# PHYSICS
## For the Life Sciences

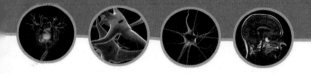

# PHYSICS
## For the Life Sciences

MARTIN ZINKE-ALLMANG

University of Western Ontario

NELSON / EDUCATION

# NELSON / EDUCATION

**Physics for the Life Sciences**
by Martin Zinke-Allmang

**Associate Vice President, Editorial Director:**
Evelyn Veitch

**Editor-in-Chief, Higher Education:**
Anne Williams

**Executive Editor:**
Paul Fam

**Marketing Manager:**
Sean Chamberland

**Developmental Editor:**
Tracy Yan

**Photo Researcher and Permissions Coordinator:**
Terry Rothman

**Content Production Managers:**
Carrie McGregor and Karri Yano

**Production Service:**
Newgen–Austin

**Copy Editor:**
Kelli Howey

**Proofreader:**
Christine Gever

**Indexer:**
Janet Mazefsky

**Manufacturing Coordinator:**
Pauline Long

**Design Director:**
Ken Phipps

**Managing Designer:**
Katherine Strain

**Interior Design and Cover Design:**
Dianna Little

**Cover Image:**
Main image: Mike Powell/ Getty Images
Left to right: Jim Wehtje/ Getty Images, © iStockphoto.com/ James Steidl, © iStockphoto.com/ Christian Anthony, © iStockphoto .com/Eraxion

**Compositor:**
Newgen

**Printer:**
RR Donnelley

Library and Archives Canada Cataloguing in Publication Data

Main entry under Physics for the Life Sciences:

Zinke-Allmang, Martin, 1958–
    Physics for the life sciences / Martin Zinke-Allmang

Includes index.
ISBN 978-0-17-644259-0

    1. Physics—Textbooks.   2. Life sciences—Textbooks.   I. Title.

QC23.2Z55 2008   530.02′457
C2007-904968-0

# CONTENTS

# PART 3   Yin and Yang

# PART 4   Tamaso Ma Jyotir

# PART 5   Ka

# PREFACE

This book is the result of a rather straightforward idea: to offer life sciences students a "Physics for the Life Sciences" course. Originally created at the author's institution in 1999, the author was pleased to see the course become very popular among students, and first-year physics enrolments saw a corresponding—and unprecedented—dramatic increase. The new course was also well received by colleagues in biology, medicine, and other basic life sciences areas, who consequently added or strengthened the physics requirements in their own programs. The great level of interest expressed by colleagues in Canada and abroad motivated us to make this book available through a market-wide release.

An introductory-level university course must meet two key objectives: to provide a comprehensive synopsis of the subject matter relevant to the student's interests and career aspirations, and to present the material in a fashion that encourages retaining acquired knowledge. In teaching physics to future life science professionals, meeting these objectives requires a major shift in content, order, and focus. We have undertaken the shift in *Physics for the Life Sciences*, and this preface aims to highlight what differentiates this text from others in the market.

## PRINCIPLE 1: GET THE STORYLINE STRAIGHT AND STICK TO IT

In the past, physics textbooks have been written to appeal to the entire market with a one-size-fits-all approach. In my experience, this approach did not work and two types of texts have evolved: texts that are tailored to the engineering students' needs, and texts that drift aimlessly through the material, mostly portraying physics as a collection of discoveries in centuries long gone. Neither approach is suitable for future life science professionals. By focusing on the needs and priorities of this audience, the textbook maintains a consistent and modern thread that guides the reader through the subject matter. Every concept originates with key physiological, biological, or medical applications. The physics essential for understanding these concepts is then developed in a fashion that is appealing to university students with interests in the biological, medical, or health-related sciences. Note that the anchoring topics in each chapter's introduction are ones that students will encounter again in upper-level courses of their programs or professional school. Frequent application will further enhance material retention and deepen topic mastery.

## PRINCIPLE 2: KEEP IT SHORT AND TO THE POINT

This textbook has approximately 800 pages. Requiring more pages (it's not uncommon to find physics textbooks with 1200 to 1600 pages) is a symptom of either one of two misconceptions: a desire to achieve encyclopaedic completeness with no willingness to distinguish relevant material from minor details; or the belief that many students are somehow academically weak and require endless repetition of the same message. In the first case, the textbook contains a huge amount of material that cannot be covered in a first-year course. The student is then left with numerous pages that contain no guidance as to what to study and what to skip. In the second case, the lecturer is stuck with a textbook that has been written with a lack of understanding of the audience and the idea of higher learning in a competitive marketplace: students attend the first-year physics course because they either need the factual knowledge as background for more intensive studies in another subject area, or because it will suit them well as part of their later professional expertise.

## PRINCIPLE 3: DON'T HIDE THE BEAUTY OF PHYSICS

Physics represents an enormous body of knowledge and methodology, and almost all of it has a huge impact on the understanding of the life sciences. In a first-year course—particularly if it might be the only physics course some students will ever take—this impact of physical facts and thought has to be presented to the fullest extent possible. Even students with other interests should appreciate at the end of the course that physics is relevant for their future careers, and is an integral part of our shared human culture. The textbook supports the lecturer in making pertinent choices by providing established methods of discussion of this science. Conceptual learning is stimulated with Concept Questions in the text and at the end of each chapter; many of these are suitable for discussion among students or in tutorial settings. Examples and end-of-chapter problems allow the reader to probe the subject matter by taking a quantitative, problem-solving approach.

## PRINCIPLE 4: BUILD ON WHAT YOU HAVE TAUGHT ALREADY

The modern university student is faced with a tremendous body of knowledge and breadth of required skills that have to be acquired in a few short years in university. Success or failure in teaching these students the essential elements of physics has a particularly high impact in times when modern medicine increasingly relies on technology that provides advanced insights into the functioning of the human body by exploiting physics concepts. Yet, physics has to compete with microbiology, biochemistry, and physiology for the student's attention. Here, the old-fashioned physics course—with its focus on pulleys, inclined planes, and simple electric circuitry with dimming light bulbs—fails miserably. In turn, a physics course that provides the student room to grow academically will keep their attention if it moves at a suitable pace through the modern applications of physics in medicine and physiology.

We have implemented this reasoning in the textbook by assuming an average high-school proficiency at the beginning, but then introducing more advanced concepts as required by the subject matter. We compromise on this principle to allow instructors reasonable freedom to choose the order in which they discuss the material: more advanced concepts are also included in the earlier chapters, but are placed at the end of the chapter so that lecturers can fine-tune to their students' needs. The logic in this is that we believe intelligent and self-aware students can select the depth to which they want to probe and acquire the offered material, as required by their program needs and career interests. The lecturer will support the students in making these choices, allowing those who are excited about physical thought to fathom deeper while focussing on basic concepts for those who need only a general introduction to the field.

One exception to this principle is the required proficiency in mathematics. The use of mathematics is kept to a necessary minimum, but tools widely used in the life sciences are introduced and applied frequently. These include in particular logarithmic and double-logarithmic plots. Basic vector algebra is included; calculus is not used in this text, as it is not required for students in their further studies in many life sciences.

## PRINCIPLE 5: THE SCIENCES HAVE BECOME INTERDISCIPLINARY, AND SO MUST A MODERN PHYSICS COURSE

The times are long gone when it was justifiable to erect boundaries around subject areas such as physics, biology, or chemistry. Pretending that we still can study one of these sciences in isolation misrepresents what drives modern science and technology. This is no longer a challenge for younger faculty members, who often have taken basic courses in biology and chemistry during their own studies, or for the increasing number of faculty with specialization in biophysics and medical physics. The current text is written in a fashion that faculty members without this background can also appreciate and teach from; after all, the basic physics concepts are the same as those studied in the traditional context, and the life sciences aspects can be picked up from this book during lecture preparation.

An interdisciplinary approach is occasionally inconsistent with the order of subject topics in an underlying science. Since this book focusses on the introduction of physical thought to the life sciences, we tried to maintain the traditional order of physics when possible. This often leads to "forward cross-links", i.e., the need to refer to an aspect that will be discussed in detail later. When implementing such forward cross-links we use them concurrently to stimulate interest and in anticipation of the later material.

Students in this course are expected to solve real-world problems very early in their professional careers. As much as possible, we have chosen numerical values for variables that are realistic for the respective application, and we have provided tables and a large number of figures with quantitative axes to provide actual data.

## Acknowledgments

A large number of highly skilled people contributed to the success of this textbook as an integral part of a modern physics curriculum in the life sciences. I acknowledge the support of the following individuals:

Dr. J. Mansfield (Toronto) and Dr. D. Fraser (Pittsburgh) for numerous text revisions; Alfredo Louro (University of Calgary), Anne Topper (Queen's University), Eduardo Galindo Riveros (Laurentian University), Peter Blunden (University of

Manitoba), Randy Kobes (University of Winnipeg), Reza Nejat (McMaster University), Len Zedel (Memorial University), Stephen Shorlin (Memorial University), and Ken Sills (McMaster University) for their careful and thoughtful reviews of the text; M. Rasche for her extensive original artwork; at the University of Western Ontario: Drs. Fred Longstaffe (Dean's Office, Science), Eugene Wong, Kevin Jordan (London Regional Cancer Centre), Frank Prato (St. Joseph's Hospital, London), Blaine Chronik, Mahi Singh (Physics and Astronomy), Jerry Battista, Ian MacDonald, Chris Ellis (Medical Biophysics), Rob Lipson (Chemistry), Dan Lajoie (Biology), Ted Lo (Biochemistry), John Ciriello (Physiology), and Volker Nolte (Kinesiology) for helpful suggestions; Drs. Brock Fenton, Tom Haffie, Denis Maxwell (Biology, University of Western Ontario), Ken Davey (York University, Toronto), and Heather Addy (University of Calgary) for discussions about their upcoming biology textbook with the same publisher; At Nelson: Tracy Yan, Sean Chamberland, Terri Rothman, and particularly my editor, Paul Fam, for patient collaboration and professional support.

*Martin Zinke-Allmang*
*London, Ontario*
*Fall 2007*

# ABOUT THE AUTHOR

The author studied physics and chemistry at the University of Heidelberg in Germany. After completing his Ph.D. thesis at the Max Planck Institute for Nuclear Physics, he moved to New Jersey for a post-doctoral fellowship at AT&T Bell Laboratories and later settled in Canada at the University of Western Ontario, where he is currently the Director of the Centre for Interdisciplinary Studies in Chemical Physics.

He has published more than 80 scientific articles, including two major review articles in *Surface Science Reports* and *Thin Solid Films*. He has supervised more than 25 M.Sc. students, Ph.D. candidates, and post-doctoral fellows, most recently in the graduate program in medical biophysics.

Together with colleagues in the Faculty of Science and the Schulich School of Medicine & Dentistry, he is currently involved in the development of an interdisciplinary undergraduate program in medical physics.

He lives with his wife and two children, Stefan and Anja, in London, Ontario, where he enjoys gardening and playing with the two family dogs.

# CHAPTER 1

# PHYSICS AND THE LIFE SCIENCES
## An Introduction

Physics and biology are two very different sciences. They differ not only in their respective objects of inquiry, but also in their experimental and conceptual methods, in their history, and even in their contributions to culture and philosophy. Physicists explain the properties of the natural world on the basis of universal laws— biologists, instead, focus on diversity, singular events, the individual history of species, or the evolution of specific traits. Why, then, should those interested in biology and the life sciences familiarize themselves with the concepts and methods used by physicists? A trivial answer rests with the fact that physics is a formal requirement for many professional programs and that it is often a subject on admissions tests. This, however, only rephrases the question: Why is physics a prerequisite for advanced studies in the life sciences? We first provide a practical answer based on an example from zoology, and then a deeper fundamental answer based on the hierarchy of complexity observed in the biosphere.

The best way to establish a practical reason for studying physics as part of an education in the life sciences is to illustrate that the modern researcher in these fields relies on extensive physics expertise. We choose an example that at first seems to be as far from physics as we can imagine: the progress made in zoology to understand the life of **dolphins**.

## Case Study: The Hearing of Dolphins Under Water

Humans have shown a great deal of affection for dolphins throughout history. In mythology and literature, theme parks and motion pictures, dolphins have been identified as our friends in the sea. Yet we still know little about their lives in the wild, which has become a problem for their preservation in the early 21st century. To understand these mammals through scientific research is our only hope in the race against their extinction.

Dolphins are distinct from most other mammals because they spend their entire life in water. This raises a wide range of questions about their ways of coping with this environment, including the interesting question we pursue in this section: Can dolphins communicate; i.e., can they speak and **hear under water**?

### What Dolphins Hear

The scientific approach starts with a fact-finding stage in which we address the question, "Do dolphins hear, and, if so, what do dolphins hear?" From observations of their vocalizations in the open sea or during tests with animals in captivity, we conclude that dolphins can hear. However, to specify *what* dolphins hear we immediately require definitions, concepts, and methods from physics. A **hydrophone** is used to record sounds in the form of frequency spectra, sound intensities, and sound amplitudes, all terms that are discussed in Chapter 17. For dolphins, these data allow us to distinguish almost constantly emitted clicking sounds (about 300 sounds per second) and whistle sounds. With a proper combination of acoustic receivers we also can establish that the clicking sounds are focussed forward, like the headlights of a car. Therefore, we expect to find two different methods of sound generation in dolphins.

Observations with live animals are supplemented with findings from the anatomy of dolphins. The features of interest to the current discussion are visible

**FIGURE 1.1**

Dolphins can vocalize, hear, and interpret a wide range of clicking and whistle sounds. The clicking sounds are focussed in the forward direction by the oily melon, which is seen as a protrusion of the forehead in front of the blowhole. The dolphin's ear consists of an inner ear and a middle ear, but lacks the outer ear of land mammals. Arriving sound is transmitted to the middle ear by bone conduction in the skull.

in Fig. 1.1. The **oily melon**, located in the forehead, is a unique organ that acts as an **acoustic lens**. Lenses allow wave energy to be focussed, as discussed in Chapter 18. Thus, we suggest that the forward-focussed clicking sounds are related to the lens-like oily melon. Whales developed the oily melon even further as a powerful weapon, emitting shockwaves that can stun squids and render them defenceless.

Dolphins share with all other mammals an inner and a middle ear. However, they don't have an outer ear. For the following discussion we keep in mind that the outer ear of humans consists of the external pinna and the auditory canal, which collect sound waves and guide them to the eardrum. Instead, dolphins have a unique fatty organ that connects the ends of the lower jaw bone to the middle ear sections. Sound generation and sound detection therefore must be different from our own.

Most of the above information was obtained from **bottlenosed dolphins**. Similar animals are studied to get a better understanding of these mechanisms, such as other dolphins, **whales**, and **porpoises**, all of which form the order *Cetacea*. Such studies show that the clicking sound is observed only among the **toothed whales**, such as belugas, narwhals, sperm whales, dolphins, and porpoises. The **baleen whales**, including blue whales, fin whales, bowheads, and minke whales, generate only whistle sounds but in widely varying forms—such as the famous "songs" of the humpback whales.

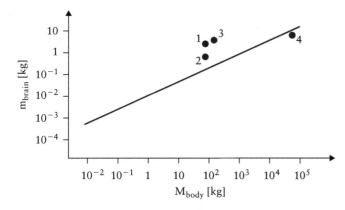

**FIGURE 1.2**

The brain size is not a measure of a mammal's intelligence but is a measure of its body size. This is illustrated with a double-logarithmic plot that relates the body mass $M_{body}$ to the brain mass $m_{brain}$. Both axes are given in unit kg. Four species with comparably large brains are highlighted: humans (1), chimpanzees (2), porpoises (3), and blue whales (4).

Studies of animal behaviour demonstrate that the sounds of dolphins are not just species- or mate-identification patterns. The whistle sounds in particular are used to communicate with other dolphins of the same species, to express alarm, sexual excitement, and likely a range of other emotions. The clicking sounds are used to navigate in the physical terrain, to move within the pod, and to hunt fish, squid, and shrimp. Technological imitations of these methods are called **sonar systems**, in which sonar stands for <u>so</u>und <u>na</u>vigation <u>r</u>anging.

As we observe in ourselves, the ability to communicate requires two attributes besides a variable vocalization: good hearing, and a large brain to process the information. Fig. 1.2 demonstrates that dolphins and porpoises have unusually large brains. The figure is a double-logarithmic plot of **brain mass** versus body mass for various mammals. The solid line illustrates that larger animals usually have larger brains, with the brain mass of the blue whale exceeding our brain mass. More interestingly, we see from the figure that some species deviate from the general trend in that they possess particularly large brains for their body size. These species are found above the solid line in the figure; humans and porpoises are particularly distinguished in that respect. The large size of dolphins' brains reinforces our assumption that they display a well-developed ability to hear. Logarithmic and double-logarithmic graphs are frequently used in the life sciences, with several examples provided in this book. We use the problem sets in this chapter to practise graph analysis for these plots. A quantitative

analysis method is introduced at the end of this chapter in the sections of the Math Review entitled "Powers and Logarithms" and "Graph Analysis Methods."

## How Dolphins Hear

In the second stage of scientific inquiry, we use these observations and anatomical data to address the question, "How do dolphins generate these sounds, and how do they hear sounds?" To determine the mechanisms, we develop a theoretical model. We then conduct quantitative tests to validate or refute it.

For dolphins, the following model is proposed: The whistle sounds originate from deep in the larynx, but the clicking sounds are generated by moving air in and out of air sacs near the blowhole. This sound is then focussed forward by the oily melon. The clicking sounds are used for **echolocation** in the same fashion as used by bats. The whistle sounds of other dolphins and the echo of the clicking sounds are received by the lower jaw bone and then transmitted to the middle ear through the fatty organ between the rear end of the lower jaw bone and the middle ear.

To see that this model is scientifically sound, we rely on well-established physical concepts of the generation, transmission, and reception of sound waves. Focussing the clicking sound with the oily melon allows the dolphin to increase the range of the initial sound energy, which is necessary because sound energy attenuates fast as it travels away from the sound source. These sound waves reflect off an object when it has a higher or lower density than the surrounding seawater. Receiving the reflected sound allows for navigation by echolocation. Dolphins use echolocation not only to locate an object, but also to determine that object's direction of motion and speed based on the Doppler effect (as described in Chapter 17). Even though dolphins have eyesight comparable to that of cats, the echolocation system is necessary at depths greater than 70 metres, beyond which sunlight cannot penetrate seawater. Dolphins often dive to such depths; they have been observed as deep as 300 metres below the sea surface. Such dives don't take long, because dolphins can swim at sustained speeds of 30 km/h. Still, their lungs and cardiovascular systems require modifications to avoid the dangers of diving (which we discuss in Chapter 9).

To establish the method by which dolphins hear, we must review the mechanisms of our own hearing. The anatomy of the **human ear** is illustrated in Fig. 1.3. For a mammal to hear, an external sound has to cause an excitation of sound-sensitive cells in

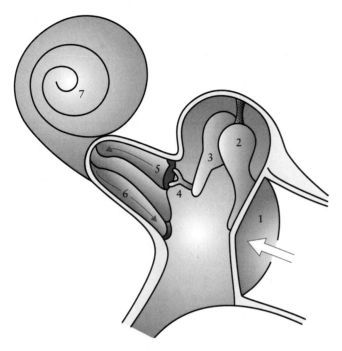

**FIGURE 1.3**

The anatomy of the human ear represents 300 million years of evolutionary adaptation to hearing in air. The arriving sound (open arrow) causes the eardrum (1) to vibrate. This vibration is mechanically transmitted to the oval window (5) of the cochlea (7, solid arrows). The sound is amplified by a factor of 30 due to the arrangement of the three ossicles, the hammer (2), the anvil (3), and the stirrup (4). The middle ear converts a sound wave in air into a sound wave in the fluid (perilymph, 6) of the inner ear.

the inner ear. Sound travels to the inner ear in two physical ways:

- External sounds enter the outer ear, move through the auditory canal, and set the eardrum in vibration. The ossicles of the middle ear amplify this vibration (by a factor of 30 in humans) and transmit it to the oval window, which separates the inner ear from the middle ear. The sound then propagates through the liquid-filled medium of the inner ear and excites the sound-sensitive cells of the organ of Corti. (This process is described in Chapter 17.)
- Alternatively, external sound waves cause vibrations of the skull bones surrounding the ear. These vibrations directly stimulate the sound-sensitive cells of the inner ear in a process called **bone conduction.**

Both mechanisms contribute to human hearing; we are not consciously aware of bone conduction, despite the fact that it is the main mechanism by which we hear ourselves speak. You can test this on yourself: tightly cover both your ears while speaking. You hear your voice equally clearly with closed ears.

In audiology, the branch of science investigating hearing and hearing impairments, bone conduction is used in two tests to distinguish hearing impairments caused by diseases of the middle ear versus diseases of the inner ear. Chronic hearing impairments of the middle ear are caused by *otitis media* (bacterial middle ear infection) or by *otosclerosis* (chronic progressive deafness, especially for low frequencies). Otitis media leads to malformed tissue in the middle ear that negatively affects the mobility of the eardrum and the ossicles. Otosclerosis affects one percent of the adult population and leads to an abnormal amount of spongy bone deposition between the stapes and the oval window, which immobilizes the stapes. Both diseases lead to a loss of sound transmission from the eardrum to the oval window. Hearing impairments of the inner ear, on the other side, are usually associated with damaged organs of Corti; i.e., sound is not properly processed into electric impulses in the sound-sensitive cells.

Two audiological tests are illustrated in Fig. 1.4. The test shown in Fig. 1.4(a) is the **Weber test:** An $A_1$ tuning fork, vibrating at 55 Hz, is brought into contact with the top centre of the patient's head. A healthy patient locates the source of the sound at the centred position. A patient with a disease of the middle ear locates the source of the sound near the ailing ear, because these patients rely more strongly on bone conduction on the ailing side. In turn, a patient with a hearing impairment of the inner ear locates the source of the sound near the healthy ear, because the ailing side does not receive a strong signal by either mechanism.

The test shown in Fig. 1.4(b) is the **Rinne test.** In this test, a vibrating $A_1$ tuning fork is first brought into contact with the *mastoid process,* which is an extension of the temporal bone behind the auricle. When the patient doesn't hear the diminishing sound any longer, the tuning fork is brought in front of the auricle. A healthy person or a person with a hearing impairment in the inner ear now hears the sound again, since bone conduction in humans is less effective than hearing a sound that is transmitted through air to the eardrum. However, a patient with a hearing impairment in the middle ear does not pick up the sound of the moved tuning fork; this is due to the ability to circumvent the middle ear mechanism with bone conduction but not for sound arriving at the eardrums.

Bone conduction is more important for hearing under water. Adjustments in the lower jaw of dolphins and the development of the fatty organ to connect the lower jaw to the middle ear are improvements of the hearing by bone conduction. This can be explained by physical concepts such as resonant cou-

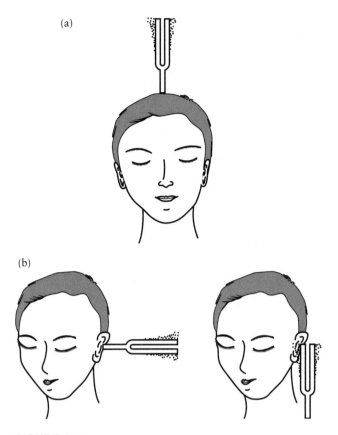

(a)

(b)

**FIGURE 1.4**

Bone conduction is employed in two audiological tests that allow us to distinguish between middle ear and inner ear diseases. (a) In the Weber test, a vibrating tuning fork touches the top of a patient's head. The diagnosis of the health practitioner depends on where the patient perceives the sound source. (b) In the Rinne test, the vibrating tuning fork is first brought into contact with the *mastoid process* behind the auricle until the patient can no longer hear the sound. Then the tuning fork is moved in front of the auricle. The health practitioner's diagnosis depends on whether the patient hears the sound after the tuning fork has been moved.

pling of sound waves to vibrations of the rigid bone material, and the amplification of vibrations in elastic materials like the fatty organ. We study these physical concepts in Chapters 16 and 17.

## Why Dolphins Hear

The final stage of scientific inquiry deals with the question "why." In the biological sciences, such ultimate questions usually require the study of an animal's evolutionary history. *Cetacea* is an order that developed only in the past 55 million years by radiating from early *Ungulates*, mammals whose last toe joints are encased in hooves. Emerging from furred carnivores, the early ancestors of the whales spent an increasing fraction of their lives in water, first in river deltas hunting like crocodiles, then along shallow coastlines of the Eocenic oceans. They lost their fur

about 47 million years ago, and became independent of freshwater supplies about 44 million years ago. Eventually they moved entirely into the sea, where their hind legs disappeared and their front legs became flippers. This transition was completed about 30 million years ago.

The evolutionary changes to the ear occurred about 45 million years ago, i.e., as an early adaptation to the marine environment. The loss of the outer ear is an example of an evolutionary reversal. Such reversals are evidence against a **teleonomic** (goal-oriented) interpretation of natural selection. (At the end of Chapter 5, we discuss an example of reverse evolution in humans that affected the shape of our pelvis.)

Dolphins share with us amphibian ancestors who lived part of their lives in water; then reptile ancestors who about 300 million years ago developed the egg shell to shed the last reason for a waterbound stage in their lives; and finally the early mammalian ancestors that flourished when the dinosaurs became extinct 65 million years ago. Thus, comparing the hearing of dolphins to the sound detection of fish is meaningless; dolphins are descendants of species that had adapted to life on dry land for more than 300 million years.

The ear of the dolphin is a device that initially was adapted for use in air, and then was modified for use under water. The adaptation of the ear to the use on land and its ineffectiveness when used under water are described in Chapter 17. Thus, the evolutionary adaptations of the dolphin's hearing are rooted in the physics of acoustics in water and air.

The example of the dolphin's hearing illustrates the usefulness of physical methods for a specific inquiry in biology. Many other examples exist in the various life sciences; we frequently choose such examples in this textbook.

## Hierarchy of Complexity

Using the case study in the previous section as a guide, we have addressed only the question, "What role does physics play in the life sciences?"; we have yet to answer, "Why does physics play an increasingly prominent role in the life sciences?" Addressing this question leads us away from the numerous observations in the life sciences that physics is used to explain and toward the common fundamental reason. This aspect will provide us with a second answer to the question of why life scientists—particularly those who will be active well into the 21st century—should be familiar with physical methods and concepts.

The argument is made with the extensive data set shown in Fig. 1.5. Its vertical axis is based on a widely

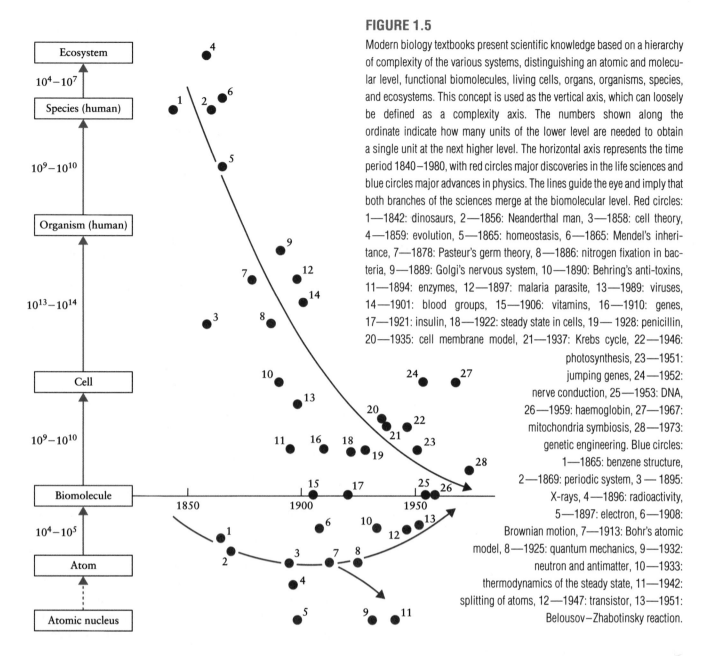

**FIGURE 1.5**

Modern biology textbooks present scientific knowledge based on a hierarchy of complexity of the various systems, distinguishing an atomic and molecular level, functional biomolecules, living cells, organs, organisms, species, and ecosystems. This concept is used as the vertical axis, which can loosely be defined as a complexity axis. The numbers shown along the ordinate indicate how many units of the lower level are needed to obtain a single unit at the next higher level. The horizontal axis represents the time period 1840–1980, with red circles major discoveries in the life sciences and blue circles major advances in physics. The lines guide the eye and imply that both branches of the sciences merge at the biomolecular level. Red circles: 1—1842: dinosaurs, 2—1856: Neanderthal man, 3—1858: cell theory, 4—1859: evolution, 5—1865: homeostasis, 6—1865: Mendel's inheritance, 7—1878: Pasteur's germ theory, 8—1886: nitrogen fixation in bacteria, 9—1889: Golgi's nervous system, 10—1890: Behring's anti-toxins, 11—1894: enzymes, 12—1897: malaria parasite, 13—1989: viruses, 14—1901: blood groups, 15—1906: vitamins, 16—1910: genes, 17—1921: insulin, 18—1922: steady state in cells, 19— 1928: penicillin, 20—1935: cell membrane model, 21—1937: Krebs cycle, 22—1946: photosynthesis, 23—1951: jumping genes, 24—1952: nerve conduction, 25—1953: DNA, 26—1959: haemoglobin, 27—1967: mitochondria symbiosis, 28—1973: genetic engineering. Blue circles: 1—1865: benzene structure, 2—1869: periodic system, 3 — 1895: X-rays, 4—1896: radioactivity, 5—1897: electron, 6—1908: Brownian motion, 7—1913: Bohr's atomic model, 8—1925: quantum mechanics, 9—1932: neutron and antimatter, 10—1933: thermodynamics of the steady state, 11—1942: splitting of atoms, 12—1947: transistor, 13—1951: Belousov–Zhabotinsky reaction.

used approach in biology textbooks where the presentation of knowledge is organized along a **hierarchy of complexity**: An overview of the simple molecules in the inanimate environment and the most frequently occurring biomolecules is followed by a tour of the living cell. This leads to the physiology of tissues and organ systems, and from these to the entire organism. At a higher level species and their evolution are discussed, which finally leads to ecosystems and the entire biosphere. To turn the progressive complexity into an axis of a plot, we need to quantify the level of complexity. For this, we use the number of units of the respectively lower level to form the next higher level. The numbers shown are rough estimates: $10^4$ to $10^5$ atoms are required to form, e.g., a haemoglobin molecule (molecular mass 68 000 g/mol); $10^9$ to $10^{10}$ biomolecules form a cell, based on a cell size of 20 $\mu$m and the density of water. An adult human body contains about $5 \times 10^{13}$ cells; we will reach 7 billion people by 2015. The biosphere accommodates more than one million taxonomically classified species, and probably another 10 to 30 million yet unknown species.

The reason why physics and the life sciences have very distinct histories, as stated at the beginning of this chapter, becomes evident when we add a *horizontal* axis to Fig. 1.5. This axis shows the time period from 1840 to 1980. Major discoveries during that period in the life sciences are shown as red circles, and major advances in physics are shown as blue circles. These events are drawn at the approximate level of complexity they address. The entries in Fig. 1.5 are selected with no claim to completeness; however, they illustrate the points we want to draw from the figure. The life sciences developed from top to bottom along our complexity axis with an early emphasis on macroscopic systems. The availability of advanced microscopes allowed biologists to approach the mechanisms of individual biomolecules only in the late 1900s. In the past, physics was primarily interested in systems below the complexity level of biomolecules, with a focus on atomic and molecular systems since the late 1800s. After Bohr's atomic model was accepted, it branched into sub-atomic physics disciplines and the physics of increasingly complex atomic and molecular structures. Condensed matter has dominated this branch since the 1930s, with surface and polymer physics, biomaterials, and medical imaging as new developments since the 1970s, initially driven by improvements in vacuum technology.

Fig. 1.5 illustrates two critical issues:

- The traditional focus of physics and chemistry research at the lowest level of complexity attributes a key role to these sciences when life is explained from bottom to top along the hierarchy of complexity employed by modern biology.

- The convergence at the biomolecular level of complexity of biological and medical research on one side, and physics and chemistry on the other side, requires a combination of methods from all of these sciences to ensure future discoveries. In the realm of biomolecules and sub-cellular processes, physics, chemistry, biology, and physiology merge at the beginning of the 21st century into one scientific method of inquiry.

## MULTIPLE CHOICE AND CONCEPTUAL QUESTIONS

**Q–1.1.** The statement "We are smarter than chimpanzees because we have a bigger brain" had better be wrong, because otherwise Fig. 1.2 would imply that we are dumber than porpoises *and* blue whales. Based on Fig. 1.2, how would you formulate a similar comparative statement about the human brain mass that would address our perception that we are also smarter than *Cetacea* with bigger brains?

**Q–1.2.** A straight line in the double-logarithmic plot in Fig. 1.2 implies that (A) $m_{\text{brain}}$ is proportional to $M_{\text{body}}$; (B) $m_{\text{brain}}$ depends linearly on $M_{\text{body}}$; (C) the dependence of the two masses can be written in the form $m_{\text{brain}} = \exp(a \cdot M_{\text{body}})$, with factor $a$ a constant; (D) the dependence of the two masses is a power law of the form $m_{\text{brain}} = a \cdot (M_{\text{body}})^b$, with factors $a$ and $b$ constant; (E) the dependence of the two masses can be written in the form $m_{\text{brain}} = a \cdot M_{\text{body}} + b$, with factors $a$ and $b$ constant.

**Q–1.3.** (a) If $m_{\text{brain}}$ and $M_{\text{body}}$ were directly proportional to each other, i.e., $m_{\text{brain}} \propto M_{\text{body}}$, the slope of the line in Fig. 1.2 would have to be (A) zero; (B) $-1$; (C) $+1$; (D) $-2$; (E) $+2$. (b) If we replot Fig. 1.2 with the brain mass shown in unit gram (g), the slope (A) increases; (B) decreases; (C) remains unchanged; (D) cannot be predicted before the replotting of Fig. 1.2 is completed.

**Q–1.4.** Next time you are in a swimming pool, first try swimming like a whale, then like a fish. In the first case you hold your legs together and move them up and down. To simulate a fish, you hold your legs together and move them sideways. Which works better? Which way would a mermaid most likely move her tail when swimming?

## ANALYTICAL PROBLEMS

**P–1.1.** (a) Plot in double-logarithmic representation the two functions (I) $y = 4x^2$ and (II) $y = 4x^2 + 1$ in the interval $0.1 \leq x \leq 10.0$. (b) What drawback of double-logarithmic plots can you identify?

**P–1.2.** For the function $y = 2e^{3x}$, (a) plot $y$ versus $x$ for $0 \leq x \leq 2$, (b) plot ln $y$ versus $x$ for $0 \leq x \leq 2$, (c) show that the slope of the logarithmic plot is 3,

and (d) show that the intercept of the logarithmic plot is ln 2.

**P–1.3.** For the function $y = 4x^3$ (a) plot $y$ versus $x$ for $0 \leq x \leq 4$, (b) plot ln $y$ versus ln $x$ for $0 \leq x \leq 4$, (c) show that the slope of the double-logarithmic plot is 3, and (d) show that the intercept of the double-logarithmic plot is ln 4.

**P–1.4.** Fig. 1.2 shows a double-logarithmic plot of brain mass versus body mass, both in unit kg, for a wide range of mammals. Using the formula

$$m_{\text{brain}} = a \cdot M_{\text{body}}^b \qquad [1]$$

to describe the plot, determine (a) the exponent $b$, and (b) the prefactor $a$.

**P–1.5.** We develop an empirical formula connecting the wingspan and the mass of some species able to fly. Then we evaluate a few interesting consequences. (The first to make these considerations was Leonardo da Vinci.) (a) Use the data in Table 1.1 to draw a double-logarithmic plot $\ln W$ versus $\ln M$ where $W$ is the wingspan and $M$ is the mass. Determine the constants $a$ and $b$ in a power law relation $W = a \cdot M^b$. (b) The largest animal believed ever to fly was a late Cretaceous pterosaur species found in Texas and named *Quetzalcoatlus northropi*. It had an 11-m wingspan. What is the maximum mass of this pterosaur? *Note:* The largest wingspan of a living species is 3.6 m, for the wandering albatross. (c) Assume that a human wishes to fly like a bird. What minimum wingspan would be needed for a person of 70 kg to take off?

### TABLE 1.1

**Mass and wingspan of various birds**

| Bird | Wingspan (cm) | Mass (g) |
|------|--------------|----------|
| Hummingbird | 7 | 10 |
| Sparrow | 15 | 50 |
| Dove | 50 | 400 |
| Andean condor | 320 | 11 500 |
| California condor | 290 | 12 000 |

## MATH REVIEW

### POWERS AND LOGARITHMS

Definitions: $a^1 = a$, $a^0 = 1$, and $a^{-n} = 1/a^n$. Calculation rules with powers:

$$a^x \cdot a^y = a^{x+y}$$

$$a^x \cdot b^x = (a \cdot b)^x$$

$$\frac{a^x}{a^y} = a^{x-y}$$

$$\frac{a^x}{b^x} = \left(\frac{a}{b}\right)^x$$

$$(a^x)^y = a^{x \cdot y}$$

Logarithms were introduced by John Napier in 1614 to simplify mathematical operations. As you see below, when using logarithms we can use multiplications instead of powers, and additions instead of multiplications. The use of logarithms also proves useful when we analyze data graphically, as discussed in the section on "Graph Analysis Methods."

Definitions: the term $c = \log_b a$ represents the number $c$, which satisfies the equation $b^c = a$; i.e., the logarithm is the inverse operation to raising to a power. In the textbook, only two types of logarithm functions are used: logarithms with base $b = 10$ (usually labelled log without a subscript), and natural logarithms with base $b = e = 2.71828\ldots$, in which $e$ is Euler's number. This logarithm function is labelled ln. Thus:

$$\log_{10} a = \log a = c \quad \Leftrightarrow \quad a = 10^c$$

$$\log_e a = \ln a = c \quad \Leftrightarrow \quad a = e^c = \exp(c)$$

The following rules apply to logarithms with any base; here, we write them specifically for the case of base $b = 10$:

$$\log(x \cdot y) = \log x + \log y$$

$$\log\left(\frac{x}{y}\right) = \log x - \log y$$

$$\log x^y = y \cdot \log x$$

and for the case of base $b = e$:

$$\ln(x \cdot y) = \ln x + \ln y$$

$$\ln\left(\frac{x}{y}\right) = \ln x - \ln y$$

$$\ln x^y = y \cdot \ln x$$

For the same variable, the two logarithm functions are related by a factor of $\ln 10$:

$$\ln x = \ln 10 \cdot \log x$$

$$\Rightarrow \quad \ln x = 2.3026 \cdot \log x$$

## GRAPH ANALYSIS METHODS

Scientific progress is based on experimental data. These data often are plotted and presented without a (yet) conclusive model that would provide a mathematical formula for the relation between the shown parameters. The three most frequently used methods of representing such data are the linear plot, the logarithmic plot, and the double-logarithmic plot.

### Linear Plots

In this most frequently used graph, the variation of a dependent variable ($y$) is illustrated as a function of an independent variable ($x$) by plotting $y$ versus $x$, as shown in Fig. 1.6. We say that "$y$ is linear in $x$" in the $x$-interval $[x_1, x_2]$ if the data in that interval can be fitted with a straight line, such as the one in the figure. Mathematically, this linear behaviour is described by the equation

$$y = a \cdot x + b$$

in which $a$ and $b$ do not depend on the variables $x$ and $y$. $a$ is called the slope of the curve and is determined from:

$$a = \frac{y_4 - y_3}{x_4 - x_3}$$

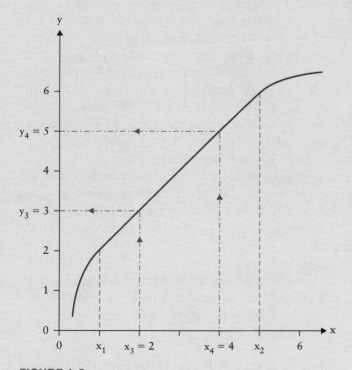

**FIGURE 1.6**

Linear plot of a function $y = f(x)$ with a linear dependence of $y$ on $x$ in the interval $[x_1, x_2]$.

where the values $x_3$ and $x_4$ must lie within the interval $[x_1, x_2]$; $b$ is called the intercept of the $y$-axis and is the value of $y$ at $x = 0$. The value of $b$ is read from the plot directly if the point $x = 0$ lies within the interval $[x_1, x_2]$. If this is not the case, like in Fig. 1.6, then we choose a particular point on the curve and substitute it together with the result for $a$ in the general linear equation.

### Example 1.1

Determine the slope and the intercept with the $y$-axis for the curve shown in interval $[x_1, x_2]$ of Fig. 1.6.

*Solution:* We choose $x_3 = 2$ and $x_4 = 4$. The corresponding $y$-values are read from the graph (using the dash-dotted lines) as $y_3 = 3$ and $y_4 = 5$. Thus, we find $a = (5 - 3)/(4 - 2) = +1$. For $b$, we choose the point with $x_3 = 2$ and $y_3 = 3$. These data are then substituted in the general linear equation $y = a \cdot x + b$, leading to $3 = 1 \cdot 2 + b$. Thus, $b = +1$.

### Logarithmic Plots

Graphs other than linear plots are usually used for two purposes. Either a large variation in the data leads to an undesirable appearance of the plot, or the data are tested for an exponential dependence. In an exponential dependence the independent variable $x$ and the dependent variable $y$ are connected in the form

$$y = a \cdot e^{b \cdot x} = a \cdot \exp(b \cdot x)$$

How can you convince yourself that this equation describes a given experimental set of data? Often, data sets show an increasing upward trend if plotted in a coordinate system with a $y$- and an $x$-axis. However, such a trend is not sufficient. You have two options: if you have logarithmic paper available or your graphics software allows you to use logarithmic axes, you show the data in the form $y$ versus $x$ using a logarithmic scale for the $y$-axis (ordinate). Alternatively, we can plot $\ln y$ versus $x$ where the natural logarithm of the $y$-data has been calculated first.

If the data points can be represented by a straight line segment in a logarithmic plot, such as in the interval $[x_1, x_2]$ in Fig. 1.7, then we know that the exponential function applies to the data in that interval. From the logarithmic plot we determine the coefficients $a$ and $b$, since the logarithmic plot corresponds mathematically to $\ln y = \ln a + b \cdot x$; i.e., the slope of the straight line segment in Fig. 1.7 gives the prefactor in the exponent, $b$, and the intercept with the $y$-axis gives the logarithm of the prefactor of the exponential term, $\ln a$.

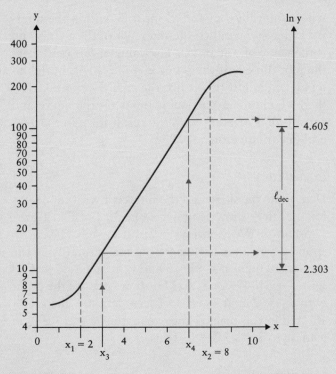

**FIGURE 1.7**

Logarithmic plot of a function $y = f(x)$ with an exponential dependence of $y$ on $x$ in $[x_1, x_2]$.

### Example 1.2

For Fig. 1.7, determine the parameters $a$ and $b$ in the interval where the exponential function applies.

*Solution*: We need two data points from within the interval $[x_1, x_2]$, since two unknown parameters $a$ and $b$ exist. For these we choose $x_3 = 3$ and $x_4 = 7$. Notice that the values given on the $y$-axis are $y$-values, not $\ln y$-values. You can tell this first because the axis is labelled $y$ and not $\ln y$, and also because the scale is not linear; i.e., the distance between the $y = 0$ and $y = 100$ tick-marks is not equal to the distance between the $y = 100$ and $y = 200$ tick-marks. In other plots it might be the case that the $y$-data are given as $\ln y$ with a linear scale. In that case we would read the corresponding $\ln y$ values directly off the $y$-axis of the graph.

However, in the present case an intermediate step in the data analysis is needed. In this step, we add a new ordinate, done in Fig. 1.7 at the right side, where the $y$-data are converted into $\ln y$-data. Notice that the new axis is linear (the distance between the $y = 0$ and $y = 2.303$ tick-marks is the same as that between the $y = 2.303$ and $y = 4.605$ tick-marks). With the new support scale established, we read the $\ln y$-values from this new axis and list them in Table 1.2. We illustrate how we arrive at the value $\ln(y_3) = 2.600$ as an example. Each decade on a $\ln$-grid

### TABLE 1.2

**Data sets from Fig. 1.7**

| $i$ | $x_i$ | $\ln(y_i)$ |
|---|---|---|
| 3 | 3.0 | 2.600 |
| 4 | 7.0 | 4.740 |

corresponds to an increment of $\ln 10 = 2.303$. This increment corresponds to the length $l_{dec}$ (expressed in unit cm as measured from Fig. 1.7). The value of $\ln(y_3)$ is a distance of $0.129 \cdot l_{dec}$ above the next lower full decade (in this case, $y = 10$). Thus $\ln(y_3) = 0.129 \cdot 2.303 + 2.303 = 2.600$.

With the data in Table 1.2, we determine in the next step the coefficient $b$ from $\ln y = \ln a + b \cdot x$:

$$b = \frac{\ln(y_4) - \ln(y_3)}{x_4 - x_3}$$

Substituting the data from Table 1.2 for the coefficient $b$ leads to $b = (4.74 - 2.6)/(7.0 - 3.0) = 0.54$. In the last step we substitute the data pair $x_3$ and $\ln(y_3)$: $2.6 = \ln a + 0.54 \cdot 3.0$, which yields $a = 2.66$.

### Double-Logarithmic Plots

If logarithmic plots do not lead to straight line segments, a double-logarithmic plot can be used to reveal whether the $y$-data depend on the $x$-variable in the form of a power law. Even if the real dependence is more complicated, a double-logarithmic plot often leads to straight line segments as shown for the interval $[x_1, x_2]$ in Fig. 1.8, as power laws are often good approximations to the actual physical or biological law.

Again, a double-logarithmic plot can take one of two equivalent forms: either the $x$ and $y$ data are plotted directly on paper, with logarithmic grids for the abscissa and ordinate, as done in Fig. 1.8, or $\ln x$ and $\ln y$ can be plotted on paper with a linear grid.

For the straight line segment in Fig. 1.8, the mathematical dependence of the dependent variable $y$ on the independent variable $x$ is then given in the form of a power law with $a$ and $b$ constant:

$$y = a \cdot x^b$$

When we rewrite both sides of this equation as the respective logarithmic values, we find

$$\ln y = \ln a + b \cdot \ln x$$

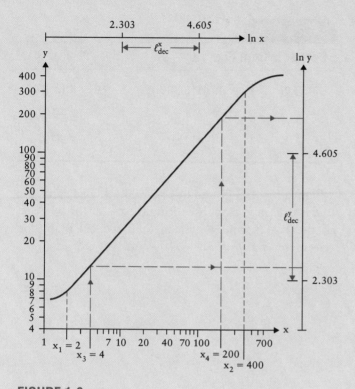

**FIGURE 1.8**

Double-logarithmic plot of a function $y = f(x)$ with a power law dependence of $y$ on $x$ in $[x_1, x_2]$.

## TABLE 1.3

### Molecular mass and radius of various molecules

| Substance | $M$ (g/mol) | $R$ $(10^{-10}$ m) |
| --- | --- | --- |
| Water | 18 | 1.5 |
| Oxygen | 32 | 2.0 |
| Glucose | 180 | 3.9 |
| Mannitol | 180 | 3.6 |
| Sucrose | 390 | 4.8 |
| Raffinose | 580 | 5.6 |
| Inulin | 5 000 | 12.5 |
| Ribonuclease | 13 500 | 18 |
| $\beta$-lactoglobulin | 35 000 | 27 |
| Haemoglobin | 68 000 | 31 |
| Albumin | 68 000 | 37 |
| Catalase | 250 000 | 52 |

i.e., the slope of the straight line segment corresponds to $b$ and the intercept of the ordinate equals $\ln a$. For practice, analyze Fig. 1.8 yourself. You follow the same approach we took for the logarithmic axis in Fig. 1.7, except the procedure must be applied to both axes in Fig. 1.8, as shown with the additional axes at the right side and at the top of the figure. For the two coefficients, you should find values close to $b = 0.68$ and $a = 5.07$.

### Example 1.3

The molecular masses $(M)$ and the radii $(R)$ of some molecules are given in Table 1.3. Plot the data in double-logarithmic representation and develop an empirical relationship between the two quantities in the form $R = f(M)$, in which the notation $f(\cdots)$ means "function of."

*Solution:* The double-logarithmic plot of the data in Table 1.3 is shown in Fig. 1.9, where the abscissa values are taken from the first column of the table and the ordinate values from the second column in unit metre (m). Note that the single data points deviate slightly from a straight line. It is possible, however, to draw a reasonably straight line through the points (mathematically, this is called the *best fit*). Using this straight line for the analysis of the constants

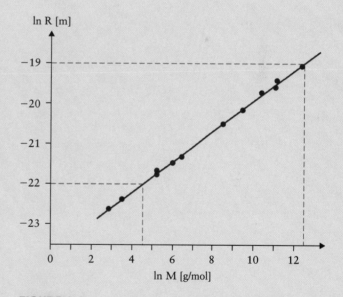

**FIGURE 1.9**

Double-logarithmic plot of the molecular mass $M$ versus the molecular radius $R$ for a wide range of molecules, based on Table 1.3.

$a$ and $b$, instead of any particular data points, reduces the statistical error in the result.

To determine the constants $a$ and $b$ in the power law $R = a \cdot M^b$, we again analyze the problem in the form $\ln R = \ln a + b \cdot \ln M$ as described above. From Fig. 1.9 we read two data pairs $\ln R$ and $\ln M$ (dashed lines), as listed in Table 1.4. This table allows us to write two linear formulas in the form $\ln y = \ln a + b \cdot \ln x$:

$$\text{(I)} \qquad -22.0 = b \cdot 4.5 + \ln a$$

$$\underline{\text{(II)} \qquad -19.0 = b \cdot 12.5 + \ln a}$$

$$\text{(II)} - \text{(I)} \quad +3.0 = b \cdot (12.5 - 4.5)$$

**TABLE 1.4**

**Data sets from Fig. 1.9**

| Data set | $\ln(M \,(\text{g/mol}))$ | $\ln(R \,(m))$ |
|---|---|---|
| #1 | 4.5 | −22.0 |
| #2 | 12.5 | −19.0 |

Thus, $b = 0.375$ and $\ln a = -23.69$. The value for $\ln a$ is obtained by substituting the result for $b$ in one of the two formulas. From $\ln a$ we calculate the parameter $a$ as $a = 5.2 \times 10^{-11}$ m.

# PART 1
# PANTA RHEI

Newton's three laws of mechanics represent a common bracket for the first part of this book. In the following group of four chapters, the parameters of motion are linked to the concept of force by Newton's second law. The concept of momentum and its conservation are anchored in the second and third laws. Mechanical equilibrium is established using the first law.

This first part introduces **change** as a major theme. Forces can change freely at any instant. Acceleration, the consequence of an unbalanced net force on an object, is the rate of change of velocity, which in turn is the rate of change of the position of the object. The momentum of an individual object changes with each collision.

Continuous change is a major subject in all sciences. Chemistry is about reactions, biology is based on evolution, and the earth sciences describe the drifts of huge segments of Earth's crust as plate tectonics. Change is even more obvious in physical processes, yet it took more than 2200 years, from the early beginnings of scientific reasoning in the Pythagorean school to the publication of *Principia Mathematica* in 1687, to establish the laws of mechanics because our way of thinking is profoundly challenged by the idea that a rate of change is at the centre of the natural order of things.

*Panta rhei* means "everything flows." It was the main thesis of the Greek philosopher Heracleitus around 500 BC. Even though it has since formed part of the European cultural heritage, it required Newton's genius to realize its implications for the natural sciences.

# CHAPTER 2

# LOCOMOTION I
## Kinematics

**M**otion is quantified through the physical parameters of position, time, velocity, and acceleration. The velocity is the change of position with time, and the acceleration is the change of velocity with time. Position, velocity, and acceleration are *vectors,* because motion occurs in three-dimensional space. The term *speed* is used for the magnitude of the velocity.

A wide range of motion patterns is possible because of the many ways an object can be accelerated. Free fall is a simple one-dimensional motion based on a constant vertical acceleration (gravitational acceleration) that acts in the direction of the velocity of the object. If we combine free fall with a horizontal motion that is not accelerated, parabolic paths result that are called *projectile trajectories*.

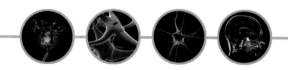

Motion attracts our attention. Particularly at night or when we are in unfamiliar places we are highly alert to objects that move around us. We subconsciously distinguish normal and unusual motion to minimize the flow of data our brains have to process. Normal motion is faded out from the conscious perception because it is seen as non-threatening. This can include quite complex motion patterns, such as water flowing down a creek, tree branches swaying in a breeze, or autumn leaves being blown around by the wind. Unusual motion in turn causes us to look carefully and investigate. Such motion can be as simple as a slow-crawling caterpillar on the sidewalk.

What distinguishes these types of motion is not whether the object is alive or not. The difference is whether the motion is passive, i.e., in response to interactions caused by the object's environment, or whether it is intentional, i.e., caused by the object on its own. This distinction makes sense behaviourally: we have no problem touching a passively moving object to stop it from hitting something, but we hesitate to touch an object that moves intentionally since the intent could change toward action against our hands.

Intentional motion is more complicated than an expression of free will. It contains many common elements with passive motion as the environment and the physical laws of nature govern what is possible and what makes sense.

Whether sensibility is always a requirement of intentional motion can be debated: if you have catnip herbs in your garden, their strong scents attract cats to chew on the perennial mint's leaves. The scent then causes the cat to roll in ecstasy or even to hallucinate, trying to catch invisible birds or mice.

However, no means exist to circumvent physical laws as a limiting factor to intentional motion. Subconsciously we take these laws into account. Nobody attaches feathers to his or her arms, spreads them, and leaps out a window to fly—even though this had been suggested as a viable means of escape from Crete for Daedalus and Icarus in mythological times.

A scientifically sound discussion of intentional motion has to explain the choices for the moving individual within the framework of applicable physical laws and physiological constraints. Combining these with free will allows for a tremendous multitude of observable motion patterns. For example, more than 9000 species of birds exist. Yet, an ornithologist (and some amateur bird watchers) can essentially distinguish these by observing a bird's flight pattern, velocity, and wing stroke. Fig. 2.1 illustrates 13 major flight patterns. Most species apply a combination of these patterns, usually selected according to circumstances not obvious to the observer. They are all adaptations to the aerodynamic properties of the bird's body. Horizontal air movement (wind) or vertical air motion (thermals) can require adjustments or enable certain manoeuvres. The physiology of the wing apparatus causes major variations in energy requirements for various flight patterns, an important factor during long-distance flights, e.g., during migration.

Thirteen flight patterns alone aren't sufficient to distinguish the large diversity of birds that have developed since *Archaeopteryx* 140 million years ago. A quantitative parameter is needed to separate the many bird species. This parameter is the bird's velocity in flight, because velocity characterizes motion in a quantitative fashion. The purpose of this chapter is to relate velocity to other parameters of motion, such as position, time, and acceleration. This will be done by means of definitions, which we need later in order to use these terms consistently. We note that the parameters of motion cannot be varied freely because these definitions relate them to each other. This means that one motion parameter can freely be chosen while the others then fall automatically in place.

In the case of recognizing bird species, we identify the velocity as a useful motion parameter. Velocity is chosen in that case not because it is the best parameter for bird identification, but because it is a convenient motion parameter for the observer. We discuss this further in the last section of this chapter. In Chapter 3, we will argue that the best parameter to characterize motion is acceleration.

# Basic Types of Motion of Inanimate Matter

We want to narrow down the many motion patterns to a few types we can handle. Since motion is the result of underlying causes that we do not discuss in this chapter, this selection may at first appear arbitrary. However, we apply two obvious criteria: the importance and/or frequency of occurrence, and scientific relevance for fundamental physical concepts. Three types of motion are distinguished this way, loosely referred to as **simple motion**:

- linear motion with constant acceleration,
- circular motion with constant acceleration toward the centre of curvature, and
- harmonic motion with a sinusoidal acceleration in one direction.

All three will be discussed in this textbook; however, we postpone circular motion to Chapter 21, when it becomes important for the motion of satellites

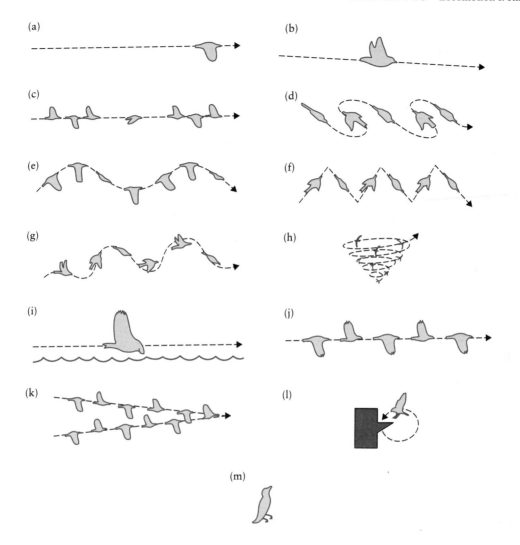

**FIGURE 2.1**

Thirteen distinguishable flight patterns of birds: (a) steady flight with regular wing beats along a straight line (all warbler species in North America), (b) partially or fully extended wings held steady during glide (hawks glide from one thermal to the next during migration), (c) flap and glide with alternate bursts of wing beats and a level glide (black vulture of southeastern United States), (d) dynamic soaring, which is a combination of downward glides, 180° turns, and lift against the wind (all albatross species), (e) undulating by rising with a couple of wing beats and then folding the wings and darting through the air (red-bellied woodpecker of eastern North America), (f) zigzag motion off the ground to evade predators (common snipe), (g) erratic or bouncy slow flight similar to a moth (common nighthawk), (h) static soaring in thermals (golden eagle of western North America), (i) steady course close to water surface with lower mandible cleaving the water surface (black skimmer), (j) straight line formation flight (American white pelican), (k) V-formation flight (Canada goose), (l) flying up from the ground or down from an aerial perch to seize prey, called hawking (American and Mexican kingbird species), (m) flightless motion (Canadian great auk, extinct since 1844).

around Earth and the motion of the electron in Bohr's atomic model, and we postpone harmonic motion to Chapter 16, when we need it to describe macroscopic and molecular vibrations. This leaves the linear motion with constant acceleration to be discussed in the current chapter. This discussion is done in two steps: first, the kinematic terms *velocity, speed,* and *acceleration* are defined, and then their mathematical relations for the specific case are developed. We repeat this approach, first for motion along a straight line and then for motion in a plane.

# One-Dimensional Motion

The place at which you sit reading this book is a position in space. You may choose it, for convenience, as your reference position for what we discuss next. Mathematically, we say that you choose it as the **origin**. Now look up and choose a particular point at the wall ahead. Imagine a straight line connecting you to that point. This line defines an **axis**. Along this axis we assign each point a numerical value, using a reference stick that has a preset length—let's say, one metre. We call this the $x$-axis, and assume that it continues beyond the point at the wall to infinity, and also continues behind you, with negative values, to negative infinity. If you can move only along this line, we call your motion **one-dimensional motion**. This motion is quite restricted—for example, you can never travel along a curved path.

Even this one-dimensional motion requires one more parameter for quantitative evaluation: time. We already referred to your current position as the origin in space. Let's now further call it the **initial instant,** for which we conveniently define time as zero, $t = 0$. Time is a second axis. Each instant along this axis is assigned a numerical value; this is done with a clock. Motion is then defined by the change of your position as a function of time.

## Definition of Velocity and Acceleration

We develop the concept of motion along the $x$-axis quantitatively with two examples from track and field events: 100-metre sprint and long jump. The box in Fig. 2.2(a) represents the sprinter at the starting line (index 1) and at the finish line (index 2), or the long jump competitor at the start of the approach (index 1) and at the point of takeoff (index 2). Fig. 2.2(b) is a plot with a vertical $x$-axis (ordinate) and a horizontal $t$-axis (abscissa). The solid curve in Fig. 2.2(b) is a possible description of the motion of each of the athletes as they get from position $x_1$ (starting position) to position $x_2$ (final position). The distance between $x_1$ and $x_2$ is called the **displacement** $\Delta x$, $\Delta x = x_2 - x_1$. During the early stage of the sprint or approach, i.e., near time $t_1$, the athlete covers a comparably smaller distance per time unit than during the late stage near time $t_2$. In the case of the sprinter, this is due to increasing the velocity toward a maximum value; in the case of the long jump competitor, this is done to achieve maximum takeoff velocity.

The simplest approach to define a velocity from the data in Fig. 2.2(a) is based on dividing the displacement $\Delta x$ by the corresponding time interval $\Delta t$, $\Delta t = t_2 - t_1$:

$$v_{\text{average}} = \frac{\Delta x}{\Delta t} = \frac{x_2 - x_1}{t_2 - t_1} \qquad [1]$$

With the displacement given in unit metre (m) and the time interval in unit second (s), the velocity has unit m/s. This is its standard unit; it is recommended to convert all other velocity units, such as the km/h unit used in everyday life, into standard units prior to

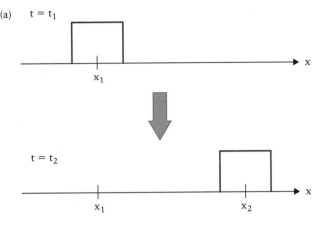

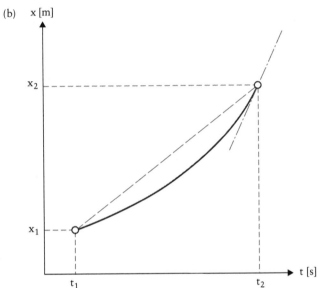

**FIGURE 2.2**

(a) The difference between the average velocity and the instantaneous velocity is illustrated for an object that moves from position $x_1$ at time $t_1$ to position $x_2$ at time $t_2$. (b) A graph illustrating how the position of the object changes with time (solid line). If we measure position and time only twice, at instant 1 and at instant 2 as indicated by two open circles, then we obtain the average velocity as the travelled distance, $\Delta x = x_2 - x_1$, divided by the elapsed time, $\Delta t = t_2 - t_1$ (dashed line). To provide a value for the velocity at instant 2, we need to record the first position at shorter intervals $\Delta t$. We can extrapolate such measurements to $\Delta t = 0$, which yields the instantaneous velocity as the tangent to the path, shown as the dash-dotted line.

further scientific calculations. (You will notice that we use non-standard units at times in this textbook; we do this when it is common practice in related research areas.) The velocity conversions are:

$$1.0 \, \frac{\text{km}}{\text{h}} = \frac{1000 \, \text{m}}{3600 \, \text{s}} = 0.278 \, \frac{\text{m}}{\text{s}}$$

$$[2]$$

$$1.0 \, \frac{\text{m}}{\text{s}} = \frac{1.0 \times 10^{-3} \, \text{km}}{(1/3600) \, \text{h}} = 3.6 \, \frac{\text{km}}{\text{h}}$$

In everyday language, the term *speed* is used synonymously with the term *velocity*. Scientifically, the two terms are defined differently. We introduce that distinction in the next section, when we study motion in a plane.

Eq. [1] corresponds graphically to the dashed line in Fig. 2.2(b), which is the **secant** to the solid curve. We call the slope of the secant the **average velocity** of the object between the two positions $x_1$ and $x_2$, $v_{average}$. The dashed line in Fig. 2.2(b) does not follow the solid line, meaning that the actual velocity of the athlete varies with position and is at most points different from the average velocity.

To discuss the usefulness of Eq. [1], the sprinter and the long jump competitor are compared more carefully. The definition of velocity in Eq. [1] is useful for the sprinter's coaching team. For example, you could plot the average velocity of a 100-m sprint, a 200-m dash, and a 400-m race for the same sprinter to obtain information about the endurance performance of the leg muscles. However, we more often want to know the velocity of an object at a particular instant in time. For example, the average velocity of the long jump competitor during the approach run is useless for the coaches. They are interested in the instantaneous velocity at takeoff.

The **instantaneous velocity** at a particular instant or position is obtained from the velocity definition in Eq. [1]. We start with the open circles in Fig. 2.2(b) and assume that they provide a first estimate for the instantaneous velocity at point $x_2$, based on Eq. [1]. Then we improve that estimate of the velocity by determining the average velocity for a shorter and shorter time interval $\Delta t$, each ending at time $t_2$. This is illustrated in Fig. 2.3; the slopes of the dash-dotted, dashed, and solid blue lines are successively better estimates of the slope at time $t_2$.

The instantaneous velocity at point $x_2$ is written as $v_{instantaneous}$ and follows when we extrapolate to $\Delta t = 0$ as shown by the slope of the dash-dotted line in Fig. 2.2(b). This line is the **tangent** to the solid curve

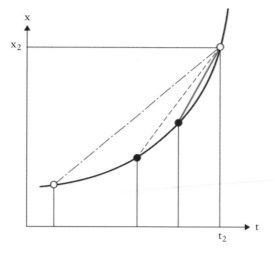

**FIGURE 2.3**

Repeat of Fig. 2.2 with the initial instants (open and solid dots) chosen successively closer to the final instant. The secant through the two respective points on the curve increasingly approaches the tangent at the final instant.

at position $x_2$, and the value of the instantaneous velocity is the slope of the tangent:

$$v_{instantaneous} = \lim_{\Delta t \to 0} \frac{\Delta x}{\Delta t} \qquad [3]$$

We use the mathematical limit notation in Eq. [3]; i.e., $v_{instantaneous}$ is the limit of the function $\Delta x/\Delta t$ as $\Delta t$ approaches zero. This is an approximation because we cannot simply set $t_2 = t_1$ in Eq. [1], as a division by zero is undefined. Since the instantaneous velocity is used in almost all physical applications, we drop the subscript *instantaneous* and require that all reported velocities are instantaneous unless explicitly stated otherwise.

## ● EXAMPLE 2.1

(a) You travel a distance $\Delta x_0 = 100$ km for each leg of a round trip. On the first leg light traffic allows you to maintain an average velocity of 80 km/h. On the return trip traffic has increased, and you can travel with an average velocity of only 40 km/h. For the round trip, what was your average velocity? Neglect the time spent at the destination. (A) $v_{\text{average}} = 40$ km/h. (B) 40 km/h $<$ $v_{\text{average}} < 60$ km/h. (C) $v_{\text{average}} = 60$ km/h. (D) 60 km/h $< v_{\text{average}} < 80$ km/h. (E) $v_{\text{average}} = 80$ km/h. (b) Generalize your result from part (a) and show that it is always correct in the generalized form. *Hint:* Use the problem-solving strategy outlined at the end of this chapter in the Math Review entitled "Problem-Solving Strategy."

*Solution to part (a):* Choice (B).

### Schematic Approach

Fig. 2.4 shows a sketch for this trip. We assume that the travel is one-dimensional with the $x$-axis along the road. The initial position is labelled $x_1$ and the destination is at $x_2$. What we do not know is the time required to travel each leg.

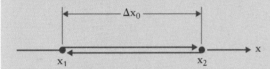

**FIGURE 2.4**

Sketch for a person on a return trip between two points along a straight line. The two positions are defined as $x_1$ (original position) and $x_2$ (destination).

### Physical Model

To calculate the average velocity for the round trip the total distance travelled is required, which is $2 \cdot \Delta x_0$. The total time required for the round trip is the sum of the times $\Delta t_1$ needed to the destination point and $\Delta t_2$ back. These two times must be calculated first.

### Quantitative Treatment

We use Eq. [1] to calculate the two travel times:

$$\Delta t_1 = \frac{\Delta x_0}{v_1} = \frac{100 \text{ km}}{80 \dfrac{\text{km}}{\text{h}}} = 1.25 \text{ h}$$

$$\Delta t_2 = \frac{\Delta x_0}{v_2} = \frac{100 \text{ km}}{40 \dfrac{\text{km}}{\text{h}}} = 2.5 \text{ h}$$

[4]

This allows us to calculate the average velocity for the round trip:

$$v_{\text{average}} = \frac{2 \cdot \Delta x_0}{\Delta t_1 + \Delta t_2} = \frac{200 \text{ km}}{1.25 \text{ h} + 2.5 \text{ h}}$$

$$= 53 \frac{\text{km}}{\text{h}}$$

[5]

Note that the result is not 60 km/h, which is the arithmetic average of the two given velocities.

*Solution to part (b):*

### Schematic Approach

A hypothesis is formulated. We state: The average velocity travelling a given route between two points is always less than the arithmetic average of the average velocities for each leg.

### Physical Model

Eq. [1] shows that the average velocity is inversely proportional to the time interval $\Delta t$. This is illustrated in Fig. 2.5. The horizontal and vertical solid lines indicate the points on the curve that correspond respectively to the two legs of the trip. The horizontal dashed line, drawn at the arithmetic average of the two velocities, and the vertical dash-dotted line, drawn at the arithmetic average of the required time intervals for the two legs, do not intersect on the curve because the two parameters of the plot are not related linearly.

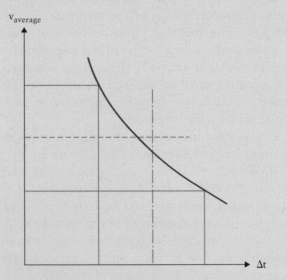

**FIGURE 2.5**

The average velocity as a function of required time for a given distance travelled. The solid lines indicate trips with larger and smaller velocity. The arithmetic average of these two velocities and the average time required do not yield a point on the curve because average velocity and time are not related linearly.

## Quantitative Treatment

We write separately the average velocity and the arithmetic average of the single-leg velocities. The average velocity of the return trip is taken from Eq. [5]:

$$v_{\text{average}} = \frac{2 \cdot \Delta x_0}{\Delta t_1 + \Delta t_2} \quad [6]$$

The arithmetic average of the two single-leg velocities is:

$$\langle v \rangle = \frac{1}{2} \left( \frac{\Delta x_0}{\Delta t_1} + \frac{\Delta x_0}{\Delta t_2} \right) \quad [7]$$

in which the notation $\langle \cdots \rangle$ refers to the arithmetic average. Now we use the hypothesis and combine Eqs. [6] and [7] such that we make a true mathematical statement if the hypothesis is correct:

$$v_{\text{average}} \text{ smaller than } \langle v \rangle \quad [8]$$

i.e.,

$$\frac{2 \cdot \Delta x_0}{\Delta t_1 + \Delta t_2} < \frac{1}{2} \left( \frac{\Delta x_0}{\Delta t_1} + \frac{\Delta x_0}{\Delta t_2} \right) \quad [9]$$

We use valid mathematical operations to rewrite Eq. [9] until we are convinced that it is correct (or prove it wrong). First, we divide on both sides by $\Delta x_0$ and write the bracket on the right side with a common denominator:

$$\frac{2}{\Delta t_1 + \Delta t_2} < \frac{1}{2} \left( \frac{\Delta t_1 + \Delta t_2}{\Delta t \cdot \Delta t_2} \right) \quad [10]$$

In the next step the respective denominators are brought to the other side of the inequality:

$$4 \cdot \Delta t_1 \cdot \Delta t_2 < (\Delta t_1 + \Delta t_2)^2$$
$$= \Delta t_1^2 + 2 \cdot \Delta t_1 \cdot \Delta t_2 + \Delta t_2^2 \quad [11]$$

In the last step the term on the left side is brought to the right side:

$$0 < \Delta t_1^2 - 2 \cdot \Delta t_1 \cdot \Delta t_2 + \Delta t_2^2 = (\Delta t_1 - \Delta t_2)^2 \quad [12]$$

We recognize that Eq. [12] is correct for all values $\Delta t_1 \neq \Delta t_2$, which we wanted to prove. The only exception occurs for $\Delta t_1 = \Delta t_2$; i.e., when we observe the same velocity throughout the round trip.

---

If the velocity of an object changes with time, we say that it accelerates. Thus, **acceleration** can be defined through its relation to the velocity in the same fashion as the velocity has been defined through its relation to the position in Eqs. [1] and [3]. The same arguments we made for the velocity with respect to

average and instantaneous values apply to acceleration. Therefore, we write only the instantaneous acceleration, in analogy to Eq. [3], as the average acceleration in a time interval $\Delta t$ with $\Delta t$ extrapolated to zero:

$$a = \lim_{\Delta t \to 0} \frac{\Delta v}{\Delta t} \quad [13]$$

The standard unit of acceleration is m/s$^2$. Eqs. [3] and [13] state:

*The velocity is the change of position with time and acceleration is the change of velocity with time. Instantaneous values of velocity and acceleration are obtained from the slope of the tangent at the instant of interest in an x(t) or v(t) plot of the motion, respectively.*

### Concept Question 2.3

**We will often treat the case of an object at rest and an object that moves with constant velocity as equivalent. What do these two states of motion have in common?**

ANSWER: In both cases, the acceleration is zero. When the object is at rest, its velocity is $v = 0$ m/s, which is a constant value as any other numerical value would be.

## Linear Motion with Constant Acceleration

We start with an experiment you can easily do as you read this book. Take an object like an eraser, place it on your flat palm, and turn your hand over. Obviously, the object will drop straight down to the ground. You may know from experience that it became faster and faster as it approached the floor, but you could argue that this detail of the motion is hard to observe during the short time the object was falling to the ground. So, let's do a second experiment. Place the object again on your flat palm, but this time release it by moving your hand upward until you suddenly pull it away from under the object. You observe that the object continues to move upward for a while, then momentarily comes to rest and then falls straight down to the ground. This time no doubt occurs about the object changing its velocity: it has initially a velocity upward, slows down to zero velocity at the instant it reaches its greatest height, and finally becomes faster but with a downward-directed velocity.

We learned earlier in this chapter that an object that changes its velocity is accelerated. We cannot explain in this chapter what accelerates the object and how, because this requires an understanding of the underlying laws of mechanics that we introduce in the next chapter. However, we can experimentally measure how the object moves and confirm that it accelerates with a constant acceleration of 9.8 m/s² straight downward. No acceleration in turn occurs in the horizontal direction. Since this acceleration is the same everywhere on the surface of Earth, the constant acceleration case is important and is therefore studied in more detail in this section.

**Kinematics** describes the motion of objects using the variables position, velocity, acceleration, and time. In particular, Eqs. [13] and [3] allow us to calculate how this acceleration is related to the velocity of the object, and its position as a function of time, respectively. When limiting the discussion to a constant acceleration, we also neglect any effects that may contribute additional horizontal or vertical acceleration terms. The resulting **kinematic relations** are used frequently in later chapters.

For a constant acceleration the instantaneous and average values are the same, as discussed in Concept Question 2.2. Thus, the acceleration can be written for any initial and final instants in analogy to Eq. [1]:

$$a = \frac{v_{\text{final}} - v_{\text{initial}}}{t_{\text{final}} - t_{\text{initial}}} \qquad [14]$$

Choosing $t_{\text{initial}} = 0$, this leads to:

$$v_{\text{final}} = v_{\text{initial}} + a \cdot t_{\text{final}} \qquad [15]$$

To generalize Eq. [15], we allow the final instant to vary; i.e., we drop the subscript *final*:

$$v(t) = v_{\text{initial}} + a \cdot t \qquad [16]$$

The notation $v(t)$ is a condensed notation for $v = f(t)$ where $f(\cdots)$ means *a function of*. Eq. [16] expresses the velocity at any time $t > 0$ and is the **first kinematic relation** relating velocity, acceleration, and time. We note that the velocity depends linearly on time. This is illustrated in Fig. 2.6. This observation allows us to write the average velocity in two ways:

- as the arithmetic average between the initial and final time instant in Fig. 2.6:

$$v_{\text{average}} = \frac{v_{\text{initial}} + v_{\text{final}}}{2} \qquad [17]$$

- and as the total displacement $\Delta x$ divided by the elapsed time $\Delta t$:

$$v_{\text{average}} = \frac{x_{\text{final}} - x_{\text{initial}}}{t_{\text{final}} - t_{\text{initial}}} \qquad [18]$$

Eqs. [17] and [18] are combined. The initial time is again chosen to be zero, $t_{\text{initial}} = 0$:

$$x_{\text{final}} - x_{\text{initial}} = \frac{t_{\text{final}}}{2} (v_{\text{final}} + v_{\text{initial}}) \qquad [19]$$

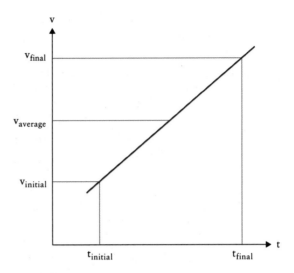

**FIGURE 2.6**

An object moves with constant acceleration. The acceleration is defined as the rate of change of the velocity with time. Therefore, the velocity changes linearly with time from an initial value $v_{\text{initial}}$ to a final value $v_{\text{final}}$. $v_{\text{average}}$ is the average velocity for the time interval from initial time $t_{\text{initial}}$ to final time $t_{\text{final}}$.

We generalize Eq. [19] again by dropping the subscript *final*. We also substitute Eq. [15] for $v_{\text{final}}$. This yields an equation that expresses the position as a function of time and acceleration:

$$x - x_{\text{initial}} = \frac{t}{2} (2 \cdot v_{\text{initial}} + a \cdot t) \qquad [20]$$

which leads to the second kinematic relation:

$$x = x_{\text{initial}} + v_{\text{initial}} \cdot t + \frac{1}{2} a \cdot t^2 \qquad [21]$$

The first two kinematic relations can be combined to eliminate the variable time. This is useful when we are interested in the path of an object as opposed to the timing of the motion. First the time variable $t$ is isolated in Eq. [16]:

$$t = \frac{v - v_{\text{initial}}}{a} \qquad [22]$$

Next, Eq. [22] is substituted into Eq. [21]:

$$x = x_{\text{initial}} + v_{\text{initial}} \frac{v - v_{\text{initial}}}{a} + \frac{a}{2} \left( \frac{v - v_{\text{initial}}}{a} \right)^2 \qquad [23]$$

which leads to the third kinematic relation:

$$v^2 = v_{\text{initial}}^2 + 2 \cdot a \cdot (x - x_{\text{initial}}) \qquad [24]$$

The term $x - x_{\text{initial}}$ represents the displacement $\Delta x$ between the initial and a variable final position of the object. Eq. [24] is also used with the acceleration written as the dependent variable:

$$a = \frac{v_{\text{final}}^2 - v_{\text{initial}}^2}{2 \cdot \Delta x} \qquad [25]$$

## Concept Question 2.4

Based on the three kinematic relations, which parameter pairs are suitable as parameter 1 and parameter 2 in Fig. 2.7?

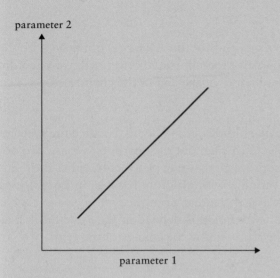

**FIGURE 2.7**

Linear plot for parameter 1 as the independent and parameter 2 as the dependent variable.

ANSWER: The graph shows that the two parameters are related in a linear fashion. We survey Eqs. [16], [21], and [24]. Keep in mind that $a$ = const was required to derive these equations; thus $a$ is not a variable. The only linear parameter pair is velocity and time in Eq. [16]. Position and time are related linearly only when $a = 0$ in Eq. [21].

## Concept Question 2.5

Animals that hunt by striking their prey need to significantly increase the velocity of their weapons over a short distance (e.g., fangs for snakes and beaks for birds). How does the required acceleration depend on the range $\Delta x$ if the weapon must strike from rest with 100 m/s or more?

ANSWER: We use Eq. [25] with $v_{initial} = 0$ and $v_{final} = 100$ m/s. This yields $a \propto 1/\Delta x$; i.e., the required acceleration is inversely proportional to the distance to the prey. Small animals with a short range, such as the Mantis shrimp we discuss later in this chapter, need to develop particularly large accelerations.

## ● EXAMPLE 2.2

An object initially at rest falls vertically from a tree branch $h = 4.0$ m above the ground. Neglecting air resistance, how long does the object travel through air?

*Supplementary physical information:* Objects near the surface of Earth are subject to a vertical acceleration downward of $g = 9.8$ m/s². This acceleration is called the gravitational acceleration. We treat it as constant even though minor variations occur due to local density variations in the lithosphere or to nearby massive mountain ranges. Indeed, variations in gravity have been used to locate the buried meteor impact crater near Chicxulub, Mexico, which most probably caused the mass extinction at the end of the Cretaceous (65 million years ago) that wiped out the dinosaurs.

*Solution:* We again use the problem-solving strategy outlined at the end of the chapter in the Math Review section "Problem-Solving Strategy."

### Schematic Approach

The problem is summarized in Fig. 2.8. The $x$-axis is identified as the vertical axis with the initial position a distance $h$ above the final position.

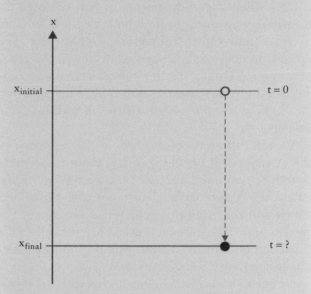

**FIGURE 2.8**

Sketch of an object falling straight off a tree branch. Its initial position is shown by an open dot, its final position by a solid dot.

### Physical Model

The second kinematic relation (Eq. [21]) connects the appropriate parameters position and time. We note that $a = -g$ because the acceleration points downward, against the direction of the $x$-axis. Further, $v_{initial} = 0$ (the object falls from rest) and

● **EXAMPLE 2.2** (*continued*)

$x_{\text{final}} - x_{\text{initial}} = -h$. Note that this is a negative value because the object travels downward, i.e., in the direction opposite to the $x$-axis.

### Quantitative Treatment

We substitute the above values in Eq. [21]:

$$x_{\text{final}} - x_{\text{initial}} = -h = \frac{1}{2}(-g)t^2 \quad [26]$$

This yields for the time:

$$t = \sqrt{\frac{2 \cdot h}{g}} = \sqrt{\frac{2 \cdot 4 \text{ m}}{9.8 \frac{\text{m}}{\text{s}^2}}} = 0.9 \text{ s} \quad [27]$$

# Two- and Three-Dimensional Motion

## Velocity and Acceleration as Vectors

The definitions of velocity and acceleration we introduced above for one-dimensional motion remain correct when we study motion in two or three dimensions. However, we now have to allow for two or three independent directions, respectively. The greater number of directions allows for more types of motion: a circular motion differs from an accelerated motion along a straight line only in the direction of the acceleration relative to the direction of the velocity.

We return to our observations at the beginning of the discussion of one-dimensional motion. We now introduce two more axes in the same way we introduced the $x$-axis earlier: these are the horizontal $y$-axis and the vertical $z$-axis. When these axes are chosen with 90° angles to each other we call this a **Cartesian coordinate system**. Any position in three-dimensional space is described by a vector. Vectors and some of their mathematical properties are introduced at the end of the chapter in the Math Review entitled "Vectors and Basic Vector Algebra."

Repeating the arguments that led to the definitions of velocity and acceleration in the one-dimensional case leads to their components along the three Cartesian axes. We write the position vector as $\mathbf{r} = (x(t), y(t), z(t))$ in which each component is a function of time. The velocity vector is then defined as $\mathbf{v} = (v_x(t), v_y(t), v_z(t))$ with:

$$\mathbf{v} = \lim_{\Delta t \to 0} \frac{\Delta \mathbf{r}}{\Delta t} \quad [28]$$

This is equivalent in component form to:

$$v_x = \lim_{\Delta t \to 0} \frac{\Delta x}{\Delta t}$$

$$v_y = \lim_{\Delta t \to 0} \frac{\Delta y}{\Delta t} \quad [29]$$

$$v_z = \lim_{\Delta t \to 0} \frac{\Delta z}{\Delta t}$$

The magnitude of the velocity is obtained with the Pythagorean theorem (see the Math Review section on "Geometry" at the end of the chapter):

$$|\mathbf{v}| = \sqrt{v_x^2 + v_y^2 + v_z^2} \quad [30]$$

The magnitude of the velocity is called the **speed** of the object. Throughout this textbook we use two notations for the magnitude of a vector, either the bold-faced variable with absolute bars, as in Eq. [30], or the variable in regular print, i.e., $|\mathbf{v}| = v$.

The acceleration is defined in the same fashion as a vector representing the change of the velocity of an object with time:

$$\mathbf{a} = \lim_{\Delta t \to 0} \frac{\Delta \mathbf{v}}{\Delta t} \quad [31]$$

This equation is written in component form:

$$a_x = \lim_{\Delta t \to 0} \frac{\Delta v_x}{\Delta t}$$

$$a_y = \lim_{\Delta t \to 0} \frac{\Delta v_y}{\Delta t} \quad [32]$$

$$a_z = \lim_{\Delta t \to 0} \frac{\Delta v_z}{\Delta t}$$

The velocity and acceleration variables in Eqs. [28] to [32] are instantaneous values because they apply at a given time instant. As before, the adjective *instantaneous* has been omitted because we always mean instantaneous velocities or accelerations unless otherwise specified.

### Concept Question 2.6

Eq. [32] relates the three acceleration components to the respective velocity components. Each formula in turn contains only $x$-, $y$-, or $z$-components. Does this mean that the acceleration and velocity vectors are always parallel to each other, i.e., $a \parallel v$ ($\parallel$ means "parallel to")?

ANSWER: No. The acceleration and the change of velocity with time are parallel, but the velocity vector itself can point in a different direction. If $\mathbf{a} \parallel \mathbf{v}$, motion along a straight line results. In all other cases a curved path is observed.

## Kinematics in a Two-Dimensional Plane

The kinematic relations connecting displacement, velocity, and acceleration have been derived for the one-dimensional case in the previous section. In this section we assume that the motion of the object is confined to the $xy$-plane and both acceleration components in that plane are constant, i.e., $a_x =$ const and $a_y =$ const. The first kinematic relation is then written in vector notation as follows:

$$\mathbf{v} = \mathbf{a} \cdot t + \mathbf{v}_{\text{initial}} \qquad [33]$$

and the second kinematic relation reads:

$$\mathbf{r} = \frac{1}{2}\mathbf{a} \cdot t^2 + \mathbf{v}_{\text{initial}} \cdot t + \mathbf{r}_{\text{initial}} \qquad [34]$$

For all practical purposes, the respective component formulas are used:

$$x\text{-direction:} \quad v_x = a_x \cdot t + v_{\text{initial},x}$$
$$y\text{-direction:} \quad v_y = a_y \cdot t + v_{\text{initial},y} \qquad [35]$$

and

$$x\text{-direction:} \quad x = \frac{1}{2}a_x \cdot t^2 + v_{\text{initial},x} \cdot t + x_{\text{initial}}$$
$$y\text{-direction:} \quad y = \frac{1}{2}a_y \cdot t^2 + v_{\text{initial},y} \cdot t + y_{\text{initial}} \qquad [36]$$

## ● EXAMPLE 2.3

The current theory of the evolution of flight requires intermediate species to benefit from **gliding** off tree branches. We can observe such behaviour in animals such as the Malayan Wallace's tree frog or the flying dragon, a Southeast Asian lizard shown in Fig. 2.9. These animals have membranous extensions in various places along their bodies that they can unfold to sustain a gliding fall after jumping off a tree. As a reference, (a) what formula describes the falling of an animal that jumps off a tree but cannot glide, e.g., a human, and (b) how must this formula vary for a Wallace's tree frog or a flying dragon for us to accept that the animal displays a successful glide?

*Solution to part (a):*

**Schematic Approach**

The first step we take in solving this problem is a simplification that is almost always justified in mechanical problems: we identify a two-dimensional plane in space in which the relevant physical parameters vary and the resulting motion occurs. This plane is defined as the $xy$-plane, allowing us to use Eqs. [35] and [36] instead of the corresponding three-dimensional formulas. We have to include

**FIGURE 2.9**

Flying dragon. A membrane is stretched between elongated ribs that act as struts.

## ● EXAMPLE 2.3 (continued)

full three-dimensional considerations in cases where the motion is not confined to a plane; when such cases occur later in the textbook, we will specifically point this out.

We can draw an initial sketch of what happens based on our everyday experience. This sketch is shown in Fig. 2.10(a). The object starts at an initial position with a given initial velocity vector. If distance matters to the jumping animal it will choose this velocity vector above the horizontal. We calculate the actual path without gliding in this part. If a person jumps off a tree and you observe the event looking at the plane of motion from the side, you observe the path sketched in Fig. 2.10(a).

### Physical Model

We define the horizontal direction as the $x$-axis and the vertical direction as the $y$-axis. The object is not accelerated horizontally ($a_x = 0$), and accelerates vertically with $a_y = -g$, as discussed in Example 2.2. The $y$-component of the acceleration is negative because the gravitational acceleration is pointing downward, i.e., in the negative $y$-direction.

For convenience, the initial position is chosen as the origin. This means that we modify the sketch we made in the schematic approach as shown in Fig. 2.10(b):

$$(x_{initial}, y_{initial}) = (0, 0) \qquad [37]$$

### Quantitative Treatment

We substitute the two acceleration components and Eq. [37] in Eq. [36]:

$$x\text{-direction:} \quad x = v_{initial,x} \cdot t$$

$$y\text{-direction:} \quad y = -\frac{g}{2} \cdot t^2 + v_{initial,y} \cdot t \qquad [38]$$

The two formulas in Eq. [38] are now combined to eliminate the time. We do this because we want to determine the path of the object. A path in two dimensions is a function of the form $y = f(x)$. We isolate the time $t$ in the first formula of Eq. [38] and then substitute it into the second formula:

$$y = -\frac{1}{2} g \left( \frac{x}{v_{initial,x}} \right)^2 + v_{initial,y} \frac{x}{v_{initial,x}}$$

$$= \frac{v_{initial,y}}{v_{initial,x}} \cdot x - \frac{g}{2v_{initial,x}^2} \cdot x^2 \qquad [39]$$

which is mathematically the form of a parabola ($y \propto x^2$). Thus, an animal or person that cannot glide will travel along a parabola from the branch to the ground. This path is shown in Fig. 2.10 and is called a **projectile trajectory**, because any object under the exclusive control of gravity follows it.

*Solution to part (b):* Any path with $y(x) > y_{projectile}$ means that the object is at a greater height than a freely falling object. Thus, that object is gliding.

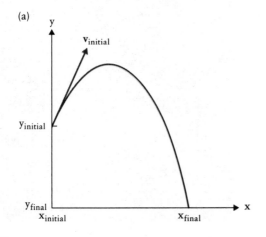
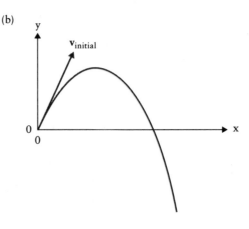

### FIGURE 2.10

(a) Sketch of the path of an object released at position ($x_{initial}$, $y_{initial}$) with an initial velocity vector $\mathbf{v}_{initial}$. The object is not accelerated horizontally and moves with a constant gravitational acceleration downward. The mathematical treatment of the motion yields a parabolic path that is called a projectile trajectory. (b) The calculations are greatly simplified by choosing the position ($x_{initial}$, $y_{initial}$) as the origin (0, 0) in this case.

## ● EXAMPLE 2.4

Mantis shrimp, such as the one shown in Fig. 2.11, have some of the most lethal weapons in the animal kingdom. They either stab or smash their prey to death with their limbs. Those that smash use calcified clubs to crush the shells of crabs or lobsters. Those that stab use spear-like arms to strike soft-bodied prey such as shrimp, fish, and squid. The prey has no chance in these encounters because the spear-like arm is accelerated from rest to 10 m/s in just 4 milliseconds. Taking into account that a F16 fighter jet has a maximum acceleration of $10 \cdot g$ where $g$ is the gravitational acceleration constant, by what factor does the mantis shrimp beat the F16 technology?

*Solution:* We first calculate the acceleration of the shrimp's arm. Then the ratio of the shrimp's acceleration to the maximum acceleration of the fighter jet is determined. We use Eq. [13], in which the limit can be dropped because we assume the shrimp applies a constant acceleration:

$$a = \frac{\Delta v}{\Delta t} \qquad [40]$$

$\Delta v$ is the change in velocity obtained in the time interval $\Delta t$. From the data given in the example text, we obtain:

$$a_{\text{shrimp}} = \frac{\Delta v}{\Delta t} = \frac{10 \text{ m/s}}{4 \cdot 10^{-3} \text{ s}} = 2500 \, \frac{\text{m}}{\text{s}^2} \qquad [41]$$

Note that we rewrote the 4 millisecond time interval by using the standard time unit seconds (s) without the prefix. The prefix represents a multiple of 10 and must be entered as such into the calculation. The result in Eq. [41] is equal to $a_{\text{shrimp}} = 255 \cdot g$. This value is obtained by dividing

Eq. [41] by $g = 9.8$ m/s$^2$. The ratio of the two accelerations is determined with the value for the fighter jet given in the example text:

$$\frac{a_{\text{shrimp}}}{a_{\text{F16}}} = \frac{255 \cdot g}{10 \cdot g} = 25.5 \qquad [42]$$

The shrimp accelerates its weapon over 25 times more strongly than a fighter jet. It is worthwhile to note, though, that the acceleration of the fighter jet does not represent an engineering limit but the physiological limit for the pilot. After all, you need the pilot still alive and conscious after take-off!

## Concept Question 2.9

With the shrimp's weapon in Example 2.4 operating not unlike the javelin of a competitive javelin thrower, should the shrimp adopt the results of state-of-the-art kinesiological research and choose a release angle in the range of 30° to 45° above the horizontal?

ANSWER: No. The stated release angle is optimum when the objective is to throw an object a maximum distance, as applicable to the javelin thrower. The shrimp is an ambush predator and kills at short distance (at most the range of its arm). The shrimp aims straight at the most vulnerable part of its prey. Does this mean that the shrimp is in danger of missing its target due to the action of gravity on its weapon? No, for several reasons. First, note that in Example 2.4 we found a forward acceleration of the shrimp's weapon of $255 \cdot g$; the action of $1.0 \cdot g$ vertically does not lead to a noticeable deviation of the weapon at impact. Secondly, the shrimp does its astonishing action underneath the surface of seawater. Its weapon would not fall to the ground even if the shrimp were to throw it at a leisurely pace forward. We discuss in Chapter 11 how buoyancy essentially compensates gravity in this case.

**FIGURE 2.11**
Mantis shrimp.

# Physiological Detection of Acceleration

Since acceleration plays a key role in kinematics, particularly in predicting the motion of an object, it is crucial for organisms to detect and measure accelerations. Interestingly, vision is not particularly effective for this purpose. You know this from your everyday experience: if somewhere in your field of vision a small bug

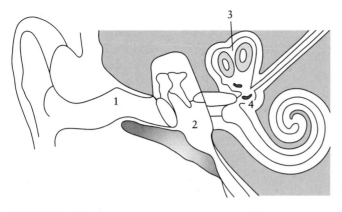

**FIGURE 2.12**

Overview of the human ear. We can distinguish three main sections of the ear: the outer ear with the auditory canal (1) ending at the eardrum, the middle ear with the three ossicles, hammer, anvil, and stirrup (from left, 2), and the inner ear with the vestibular organ. The vestibular organ includes the semicircular canals (3), which we discuss in the context of acceleration detection in the head, and the maculae (4), which we discuss in the context of gravity detection.

moves slowly, you turn your attention immediately to it. Compare this to your visual sensitivity for accelerations. When you sit in an airplane you feel the thrust of the aircraft immediately when the pilot receives clearance for take-off (as the acceleration pushes you into your seat). But if you watch the initial acceleration from an observation deck you have the impression that the airplane takes forever to get off the end of the tarmac. Thus, our vision is not sensitive to acceleration, but only to velocities.

The human body is capable of detecting accelerations in two ways: accelerations of our own body, particularly the head, and accelerations of objects in contact with our skin. Detection of the latter is achieved by **Pacinian corpuscles,** which are acceleration sensors located in the skin; these will be discussed in Chapter 3 (see Example 3.12).

Our sense of acceleration is located in our head as part of the ear. Fig. 2.12 presents an overview of the ear. The vestibular organ consists of two components:

• the orthogonal semicircular canals highlighted in yellow, which allow the measurement of accelerations, and

• the maculae (plural of *macula*), which are 0.3-mm-wide spots located just below the semicircular canals. The maculae are indicated in Fig. 2.12 as elongated red bars. The upper one is called the **utricular macula,** and the lower one the **saccular macula,** because they are located in small chambers called the *utricle* and the *saccule*, respectively. Both maculae measure the orienta-

tion of the head relative to the direction of gravity. We discuss them in detail in Chapter 3 (see Example 3.11).

Accelerations of our head are measured by the **semicircular canals** of the **vestibular organ.** The semicircular canals consist of three orthogonal, crescent-shaped tubes that are filled with a fluid called the **endolymph.** The orthogonal orientation of the three tubes provides the brain with a decoupled **acceleration detection** along the three Cartesian coordinates: the acceleration component sideways, back and forth, and up and down.

The mechanism of the semicircular canals is illustrated in Fig. 2.13. Resting on the crista is the swivel-mounted **cupula.** Dendrites reach from the neuron embedded in the crista into the cupula. While the head is motionless, the endolymph surrounding the cupula is at rest. When the head accelerates parallel to the orientation of a semicircular canal, the inertia of the endolymph results in a flow of the endolymph in the direction opposite to the direction of the acceleration. (We will explain inertia with Newton's first

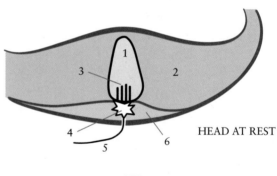

HEAD AT REST

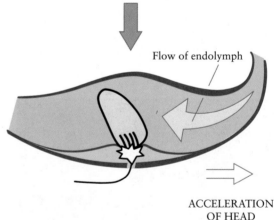

Flow of endolymph

ACCELERATION OF HEAD

**FIGURE 2.13**

(a) Sketch of the mechanism of the semicircular canals in the vestibular organ of the inner ear. The top part shows the head motionless. When the head accelerates toward the right, as shown at the bottom, the endolymph (2) flows because of its inertia toward the left. This pushes the cupula (1) resting on the crista (6). The cupula tilts, bending the dendrites (3) that belong to a neuron (4) embedded in the crista, triggering a signal in a nerve (5) to the brain.

law in Chapter 3.) This phenomenon can be simulated by holding a half-full glass of water in your hand and suddenly accelerating it. Its inertia causes the water to stay behind. The flow of the endolymph pushes the cupula to the side, so that the tilting is sensed by the nerve endings in the cupula and communicated to the brain. Note that the semicircular canals cannot sense speed, because motion with constant speed does not cause an acceleration of the endolymph against the cupula. If you move your head with constant speed the endolymph is at rest and the cupula retains an upright position, in the same fashion as if the head were motionless.

Acceleration detectors developed early in animals and are widespread among vertebrates. The **lateral line system** in fish is illustrated in Fig. 2.14. You see this canal system as lines running the full length of the fish from the gills to the tail along both sides (trunk canals); the pattern at the head is highlighted in Fig. 2.14(a). The canals lie below the scales of the fish. When the fish accelerates, water pushes against **neuromasts** (see Fig. 2.14(b)), which are the equivalent component to the cupula of the semicircular canal system in the human ear. Water flowing past the bendable neuromast causes dendrites that reach into the neuromast to bend and trigger a nerve signal to the brain of the animal. The lateral line system allows fish to monitor not only their own accelerations, but also water pressure changes due to other moving objects (such as predators or prey) and low-frequency sounds carried through the water.

(a)

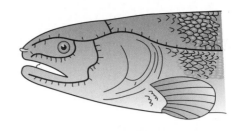

(b)

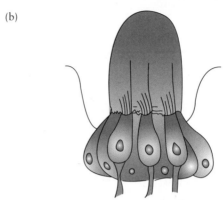

**FIGURE 2.14**

The mechanism of the lateral line system of fish. Fish can detect the acceleration of the water passing past their body. (a) The lateral line system consists of a system of canals with external openings that are running below the fish's epidermis between the scales. The line system in the head region is highlighted by thick lines. Acceleration receptors are located at various points along these canals, indicated by small tick-marks along the highlighted lines. (b) The receptor consists of a very similar arrangement to that of the cupula in the semicircular canals of the vestibular organ: the cupula rests on hair cells with hair-like sensory extensions reaching into the base of the cupula. When these sensory hairs are bent, a nerve signal is sent to the centre of the nervous system of the fish.

# MULTIPLE CHOICE AND CONCEPTUAL QUESTIONS

### VECTORS

**Q–2.1.** (a) What is the sum of the two vectors $\mathbf{a} = (5, 5)$ and $\mathbf{b} = (-14, 5)$? (b) What are the magnitude and direction of $\mathbf{a} + \mathbf{b}$?

**Q–2.2.** If vector $\mathbf{a}$ is added to vector $\mathbf{b}$, the result is the vector $\mathbf{c} = (6, 2)$. If $\mathbf{b}$ is subtracted from $\mathbf{a}$, the result is the vector $\mathbf{d} = (-5, 8)$. (a) What is the magnitude of vector $\mathbf{a}$? (b) What is the magnitude of vector $\mathbf{b}$?

### ONE-DIMENSIONAL MOTION

**Q–2.3.** We become uncomfortable if an elevator accelerates downward at a rate such that it reaches or exceeds a velocity of 6 m/s while travelling ten floors (30 metres). What value comes closest to the acceleration of such an elevator? (A) 0.3 m/s$^2$, (B) 0.6 m/s$^2$, (C) 1.2 m/s$^2$, (D) 2.0 m/s$^2$, (E) 10 m/s$^2$.

**Q–2.4.** If an object travels with positive velocity in the $x$-direction, can it have a negative acceleration along the $x$-axis at the same time?

**Q–2.5.** If the average velocity of an object is zero in a given time interval, what do we know about its displacement during the same time interval?

**Q–2.6.** Can the instantaneous velocity of an object at a given time instant be greater than the average velocity over a time interval that includes the given time instant? Can it be less?

**Q–2.7.** An object is thrown vertically upward. (a) What are its velocity and acceleration when it reaches its highest altitude? (b) What is its acceleration on its way downward half a metre above the ground?

**Q–2.8.** A dog and its master walk toward their home. When they are within 1 km of the door ($t = 0$), the dog starts to run twice as fast as the master walks, back and forth between master and door until the master reaches home. How far did the dog run after $t = 0$?

## TWO-DIMENSIONAL MOTION

**Q–2.9.** (a) Can an object accelerate if its speed is constant? (b) Can an object accelerate if its velocity is constant?

**Q–2.10.** Is there any point along the path of a projectile where its velocity and acceleration vectors are (a) perpendicular to each other, or (b) parallel to each other?

**Q–2.11.** An object is thrown upward by a person on a train that moves with constant velocity. (a) Describe the path of the object as seen by the person throwing it. (b) Describe the path of the object as seen by a stationary observer outside the train.

**Q–2.12.** (a) Why do athletes in jumping or throwing disciplines use an approaching run as part of their action? (b) Neglecting air resistance and aerodynamics, what would be the best angle of release in discus throwing?

## ANALYTICAL PROBLEMS

### UNIT CONVERSIONS

**P–2.1.** A competitive sprinter needs 9.9 seconds for 100 metres. What is the average velocity in units m/s and units km/h?

### VECTOR APPLICATIONS

**P–2.2.** Fig. 2.15(a) shows a shear fracture of the neck of the femur. In a shear fracture opposite fracture faces have slid past each other. Fig. 2.15(b) shows a sketch of a fracture with the net displacement $AB$ along the fracture plane. (a) What is the net displacement $AB$ for a horizontal slip of 4.0 mm and a vertical slip of 3.0 mm? (b) If the fracture plane is tilted by $\theta = 20°$ to the plane perpendicular to the bone, by how much have the two bones moved relative to each other along the bone's axis?

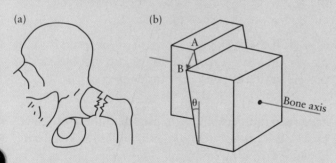

**FIGURE 2.15**

**P–2.3.** Fig. 2.16 shows a back view of an adult male and an adult female human (accompanied by two children). (a) For a typical male, the vertical distance from the bottom of the feet to the neck is $d_1 = 150$ cm and the distance from the neck to the hand is $d_2 = 80$ cm. Find the vector describing the position of the hand relative to the bottom of the feet if the angle at which the arm is held is $\theta = 35°$ to the vertical. (b) Repeat the calculation for a typical female with $d_1 = 130$ cm, $d_2 = 65$ cm, and the same angle $\theta$.

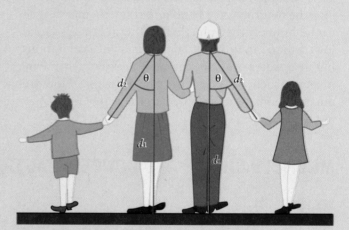

**FIGURE 2.16**

**P–2.4.** Fig. 2.17 shows (left) a front view and (right) a side view of a human skull. Two perpendicular projections such as these are often used to determine distances and angles in three-dimensional bodies, e.g., for focussed radiation therapy with high-energy X-ray beams. (a) Assuming that the diameter of the skull at the dashed line shown with the left-hand skull in Fig. 2.17 is 16 cm, determine the distance from the tip of the nasal bone (point $A$) to the centre of the last molar in the upper jaw (point $B$). (b) Determine the angle between two lines connecting the point halfway between the two central maxilla incisor teeth and the last maxilla molars on either side.

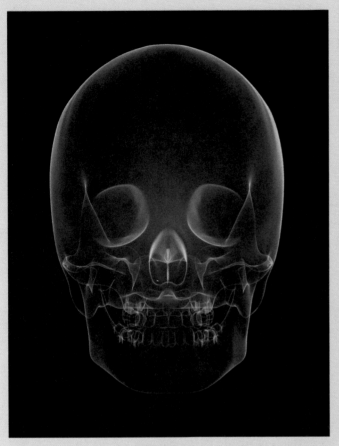 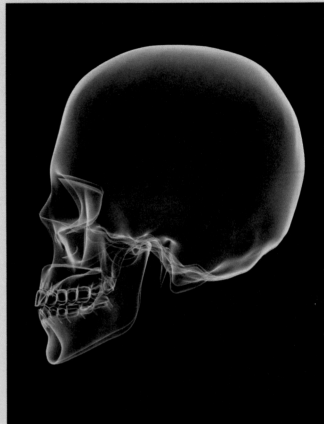

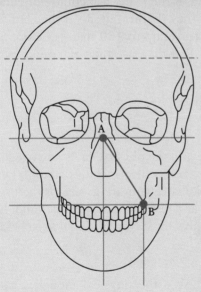 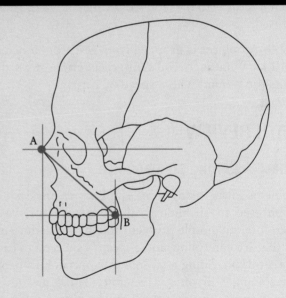

**FIGURE 2.17**

(c) Compare the result in (b) with the result obtained from Fig. 2.18, which shows a top view of the permanent dentition.

## ONE-DIMENSIONAL MOTION

**P–2.5.** A bacterium moves with a speed of 3.5 $\mu$m/s across a petri dish with radius $r = 8.4$ cm. How long does it take the bacterium to traverse the petri dish along its diameter?

**P–2.6.** In 1865, Jules Verne suggested sending people to the Moon by launching a space capsule with a 220-m-long cannon. The final speed of the capsule must reach 11 km/s. What acceleration would the passengers experience, and would they survive the launch?

**P–2.7.** An object is released at time $t = 0$ upward with initial speed 5.0 m/s. Draw an $x(t)$ plot for the time period until it returns to its initial position.

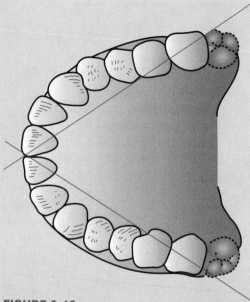

**FIGURE 2.18**

**P–2.8.** An object is thrown vertically upward with a speed of 25 m/s. (a) How high does it rise? (b) How long does it take to reach this highest altitude? (c) How long does it take to hit the ground after it reaches the highest altitude? (d) What is its speed when it returns to the level from which it was initially released?

**P–2.9.** An object is dropped from rest from a height of 10 m. What is its constant acceleration upward if it hits the ground with a speed of 1 m/s?

## TWO-DIMENSIONAL MOTION

**P–2.10.** A long jumper leaves the track at an angle of 20° with the horizontal and at a speed of 11 m/s. (a) How far does the athlete jump, disregarding arm and leg motion and air resistance? (b) What is the maximum height reached during the jump?

**P–2.11.** The best major league baseball pitchers can throw a baseball with velocities exceeding 150 km/h. If a pitch is thrown horizontally with that velocity, how far does the ball fall vertically by the time it reaches the catcher's glove 20 metres away?

**P–2.12.** In American football, place kickers often decide a game with an attempt to kick the football from as far as 40 metres through a goal that has a lower crossbar 3 metres above the ground. In a typical kick, the ball is set in motion with an initial velocity of 20 m/s at an angle of 53° to the horizontal. Does the ball clear the crossbar?

**P–2.13.** Fish use various techniques to escape a predator. Forty species of flying fish exist—such as the California flying fish, which has a length of 50 cm. These animals escape by leaving the water through the surface, propelled by their tails to typical speeds of 30 km/h. If the flying fish could not glide, (a) how far would they fly through air if they left at 45°? (b) They can travel up to 180 metres before re-entering the water. Did they use their wing-like pectoral fins to glide?

# MATH REVIEW

## PROBLEM-SOLVING STRATEGY

Problems in the many sub-disciplines of physics can be phrased in an almost infinite number of ways. Therefore, no simple problem-solving procedure exists that we can follow and expect to succeed in each case. Still, providing a structured approach to problem solving will often save time. Thus, we devise three general steps that are useful in most contexts.

### Schematic Approach

In the first step, you compile the known facts about the problem and note what you do not know. If a sketch is given with the problem, familiarize yourself with it during this step. If one is not given you may want to make your own sketch.

### Physical Model

In the second step you address the physical aspects of the problem, including the physical parameters that play a role and the physical laws you need to solve it. A physical model also includes simplifying assumptions. Make sure you are aware of the assumptions you make and test whether they are valid. In this step you may have to draw additional sketches.

### Quantitative Treatment

In the last step the physical model is transformed into mathematical equations and the known parameters are substituted such that an explicit solution is provided.

## GEOMETRY

Often you will evaluate angles in sketches accompanying a problem. To do this, it is necessary to know which angles in a given situation are equal, and which angles add up to 90° or 180°. Inspecting Figs. 2.19 and 2.20, confirm that $\alpha = \gamma$, $\alpha + \beta = 180°$, $\varepsilon = \phi$, $\varepsilon = \theta$, and $\delta + \theta = 180°$.

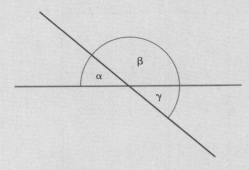

**FIGURE 2.19**

The three angles adjacent to an intersection of two straight lines are related in the form $\alpha = \gamma$, $\alpha + \beta = 180°$, and $\beta + \gamma = 180°$.

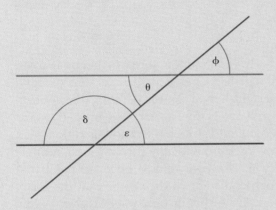

**FIGURE 2.20**

The four angles $\delta$, $\varepsilon$, $\theta$, and $\phi$, which are adjacent to a straight line that intersects with two parallel straight lines, are related in the form $\varepsilon = \phi$, $\varepsilon = \theta$, and $\delta + \theta = 180°$.

We use three trigonometric functions in the text, the sine function ($\sin \theta$), the cosine function ($\cos \theta$), and the tangent function ($\tan \theta$). It is important to know how they are connected for a right triangle. Defining one angle other than the 90° angle in the triangle as $\theta$, the trigonometric functions are given as follows:

$$\sin \theta = \frac{\text{length of side opposite to } \theta}{\text{length of hypotenuse}}$$

$$\cos \theta = \frac{\text{length of side adjacent to } \theta}{\text{length of hypotenuse}}$$

$$\tan \theta = \frac{\text{length of side opposite to } \theta}{\text{length of side adjacent to } \theta}$$

The following relations apply for negative angles:

$$\sin(-\theta) = -\sin \theta$$

$$\cos(-\theta) = \cos \theta$$

$$\tan(-\theta) = -\tan \theta$$

Relations between the sine and cosine functions follow from the basic definitions:

$$\sin(90° - \theta) = \cos \theta$$

$$\cos(90° - \theta) = \sin \theta$$

### Example 2.5

In the triangle given in Fig. 2.21 identify the trigonometric functions for angles $\psi$ and $\phi$.

*Solution*: The following relations hold:

$$\sin \psi = \frac{a}{c} \quad \cos \psi = \frac{b}{c} \quad \tan \psi = \frac{a}{b}$$

$$\sin \phi = \frac{b}{c} \quad \cos \phi = \frac{a}{c} \quad \tan \phi = \frac{b}{a}$$

The Pythagorean theorem states that, for a right triangle in which $c$ is the length of the hypotenuse and $a$ and $b$ are the lengths of the sides opposite and adjacent to the angle $\theta$:

$$c^2 = a^2 + b^2$$

This is illustrated in the left sketch of Fig. 2.22. The two sketches on the right side of the figure demonstrate how simply the Pythagorean theorem is proven: the four triangles in the left box are arranged to leave open the area $c^2$. They are then rearranged in the same box at right to leave open two areas, $a^2$ and $b^2$.

### Example 2.6

(a) Confirm that the corners of the area labelled $c^2$ in the middle panel of Fig. 2.22 are right angles.
(b) Use the Pythagorean theorem to prove the following formula:

$$\sin^2 \phi + \cos^2 \phi = 1$$

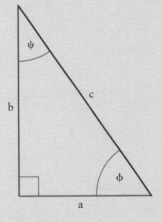

**FIGURE 2.21**

A right triangle with all three sides and angles labelled.

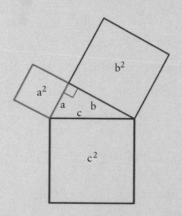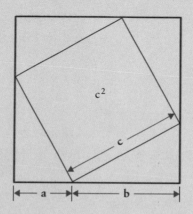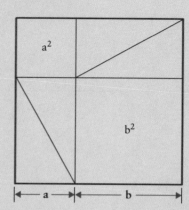

**FIGURE 2.22**

Left panel: Illustration of the Pythagorean theorem for a right triangle with hypotenuse $c$. Middle and right panel: Simple geometric proof of the Pythagorean theorem. Each box has the total area $(a + b)^2$. Inserting four right triangles, with sides $a$ and $b$ meeting at the right angle, an area $c^2$ is left open in the middle panel and, after rearranging the four triangles in the right panel, the areas $a^2$ and $b^2$ are left open.

(c) Use Fig. 2.21 to prove the following formula, which applies as long as $\cos \phi \neq 0$:

$$\tan \phi = \frac{\sin \phi}{\cos \phi}$$

*Solution to part (a):* The sum of the three angles in a triangle is 180°, and therefore the sum of the angles excluding the right angle in a right triangle is equal to 90°. Choosing the lower corner of the tilted area within the larger box in the middle panel of Fig. 2.22, we see that the two angles between the side of the larger box and the sides of the inner box are equal to the sum of the two angles (excluding the right angle) in either one of the four identical triangles. Thus, the angle of the corner is 90° since this sum equals 90°, and the larger box describes an angle of 180° at the corner point.

*Solution to part (b):* We calculate $\sin^2 \phi$ and $\cos^2 \phi$ from Fig. 2.21. Then we use the Pythagorean theorem to simplify the result:

$$\sin^2 \phi + \cos^2 \phi = \frac{b^2}{c^2} + \frac{a^2}{c^2} = \frac{a^2 + b^2}{c^2}$$

which yields

$$\sin^2 \phi + \cos^2 \phi = \frac{c^2}{c^2} = 1$$

*Solution to part (c):* The proof is based on Fig. 2.21:

$$\frac{\sin \phi}{\cos \phi} = \frac{b/c}{a/c} = \frac{b}{a} = \tan \phi$$

## VECTORS AND BASIC VECTOR ALGEBRA

The Cartesian coordinate system (named after René Descartes, *La Géométrie*, 1637) is suitable for describing a three-dimensional mathematical space

(Fig. 2.23). It is based on three orthogonal axes, which are labelled, in order, $x$-axis, $y$-axis, and $z$-axis. The **right-hand rule** was developed to confirm that a coordinate system is labelled properly: take your right hand and stretch the thumb and the index finger. They are automatically forming a right angle between them. Use your middle finger to point in a direction perpendicular to the thumb and the index finger. You can do this in only one direction. Now point the thumb in the direction of the $x$-axis. Then turn your hand such that the index finger points in the $y$-direction. At this point your middle finger points automatically in the $z$-direction.

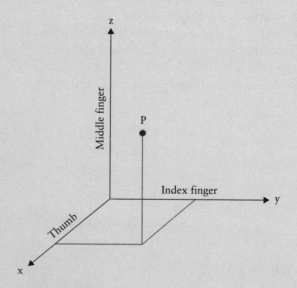

**FIGURE 2.23**

Three-dimensional, perpendicular coordinates (Cartesian coordinate system). The order of the axes is determined by the right-hand rule described in the text.

The three axes intersect at the **origin**. Three numbers are assigned to any point $P$ that are proportional to the distances from the origin along each axis. These numbers are called the *coordinates*, and are labelled using indices to identify the axis: $p_x$, $p_y$, and $p_z$. This is illustrated in Fig. 2.24, where, for clarity, only a two-dimensional space is shown.

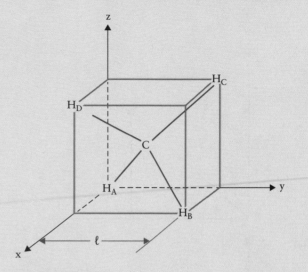

**FIGURE 2.25**

The geometry of the tetrahedral methane molecule $CH_4$ is best described by placing the molecule in a cube of side length $l$ in a Cartesian coordinate system. The four hydrogen atoms form four corners of the cube as shown. They are indistinguishable in a real molecule but have been labelled in the sketch with different indices for calculation purposes.

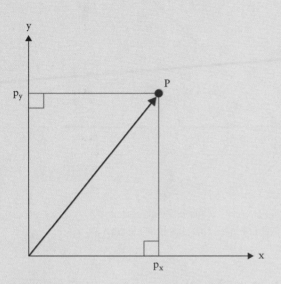

**FIGURE 2.24**

Coordinates of point $P$ in a two-dimensional Cartesian coordinate system. The coordinates are proportional to the lengths of the axes from the origin to the points of perpendicular projection of point $P$ onto the axes.

Associated with point $P$ is an arrow reaching from the origin to point $P$, called vector **p**. A vector is represented by two or three numbers (with the number of coordinates depending on the dimensionality of the considered space), $\mathbf{p} = (p_x, p_y, p_z)$, or, as in Fig. 2.24, $\mathbf{p} = (p_x, p_y)$. Note that vectors are typographically indicated by bold-faced letters.

Vectors must be distinguished from *scalars*, which are just simple numbers. In contrast, vectors have both magnitude (i.e., a simple number) and direction. The physical quantities discussed in this textbook are either described by a scalar (e.g., temperature) or by a vector (e.g., force). Even if a problem is one-dimensional, vector quantities retain their directional information, then carrying a + or − sign.

**Example 2.7**

We use the methane molecule as an example of the vector algebra concepts introduced in this section. The methane molecule, $CH_4$, is placed in a cube of side length $l$ in Fig. 2.25. Express the positions of the four hydrogen atoms and the carbon atom in the methane molecule in Cartesian coordinates.

*Solution:* The positions of the five atoms are C: $(0.5l, 0.5l, 0.5l)$, $H_A$: $(0, 0, 0)$, $H_B$: $(l, l, 0)$, $H_C$: $(0, l, l)$, and $H_D$: $(l, 0, l)$.

An alternative way to describe vectors is to use polar coordinates. We apply these in this textbook only for two-dimensional systems. The length $|\mathbf{p}|$ and the angle $\theta$ between the vector and the positive $x$-axis replace the two Cartesian coordinates $p_x$ and $p_y$, as shown in the top sketch of Fig. 2.26. The bottom sketch of Fig. 2.26 illustrates how the polar coordinates and the Cartesian coordinates are related to each other: $\sin \theta = p_y/|\mathbf{p}|$ and $\cos \theta = p_x/|\mathbf{p}|$. With the basic vector definitions established, the fundamental vector operations can be introduced.

**Magnitude or Length of a Vector**

With the Pythagorean theorem, we find for the triangle in the bottom sketch of Fig. 2.26:

$$|\mathbf{p}| = \sqrt{p_x^2 + p_y^2}$$

For example, the length of the two-dimensional vector $\mathbf{p} = (3, 4)$ is $|\mathbf{p}| = 5$.

**Vector Addition: $a + b = r$**

The vector addition is sketched in Fig. 2.27. For practical applications, each component of a Cartesian coordinate system is added separately:

$x$-component: $\quad a_x + b_x = r_x$

$y$-component: $\quad a_y + b_y = r_y$

$z$-component: $\quad a_z + b_z = r_z$

(a)

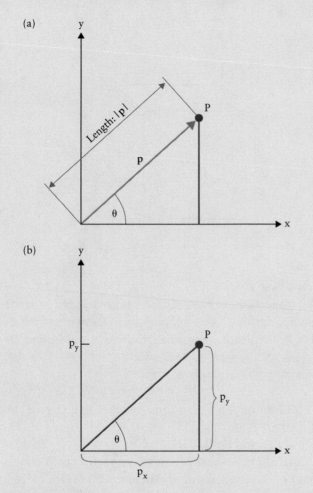

(b)

**FIGURE 2.26**

Representation of the position of a point *P* using polar coordinates. (a) Definition of angle $\theta$ and length of vector, |**p**|. (b) Sketch highlighting the trigonometric relations between the polar coordinates and the Cartesian coordinates.

Thus, all algebra rules apply; e.g., the commutative law in the form $\mathbf{a} + \mathbf{b} = \mathbf{b} + \mathbf{a}$.

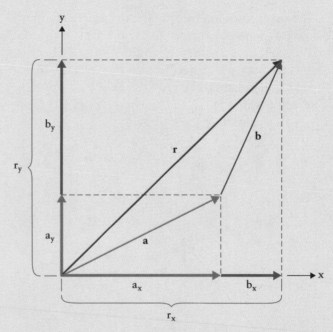

**FIGURE 2.27**

Vector addition of vectors **a** and **b** and the relation of the components of the resulting vector **r** to the components of **a** and **b**, i.e., $a_x + b_x = r_x$ and $a_y + b_y = r_y$.

**Multiplication of a Vector with a Scalar: *na = r***

Again, the operation is done for each component separately:

$x$-component: $\quad na_x = r_x$

$y$-component: $\quad na_y = r_y$

$z$-component: $\quad na_z = r_z$

Combining the multiplication and addition of vectors, we introduce the subtraction of vectors in the form: $\mathbf{a} - \mathbf{b} = \mathbf{a} + (-1)\mathbf{b}$.

# SUMMARY

**DEFINITIONS**

• Instantaneous velocity:
  • in one dimension:

$$v_{\text{instantaneous}} = \lim_{\Delta t \to 0} \frac{\Delta x}{\Delta t}$$

$\Delta x$ is displacement, $\Delta t$ is time interval.

• vector notation for motion in two- or three-dimensional space:

$$\mathbf{v} = \lim_{\Delta t \to 0} \frac{\Delta \mathbf{r}}{\Delta t}$$

**r** is the position vector, $\mathbf{r} = (x, y, z)$.

• vector components for motion in $xy$-plane:

$$v_x = \lim_{\Delta t \to 0} \frac{\Delta x}{\Delta t}$$

$$v_y = \lim_{\Delta t \to 0} \frac{\Delta y}{\Delta t}$$

• Speed:

$$|\mathbf{v}| = \sqrt{v_x^2 + v_y^2 + v_z^2}$$

• Instantaneous acceleration:
  • in one dimension:

$$a = \lim_{\Delta t \to 0} \frac{\Delta v}{\Delta t}$$

- vector notation for motion in two- or three-dimensional space:

$$\mathbf{a} = \lim_{\Delta t \to 0} \frac{\Delta \mathbf{v}}{\Delta t}$$

- vector components for motion in $xy$-plane:

$$a_x = \lim_{\Delta t \to 0} \frac{\Delta v_x}{\Delta t}$$

$$a_y = \lim_{\Delta t \to 0} \frac{\Delta v_y}{\Delta t}$$

## UNITS

- Position, position component, distance, displacement: m (metre)
- Time $t$: s (second)
- Velocity components and speed $v$: m/s
- Acceleration $a$: m/s$^2$

## LAWS

- First kinematic relation for constant acceleration
  - in one dimension:

$$v(t) = v_{initial} + a \cdot t$$

  - vector notation for motion in two- or three-dimensional space:

$$\mathbf{v} = \mathbf{a} \cdot t + \mathbf{v}_{initial}$$

- vector components for motion in $xy$-plane:

$x$-direction:  $v_x = a_x \cdot t + \mathbf{v}_{initial,x}$

$y$-direction:  $v_y = a_y \cdot t + \mathbf{v}_{initial,y}$

- Second kinematic relation for constant acceleration
  - in one dimension:

$$x = x_{initial} + v_{initial} \cdot t + \frac{1}{2} a \cdot t^2$$

  - vector notation for motion in two- or three-dimensional space:

$$\mathbf{r} = \frac{1}{2} \mathbf{a} \cdot t^2 + \mathbf{v}_{initial} \cdot t + \mathbf{r}_{initial}$$

  - vector components for motion in $xy$-plane:

$x$-direction:  $x = \frac{1}{2} a_x \cdot t^2 + \mathbf{v}_{initial,x} \cdot t + x_{initial}$

$y$-direction:  $y = \frac{1}{2} a_y \cdot t^2 + \mathbf{v}_{initial,y} \cdot t + y_{initial}$

- Third kinematic relation for constant acceleration:
  - in one dimension:

$$v^2 = v_{initial}^2 + 2 \cdot a(x - x_{initial})$$

  - with acceleration as dependent variable:

$$a = \frac{v_{final}^2 - v_{initial}^2}{2 \cdot \Delta x}$$

# CHAPTER 3

# BIOMECHANICS
## Forces and Newton's Laws

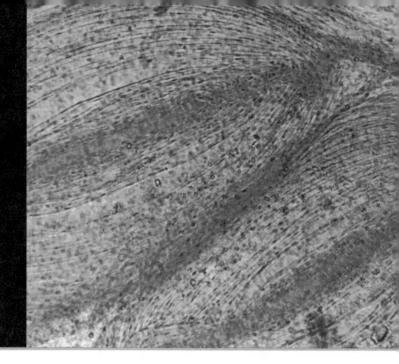

A force is defined by the interaction between separate objects. It is characterized by two properties, a magnitude and a direction. Newton identified three laws that govern all forces, called the *laws of mechanics:* (1) An object is in mechanical equilibrium if the forces that act on the object are balanced, resulting in no change of its velocity. (2) If instead a set of unbalanced forces acts on the object, it accelerates proportional to the magnitude of the net force, and in the direction in which the net force acts. (3) Any two interacting objects exert equal but opposite forces upon each other; such forces are called an action–reaction pair.

The laws of mechanics allow us to understand the anatomical design and physiological function of muscles as a source of forces, and the skeleton as the frame against which these forces act. Organisms have a range of receptors that detect external forces directly or by measuring the resulting acceleration. These receptors are called mechano-receptors, and they provide us with interesting applications of Newton's laws.

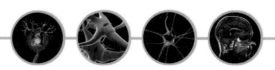

The widely accepted **definition of life** consists of three necessary conditions: (a) metabolism and growth, (b) recognition of external stimuli, combined with the ability to respond, and (c) reproduction. It is interesting to note that the second condition does not specify the response to stimuli as locomotion (which is the motion from one place to another), even though locomotion first comes to mind: bacteria and protists propelling themselves with flagellar action along chemical gradients in their environment, fungi and plants adjusting to the direction of sunlight, and animals pursuing prey or evading predators. The wording of the second condition is proper from a physical point of view: locomotion is not a direct response of an organism but is one possible consequence of the primary response, which is to **exert a force**. Indeed, organisms more often exert forces to *prevent* motion, e.g., when we hold objects or keep our body in a particular posture.

The predominance of forces over locomotion is also seen in the hierarchy of specialized tissues that have developed in the animal kingdom: muscle tissue serves the specific purpose of exerting forces; locomotion in turn is achieved when several muscles and other tissues, such as bones, cooperate. We therefore need to start our discussion with the basic muscle tissue and the properties of the forces it generates.

We turn our attention in the current chapter also to the methods of **mechanical stimulus detection**, the question of why we are sensitive to environmental forces, in particular gravity and the various contact forces.

To fully describe forces requires that we measure both their magnitude and direction; i.e., we require vector algebra in this chapter as a mathematical tool. The mathematical definition of a vector and an overview of vector algebra operations are given in a Math Review at the end of Chapter 2.

## Muscles as the Origin of Forces

**Muscle tissues** are distinguished in anatomy on the basis of their structural differences and in physiology on the basis of their functional purposes. Both approaches lead to the same three categories, reinforcing the close relation between design and function in living organisms: **skeletal muscles** that are attached to bones, **smooth muscles** that surround abdominal organs and blood vessels, and **cardiac muscles** that operate the heart. Defining the muscle function based on the tissue onto which a muscle exerts a force is justified because of the underlying physics: physics is primarily concerned with the object on which a force

acts. Even though all three muscle tissues share a common mechanism, we limit the current discussion to skeletal muscles because their actions relate most directly to the everyday experience with our bodies. The action of smooth muscles is briefly discussed in Q–3.18, and the action of cardiac muscles is discussed in more detail in Chapter 15.

Three **types of skeletons** evolved in the animal kingdom. The bodies of jellyfish and sea anemones, flatworms, roundworms, and segmented worms contain a **hydrostatic skeleton** against which their muscles operate. A hydrostatic skeleton consists of a liquid held under pressure in closed body compartments. The hydrostatic pressure maintains the total volume of the animal. Muscle action causes rhythmic reshaping of the body; the reshaping segments interact with the underlying solid surface to propel the animal forward. Hydrostatics and the principles governing the hydrostatic skeleton are discussed in Chapter 11.

An external rigid or semirigid skeletal structure is called an **exoskeleton**. It provides protection and static support for soft tissues. The exoskeleton can be composed of different materials: amoeba build such exoskeletons with calcium or silica secretion and sponges use *spongin,* a tough but elastic substance. A very well-known example of an exoskeleton is the stony material deposited by corals. As animal life developed to higher complexity, increased mobility became advantageous for individual creatures. This was achieved by subdividing the exoskeleton into a larger number of connected plates, such as a separated head, thorax, and abdomen in insects. The exoskeletal plates are connected by elastic tissue to provide good flexibility, particularly along the legs.

Fig. 3.1 illustrates the interaction of skeletal muscles with an exoskeleton. Shown are two cross-sections of a horsefly thorax (dashed lines). The exoskeleton of the thorax section consists of a top plate (*tergal plate*) to which the wings are attached, two side plates (*pleural plates*) on which the wings are pivoted, and a bottom plate (*sternal plate*). One set of muscles connects the tergal and sternal plates vertically (*dorsoventral flight muscles*) and a second set connects the two ends of the tergal plate along the body axis (*longitudinal flight muscles*). An upstroke of the wings results when the fly contracts its dorsoventral flight muscles. In turn, a downstroke is the result of the contraction of the longitudinal flight muscles. The need for two complementary sets of muscles is rooted in the physical mechanism of muscle action: a muscle can only contract actively, but then has to be stretched passively as another muscle contracts. In biology, this is called **antagonistic action**.

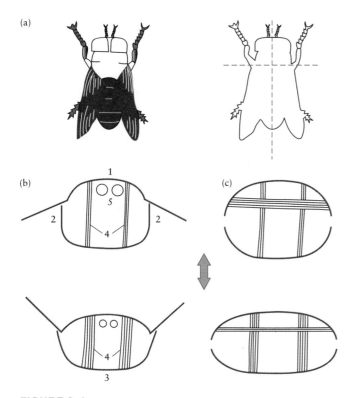

**FIGURE 3.1**

The flight mechanism of a horsefly. (a) Two perpendicular cross-sections through the thorax are defined by the dashed lines in the right sketch. (b) The motion of the top plate (tergal plate, 1) including wings, the two side plates (pleural plates, 2) on which the wings are pivoted, and the bottom plate (sternal plate, 3) through a complete wing beat cycle in front view. Vertical muscles connect the tergal and sternal plates (dorsoventral flight muscles, 4) and longitudinal muscles connect the two ends of the tergal plate along the body axis (longitudinal flight muscles, 5). (c) The corresponding motion in side view, highlighting the alternating contraction of the dorsoventral and the longitudinal flight muscles.

Keep in mind that the muscle action in Fig. 3.1 always exerts a force on a component of the skeleton, but does not necessarily cause locomotion. Bumblebees survive in cooler climates (e.g., more northern latitudes or alpine altitudes) than most other insects because they can raise their body temperature through rapid wing movement. The muscle action in this case serves the purpose of increasing the animal's metabolism, of which heat dissipation is a byproduct (as we discuss in detail in Chapter 10).

The third type of skeleton is the internal skeleton of vertebrates, called the **endoskeleton**. The most primitive of these endoskeletons is the *notochord,* like that found in the cartilaginous bone of fish. In more advanced animals, the skeleton formed in the embryo is initially cartilaginous and hardens as the animal matures. This process is complete in humans with the ossification of the breastbone at the age of 25.

Skeletal muscles consist of bundles of fibres running the length of the muscle. The diameter of such

a bundle lies in the range of 0.1 to 1 mm. Each fibre is a cell, which is subdivided into smaller repetitive units called *myofibrils*. Muscle cells each contain about 100 myofibrils. This functional component has a diameter of about 1 $\mu$m. In the elongated direction the myofibril is divided into **sarcomeres**, the basic contractile units of the muscle. A sarcomeric unit is shown schematically in Fig. 3.2(a) and in the micrograph in Fig. 3.2(b). Each sarcomere has an average length of 2.1 $\mu$m. It is confined at both ends by stiff Z-discs. **Actin filaments** are anchored in these discs and extend by 1.0 $\mu$m to 1.2 $\mu$m on both sides. **Myosin filaments** of 1.65 $\mu$m length bridge the gap between the actin filaments of two adjacent Z-discs. Actin proteins are present in all eukaryotic cells. They form part of the cytoskeleton, allowing the cell to bear tensile (pulling) forces. The myosin protein acts as a motor molecule by walking along the actin rods. This combined action of both proteins evolved early and was already applied by amoeba to move with extruding *pseudopodia* (false feet).

The microscopic mechanism of muscle contraction is called the **sliding filament model** and is illustrated in Fig. 3.3. The top frame shows a resting muscle. A nerve signal triggers the release of $Ca^{2+}$ ions from the sarcoplasmic reticulum. The calcium ions attach to troponin molecules. As a result, the tropomyosin protein strands that are coiled around the actin filament loosen. This allows the ends of the myosin filament to bond to the actin filaments. With a 21-nm-long myosin head attached to the actin filament, a tilt from an angle of 90° to about 45° shortens the sarcomere. At the same time, the sarcoplasmic reticulum reabsorbs the calcium ions, causing the muscle fibre to regenerate as the actin–myosin bond is severed by the reactivated troponin. This cycle repeats for every new nerve impulse arriving at the muscle. Such impulses arrive at rates between 20 and 100 Hz (hertz is a unit of frequency: 1 Hz = 1 s$^{-1}$; thus, 20 Hz means that 20 nerve impulses arrive per second). This leads to an appreciable contraction of the muscle in a short time.

The limit of contraction of sarcomeres can be determined from Fig. 3.2. When the myosin filament hits the Z-discs on both sides, a further shortening of the muscle would require filament crumbling, which does not occur. Thus, the maximum shortening of a sarcomere occurs from the average length of $L_{average} = 2.1$ $\mu$m to a minimum length of $L_{min} = 1.65$ $\mu$m. This means that each sarcomere, and therefore the entire muscle, can shorten by slightly more than 20%. Mechanisms discussed in Chapter 16 protect muscles against overstretching, which occurs when a sarcomere is elongated by more than 35%.

(a)

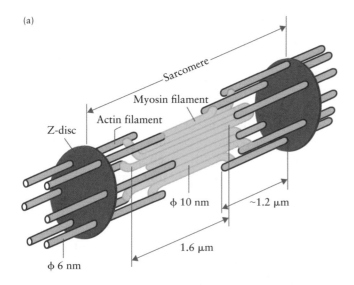

**FIGURE 3.2**

(a) The sarcomere is the contractile unit of the myofibrils in the muscle cell. The length of the sarcomere is defined by the distance between two adjacent Z-discs. This length varies during muscle action when the myosin filaments crawl along the actin filaments, which are connected to the Z-discs. The actin filaments extend by about 1.2 $\mu$m beyond the Z-disc at each side. Combined with a 1.65-$\mu$m length of the myosin filament, the sarcomere length can typically vary between 1.6 $\mu$m and 3.0 $\mu$m while maintaining an effective overlap between both filaments. (b) Coloured transmission electron micrograph (TEM) of a section through a skeletal muscle. The muscle myofibrils are orange and run from upper left to bottom right. Z-discs are red and mitochondria are red ovals, e.g., at the lower right.

## ● EXAMPLE 3.1

We see in Fig. 3.3 that each myosin head of 21 nm length tilts to an angle of 45° and relaxes to an angle of 90° relative to the rest of the myosin molecule once per nerve impulse. (a) Calculate the contraction (change in length) of a sarcomere per nerve impulse. *Note:* Fig. 3.4(a) shows that two myosin heads tilt simultaneously per myosin molecule, one at each end. (b) Express the contraction of the muscle per nerve impulse as a fraction of the average length of the sarcomere. For this part, use $L_{average}$ = 2.1 $\mu$m. (c) How long does it take to contract a muscle from its average length by 20% if we assume 60 impulses per second?

*Solution to part (a):* Fig. 3.4(b) shows the geometry of a tilting myosin head. The solid ellipse shows the myosin head in the relaxed position and the dashed ellipse when tilted to 45°. The figure indicates the displacement $\Delta x$ of the lower tip of the myosin head in the direction parallel to the myosin filament. This is also the displacement of the actin filament relative to the myosin filament achieved in a single cycle of the sliding filament model. The question in part (a) requires us to calculate $2 \cdot \Delta x$ because a second myosin head undergoes the same tilt at the other end of the myosin molecule, as illustrated in Fig. 3.4(a). We find:

$$2 \cdot \Delta x = 2 \cdot (21 \text{ nm})\sin 45° = 29.6 \text{ nm} \quad [1]$$

The length of the sarcomere shortens by about 30 nm per nerve impulse.

*Solution to part (b):* The sarcomere has an average length of $L_{average}$ = 2.1 $\mu$m = 2100 nm. Thus, the contraction length as a fraction of the average length, $2 \cdot \Delta x / L_{average}$, is given by:

$$\frac{2 \cdot \Delta x}{L_{average}} = \frac{29.6 \text{ nm}}{2100 \text{ nm}} = 0.014 = 1.4\% \quad [2]$$

A single nerve impulse shortens each sarcomere and therefore the entire muscle by 1.4%.

*Solution to part (c):* In one second 60 impulses are received, each shortening the sarcomere by 1.4% of its average length as found in part (b). If the sliding filament model operates for one second, a shortening of $60 \cdot 1.4\% = 84\%$ would occur. However, the maximum contraction of a sarcomere is 20%. We can solve for the time interval $\Delta t$ for a 20% shortening by equating two fractions:

$$\frac{84\%}{1.0 \text{ s}} = \frac{20\%}{\Delta t} \quad [3]$$

This yields $\Delta t$ = 0.24 seconds: a complete muscle contraction can be achieved in a quarter of a second, which is consistent with our everyday experience.

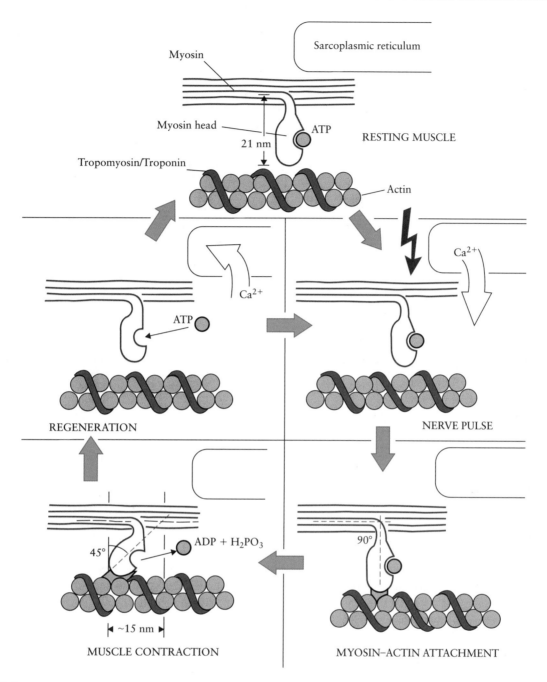

Sarcoplasmic reticulum

Myosin

Myosin head

ATP

RESTING MUSCLE

21 nm

Tropomyosin/Troponin

Actin

Ca²⁺

Ca²⁺

ATP

REGENERATION

NERVE PULSE

45°

ADP + H₂PO₃

90°

~15 nm

MUSCLE CONTRACTION

MYOSIN–ACTIN ATTACHMENT

## FIGURE 3.3

Illustration of the sliding filament model. A resting muscle is shown at the top with its major components: the sarcoplasmic reticulum at the upper right, the myosin filament with the myosin head charged with an ATP molecule below, and the intertwined actin and troponin/tropomyosin filaments at the bottom. When a nerve impulse arrives (indicated by a lightning bolt), a cycle of processes unfolds as shown in the four lower boxes. First, the nerve impulse triggers $Ca^{2+}$ release from the sarcoplasmic reticulum. The calcium ions bond with troponin, deactivating the tropomyosin filament and allowing the myosin head to bond to the actin strand (bottom right box). When the myosin head is firmly attached to the actin filament it tilts to 45°. An ATP dissociation provides the energy for this step. Concurrent with the tilting of the myosin head, calcium is pumped back into the sarcoplasmic reticulum. This reactivates the troponin/tropomyosin, and the myosin–actin bond breaks. Further nerve impulses lead to a repetition of this cycle.

In vertebrates, muscles are not directly connected to bones but extend as connective tissues called **tendons** that are attached to the bones. Thus, the force of the muscle is transferred to the bone via a tendon. Tendons act like extremely strong strings that are flexible but do not stretch. They are made of large strands of white, fibrous proteins, called *collagen*. This is different from the muscle tissue but originates

(a)

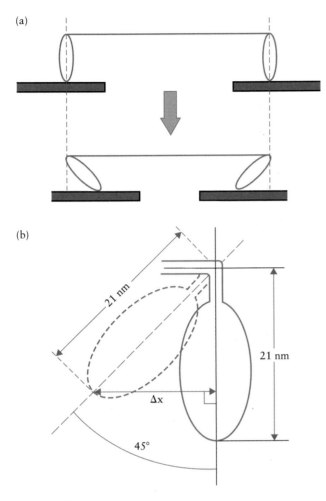

(b)

**FIGURE 3.4**

(a) Each cycle of the sliding filament model causes a shortening of the sarcomere. This is achieved by the synchronous tilting of myosin heads at both ends of the myosin molecule. (b) The tilting of a myosin head is highlighted by comparing the relaxed vertical position (solid ellipse) and the head at maximum 45° tilt (dashed ellipse). The myosin head has a length of 21 nm, measured from the axis of rotation to the tip. The tip is attached to the actin filament. The length $\Delta x$ represents the distance by which the myosin head pulls the myosin filament along the actin filament per nerve impulse.

within the muscle to provide maximum strength. You may have noticed these anatomical features when eating chicken legs.

An example of the relative arrangement of muscle, tendon, and bone in humans is shown in Fig. 3.5 for the **Achilles tendon**, the thickest and strongest tendon in our body. It extends from the calf muscle to the heel bone. This tendon is named for Achilles, the greatest of the Achaean heroes during the Trojan war of the 13th century BC, son of king Peleus and goddess Thetis. To extend immortality to her son, Thetis dipped Achilles in the sacred waters of the river Styx, holding the infant by the heels. As reported in

(a)                    (b)

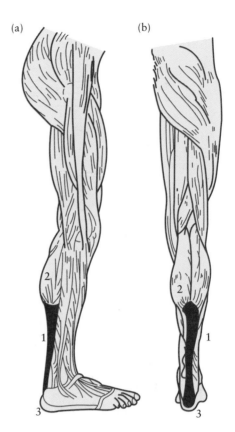

**FIGURE 3.5**

(a) Side view and (b) rear view of the lower leg of a human showing the Achilles tendon (1), connecting the calf muscle (2) to the heel bone (3). The Achilles tendon (highlighted) stretches as a narrow band along the lower one-third of the back of the lower leg. You can easily feel the Achilles tendon in your own leg because it runs shallow underneath the skin.

Homer's *Iliad*, an arrow was later shot at this vulnerable spot by Paris (whose seduction of Helen caused the war), killing the hero.

# What Is a Force?

The muscle, tendon, and bone in Fig. 3.5 are three separate tissues that interact as a particular functional group. We want to introduce the term **force** for this interaction. In the sciences we first generalize such observations before formulating fundamental definitions and laws. The most inclusive definition follows when essential features have been separated from system-specific properties. The muscle and the bone from Fig. 3.5 are replaced by the more general term **object** because we want to apply the force concept to other systems as well—e.g., the action of myosin on actin filaments in Fig. 3.3, or the action of a person on some equipment in a gym. It is common, though, to always identify two distinguishable objects: we never think of an object acting on itself, and later will see that we have to exclude this specifically, as done by Newton's third law. These considerations lead to the broadest possible definition of force:

*Forces represent the interaction of distinguishable objects.*

Surveying the many ways in which objects affect each other, we group forces into two types: **contact forces** and **contact-free forces**. Contact forces act only when physical contact between the objects is established; contact-free forces act over a distance. Thus, the calf muscle cannot exert a contact force on the heel bone in Fig. 3.5 because the muscle and the bone are not in contact with each other. The tendon creates this contact; thus, the calf muscle exerts a force on the Achilles tendon, and in turn the Achilles tendon exerts a force on the heel bone.

A list of commonly observed forces is provided in Table 3.1. The table illustrates that we identify four fundamental forces in physics, i.e., forces that are not composite forces of one or several fundamental forces: gravity, the electric force, the strong (nuclear) force, and the weak force. All but the weak force are discussed in this textbook; the electric and nuclear forces are introduced in Chapters 13 and 23, respectively. Note that all four fundamental forces are contact-free forces. Table 3.1 also illustrates that a wide range of contact forces exist, of which we introduce only a few in this chapter. A common characteristic of contact forces is that they are macroscopic interactions that result from a large number of microscopic electrostatic interactions.

## TABLE 3.1

### The main forces discussed in the textbook

| Force | Example |
| --- | --- |
| **Contact-free forces** | |
| Gravity | Attraction between Earth and Sun |
| Weight | Object falling to the surface of Earth |
| Electric force | Static electricity |
| Magnetic force | Alignment of a compass needle |
| Nuclear force | Radioactive decay |
| **Contact forces** | |
| External force | Your hand pushing an object |
| Normal force | Table holding an object up |
| Tension | Pulling an object with a string |
| Buoyant force | A fluid supporting a floating object |
| Friction | Resistance against fluid flow in a tube |

Force is a scientifically useful concept because it can be quantified. We illustrate this with a simple self-test. Hold a pen in your hand, with your arm relaxed beside your body. Then bend the lower arm at the elbow until the pen touches your shoulder. To complete this test you had to exert a force on the pen, which you barely felt. Now exchange the pen with this textbook and repeat the self-test. This time you note that you have to exert a larger force. If you are not sure, repeat each of the two self-tests ten times and observe the exhaustion of your biceps muscle. We conclude that the quantitative definition of force must allow for a variability in the magnitude of a force.

Now we perform a self-test to explore the directional feature of forces: Start again with the pen in your hand and the arm relaxed. Bend the lower arm at the elbow to a right angle, once to hold the pen in front of you as if giving it to another person, and once in front of your chest as if carrying it in the rain under an umbrella. You note that you need the same magnitude of force in both cases, but the result is different because the pen ends up in different places. We conclude that a force can act in different directions; thus, direction is a property of the force. Physical quantities that have a magnitude and a direction in space are described by **vectors**. The Math Review "Vectors and Basic Vector Algebra" at the end of Chapter 2 introduces the mathematical definition of a vector and some basic vector operations we will need later in this chapter.

We are now ready to quantify a few specific forces and start with contact forces, for which we have already established the muscle force as an example. A self-test helps us to identify another contact force. Stand upright with both legs on a levelled floor, as shown in Fig. 3.6. Contact forces can always be identified by a visible contact between the object that exerts the force and the object on which the force acts. When standing on the floor, we note that it pushes the body up through the contact point with each foot. If this were not the case—i.e., if the magnitudes of both upward-directed forces were zero—then the floor would not have an effect on the body and we would fall through the floor (think of trying to stand on a cloud). We call the force we have identified in this case a **normal force** because it acts in the direction normal (perpendicular) to a surface; in Fig. 3.6 this surface is the floor. $N_1$ and $N_2$ are labelled with different subscripts because they may differ in magnitude, e.g., when you shift your upper body over the left or the right leg.

We can also identify a contact-free force in the self-test of Fig. 3.6: gravity. Gravity pulls the body down. Sir Isaac Newton was the first to quantitatively

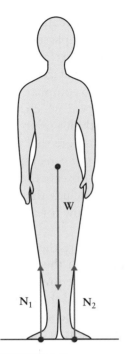

**FIGURE 3.6**

The forces acting on a person standing on both legs. The gravitational force is present everywhere on Earth's surface. It is directed straight downward toward the centre of Earth. We call this force weight and label it **W**. Upward-directed forces act on each foot on the ground. These forces are directed perpendicular to the supporting surface and are therefore called normal forces. The normal force is identified as **N**₁ for the right foot and **N**₂ for the left foot. These two forces may differ, as the person can shift from one foot to the other.

describe gravity as the attractive force between two objects of masses $m$ and $M$. Its magnitude is given as:

$$F_{\text{gravity}} = G^* \frac{m \cdot M}{r^2} \qquad [4]$$

The factor $G^*$ is the gravitational constant with a value of $G^* = 6.67 \times 10^{-11}$ N · m²/kg². The right-hand side of Eq. [4] further contains $r$, which is the centre-to-centre distance of the two objects that attract each other. In the general form given in Eq. [4], the law of gravity is primarily applied in astronomy. We will use it in that form for some discussions of the effect of weightlessness on the human body in Chapter 21. When gravity is observed at or near the surface of Earth, which is the origin of the force, we call it **weight** and label it **W**.

A simpler formula than Eq. [4] is sufficient to describe the magnitude of the weight:

$$W = m \cdot g \qquad [5]$$

Eq. [5] quantifies the magnitude of the weight, with the constant $g$ the gravitational acceleration. Note that $g$ is not a force but an acceleration, as defined in Chapter 2. The numerical value of $g$ is obtained from Eq. [4] by substituting for $r$ the radius of Earth,

$r_{\text{Earth}} = 6400$ km $= 6.4 \times 10^6$ m, and for $M$ its mass, $M_{\text{Earth}} = 6 \times 10^{24}$ kg:

$$g = \frac{G^* M_{\text{Earth}}}{r_{\text{Earth}}^2}$$

$$= \frac{\left(6.67 \times 10^{-11} \dfrac{\text{N} \cdot \text{m}^2}{\text{kg}^2}\right)(6 \times 10^{24} \text{ kg})}{(6.4 \times 10^6 \text{ m})^2}$$

$$= 9.8 \frac{\text{m}}{\text{s}^2} \qquad [6]$$

Contact forces, particularly muscle forces, are often identified within our body. This is illustrated in Fig. 3.7 for the main forces acting on the arm of a person intending to do one-arm dumbbell rows in a gym. You can confirm the observations in Fig. 3.7 when holding this textbook with your arm relaxed beside your body (we used this self-test before). You notice that the book pulls your arm down, that the arm's own weight also pulls it down, and that your shoulder is pulling the arm upward. In the figure we label the weight of the arm $\mathbf{W}_{\text{arm}}$, the tension force the trapezius muscle in the shoulder exerts on the arm **T**, and the force the book or the dumbbell exerts on the fist **F**. Note that we did not call the latter force the weight of the book or the dumbbell because we defined the weight as a force acting on the object due to its own mass; in Fig. 3.7, in turn, the dumbbell exerts a force on the arm of the person.

The **tension** is a new force in Fig. 3.7. We call a force a tension when it is exerted by a massless string

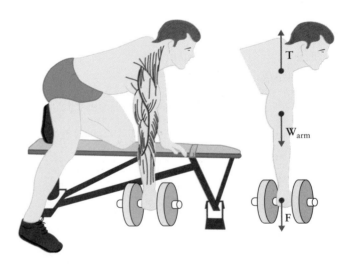

**FIGURE 3.7**

Forces also act between different parts of an organism. As an example, three major forces are highlighted as they act on the arm of a person intending to do one-arm dumbbell rows in a gym. The forces are indicated at the right: **F** is a downward-directed force due to the weight of the dumbbell; $\mathbf{W}_{\text{arm}}$ is the weight of the arm; and **T** is the force pulling the arm up due to the tension in muscles and ligaments connecting the trunk and the arm.

attached to the object of interest; the tension always acts in the direction of the string. Tensions occur often in physiological and kinesiological problems because we usually model tendons as massless strings. Note that the force is not labelled a tension if the string's mass is included. We discuss this point in Concept Question 3.9.

### Concept Question 3.1

**(a) Can the weight $W$ in Eq. [5] be written as a vector? (b) The biceps tendon is attached to the radius, which is a bone in your lower arm. Does the biceps tendon exert a force on the radius? (c) Can the radius exert a force on the biceps tendon?**

ANSWER TO PART (a): Yes. The magnitude of the weight varies with the mass of the object. Its direction is fixed (always straight down toward the centre of Earth), but it has that direction nevertheless. A quantity with magnitude and direction is a vector, regardless of whether magnitude and direction can vary.

ANSWER TO PART (b): Not always. You can relax your muscle at its resting length. In that state, the tendon does not exert a force on the bone even though they are always connected with each other.

ANSWER TO PART (c): Yes. Recall that a force represents an interaction between two objects. The radius interacts with and affects the attached tendon. Imagine for a moment that the radius/biceps interaction did not exist while you stretch your arm. In this case, the biceps would not be stretched and later could no longer serve its purpose.

### Concept Question 3.2

**If you read Eq. [5] as a mathematical formula, the following statement is correct: to double $m$ while holding $W$ constant, we have to reduce $g$ to one-half of its original value. Using Eq. [5] to express the physical relation between mass, gravitational acceleration, and weight, is this statement still correct?**

ANSWER: No. The gravitational acceleration is constant for experiments done in a laboratory on Earth; thus, we cannot vary $m$ while holding $W$ constant in Eq. [5]. While this argument may appear trivial for the simple formula in Eq. [5], the distinction between the meaning of mathematical and physical formulas is fundamental to mastering physics. We will therefore reiterate this issue throughout the textbook.

### Concept Question 3.3

**Fig. 3.8 shows an object as a white circle on an inclined surface. Six forces act on the object. Identify (a) the normal force and (b) the weight.**

ANSWER TO PART (a): $F_6$ is the normal force, acting on the object in the direction normal to the underlying surface. Note that force $F_3$ also acts perpendicular to the underlying surface, but cannot be exerted by that surface on account of its direction. For objects on a levelled surface, $F_5$ represents the direction in which the normal force acts. However, on an inclined surface the direction perpendicular to the surface is no longer vertical.

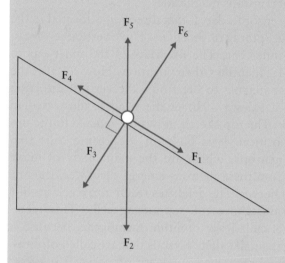

**FIGURE 3.8**

Object (dot) on an inclined surface. Six forces act on the object in different directions.

ANSWER TO PART (b): The weight is a force on an object that is always directed vertically downward, regardless of the orientation of surfaces in contact with the object. Thus, $F_2$ is the weight. Force $F_5$ also acts in the vertical direction; however, it cannot be caused by Earth because the gravitational force always attracts objects toward Earth's centre.

## Can Our Bodies Detect Forces?

In this section our awareness of the contact-free gravitational force and a typical contact force is surveyed. It is always instructive to start with a self-test. This allows us to locate the detection system in our bodies. We then describe the anatomical features of the detection system to later allow us to apply physical methods to quantify their function.

## Detection of the Direction of Gravity

Close your eyes, stretch your arms, concentrate on your hands, and turn them to the side. The sensation in your hands has not changed despite the change of orientation. Thus, no gravity detector exists in your hands. Now, close your eyes again and lean your head to the side. This time you can even estimate the angle of tilt without a visual impression of your environment. The awareness of the direction of gravity resides in our heads. Note that the magnitude of the gravitational force during this self-test did not change; it is $W = m \cdot g$, in which $m$ is the mass of the object, which our bodies use to detect this force. Thus, we detect a change in the direction of a force of constant magnitude.

The sensor to detect that direction is located in the maculae (plural of *macula*) of the **vestibular organ** in the inner ear. The overview of the inner ear in Fig. 2.12 identifies their location. How we use the utricular macula to determine the vertical direction during a sideways tilt of the head is illustrated in Fig. 3.9. The top sketch shows the macula in the upright position. It is built on supporting cells that house neurons, which are the main body of nerve cells. From these neurons emerge dendrites, the fine ends of nerves. The dendrites reach into a gelatin-like membrane above the supporting cells. This membrane is called the **otolithic membrane**, because it supports small calcite crystals that are called **otoliths**. The membrane has a density of about 1.0 g/cm$^3$ (close to the density of water) and supports CaCO$_3$ otoliths with a density of 3.0 g/cm$^3$, comparable to the density of rocks. If the head is turned, as shown in the bottom sketch of Fig. 3.9, the heavier otoliths pull the soft membrane in the direction of gravity, exerting a force on the dendrites. This force causes the dendrites to fire nerve impulses that travel to the brain (nerve impulse transport is discussed in Chapter 14). We will calculate the forces acting on an otolith in the macula in Example 3.11. At that point we will also find out why we have two maculae in each ear.

## Detection of the Weight of an Object

When you close your eyes and lay an object on your hand with the palm up, you notice at what position the object pushes on your skin. Note also that you sense the object continuously even though it does not move. When you hold a different object you can tell which of the two objects is heavier. If you instead push the object against your hand from below, you also sense where the object touches you. This time,

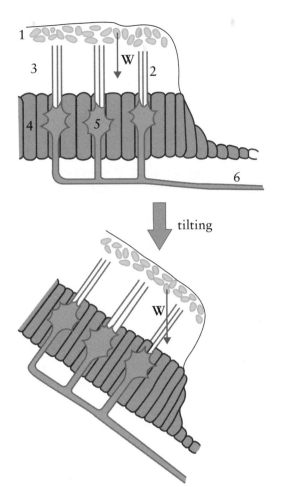

**FIGURE 3.9**

The mechanism of gravity detection in a macula is illustrated for a person tilting the head to one side. Above, the macula is shown in an upright position; below, the head is tilted. The components highlighted in the upper plot are the otoliths (1), the dendrites (2), which are embedded in the otolithic membrane (3), the supporting cells (4) containing the neurons (5), and the nerve to the brain (6).

however, you do not measure the weight of the object but rather how hard it is pushed against your skin. Therefore, unlike our sense of gravity, the sensitivity for contact forces exists locally in the hand.

Fig. 3.10 shows an overview of the near-surface structure of the palm, including the corpuscles typically contained in the skin. The outermost layer of the skin is called the *epidermis*. It varies in thickness between 30 $\mu$m and 4 mm. The next layer consists of 0.3- to 4-mm-thick connective tissue called *corium*; the fat cells below form the *subcutis*. Large numbers of various corpuscles are located in the shallower sections of the skin just below the epidermis, with other corpuscle types found deeper. We will discuss all of these corpuscles in this textbook because they measure various physical parameters. The deep corpuscles (*Pacinian corpuscles*) are discussed in this chapter as acceleration detectors, and the beehive-shaped corpuscles (*Meissner's corpuscles*) are discussed in Chapter 6 as velocity detectors. Here we focus on the disc-shaped corpuscles, which are sensitive to contact forces. These are called **Merkel's corpuscles** (shown in Fig. 3.11) and are located just below the epidermis.

Merkel's corpuscles appear in high density in the palms of our hands and in the soles of our feet. The function of Merkel's corpuscles is illustrated most easily when we repeat our self-test placing objects of varying mass on the open hand with the palm up.

Fig. 3.12 shows the nerve impulse rate (impulses per second) of the dendrites ending in Merkel's corpuscles as a function of mass with the mass varied between 1 g and 100 g. Fig. 3.12(a) is a **linear representation** of the data. It shows that the impulse rate depends on the weight—but not in a linear fashion, because the curve is not a straight line. We can conclude from the linear plot that Merkel's corpuscles are suitable to detect the weight of an object because the impulse rate varies monotonically with the weight. However, we also note that (i) the linear graph is inconvenient for quantitative data analysis, and that (ii) it is not sufficient to judge whether a single or several mechanisms are needed to describe the response of Merkel's corpuscles. The **double-logarithmic plot** in Fig. 3.12(b) helps to clarify these issues because it yields a straight line.

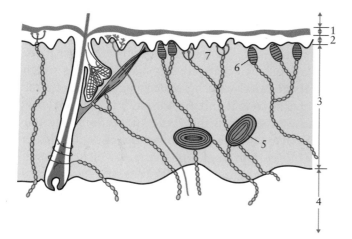

**FIGURE 3.10**

Cross-section through a section of skin with hair (left) and without hair (right). The skin is divided into four distinguishable layers: the epidermis (1 and 2) at the outer surface, and the corium (3) and the subcutis (4) forming its inner boundary. The skin contains a large number of receptor systems that measure a wide range of external parameters. Highlighted in the figure are four types of mechano-receptors, three corpuscle systems, and the hair for detecting mechanical stimuli. The Pacinian corpuscles (5), which measure the acceleration of the body, are located in the subcutis; Meissner's corpuscles (6), measuring the speed of incoming objects, and Merkel's corpuscles (7), measuring the weight of objects resting on the skin, lie in a shallow region below the epidermis.

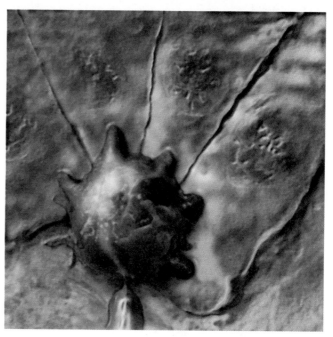

**FIGURE 3.11**

Micrograph of a Merkel's corpuscle at the basal layer of the epidermis.

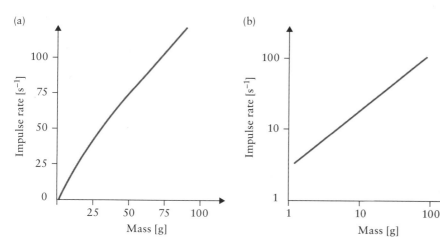

(a)

(b)

**FIGURE 3.12**

Quantitative analysis of the impulse rate of the dendrites terminating in Merkel's corpuscles, as a function of the mass of an object placed on the open hand with the palm facing up. The impulse rate is the number of impulses sent to the brain per second and therefore carries the unit $s^{-1}$. (a) Linear representation of the data. The impulse rate is not linearly proportional to the mass because the curve is not a straight line. (b) Double-logarithmic representation of the data. The straight line confirms that a power law describes the mass dependence of the impulse rate.

Therefore, a single mechanism with a single power law is sufficient to describe the response of Merkel's corpuscles.

## ● EXAMPLE 3.2

For Merkel's corpuscles, Fig. 3.12 shows the number of nerve impulses per second (rate) as a function of the mass of an object resting on the skin. Fig. 3.12(a) is a linear plot and Fig. 3.12(b) is a double-logarithmic plot of the same data. Determine the power law relation between the impulse rate ($P$ in unit 1/s) and the mass ($m$ in unit g); i.e., find the parameters $a$ and $b$ in $P = a \cdot m^b$. A detailed discussion of the approach taken to analyze a double-logarithmic plot is provided in Math Review "Graph Analysis Methods" at the end of Chapter 1.

*Solution:* Following the procedure in the Chapter 1 Math Review, the two data sets in Table 3.2 are taken from the plot in Fig. 3.12(b). We rewrite the power law relation $P = a \cdot m^b$ in logarithmic form as:

$$\ln P = b \cdot \ln m + \ln a \qquad [7]$$

Substituting the two data sets from Table 3.2 in Eq. [7], we find:

$$\text{set 1} \quad 2.303 = b \cdot 1.50 + \ln a$$
$$\text{set 2} \quad 4.606 = b \cdot 4.39 + \ln a \qquad [8]$$

$$(\text{set 2} - \text{set 1}) \quad 2.303 = b(4.39 - 1.50)$$

This yields $b = 0.8$. Substituting $b$ in the formula for set 1 in Eq. [8] yields:

$$\ln a = 2.303 - 0.8 \cdot 1.50 = 1.103 \qquad [9]$$

This yields $a = 3.0$.

Note that the relation between impulse rate and mass is not linear, because we found a value for $b$ that is not unity ($b \neq 1$): $P \propto m^{0.8}$. This is confirmed by the fact that the curve in Fig. 3.12(a) is not a straight line.

## TABLE 3.2

### Data sets taken from Fig. 3.12(b) for the nerve impulse response of Merkel's corpuscles

| Data set | $\ln(P\,(s^{-1}))$ | $\ln(m\,(g))$ |
|---|---|---|
| #1 | 2.303 | 1.50 |
| #2 | 4.606 | 4.39 |

A more detailed physiological description of the mechanism of Merkel's corpuscles requires input from Chapter 16, in which the elastic response of tissue to external forces is discussed.

# Newton's Laws of Mechanics

We now will establish forces as the cause of acceleration. We start with a simple experiment that allows us to isolate the action of individual forces. Again, this is an experiment you can do yourself: You need a slippery surface, such as a frozen pond, and an object with a smooth surface, such as a hockey puck. The forces we focus our attention on are the horizontal forces we use to push the object. Other forces that act on the object are associated with its weight and its contact with the underlying surface (normal force). The weight and the normal force are neglected because both act in the vertical direction. The only forces that act in the horizontal direction are the external force (pushing) and friction. We chose a slippery ice surface and a smooth object to be in a position to neglect friction.

First, let's consider the following three experiments: (i) We place the puck on the ice surface, so that it is initially at rest. We observe that the puck remains at rest if we do not push it. (ii) Next, we set the puck in motion. We observe that it maintains its velocity (magnitude and direction) once we no longer touch it. (iii) Lastly, we push the puck, which is again at rest, with two hands. You can do this with varying forces, including conditions such that the puck remains at rest. This means that an object may remain at rest even though several forces act on it.

The last observation motivates us to introduce the term **net force**. For an object on which $n$ forces act, the net force is:

$$\mathbf{F}_{net} = \sum_{i=1}^{n} \mathbf{F}_i \qquad [10]$$

The summation symbol is defined in the Math Review "Summations" at the end of this chapter. To simplify the calculations in this chapter, we limit our discussion to cases in which the forces acting on an object and its motion occur in a two-dimensional plane, which we define as the $xy$-plane. In these cases, the net force has two components:

$$x\text{-direction:} \quad F_{net,x} = \sum_{i=1}^{n} F_{ix}$$
$$y\text{-direction:} \quad F_{net,y} = \sum_{i=1}^{n} F_{iy} \qquad [11]$$

The net force is a key concept in the applications of the laws of mechanics. We introduce, therefore, a particular plot, called the **free-body diagram**, to combine in graphic form all forces that contribute to the net force.

*A free-body diagram is a line drawing that consists of all forces that act on the system of interest. No other physical features of the system are included, such as its velocity or acceleration. A coordinate system and labels for angles are often added.*

To draw a free-body diagram, you begin with a dot that represents the object of interest. Next, attach to the dot all the forces in your list. The forces are drawn as arrows; be careful to draw them in the direction in which they act.

With the net force defined we summarize the experimental observations of the puck on the ice surface in quantitative form:

$$\mathbf{F}_{net} = 0 \quad \Rightarrow \quad \mathbf{a} = 0 \quad \text{and} \quad \mathbf{v} = \text{const} \quad [12]$$

i.e., no acceleration occurs in the three experiments, because in each a zero net force acts on the object.

Now we proceed with two more experiments: (iv) We exert a single force on the hockey puck. We observe that the object accelerates in the direction in which the force is exerted. (v) We further push the object with two hands at the same time but make sure that the two contact forces we use differ in magnitude and/or are not directed opposite to each other. We observe that the object accelerates in the direction of the net force:

$$\mathbf{F}_{net} \neq 0 \quad \Rightarrow \quad \mathbf{a} \neq 0 \quad \text{and} \quad \mathbf{v} \neq \text{const} \quad [13]$$

We identify Eq. [12] as **Newton's first law**; Eq. [13] leads to Newton's second law. We discuss these two laws in order, each with several examples.

## Newton's First Law

Newton's first law requires the net force acting on an object to be zero. This is written in component form for an object that is confined to the $xy$-plane:

$$F_{net,x} = \sum_{i=1}^{n} F_{ix} = 0$$
$$F_{net,y} = \sum_{i=1}^{n} F_{iy} = 0 \qquad [14]$$

The first law can be stated in the following form:

*An object at rest or in motion with constant velocity remains that way unless acted upon by a net force. If in turn the object does not accelerate along the x-axis (y-axis), the sum of the x-components (y-components) of all forces acting on it must be zero. The cases in which these formulas apply are called* **mechanical equilibrium**; *the first law is also referred to as the* **law of inertia**.

Often, we are not interested in a particular force component but seek the magnitude of the force. The force magnitude is calculated from its components by using the Pythagorean theorem (see the Math Review "Geometry" at the end of Chapter 2):

$$|\mathbf{F}| = \sqrt{F_x^2 + F_y^2} \qquad [15]$$

In your later work, keep in mind that the net force $\mathbf{F}_{net}$ being equal to zero does not imply that any force $\mathbf{F}_i$ in Eq. [10] is separately zero. The first law does not allow us to identify the unit of force, which is possible only when Newton's second law is introduced in the next section. However, we need this unit for calculations. Since we already know that the gravitational acceleration $g$ has the unit m/s² and that the weight of an object is a force written as $W = m \cdot g$, we note that kg · m/s² is the standard unit of force. A new unit, **newton** (N), with 1 N = 1 kg · m/s², is introduced for force since we deal with it so often.

**Concept Question 3.4**

For each of the six objects in Fig. 3.13, the arrows indicate forces of equal magnitude that act in the directions shown. Which of the six objects are not in mechanical equilibrium?

ANSWER: Objects (3), (4), and (6). Mechanical equilibrium requires a balance of forces in every direction. We need to test only along the Cartesian coordinates, i.e., in Fig. 3.13 the horizontal $x$-axis and the vertical $y$-axis.

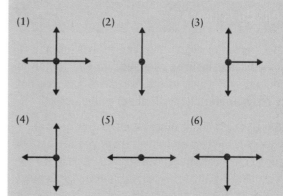

**FIGURE 3.13**
Six arrangements of equal-magnitude forces acting on an object.

## Concept Question 3.5

Three forces are shown to act on a human leg in Fig. 3.14: the weight **W** of the leg, the normal force **N** acting at the sole, and the force **F** the hip bone exerts on the head of the femur. Is the leg in mechanical equilibrium?

ANSWER: No. There is only one force, **F**, that has a component in the horizontal direction. Thus, in the horizontal direction no balance of the force components exists as required by Eq. [14]. We need to apply Newton's second law to the leg.

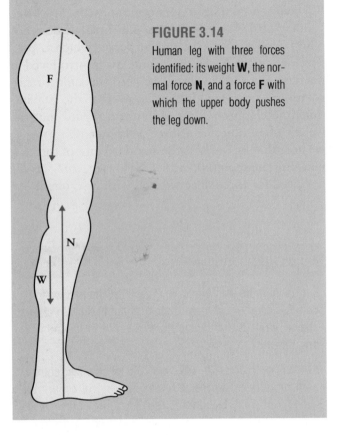

**FIGURE 3.14**

Human leg with three forces identified: its weight **W**, the normal force **N**, and a force **F** with which the upper body pushes the leg down.

## Concept Question 3.6

Fig. 3.15 shows an object attached to a string and in contact with an inclined surface in five different arrangements. In which of the five cases can you not identify three or more forces that act on the object?

ANSWER: Case (C). In the other four cases, you can identify the weight, the tension in the string, and the normal force due to the adjacent inclined surface. In case (C) the contact with the inclined surface is accidental; i.e., removing the inclined surface has no effect on the object. Even if you choose to argue that some molecular interactions between both surfaces occur in case (C), these constitute

a force much smaller than the weight and the tension, and are therefore neglected. The free-body diagrams for all five cases are shown in Fig. 3.16.

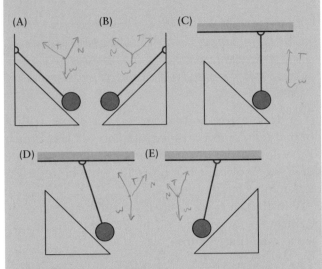

**FIGURE 3.15**

Object (green circle) in five different positions relative to an inclined surface.

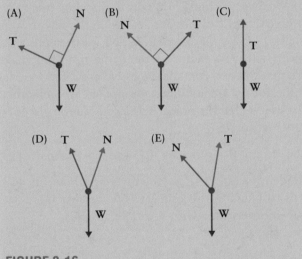

**FIGURE 3.16**

Five free-body diagrams for the sketches in Fig. 3.15.

## ● EXAMPLE 3.3

Fig. 3.17 shows two objects with masses $m$ and $M$ that are connected with a taut string running over a pulley. The two masses are given as $M = 5.0$ kg and $m = 3.0$ kg, with the heavier object being connected to the ceiling by another taut string. Assuming that both strings and the pulley are massless, and that the pulley rotates without friction, calculate (a) the tension in the string running over

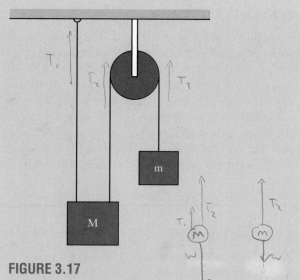

**FIGURE 3.17**

Two objects with masses *m* and *M* are connected by a massless string, which runs over a massless, frictionless pulley. The heavier object with mass *M* is further connected to the ceiling by another vertical, massless string.

the pulley, and (b) the tension in the string connected to the ceiling.

*Supplementary information:* We highlight in this problem the use of the problem-solving strategy we introduced in a Math Review at the end of Chapter 2. In the context of Newton's laws, the Schematic Approach includes specifically the identification of the object of interest. In anticipation of discussions in later chapters, we frequently call the object of interest the **system**. Then we identify all other objects that interact with the system and call them the **environment**. Developing the Physical Model requires you to first list all the forces acting on the system. Do not include any forces that the system exerts on the environment! Then draw the free-body diagram as discussed above. In the last step, the Quantitative Treatment, the physical model is used to solve the problem.

*Solution:* In this example problem, parts (a) and (b) are considered together until we reach the last step of the problem-solving strategy.

## Schematic Approach

Likely candidates for the object of interest are the two objects with masses $M$ and $m$. We decide whether both or just one of these has to be taken into account based on two considerations:

(i) If a variation of the mass of an object alters the outcome of the experiment, the object has to be included. If we were to increase mass $m$ such that $m > M$, or if we were to decrease mass $M$ such that $M < m$, we no

longer would have a mechanical equilibrium, but the object of mass $M$ would accelerate upward and the string to the ceiling would no longer be taut. Thus, we have to consider both objects.

(ii) We check whether the two objects can be combined as a single system. This option has to be ruled out if any of the forces acting between the two objects plays a role in the problem. In the current case, the problem text refers to a tension in the string between the two objects. Thus, we cannot combine the two objects into a single system.

Our last observation studying Fig. 3.17 is that the system is in mechanical equilibrium, because neither one of the two objects accelerates at any stage of the experiment.

## Physical Model

We need to organize the various labels we use to refer to the different forces in the problem. Note that there is no reason to assume that the tensions in the two strings are equal; thus, we need distinguishable variables for them. We define the string running to the ceiling as string 1. Tension $\mathbf{T}_1$ is the force acting on the objects attached at the end of string 1. We define the string running over the pulley as string 2. Tension $\mathbf{T}_2$ is the force acting on objects at either end of string 2. Note that we can identify the same magnitude $T_2$ at both ends of the string because the string is massless. This is justified in Concept Question 3.9. We are asked to calculate the magnitude of the tension $\mathbf{T}_2$ in part (a) and the magnitude of the tension $\mathbf{T}_1$ in part (b). We are also given the masses of the two objects, $M$ and $m$. We label their weights respectively as $\mathbf{W}_M$ for the object of mass $M$ and $\mathbf{W}_m$ for the object of mass $m$.

We group the forces acting on each of the two systems separately. On the object of mass $m$ we deal with its own weight and the tension of string 2, and on the object of mass $M$ we need its own weight and the tensions of both strings. These forces are combined in two free-body diagrams, which are displayed in Fig. 3.18.

## Quantitative Treatment

The forces in a free-body diagram are distinguished by their magnitudes and directions. In this particular case these directions are collinear, but forces are then still parallel or anti-parallel to each other. Next we choose the positive *x*-axis upward in both free-body diagrams. The first formula in Eq. [14] is then used to quantify the mechanical equilibrium. Using Fig. 3.18, one

## ● EXAMPLE 3.3 (*continued*)

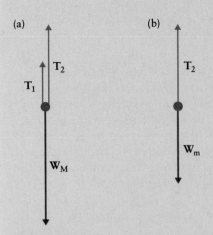

(a)          (b)

**FIGURE 3.18**
Free-body diagrams for the two objects shown in Fig. 3.17. (a) Three forces act on the object of mass $M$: its own weight $\mathbf{W}_M$ and the tensions in the two strings, $\mathbf{T}_1$ and $\mathbf{T}_2$. (b) Two forces act on the object with mass $m$: its weight $\mathbf{W}_m$ and the tension in the string $\mathbf{T}_2$.

equation is written for each of the two systems. These are:

system with mass $M$:

$$F_{net,M} = T_1 + T_2 - W_M = 0$$

[16]

system with mass $m$:

$$F_{net,m} = T_2 - W_m = 0$$

in which $T_{1,x} = T_1$, $T_{2,x} = T_2$, $W_{M,x} = -W_M$, and $W_{m,x} = -W_m$ are the four $x$-components of the forces. The first formula applies to the object of mass $M$ and contains two positive and one negative component based on our choice of axis in Fig. 3.18. The second formula applies to the object of mass $m$ and has two components with opposite signs.

*Solution to part (a):* We use the second formula in Eq. [16] to find the magnitude of the tension $\mathbf{T}_2$. With $W_m = m \cdot g$, we get:

$$T_2 = W_m = m \cdot g = (3.0 \text{ kg})\left(9.8 \frac{m}{s^2}\right)$$
$$= 29.4 \text{ N}$$

[17]

The magnitude of the tension in the string running over the pulley is $T_2 = 29.4$ N.

*Solution to part (b):* Substituting the result of part (a) into the first formula of Eq. [16] yields:

$$T_1 = W_M - T_2 = W_M - W_m = (M - m)g$$
$$= (2.0 \text{ kg})\left(9.8 \frac{m}{s^2}\right) = 19.6 \text{ N}$$

[18]

The magnitude of the tension in the string running to the ceiling is $\mathbf{T}_1 = 19.6$ N.

## ● EXAMPLE 3.4

An object of mass $m = 1.0$ kg is attached to a taut string of length $L = 20$ cm. The object is pulled to the position shown in Fig. 3.19 with $\theta = 30°$. At this position the object is held stationary by a horizontal external force, $\mathbf{F}_{ext}$, as shown. (a) What is the magnitude of the tension $\mathbf{T}$ in the string? (b) What is the magnitude of the force $\mathbf{F}_{ext}$? Note that we use the term *external force* for a wide range of forces, including all intentionally exerted forces.

*Solution:* We again apply the problem-solving strategy.

### Schematic Approach

The object is the system. The massless string is part of the environment. The sketch indicates that the object, if free to move, would move along a circular path. The axis of that motion is the point at which the string is attached to the ceiling (centre of curvature) and the length $L$ of the string is the radius of the path. However, the problem text implies that the object does not move, i.e., that Newton's first law applies.

### Physical Model

Studying the problem text and Fig. 3.19 reveals that three forces act on the object. The first is the gravitational force exerted by Earth, labelled weight $\mathbf{W}$, with magnitude $W = m \cdot g$. The second force is the contact force exerted on the object by the massless string, labelled tension $\mathbf{T}$. The tension is not negligible. This becomes clear when you think about the consequence if this force were

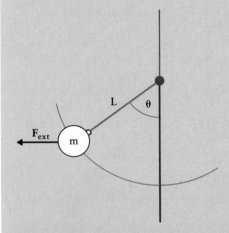

**FIGURE 3.19**
An application of the first law of mechanics. An object of mass $m$ is attached to a string of length $L$ and pulled to the left side. The object is then held stationary by an external force $\mathbf{F}_{ext}$ with the string forming an angle $\theta$ with the vertical. Compare this arrangement with a similar problem shown in Fig. 3.58.

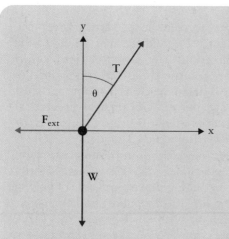

**FIGURE 3.20**

The free-body diagram for the example shown in Fig. 3.19. The dot represents the object. Note that only forces acting on the object are included; these are the tension **T** in the string, the weight **W** of the object, and the external force **F**ext. In addition to the three forces, the angle θ and a coordinate system are shown. θ is the angle between the tension and the vertical direction. The coordinate system is chosen such that two of the three forces, **W** and **F**ext, coincide with the axes.

not present (e.g., if the string were cut): instead of being stationary, the object would fall. The third force is the external force, **F**ext, exerted by the person (not shown) holding the object in place. The external force is also not negligible since releasing the object would cause it to swing. At this point make sure that no force has been overlooked, because you will not be able to solve the problem if you have missed one!

Next, we construct the free-body diagram as shown in Fig. 3.20. We draw a dot for the system, then enter the weight as a vector pointing downward. The tension is added, drawn in the direction of the string because all contact forces act in the direction along which the contact with the system occurs. The external force **F**ext is added in the direction given in the problem text.

## Quantitative Treatment

You may add only two other things to a free-body diagram: a coordinate system and the angles between the forces and the axes. Do not combine the free-body diagram with any other sketch that you make, because you need it to write the appropriate set of Newton's equations. Two orthogonal directions are identified in the free-body diagram as x- and y-axes. As a rule of thumb, choose the axes such that the greatest possible number of forces in the free-body diagram coincide with these axes. Although any choice is just as valid, a good choice reduces the extent of later calculations. In the case

of Fig. 3.20, we choose a horizontal x-axis and a vertical y-axis. Thus, the weight is parallel to the y-axis and the external force **F**ext is parallel to the x-axis.

Using Fig. 3.20 we write Eq. [14] for the specific forces shown in the free-body diagram. It is important not to confuse x- and y-components; complete the x-component formula first before you proceed to the y-component formula:

x-direction:  $-F_{ext} + T \cdot \sin \theta = 0$

$$y\text{-direction:} \quad -W + T \cdot \cos \theta = 0 \qquad [19]$$

*Solution to part (a):* From the second formula in Eq. [19], we find:

$$T \cdot \cos \theta = W = m \cdot g \qquad [20]$$

With the given values of θ and m, we obtain:

$$T = \frac{m \cdot g}{\cos \theta} = \frac{(1.0 \text{ kg})\left(9.8 \dfrac{m}{s^2}\right)}{\cos 30°} = 11.3 \text{ N} \quad [21]$$

The tension in the string has a magnitude of T = 11.3 N.

*Solution to part (b):* In the next step, the result of part (a) is substituted into the first formula in Eq. [19]:

$$F_{ext} = T \cdot \sin \theta = m \frac{g}{\cos \theta} \sin \theta$$

$$= m \cdot g \cdot \tan \theta \qquad [22]$$

which leads to:

$$F_{ext} = (1.0 \text{ kg})\left(9.8 \frac{m}{s^2}\right)\tan 30° = 5.7 \text{ N} \quad [23]$$

For mechanical equilibrium, the external force must have a magnitude of $F_{ext} = 5.7$ N, about half of the force found for the tension in the string.

## ● EXAMPLE 3.5

Two objects with m = 2.0 kg and M = 3.0 kg are connected by massless strings, as shown in Fig. 3.21. The string to the vertical wall forms an angle of θ = 45° with the horizontal. What is the magnitude of the external force **F**ext, with which the object of mass m has to be pulled toward the left in order to hold both objects stationary?

● **EXAMPLE 3.5 (*continued*)**

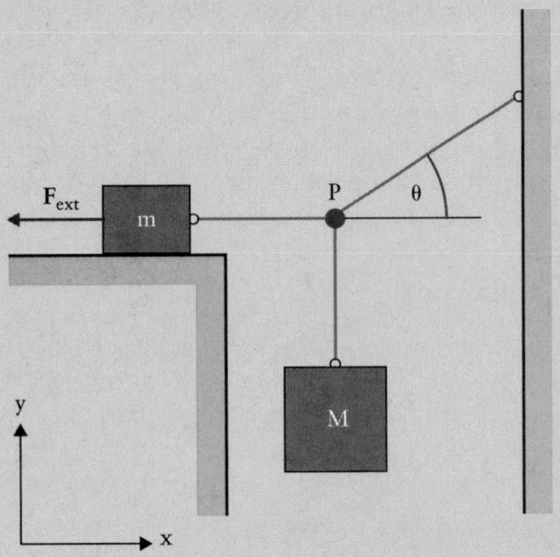

**FIGURE 3.21**

An application of the first law of mechanics. Two objects of masses *m* and *M* are connected with each other and a vertical wall using three massless strings. The string to the wall forms an angle *θ* with the horizontal. The two objects are held stationary; i.e., they do not move. To accomplish this, an external force $\mathbf{F}_{ext}$ is required. Note that a choice of coordinate system for this problem is indicated with the figure.

*Solution:*

**Schematic Approach**

We choose the object of mass *m* (called object *m*) as a system because the problem text asks for $\mathbf{F}_{ext}$, which acts on that object. However, the answer will also depend on the mass of the second object of mass *M* (called object *M*) since by changing *M* the force $\mathbf{F}_{ext}$ would also have to be changed in order to maintain mechanical equilibrium. This observation requires that object *M* be included as a second system.

We further expect the angle *θ* of the string attached to the vertical wall to influence the result. Again, think about changing this angle: the tension in the string would change and all other forces would change with it. This means that the point *P*, at which the three strings are connected, is a third system. *P* qualifies as a system even though its mass is zero, and it will not be assigned a weight. In turn, the three massless strings, the vertical wall, and the horizontal surface remain part of the environment because we need not write full-fledged formulas for them.

**Physical Model**

We find the forces acting on each of the three systems. Four forces act on object *m*: its weight $\mathbf{W}_m$

and the normal force **N** in the vertical direction, the external force $\mathbf{F}_{ext}$ and the tension $\mathbf{T}_m$ in the horizontal direction. The subscript *m* is added to the tension because the other two strings in Fig. 3.21 have different tensions. For object *M*, just two forces are identified, both acting in the vertical direction: one is its weight $\mathbf{W}_M$ and the other is the tension in the vertical string, $\mathbf{T}_M$.

The three strings yield three tensions acting on point *P*. Using the index *w* for the wall we identify (i) a tension $\mathbf{T}_1$ pulling downward, (ii) $\mathbf{T}_2$ pulling toward the left, and (iii) $\mathbf{T}_w$ pulling under an angle *θ* toward the wall. With all the forces identified, three separate free-body diagrams are drawn. These are shown in Fig. 3.22. At this point we use the information that the strings are massless. As discussed in detail in Concept Question 3.9, the magnitude of tension is constant at both ends of a massless string. This means $T_1 = T_M$ and $T_2 = T_m$. Note that these two relations apply to the magnitude of the tension; as a vector the tension

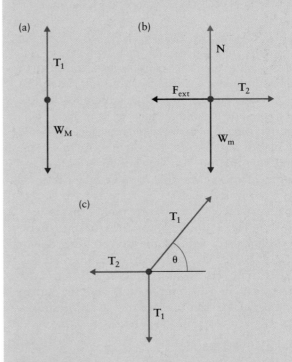

**FIGURE 3.22**

We need three free-body diagrams for the problem shown in Fig. 3.21, one for each object and one for the massless point *P* at which the three strings meet. (a) The free-body diagram for the object of mass *M* contains its weight and the tension in the vertical string. (b) The free-body diagram of the object of mass *m* contains its weight and the normal force due to the table in the vertical direction, and the external force and the tension in the horizontal string in the horizontal direction. (c) The free-body diagram for point *P* consists of the tensions in the three strings.

exerted at the left end and the right end of a taut string point in opposite directions. Thus, $\mathbf{T}_1 = -\mathbf{T}_M$ and $\mathbf{T}_2 = -\mathbf{T}_m$ when writing the tensions as vectors.

## Quantitative Treatment

Most forces coincide with the $x$- and $y$-axes when the two axes are chosen, as indicated in Fig. 3.21 for each of the three systems. Based on the free-body diagrams in Fig. 3.22 and using $T_1 = T_M$ and $T_2 = T_m$, we write five formulas using Eq. [14]:

$$
\begin{aligned}
\text{object } m, x\text{-direction:} & \quad T_m - F_{ext} = 0 \\
\text{object } m, y\text{-direction:} & \quad N - W_m = 0 \\
\text{object } M, y\text{-direction:} & \quad T_M - W_M = 0 \\
\text{point } P, x\text{-direction:} & \quad T_w \cdot \cos\theta - T_m = 0 \\
\text{point } P, y\text{-direction:} & \quad T_w \cdot \sin\theta - T_M = 0
\end{aligned}
\tag{24}
$$

Unknown in Eq. [24] are the three tensions, the normal force, and the external force. Thus, we have five equations and five unknown variables. However, the normal force is not asked for nor required to solve for any other variable, so the second formula in Eq. [24] can be neglected. From the formula for object $M$, we find:

$$
T_M = W_M = M \cdot g = 29.4 \, \text{N} \tag{25}
$$

We substitute this result in the last formula of Eq. [24]:

$$
T_w = \frac{T_M}{\sin\theta} = \frac{29.4 \, \text{N}}{\sin 45°} = 41.6 \, \text{N} \tag{26}
$$

Next, we substitute $T_w$ into the $x$-direction formula for point $P$:

$$
\begin{aligned}
T_m = T_w \cdot \cos\theta &= (41.6 \, \text{N})\cos 45° \\
&= 29.4 \, \text{N}
\end{aligned}
\tag{27}
$$

Finally, using the $x$-direction formula for object $m$, we calculate:

$$
F_{ext} = T_m = 29.4 \, \text{N} \tag{28}
$$

Note that the mass $m$ of the object on the table did not enter into the calculations.

# Newton's Second Law

We consider the experimental result in Eq. [13]. This is the case in which the net force does not equal zero and therefore no mechanical equilibrium exists. To quantify the properties of a system with a non-vanishing net force, we consider once more a hockey puck sliding across an ice surface. We note that the harder we push the object the faster it moves in the direction of the net force after losing contact with the hand. To achieve a faster motion, a larger acceleration is required. Thus, we propose $\mathbf{F}_{net} \propto \mathbf{a}$. This implies not just that both magnitudes increase concurrently, but more specifically that, e.g., doubling the force leads to a doubling of the acceleration. We call this a **linear relation** or **direct proportionality** between the two parameters net force and acceleration. Whenever two variables are related linearly we know that the most general equation describing their relation is $\mathbf{F}_{net} = m \cdot \mathbf{a} + \mathbf{F}_0$, with $m$ and $\mathbf{F}_0$ as yet undetermined constants. In the case of an object accelerating due to a net force, however, we know from Newton's first law that $\mathbf{a} = 0$ for $\mathbf{F}_{net} = 0$, yielding $\mathbf{F}_0 = 0$. This leads to the second law of mechanics for a system of $n$ forces:

$$
\mathbf{F}_{net} = \sum_{i=1}^{n} \mathbf{F}_i = m \cdot \mathbf{a} \tag{29}
$$

in which $m$ is the mass of the object. Eq. [29] is often referred to as the **equation of motion**. It confirms the unit of force as $\text{N} = \text{kg} \cdot \text{m/s}^2$. Applying the second law requires that we use Eq. [29] in component form. Confining the discussion again to motion in the $xy$-plane, we write:

$$
F_{net,x} = \sum_{i=1}^{n} F_{ix} = m \cdot a_x
$$

$$
F_{net,y} = \sum_{i=1}^{n} F_{iy} = m \cdot a_y
\tag{30}
$$

Note that the acceleration in the $x$-direction depends only on force components in the $x$-direction. Equally, the acceleration in the $y$-direction depends only on force components in the $y$-direction. Eq. [29] allows us to state **Newton's second law** in the following form:

*If a net force is applied to an object of mass m it accelerates in the direction of the net force. The magnitude of the object's acceleration is directly proportional to the magnitude of the net force and inversely proportional to the mass of the object.*

## ● EXAMPLE 3.6

We consider the same arrangement as in Example 3.3, except that we cut the string connecting the object with the larger mass $M$ to the ceiling, as illustrated in Fig. 3.23. Calculate (a) the acceleration of the object of mass $M$, (b) the acceleration of the object of mass $m$, and (c) the tension in the string.

*Solution:*

### Schematic Approach

Most of our considerations from Example 3.3 still apply. We continue to treat both objects as separate systems. We use again $W_m$ and $W_M$ as the two objects' respective weights. The tension in the string is now labelled $T$, since only one string is left. We note that the two objects are no longer in mechanical equilibrium as the heavier one accelerates downward, pulling the lighter object upward. Thus, we need Newton's second law for this problem.

Initially, we assign two accelerations to the systems, $a_m$ and $a_M$. We can already comment further on these accelerations. Note that the string remains taut throughout the experiment while the heavier object falls downward. This means that the distance between the two objects, measured along the string, never changes. As a consequence, we know that both accelerations must be equal *in magnitude*. This fact is written in the form $a_m = a_M = a$. It is very important to understand that this does not necessarily imply that $\mathbf{a}_m = \mathbf{a}_M$; indeed, we will find this to be wrong in the current

problem. The reason is linked to our choice of coordinate system, a choice we make only later. However, you can already see now why the two vertical acceleration components may differ in sign: when we choose the positive axis for each object upward, $\mathbf{a}_m = \mathbf{a}_M$ would imply that both objects accelerate upward—an impossible outcome of the experiment. Having established these findings about the two accelerations we can consider parts (a) and (b) of the problem together in our solution.

### Physical Model

The three forces we need to take into consideration are the tension $\mathbf{T}$ and the weights of the two objects. We draw a free-body diagram for each of them, Fig. 3.24(a) applying to the object of mass $M$ and Fig. 3.24(b) to the object of mass $m$. We have chosen the positive $y$-axis upward in both cases, as we did in Example 3.3.

### Quantitative Treatment

The second formula in Eq. [30] is used twice to quantify the equation of motion for each object. Using Fig. 3.24, we find:

$F_{net} = T - W = M \cdot a$

system with mass $M$:

$$F_{\text{net},M,y} = T - W_M = M \cdot a_{M,y} \quad [31]$$

system with mass $m$:

$$F_{\text{net},m,y} = T - W_m = m \cdot a_{m,y}$$

Using our chosen $y$-axis and the fact that $a_m = a_M = a$, we note that $a_{M,y} = -a$ and $a_{m,y} = +a$; i.e., the two acceleration components in the $y$-direction have opposite signs. This allows us to rewrite Eq. [31]:

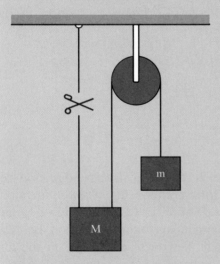

**FIGURE 3.23**

We study once more the arrangement of Fig. 3.17; however, we assume this time that the string between the object of mass $M$ and the ceiling is cut as indicated. With this connection eliminated, the two objects accelerate unless $M = m$.

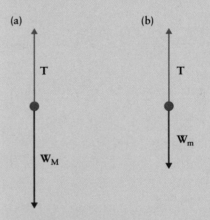

(a)      (b)

**FIGURE 3.24**

The free-body diagrams for the two objects shown in Fig. 3.23. (a) The forces acting on the object of mass $m$: its own weight $\mathbf{W}_M$ and the tension in the string $\mathbf{T}$. (b) The weight $\mathbf{W}_M$ and the tension $\mathbf{T}$ act on the object of mass $m$. We do not distinguish the two tensions because the string is massless.

system with mass $M$:  $T - W_M = -M \cdot a$

system with mass $m$:  $T - W_m = m \cdot a$

$$[32]$$

Note the negative sign at the right-hand side of the first formula in Eq. [32]. This sign is caused by the downward direction of the resulting acceleration of the object of mass $M$. Eq. [32] contains two unknown variables, $T$ and $a$. Since we have two independent formulas we can solve for both variables. One way to find the acceleration $a$ is to multiply the first formula in Eq. [32] with $-1$, then add the two formulas. This yields:

$$-T + W_M + T - W_m = M \cdot a + m \cdot a \quad [33]$$

The two weights are combined on the left-hand side and the acceleration is isolated on the right-hand side:

$$M \cdot g - m \cdot g = (M - m)g = (M + m)a \quad [34]$$

which yields:

$$a = \frac{M - m}{M + m} g = \left(\frac{5\text{ kg} - 3\text{ kg}}{5\text{ kg} + 3\text{ kg}}\right)9.8\frac{m}{s^2}$$

$$= 2.45\frac{m}{s^2} \quad [35]$$

Both objects accelerate with 2.45 m/s² in opposite directions.

*Solution to part (c):* We substitute the result from Eq. [35] into either one of the two formulas in Eq. [32] to find the magnitude of **T**:

$$T = W_M - M \cdot a = M(g - a)$$

$$= 5\text{ kg}\left(9.8\frac{m}{s^2} - 2.45\frac{m}{s^2}\right)$$

$$= 36.8\text{ N} \quad [36]$$

The tension in the string running over the pulley is now $T = 36.8$ N, which is notably higher than the tension in the same string before the second string in Fig. 3.23 was cut.

## Concept Question 3.7

Eq. [35] provides the formula for the acceleration of both objects in Fig. 3.23. How would you change the parameters in Example 3.6 to observe an acceleration that is lower than the value calculated in Eq. [35]?

ANSWER: Several ways to achieve a smaller acceleration exist. We can lower the difference $M - m$ in the numerator of Eq. [35], i.e., choose more similar masses. In particular, $M = m$ leads to $a = 0$. Another way is to increase the sum $M + m$ in the denominator of Eq. [35], e.g., by adding the same amount of mass to both objects.

## Concept Question 3.8

In kinesiology, the movements of the human body and the use of sports equipment are often modelled in computer simulations to optimize performance conditions. Usually a large number of factors play a role, even when focussing only on the released equipment in an overhanded throwing action. For example, for a javelin throw the optimum angle of release depends on the height above ground, the air resistance (which is a function of the stadium location), the wind direction, and the speed of the athlete at the instant of release. These conditions, combined with the aerodynamic properties of the javelin itself, lead to optimum release angles lower than intuitively expected, e.g., as low as 30° above the horizontal. Assume that we include in a simplified algorithm to simulate the maximum distance as a function of angle of release only the weight of the javelin, neglecting its aerodynamic properties and air resistance. How do Newton's laws enter into this algorithm?

ANSWER: You choose the vertical and the horizontal directions as your $x$- and $y$-axes. This allows you to use Newton's first law (i.e., the first formula in Eq. [14]) for the horizontal direction and Newton's second law (i.e., the second formula in Eq. [30]) for the vertical direction. Newton's first law applies horizontally, because the javelin does not accelerate in that direction (note that we excluded air resistance from the model). Newton's second law must be used in the vertical direction, because the javelin's weight continuously acts on it.

## ● EXAMPLE 3.7

Two objects with $m_1 = 3.0$ kg and $m_2 = 2.0$ kg are connected by a massless, taut string that runs over a massless and frictionless pulley, as shown in Fig. 3.25. The inclined surface at the left is tilted at an angle $\theta_1 = 45°$ toward the vertical, and the inclined surface at the right at $\theta_2 = 30°$. Both surfaces permit the frictionless motion of objects. (a) Find the magnitude of the acceleration of the object of mass $m_1$, and (b) find the magnitude of the acceleration of the object of mass $m_2$.

*Solution:*

### Schematic Approach

Both objects have to be treated as independent systems, leaving the massless string, the massless and frictionless pulley, and the frictionless inclined surfaces as components of the environment. For the purpose of practice you may convince yourself that identifying only one object as a

## ● EXAMPLE 3.7 (*continued*)

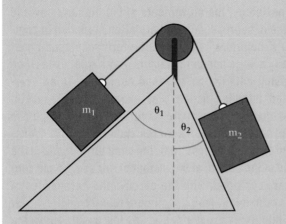

**FIGURE 3.25**

Sketch of two connected objects of masses $m_1$ and $m_2$, which are placed on two inclined surfaces of different angles $\theta_1$ and $\theta_2$. The connection between the objects is a taut, massless string running over a massless and frictionless pulley.

system does not lead to a wrong answer. Instead, you will find that you just do not obtain enough formulas to solve the problem, forcing you back to this step to include the other object as a second system.

### Physical Model

Three forces act on each object: its weight, the normal force exerted by the surface, and the tension along the string. Since these forces differ, we must identify each with the respective index of the object, 1 or 2. The resulting two free-body diagrams are shown in Fig. 3.26.

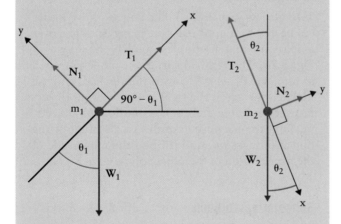

**FIGURE 3.26**

The two free-body diagrams for the objects shown in Fig. 3.25. Note that we choose two different coordinate systems. The angles taken from Fig. 3.25 are also shown because they are needed to identify the x- and y-components of the weights.

### Quantitative Treatment

A choice of axes is included in Fig. 3.26. Note that one axis is chosen parallel and one perpendicular to the inclined surface. The coordinate systems for the two objects do not have to be the same because no force appears in both free-body diagrams; choosing the coordinate systems for each system separately is often useful to minimize the amount of later calculations.

We notice that nothing interesting is happening in either of the y-directions perpendicular to the inclined surface. Thus, we need not write all four formulas for the two systems using Newton's laws, but can confine the discussion to the two component formulas in the directions along the inclined surfaces. These formulas are:

System 1:    $-m_1 \cdot g \cdot \cos \theta_1 + T = m_1 \cdot a$

System 2:    $-T + m_2 \cdot g \cdot \cos \theta_2 = m_2 \cdot a$    [37]

in which we used $T_{1x} = T$ and $T_{2x} = -T$. This actually means two things. First, we note that the magnitudes of both tension vectors are equal because the string is massless. Second, the only non-zero component of the tension is the x-component in each case, and therefore the value of that component is equal to the magnitude of the vector. However, tension $\mathbf{T}_1$ runs in the positive x-direction and tension $\mathbf{T}_2$ runs in the negative x-direction, each based on the respective free-body diagram.

We would get the same results if we had chosen a different coordinate system: had we chosen the x-direction in the free-body diagram at the right in Fig. 3.26 upward along the inclined surface, then the sign of the respective tension component would be opposite to the sign used in Eq. [37]. In this case the sign of the acceleration would also change in the formula for system 2.

The use of tensions in this problem reminds us yet again to carefully distinguish between the magnitude of a vector, which is always positive, and the non-zero component of the vector when it is directed parallel to one of the fundamental axes in the problem.

*Any vector **p** has a magnitude (or length) $+p$ regardless of the orientation of the vector. If **p** is directed along the x-axis, then the x-component of **p** is either $p_x = +p$ if **p** is directed along the positive x-direction or $p_x = -p$ if the vector is directed along the negative x-direction.*

We also use in Eq. [37] $a_{1x} = a_{2x} = a$; i.e., the x-components of the accelerations of both systems are equal. This follows from the same reasoning as just applied to the tensions: the magnitudes of both accelerations are the same since the string is and remains taut; the distance between both objects, as measured along the string, does not change. Further, both $x$-components of the accelerations are directed in the same direction based on the chosen coordinate systems; i.e., they must both be positive or both be negative, because otherwise the two objects would eventually collide or drift apart.

*Solution to part (a):* The magnitude of the acceleration $a$ is sought first. In Eq. [37] we eliminate the second unknown variable, the magnitude of the tension $\mathbf{T}$, by adding the two formulas:

$$(-m_1 \cdot \cos 45° + m_2 \cdot \cos 30°)g = (m_1 + m_2)a \quad [38]$$

This allows us to calculate the acceleration:

$$a = \frac{m_2 \cdot \cos 30° - m_1 \cdot \cos 45°}{m_1 + m_2} g$$

$$= -0.76 \, \frac{m}{s^2} \quad [39]$$

We found a negative result! By definition, this must be wrong. However, it is useful to analyze the origin of the mistake, as it is essentially unavoidable and is easy to correct. The result in Eq. [39] is negative because we assumed $a_{1x} = a_{2x} = a$, but should have used $a_{1x} = a_{2x} = -a$. That means we made a mistake by assuming that both objects move toward the right when they actually move toward the left: the object with $m_2 = 2$ kg moves up the inclined surface and the object with $m_1 = 3$ kg slides down. Note that the acceleration is quite small in comparison to the gravitational acceleration constant $g$! For that reason it was next to impossible to guess without the above calculation which way the two objects move. In turn, we can easily correct the mistake by stating the direction of motion correctly, then assigning an acceleration of $a = 0.76$ m/s$^2$.

*Solution to part (b):* We already established $a_{1x} = a_{2x}$ before solving part (a). Thus, Eq. [39] also gives the answer to this part.

### ● EXAMPLE 3.8

Fig. 3.27 shows an object of mass $m = 10.0$ kg held by a massless string on a frictionless inclined surface. (a) What is the tension in the string if $\theta = 35°$, and (b) what force does the surface exert on the object? (c) When the string is cut, with what acceleration does the object move along the inclined surface?

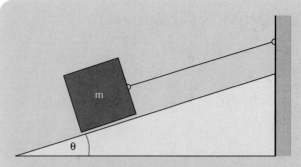

**FIGURE 3.27**

A combined application of the first and second laws of mechanics. An object of mass $m$ on an inclined frictionless surface is connected by a massless string to a vertical wall. We can determine the normal force and the tension using Newton's first law. When the string is cut, the problem becomes an application of the second law of mechanics because the object accelerates downhill.

*Solution:*

### Schematic Approach

The object of mass $m$ is the system. The inclined surface, the massless string, and the person cutting the string are part of the environment.

### Physical Model

For parts (a) and (b), three forces act on the object: the tension $\mathbf{T}$ along the inclined surface, the weight $\mathbf{W}$ down, and the normal force $\mathbf{N}$ in the direction normal (perpendicular) to the surface. For part (c) the tension is eliminated. The free-body diagram for parts (a) and (b) is shown in Fig. 3.28.

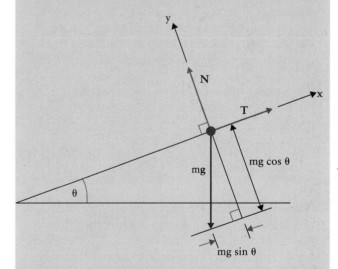

**FIGURE 3.28**

We draw the free-body diagram for the object with the string as shown in Fig. 3.27. Note that the coordinate system is chosen with the $x$-axis parallel to the inclined surface. The figure indicates how the two components of the weight are obtained. Note that these components can be negative, which depends on the choice of direction of the coordinate system axes.

● **EXAMPLE 3.8 (continued)**

**Quantitative Treatment**

The coordinate system is chosen with the $x$-axis parallel to the inclined surface and the $y$-axis perpendicular to it. Thus, **T** and **N** are parallel to major axes. The components of the weight are determined from the free-body diagram: $W_x = -m \cdot g \cdot \sin \theta$, and $W_y = -m \cdot g \cdot \cos \theta$. These components are needed when we apply Newton's laws along each axis separately.

*Solutions to parts (a) and (b):* The first two parts of the example are applications of the first law of mechanics as given in Eq. [14], because the object remains at rest. From the free-body diagram in Fig. 3.28, we find:

$$x\text{-direction:} \quad T - m \cdot g \cdot \sin \theta = 0$$
$$y\text{-direction:} \quad N - m \cdot g \cdot \cos \theta = 0 \quad [40]$$

From the first formula, we derive:

$$T = m \cdot g \cdot \sin \theta = (10 \text{ kg})\left(9.8 \frac{\text{m}}{\text{s}^2}\right)\sin 35°$$
$$= 56 \text{ N} \quad [41]$$

From the second formula, we obtain:

$$N = m \cdot g \cdot \cos \theta = 80 \text{ N} \quad [42]$$

Note that this example demonstrates that you cannot assume $N = m \cdot g$ in all cases!

*Solution to part (c):* We have to go back to the free-body diagram in Fig. 3.28. Eliminating the tension by cutting the string reduces the free-body diagram to just two forces, **N** and **W**. Keeping the coordinate system as chosen before, we have to revise Eq. [40]. This time, the problem is an application of the second law of mechanics along the $x$-direction because the two remaining forces do not balance each other (two non-parallel forces never balance each other). Thus, Eq. [40] is replaced by:

$$x\text{-direction:} \quad -m \cdot g \cdot \sin \theta = -m \cdot a$$
$$y\text{-direction:} \quad N - m \cdot g \cdot \cos \theta = 0$$
$$[43]$$

with the acceleration component $a_x = -a$ because the object accelerates downhill while the $x$-axis is pointing uphill. Note that the second formula in Eq. [43] has not changed from Eq. [40] and remains an application of the first law of mechanics because the object does not move in the $y$-direction at any time. Comparing Eqs. [40] and [43] illustrates why we have chosen the coordinate system with one axis parallel to the inclined surface: the lack of motion perpendicular to the inclined surface allows us to use Newton's first law in the $y$-direction in part (c), and the acceleration

doesn't need to be written as two components. Part (c) is solved with the first formula in Eq. [43]:

$$a = g \cdot \sin \theta = \left(9.8 \frac{\text{m}}{\text{s}^2}\right)\sin 35° = 5.6 \frac{\text{m}}{\text{s}^2} \quad [44]$$

The magnitude of the acceleration has the value $|a| = 5.6 \text{ m/s}^2$. The vector component along the $x$-axis is $a_x = -5.6 \text{ m/s}^2$.

A final comment about Newton's first and second law. Based on the discussion above, one may think that the first law is a special case of the second law for **a** = 0. This is not the case, for two reasons:

- In conceptual physics, the two laws are considered independent because of an aspect of the first law that we do not pursue further in this textbook. We define a frame of reference as a set of points or axes relative to which motion is described. The first law defines when a particular reference frame is an *inertial frame of reference*, in which an object that does not interact with other objects does not accelerate. The second and third laws then apply only in inertial frames of reference.

- For the applications in this book, another distinction between the two laws will have a big impact on our discussion: the first law leads to static issues and the second law to dynamic cases. As we progress through later chapters, in particular thermodynamics, the discussion of systems in equilibrium requires distinctively different concepts than the description of systems outside the equilibrium.

## Newton's Third Law

The last law focusses on the interaction of the system with its environment. We state this law in the following form:

*If an object A exerts a force **F** on an object B, then object B exerts a force equal in magnitude and opposite in direction on object A.*

Calling the force exerted by object A on object B $\mathbf{F}_{Ba}$, and the force exerted by object B on object A $\mathbf{F}_{Ab}$, we write this law quantitatively:

$$\mathbf{F}_{Ab} = -\mathbf{F}_{Ba} \quad [45]$$

We call the two forces in Eq. [45] an **action–reaction pair**. It is very important to note that an action force and its reaction force never act on the same object!

## Concept Question 3.9

A person's calf muscle pulls on the Achilles tendon attached to the heel bone. How are the various forces in the lower leg related when the person does push-ups? Fig. 3.29 shows a simplified sketch of the muscles and bones of a human body during a push-up. Note that the calf muscle connects to the heel via the Achilles tendon. An anatomically correct side view of the muscles in the lower leg is given in Fig. 3.5.

ANSWER: We apply the problem-solving strategy to illustrate that it can be used for conceptual questions as well.

### Schematic Approach

Notice in Fig. 3.29 that the heel bone, the Achilles tendon, and the calf muscle all are lined up horizontally when the body is in the position shown. This allows us to neglect the weight as a force because we are interested only in the horizontal interactions. A careful labelling must take place, because three systems are considered: we label the calf muscle "M," the Achilles tendon "T," and the heel bone "B." We include the tendon since it may not be possible to assume that it is a massless string. For the discussion of this problem, we need only the forces the three parts of the leg exert on each other.

### Physical Model

We develop (partial) free-body diagrams for Fig. 3.29. This problem is a typical application of the third law of mechanics since several objects are involved. Fig. 3.30 shows the important forces for each system; note that the tendon is drawn as a bar. We identify the horizontal interaction forces in each case. The muscle pulls the tendon to the left. Labelling the object on which the force acts with a capital letter and the object exerting the force with a lower-case letter, this force is $F_{Tm}$. At the same time, the

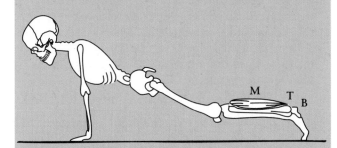

**FIGURE 3.29**

Anatomical sketch of a standard man doing push-ups. This side view highlights the relative position of the heel bone (B), the Achilles tendon (T), and the calf muscle (M). Note that the three elements are located along a horizontal line during push-ups.

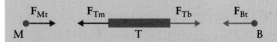

**FIGURE 3.30**

The major horizontal forces acting on each of the three systems in Fig. 3.29, the heel bone (B), the Achilles tendon (T), and the calf muscle (M). The tendon is shown as an elongated box. Each force is identified by a double index with the capital letter indicating on which system the force acts and the lowercase letter indicating which other object exerts the force. For example, $F_{Mt}$ is the force exerted by the tendon on the muscle.

muscle is pulled in the opposite direction by the tendon. This force is labelled $F_{Mt}$. At the other end, the tendon pulls on the bone with force $F_{Bt}$. The bone exerts an equal but opposite force on the tendon, labelled $F_{Tb}$.

### Quantitative Treatment

Among these forces are the following action–reaction pairs:

$$\mathbf{F}_{Tm} = -\mathbf{F}_{Mt}$$
$$\mathbf{F}_{Bt} = -\mathbf{F}_{Tb} \qquad [46]$$

Note that $F_{Tb}$ and $F_{Tm}$ are not an action–reaction pair, because both forces act on the same object! Actually, these two forces need to be different for the muscle to succeed in moving the heel. In that case we write the second law of mechanics for the horizontal component of the net force on the tendon:

$$\text{horizontal direction:} \quad F_{net} = F_{Tb} - F_{Tm} = m_T \cdot a \qquad [47]$$

in which the magnitude of **a** is equal to the horizontal acceleration component of the tendon. Eq. [47] is applied for a tendon in two ways:

- For a given mass $m_T$ of the tendon, an acceleration can be determined. Note, however, that we need to identify two different forces, one at each end of the tendon.

- If we assume $m_T = 0$—i.e., that the mass of the tendon is negligible—then Eq. [47] simplifies to

$$F_{Tb} = F_{Tm} = T \qquad [48]$$

This equation defines the magnitude of the tension **T**. This case is simpler since only one force magnitude is associated with the tendon.

## Concept Question 3.10

Newton's third law states that a reaction force exists for each force, and that the two forces are equal but opposite in direction. Would we not need some forces that have no reaction force for an object to achieve an acceleration, since all action–reaction pairs each add up to a zero net force?

ANSWER: This is a frequently stated misconception. Keep in mind that action and reaction forces must act on different objects, but only forces that act on the object of interest determine the net force that is then used in Newton's first or second law. No forces exist without a reaction force.

## Concept Question 3.11

Fig. 3.31 shows an object that is suspended by a string from the ceiling. The right side of the figure shows three (partial) free-body diagrams for the object, the string, and the hook, respectively, from bottom to top. For which of the six forces are no reaction forces shown, and what objects cause those reaction forces?

ANSWER: $F_2$ and $F_3$, and $F_4$ and $F_5$, are action–reaction pairs of forces. $F_1$ is the force the ceiling exerts on the hook with the force exerted by the hook on the ceiling not shown. $W$ is the weight of the object. The force exerted on Earth caused by the gravitational attraction due to the object is not shown.

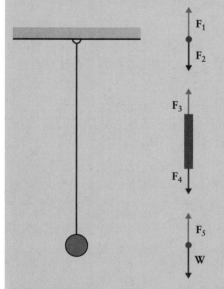

**FIGURE 3.31**

An object (green circle) is suspended from the ceiling with a string (left). Partial free-body diagrams are shown at the right for the hook (top), the string (centre), and the object (bottom).

## ● EXAMPLE 3.9

A sprinter wants a maximum forward acceleration during the initial stage of a sprint. This is achieved from a crouching position with the upper body of the sprinter well in front of the feet, as shown in Fig. 3.32(a). If the sprinter has a mass of $m = 70$ kg, calculate the force the sprinter must apply against the starting block to achieve a horizontal acceleration of 15 m/s$^2$.

*Note:* The starting block must be tilted such that the vertical component of the force the starting block exerts on the sprinter compensates for the weight of the sprinter. Otherwise, the sprinter would either fall to the ground or jump upward instead of accelerating forward.

*Solution:*

### Schematic Approach

Fig. 3.32(a) indicates why this problem is an application of Newton's third law: We are asked about a force acting on the starting block, but we cannot treat the starting block as the system because we know too little about it. On the other side, we know everything necessary to determine the force exerted by the starting block on the sprinter. Anticipating the use of the third law at the end of the discussion, we therefore treat the sprinter as the system, solve for the magnitude of the force between sprinter and starting block, and then answer the question without further calculations.

### Physical Model

From Fig. 3.32(a), we can identify two forces acting on the system: the weight pulling the sprinter downward and the contact force (normal force) exerted by the starting block. Note that the normal force does not act vertically since the starting block is tilted. The free-body diagram is shown in Fig. 3.33.

### Quantitative Treatment

The best choice of coordinate system is horizontal $x$- and vertical $y$-axes, because the text refers to the horizontal component of the acceleration. This means that we have to split the normal force into a vertical and a horizontal component in the free-body diagram.

The free-body diagram leads to two formulas: a mechanical equilibrium based on Eq. [14] in the $y$-direction as indicated in the problem text, which states there is no change of motion in the $y$-direction, and an equation of motion based on Eq. [30] along the $x$-direction, in which an acceleration occurs:

$$x\text{-direction:} \qquad N_x = m \cdot a$$
$$y\text{-direction:} \quad N_y - W = 0 \qquad [49]$$

(a)

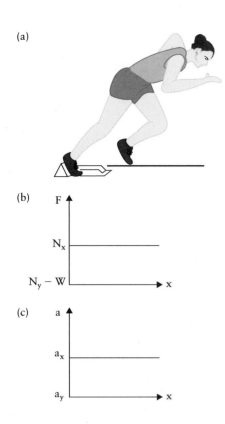

(b)

**FIGURE 3.32**

(a) An application of the third law of mechanics: a sprinter in the initial stage of a sprint. At this stage the sprinter has no contact with the horizontal ground but only with the inclined starting block. The sprinter accelerates in the horizontal direction. (b) The x- and y-components of the net force acting on the sprinter, and (c) the x- and y-components of the acceleration of the sprinter in the initial stage of the sprint.

(c)

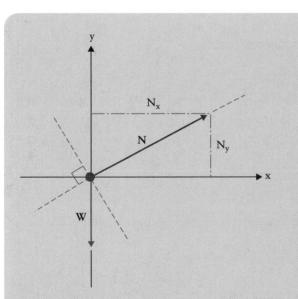

**FIGURE 3.33**

The free-body diagram and coordinate system for the sprinter in Fig 3.32. The weight **W** is compensated by the vertical component of the normal force, $N_y$. The horizontal component of the normal force, $N_x$, leads to the acceleration. Note that we do not develop a free-body diagram for the starting block, even though the problem asks for the magnitude of a force acting on it.

The x- and y-components of the net force are shown in Fig. 3.32(b), and the respective acceleration components are illustrated in Fig. 3.32(c). From the two formulas in Eq. [49], we find the two components of the normal force:

$$x\text{-direction:} \quad N_x = m \cdot a = (70 \text{ kg})\left(15 \frac{\text{m}}{\text{s}^2}\right)$$
$$= 1050 \text{ N}$$
$$y\text{-direction:} \quad N_y = W = m \cdot g = 685 \text{ N}$$

[50]

The two components are combined to calculate the magnitude of the normal force:

$$|\mathbf{N}| = \sqrt{N_x^2 + N_y^2} = 1255 \text{ N} \qquad [51]$$

Note that Eq. [51] does not answer the initial question. We were not asked for the force the starting block exerts on the sprinter, but for the force the sprinter exerts on the starting block. As anticipated, at this point the third law of mechanics comes into play. The force exerted by the sprinter on the starting block is equal in magnitude but opposite in direction to the normal force we calculated. Therefore, the sprinter pushes with a force of 1255 N into the starting block.

# Physiological Applications of Newton's Laws

In this section, three examples highlight how the laws of mechanics are applied in kinesiology and physiology.

## A Standard Man in the Gym

In physiology we are often concerned with humans in general, not with the features of a particular person. For this purpose, a **standard man** has been defined and the standard man's data, summarized in Table 3.3, are used in calculations.

● **EXAMPLE 3.10**

The standard man in Fig. 3.34 intends to do *concentration curls* in a gym. At the beginning of this exercise, the person holds with the left arm vertically a dumbbell of mass $M = 4$ kg. We are interested in the arm of the standard man and consider the following forces: the weight of the dumbbell, the force pulling down the fist, the weight of the arm, and the tension in the shoulder. This tension is primarily caused in the tendon of the deltoid muscle and several ligaments that run across the interface between the trunk and the arm. The weight of the dumbbell and the force pulling the fist down are equal in magnitude. Calculate the ratio of the magnitude of the tension in the shoulder to the magnitude of the force that pulls the fist down.

*Solution:*

### Schematic Approach

We choose the left arm as our system because the problem text refers to several forces acting on that arm. We note, however, that the weight of the dumbbell is a force acting not on the arm but on the dumbbell. It is identified because it allows us to quantify the force pulling on the fist. Using Table 3.3, we know that the body mass of the standard man is 70 kg, and that the mass of the left arm is 6.5% of this value, i.e., 4.6 kg.

Note also that the question does not ask for a numerical value for one of the unknown parameters, but asks for a ratio instead. This type of question occurs frequently, because such ratios help us to develop an intuitive idea of the magnitude of the effects we study. Note how this type of question leads to a slightly different approach in the quantitative treatment.

The text indicates that the person holds the dumbbell in the position shown before doing an intended exercise with it. Thus, the dumbbell is at rest and the problem is an application of Newton's first law.

### Physical Model

The forces we need to consider are all given in the problem text. You will find this to be typical for physiological or biological problems in this textbook, because identifying the major forces

**TABLE 3.3**

### Standard man data. The percentage values indicate the fraction of the total body mass

| General data | |
|---|---|
| Age | 30 years |
| Height | 173 cm |
| **Mass distribution** | |
| Body mass $M_{total}$ | 70 kg |
| Mass of the trunk | 48% |
| Muscle mass | 43% |
| Mass of each leg | 15% |
| Fat mass | 14% |
| Bone mass | 10% |
| Mass of the head | 7% |
| Mass of each arm | 6.5% |
| Brain mass | 2.1% |
| Mass of both lungs | 1.4% |
| **Homeostasis data** | |
| Surface area | 1.85 m² |
| Body core temperature* | 310 K |
| Specific heat capacity | 3.60 kJ/(kg · K) |
| **Respiratory data** | |
| Total lung capacity | 6.0 L |
| Tidal volume (lungs) | 0.5 L |
| Breathing rate | 15 breaths/min |
| Oxygen consumption | 0.26 L/min |
| Carbon dioxide production | 0.208 L/min |
| **Cardiovascular data** | |
| Blood volume | 5.1 L |
| Cardiac output | 5.0 L/min |
| Systolic blood pressure | 16.0 kPa |
| Diastolic blood pressure | 10.7 kPa |
| Heart rate | 70 beats/min |

\* Skin surface temperatures vary with environmental temperature; see Fig. 10.5.

**FIGURE 3.35**

Free-body diagram for the system (arm) in Fig. 3.34. The three forces act in the vertical direction, with the weight of the arm and the pull of the dumbbell directed downward, and the tension in the shoulder directed upward.

acting in our body for a given exercise requires anatomical knowledge you may not yet have. Note that any one of these problems could be defined as a kinesiological research project, where identifying the major forces would consume most of the time invested in the project.

Finally, we draw the free-body diagram for the arm. This is shown in Fig. 3.35. We label the tension in the shoulder **T** and the force pulling the fist down **F**. The force **T** acts in the upward direction and **F** and $W_{arm}$ downward. We choose the vertical direction upward as the $y$-axis.

### Quantitative Treatment

Using the free-body diagram in Fig. 3.35, we write Newton's first law (i.e., the second formula in Eq. [14]) for the arm in Fig. 3.34 in the form:

$$F_{net,y} = T - W_{arm} - F = 0 \qquad [52]$$

Substituting $F = W_M$, in which $W_M$ is the magnitude of the weight of the dumbbell, and writing $W_{arm} = 0.065 \cdot W_{total}$, in which $W_{total}$ is the magnitude of the weight of the standard man, we find:

$$T = 0.065 \cdot W_{total} + W_M \qquad [53]$$

We can now calculate the ratio $T/F$, which we are asked to find:

$$\frac{T}{F} = \frac{0.065 \cdot W_{total}}{W_M} + 1$$

$$= \frac{(4.6 \text{ kg}) \, g}{(4.0 \text{ kg}) \, g} + 1 = 2.15 \qquad [54]$$

The tension in the shoulder is more than twice as large as the force pulling on the fist.

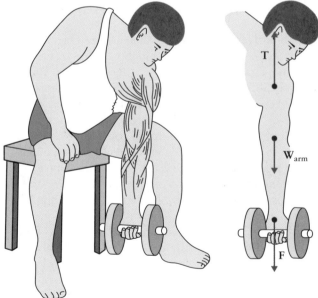

**FIGURE 3.34**

A standard man intends to do *concentration curls*. The sketch at the bottom right indicates the major forces acting on the arm of the person: the tension **T** in the muscles and ligaments connecting the arm to the trunk, the weight of the arm $W_{arm}$, and a force **F** acting on the fist due to the weight of the dumbbell.

Why can we substitute $F = W_M$ in Example 3.10 when deriving Eq. [53] from Eq. [52]? Recall that $W_M$ is the weight of the dumbbell in the standard man's hand. Specifically, was it necessary to provide this information with the example text?

ANSWER: Let's consider the dumbbell as our object of interest. Two forces act on it, a force exerted upward by the standard man to compensate for the dumbbell's weight $W_M$. We call the force exerted by the standard man $\mathbf{F}^*$ and note $\mathbf{W}_M = -\mathbf{F}^*$ since this establishes the mechanical equilibrium for the dumbbell. Now we turn our attention to the standard man, but focus still on the interaction with the dumbbell. From Newton's third law we recognize that $\mathbf{F} = -\mathbf{F}^*$; i.e., the standard man exerts the same force on the dumbbell as the dumbbell exerts on the standard man's hand, only in the opposite direction. Thus, stating $F = W_M$ is not necessary since it can be determined from the laws of mechanics.

## Gravity Detection in the Maculae

● **EXAMPLE 3.11**

Determine the force acting perpendicular to the dendrites of each neuron in the **utricular macula** (a) when the head is upright and (b) when it is tilted sideways by 30°. *Hint:* Fig. 3.9 shows the side view of the macula in the upright and the tilted position. The mechanism of the macula was described earlier with Fig. 3.9.

*Note:* This is the first example where we no longer explicitly highlight the specific steps of the problem-solving strategy. Continue to identify the three steps in this and later examples.

*Solution to part (a):* We start with the identification of the system and the forces acting on it. We define a single calcite **otolith** as our system, and consider the **otolithic membrane** of the macula as the environment. This choice requires that we later use Newton's third law, because the problem text asks for a force acting on the dendrites. We cannot choose the dendrites directly as our system because we know too little about them, but we know that action–reaction pairs of forces relate the otoliths to the otolithic membrane, and in turn the otolithic membrane to the dendrites.

Two forces act on the otolith in Fig. 3.9(a):

- Earth exerts a gravitational force leading to the otolith's weight $\mathbf{W}$, and
- the otolithic membrane exerts a normal force $\mathbf{N}$.

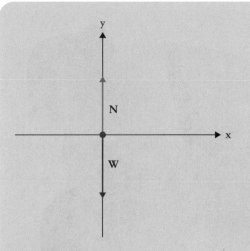

**FIGURE 3.36**
The free-body diagram of a single otolith in the macula when the head is held upright.

The free-body diagram is developed and Cartesian coordinates are assigned in Fig. 3.36. The dot at the centre represents the otolith (the system). The weight acts downward and the normal force pushes the otolith upward. We choose the $x$-axis toward the right and the $y$-axis upward. The otolith is in mechanical equilibrium in both directions: in the $x$-direction no forces act on it, and in the $y$-direction we use Newton's first law:

$$y\text{-direction:} \quad -W + N = 0 \qquad [55]$$

The answer to part (a) is that no force acts perpendicular to the dendrites in the upright position.

We can still use Eq. [55] to quantify the force the otolithic membrane has to exert on the otolith to keep it in place. This calculation illustrates the use of the density information provided earlier. The magnitude of the normal force is $N = W = m \cdot g$. To quantify $N$ we need the mass of an otolith, which we don't know. Instead, we have information about its size and its density. The **density** is defined as $\rho = m/V$, where $V$ is the volume. For calcite, $\rho = 3.0$ g/cm$^3$ = $3.0 \times 10^3$ kg/m$^3$. From microscopic images of the macula we find that the length of an average otolith is about 5 $\mu$m, which corresponds to a volume $V = (5 \ \mu\text{m})^3$ or $V = 1.25 \times 10^{-16}$ m$^3$. The mass of the otolith is then $m = \rho \cdot V = 3.75 \times 10^{-13}$ kg. By multiplying with $g$ we find the magnitude of the normal force, $N = 3.7 \times 10^{-12}$ N for a single otolith.

*Solution to part (b):* Fig. 3.37(a) shows a simplified sketch of the otolith and the adjacent dendrites when the head is turned sideways by an angle $\theta$. This posture results in the free-body diagram in the bottom part of the figure. Again, the otolith is represented as the dot at the centre. The weight acts downward; the normal force is directed perpendicular to the otolithic membrane surface. If there were no other forces, no mechanical equilibrium could exist along the membrane surface and, according to Newton's second law, the otolith would accelerate toward the right. This does not happen, because one more force is to be considered: a contact force along the interface between the otolithic membrane and the otolith. This contact force resists the slipping of the otolith, i.e., the gelatin pushes the otolith upward along the inclined surface. We call this force $\mathbf{F}_{gel}$. Remember that we are asked to find the force acting perpendicular to the dendrites; thus the answer will be based on $\mathbf{F}_{gel}$.

Once all three forces are included in the free-body diagram, directions for the Cartesian coordinates have to be chosen. To have most forces coincide with the main axes, we choose $y$- and $x$-directions perpendicular and parallel to the surface plane of the membrane, respectively.

Note that the free-body diagram contains one force that is not in the direction of a fundamental axis. The next step is to determine the $x$- and $y$-components of this force as shown in Fig. 3.37(b): $W_x = W \cdot \sin \theta$ and $W_y = -W \cdot \cos \theta$.

We use Newton's first law (Eq. [14]) because the otolith is in mechanical equilibrium in both the $x$- and $y$-directions:

$$x\text{-direction:} \quad -F_{gel} + W \cdot \sin \theta = 0$$
$$y\text{-direction:} \quad -W \cdot \cos \theta + N = 0 \qquad [56]$$

The first formula in Eq. [56] leads to the force exerted by the otolithic membrane:

$$F_{gel} = W \cdot \sin \theta = (3.7 \times 10^{-12}\text{ N})\sin 30°$$
$$= 1.85 \times 10^{-12}\text{ N} \qquad [57]$$

in which $\mathbf{W}$ was taken from the solution of part (a). The force calculated in Eq. [57] is the force exerted by the otolithic membrane on a single otolith. However, due to the third law of mechanics, a force of the same magnitude is exerted by the otolith on the membrane, and in turn on the dendrites embedded in it. To determine the total lateral force on the dendrites of a single neuron, we multiply $F_{gel}$ by the number of otoliths that interact with each neuron. This number is estimated from microscopic images to be about 15 otoliths per neuron. Since forces can be added, we estimate the magnitude of the lateral force on all dendrites of a single neuron to be $|\mathbf{F}_{\text{lateral on neuron}}| = 2.8 \times 10^{-11}$ N. Table 3.4 allows us to compare this force with other typical forces. Note that the

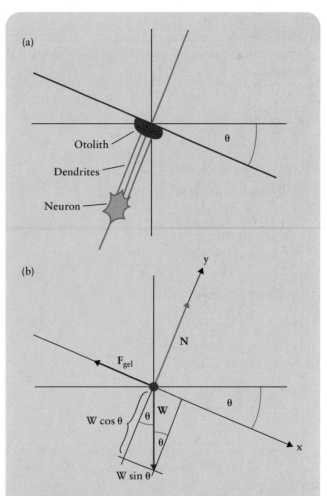

(a)

(b)

**FIGURE 3.37**

(a) Sketch of an otolith near the membrane surface of the utricular macula with the head tilted sideways by an angle $\theta$. Dendrites near the otolith illustrate the geometry of the otolith–membrane–dendrite interaction. (b) The free-body diagram of a single otolith as shown in part (a) with three forces acting on the system: its weight $\mathbf{W}$, the normal force $\mathbf{N}$, and a force parallel to the surface layer of the otolithic membrane $\mathbf{F}_{gel}$. The Cartesian coordinates are chosen with the $x$-axis parallel and the $y$-axis perpendicular to the membrane surface. Based on the choice of the directions of these axes, vector components can be negative.

calculated force is comparably small due to the size of the objects involved.

*Additional comments:* The physical concepts we quantified in Example 3.11 explain why we are equipped with an utricular macula. The ability to detect the vertical direction allows us to judge the alignment of our head with the vertical; this information in turn allows our brain to coordinate our locomotion and correct the information received from other sensory components, such as the eyes. Indeed, due to the importance of our vision, a sideways tilt of the head leads to a horizontal realignment of the eyes.

## TABLE 3.4

### Some typical forces of physiological or biological relevance

| Force | Magnitude $N$ |
|---|---|
| Weight of a female blue whale (with a mass of up to 144 tonnes) | $1.4 \times 10^6$ |
| Weight of a male beluga whale | $1.5 \times 10^4$ |
| Typical contact force in a stressed joint (e.g., hip on head of femur) | $1.7 \times 10^3$ |
| Typical force exerted by a muscle on a large bone (e.g., abductor muscle on hip bone) | $1.1 \times 10^3$ |
| Weight of a standard man | $6.9 \times 10^2$ |
| Weight of an insect egg | $3.5 \times 10^{-6}$ |
| Weight of a single otolith in the macula of the vestibular organ | $3.7 \times 10^{-12}$ |
| Weight of a bacterium | $2.0 \times 10^{-18}$ |

But why do we have two maculae in each ear? Figs. 3.37 and 3.38 provide the answer: We need a sensitive measure of the angle between the axis of our head and the vertical for every possible orientation of the head. A single macula cannot provide that information. We illustrate this with Fig. 3.38(a), which shows the variation of the force on the dendrites as a fraction of the maximum force for the utricular macula. The solid line applies to tilting the head sideways and the dashed line to tilting back and forth. These two curves are not identical, because you need to tilt your head forward by 30° to bring the utricular macula into a levelled position.

The limitations of a single macula are explained by first focussing on the solid line in Fig. 3.38(a). This curve represents the case when the head is tilted sideways. When your head is upright, no force acts on the dendrites in the sideways direction. While you tilt your head to an angle $\theta$, Eq. [57] describes the force acting on the dendrites as $F/F_{max} = \sin \theta$. Note that the solid curve in Fig. 3.38(a) varies fastest for small angles up to 60°. However, due to the sine function, the curve varies much less between 75° and 105°. This means that the signal your brain receives from the utricular macula allows you to judge angles near the vertical position of the head, while the detection of changes of the angle near 90° is poor.

We often hold our heads at angles near 90°, e.g., when lying down. Our ability to judge angles relative

to vertical in that position, even with closed eyes, is not reduced. This is due to the saccular macula, which is tilted by 90° relative to the utricular macula, as illustrated in the anatomical sketch in Fig. 3.39. The dependence of the force on the dendrites in the saccular macula as a function of the angle between the axis of the head and the vertical is shown in Fig. 3.38(b). The solid line applies to a sideways tilt and the dashed line to tilting back and forth. We compare the solid curves in Figs. 3.38(b) and 3.38(a) for the same sideways tilt of the head. Due to the difference in orientation of both maculae in Fig. 3.39, the force on the dendrites in Fig. 3.38(b) is shifted by 90° relative to the corresponding curve in Fig. 3.38(a). Thus, the saccular macula is most sensitive near tilts of the head of 90°, the range of least sensitivity of the utricular macula. Both maculae supplement each other for sideways tilts.

We compare both maculae with respect to tilting the head back and forth in the same fashion. In Fig. 3.38, the dashed curves apply to this case. Note that the 30° tilt of the utricular macula is important

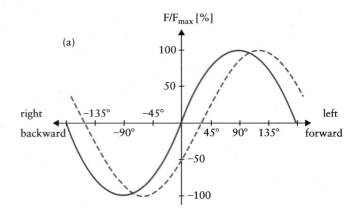

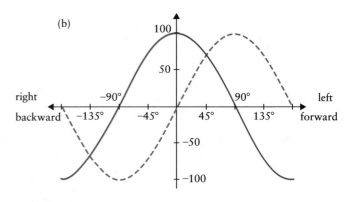

### FIGURE 3.38

The force on the dendrites in the maculae as a function of the tilt of the head. The force is shown relative to the maximum force. The solid lines apply to sideways tilting; the dashed lines apply to tilting back and forth. (a) The angular dependence of the force in the utricular macula. (b) The angular dependence of the force in the saccular macula.

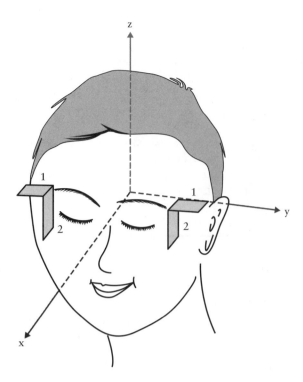

**FIGURE 3.39**

Anatomical sketch of the human head illustrating the orientation of the surface of the otolithic membrane of the utricular (1) and saccular (2) maculae.

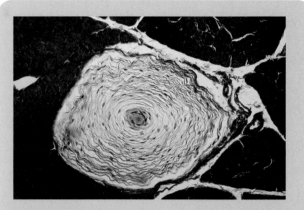

**FIGURE 3.40**

Light micrograph of a sectioned Pacinian corpuscle (bright oval structure at centre). The darker central dendrite is surrounded by a lamellar arrangement of cell membranes. Extracellular fluid surrounds the dendrite inside the innermost cell membrane. The dendrite in the corpuscle is better seen in the chapter-opening micrograph, with the nerve axon leaving the corpuscle at the upper right.

because otherwise both dashed curves would be identical and we would have limited sensitivity to tilts of 90° in this direction, e.g., when lying on the back of our head.

## Acceleration Detection in the Hand: Pacinian Corpuscles

### ● EXAMPLE 3.12

What horizontal force acts on the central dendrite in a **Pacinian corpuscle** when your hand in pronation accelerates with $90 \text{ m/s}^2$ horizontally? Note that this is a typical acceleration for a discus thrower just before releasing the discus.

*Supplementary anatomical information:* The term *pronation* describes the way the hand is held. Pronation means palm down and supination means palm up. In the current context, we conclude that the acceleration occurs parallel to the surface of the palm.

Fig. 3.40 shows a cross-section of a Pacinian corpuscle; the picture used at the beginning of the chapter shows the same corpuscle in a cross-section side view. These corpuscles are about 0.5 mm long and have a 0.2 mm diameter. They consist of more than 50 lamellar cells (cells that are arranged like the layers of an onion). In the centre of the corpuscle is a dendrite. The space between the lamellar cell membranes is filled with extracellular fluid, and the entire corpuscle is encapsulated by elastic connective tissue. The corpuscles are located deep below the epidermis (see Fig. 3.10), with the central dendrite either oriented parallel to the skin surface or at about 45°. They are primarily found in the skin of the palms of our hands and the soles of our feet and serve as acceleration or vibration (cyclic acceleration) detectors.

*Solution:* We first identify the system and the forces so that we can draw a free-body diagram. Fig. 3.41(a) shows a schematic sketch of a Pacinian corpuscle. The $x$-axis is defined parallel and the $y$-axis perpendicular to the palm surface. Fig. 3.41(b) shows the free-body diagram of the forces acting on the central dendrite. Four forces are identified:

- The weight **W** in the vertical direction downward,

- The buoyancy force $\mathbf{F}_{\text{buoyant}}$, caused by the liquid in the vertical direction upward. The buoyant force is associated with the weight of the displaced fluid and is the reason why a diver can float underwater. It will be discussed in more detail in Chapter 11.

- Two non-vertical contact forces that are due to the resting fluid pushing perpendicularly on the nerve from both sides: $\mathbf{F}_{\text{fluid,left}}$ is the

● **EXAMPLE 3.12** (*continued*)

(a)

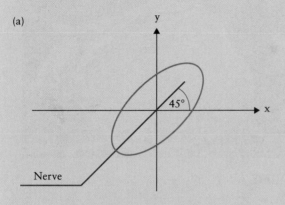

(b)

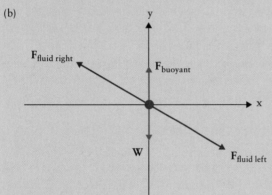

**FIGURE 3.41**

(a) Sketch of the dendrite (the system) in a Pacinian corpuscle tilted by 45° with respect to the palm. The *x*-coordinate is chosen parallel to the palm because it is the direction of the acceleration of the hand. (b) The corresponding free-body diagram shows four forces acting on the dendrite: the weight and the buoyant force in the vertical direction, and two contact forces between the extracellular fluid and the dendrite surface.

force pushing the dendrite from the upper left side, and

- $F_{fluid,right}$ is the force pushing the dendrite from the lower right side.

While the palm and thus the Pacinian corpuscle is at rest, a mechanical equilibrium exists in both directions, i.e., along the *x*- and *y*-axes. According to Newton's first law, the respective formulas are:

*x*-direction:   $F_{fluid\ left,x} - F_{fluid\ right,x} = 0$

*y*-direction:                                                          [58]

$F_{buoyant} - W + F_{fluid\ right,y} - F_{fluid\ left,y} = 0$

We must modify Eq. [58] because the question asks about the hand when it accelerates. Since the acceleration occurs only in the *x*-direction, a

mechanical equilibrium still exists in the *y*-direction; i.e., the second formula in Eq. [58] remains unchanged. The modified first formula reads:

$$F_{fluid\ left,x} - F_{fluid\ right,x} = m \cdot a_x \qquad [59]$$

with $a_x = |a|$ since the acceleration occurs exclusively along the *x*-axis. As a result of $m \cdot a_x \neq 0$, the force of the fluid on the dendrite from the left is larger than the force from the right.

Using Fig. 3.41, we quantify the difference between the forces in Eq. [59]. To do so, we need the mass *m* of the dendrite. We estimate this mass from its volume and density. The dendrite in a typical Pacinian corpuscle extends slightly more than half the length of the corpuscle, $l \approx 0.33$ mm. It is an unmyelinated nerve, as defined in Chapter 14, with a typical diameter of 10 $\mu$m. We use the density of water ($\rho = 1.0$ g/cm$^3$) as an approximate value for the nerve material. Modelling the nerve as a cylinder, we determine first its volume *V*:

$$V = \pi \cdot r^2 \cdot l = \pi(5 \times 10^{-6} \text{ m})^2(3.3 \times 10^{-4} \text{ m})$$
$$= 2.6 \times 10^{-14} \text{ m}^3 \qquad [60]$$

Using this volume, we find the mass of the nerve:

$$m = \rho \cdot V = \left(1 \times 10^3 \frac{kg}{m^3}\right)(2.6 \times 10^{-14}\, m^3)$$
$$= 2.6 \times 10^{-11} \text{ kg} \qquad [61]$$

The difference in magnitude between both contact forces on the central dendrite in Eq. [59] is:

$$\Delta F = F_{fluid\ left,x} - F_{fluid\ right,x}$$
$$= (2.6 \times 10^{-11} \text{ kg})\left(90\, \frac{m}{s^2}\right)$$
$$= 2.3 \times 10^{-9} \text{ N} \qquad [62]$$

This is the answer to the problem. What does this result mean? In order to accelerate a Pacinian corpuscle, the fluid must push the dendrite faster and faster to the left. In the same way the elastic capsule pushes the liquid, the skin pushes the Pacinian corpuscle, and the person moves the whole hand. Due to Newton's third law, the dendrite pushes in the opposite direction, i.e., toward the extracellular fluid that encloses it from the left. Since a fluid can flow, this force causes an evasion of the fluid. As this happens, the dendrite bends slightly to the left, triggering a signal in the nerve.

# MULTIPLE CHOICE AND CONCEPTUAL QUESTIONS

## FORCE CONCEPT

**Q–3.1.** Fig. 3.42 shows five experimental arrangements. In part (A), the object is vertically attached to a string, in parts (B) and (C) the object is in a bowl-shaped structure, in part (D) it lies on a horizontal table, and in part (E) the object is held by a string on an inclined surface. In which case is the object not in mechanical equilibrium?

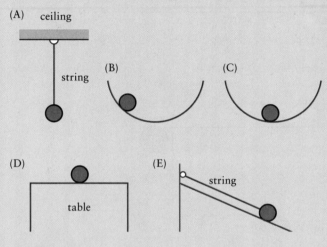

**FIGURE 3.42**

**Q–3.2.** The more forces act on a body part of interest the more anatomical, physiological, and physical data are required for the quantitative evaluation of a mechanical system. To deal with this, we often want to limit the number of forces that have to be taken into account. Under what circumstances can the weight of the body part be neglected? Can you suggest an example?

**Q–3.3.** In Example 2.4, we discussed the Mantis shrimp's ability to achieve astonishing accelerations with its spear-like arms, allowing it to kill its prey without the victim ever noticing the attack. Assume that the mantis shrimp uses a constant force to accelerate its weapon and is at a distance $d_0$ from its prey. (a) Which of the three plots in Fig. 3.43 shows the

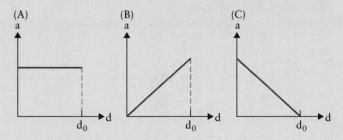

**FIGURE 3.43**

acceleration as a function of position $d$? (b) Which of the three plots in Fig. 3.44 shows the velocity of the weapon as a function of position $d$?

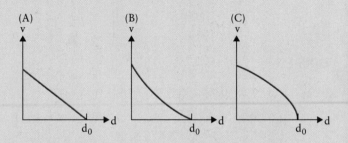

**FIGURE 3.44**

**Q–3.4.** Which of the three forces shown to act on a standard man's arm in Fig. 3.7 are contact forces? (A) All three forces; (B) $\mathbf{T}$ and $\mathbf{W}_{arm}$; (C) $\mathbf{T}$ and $\mathbf{F}$; (D) $\mathbf{W}_{arm}$ and $\mathbf{F}$; (E) only the force $\mathbf{F}$? *Note:* The standard man is defined in Example 3.10 and in Table 3.3.

**Q–3.5.** The dumbbell in Fig. 3.7 has a weight $\mathbf{W}_{dumbbell}$. Why do we not include this force when discussing the mechanics of the lower arm of the standard man in the figure? (A) The force $\mathbf{W}_{dumbbell}$ acts in another direction than the listed forces and therefore has to be omitted; (B) The force $\mathbf{W}_{dumbbell}$ has no reaction force in the figure, and for that reason cannot be considered in Newton's laws; (C) The force $\mathbf{W}_{dumbbell}$ does not act on the standard man's arm and has to be excluded when Newton's law is applied to the arm; (D) We have already included the weight of the arm, $\mathbf{W}_{arm}$, and no way exists to include two different weights in Newton's laws; (E) The dumbbell is not alive and can therefore not exert a force on another object.

**Q–3.6.** What forces act on a football at the top of its path after having been kicked? Neglect air resistance. (A) The force due to the horizontal motion of the football. (B) The force of gravity. (C) The force exerted by the kicker. (D) The force exerted by the kicker and gravity.

## NEWTON'S FIRST LAW

**Q–3.7.** Fig. 3.45 shows a round blue object on a table touching a green block. Which of the following six equations is the proper application of Newton's laws in the vertical direction describing the forces acting on the round object? *Hint:* We label $\mathbf{N}$ the normal force, $\mathbf{W}$ the weight, and $\mathbf{F}$ the contact force with the block.

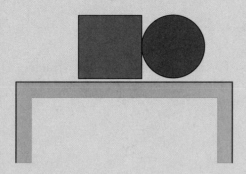

**FIGURE 3.45**

(A) $F + W = 0$     (B) $F - W = 0$

(C) $N + W = 0$     (D) $N - W = 0$     [63]

(E) $N - F = 0$     (F) $N + F = 0$

**Q–3.8.** We study a person in a gym intending to do *seated rows*. In this exercise, the person sits on a bench facing the exercise equipment. The feet are placed against the foot stops. The person leans toward a pulley and holds the handle on a string. Then the person arches the back and pulls the handle until it touches the lower ribcage. The main muscles needed in this exercise are the deltoid muscle in the shoulder and the upper back muscles. When the arms are stretched out horizontally, the major forces acting on the arm include the tension in the deltoid/back muscles, **T**, which acts in the direction away from the pulley; the force, **F**, due to the shoulder bones pushing the upper arm bone against the pull of the tension force; the weight of the arm, $\mathbf{W}_{arm}$; and a force $\mathbf{F}_{handle}$ due to the mass of the handle. Which choice in Fig. 3.46 is the correct free-body diagram for the horizontal forces acting on the person's arm?

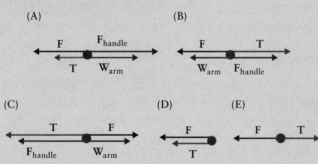

**FIGURE 3.46**

**Q–3.9.** Two forces act on a system, $\mathbf{F}_1 = (F_1, 0)$ along the x-axis and $\mathbf{F}_2 = (0, F_2)$ along the y-axis. What is the minimum number of forces required in this case to establish mechanical equilibrium? (A) two; (B) three; (C) four; (D) five; (E) the number depends on further information not provided.

**Q–3.10.** Fig. 3.47 shows an object attached to a string. The object is in mechanical equilibrium in the position shown because a table prevents it from moving toward the lower left. Which of the following six equations is the proper application of Newton's laws in the x-direction of this case? *Note:* We label the normal force **N**, the weight **W**, and the tension **T**.

(A) $-W + T \sin \theta = 0$     (B) $-W + T \cos \theta = 0$

(C) $+N - T \cos \theta = 0$     (D) $-N + T \cos \theta = 0$

(E) $+N - T \sin \theta = 0$     (F) $-N + T \sin \theta = 0$

[64]

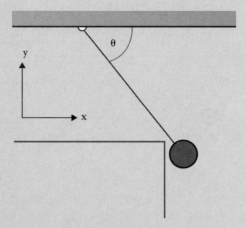

**FIGURE 3.47**

**Q–3.11.** Fig. 3.48 shows a free-body diagram with three forces, a tension **T**, a normal force **N**, and a weight **W**. For which of the five cases shown in Fig. 3.15 is this free-body diagram correct?

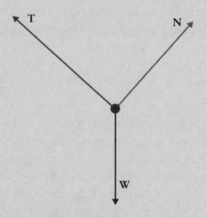

**FIGURE 3.48**

## NEWTON'S SECOND LAW

**Q–3.12.** Only one force acts on an object. Can the object be at rest?

**Q–3.13.** Is it possible for an object to move if no net force acts on it?

**Q–3.14.** Let's consider a case we quantify later: Fig. 5.52 shows a person lifting an object of mass M with the aid of a pulley. The upper arm is held vertical.

Consider the following four forces: (i) the tension **T** in the string of the handle, (ii) the weight **W** of the lower arm and hand, (iii) the tension $F_1$ due to the triceps muscle, and (iv) the force $F_2$ due to the (vertically held) humerus. Assume that the triceps muscle pulls in the vertical direction. (a) Which of the four free-body diagrams in Fig. 3.49 applies if the person holds the object of mass $M$ at rest? (b) Which of the four free-body diagrams in Fig. 3.49 applies if the person moves the object of mass $M$ upward with constant velocity?

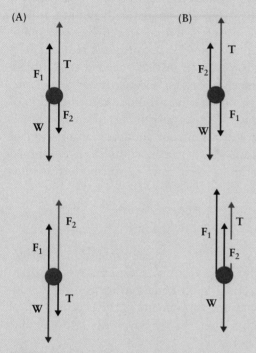

**FIGURE 3.49**

**Q–3.15.** Two forces $F_1$ and $F_2$ act on an object. It accelerates in a particular direction. Under what circumstances can you predict the direction of force $F_1$ regardless of the specific value of force $F_2$?

**Q–3.16.** If no forces other than the three forces shown act on the leg in Fig. 3.14, (a) what is the state of motion of the leg, and (b) in what direction would a fourth force have to act to establish mechanical equilibrium for the leg? Can you suggest the origin of such a force? (c) Identify the reaction force to each of the three forces shown in Fig. 3.14.

**Q–3.17.** An object of mass $m$ accelerates with acceleration $a$. How does the acceleration change if we double the mass of the object but keep the accelerating force unchanged? (A) the acceleration remains unchanged; (B) the magnitude of the acceleration doubles; (C) the magnitude of the acceleration increases by a factor of 4; (D) the magnitude of the acceleration is halved; (E) only the direction of the acceleration changes, but not its magnitude.

## NEWTON'S THIRD LAW

**Q–3.18.** Fig. 3.50 shows the mechanism by which hairs on the arms are tilted upward when a person gets goose bumps, i.e., a roughness of the skin produced from cold, fear, or sudden excitement. The contracting muscle is called *arrector pili* and connects to the epidermis and the root sheath. This example illustrates that the arrector pili, which is a smooth muscle, operates in a very similar fashion to skeletal muscles. Can you identify an action–reaction pair of forces that is involved in its action?

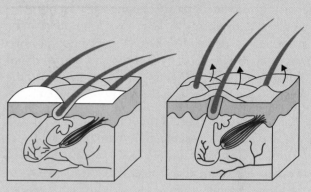

**FIGURE 3.50**

**Q–3.19.** Due to Newton's third law we can make the following statement about the forces in Fig. 3.7: (A) The arm exerts on the trunk a force that equals $-T$; (B) The weight $W_{arm}$ is equal in magnitude to the tension **T**; (C) Forces $W_{arm}$ and **T** are an action–reaction pair of forces; (D) Forces $W_{arm}$ and **F** are an action–reaction pair of forces; (E) The weight of the arm has no reaction force.

**Q–3.20.** Fig. 3.29 shows a standard man doing push-ups. We used the figure to discuss how the various forces in the lower leg are connected. Choose the answer that correctly completes the following statement: "*We probably need Newton's third law to describe the interaction between the bone, the tendon, and the muscle because . . .* (A) the tendon is modelled as a massless string"; (B) we always need all three of Newton's laws to deal with mechanical problems"; (C) we may not have enough information about the system in the stated problem about the standard man"; (D) Newton's third law is required to solve all problems in kinesiology"; (E) we do not need Newton's third law to solve any problem about a standard man doing push-ups."

**Q–3.21.** Two objects are connected with a string. In the quantitative treatment of the problem we assume that the string exerts a tension force of magnitude $T$ on each of the two objects. What has to be the case for this assumption to be valid? (A) the string hangs loose between the objects; (B) the string does not pass over a pulley; (C) the string is massless; (D) the two objects are not on a collision course with each other.

**Q–3.22.** (The following story is reported in the incredible adventures of Freiherr Karl Friedrich Hieronymus von Münchhausen [1720–1797].) Von Münchhausen participated in a hunting party of the king of Lithuania. As guest of honour he had been given the fastest horse of the royal stables, and so he arrived first at a local river in pursuit of a stately elk. Underestimating the depth of the water, von Münchhausen made the horse run straight into it. He noticed the mistake too late, already sinking with the poor animal toward an untimely death. With no other hope for rescue, he decided to take things into his own hands—literally indeed, by grabbing his long hair and pulling himself and the horse straight up out of the water. What is wrong with this story . . . and why?

**Q–3.23.** Newton reported the following observation in *Principia*: Let's assume that two objects attract each other. Contrary to the third law of mechanics, however, we assume that object B is attracted by object A more strongly than object A is attracted by object B. To test this case further, we connect objects A and B with a stiff but massless string, forcing both objects to maintain a fixed distance. Since the force on object B is stronger than on object A, a net force acts on the combined object: it will accelerate without the action of an external force. Since this contradicts the first law of mechanics, we conclude that no violation of the third law is possible and that the third law is already included when we introduced the first law. Indeed, is the third law based on this argument not required as a separate law?

**Q–3.24.** The full title of Newton's seminal work on mechanics is *Philosophiae Naturalis Principia Mathematica* and it contains four statements labelled *lex prima, lex secunda, lex tertia,* and *lex quarta.* The second law, *lex secunda,* is formulated in a different way than we have used it in this chapter, but we will provide Newton's original formulation in Chapter 4. Newton's *lex quarta* states in translated form that "forces can be added like vectors." Why do we no longer identify this statement as Newton's fourth law? (A) Because it is wrong—even Newton made errors once in a while; (B) Because it is redundant—the information it contains isn't needed to establish the laws of mechanics; (C) Because it has been combined with the first law in our modern formulation of Newton's laws; (D) Because it has been combined with the second law in our modern formulation of Newton's laws; (E) Because it has been combined with the first and second laws in our modern formulation of Newton's laws.

### PHYSIOLOGICAL APPLICATIONS

**Q–3.25.** We live in a three-dimensional space. Consequently, each vestibular organ contains three orthogonal semicircular canals to measure the independent Cartesian components of the acceleration of the head. Why, then, do we have only two maculae per ear and not three?

# ANALYTICAL PROBLEMS

### DENSITY

**P–3.1.** One cubic centimetre (1 cm³) of water has a mass of one gram (1 g). (a) Determine the mass of one cubic metre (1 m³) of water. (b) Assume that a spherical bacterium consists of 98% water and has a diameter of 1.0 $\mu$m. Calculate the mass of its water content. (c) Modelling a fly as a water cylinder of 4 mm length and 1 mm radius, what is its mass? *Note:* Important formulas for volume and surface of two- and three-dimensional symmetric objects are listed in the Math Review section "Symmetric Objects" at the end of this chapter.

### ONE-DIMENSIONAL MOTION WITH COLLINEAR FORCES

**P–3.2.** A standard man stands on a bathroom scale. What are (a) the standard man's weight, and (b) the normal force acting on the standard man? (c) What does the standard man read off the scale if it is calibrated in unit N? Can you suggest reasons why that reading may deviate from the actual value? In particular, can you identify a reason why a balance scale might be more precise for a weight measurement? *Note:* The standard man is defined in Example 3.10 and in Table 3.3.

**P–3.3.** Fig. 3.51 shows a standard man intending to do *reverse curls* in a gym. The person holds the arms straight, using an overhand grip to hold the bar. If the mass of the bar is 100 kg, what is the tension in each of the shoulders? Consider the weight of the arm (see Table 3.3) and forces due to the weight of the bar.

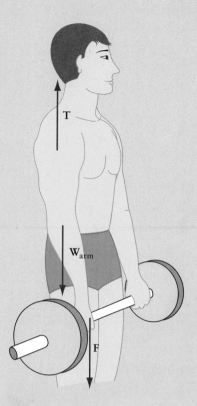

**FIGURE 3.51**

**P–3.4.** Fig. 3.52 shows a standard woman intending to do *closed-grip lat pulldowns* in a gym. In this exercise,

**FIGURE 3.52**

the person pulls the weight of the upper body (arms, head, and trunk) upward using a handle while the legs are wedged under a restraint pad. What is the magnitude of the force exerted by the handle on each of the standard man's hands?

**P–3.5.** Large hawks, eagles, vultures, storks, the white pelican, and gulls are North American birds that sail on rising columns of warm air. This static soaring requires only 5% of the effort of flapping flight. The birds are essentially in a level flight, holding their wings steadily stretched. The weight of the bird is balanced by a vertical lift force, which is a force exerted by the air on the bird's wings. How large is the lift force for (a) a Franklin's gull (found in Alberta, Saskatchewan, and Manitoba) with an average mass of 280 g, and (b) an American white pelican (found in Western Canada) with an average mass of 7.0 kg?

**P–3.6.** Fig. 3.53 shows two horizontal forces, $F_1$ and $F_2$, acting on an object of mass $M = 1.5$ kg. The magnitude of $F_1$ is $F_1 = 25$ N. The object moves strictly along the horizontal $x$-axis, which we choose as positive to the right. Find the magnitude of $F_2$ if the object's horizontal acceleration component is (a) $a_x = 10$ m/s$^2$, (b) $a_x = 0$ m/s$^2$, and (c) $a_x = -10$ m/s$^2$.

**FIGURE 3.53**

**P–3.7.** Fig. 3.54 shows two objects in contact on a frictionless surface. A horizontal force **F** is applied to the object with mass $m_1$. (a) Use $m_1 = 2.0$ kg, $m_2 = 1.0$ kg, and $F = 3.0$ N to calculate the magnitude of the force f between the two objects. (b) Find the magnitude of the force f between the two objects if the force **F** is instead applied to the object of mass $m_2$ but in the opposite direction.

**FIGURE 3.54**

**P–3.8.** Fig. 3.55 shows two objects of masses $M$ and $m$. The horizontal surface allows for frictionless motion. The string tied to the two objects is massless and passes over a massless pulley that rotates without friction. (a) What resulting motion of the two objects do you predict? If $M = 3.0$ kg and $m = 2.0$ kg,

(b) find the magnitude of the acceleration of the sliding object, (c) find the magnitude of the acceleration of the hanging object, and (d) find the magnitude of the tension in the massless string.

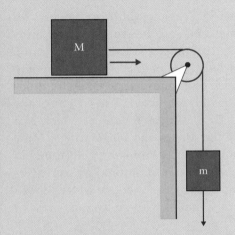

**FIGURE 3.55**

**FIGURE 3.57**

**P–3.9.** Fig. 3.56 shows two objects that are connected by a massless string. They are pulled along a frictionless surface by a horizontal external force. Using $F_{ext} = 50$ N, $m_1 = 10$ kg, and $m_2 = 20$ kg, calculate (a) the magnitude of the acceleration of the two objects, and (b) the magnitude of the tension **T** in the string.

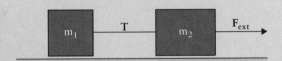

**FIGURE 3.56**

**P–3.10.** Fig. 3.57 illustrates the treatment of fractures of the humerus shaft with a cast of the upper arm bent by 100° to 110° at the elbow joint, and an attached traction device. The traction device keeps the upper arm under tension to lower the risk of fracture dislocation due to muscle contraction. Similar traction devices can be applied for most fractures of the appendicular skeleton and for the cervical vertebrae after neck injuries. What is the range of masses for the traction device used if the muscle force it must compensate ranges from 5 N to 10 N?

## MOTION IN TWO DIMENSIONS WITH NON-COLLINEAR FORCES

**P–3.11.** We study once more Example 3.4, except that the direction of the external force is changed to act tangentially to the circular path of the object of mass $m = 1.0$ kg, as shown in Fig. 3.58. We assume again that the object is held at a position where the string forms an angle $\theta = 30°$ with the vertical. (a) What is the magnitude of the tension **T** in the string? (b) What is the magnitude of the force $\mathbf{F}_{ext}$? (c) Why is it not possible to repeat the calculation with the external force $\mathbf{F}_{ext}$ acting vertically upward?

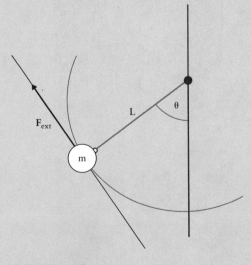

**FIGURE 3.58**

**P–3.12.** Fig. 3.59 shows an object on a frictionless surface that forms an angle $\theta = 40°$ with the horizontal. The object is pushed by a horizontal external force $F_{ext}$ such that it moves with constant speed. If the mass of the object is $M = 75$ kg, calculate (a) the magnitude of the external force $F_{ext}$, and (b) the direction and the magnitude of the force exerted by the inclined surface on the object.

$\theta_2 = 10°$ between the vertical and the direction of the tension below the kneecap, as shown in Fig. 3.61(a). What are the magnitude and the direction of the resultant force exerted on the femur, labelled $-R$ in Fig. 3.61(b)?

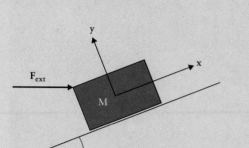

**FIGURE 3.59**

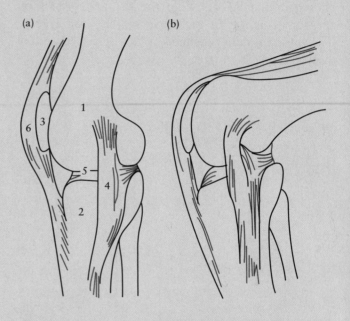

**FIGURE 3.60**

(1) femur, (2) tibia, (3) patella (kneecap), (4) collateral ligaments, (5) meniscus, (6) tendon of quadriceps femoris muscle.

**P–3.13.** Fig. 3.60 shows the human leg (a) when it is stretched and (b) when it is bent. Note that the kneecap (3) is embedded in the quadriceps tendon (6) and is needed to protect the quadriceps tendon against wear and tear due to the femur (1) in the bent position. Assume that the magnitude of the tension in the quadriceps tendon of a bent knee is $T = 1400$ N. Use an angle $\theta_1 = 20°$ between the horizontal and the direction of the tension above the kneecap and

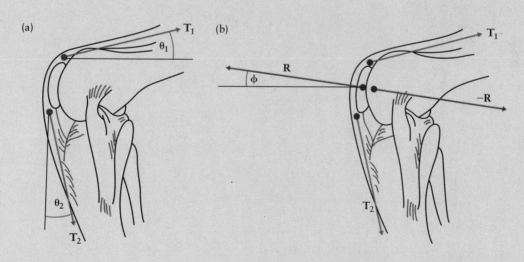

**FIGURE 3.61**

**P–3.14.** Fig. 3.62 shows a standard man hanging motionless from a horizontal bar. (a) Assume that the arms are stretched at 20° to the vertical on either side, as shown in the middle sketch. Find the magnitude of the force acting on each arm. (b) Assume that the arms are held at the two different angles shown in sketch (c). What are the magnitudes of the forces acting in each arm in this case? *Note:* The standard man is defined in Example 3.10 and in Table 3.3.

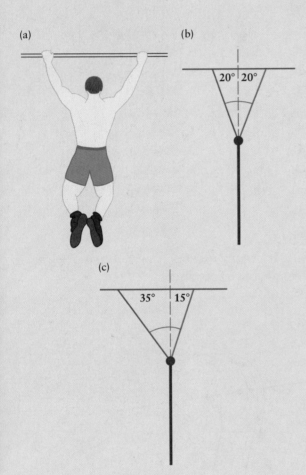

FIGURE 3.62

**P–3.15.** In Fig. 3.63, a standard man does *cable crossover flys* in the gym. In this exercise, the person holds two handles with the arms spread, the chest slightly leaning forward, and the elbow slightly bent. During the action, the handles are pulled forward until the hands touch; this contraction is accompanied by a lifting of two objects of equal masses $M = 20$ kg that are connected to the handles via pulleys (not shown). If the standard man locks the hands together at maximum contraction, what angle $\theta$ must the cable form with the vertical for the standard man

to apply a force of 300 N vertically downward? Neglect the mass of the handles.

FIGURE 3.63

**P–3.16.** In Fig. 3.64 a standard man uses crutches. The crutches each make an angle $\theta = 25°$ with the vertical. Half of the standard man's weight is supported by the crutches; the other half is supported by the normal forces acting on the soles of the feet. Assuming that the standard man is motionless, find the magnitude of the force supported by each crutch.

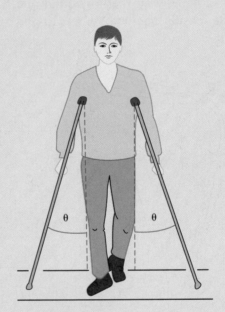

FIGURE 3.64

**P–3.17.** Fig. 3.65 shows the top view of an object on a frictionless surface. Two horizontal forces act on the object. The force $\mathbf{F}_1$ acts in the positive $x$-direction and has a magnitude of 10 N; the force $\mathbf{F}_2$ acts toward the lower left (third quadrant). If the object accelerates in a direction that forms an angle $\theta = 30°$ with the negative $y$-axis and has magnitude

$a = 10 \text{ m/s}^2$, calculate the force $\mathbf{F}_2$ (a) in component notation, and (b) as a magnitude and direction.

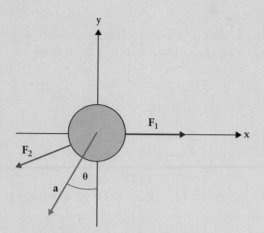

**FIGURE 3.65**

**P–3.18.** Fig. 3.66 shows an object (green box) of mass $m_1 = 1.0$ kg on an inclined surface. The angle of the inclined surface is $\theta = 30°$ with the horizontal. The object $m_1$ is connected to a second object of mass $m_2 = 2.5$ kg on a horizontal surface below an overhang that is formed by the inclined surface. Further, an external force of magnitude $F_{ext} = 10$ N is exerted on the object of mass $m_1$. We observe both objects to accelerate. Assuming that the surfaces and the pulley are frictionless, and the pulley and the connecting string are massless, what is the tension in the string connecting the two objects?

**P–3.19.** An object of mass $m = 6.0$ kg accelerates with $2.0 \text{ m/s}^2$. (a) What is the magnitude of the net force acting on it? (b) If the same force is applied on an object with mass $M = 4.0$ kg, what is the magnitude of that object's acceleration?

**P–3.20.** A football punter accelerates a football from rest to a speed of 10 m/s during the time in which the shoe makes contact with the ball, typically $t = 0.2$ s. Using $m = 0.5$ kg as the mass of the football, what average force does the punter exert on the football?

**P–3.21.** The leg and cast in Fig. 3.67 have a mass of 22.5 kg. Determine the mass of object 2 and the angle $\theta$ needed in order that there be no force acting on the hip joint by leg plus cast. Note that object 1 has a mass of 11 kg and $\phi = 40°$.

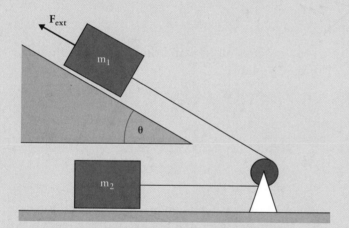

**FIGURE 3.66**

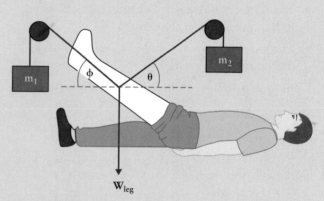

**FIGURE 3.67**

# MATH REVIEW

## SUMMATIONS

When adding more than two terms, it is convenient to use a condensed notation for the summation (sigma notation):

$$\sum_{i=1}^{N} F_i = F_1 + F_2 + F_3 + \cdots + F_N$$

in which $i$ is an index that runs from 1 to $N$ so that $N$ terms of the quantity $F$ are added. As an example, let us add the square numbers from 1 to 5. This can be written in two ways:

$$1^2 + 2^2 + 3^2 + 4^2 + 5^2 = 55$$

$$\text{or} \quad \sum_{i=1}^{5} i^2 = 55$$

## SYMMETRIC OBJECTS

(I)   *Circle.* Defining C as the circumference and A as the area for a two-dimensional circle of radius $r$, we get $C = 2 \cdot \pi \cdot r$ and $A = \pi \cdot r^2$.

(II)  *Triangle.* For a triangle with base $a$ and height $h$, the area A is given as $A = a \cdot h/2$.

(III) *Sphere.* Defining A as the surface area and V as the volume for a three-dimensional sphere of radius $r$, we get $A = 4 \cdot \pi \cdot r^2$ and $V = 4 \cdot \pi \cdot r^3/3$.

(IV)  *Cylinder.* Defining A as the mantle surface area and V as the volume for a right circular cylinder of radius $r$ and height $h$, we get $A = 2 \cdot \pi \cdot r \cdot h$ and $V = \pi \cdot r^2 \cdot h$.

# SUMMARY

## DEFINITIONS

- Forces represent the interaction of distinguishable objects.
- Specific forces:
  - The weight **W** with magnitude $W = m \cdot g$ acts near Earth's surface with $g$ the gravitational acceleration. The force is directed toward the centre of Earth.
  - The normal force **N** is due to contact with a surface. It is directed perpendicular to the surface.
  - The tension **T** is due to a taut, massless string. It is directed along the string.
  - The external contact force $\mathbf{F}_{ext}$ acts along the direction of the push.
- Density $\rho = m/V$ with $m$ for mass, $V$ for volume

## UNITS

- Mass $m$: kg (kilogram)
- Force and force components: N (newton) with $1\ N = 1\ kg \cdot m/s^2$
- Volume $V$: $m^3$
- Density $\rho$: $kg/m^3$

## LAWS

Newton's first law (law of inertia) for an object in mechanical equilibrium:

$$\mathbf{F}_{net} = \sum_{i=1}^{n} \mathbf{F}_i = 0$$

If the system's motion and the forces are confined to the $xy$-plane:

$$F_{net,x} = \sum_i F_{ix} = 0$$

$$F_{net,y} = \sum_i F_{iy} = 0$$

- Newton's second law (equation of motion) for an accelerating object of mass $m$:

$$\mathbf{F}_{net} = \sum_{i=1}^{n} \mathbf{F}_i = m \cdot \mathbf{a}$$

If the system's motion and the forces are confined to the $xy$-plane:

$$F_{net,x} = \sum_i F_{ix} = m \cdot a_x$$

$$F_{net,y} = \sum_i F_{iy} = m \cdot a_y$$

- Newton's third law:

When an object A acts on an object B with force $\mathbf{F}_{Ba}$, then there is a force $\mathbf{F}_{Ab}$ exerted by object B on object A with:

$$\mathbf{F}_{Ab} = -\mathbf{F}_{Ba}$$

# CHAPTER 4

# LOCOMOTION II
## Linear Momentum and Friction

Newton's mechanics is tested for its adequacy to describe locomotion. New challenges arise from the need to accurately quantify the interaction of an organism with its physical environment. This not only motivates us to establish friction as an additional force, but also leads us to re-interpret Newton's second and third laws by introducing the linear momentum as a new concept.

The linear momentum of an object is a vector variable calculated as the product of its mass and velocity. The linear momentum is conserved for an isolated system, which is a system with no net external force acting on it and may consist of one or more distinguishable objects. The linear momentum and its conservation are useful to describe collisions in multi-object systems, or to simplify the description of its motion by introducing the centre of mass position. If the system interacts with its environment, Newton's second law allows us to link the net force that acts on the system to a change of its linear momentum with time. Flight of insects and birds can be quantified by using this concept, leading to the momentum disc theory of animal flight.

When an organism moves, resistance to its motion originates from the interaction with air, water, or solid ground. The velocity dependence of these friction forces varies, leading to a range of new phenomena, such as the terminal speed of a falling or sliding object, or a threshold force that delays the onset of motion when an unbalanced force acts on an object.

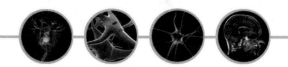

In Chapter 3, we introduced muscles as the physiological means by which animals exert forces. These forces are contact forces that are applied against other anatomical components of the animal's body, most prominently bones of the endoskeleton or plates of the exoskeleton. **Locomotion** is the act of moving from place to place, and is one of the possible responses of animals to external stimuli. Animals can move in several different ways; these ways have in common only that their description benefits from the introduction of additional mechanical concepts. For this reason, the mechanisms of locomotion have to be discussed in several steps throughout this textbook. However, we dedicate two chapters at this point exclusively to this issue: the current chapter focusses on locomotion of the whole body in a medium such as water or air, or on a solid surface. The next chapter deals specifically with the mechanism by which vertebrates achieve movement using their limbs.

## The Flight of Birds and Insects

The ability of **powered flight** has developed at least four times on Earth: first among insects, twice during the reign of the dinosaurs, and once among mammals. The fact that all four groups share common features through convergent evolution points toward common physical principles that govern the ability to fly. We present a brief overview of flight among birds and insects not only to identify the common features for discussion in this chapter, but also to point to details that will be addressed later.

Birds and insects share a common characteristic, **wings.** These must move relative to the surrounding air to provide a lift force. This force has to exceed the weight of the animal to lift off and while it increases its altitude above ground; lift has to be equal to the weight in level flight. Motion of the wings relative to air does not automatically require movement of the wings. For example, large birds such as eagles often soar with still wings while searching the ground for food or rising in thermal updrafts. In this case, the wings still move relative to the surrounding air as the bird exceeds a minimum speed.

Unlike airplanes, both insects and birds have to rely on their wings for more than the lift force. The wings must also provide the forward thrust of propellers or jet engines, whether to accelerate the flight or to maintain a constant speed against the drag effect. This requires a more complex wing than those of airplanes; i.e., we have to be careful when using airplane wings as models in explaining animal flight. Birds, for example, have different types of feathers along their wings: large primaries attached to the hand at the end of the wing, secondaries behind the forearm, and tertiaries that cover the space between the secondaries and the bird's body. During the **downstroke** of a large bird, the hand turns the primaries so that a forward thrust is achieved while the secondaries provide a closed wing surface to generate the lift. Birds also can change the length of their wings by flexing at the wrist, elbow, and shoulder. They use these changes during the **recovery stroke** to minimize air resistance and to get the wings back as fast as possible for the next downstroke. Therefore, both strokes serve different purposes, which is the reason for a *big pectoral muscle* (used in the downstroke) that is about ten times stronger compared to the *weak pectoral muscle* used for the recovery stroke.

Flying insects achieve the same degree of mobility in a different fashion. Their wings are part of the exoskeleton as extensions of the tergal plate (see Fig. 3.1). The main difference is that insects and a few birds, such as hummingbirds, achieve lift during both the downstroke and the upstroke. We confirm this from their anatomy, because both strokes are powered by similarly strong muscles. This requires a greater degree of variability in the tilt of the wing, which is achieved in insects by pivoting it on a protrusion of the pleural plate, called the **pleural wing process.** The wing shifts over the pleural wing process driven by small muscles attached at its base. Tilting its wings allows a variable angle of attack during flight, a feature that is achieved by the up or down motion of inboard and outboard flaps on airplane wings. Insects, unlike birds, cannot flex or extend their wings, and only a few species—such as grasshoppers—have pleated hind wings that allow alterations to the overall wing surface.

Insects must in general be able to create an even greater lift than birds because they can hover at a fixed location, for example, when bumblebees sample flowers on a plant. A first adaptation is a very high wingbeat frequency. This is accomplished by the **click mechanism,** which allows the insect to release its muscle force more explosively than by direct muscle contraction. We can qualitatively see this mechanism in Fig. 3.1: when the **tergal plate** is pulled down by the **dorsoventral muscles** to raise the wings, the **pleural plates** are forcibly bent outward. This strains the plates until a critical point is reached from which they snap back and drive the wings at a high speed. How the click mechanism allows an insect, such as the fruit fly in Fig. 4.1(b), to overcome the natural limitation of the speed of muscle contraction is illustrated in Fig. 4.1(a): we start with the top frame, which shows the cross-section of the insect in

(a)

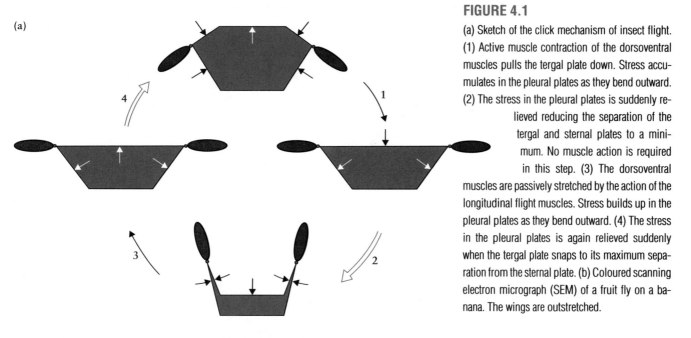

**FIGURE 4.1**

(a) Sketch of the click mechanism of insect flight. (1) Active muscle contraction of the dorsoventral muscles pulls the tergal plate down. Stress accumulates in the pleural plates as they bend outward. (2) The stress in the pleural plates is suddenly relieved reducing the separation of the tergal and sternal plates to a minimum. No muscle action is required in this step. (3) The dorsoventral muscles are passively stretched by the action of the longitudinal flight muscles. Stress builds up in the pleural plates as they bend outward. (4) The stress in the pleural plates is again relieved suddenly when the tergal plate snaps to its maximum separation from the sternal plate. (b) Coloured scanning electron micrograph (SEM) of a fruit fly on a banana. The wings are outstretched.

(b)

the mechanically stable (relaxed) down-bent position of the wings. As the tergal plate is pulled down by the dorsoventral muscles (step 1), strain builds up in the pleural plates at both sides. The right frame shows the instant when the wing position becomes unstable against snapping into the bottom frame (step 2), which represents the end of the recovery stroke. In step 3, the longitudinal flight muscles contract, moving the tergal plate up until it reaches the unstable arrangement in the left frame and then in step 4 snaps back into the initial position, completing the downstroke. This mechanism allows the insect to exceed the beat frequency due to muscle contraction at about 100 cycles per second by a factor of up to 8.

Lift is due to the flow of air past the wing. We discuss this effect in detail in Chapter 12, where we study the flow of fluids past solid objects. This allows birds to soar and insects to fly fast. But the hovering of insects needs to be addressed further, in particular the question of how they can hover stationary as

opposed to bobbing while the wings move backward during the recovery stroke.

The best way to understand this observation is based on a physical model of the wing motion. The insect's wings move in a plane that is inclined to the body axis, with the wing tips below and in front of the insect's body at the end of the downstroke, and above and behind at the end of the recovery stroke. This plane, shown in Fig. 4.2 for a horsefly in side and top views, is called the **stroke plane**. With the stroke plane defined we introduce the **momentum disc theory of animal flight** in Fig. 4.3. The wing action causes an air flow perpendicular through the stroke plane, comparable to that of a helicopter rotor. The air transported through the stroke plane is also accelerated; i.e., it moves faster out of the stroke plane than it is drawn into it. For a tilted stroke plane, this provides lift and thrust at the same time and the insect moves forward (Fig. 4.3(a)); when the stroke plane is almost horizontal, only lift is achieved and the insect hovers (Fig. 4.3(b)). The animal controls the stroke plane orientation with the tilt of the wings about the pleural wing process, and the air flow rate with the angle of attack of its wings.

Applying Newton's laws to Fig. 4.3 isn't straightforward. As the name of the mechanism—momentum disc theory—implies, a new mechanical concept is more suitable in this case: linear momentum as opposed to force or acceleration. We will see, though, that at the same time the momentum concept is rooted in Newton's third law, particularly that law's emphasis on the role of the environment and its interaction with the system.

**FIGURE 4.2**

Stroke plane of a horsefly in flight. (a) Side view of the animal with (c) the stroke plane shown at an angle $\theta$ with the horizontal. (b) Top view of the insect with spread wings. (d) The stroke plane is essentially circular with radius $R$ where $2 \cdot R$ is the wingspan.

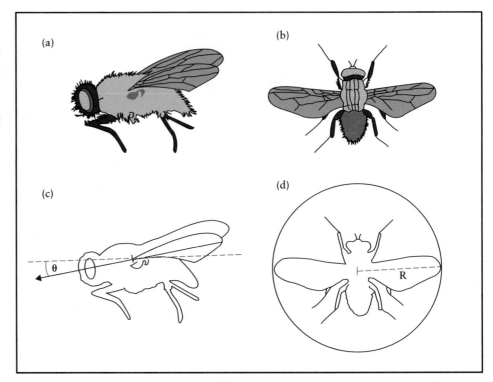

**FIGURE 4.3**

Motion of air through the stroke plane to generate lift. (a) Insect with a tilted stroke plane to generate thrust (horizontal component, $\mathbf{F}_p$) and lift (vertical component, $\mathbf{F}_L$). (b) A hovering insect uses a horizontal stroke plane that generates only a lift force. The positive $y$-axis indicates the direction upward. The red arrows indicate the magnitude and direction of the velocity of air movement through the stroke plane.

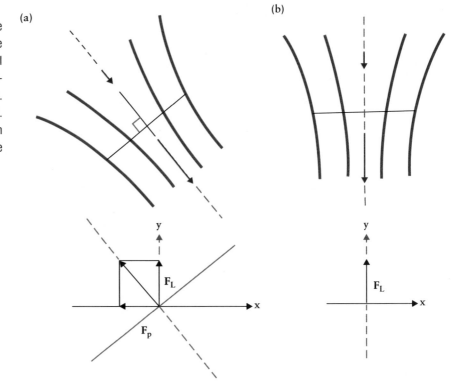

# Linear Momentum and Its Conservation

A re-interpretation of Newton's third law allows us to define the linear momentum concept as the product of mass and velocity of an object, $m \cdot \mathbf{v}$. This connection to Newton's laws ensures that the definition of linear momentum is consistent with our previous discussion, but does not explain why we introduce it. Note that this question becomes even more interesting in Chapter 6, when we introduce yet another combination of velocity and mass of an object, the term $\frac{1}{2}m \cdot v^2$, which we will call *kinetic energy*. Why do we introduce these terms, and why not other combinations of mass and velocity? The answer is based on a new phenomenon: both linear momentum and energy are conserved under broadly applicable circumstances. If a quantity is conserved it receives great attention in physics, both from a fundamental and an applied point of view. We will stress the benefits of using conservation arguments with several examples, primarily the flight of insects and birds.

## Newton's Third Law and Linear Momentum

Let's consider two objects, 1 and 2, that interact with each other. Object 1 exerts a force $\mathbf{F}_{12}$ on object 2. If no other forces act on object 2, this force accelerates object 2 based on Newton's second law: $\mathbf{F}_{12} = m_2 \cdot \mathbf{a}_2$. In turn, object 2 exerts a force $\mathbf{F}_{21}$ on object 1. If no other force acts on object 1, Newton's second law gives us the acceleration of object 1 as $\mathbf{F}_{21} = m_1 \cdot \mathbf{a}_1$.

We call the combined system of objects 1 and 2 an **isolated system** if no other forces than the interaction force between objects 1 and 2 act on either object. In this case, the only forces that we need to consider are $\mathbf{F}_{21}$ and $\mathbf{F}_{12}$, for which we know from Newton's third law that $\mathbf{F}_{21} = -\mathbf{F}_{12}$. Thus, we find for the combined system of two objects:

$$\mathbf{F}_{\text{net}} = \mathbf{F}_{21} + \mathbf{F}_{12} = 0 = m_1 \cdot \mathbf{a}_1 + m_2 \cdot \mathbf{a}_2 \quad [1]$$

Each term on the right-hand side contains the mass and the acceleration of the object. We want to analyze Eq. [1] further by re-interpreting the acceleration based on its definition as the change of velocity of the object with time, which we write as $\Delta\mathbf{v}/\Delta t$:

$$m_1 \cdot \frac{\Delta\mathbf{v}_1}{\Delta t} + m_2 \cdot \frac{\Delta\mathbf{v}_2}{\Delta t} = 0 \quad [2]$$

If the two masses in Eq. [2] are time-independent, we can combine them with the velocity without mathematically altering the equation. Thus, for the change of the product mass times velocity with time for objects of given masses, we note:

$$\frac{\Delta(m_1 \cdot \mathbf{v}_1)}{\Delta t} + \frac{\Delta(m_2 \cdot \mathbf{v}_2)}{\Delta t} = 0 \quad [3]$$

Eq. [3] can also be written as the change of both terms in the sum with time:

$$\frac{\Delta(m_1 \cdot \mathbf{v}_1 + m_2 \cdot \mathbf{v}_2)}{\Delta t} = 0 \quad [4]$$

If a term does not change with time, the term itself is constant, i.e.:

$$m_1 \cdot \mathbf{v}_1 + m_2 \cdot \mathbf{v}_2 = \text{const} \quad [5]$$

Eq. [5] tell us that the sum of the products of mass and velocity is a useful quantity because the sum of the two terms does not change with time under two assumptions: (i) that the system of objects is isolated, and (ii) that the mass of the objects is fixed. We will discuss the second assumption a bit further below and see that it can be dropped.

We give the product of mass and velocity a name: the **linear momentum**. The prefix "linear" is used because in Chapter 21 we introduce the angular momentum as a related quantity for circular motion. A new variable $\mathbf{p}$ is introduced for the linear momentum:

$$\mathbf{p} = m \cdot \mathbf{v} \quad [6]$$

The standard unit of linear momentum is $\text{kg} \cdot \text{m/s}$. No derived unit is introduced. Eq. [6] shows that the linear momentum is mathematically a vector; thus, Eq. [6] is usually applied in component form:

$$\begin{aligned} x\text{-direction:} \quad & p_x = m \cdot v_x \\ y\text{-direction:} \quad & p_y = m \cdot v_y \\ z\text{-direction:} \quad & p_z = m \cdot v_z \end{aligned} \quad [7]$$

With the definition in Eq. [6], we can write Eq. [5] for the isolated system of two objects as:

$$\mathbf{p}_1 + \mathbf{p}_2 = \text{const} \quad [8]$$

The reasoning we used in Eqs. [1] to [8] also applies to an isolated system of more than two objects. To generalize the arguments, we define the total linear momentum $\mathbf{P}$ as the vector sum of the individual linear momentums $\mathbf{p}_i$, where $i$ is the index identifying the individual objects that constitute the isolated system. This sum is constant if the multi-object system is isolated ($\mathbf{F}_{\text{net}} = 0$):

$$\mathbf{P} = \sum_i \mathbf{p}_i = \text{const} \quad [9]$$

Eq. [9] states that the total linear momentum of an isolated system does not change with time. A quantity that does not change with time is **conserved**, and the law that establishes this fact is called a *conservation law*. Thus, Eq. [9] establishes the **conservation of linear momentum** for an isolated system. Note that this isn't a foolproof statement: the linear momentum is usually not conserved in a non-isolated system, i.e., a system that interacts with its environment.

*The product of mass and velocity of an object defines the linear momentum. The total linear momentum of an isolated system of objects, i.e., a system on which no external forces act, is conserved.*

Identifying an initial and final state of interest, we write Eq. [9] in component form:

$$x\text{-direction:} \quad \sum_i p_{i,x,\text{initial}} = \sum_i p_{i,x,\text{final}}$$

$$y\text{-direction:} \quad \sum_i p_{i,y,\text{initial}} = \sum_i p_{i,y,\text{final}} \quad [10]$$

$$z\text{-direction:} \quad \sum_i p_{i,z,\text{initial}} = \sum_i p_{i,z,\text{final}}$$

Applying Eqs. [1] to [10] requires vector algebra, and Eqs. [9] and [10] contain a summation symbol. These are discussed in more detail in the Math Review at the end of Chapters 2 and 3, in the sections "Vectors and Basic Vector Algebra" and "Summations."

One type of physical process for which the linear momentum is particularly useful is **collisions**. Several different types of collisions between objects exist. The most fundamental types are the *elastic collision* (the collision of two billiard balls comes close to this case) and the **perfectly inelastic collision** we discuss in Example 4.1. Elastic collisions are more important for interactions at a microscopic level; however, we postpone their discussion to Chapter 6, when the energy concept is introduced, because the elastic collision is defined by the conservation of both linear momentum and energy.

## ● EXAMPLE 4.1

We study the perfectly inelastic collision illustrated in Fig. 4.4: an object of mass $m_1$ hits with initial velocity $\mathbf{v}_{1,\text{initial}}$ a second object with mass $m_2$ and initial velocity $\mathbf{v}_{2,\text{initial}}$. Objects 1 and 2 merge in the collision, forming a combined object that moves with final velocity $\mathbf{v}_{\text{final}}$ after the collision. We assume in this and all other examples that the motion of the objects is confined to the

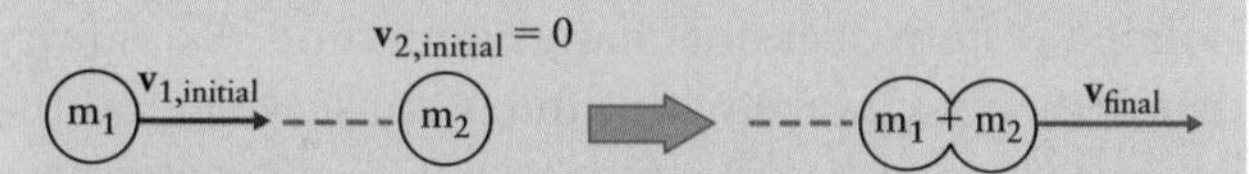

**FIGURE 4.4**

A specific case of an inelastic collision in which the two particles merge. Initially, the object with mass $m_1$ moves with velocity $\mathbf{v}_{1,\text{initial}}$ and the object with mass $m_2$ is at rest (seen at the left). The merged object moves with velocity $\mathbf{v}_{\text{final}}$ after the collision (seen at the right).

$xy$-plane. Eq. [10] is written in this case as two component equations:

$x$-direction:
$$m_1 \cdot v_{1,x,\text{initial}} + m_2 \cdot v_{2,x,\text{initial}} = (m_1 + m_2)v_{x,\text{final}}$$
$y$-direction:
$$m_1 \cdot v_{1,y,\text{initial}} + m_2 \cdot v_{2,y,\text{initial}} = (m_1 + m_2)v_{y,\text{final}} \quad [11]$$

(a) Determine the speed $v_{\text{final}}$. (b) What do you observe when $m_1 \gg m_2$, or (c) when $m_1 \ll m_2$?

*Solution to part (a):* In the case of a perfectly inelastic collision with one object at rest, $\mathbf{v}_{1,\text{initial}}$ and $\mathbf{v}_{\text{final}}$ must be parallel; i.e., the entire motion occurs along a straight line, which we define as the $x$-axis. This means that $\mathbf{v}_{1,\text{initial}} = (v_{1,\text{initial}}, 0)$ and $\mathbf{v}_{\text{final}} = (v_{\text{final}}, 0)$; i.e., we need only the first formula of Eq. [11]:

$$m_1 \cdot \mathbf{v}_{1,\text{initial}} = (m_1 + m_2)v_{\text{final}} \quad [12]$$

where we used $v_{2,\text{initial}} = 0$ because the second object is initially at rest. The same final speed applies to both objects because they remain attached to each other after the collision. Eq. [12] is solved for the final speed:

$$v_{\text{final}} = \left( \frac{m_1}{m_1 + m_2} \right) v_{1,\text{initial}} \quad [13]$$

This is the final result because no specific values were given in part (a). Note that writing the result in the form of Eq. [13] is useful for discussing possible cases, as we illustrate with the two asymptotic cases in parts (b) and (c).

*Solution to part (b):* Eq. [13] illustrates that the final speed depends linearly on the initial speed of object 1 when the two mass values are given. More interesting for applications, though, is the dependence of the ratio $v_{\text{final}}/v_{1,\text{initial}}$ on the two masses; $m_1 \gg m_2$ implies that an object approaches and then collides with a much lighter object. Examples of a predator/prey system include a bat catching a slow-flying moth, a cougar ambushing an unsuspecting rabbit, or a dolphin feeding on a school of fish. We expect the effects predicted by Eq. [13] in these cases to be physiologically acceptable to the predator (i.e., the object of mass $m_1$) because they would otherwise not use a hunting method that is based on a perfectly inelastic collision. Mathematically, we find:

$$\frac{v_{\text{final}}}{v_{1,\text{initial}}} = \lim_{m_1 \gg m_2} \left( \frac{m_1}{m_1 + m_2} \right) = 1 \quad [14]$$

Thus, the speed of the heavy object remains essentially unchanged; the predator can run full speed into the prey without a serious change of the linear momentum it has to accommodate. The prey is less lucky, as it is suddenly accelerated—which probably smashes a moth into the fangs of a bat before the bat has to close its bite. Indeed, the sudden change of linear momentum as endured by the prey is part of the tactics of a heavy ambush-predator.

*Solution to part (c):* Next, we consider the case where the predator is lighter than the prey. Wolves are small compared to a moose they try to bring down; piranhas don't size up to a cow or a pig that falls into their South American river; and prehistoric men were dwarfed by mammoths. Let's see whether the same hunting practices discussed in part (b) make sense in these cases. We use $m_1 \ll m_2$ in Eq. [12]:

$$\frac{v_{\text{final}}}{v_{1,\text{initial}}} = \lim_{m_1 \ll m_2} \left( \frac{m_1}{m_1 + m_2} \right) = 0 \quad [15]$$

We find a negligible change in linear momentum for the prey (object 2), while a big change occurs for the predator (object 1). The predator, when stuck to the prey, would have to shake off the physical effects of a sudden change in speed while the prey could address the nuisance of the attack in comparable comfort. Thus, other hunting methods have been developed to bring down heavy prey, in particular hunting in packs. However, we cannot conclude that any light predator hunts (or has hunted) heavy prey in packs, because coordination among the members of the pack requires a rather well-developed brain. This is one reason why predatory dinosaurs were initially suspected to have been scavengers: only one 25-kg Velociraptor was needed to enjoy feasting on an 180-kg Protoceratops that had already dropped dead. We required fossil discoveries such as the famous 1924 find of a Velociraptor and a Protoceratops locked in battle to appreciate predatory dinosaurs as fierce and swift hunters. This issue deserves further discussion, and we return to dinosaurs in Chapter 6.

A second advantage to hunting larger prey in packs exists. The risk of injury is great, even for an ambush hunter with an 80% success rate, such as the North American cougar. A wolf with a broken bone can recover while the pack provides for its food; a cougar is doomed. Indeed, 25% of all cougars are estimated to die as the result of a hunting accident.

**10 m/s. (a) With what speed would the battling pair have been sliding immediately after the impact? (b) In which direction would they have been sliding?**

ANSWER TO PART (a): We treat the surface as frictionless; i.e., the surface does not exert a horizontal force on objects. Thus, the interaction between the two dinosaurs in the horizontal direction can be treated as an interaction in an isolated system. Since the two dinosaur bodies are locked in battle after the Velociraptor (object 1) jumps onto the Protoceratops (object 2), the attack can be modelled as a perfectly inelastic collision, for which Eq. [12] applies:

$$m_1 \cdot v_{1,\text{initial}} = (25 \text{ kg})\left(10 \frac{\text{m}}{\text{s}}\right) = (m_1 + m_2)v_{\text{final}}$$

$$= (25 \text{ kg} + 180 \text{ kg})v_{\text{final}} \quad [16]$$

which yields:

$$v_{\text{final}} = \frac{25 \text{ kg}}{25 \text{ kg} + 180 \text{ kg}}\left(10 \frac{\text{m}}{\text{s}}\right) = 1.2 \frac{\text{m}}{\text{s}} \quad [17]$$

This speed is small compared to the initial speed of the Velociraptor; indeed, the Velociraptor's impact on the Protoceratops was likely not sufficient to cause the larger dinosaur to fall. This was not the Velociraptor's intention anyway, as a falling Protoceratops could well have crushed it to death. Instead, the success of the Velociraptor's attack depended on positioning itself on the Protoceratops such that it could bring its long, curved, blade-like claw on the second toe to devastating use, e.g., by slitting open the Protoceratops's unprotected belly. This was no doubt on the mind of the Velociraptor that battled with a Protoceratops about 70 million years ago in Mongolia when both were buried and eventually fossilized; its claw is still embedded in the larger dinosaur's belly section. Despite possession of this deadly weapon, Velociraptors had developed large brains for a dinosaur, suggesting that they were able to coordinate with each other in a pack hunt.

ANSWER TO PART (b): Any perfectly inelastic collision occurs along a single axis. Thus, the direction of the incoming Velociraptor determines the direction of motion for the battling pair.

---

## Concept Question 4.1

Assume that the 180-kg Protoceratops in the above-mentioned fossil find was standing on a slippery surface, such as an easily shifting sand layer, when the 25-kg Velociraptor jumped on its back with a speed of

---

## Concept Question 4.2

Comment on the practice among adult male Bighorn sheep to run at great speed head-first into each other, as illustrated in Fig. 4.5. What is the linear momentum of each sheep at impact? What is the change in the

## Concept Question 4.2 (continued)

linear momentum of both sheep together at impact? Is a perfectly inelastic collision preferable for the Bighorn sheep (compared to any other type of head-on collision)? Note: Adult male Bighorn sheep typically have a mass of 125 kg (females range from 50 to 90 kg but don't participate), and reach maximum speeds of 50 km/h on flat terrain.

**FIGURE 4.5**
Bighorn sheep.

ANSWER: This case differs from the two cases discussed in Example 4.1 in two ways: (i) both objects have about the same mass, and (ii) both objects approach the collision with similar but opposite velocities. To evaluate this case, we have to go back to the first formula in Eq. [11]. We don't need the second formula, because we can assume that both Bighorn sheep move along a straight line before and after the collision:

$$m_1 \cdot v_{1,\text{initial}} + m_2 \cdot v_{2,\text{initial}} = (m_1 + m_2)v_{\text{final}} \quad [18]$$

The left-hand side of Eq. [18] yields zero, because $m_1 = m_2$ and $v_{1,\text{initial}} = -v_{2,\text{initial}}$. As a result of a perfectly inelastic collision of the two Bighorn sheep, they end up at rest with their heads pressed against each other. In reality, their collision is not perfectly inelastic. This makes the collision even worse, as both sheep bounce backward because that is the only direction in which they can move away from the impact. Each Bighorn sheep reaches the collision with a linear momentum of:

$$p_{\text{Bighorn}} = m_{\text{Bighorn}} \cdot v_{\text{Bighorn}} = (125 \text{ kg})\left(14 \frac{\text{m}}{\text{s}}\right)$$

$$= 1750 \frac{\text{kg} \cdot \text{m}}{\text{s}} \quad [19]$$

This is a large value; it is 20 times the linear momentum of a standard man accidentally walking into a wall at 4 km/h: $p_{\text{standard man}} = 80 \text{ kg} \cdot \text{m/s}$. Anyone who has walked into a wall once (and therefore came to rest instantly) knows that this is not a pleasant experience. The Bighorn sheep needs extra protection to get away with it, particularly since some of them do it as often as five times an hour in battles that may last as long as 24 hours! Their skulls are double-layered with extra struts of bone, and they have a broad, massive tendon linking the skull and the spine to help the head recoil from blows. Note that the total linear momentum before and after collision is the same: zero in this case. The conservation of linear momentum applies universally, independent of type of collision or process studied.

So why do the Bighorn sheep do it? These collisions are part of butting contests during mating season from mid-September to late October and therefore represent an example of sexual selection rather than natural selection. With few natural predators to fear, sexual selection guarantees the survival of the species.

## ● EXAMPLE 4.2

Fig. 4.6(a) shows two objects of masses $m_1$ and $m_2$ travelling with velocities $\mathbf{v}_1$ and $\mathbf{v}_2$ toward a collision point (chosen at the origin). After a perfectly inelastic collision, the combined object travels with angle $\phi$ relative to the positive $x$-axis, as indicated in Fig. 4.6(b). (a) Calculate the $x$- and $y$-component formulas for the velocity of the combined object after the collision. (b) Choosing $m_1 = m_2$, $v_1 = v_2$, and $\theta = 45°$, calculate the angle $\phi$.

*Solution to part (a):* Inelastic collisions are governed by the conservation of momentum from Eq. [9]. We use the first two formulas from Eq. [10] because both objects in this example

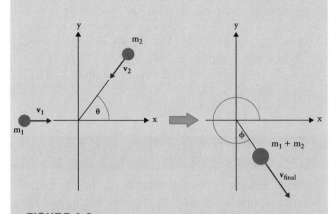

**FIGURE 4.6**
Inelastic collision of two moving objects in the $xy$-plane.

move in a common plane, which we define as the $xy$-plane. Fig. 4.6(a) indicates that object 1 travels along the $x$-axis; i.e., its velocity components are $(v_1, 0)$. Object 2 travels at an angle to the $x$-axis. Its velocity components are $(-v_2 \cos \theta, -v_2 \sin \theta)$. You can confirm this with the Math Review "Geometry" at the end of Chapter 2. The velocity of the combined object after the collision is written as $(v_{x,\text{final}}, v_{y,\text{final}})$. Substituting these components in the first two formulas of Eq. [10], we find:

$x$-direction:
$$m_1 \cdot v_1 - m_2 \cdot v_2 \cdot \cos \theta = (m_1 + m_2)v_{x,\text{final}}$$
$y$-direction: [20]
$$-m_2 \cdot v_2 \cdot \sin \theta = (m_1 + m_2)v_{y,\text{final}}$$

which for the final velocity components yields:

$$v_{x,\text{final}} = \frac{m_1}{m_1 + m_2} v_1 - \frac{m_2}{m_1 + m_2} v_2 \cdot \cos \theta$$

$$v_{y,\text{final}} = -\frac{m_2}{m_1 + m_2} v_2 \cdot \sin \theta \qquad [21]$$

*Solution to part (b):* Eq. [21] is rewritten for the special case of $m_1 = m_2$, $v_1 = v_2 = v$, and $\theta = 45°$:

$$v_{x,\text{final}} = \frac{v}{2}(1 - \cos 45°)$$

$$v_{y,\text{final}} = -\frac{v}{2}(\sin 45°) \qquad [22]$$

which for the angle $\phi$ yields:

$$\tan \phi = \frac{v_{y,\text{final}}}{v_{x,\text{final}}} = \frac{-\sin 45°}{1 - \cos 45°} = -2.41 \quad [23]$$

This yields $\phi = -67.5° = 292.5°$.

## Changes of Linear Momentum and Newton's Second Law

With the concept of momentum introduced, we can now remove the requirement of an isolated system. We consider first a system with a single object on which a non-zero external force acts. Newton's second law is re-written with the linear momentum definition from Eq. [6]:

$$\mathbf{F}_{\text{net}} = m \cdot \mathbf{a} = m \frac{\Delta \mathbf{v}}{\Delta t} = \frac{\Delta(m \cdot \mathbf{v})}{\Delta t} = \frac{\Delta \mathbf{p}}{\Delta t} \quad [24]$$

Recall we discussed earlier that the inclusion of the mass with the velocity is mathematically correct as long as the mass of the object is time-independent. Newton evaluated Eq. [24] carefully, and in *Principia* decided to write the second law of mechanics in

the form $\mathbf{F}_{\text{net}} = \Delta \mathbf{p}/\Delta t$ and not in the form we used earlier, i.e., $\mathbf{F}_{\text{net}} = m \cdot \mathbf{a}$. Taking a fundamental view that physical laws are written such that a minimum of necessary assumptions are required, Newton chose the form connecting the linear momentum and the net force because he realized the assumption of a constant mass of the studied objects is not necessary: the laws of mechanics apply equally well to objects of variable mass. We will see several examples below that use this fact to derive interesting results, such as strategies of some sea animals to escape their predators swiftly in Example 4.3. In turn, when Newton realized that the laws of mechanics are not limited to objects of fixed masses, the formulation $\mathbf{F}_{\text{net}} = m \cdot \mathbf{a}$ for the second law became undesirable because it does not describe properly the motion of a system with varying mass. Thus, the most general formulation of Newton's second law reads:

*The time change in linear momentum of a system is equal to the net force that acts on the system.*

Eq. [24] is correct with respect to units; the force is given in unit $kg \cdot m/s^2$ while the linear momentum is given in unit $kg \cdot m/s$. The time change of the linear momentum, $\Delta \mathbf{p}/\Delta t$, then, carries the unit $kg \cdot m/s^2$, i.e., the same unit as force. Eq. [24] is applied in component form in Example 4.3.

## ● EXAMPLE 4.3

Squid have a streamlined shape, with flap-like fins that stabilize them in water. They either move slowly by rippling their fins or dart very fast forward using a kind of jet propulsion, squirting water rapidly out of the breathing tube (siphon). They use the latter movement to escape predators they can spot early as a result of their good vision. What is the initial acceleration a squid can achieve when starting from rest? For the density of seawater, use $\rho = 1025 \ kg/m^3$ and an initial mass of the squid of 50 kg. The opening of the breathing tube has an area of 7 $cm^2$, and water is ejected at 15 m/s. *Note:* We ask about the initial acceleration only because this allows us to neglect (i) drag effects when moving with notable speed through water (see the discussion of friction later in the chapter), and (ii) the change of the mass of the squid as water is ejected.

*Solution:* The squid ejects water in a stream with a cross-sectional area of 7 $cm^2$ and a speed of 15 m/s. Multiplying these two quantities leads to a term of the form $\Delta V/\Delta t$, which is called **volume flow rate** with unit $m^3/s$: $\Delta V/\Delta t = 0.0105 \ m^3/s = 10.5$ L/s. Multiplying the volume flow rate with

## ● EXAMPLE 4.3 (*continued*)

the density leads to a term of the form $\Delta m / \Delta t$, which is called the **mass flow rate** with unit kg/s. The mass flow rate of ejected water is found:

$$\frac{\Delta m}{\Delta t} = \rho \frac{\Delta V}{\Delta t} = \left( 1025 \frac{\text{kg}}{\text{m}^3} \right) \left( 0.0105 \frac{\text{m}^3}{\text{s}} \right)$$

$$= 10.8 \frac{\text{kg}}{\text{s}} \qquad [25]$$

Note that this is only an initial rate; obviously, the squid cannot sustain that rate of expulsion of water for too long! The result in Eq. [25] is then multiplied with the speed of the ejected water to obtain the time change of linear momentum resulting for the water as it is brought from rest in the squid's body to ejection speed:

$$\frac{\Delta |\mathbf{p}_{\text{water}}|}{\Delta t} = \frac{\Delta m}{\Delta t} v = \left( 10.8 \frac{\text{kg}}{\text{s}} \right) \left( 15.0 \frac{\text{m}}{\text{s}} \right)$$

$$= 162 \frac{\text{kg} \cdot \text{m}}{\text{s}^2} \qquad [26]$$

Note that we wrote the time change of the linear momentum as the time change of the mass multiplied with the speed of the water. This is correct because that speed does not vary with time. Using Eq. [24], we note that 162 N is the net force acting on the water as it is ejected. Due to Newton's third law an equal but opposite force acts on the body of the squid as the net force calculated in Eq. [26] is exerted by the squid on the water. Thus, the water pushes the squid in the direction opposite to the ejected water with an acceleration of:

$$a_{\text{squid}} = \frac{F_{\text{net}}}{m_{\text{squid}}} = \frac{162 \frac{\text{kg} \cdot \text{m}}{\text{s}^2}}{50 \text{ kg}} = 3.2 \frac{\text{m}}{\text{s}^2} \quad [27]$$

This acceleration will often be sufficient as it moves the squid a distance $d = \frac{1}{2} a t^2 = 1.6$ m within the first second of escape.

Note that we did not use a vector notation in this problem but treated the line along which the squid moves as the *x*-axis in Eq. [24]. This simplified the calculation because we note that the magnitude of the force and the acceleration are equal to (except for a possible minus sign) their *x*-components.

## Concept Question 4.3

**(a) A bumblebee hovers at a fixed position, as seen in Fig. 4.7. Assuming that its stroke plane is horizontal, as shown in Fig. 4.3(b), develop the formula that**

describes the speed to which the bumblebee must accelerate the air that passes the stroke plane. **(b)** Estimate the speed in unit m/s using this formula. **(c)** If the bumblebee tilts its stroke plane $\theta = 30°$ with the vertical as defined in Fig. 4.8, what forward acceleration is achieved?

**FIGURE 4.7**

A bee hovering near a flower.

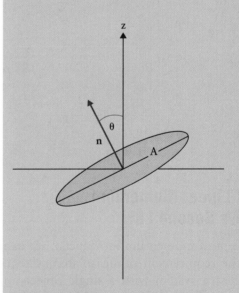

**FIGURE 4.8**

The stroke plane is defined by a vector that is oriented perpendicular to the surface, **n**. The magnitude of **n** represents the area *A*. The angle between **n** and the *z*-axis, $\theta$, defines the orientation of the plane.

ANSWER TO PART (a): Whether we deal with a squid in water or a bumblebee in air does not change the basic physical principles. Thus, the same reasoning is applied as in Example 4.3. We make the simplifying assumption that the air flows into the stroke plane at negligible speed.

Calling $A$ the area of the stroke plane, $\rho$ the density of the medium air, and $v$ the speed of air as ejected from the stroke plane, we find for the mass flow rate at which air flows through the stroke plane:

$$\frac{\Delta m}{\Delta t} = \rho \, \frac{\Delta V}{\Delta t} = \rho \cdot A \cdot v \qquad [28]$$

We treat the air that moves through the stroke plane as a mechanical system, for which we need to determine the time change of the linear momentum. For this we multiply Eq. [28] with the speed of air passing through the stroke plane. This yields on the left-hand side of Eq. [28] $v \cdot \Delta m/\Delta t = \Delta(mv)/\Delta t = \Delta p/\Delta t$, with $p$ the magnitude of the linear momentum. On the right-hand side we find the product of density, stroke plane area, and the square of the air speed beyond the stroke plane:

$$\frac{\Delta p}{\Delta t} = \rho \cdot A \cdot v^2 \qquad [29]$$

Newton's second law in the form of Eq. [24] allows us to interpret Eq. [29] as the net force acting on the air as it is pushed downward through the stroke plane. Newton's third law identifies this force with same magnitude but directed upward, as the force acting on the bumblebee due to the rushing air. We call this force the **lift force**. The insect remains at constant height above ground when it generates enough lift to compensate its weight, $F_{lift} = W$. Thus, the speed of air rushing through the stroke plane must be fine-tuned by the bee to guarantee:

$$m \cdot g = \rho \cdot A \cdot v^2$$
$$v = \sqrt{\frac{m \cdot g}{\rho \cdot A}} \qquad [30]$$

Eq. [30] is the key formula of the **momentum disc theory of animal flight**. Let's discuss it first qualitatively and then quantitatively in parts (b) and (c).

Hovering in air is harder than hovering below water because the density of air is about 1000 times smaller than the density of water. Thus, the speed to which an insect must accelerate the air is 30 times (square root of 1000) greater than the speed to which an animal hovering under water has to accelerate the surrounding water. However, the real advantage for the animal underwater comes from the numerator in the square root of Eq. [30], which has to be replaced with the much smaller difference between weight and buoyant force. (We discuss buoyancy in Chapter 11.) These two adjustments reduce the speed in Eq. [30] significantly enough that underwater animals do not need large, fast-flapping wings to hover in a given place. Conquering three-dimensional motion underwater

is therefore much easier than conquering three-dimensional motion in air.

Eq. [30] also explains why a bumblebee appears less capable of flight than a dragonfly. Note that both can hover in place, something butterflies cannot do. For this reason, comparing the bumblebee or dragonfly with a butterfly is futile; however, comparing them to each other is a meaningful exercise. The dragonfly has a larger stroke plane, while its slender body makes it lighter than the bee. Since the density of air is fixed, the only way for the bumblebee to make up for its disadvantages is to increase $v$ in Eq. [30], i.e., flap its wings faster than the dragonfly. We mentioned already the length to which nature has gone to allow an insect such as the bumblebee to flap its wings faster than the limit of muscle contraction would allow. Still, the bumblebee is lucky that Eq. [30] contains a square-root dependence; without the square root, the bumblebee would have to watch the elegant dragonfly from the ground!

ANSWER TO PART (b): Let's see whether we can estimate a reasonable value of $v$ from Eq. [30]. This is an important step before accepting a formula as a proper representation of a physical process: we always make assumptions when deriving equations, and sometimes assumptions are not justified. The stroke plane of a bumblebee is about $A = 5 \text{ cm}^2$, based on a size of the bumblebee of 2 to 3 cm and a wingspan of the same length. The density of air is $1.2 \text{ kg/m}^3$. The mass of a bumblebee varies between 0.04 and 0.6 g for workers. Using an average value of 0.3 g, we find a weight of $2.9 \times 10^{-3}$ N. Inserting these values in Eq. [30] yields:

$$v = \sqrt{\frac{m \cdot g}{\rho \cdot A}} = \sqrt{\frac{2.9 \times 10^{-3} \text{ N}}{\left(1.2 \, \dfrac{\text{kg}}{\text{m}^3}\right)(5 \times 10^{-4} \text{ m}^2)}}$$
$$= 2.2 \, \frac{\text{m}}{\text{s}} \qquad [31]$$

which is a moderate value compared to the 15 m/s with which the squid ejects water. We know that the bumblebee is capable of beating its wings as often as 1000 times per second. That means it has to push the air a distance of about 2 to 3 mm per wingbeat, which is well within the range of wing movement of the insect.

ANSWER TO PART (c): The net force acting on the bumblebee's body points in the direction of the normal vector that describes the stroke plane in Fig. 4.8. Assuming that the bumblebee tilts this direction by 30° relative to the hovering effort in part (b), a division of the net force in a vertical lift component and a horizontal thrust component

## Concept Question 4.3 (continued)

occurs. The net force in part (b) is equal to the weight of the bumblebee with $W = 2.9 \times 10^{-3}$ N; Fig. 4.9 illustrates that this yields a thrust of $W \cdot \sin 30°$ and a lift of $W \cdot \cos 30°$. The latter could be a problem, because we needed the entire net force in part (b) to compensate the weight. If we divert a fraction of this force away from the lift, the bumblebee should crash to the ground. However, the bumblebee now flies in a forward direction and receives its lift from the same effect as airplane wings: the flow of air past the wings. (We quantify this effect in Chapter 12.) Using the value from part (b), the thrust in part (c) is $\sin 30° = 0.5$ times the gravitational acceleration, i.e., 4.9 m/s$^2$. This huge acceleration is not necessary to overcome drag in the air, as bees typically fly with speeds of up to 25 km/h. Thus, the actual tilt a bumblebee applies to achieve forward thrust is much smaller than 30°. The bumblebee may also reduce its wingbeat frequency to conserve energy when switching to level forward flight, which requires less effort.

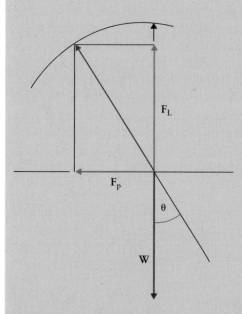

**FIGURE 4.9**

During hovering, an insect must generate a lift force that is equal in magnitude to its weight. When the insect tilts the stroke plane, the insect generates the same force by moving air through its stroke plane. This force has two components, $\mathbf{F}_L$ is the lift force and $\mathbf{F}_p$ is a forward thrust.

## Concept Question 4.4

**Cuttlefish use rapidly elongating tentacles to snatch crabs and other prey. A pair of tentacles is hidden within the visible outer ring of arms. Despite the resistance of** water, the cuttlefish's killing tentacles can accelerate with $25 \cdot g$, i.e., 25 times the gravitational acceleration. What is the effect on the cuttlefish when it unleashes its tentacle? Does the targeted crab benefit from the backlash; i.e., does this effect increase the crab's chance of surviving the attack? Assume that the deadly tentacle represents 1/20th of the mass of the cuttlefish.

ANSWER: We use the conservation of linear momentum. The cuttlefish is initially motionless; i.e., its total linear momentum is zero. This must remain the case while the tentacle elongates forward; i.e., the rest of the cuttlefish must concurrently accelerate backward. This sounds good to the threatened crab, because it means that the cuttlefish moves away from the crab during the attack. But is the effect large enough to put the cuttlefish out of its tentacles' reach before the crab is snatched? We expect the answer to be no, as otherwise the cuttlefish would have become extinct a long time ago.

We use Eq. [24] to write the time change of the linear momentum for the cuttlefish's tentacle:

$$\frac{\Delta p_{\text{tentacles}}}{\Delta t} = m_{\text{tentacles}} \cdot a_{\text{tentacles}} = \frac{m_{\text{cuttlefish}}}{20} 25 \cdot g$$
$$= 1.25 \cdot W_{\text{cuttlefish}} \qquad [32]$$

This net force acts on the remaining body of the cuttlefish (labelled "rest") due to Newton's third law:

$$1.25 \cdot W_{\text{cuttlefish}} = m_{\text{rest}} \cdot a_{\text{rest}} = \frac{19}{20} m_{\text{cuttlefish}} \cdot a_{\text{rest}}$$
$$[33]$$

which yields $a_{\text{rest}} = 1.3 \cdot g$. Receiving a backward acceleration larger than the gravitational acceleration isn't a negligible effect. Let's assume that a tentacle has a length $L$. It will be fully extended in time $t$, which we calculate from

$$L = \frac{1}{2} a_{\text{tentacle}} \cdot t^2$$
$$t = \sqrt{\frac{2 \cdot L}{25 \cdot g}} \qquad [34]$$

During this time, the rest of the cuttlefish is pushed backward a distance $d$:

$$d = \frac{1}{2} a_{\text{rest}} \cdot t^2 = \frac{1}{2} (1.3 \cdot g) \frac{2 \cdot L}{25 \cdot g} = \left(\frac{1.3}{25}\right) L$$
$$[35]$$

i.e., about 5% of the tentacle's length. That isn't as bad as it looked at first; however, can the cuttlefish rely on an undetected approach? Apparently not, because the cuttlefish developed another amazing feature: while approaching prey, it displays fast-flashing colour changes to confuse the prey long enough to get within reach before the prey recovers its alertness and attempts to escape.

We still want to discuss the role of Eq. [24] for a non-isolated multi-object system. However, before we can do this the concept of centre of mass has to be introduced.

# Multi-Object Systems and Their Motion

So far, we have limited our discussion to systems with two or three objects. The concept of linear momentum allows us now to address more complex systems that consist of a very large number of objects. We approach such systems in several steps, first defining a new concept, the *centre of mass,* and then illustrating for an increasing number of objects in the system how the centre of mass allows us to simplify the description of physical processes. This is an important step because life science systems are rarely single-object systems. Our approach will lead to a new model system that we call a *rigid object.* The rigid object model will accompany us, then, into the next chapter.

## Centre of Mass Definition

The **centre of mass** is a position in space, mathematically described by a vector $\mathbf{r}_{c.m.}$:

$$\mathbf{r}_{c.m.} = \frac{1}{M}\sum_{i=1}^{n} m_i \cdot \mathbf{r}_i \qquad [36]$$

In component form, this vector is given by $\mathbf{r}_{c.m.} = (x_{c.m.}, y_{c.m.}, z_{c.m.})$, with:

$$x\text{-direction:} \quad x_{c.m.} = \frac{1}{M}\sum_{i=1}^{n} m_i \cdot x_i$$

$$y\text{-direction:} \quad y_{c.m.} = \frac{1}{M}\sum_{i=1}^{n} m_i \cdot y_i \qquad [37]$$

$$z\text{-direction:} \quad z_{c.m.} = \frac{1}{M}\sum_{i=1}^{n} m_i \cdot z_i$$

$M$ represents in both equations the total mass of the system, which consists either of $n$ objects with negligible volume at respective positions $(x_i, y_i, z_i)$ or of a continuous, extended object that we divide into $n$ small objects.

In Eq. [37], we multiply for each object its mass with its position vector, then divide by the total mass of the system. The discussion below and the usefulness of this definition in later chapters justifies the introduction of Eqs. [36] and [37]. The centre of mass is a position that typically lies within the space that is taken up by the system.

For systems that consist of a small number of objects, Eq. [37] is used as given to calculate this position. This is illustrated in Case I below. Most objects, however, have a more complex distribution of mass. Eq. [37] is not suitable in these cases because the system would have to be broken down into a large number of small objects and the sum in Eq. [37] would be quite extensive. Further, we may not know the structural details of the system well enough, and a division into small objects would be arbitrary. Two alternative approaches are available in these cases:

- we assume that all parts of the object are at fixed relative positions to each other and use a modified form of Eq. [37], as discussed in Case II, or
- we make no assumptions but use experimental methods or even "educated guesses," as illustrated in Case III. This includes all cases where the relative positions of the small objects that constitute the system vary as a function of time.

## CASE I: A SYSTEM CONSISTING OF FEW OBJECTS OF NEGLIGIBLE VOLUME

In this textbook we frequently discuss objects that can be treated as if their volume is negligible. To simplify the discussion in the current section, where we also discuss extended objects, we introduce the term **particle** for an object with negligible volume. Most molecules consist of a small number of atoms that can be treated as $n$ localized particles with given masses. The relative positions of the particles within a molecule are well defined. The simplest case is binary molecules, such as carbon monoxide. We consider this simple case first as it allows us to connect Eq. [37] with our well-developed intuition for the centre of mass in everyday situations.

We choose the line through the two particles of a binary system as the $x$-axis, as illustrated in Fig. 4.10. Thus, we need to consider only the first formula in Eq. [37]. For $n = 2$, that formula transforms into:

$$x_{c.m.} = \frac{x_1 \cdot m_1 + x_2 \cdot m_2}{m_1 + m_2} \qquad [38]$$

because the total mass is $M = m_1 + m_2$.

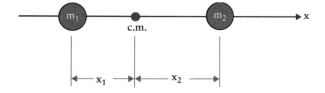

**FIGURE 4.10**

Illustration of the centre of mass for two objects positioned along the *x*-axis. Their masses are $m_1$ and $m_2$. The centre of mass is labelled c.m.

A frequently occurring case is a system with two particles of equal mass ($m_1 = m_2$), e.g., molecules such as oxygen or nitrogen. In this special case, the centre of mass lies halfway between the two particles at the position $x_{\text{c.m.}} = \frac{1}{2}(x_1 + x_2)$. Another frequently occurring case is a system in which one particle has a mass much greater than the other particle, e.g., $m_1 \gg m_2$; examples include molecules such as HCl, HBr, and HI. This case leads to $x_{\text{c.m.}} = x_1$; i.e., the centre of mass is at the position of the much heavier particle. (This assumption will be used in Chapter 16 when we discuss the molecular vibrations of the HCl molecule.)

**Concept Question 4.5**

**Why does the Fosbury flop allow an athlete to jump higher than the traditional straddle technique?**

*Supplementary information from kinesiology:* In the straddle technique of high jumping, the athlete ran toward the bar from an angle, then leaped while facing the bar. The jump consisted of swinging first one leg and then the other over the bar in a scissoring motion. At the highest point the athlete's body was oriented parallel to the bar facing downward.

In 1968, Dick Fosbury introduced a new technique called the Fosbury flop on his way to winning the Olympic gold medal in Mexico City. In this technique athletes turn as they leap, flinging their body backward over the bar with the back arched. Throughout the jump the athlete's body is oriented perpendicular to the bar.

ANSWER: For this example, we simplify the human body as a binary system of two particles of equal mass, as illustrated in Fig. 4.11(a). One particle is located at the upper chest, and one in the pelvis area. The two particles are

**FIGURE 4.11**

Comparison of the motion of the centre of mass of an athlete using the two main techniques for high jump. (a) For the comparison of the two techniques it is sufficient to simplify the human body as two equal point-like objects, located at the chest and at the pelvis. The two objects are connected with a massless string of fixed length. (b) For the straddle technique, the critical stage of the jump is highlighted, illustrating that both point-like objects pass over the bar at the same time. (c) For the Fosbury flop, three sequential frames of the jump show the two objects move across the bar, illustrating that the centre of mass of the athlete is never above the bar. Note that the centre of mass lies along a straight line between the two massive dots describing the athlete, i.e., not along their connection line if it is curved. (d) Fosbury flop executed by an athlete (see next page).

(a)

c.m.

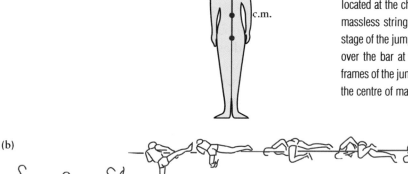

(b)

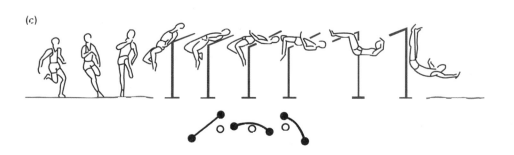

(c)

(d)

connected with a flexible, massless string of fixed length. The centre of mass is always positioned at the halfway point between the two particles.

Fig. 4.11(b) illustrates the centre of mass of the athlete at different stages of a high jump using the straddle technique. The centre of mass of the athlete is briefly positioned above the bar because both the chest and the pelvis are located above the bar at the same time. The athlete must generate a sufficient force when leaping up to allow the centre of mass to reach this height.

Fig. 4.11(c) illustrates the athlete's body at various stages of a Fosbury flop. Note that the centre of mass always lies below the bar, allowing the athlete to pass the bar with a lesser force when leaping. A photograph of an athlete executing a Fosbury flop is shown in Fig. 4.11(d).

## ● EXAMPLE 4.4

The four hydrogen atoms in the methane molecule $CH_4$ form a regular tetrahedron. Fig. 4.12 illustrates the positions of the hydrogen atoms with respect to a Cartesian coordinate system. The carbon atom is located at the centre of mass of the four hydrogen atoms. Assuming that all five atoms can be treated as particles, and using Fig. 4.12, calculate the position of the carbon atom.

*Solution:* The methane molecule is a three-dimensional structure. Thus, Eq. [37] is used to calculate the three Cartesian components of the position of the carbon atom in Fig. 4.12. In each case, the total mass of the four hydrogen atoms in the denominator is equal to $M = 4 \cdot m_H$ where $m_H$ is the mass of a single hydrogen atom. For the $x$-component of the centre of mass position, the figure contains two hydrogen atoms, $H_B$ and $H_D$, with $x_i = l$. The other two hydrogen atoms, $H_A$ and $H_C$, lead to zero-contributions to the sum because their $x$-components are $x_i = 0$. Proceed-

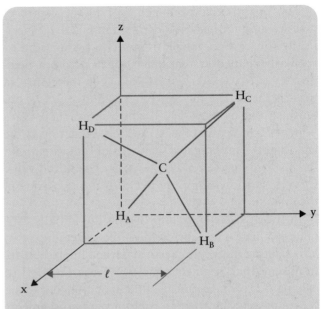

**FIGURE 4.12**

The geometry of the tetrahedral methane molecule $CH_4$ is best described by placing the molecule in a cube of side length $l$ in a Cartesian coordinate system. The four hydrogen atoms form four corners of the cube as shown. They are indistinguishable in a real molecule but have been labelled in the sketch with different indices for calculation purposes.

ing in the same fashion for the other components, we find:

$$x_{c.m.} = \frac{l \cdot m(H_B) + l \cdot m(H_D)}{4 \cdot m_H} = 0.5 \cdot l$$

$$y_{c.m.} = \frac{l \cdot m(H_B) + l \cdot m(H_C)}{4 \cdot m_H} = 0.5 \cdot l \quad [39]$$

$$z_{c.m.} = \frac{l \cdot m(H_C) + l \cdot m(H_D)}{4 \cdot m_H} = 0.5 \cdot l$$

The carbon atom is located at the centre of the cube shown in Fig. 4.12.

## CASE II: A CONTINUOUS, EXTENDED SYSTEM

An extended object can be treated as if it consists of a very large number ($n \gg 1$) of particles, which includes in particular objects that have a macroscopically continuous mass distribution. Rewriting Eq. [37] to apply to this case is greatly simplified if we assume that the position parameters $r_i = (x_i, y_i, z_i)$ for the particles in Eqs. [36] and [37] are time-independent. This condition leads to the definition of a **rigid object:**

*A rigid object is an extended object for which*

- *the distance between any two parts of the object is fixed, and*
- *the angle between the lines connecting any three parts of the object is fixed.*

The quantitative approach to find the centre of mass of a rigid object is illustrated in Fig. 4.13 specifically for its $x$-component. Fig 4.13(a) shows an irregularly shaped system that stretches from a position $x_{min}$ to $x_{max}$. An initial value for the centre of mass is the half-point between $x_{min}$ and $x_{max}$. We enter this value in Fig. 4.13(b), which shows the $x$-component of the centre of mass, $x_{c.m.}$, as a function of the length of the investigated segments of the system, $\Delta x$. In this first step, $\Delta x = x_{max} - x_{min}$. The initial value for $x_{c.m.}$ is shown halfway between the two ends of the system.

In the next step, we improve on the initially estimated value for $x_{c.m.}$ by dividing the system into two halves along the $x$-axis (vertical dashed line), then determining each segment's mass. We use Eq. [38] to calculate a second estimate of the $x$-component of the centre of mass by treating each of the two segments as particles located at the centre of the respective segment. Since both halves have a width of $\Delta x = \frac{1}{2}(x_{max} - x_{min})$, the resulting value is entered at

that abscissa value in Fig. 4.13(b). The $x_{c.m.}$ value is shown closer to $x_{max}$, which means that the right segment is heavier than the left segment.

The estimate of the centre of mass position is further improved by dividing the system into three equally long segments (vertical dash-dotted lines). We find again the mass of each of these segments and their centre positions that serve as the positions assigned to the respective particle. Using the first formula in Eq. [37] yields a sum of three terms that is the third estimate for the $x$-component of the centre of mass:

$$
\begin{aligned}
x_{c.m.} &= \frac{1}{M} \sum_i x_i \cdot \Delta m_i \\
&= \frac{1}{M} (x_1 \cdot \Delta m_1 + x_2 \cdot \Delta m_2 + x_3 \cdot \Delta m_3) \quad [40]
\end{aligned}
$$

We wrote the masses in Eq. [40] as $\Delta m_i$, noting that they become smaller with each successive division of the system. The position values $x_i$, in turn, remain finite numbers that lie equally spaced between the position at the left and right ends of the system. The third estimate is now entered into Fig. 4.13(b) at the abscissa value $\frac{1}{3}(x_{max} - x_{min})$ and is shown again closer to the $x_{max}$ position.

We repeat the last step iteratively, treating the system step by step as if composed of more and more but increasingly shorter sections. Fig. 4.13(b) shows that the plot of the estimated value of the $x$-component of the centre of mass approaches a value where the dashed line intersects the ordinate as the width $\Delta x$ decreases toward zero. Mathematically, this approach is called an **extrapolation** because the final value of $x_{c.m.}$, at $\Delta x = 0$, lies to the left of all individual points we determined along the dashed line in Fig. 4.13(b). Thus, the precise value follows from extrapolating the successive estimates of the centre of mass with smaller and smaller segment lengths.

The procedure described here is called an **algorithm**, and the specific algorithm we introduced is used to calculate a correct value for the centre of mass through extrapolation of Eq. [37]. We can write this in the following form:

$$
x_{c.m.} = \frac{1}{M} \lim_{n \to \infty} \sum_{i=1}^{n} x_i \cdot \Delta m_i \quad [41]
$$

Eq. [41] can analytically be solved for highly symmetric systems, and if the system has a uniform density $\rho$. In Eq. [41], we rewrite the formula using $\Delta m = \rho \cdot \Delta V = \rho \cdot A \cdot \Delta x$, in which $\Delta V$ is the volume of each segment, $A(x_i)$ is the cross-sectional area of the object at position $x_i$, and $\Delta x$ is a constant thick-

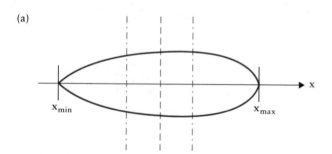

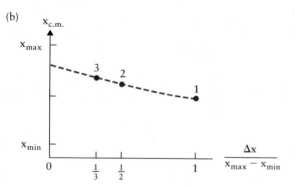

**FIGURE 4.13**

Method of finding the centre of mass on an irregularly shaped object. (a) For convenience of illustration we consider a two-dimensional object that we divide along the $x$-axis to find the $x_{c.m.}$-component. (b) The algorithm used is based on successively plotting estimated values for the centre of mass with decreasing segment lengths of the object, $\Delta x$. Shown are a first estimate based on the entire mass and the length of the object (1), a second estimate where the object is divided into two segments (dashed line in (a) and point 2 in (b)), and a third estimate with three segments (dash-dotted lines in (a) and point 3 in (b)). Each estimate leads to a value closer to $x_{max}$ for the particular object. The exact value follows from an extrapolation $\Delta x \to 0$.

ness of the thin segments into which the object is divided:

$$x_{c.m.} = \frac{\rho}{M} \lim_{n \to \infty} \sum_{i=1}^{n} x_i \cdot A(x_i) \cdot \Delta x \qquad [42]$$

where the last two terms assume that we choose very thin slices of the object and multiply their area with the thickness $\Delta x$. Experimental methods are used in more complex cases, which we discuss in Case III.

## Concept Question 4.6

The more than 30 phyla in the animal kingdom are distinguished by body symmetry, digestive system, body cavities, and segmentation. Two major body plans exist: radial symmetry or bilateral symmetry. For animals with radial symmetry the body parts are arranged regularly around a central axis. Examples include starfish and jellyfish. Animals with bilateral symmetry have a mirror-plane passing through the body from the front to the back end, giving rise to similar left and right sides. Examples are arthropods, such as flying insects, and chordates, such as birds. What do you know about the position of the centre of mass for each of these body plans?

ANSWER: We inspect Eq. [42] to see how we benefit from symmetry in uniform systems when determining the centre of mass. Note that we discuss Eq. [42] in this answer to extract useful information without mathematically solving it. Assume that the system is symmetric to the centre point between $x_{min}$ and $x_{max}$, i.e., the position $\frac{1}{2}(x_{min} + x_{max})$. The best way to see what consequences this symmetry has for Eq. [42] is to choose the centre position as the origin, i.e., $\frac{1}{2}(x_{min} + x_{max}) = 0$. This means that the cross-sectional area follows $A(x) = A(-x)$ due to the symmetry with respect to the origin along the $x$-axis. Since we multiply the cross-sectional area $A$ with the position $x_i$ in Eq. [42], we note that the sum of $x \cdot A(x)$ and $(-x) \cdot A(-x)$ is zero. Thus, we find $x_{c.m.} = 0$ for a symmetric object; the centre of mass lies at the spatial centre of the system.

For animals with radial symmetry, we choose the direction of the body axis as the $z$-direction. The symmetry then applies in both the $x$- and $y$-directions. Using the argument made with Eq. [42], we find that the centre of mass lies on the body axis.

Based on the same argument, the centre of mass lies somewhere in the mirror-plane for animals with bilateral symmetry. We took this into account when we simplified the human body in Concept Question 4.5: the two particles we used to model our body both lie on a central plane that divides our body into a left and a right side.

The centre of mass of a system is not always determined along the $x$-axis. Indeed, like any other position, the centre of mass has three vector components in three-dimensional space. We generalize Eq. [41] for numerical applications by including all three component formulas:

$$x_{c.m.} = \frac{1}{M} \lim_{n \to \infty} \sum_{i=1}^{n} x_i \cdot \Delta m_i$$

$$y_{c.m.} = \frac{1}{M} \lim_{n \to \infty} \sum_{i=1}^{n} y_i \cdot \Delta m_i \qquad [43]$$

$$z_{c.m.} = \frac{1}{M} \lim_{n \to \infty} \sum_{i=1}^{n} z_i \cdot \Delta m_i$$

or in vector notation:

$$\mathbf{r}_{c.m.} = \frac{1}{M} \lim_{n \to \infty} \sum_{i=1}^{n} \mathbf{r}_i \cdot \Delta m_i \qquad [44]$$

The centre of mass is easiest to find in highly symmetric systems such as cylinders, spheres, and rectangular prisms. Concept Question 4.6 illustrates that the centre of mass is identified in these cases without a mathematical calculation. For example, the centre of mass of a uniform sphere lies at its centre; the centre of mass of a uniform bar lies halfway between the two ends of the bar.

## CASE III: COMPLEX SYSTEMS

For an irregularly shaped rigid object, Eq. [44] is evaluated experimentally as illustrated in Fig. 4.14. The object in the figure is a two-dimensional sheet of

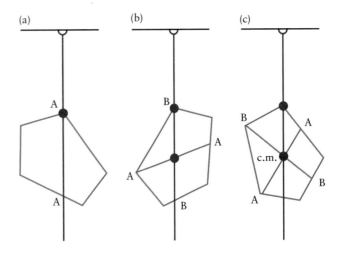

**FIGURE 4.14**

Construction of the centre of mass for an irregularly shaped two-dimensional object. (a) An arbitrary point A is chosen along the perimeter of the object. The object is then suspended at point A. When it is in mechanical equilibrium, a vertical line is drawn through point A, and is labelled with two letters A to indicate the vertex. (b) A different point B is chosen along the perimeter and the procedure is repeated. (c) The intersection of the two vertices A–A and B–B from parts (a) and (b) represents the centre of mass.

irregular shape. We pick two points along the rim of the object, A and B, and suspend the object from each of these points. The two vertical lines, which we draw on the object when it is in mechanical equilibrium in each case, intersect at the centre of mass of the object. The reason why this approach works is discussed further in the next chapter, where we introduce the *rotational equilibrium*.

## ● EXAMPLE 4.5

We use a simplified model of the human leg in the form of a uniform frustum of a right circular cone, as illustrated in Fig. 4.15. The radius of the leg at the hip is 1.4 times the radius at the foot, which we label $R$. The length of the leg is labelled $L$. Suggest a simple method to determine at what distance from the sole the centre of mass lies.

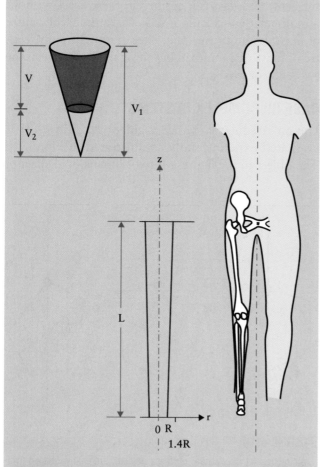

### FIGURE 4.15

Centre of mass of the human leg between hip joint and sole. The leg is modelled as a frustum of a right circular cone with base radius $R$ at the foot and base radius $1.4 \cdot R$ at the hip. The inset shows the construction of a frustum as the difference between two cone volumes, $V = V_1 - V_2$.

*Solution:* This type of problem can be solved mathematically, but requires calculus-based methods. Even though we greatly simplify the leg, these calculations turn out to be lengthy. Thus, it is more convenient to use a computer code based on Eq. [42]. If that isn't at hand, you could choose a cylindrical piece of solid material that can be machined into the shape described in Fig. 4.15. Once that model is obtained, use symmetry arguments as introduced in Concept Question 4.6 to determine that the centre of mass lies on the central axis of your machined piece. Thus, only a single experiment is needed to determine the centre of mass: you support your model with your finger while holding it sideways. When it is balanced—i.e., not tilting and falling either left or right—it is supported at the centre of mass. If you have an opportunity to do this experiment, confirm that the centre of mass of the human leg lies above the halfway point between hip and sole, at a fraction 5/9 above the sole, or 4/9 below the hip. This is due to the more massive upper leg. The effect would be even greater but for the foot and the existence of two bones in the lower leg.

The approach of Fig. 4.14 and Example 4.5 is often not feasible for biological systems, for example a tree. We cannot cut the tree just to find its centre of mass, nor can we model a tree as a simple geometric shape due to its low degree of symmetry. In these cases we place the centre of mass intuitively. This is shown in Fig. 4.16, which illustrates the correlation of the shape of coniferous trees and their usual place of growth. The tree in Fig. 4.16(a) has a low centre of mass, allowing it to grow at isolated spots. Even gale storms will not topple this tree, because the centre of mass is close to the ground. In turn, the tree shown in Fig. 4.16(b) has a high centre of mass. Such trees grow in forests where the surrounding trees break the force of a storm. In turn, the tree must grow tall with the majority of its needles near the top, as this is the only place where sufficient sunlight is available for photosynthesis. Of course, we must still prove that the effect of a force acting sideways on a tree is related to the tree's centre of mass. This will be the subject of the next chapter.

## Motion of the Centre of Mass

The benefit of introducing the centre of mass becomes evident when we determine its variation with time. We know that the time change of a position is a velocity. Thus, allowing both sides of Eq. [36] to vary

(a)        (b)

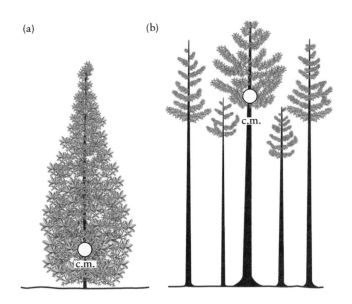

**FIGURE 4.16**

The centre of mass concept can be applied to the growth of coniferous trees. (a) The shape of isolated trees usually allows for a low centre of mass. (b) Trees in a forest often have a high-lying centre of mass. Note that we can guess the position of the centre of mass in these cases intuitively without requiring a precise calculation.

with time, we find the velocity of the centre of mass of a system:

$$\frac{\Delta \mathbf{r}_{c.m.}}{\Delta t} = \frac{1}{M}\sum_i m_i \frac{\Delta \mathbf{r}_i}{\Delta t} \qquad [45]$$

in which the masses $M$ and $m_i$ are time-independent. Eq. [45] yields the velocity of the centre of mass of a system:

$$\mathbf{v}_{c.m.} = \frac{1}{M}\sum_i m_i \cdot \mathbf{v}_i \qquad [46]$$

Transferring the total mass $M$ to the left-hand side of the equation yields:

$$M \cdot \mathbf{v}_{c.m.} = \sum_i m_i \cdot \mathbf{v}_i = \sum_i \mathbf{p}_i = \mathbf{P}_{total} \qquad [47]$$

We used the definitions of linear momentum in Eq. [6] and total linear momentum of a system in Eq. [9]. Thus, the velocity of the centre of mass is determined by the total linear momentum of the system and its total mass. In particular, when no external forces act on a system (isolated system), the total linear momentum is constant and consequently the velocity of the centre of mass is constant. This means that the centre of mass moves with constant speed along a straight line for an isolated system.

The motion of the centre of mass of a system on which a non-zero net force acts is determined from

Eq. [47] by allowing both sides of the equation to vary with time:

$$M\frac{\Delta \mathbf{v}_{c.m.}}{\Delta t} = \frac{\Delta \mathbf{P}_{total}}{\Delta t} \qquad [48]$$

which yields:

$$M \cdot \mathbf{a}_{c.m.} = \mathbf{F}_{net} \qquad [49]$$

in which we used Newton's second law in the form of Eq. [24]. Thus, we can state:

*The centre of mass accelerates under the action of a net force on the system as if the entire mass of the system were forming a point-like object at the centre of mass.*

> **Concept Question 4.7**
>
> **In Concept Question 4.5, we modelled the human body as a combination of two massive, point-like objects that are linked by a massless string. Comparing the straddle technique and the Fosbury flop in Fig. 4.11, what can be said about the centre of mass of the athlete?**
>
> ANSWER: In both techniques the weight is the only force acting on the athlete after the second foot leaves the ground. Thus, the athlete's centre of mass accelerates like an object on which only gravity acts. The motion of such objects follows the projectile trajectory we introduced in Chapter 2: the athlete's centre of mass moves along a parabola. In the case of the Fosbury flop this parabola peaks below the bar, while it must peak above the bar in the straddle technique.

## Friction

In the biosphere, none of the forces we have discussed so far can be observed in isolation. Additional forces are always acting due to the relative motion of the surrounding medium: air resistance or drag for flight, friction on solid ground, and viscosity in liquids. These forces have in common that they act against the direction of actual or anticipated motion due to contact between two systems. As a result, a moving system slows down to rest if it is not accelerated. To maintain uniform motion along a straight line requires a continuous force to overcome friction.

Friction forces originate in a complex fashion from the electrostatic and morphological microstructures of the two systems in contact. Electrostatic interactions occur between single atoms or molecules in the two adjacent surfaces. The morphological contributions at solid surfaces occur at a slightly larger length-scale where the roughness of the surface can lead to additional interactions with gases or liquids, or to interlocking with another solid surface. Both processes are too complex to allow us to calculate the macroscopic frictional effect between any two real surfaces based on the microscopic properties.

To circumvent this problem, various simplifying models have been proposed. Such simplifying models are approximations and describe frictional motion only in certain velocity domains. The macroscopic models we discuss in this section are still introduced, to provide us with a formalism to deal with major applications.

## Speed Dependence of Friction

Friction $\mathscr{F}$ is described by a vector that is directed opposite the velocity **v**. Three types of friction forces are distinguished based on their dependence on the speed of the object:

- *The magnitude of the friction does not depend on the speed:* $\mathscr{F} \neq f(v)$. This case is called **kinetic friction** (with a subscript "k" for "kinetic"). The main application is the motion at solid–solid interfaces with not-too-large or not-too-small speeds. $\mathscr{F}_k$ depends on the magnitude of the normal force, i.e., the force that pushes the two objects toward each other. The low-speed limit can be included by introducing in the same fashion a **static friction** force $\mathscr{F}_s$, which defines a threshold for the kinetic friction to take effect. We discuss this case in more detail in the next section because it applies to our own motion on solid ground.

- *The magnitude of the friction is proportional to the speed:* $\mathscr{F} \propto v$. The main application is the motion of a solid object through a liquid at moderate or low speeds. We discuss fluids in Chapters 11 and 12.

- *The magnitude of the friction is proportional to the square of the speed:* $\mathscr{F} \propto v^2$. This is the most general case, applicable for all objects at very high speeds (including the motion of a bullet through tissue in forensics) and applicable for object motion through gases with the exception of aerodynamic objects. It is then called the *drag force* or *air resistance*.

Here we discuss the last case first to study the motion with drag effects. We assume that an object travels with speed $v_{\text{system}}$ through a medium of density $\rho$. To achieve this, the object must displace the medium in its way, which it does with a speed $v_{\text{medium}}$ roughly equal to its own speed. During a time interval $\Delta t$ the amount of medium displaced is equal to the volume

of a cylinder through which the system travels in time $\Delta t$. To achieve this displacement, the object must exert a force on the medium. The reaction force to this force is the **drag force**. The magnitude of the drag force is written in the form:

$$F_{\text{drag}} = \frac{D}{2} \rho \cdot A \cdot v_{\text{system}}^2 \qquad [50]$$

in which $A$ is the cross-section of the object perpendicular to the direction of its velocity vector. $D$ is the drag coefficient that depends on the aerodynamic properties of the object. Aerodynamics causes a reduction in the ratio $v_{\text{medium}}/v_{\text{system}}$, which is best achieved by minimizing the area $A$. We find $D = 0.5$ for a spherical object moving through air, but the coefficient may be as large as $D = 2.0$ for irregularly shaped objects. In turn, the drag coefficient can be as small as 0.15 for aerodynamically optimized objects.

The consequences of drag forces on the motion of objects travelling though air can be read from Eq. [50]: if the object moves slowly, the drag force is negligible. When the object becomes faster, the drag force increases faster than any other force due to the proportionality to the square of the speed. The object will eventually reach a speed at which the drag force becomes equal to the sum of all other forces; when this speed is reached, the object can no longer accelerate. The state of the object is then called a quasi-stationary state and the speed of the object is called the **terminal speed** $v_t$. We use Newton's first law to determine the terminal speed of an object falling toward Earth through air:

$$F_{\text{drag}} - W = \frac{D}{2} \rho \cdot A \cdot v_t^2 - m \cdot g = 0 \qquad [51]$$

which yields:

$$v_t = \sqrt{\frac{2 \cdot m \cdot g}{D \cdot \rho \cdot A}} \qquad [52]$$

To determine the time it takes to reach the terminal speed, Newton's second law would have to be solved in the form $F_{\text{drag}} - W = m \cdot a$. Instead, we usually estimate the time by assuming that the object's speed increases as $v = g \cdot t$ until the terminal speed is reached. Substituting $g \cdot t$ for $v_t$, we find for the time to reach terminal speed from rest, $t_t$:

$$t_t = \sqrt{\frac{2 \cdot m}{D \cdot g \cdot \rho \cdot A}} \qquad [53]$$

● **EXAMPLE** 4.6

(a) What is the terminal speed for a standard man in air? Consider a skydiver falling with area $A = 0.7$ m$^2$ and a head-first diver with area $A = 0.15$ m$^2$. $D = 0.5$ is used for the drag coefficient. *Note:* The surface area of a standard man is 1.85 m$^2$ (see Table 3.3); thus, the cross-section of a skydiver is about 40% of the total surface area. (b) Does either of the two standard men in part (a) reach terminal speed? The typical height of a skydiving jump is 3500 m to 4500 m, and the maximum height of a regularly performed dive is 35 m (in Acapulco, Mexico). (c) What is the terminal speed for a Northern Gannet? Northern Gannets live along the northern Atlantic coast of America and hunt for fish and squid as deep as 15 m below the sea surface by plunging like an arrow from up to 50 m above the water. The average mass of a Northern Gannet is 2.9 kg and its average length is about 1 m. The bird reduces its cross-sectional area to about $A = 250$ cm$^2$ during the dive. Use $D = 0.2$; how high would the bird have to start its dive to reach maximum depth in the water?

*Solution to part (a):* Using Eq. [52] with the density of air $\rho = 1.2$ kg/m$^3$, we find for the skydiver $v_t = 57$ m/s $= 205$ km/h. The diver is aerodynamically more effective and would reach 123 m/s $= 440$ km/h.

*Solution part (b):* Using Eq. [53], we find that the skydiver needs about 6 seconds to reach the terminal speed, by which time the standard man fell less than 200 m. The diver needs almost 13 seconds to reach terminal speed; however, the standard man fell for fewer than 3 seconds to reach the water 35 m below. Were the divers to reach terminal speed and survive the dive, they could as well jump off an airplane over the ocean at any height with nothing but a bathing suit! The overall effect of air drag is nicely shown by the skydiver. Starting at 4000 m, it takes more than 70 seconds to reach ground (without a parachute). This time would be cut to fewer than 30 seconds without air drag.

*Solution to part (c):* Using Eq. [52], a terminal speed of almost 100 m/s is calculated for the Northern Gannet, which it would reach 10 seconds after commencing the dive. However, a dive from 50 metres above the water takes only 3 seconds. Thus, the Northern Gannet does not optimize its depth. To do so, a dive from a 500-m height would be needed; however, from that height the bird would no longer be able to make out prey and would risk that the prey had moved on before the bird reached the water surface. Rather, birds that hunt underwater developed the ability to dive actively in water using their wings

to propel themselves. Flapping the wings under water requires significantly greater force, a problem birds such as the penguin have solved by becoming flightless with smaller wings; this allows the Emperor Penguin in Antarctica, for example, to dive to depths greater than 500 m.

## Friction at Stationary or Slowly Moving Solid Interfaces

In this section, we discuss the case when the frictional force is independent of the speed of the object. Instead, the frictional force is related to the normal force exerted by the supporting surface, implying that the strength of the interaction between the moving object and the supporting surface determines the frictional effect.

For an object on a frictionless inclined plane, the forces acting on the object parallel to the plane are not balanced (see Example 3.8). Thus, the object accelerates in the downhill direction. If we increase the roughness of the surface of the object and the inclined plane, then either one of two types of motion may result:

• the object remains at rest as if it were glued to the plane, or

• the object moves down the inclined plane but reaches a terminal speed beyond which it does not accelerate.

Reviewing Example 3.8 more carefully, we recognize the conditions under which either of these two results can occur: an object at rest or moving with a constant speed obeys Newton's first law; i.e., the forces along the inclined plane must be balanced. In Example 3.8 this was initially accomplished by a string that introduced a tension directed upward along the inclined plane.

We first study the case in which the object remains at rest on the inclined plane. The corresponding free-body diagram is shown in Fig. 4.17(a). In addition to the forces we discussed in Example 3.8, an additional force acts in the direction opposed to the anticipated motion of the object. This direction can be determined by solving the problem for the frictionless case, as done in Example 3.8. Note that the additional force $\mathscr{F}_{s,max}$ is shown dashed in the figure. The subscript "max" indicates that the force shown is the maximum force acting on the object against the direction of motion. The subscript "s" stands for "static," since the consequence of this force is to allow the object to remain at rest. Based on Newton's first law we know that the actual force acting in the positive $x$-direction in

(a)

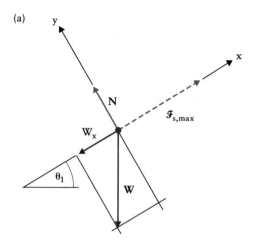

(b)

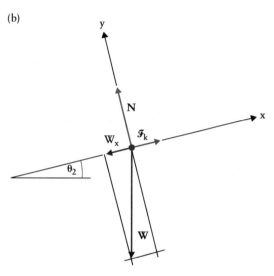

**FIGURE 4.17**

Free-body diagram for an object on an inclined plane with friction. (a) The friction force is expressed as a threshold force acting against the direction of anticipated motion while the object is at rest. (b) When the object is in motion, friction may allow the object to move with a constant terminal speed.

Fig. 4.17(a) must be equal in magnitude to $W_x$ in order to provide for a mechanical equilibrium along the inclined plane. The system remains at rest as long as the force causing the anticipated motion does not exceed the magnitude of $\mathcal{F}_{s,max}$. We can determine this threshold force experimentally by slowly increasing the angle of the inclined plane until the object starts to move. At the instant the object moves, we know that the accelerating force exceeds the **maximum static frictional force**. We introduce a proportionality factor $\mu$ for the magnitudes of $\mathcal{F}_{s,max}$ and the normal force since we already know that friction at solid interfaces is related to the normal force:

$$\mathcal{F}_{s,max} = \mu_s \cdot N \qquad [54]$$

The proportionality factor $\mu_s$ is called the **coefficient of static friction**. This coefficient depends on the materials of the two objects that are in contact.

Values for $\mu_s$ lie usually between 0.01 (a synovial joint of vertebrates) and 1.0 (rubber tire on dry concrete). The smaller this coefficient the easier it is to set the object on the surface in motion.

It is interesting to compare Eq. [54] with $W = m \cdot g$, as both are definitions of forces. On a superficial level we notice that Eq. [54] defines one force as a multiple of another force, implying that the frictional force is a secondary force, not a fundamental force such as weight. But the new feature in Eq. [54] is the proportionality factor $\mu$. We will find a large number of proportionality factors between physical parameters throughout this textbook. They belong to one of four categories:

- *Universal and Natural Constants:* Proportionality factors that occur with only a single, fixed value. The gravitational acceleration $g$ is such a natural constant because it applies specifically on the surface of Earth; the gravitational constant $G^*$ in Eq. [3.4] is a universal constant because it applies throughout the known universe. Relations between physical parameters that contain only universal or natural constants are either physical laws (e.g., Newton's law of gravity) or definitions of physical parameters (e.g., the definition of weight in Eq. [3.5]).

- *Materials Constants:* Proportionality factors with values varying from material to material. The density $\rho$ is a materials constant. Materials constants may also depend on other parameters, in particular the temperature, indicating fundamental properties at the atomic or molecular level of the material that are hidden in the materials constant when it is used to describe macroscopic observations. Relations between physical parameters that contain only materials constants and universal or natural constants are again physical laws or definitions, e.g., the relation between mass and volume for a uniform object $m = \rho \cdot V$. Values for materials constants are usually tabulated when they are introduced (e.g., diffusion coefficients in Table 10.5).

- *Conversion Factors:* Arbitrarily set but widely used factors that allow us to use physical parameters in different unit systems. An example is the conversion of lengths from the metric system to the U.S. system, e.g., that 1 metre is approximately 39.37 inches. No underlying physical principle is involved, but we need these conversion factors because no single, exclusively used unit system exists.

- *Auxiliary Constants:* Proportionality factors that are introduced *ad hoc* for a particular system.

They often have a preliminary character and are replaced by universal, natural, or materials constants as soon as the proper physical laws governing an observation are identified. Most constants introduced in the literature are of this type, and they often are referred to as "fudge factors" in laboratory jargon. Some of these auxiliary factors persist for extended periods, indicating that a fundamental law has not yet been identified or is cumbersome to use, and the relation based on the auxiliary factor remains a convenient simplification for applications. The drag coefficient $D$ and the coefficient of static friction are examples of auxiliary constants. They do not qualify as materials constants because their value varies even for the same system. This is due to the combination of microscopic electric effects and larger-scale roughness that are never the same even for otherwise macroscopically identical objects.

The fact that the coefficient of static friction in Eq. [54] is an auxiliary constant means two things: (i) we have to be careful to use a particular value even if found in a tabulation because the actual value of $\mu_s$ varies from experiment to experiment; and (ii) we need to keep an open mind when discussing frictional effects because it is a complex issue with ramifications beyond the simplified treatment that we can provide.

Next we study the case in Fig. 4.17(b): the object moves along the inclined plane, but does so with a constant terminal speed. Fig. 4.17(b) shows the free-body diagram for this case. We know that the net force along the $x$-direction is zero (an application of Newton's first law) because the object moves with a constant speed:

$$\mathscr{F}_k - W_x = 0 \qquad [55]$$

which yields $\mathscr{F}_k = W_x$. A second friction force has been introduced in Eq. [55], which is identified by the subscript "k" for "kinetic." The **kinetic friction force** is the force that resists the actual motion of an object. Eq. [55] illustrates that this force can be calculated when all other forces in the problem are known and specific conditions have been established such that the object moves with a terminal speed. We are faced with the same dilemma as before—that the kinetic friction force must be established experimentally for each case and is not predictable even for very similar cases. In analogy to the static friction force, a formula has been developed that allows a rough estimate of the magnitude of the kinetic friction force based on the normal force exerted on the sliding object:

$$\mathscr{F}_k = \mu_k \cdot N \qquad [56]$$

in which the **coefficient of kinetic friction,** $\mu_k$, is again an auxiliary constant and is usually smaller than the coefficient of static friction. This means that an object needs a larger angle of the inclined plane to overcome the threshold for motion, and that the object then needs a smaller angle of the inclined plane to cease accelerating and reach a terminal speed.

● **EXAMPLE 4.7**

(a) An object is placed on a horizontal surface, which is then tilted. When the surface tilt exceeds an angle of $\theta_1 = 14°$ with the horizontal, the object starts to slide downhill. What is the coefficient of static friction between the object and the surface? (b) The object on the same surface moves downhill with a constant speed (terminal speed) if the surface tilt is now changed to a lower angle $\theta_2$. Calculate $\theta_2$ if the coefficient of kinetic friction between the object and the surface is $\mu_k = 0.14$.

*Solution to part (a):* We identify the object on the inclined plane as the system. Fig. 4.17(a) shows the free-body diagram of the forces acting on the object. Note that the actual static friction force must be equal to the maximum static friction force at the threshold of motion, which is reached at an angle of $\theta_1 = 14°$. Thus, we use Fig. 4.17(a) to write Newton's laws for the case just before motion of the objects sets in:

$$x\text{-direction:} \quad \mathscr{F}_s - W \cdot \sin \theta_1 = 0$$
$$y\text{-direction:} \quad N - W \cdot \cos \theta_1 = 0 \qquad [57]$$

The two formulas in Eq. [57] allow us to substitute the normal force and the static friction force from Eq. [54]:

$$\mu_s = \frac{\mathscr{F}_{s,max}}{N} = \frac{W \cdot \sin \theta_2}{W \cdot \cos \theta_2} = \tan \theta_2$$
$$= \tan 14° = 0.25 \qquad [58]$$

*Solution to part (b):* Fig. 4.17(b) provides the free-body diagram when the object slides downhill. Applying Newton's laws, the following formulas are written for this case:

$$x\text{-direction:} \quad \mathscr{F}_k - W \cdot \sin \theta_2 = 0$$
$$y\text{-direction:} \quad N - W \cdot \cos \theta_2 = 0 \qquad [59]$$

in which both formulas are applications of Newton's first law because the object has reached its terminal speed. We calculate the angle $\theta_2$ from Eq. [59] by determining the ratio of friction force and normal force according to Eq. [56]:

$$\mu_k = \frac{\mathscr{F}_k}{N} = \frac{W \cdot \sin \theta_2}{W \cdot \cos \theta_2} = \tan \theta_2 \qquad [60]$$
$$\Rightarrow \theta_2 = \tan^{-1}(0.14) = 8°$$

## Concept Question 4.8

**(a) What does a coefficient of static friction $\mu_s > 1$ imply? (b) Can you name a natural system with a very large coefficient of static friction, i.e., $\mu_s \gg 1$? (c) Should an object on a horizontal surface with $\mu_s = 0$ start to slide right away?**

ANSWER TO PART (a): If we test a system by tilting the underlying plane to an angle at which it starts to slide, then the condition $\mu_s > 1$ requires that $\theta_1 > 45°$ based on Eq. [58].

ANSWER TO PART (b): Specifically, $\mu_s \gg 1$ requires an angle $\theta_1$ close to (or equal to) 90°. Such systems occur naturally when it is beneficial for an object to attach and hold on to a vertical surface. Vines can grow up along rough surfaces, such as brick or wood, plant pollen can stick to the legs of insects, and flies can hold on to smooth vertical surfaces such as glass windows.

ANSWER TO PART (c): No. Note that Eq. [54] implies that sliding occurs when horizontal forces on the object exceed the frictional force, not when they equal this threshold. Thus, a horizontal force of magnitude zero that acts on a system on a horizontal surface does not set in motion (accelerate) an object on a frictionless surface; this is consistent with Newton's first law of mechanics, which applies to all systems with and without friction.

# A Philosophical Note

Friction plays a pivotal role in that it opens a window beyond an exclusively mechanical view of life and life processes. While reading this book, you probably noticed a feeling of intellectual discomfort the first time we discussed friction. Up to that point, Newton's laws and related principles, such as the conservation of linear momentum, gave us a sense of consistency of the mechanical view of nature. With friction, we suddenly lose uniformity: the physical processes break down in cases that have to be dealt with individually and require somewhat arbitrary coefficients to match theoretical predictions with experimental observations. This is not the result of a lapse of rigour in the discussion, but an inherent fault of the idea that nature can be described by mechanical concepts alone. Frictional effects are ultimately non-mechanical, and for that reason do not fit into mechanics. It will be beneficial to the reader to keep this observation in mind throughout Chapter 5 and well into Chapter 6, as we need to dwell for a while longer on the mechanical view of nature.

In Chapter 6 we will then reach the second and final point at which a mechanical approach can no longer be sustained; while in the current chapter we introduced one of the crown jewels of mechanics in the form of the concept of conservation of linear momentum, an attempt in Chapter 6 at formulating the conservation of energy for mechanical systems will fail miserably and force us to abandon an exclusively mechanical approach.

## MULTIPLE CHOICE AND CONCEPTUAL QUESTIONS

### MOMENTUM AND INELASTIC COLLISIONS

**Q–4.1.** Stand perfectly still, then take a step forward. Before the step your momentum was zero, then it increased. Does this violate the conservation of momentum?

**Q–4.2.** An object of mass $m$ moves with speed $v$. It collides head-on in a perfectly inelastic collision with an object of twice the mass but half the speed moving in the opposite direction. What is the speed of the combined object after the collision? (A) $v_{final} = 0$. (B) $v_{final} = v/2$. (C) $v_{final} = v$. (D) $v_{final} = 2 \cdot v$. (E) A speed different from the previous four choices.

**Q–4.3.** If two objects collide and one is initially at rest, is it possible for both to be at rest after the collision?

**Q–4.4.** Two objects of equal mass $m$ and speed $|v_1| = |v_2| = v$ collide in a perfectly inelastic collision at a right angle, as illustrated in Fig. 4.18. In what direction does the combined object move after the collision?

**Q–4.5.** Fig. 4.19 shows two escape options for a squirrel (solid circle) that is being chased by a dog (small open circle) in a garden: run straight for the closest tree (large open circle) and up (Fig. 4.19(a)), or run along a tangent toward the next tree and then up on the far side (Fig. 4.19(b)). Why does the squirrel usually choose the second option? *Hint:* Consider the collision squirrel–tree and a possible collision dog–squirrel when the squirrel is running up the tree.

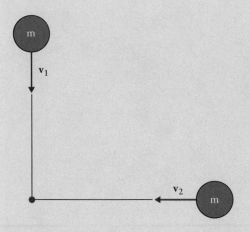

**FIGURE 4.18**

Two objects of equal mass collide perfectly inelastically at a 90° angle.

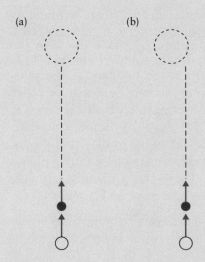

(a)      (b)

**FIGURE 4.19**

**Q–4.6.** In a sequence filmed with a high-speed camera, a Northern Goshawk (compare P–4.3) is seen catching a moth in mid-flight without any sign of change of speed of the bird. Did the hawk find a way to violate the conservation of linear momentum?

**Q–4.7.** Velvet worms use a rather cruel method of hunting: aiming at their prey for distances of up to one metre, they eject two jets of a sticky liquid from glands near their mouth. The liquid dries very fast, immobilizing the prey. The worm then injects digestive juices through a bite and later extracts its meal, which formed by internal liquefaction of the prey. Would not the conservation of linear momentum require the velvet worm's body to be accelerated backward while spraying from its two powerful nozzles?

**Q–4.8.** You want to determine the mass of an object by exposing it to a perfectly inelastic collision with

a test object. In this experiment, what is the minimum number of parameters you have to either measure or set? (A) one; (B) two; (C) three; (D) four; (E) five.

**Q–4.9.** A 1.2-kg common raven, just leaving a feeding platform at 0.2 m/s, and a 23-g Savannah sparrow in mid-flight at 10 m/s, collide with a glass window (treat the collision as a perfectly inelastic collision). Which bird exerts the larger force on the window panel? (A) the raven; (B) the sparrow; (C) they exert the same force; (D) neither exerts a force; (E) we cannot answer the question with the information given.

**Q–4.10.** In 1965, Jacques-Yves Cousteau developed a mixture of oxygen and helium to reduce the risk of human breathing in the deep-sea station *Conshelf III* (see also Q–9.3). Helium is now routinely mixed with air or oxygen in scuba diving tanks to reduce the side-effects of nitrogen under high pressure, such as narcosis (a mental function impairment) and diver's paralysis (nitrogen gas bubble formation in the cardiovascular system; see Example 9.2). Assume that we use one of these gas mixtures in a test chamber when investigating the flight of an insect with high-speed cameras. Using the momentum disc theory, describe the adjustments the insect has to attempt when flying in heliox (20% oxygen, 80% helium) of density $\rho_{heliox} = 400$ g/m$^3$ (with otherwise same conditions as air).

**Q–4.11.** Smaller birds, such as the European starling (introduced in 1890 in North America and now common across the continent) are often seen resting on small tree branches. When they take off, the branch swings momentarily downward. Can this observation be explained by the momentum disc theory?

**Q–4.12.** In Chapter 7, the kinetic gas theory is introduced as a microscopic model for gases. One of the assumptions in that model is that the gas particles move between collisions with constant speed along straight lines. For which part of a nitrogen molecule ($N_2$) should this condition exactly apply?

**Q–4.13.** A baseball player accidentally releases the bat in mid-swing. The bat sails toward the stands, spinning in the air. Neglect air resistance. (a) With the information given, can we determine any point on the baseball bat for which we can describe its motion after it left the player's hands? What motion does that point perform? (b) Assuming that the baseball bat is made of solid wood (uniform density), where along the baseball bat would you expect the point in part (a) to lie?

**Q–4.14.** We consider the water molecules in a beaker on a table as the system. We will later learn that the individual water molecules in the beaker typically move at several hundred metres per second (let $v$ be the average molecular speed). What is the state of motion of the centre of mass of this system? (A) It moves also with speed $v$ like the individual molecules; (B) It moves with speed $v$ but in the opposite direction of the individual molecules due to Newton's third law; (C) It moves with constant speed, but that speed is different from $v$; (D) It does not move, the centre of mass is at rest; (E) It accelerates downward because gravity is the only force acting on the water molecules.

**Q–4.15.** A system consists of three objects. Initially its centre of mass moves with constant speed along a straight line. What happens if I exert an external force on only one of the three objects? (A) Nothing; to change the state of motion I must exert the external force on all three objects; (B) Nothing; I cannot exert a force on just a part of a system; (C) Nothing; I need collisions among the three objects to affect the centre of mass; (D) The object I interact with accelerates, but the other two objects accelerate in the opposite direction such that the centre of mass continues to move at constant speed; (E) All three objects accelerate to allow the centre of mass to accelerate in the same fashion as the object on which I exert the external force. This is necessary because otherwise the external force causes the dismantling of the system, which is inconsistent with the definition of the system as three objects; (F) None of the above. If you chose (F), do you have a better suggestion?

## FRICTION

**Q–4.16.** (a) A single force acts on an object. Can the object be at rest? (b) An object has a zero acceleration. Does this mean that no forces act on it?

**Q–4.17.** Why do car manufacturers offer ABS systems with their products?

**Q–4.18.** Ospreys are large North American birds of prey that eat mainly fish. To catch prey they dive into the water and grab the fish with both feet, as illustrated by the image at the beginning of this chapter. Their large wingspans of 140 to 180 cm allow them to carry even large fish considerable distances. In preparation for this flight ospreys stop after the successful hunt to shake water out of their feathers and to point the head of the fish forward in the direction of flight, as seen in Fig. 4.20. Which formula, and

**FIGURE 4.20**

particularly which parameter in that formula, is changed favourably for the flight of the osprey by orienting the fish in this fashion?

**Q–4.19.** We compare the terminal speed of a raindrop of mass 30 mg and an equally heavy ice pellet during a hail storm. Noting the density difference, with a value of $\rho = 1.0$ g/cm$^3$ for liquid water and $\rho = 0.92$ g/cm$^3$ for ice, (a) do both fall with the same terminal speed (since the density of the falling object is *not* a factor in Eq. [52]), and (b) if they fall with different terminal speeds, which one is faster?

**Q–4.20.** Why is it dangerous to jump into water from great heights even if a trained performer can do it safely?

**Q–4.21.** Why is the coefficient of kinetic friction smaller than the coefficient of static friction? (a) Give a reason based on the microscopic roughness of the interface, and (b) give a logical reason by looking at Eqs. [54] and [56] and thinking about what they imply.

**Q–4.22.** "Friction cannot be a vertical force because it is a multiple of the normal force, and a vertical surface cannot exert a normal force on an object that touches it." This statement is (A) true; (B) false; (C) This question cannot be answered with the information given.

**Q–4.23.** We discussed the case of objects moving through a liquid at small speeds in which the drag force is proportional to the speed $v$ (linear relation). With the drag force being the only force acting in the horizontal direction on a fish that stops propelling its body forward, we expect that (A) The fish slows down linearly, $v \propto -t$ ($t$ is time); (B) The fish slows down until it reaches a finite terminal speed; (C) The fish slows down but not with a linear relation between its speed and time; (D) The fish comes instantaneously to rest; (E) The fish slows down and is then pushed in the opposite direction by the drag force.

**Q–4.24.** Two identically shaped objects with same surface roughness and composition are placed on the same surface. One object is hollow and has mass $M$, the other object is solid and has mass $2 \cdot M$. What is required to have both objects slide across the horizontal surface with the same frictional force? (A) Move the hollow object twice as fast; (B) Move the solid object twice as fast; (C) Have both objects move with the same speed across the surface; (D) Push the hollow object down with an additional force $M \cdot g$ while it moves; (E) Push the solid object down with an additional force $M \cdot g$ while it moves.

**Q–4.25.** (a) When we refer to the shape of an animal as being aerodynamic, what formula—and particularly what *term* in that formula—do we have in mind? (b) What is the underlying physics of an aerodynamic shape?

# ANALYTICAL PROBLEMS

## MOMENTUM AND INELASTIC COLLISIONS

**P–4.1.** Polonium-210 ($^{210}$Po) is a radioactive isotope that has an atomic nucleus with 84 protons and 126 neutrons (together 210 nucleons). It undergoes an $\alpha$-decay with a half-life of 138.4 days, resulting in a stable Lead-206 ($^{206}$Pb) isotope of a mass of $205.974 \cdot u$. Assuming that the polonium nucleus is at rest when it decays, an $\alpha$-particle ($^4$He) with a speed of $1.6 \times 10^7$ m/s is emitted. The $\alpha$-particle has a mass of 4.002 u. The atomic unit u is defined as $1\ u = 1.6605677 \times 10^{-27}$ kg. (a) In what direction does the daughter isotope $^{206}$Pb move? (b) What is the speed of the $^{206}$Pb leaving the decay zone? (c) Compare both speeds in this problem to the vacuum speed of light.

**P–4.2.** Two objects, each moving with the same speed in opposite directions, collide head-on. The smaller object of mass $m = 100$ g is embedded in the larger object of mass $M = 500$ g after the collision. How does the final speed depend on the initial speed?

**P–4.3.** Some birds of prey, such as the Northern Goshawk, hunt other birds in midair. Typically, the hawk spots the prey while soaring high above, then dives in for the kill with the deadly grip of its talons. They do not shy away from rather large prey, such as ducks and crows. We want to estimate the impact on the hawk when completing a successful kill by using the change in linear momentum when clawing into the prey, which we take to be an unsuspecting American crow. Use: mass of crow $m_C = 450$ g, horizontal flight of the crow with speed $v_C = 10$ m/s, mass of hawk $m_H = 900$ g, flight path in the same plane as crow but approaching from behind with $v_H = 20$ m/s and with an angle of $\theta = 70°$ with the horizontal, as illustrated in the side view of Fig. 4.21. (a) How fast does the hawk move immediately after catching the crow? (b) By what angle has the direction of motion of

the hawk changed at the impact? *Note:* American crows take the danger posed by high-soaring hawks very seriously. They are often seen to mob the predator as a group to drive it out of their neighbourhood.

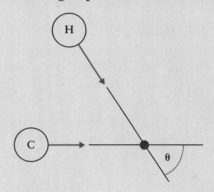

**FIGURE 4.21**

**P–4.4.** The heart of the standard man ejects 5.0 L blood per minute into the aorta. We calculate later that the average blood speed in the aorta is 22 cm/s. The density of blood is 1.06 g/cm$^3$. The mass of the heart of a standard man is 300 g (Table 3.3). Use these data to estimate (a) the average net force acting on the heart, (b) the average acceleration of the heart as a result of this force, and (c) the average acceleration of the human body as a result of this force. (d) What assumptions do we make for the value in part (c) to have a physical meaning? (e) How accurate are the values we estimated in parts (a) and (b)?

**P–4.5.** Ruby-throated hummingbirds can be watched hovering at feeders throughout eastern North America. These birds have a wingspan of 11 cm and a mass of just 3.0 g. Using the momentum disc theory, to what speed does the bird have to accelerate air downward to maintain its hovering position? Use $\rho_{air} = 1.2$ kg/m$^3$.

**P–4.6.** An object ejects 10% of its mass at time $t = 0$ along the negative $x$-axis with a speed of 1.0 m/s, and shortly after another 10% along the negative $y$-axis with the same speed. Calculate the magnitude and direction of its final speed if it started from rest.

**P–4.7.** An object of mass $m = 3.0$ kg makes a perfectly inelastic collision with a second object that is initially at rest. The combined object moves after the collision with a speed equal to one-third of the object that was initially moving. What is the mass of the object that was initially at rest?

**P–4.8.** An object of mass $m = 8.0$ g is fired into an object of mass $M = 250$ g that sat initially at rest at the edge of a table of 1.0 metre height. The lighter object becomes embedded in the larger object (perfect inelastic collision) and the combined object lands after the impact 2.0 m from the table on the floor. Determine the initial speed of the object of mass $m$.

## CENTRE OF MASS

**P–4.9.** In the ammonia molecule $NH_3$ the three hydrogen atoms are located in a plane forming an equilateral triangle with side length $a$ as shown in Fig. 4.22. The nitrogen atom oscillates 24 billion times per second up and down along a line that intersects the plane of the hydrogen atoms at the centre of mass of the three hydrogen atoms (solid circles in Fig. 4.22). (a) Calculate the length $a$ in Fig. 4.22, using for the N—H bond a length $l = 0.1014$ nm, and for the HNH-bond angle $\theta = 106.8°$. (b) Calculate the distance between the centre of mass of the three hydrogen atoms and any one of the hydrogen atoms.

**P–4.10.** A water molecule consists of an oxygen atom and two hydrogen atoms. The O—H bonds are 0.1 nm long and form an angle of 107°. Where is the molecule's centre of mass located? Consider the mass of the oxygen atom to be 16 times the mass of a hydrogen atom.

## FRICTION

**P–4.11.** (a) An object moves with initial speed $v_0 = 10.0$ m/s on a horizontal surface. It slides for a distance of 20.0 m before it comes to rest as illustrated in Fig. 4.23(a). Determine the coefficient of kinetic friction between object and surface. (b) How long does the object move until it comes to rest? (c) With what speed does the object move after the same time if the surface is tilted to an angle of $\theta = 10°$ with the horizontal and the object is sliding downhill, as illustrated in Fig. 4.23(b)?

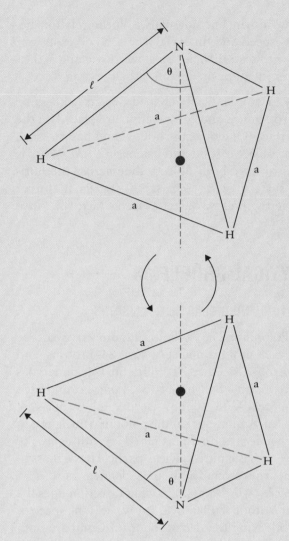

**FIGURE 4.22**

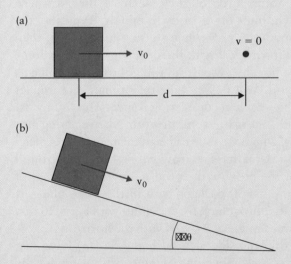

**FIGURE 4.23**

**P–4.12.** Fig. 4.24 shows two objects that are connected with a massless string. Object 1 has a mass $m_1 = 1.0$ kg and is placed on a horizontal surface with a coefficient of static friction $\mu_s = 0.35$ and a coefficient of kinetic friction $\mu_k = 0.25$. Object 2 has an unknown mass $m_2$. The connecting string passes over a massless and frictionless pulley. (a) Calculate the minimum mass $m_2$ for the two objects to start moving when released from rest. (b) Once the two objects move with $m_2$ at the value calculated in part (a), what is the magnitude of the acceleration of the two objects?

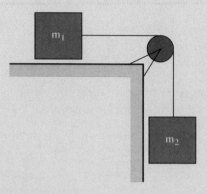

**FIGURE 4.24**

**P–4.13.** A standard man rides on a bicycle. Resistance against the forward motion is due to air resistance, friction of the tires on the road, and the metal-on-metal sliding in the lubricated axles. Combining the latter two effects as a velocity-independent friction force $\mathcal{F}$, determine the speed above which air resistance limits the cyclist's motion. $\mathcal{F}$ is determined from the fact that the cyclist rolls with constant speed downhill on a road that has a 1% slope. Use $\rho_{air} = 1.2$ kg/m³ and a cross-sectional area $A = 0.5$ m² for the bicycle/standard man system in the direction of motion. Use $D = 0.5$ for the drag coefficient.

**P–4.14.** A jellyfish floats motionless in water. At time $t = 0$ it expels water by contracting its bell, accelerating its body to a speed $v_0$. Determine the mathematical formula that describes the change of the speed of the jellyfish until it returns to rest. How long does it take for the jellyfish to come to rest? *Note:* The drag force on the moving jellyfish is modelled by Stokes's law for the drag force due to the motion of a sphere through a liquid: $\mathcal{F} = -k \cdot v$ with $k = $ const. This problem requires basic knowledge of differential equations. *Hint:* The jellyfish initially floats motionless because its weight is compensated by the buoyant force we introduce in Chapter 11. Thus, the drag force is the only unbalanced force acting on the jellyfish when in motion.

**P–4.15.** An object of mass $m = 20$ kg is initially at rest on a horizontal surface. It requires a horizontal force $F = 75$ N to set it in motion. However, once in motion, only a horizontal force of 60 N is required to keep it moving with a constant speed. Find the coefficients of static and kinetic friction in this case.

**P–4.16.** Assume that $m_1 = 10$ kg and $m_2 = 4.0$ kg in Fig. 4.24. The coefficient of static friction between the object on the table and the table surface is 0.5 while the coefficient of kinetic friction is 0.3. The system is set in motion with the object of mass $m_2$ moving downward. What is the acceleration of the object of mass $m_1$?

**P–4.17.** In Fig. 4.25, the coefficient of static friction is 0.3 between an object of mass $m = 3.0$ kg and a surface, which is inclined by $\theta = 35°$ with the horizontal. What is the minimum magnitude of force **F** that must be applied to the object perpendicular to the inclined surface to prevent the object from sliding downward?

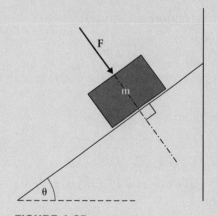

**FIGURE 4.25**

# SUMMARY

## DEFINITIONS

- Linear momentum of a single particle (point-like object) in vector notation:

$$\mathbf{p} = m \cdot \mathbf{v}$$

- Linear momentum of a single particle in component form:

  x-direction:  $p_x = m \cdot v_x$

  y-direction:  $p_y = m \cdot v_y$

  z-direction:  $p_z = m \cdot v_z$

- The position of the centre of mass (index c.m.) of a system of $n$ objects with total mass $M$:

$$\mathbf{r}_{\text{c.m.}} = \frac{1}{M}\sum_{i=1}^{n} m_i \cdot \mathbf{r}_i$$

- Centre of mass of $n$ objects of total mass $M$ in component form:

$$x_{\text{c.m.}} = \frac{1}{M}\sum_{i=1}^{n} m_i \cdot x_i$$

$$y_{\text{c.m.}} = \frac{1}{M}\sum_{i=1}^{n} m_i \cdot y_i$$

$$z_{\text{c.m.}} = \frac{1}{M}\sum_{i=1}^{n} m_i \cdot z_i$$

- A rigid object is an extended object for which (i) the distance between any two parts of the object is fixed, and (ii) the angle between the lines connecting any three parts of the object is fixed.

- Linear momentum of an extended rigid object of mass $M$:

$$M \cdot \mathbf{v}_{\text{c.m.}} = \sum_i m_i \cdot \mathbf{v}_i = \sum_i \mathbf{p}_i = \mathbf{P}_{\text{total}}$$

- Specific types of friction:
  - Drag force:

$$F_{\text{drag}} = \frac{D}{2}\rho \cdot A \cdot v^2_{\text{system}}$$

  with $\rho$ the density of the medium, $A$ the cross-section of the object, $v$ the speed of the object, and $D$ the drag coefficient.

  - Maximum static friction at a motionless solid–solid interface:

$$\mathscr{F}_{\text{s,max}} = \mu_s \cdot N$$

  with $N$ the normal force and $\mu_s$ the coefficient of static friction.

  - Kinetic friction at a sliding solid–solid interface:

$$\mathscr{F}_k = \mu_k \cdot N$$

  with $N$ the normal force and $\mu_k$ the coefficient of kinetic friction.

## UNITS

- Linear momentum $\mathbf{p}$: $\text{kg} \cdot \text{m/s}$

## LAWS

- Conservation of linear momentum for isolated multi-object system ($\mathbf{F}_{\text{net}} = 0$):

$$\mathbf{P} = \sum_i \mathbf{p}_i = \text{const}$$

- Component form of linear momentum conservation in isolated system:

$$x\text{-direction:}\quad \sum p_{ix} = \sum p_{fx}$$

$$y\text{-direction:}\quad \sum p_{iy} = \sum p_{fy}$$

$$z\text{-direction:}\quad \sum p_{iz} = \sum p_{fz}$$

- Linear momentum—net force relation for single object (Newton's second law for non-isolated system):

$$\mathbf{F}_{\text{net}} = m \cdot \mathbf{a} = m\frac{\Delta\mathbf{v}}{\Delta t} = \frac{\Delta(m \cdot \mathbf{v})}{\Delta t} = \frac{\Delta\mathbf{p}}{\Delta t}$$

- Linear momentum—net force relation for an extended rigid object (Newton's second law for an object with external forces):

$$M\frac{\Delta\mathbf{v}_{\text{c.m.}}}{\Delta t} = M \cdot \mathbf{a}_{\text{c.m.}} = \frac{\Delta\mathbf{P}_{\text{total}}}{\Delta t} = \mathbf{F}_{\text{net}}$$

- Momentum disc theory of animal flight:

$$\frac{\Delta p}{\Delta t} = \rho \cdot A \cdot v^2$$

with $A$ the area of the stroke plane, $\rho$ the density of the medium, $v$ the speed of the medium leaving the stroke plane, $\Delta p/\Delta t$ the rate of change of linear momentum acting on the animal.

# CHAPTER 5

# KINESIOLOGY
## The Action of Forces at Joints

When the size and the shape of objects are no longer negligible, more complex patterns of motion emerge. We use the **rigid object model** to address these. It is a simplifying model because it excludes vibrations and deformations, but it allows us to focus on rotations. Using the rotation of the lower arm about the elbow as a typical example, motion in a two-dimensional plane results when the rotation occurs about a fixed axis directed perpendicular to the plane of action. The axis of rotation intersects this plane at the fulcrum.

We distinguish two types of forces acting on a rigid object with a fixed axis: forces acting along a line through the fulcrum do not lead to a rotation, but forces acting in other directions cause increasingly stronger rotations as the magnitude of the force and/or the perpendicular distance from the axis of rotation increases. These variables define the torque as a measure of the strength of a rotation.

The concept of mechanical equilibrium, when applied to a rigid object, extends Newton's first law that the net force on the object must equal zero such that the sum of torques due to all forces acting on the object must also equal zero. If the latter condition is not met, the object begins to spin faster and faster. Applying the mechanical equilibrium for rigid objects to various joints in the human body reveals the large magnitude of forces acting in tendons during regular use.

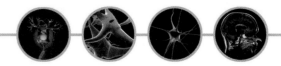

In the previous chapters we discussed the mechanics of objects when these could be modelled by a point in space. For this to be a valid assumption, the spatial extensions of the object have to be negligible. When studying the locomotive system of vertebrates, this assumption is not applicable. This not only is due to the relative size of bones compared to the body, but also has its origin in the rotational, rather than translational, mobility at joints. Since it makes no sense to define rotations for zero-dimensional points, motion at joints requires additional considerations.

In this chapter we study the various types of joints. They all share a fundamental design, illustrated in Fig. 5.1: two skeletal muscles are attached to the bones adjacent to the joint, one for clockwise and one for counter-clockwise rotation. Since the tendons connecting these muscles to the bones are usually attached close to the joint, large forces are needed to achieve locomotion. We first establish this observation by using geometrical considerations and then confirm the occurrence of large forces by applying the mechanical equilibrium condition to specific cases. These large forces are of interest in kinesiology and in medicine: joints have a relatively high likelihood of failure during their lifetime, not only as

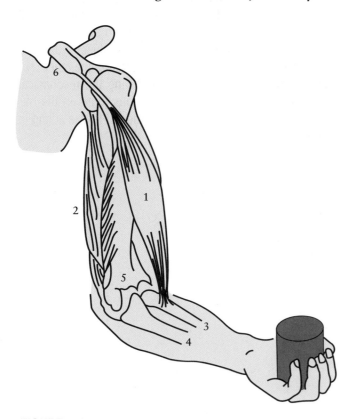

**FIGURE 5.1**

Arrangement of the biceps muscle (1) and the triceps muscle (2) in the upper arm. The biceps is connected to the scapula (6) and the radius (3), which runs parallel to the ulna (4) in the lower arm. The muscle actions of the biceps and triceps rotate the lower arm relative to the humerus (5) at the elbow.

a result of injury (tendon and ligament rupture) but also as a result of degeneration (arthrosis).

# Geometry of the Rotation at Joints
## Fundamental Types of Movable Joints

We distinguish five types of movable joints based on their possible directions of rotation. Each rotation occurs about a straight line that we call the **axis of rotation** (e.g., the straight line from geographic North pole to geographic South pole defines the axis of rotation of Earth).

The five types of movable joints are sketched schematically in Fig. 5.2: (A) the **spheroid** or **ball-and-socket joint** has three orthogonal axes of rotation. Note that only the bone farthest from the trunk rotates. (B) The **ellipsoid joint** has two orthogonal axes of rotation. The third rotation along the bone's axis is no longer possible due to the elliptical fit between the adjacent bones. (C) The **saddle joint** has two orthogonal axes of rotation. The mobility of the two adjacent bones defines the difference between the ellipsoid and saddle joints. Rotation of an ellipsoid joint involves only the bone farthest from the trunk, while both adjacent bones are responsible for one rotation each in a saddle joint. (D) The **hinge joint** has one axis of rotation perpendicular to both bones. (E) The **pivot joint** has one axis of rotation parallel to both bones.

Together with the gliding joint, which does not allow for the rotation of bones, these five movable joints all contain a lubricant called **synovial fluid** that prevents wear and tear, and are therefore collectively known as **synovial joints**. We illustrate each with a few examples.

### SPHEROID JOINT

The spheroid joint has the most rotational degrees of freedom of the five mobile joints, permitting the greatest mobility. For this reason it is most frequently found where limbs are connected to the trunk of an animal. The shoulder and hip joints shown in Fig. 5.3 are examples in the human body.

Due to their versatility, spheroid joints developed early in animal evolution, with each sea urchin's spine containing a ball-and-socket joint to provide for locomotion. The shoulder joint of primates in particular is extremely versatile; we can spin the arm through essentially all points of a hemisphere. Shoulder joints of other vertebrates, such as cats, do not have the same versatility; a similar mobility is reached only by the

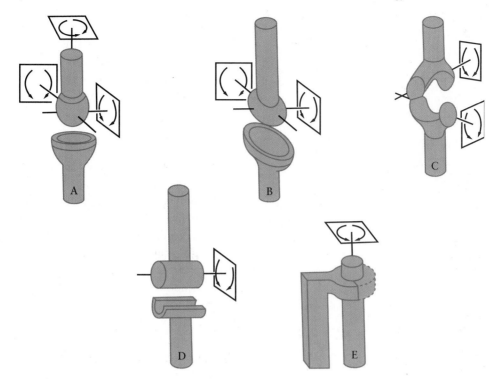

**FIGURE 5.2**

The five fundamental types of movable joints: (A) the spheroid or ball-and-socket joint with three orthogonal axes of rotation, (B) the ellipsoid joint with two orthogonal axes of rotation perpendicular to the adjacent bones, (C) the saddle joint with two axes of rotation, one for each of the two bones adjacent to the joint, (D) the hinge or ginglymoid joint with one axis of rotation, and (E) the pivot joint with one axis of rotation pointing along the axis of the adjacent bones. The possible directions of rotation are indicated in each case.

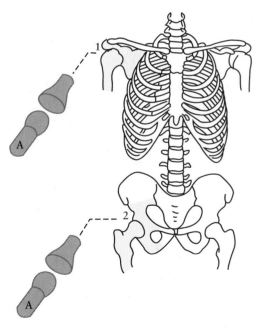

**FIGURE 5.3**

Overview of the human trunk skeleton with shaded highlighting of the shoulder joint (1) and the hip joint (2). The icons illustrate the orientation of the two ball-and-socket joints.

boneless trunk of an elephant, the boneless arms of an octopus, or the multi-boned neck of an ostrich.

The shoulder and hip joints are studied further in this chapter, with the shoulder joint used to illustrate the concept of rotation of a rigid object and the hip joint used in Example 5.5 to demonstrate the need for a well-developed mutual adaptation of two adjacent bones to guarantee the safe operation of a joint.

## ELLIPSOID JOINT

The next most mobile joints are the ellipsoid joints and the saddle joints. Of these the ellipsoid joint is much more common because it provides greater mobility for the bone farthest from the trunk. An example is the wrist joint in Fig. 5.4. This joint lies between the two arm bones, ulna and radius, on one side and the wrist bones on the other side. You can tilt your hand left/right and back/forth, but because the wrist is an ellipsoid joint you cannot rotate your hand about the axis defined by your lower arm.

## SADDLE JOINT

The carpometacarpal joint of the thumb is an example of a saddle joint. It is illustrated in Fig. 5.5. Note that the corresponding joints for the other fingers are fused, preventing any rotation. To illustrate the uniqueness of the saddle motion, note first that your thumb has two directions of rotation, toward/away from the index finger and left/right in front of the open palm. The second motion is significantly reduced when you hold the great multangular bone

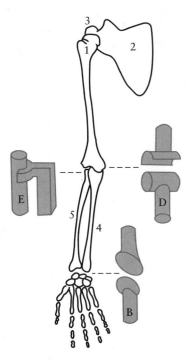

**FIGURE 5.4**

Anatomic overview of the human arm. Shown are the humerus (1), which connects to the scapula (2) and the collarbone (3) at the shoulder joint. The ulna (4) and radius (5) connect to the elbow. Note that the radius is located on the same side as the thumb. The arm displays three different types of joints, the elbow is a hinge joint, and the wrist is an ellipsoid joint. Further, a pivot joint is located between ulna and radius just below the elbow.

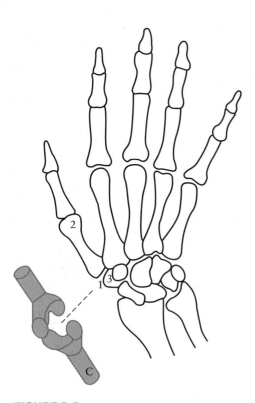

**FIGURE 5.5**

The carpometacarpal joint of the thumb (1) between the first metacarpal (2) and the trapezium (3). The icon symbolizes a saddle joint.

(labelled (3) in Fig. 5.5) with your other hand. This shows that the mobility of this joint is due to rotation of both adjacent bones. Compare this with the ellipsoid joint: neither of the two rotations of the hand at the wrist is hindered by holding your lower arm.

## HINGE JOINT

Due to the high degree of mobility of the shoulder and hip joints, limb joints farther away from the trunk maintain a high flexibility with less mobile types of joints that are in turn more sturdy. The compromise between versatility and stability is evident in the hinge joint, making it the most frequently occurring joint in vertebrate skeletons. Examples in the human body include the elbow, the knee, and the upper ankle.

The knee in Fig. 5.6 illustrates the complexity of an actual joint. Several cartilage layers and ligaments protect the joint against wear and tear due to the large forces frequently acting on it. The knee connects the femur of the upper leg to both the tibia and the fibula in the lower leg. The facing surfaces of the

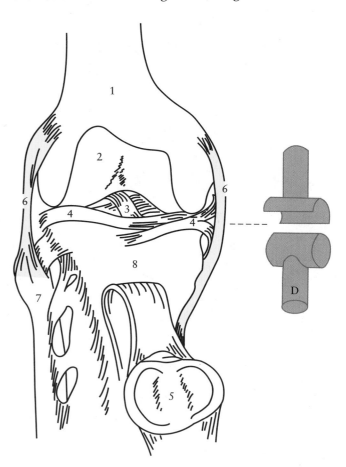

**FIGURE 5.6**

The knee is a hinge joint as indicated by the icon. Its complexity stems from the versatility and robustness required by a bipedal posture. The components shown include: (1) the femur, (2) a cartilage layer, (3) the cruciate ligaments, (4) the meniscus, (5) the patella, (6) the collateral ligaments, (7) the fibula, and (8) the tibia.

bones are covered by a cartilage layer. In arthrosis, this layer is worn down all the way to the bone. The meniscus that lies behind various ligaments acts as a shock absorber to ensure the even distribution of forces. Injury to the meniscus often accelerates the deterioration of the joint. Further ligaments, such as the cruciate ligaments and the collateral ligaments, help to stabilize the knee. Rupture or injury of these ligaments loosens the joint, accelerating the wear and tear during regular use. The kneecap (shown in the figure folded down) improves the force transfer from the quadriceps femoris muscle to the lower leg. It protects the tendon of the quadriceps femoris muscle against wear and tear due to rubbing while bending the knee (this was highlighted in P–3.13).

The complexity of the knee is the result of several design compromises that adapted the joint for an upright posture. The human knee has to endure forces up to ten times the weight of the person while running. The required stability led to a more limited ability to rotate compared to the elbow. The knees of quadrupeds do not have to meet the same

specification; we would walk like ducks without this unique adjustment.

The elbow is highlighted in Fig. 5.4 for the stretched arm and in Fig. 5.1 for the raised lower arm. We use the elbow below to discuss the implications of having the biceps and triceps muscles attached close to the joint. The upper ankle joint is used in Example 5.3 to study the action of the Achilles tendon. In that example we will highlight how large the forces get in our body during normal use of our locomotive system.

## PIVOT JOINT

The pivot joint is a rare joint type in nature. It requires two co-axial bones, as indicated in Fig. 5.2. Such a connection occurs between the first and second cervical vertebrae, highlighted in the lateral overview of the head shown in Fig. 5.7. The second cervical vertebra, which is the lower bone in the close-up of Fig. 5.7, is called *axis* and reaches through the centre hole in the doughnut-shaped first

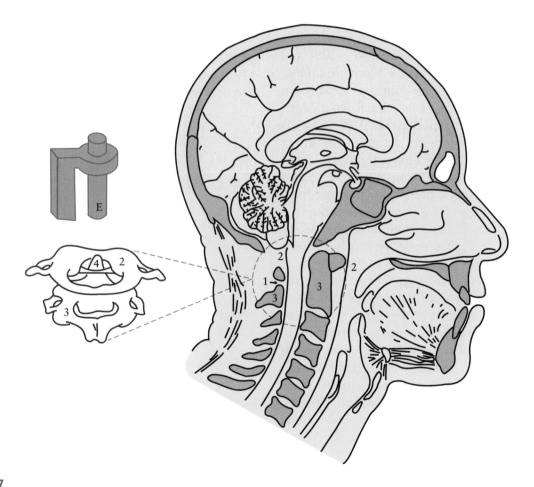

**FIGURE 5.7**

Lateral overview of the head. The first cervical vertebra (*atlas*, 2) and the second cervical vertebra (*axis*, 3) form a pivot joint (1). This joint allows the head to turn sideways. The arrangement of *atlas* and *axis* is highlighted at the left below the icon for a pivot joint. This inset illustrates how the pivot joint is realized: the pin-head of *axis* (4) reaches between *atlas* and the horizontal ligament of *atlas*.

cervical vertebra, called *atlas*. Note that in turn the *atlas/axis* joint of the predatory dinosaurs was a ball-and-socket joint.

Another example of a pivot joint is identified in Fig. 5.4 and allows for the limited rotation of the lower arm. This rotation does not occur directly in the elbow, but is due to the radius rotating about its axis in a groove of the ulna in the lower arm.

## Muscle Arrangement at the Elbow and Its Rotation

Two skeletal muscles are needed for each rotation of a joint; these are called antagonistic muscles. The action of each of the two muscles counter-balances that of the other; i.e., one is stretched because the other contracts. In Fig. 5.1 this is shown for the biceps and triceps muscles, which operate the elbow. Note that neither of the two muscles is attached to the joint itself. The biceps is attached to the radius a short distance away from the joint. This way, contracting the biceps pulls the lower arm up. The triceps in turn connects to the ulna behind the elbow and pulls the lower arm down when contracting.

We noted in Chapter 3 that each sarcomere unit in a muscle cell can vary in length between $-20\%$ and $+35\%$ of the average length of 2.1 $\mu$m. Assuming that all sarcomeres in a muscle contract or extend in a synchronous fashion, the same relative length variation limits apply to the entire muscle. This finding is important for the evolutionary design of the upper arm in Fig. 5.1. The elbow is a hinge joint that works like the hinges on a door. When you try to open a door near the hinges, you need a much larger force than far from the hinges. This is why the doorknob is found at a maximum distance from the hinges. Comparing the lower arm to the door, we conclude that a muscle attached to the radius close to the wrist (i.e., far from the elbow) would significantly reduce the amount of force required to lift the lower arm. Why, then, is the biceps attached to the radius so close to the elbow? The reason is illustrated qualitatively in Fig. 5.8, in which the humerus in the upper arm is shown as a stationary, vertical line and the radius in the lower arm is illustrated in three positions: when horizontal, tilted up by 45°, and tilted down by 45°. In each case, the "actual biceps" (short-dashed line) and the "alternative biceps attached to the wrist" (long-dashed line) are shown. Although a muscle attached to the wrist would require less force, it would in turn have to vary in length much more. With the physiological limitation of $-20\%$ and $+35\%$ of the average length, this would severely reduce the angular range of motion for the lower arm.

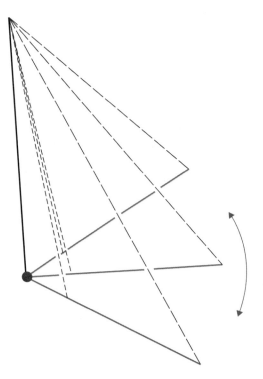

## FIGURE 5.8

A comparison of the required length of the biceps muscle and its tendons for an actual human arm with the muscle attached close to the elbow (short dashed line) and a hypothetical biceps attached close to the wrist (long dashed line). The upper arm is shown as a vertical solid line. Three positions of the lower arm are sketched (solid lines): horizontal, and rotated 45° either upward or downward.

## ● EXAMPLE 5.1

Fig. 5.9 shows a simplified sketch of the biceps muscle and bone arrangement in the human arm (compare to Fig. 5.1). Assuming that the three lengths in the figure are given as $l_1 = 38$ cm, $l_2 = 3.5$ cm, and $l_3 = 30$ cm, what is the relative contraction (in %) of the biceps and its tendons when the lower arm (a) is raised to $\psi = 45°$ above the horizontal, and (b) is lowered to $\phi = 45°$ below the horizontal? (c) If the biceps were instead connected to the end of the radius as shown in Fig. 5.8 (at distance $l_3$ from the elbow), to what angle could the person lift the lower arm when the biceps muscle contracts 20% (maximum contraction)?

*Solution:* In this solution, we again apply vector concepts. These are summarized in the Math Review "Vectors and Basic Vector Algebra" at the end of Chapter 2. Fig. 5.10 illustrates the first two parts of the problem. We call the horizontal direction the $x$-axis and the vertical direction the $y$-axis. Starting with the lower arm perpendicular to the upper arm (left sketch), we find with the

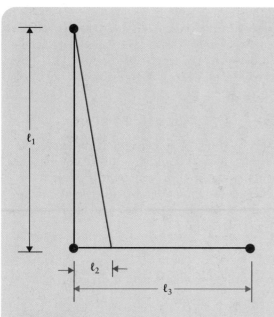

**FIGURE 5.9**

A simplified sketch of the arrangement between the biceps (red) and the upper and lower arm bones (blue and green, respectively). The sketch illustrates $l_1$, the length of the upper arm from shoulder to elbow; $l_2$, the length from the elbow to the attachment of the tendon of the biceps muscle; and $l_3$, the length of the lower arm from elbow to wrist.

Pythagorean theorem that the length of the biceps muscle and its tendons is:

$$|\mathbf{l}_m| = \sqrt{l_1^2 + l_2^2}$$
$$= \sqrt{(38\text{ cm})^2 + (3.5\text{ cm})^2}$$
$$= 38.2\text{ cm} \qquad [1]$$

This length is needed to solve the first two parts of the problem because the example asks for relative changes.

*Solution to part (a):* We assume that the lower arm is raised to an angle of $\psi = 45°$ with the horizontal as shown in Fig. 5.10(a). This leads to a shortening of the length of the biceps muscle. We use vector addition to quantify this effect. The vector describing the length and the orientation of the biceps muscle, $\mathbf{l}_m$, equals the sum of the vector of the stationary upper arm, $\mathbf{l}_1$, and the vector from the joint to the point of the lower arm at which the biceps muscle is attached, $\mathbf{l}_2$:

$$\mathbf{l}_m = \mathbf{l}_1 + \mathbf{l}_2 \qquad [2]$$

which is given in component form as:

$$\begin{aligned} x\text{-direction:} \quad l_{m,x} &= l_2 \cdot \cos\psi \\ y\text{-direction:} \quad l_{m,y} &= -l_1 + l_2 \cdot \sin\psi \end{aligned} \qquad [3]$$

Using the Pythagorean theorem, we calculate the length of the vector in Eq. [2] from its components in Eq. [3]:

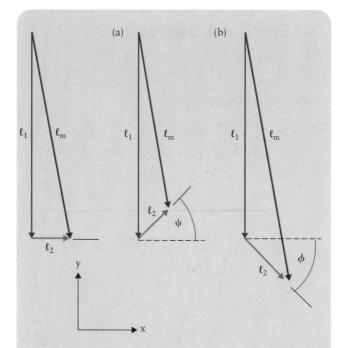

**FIGURE 5.10**

Three geometrical sketches showing the mathematical vector relations for the arrangement in Fig. 5.9: the sum of the vectors representing the upper arm $\mathbf{l}_1$, and the lower arm between the elbow and the attachment point of the biceps $\mathbf{l}_2$, equals the vector representing the biceps muscle with its tendons $\mathbf{l}_m$. The sketch at the left shows the lower arm at 90° with the upper arm, (a) the lower arm lifted by 45°, and (b) the lower arm lowered by 45°.

$$|\mathbf{l}_m| = \sqrt{l_2^2 \cos^2\psi + (l_2 \sin\psi - l_1)^2}$$
$$= \sqrt{(3.5\text{ cm})^2 \cos^2 45° + ((3.5\text{ cm})\sin 45° - (38\text{ cm}))^2} \qquad [4]$$

which yields:

$$l_m = 35.6\text{ cm} \qquad [5]$$

The result in Eq. [5] means that the length of the muscle and its tendons has changed from 38.2 cm to 35.6 cm.

This does not answer the question! In the question, the relative contraction, in percent (%), is sought. To get that number, an additional step of calculation is needed:

$$\frac{l_{m,\text{final}} - l_{m,\text{initial}}}{l_{m,\text{initial}}} = \frac{\Delta l}{l_{m,\text{initial}}}$$
$$= \frac{(38.2\text{ cm}) - (35.6\text{ cm})}{38.2\text{ cm}}$$
$$= 0.068 \qquad [6]$$

The contraction is 6.8%, well within the accessible range for the biceps muscle.

*Solution to part (b):* Studying Fig. 5.10(b), you notice that the muscle is stretched rather than

## ● EXAMPLE 5.1 (*continued*)

contracted as in part (a). The resulting length change is expected to be similar, but not the same. First we determine the length of the biceps and its tendons in Fig. 5.10(b):

$$l_m = l_1 + l_2 \qquad [7]$$

We write Eq. [7] in component form:

$$x\text{-direction:} \quad l_{m,x} = l_2 \cdot \cos \phi \qquad [8]$$
$$y\text{-direction:} \quad l_{m,y} = -l_1 - l_2 \cdot \sin \phi$$

The length of this vector is:

$$|l_m| = \sqrt{l_2^2 \cos^2 \phi + (-l_2 \sin \phi - l_1)^2}$$
$$= \sqrt{(3.5\,\text{cm})^2 \cos^2 45° + (-(3.5\,\text{cm})\sin 45° - (38\,\text{cm}))^2} \qquad [9]$$

which yields:

$$l_m = 40.6 \text{ cm} \qquad [10]$$

The length increased from 38.2 cm to 40.6 cm, and the relative change is:

$$\frac{\Delta l}{l_{m,\text{initial}}} = \frac{(40.6\,\text{cm}) - (38.2\,\text{cm})}{38.2\,\text{cm}}$$
$$= 0.063 \qquad [11]$$

The muscle has been stretched by 6.3%.

*Solution to part (c):* This part of the question is different, as the relative contraction is given but not the angle. This complicates the algebraic calculations somewhat and requires a new sketch to guide our approach. The sketch for this part is shown in Fig. 5.11, where we see in Fig. 5.11(a) the now-modified arm with the lower arm perpendicular to the upper arm, and in Fig. 5.11(b)

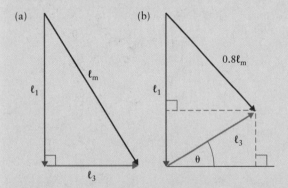

(a)    (b)

$0.8\ell_m$

$\ell_m$

$\ell_1$    $\ell_1$

$\ell_3$

$\theta$

$\ell_3$

**FIGURE 5.11**

This sketch is an analogous sketch to Fig. 5.10 when a hypothetical biceps muscle is attached to the wrist. (a) The arm with a 90° angle at the elbow, and (b) the geometrical features of the hypothetical arm raised to the point where the biceps muscle has shortened to 80%, the minimum length possible for a fully contracted muscle.

the arm when the muscle has shortened by 20%, i.e., when it is only 80% of its original length.

The new average length of the muscle is obtained from Fig. 5.11(a) by applying the Pythagorean theorem:

$$l_m = \sqrt{l_1^2 + l_3^2} = 48.4 \text{ cm} \qquad [12]$$

Eighty percent of the length $l_m$ is expressed mathematically as $0.8 \cdot l_m$. If we define the angle $\theta$ as the maximum angle to which the lower arm can be raised, as shown in Fig. 5.11(b), we obtain an equation for $0.8 \cdot l_m$ using the same approach as in parts (a) and (b):

$$0.8 \cdot l_m = l_1 + l_3 \qquad [13]$$

which is written in component form as:

$$x\text{-direction:} \quad 0.8 \cdot l_{m,x} = l_3 \cdot \cos \theta \qquad [14]$$
$$y\text{-direction:} \quad 0.8 \cdot l_{m,y} = -l_1 + l_3 \cdot \sin \theta$$

Eq. [14] yields the magnitude of the vector $0.8 \cdot l_m$ by using the Pythagorean theorem:

$$0.8 \cdot l_m = \sqrt{(0.8 \cdot l_m)_x^2 + (0.8 \cdot l_m)_y^2}$$
$$= \sqrt{l_3^2 \cdot \cos^2 \theta + (l_3 \cdot \sin \theta - l_1)^2} \qquad [15]$$

Eq. [15] is solved by first squaring both sides of the formula:

$$(0.8 \cdot l_m)^2 = l_3^2 \cdot \cos^2 \theta + l_3^2 \cdot \sin^2 \theta$$
$$- 2 \cdot l_1 \cdot l_3 \cdot \sin \theta + l_1^2 \qquad [16]$$

Eq. [16] is then simplified using the trigonometric identity $\sin^2 \theta + \cos^2 \theta = 1$ to combine the first two terms on the right-hand side:

$$0.64 \cdot l_m^2 - l_3^2 - l_1^2 = -2 \cdot l_1 \cdot l_3 \cdot \sin \theta \qquad [17]$$

Eq. [17] is finally solved for $\sin \theta$:

$$\sin \theta = \frac{(1 - 0.64)(l_1^2 + l_3^2)}{2 \cdot l_1 \cdot l_3} = 0.37 \qquad [18]$$

This yields $\theta = 21.7°$. This angle is too small for proper use of the lower arm, which you can confirm by bending your arm by just 22° in front of a mirror.

# Mechanical Properties of an Extended Rigid Object

Forces were identified as the cause for motion in Chapter 3. When acting on a point-like object, the only type of motion possible is called *translational motion,* which is a motion along a straight line.

To include rotations for a bone, two extensions of the approach taken so far are needed: firstly, we note that modelling the bone as a point-like object is no longer sufficient because the position of the joint and the position at which the various muscles act on the bone do not coincide, as illustrated in Fig. 5.1. To be able to take this into account we continue to use the rigid object model we introduced in the previous chapter. Secondly, for rotations we have to distinguish between the effect of forces that act along a line through the joint and the effect of those that act under an angle to that line. We introduce the concept of torque to make that distinction. With these two concepts introduced we revisit Newton's first law and extend it such that it allows for the definition of a mechanical equilibrium of a rigid object.

## Rigid Object as a Model for a Rotating System

We introduced the **rigid object** in Chapter 4 as an extended object for which

- the distance between any two parts of the object is fixed, and

- the angle between the lines connecting any three parts of the object is fixed.

We choose our hand as an example. It is connected to the arm at the wrist, which is a hinge joint with a single axis of rotation (see Fig. 5.2, case D). Modelling the hand as a point would be an oversimplification because it would not allow us to quantify its motions. The rigid object model in turn is suitable for the hand as long as it doesn't change its shape during the processes we study, i.e., when the forces that act on the hand are not too large. The rigid object model is still restrictive, as real bones can do several things a rigid object cannot do: bones can bend slightly under force or can break. The discussion of such cases is postponed to Chapter 16, when we introduce the *elastic object* as a new model for an extended object.

Fig. 5.12 shows a schematic sketch of (a) the top view and (b) a side view of the hand. The $z$-axis is chosen along the axis of rotation, which is a horizontal line through the joint in Fig. 5.12(a) and a line perpendicular to the plane of the paper in Fig. 5.12(b). The axis is perpendicular to the plane of action of the rigid object, which we choose as the $xy$-plane. This plane is seen from the side (dashed) in Fig. 5.12(a) and coincides with the plane of the paper in Fig. 5.12(b). The point at which the axis of rotation intersects with the plane of action is defined as the **fulcrum**. All figures in this chapter display physical situations like that in Fig. 5.12(b); i.e., the

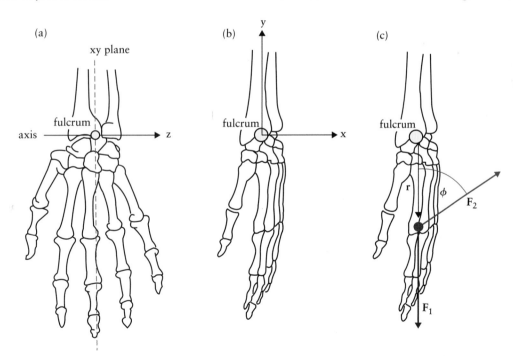

**FIGURE 5.12**

(a) Top view of the hand with wrist. We can treat the hand as an extended rigid object with the axis of rotation (chosen along the $z$-axis) toward the right. The dashed line indicates the plane perpendicular to the axis ($xy$-plane), in which the physical action takes place, i.e., the possible motion of the hand. The intersection of the axis with the $xy$-plane defines the fulcrum (yellow circle). (b) Side view of the hand. In this view, the plane of action lies in the plane of the paper. Consequently, the only point on the axis of rotation shown is the fulcrum. (c) Two forces act on the hand at the point of attack (blue circle) a distance $r$ from the fulcrum. Note that they lead to different types of motion: $\mathbf{F}_2$ causes a rotation because it does not act in the direction of the fulcrum. $\mathbf{F}_1$ leads to a linear acceleration.

fulcrum is the only point along the axis of rotation in the plane of the paper. We limit the discussion further to axes of rotation that are fixed in space, i.e., don't change their position or orientation with time. Note that this assumption may oversimplify the anatomy of some joints, as discussed in Concept Question 5.1.

---

### Concept Question 5.1

Propose a modification to the hinge joint shown in Fig. 5.2 (case D) that violates the assumption that the axis of rotation is fixed in space.

ANSWER: Fig. 5.13 shows such a modification. The radius of the head of a bone is significantly smaller than the socket of the adjacent bone. In this case, the axis is not fixed but moves within the larger socket. Such cases are not considered further.

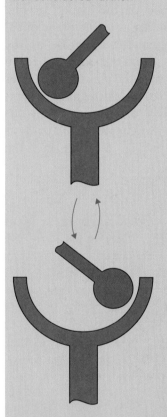

**FIGURE 5.13**
The motion of a joint is not adequately described with a fixed axis if the radius of the socket exceeds the radius of the head of the adjacent bone significantly.

Note that the simpler suggestion of a joint that moves as the result of the motion of the person is not correct. Note that all the mechanical problems for joints in this textbook are addressed with a coordinate system that is attached to the joint (fulcrum). In these coordinate systems an additional motion of the entire body is without effect.

## Torque

Starting with a fixed axis of rotation, we now study forces that act on the rigid object in Fig. 5.12(c). We investigate two types of forces in a self-experiment: $F_1$ is a force that acts on the hand along a line through the fulcrum, while $F_2$ acts in another direction. Exert $F_1$ on your own hand; i.e., try to pull your fingers straight away from the wrist. If you succeed in setting your hand in motion it will be an acceleration along a straight line, not a rotation. This type of motion has already been discussed in Chapter 3 and need not be considered further.

Now, exert $F_2$ on your hand; i.e., push your fingers in the direction shown in Fig. 5.12(c). A rotation results about the fixed axis in the wrist. The strength of the rotation varies with both the magnitude of $F_2$ and the distance $|r|$ between the fulcrum and the point at which you push your hand. It also depends on the angle $\phi$ between the directions of $r$ and $F_2$. Vary one quantity after the other and feel the strength of the rotation: you note the greatest effect when the magnitude of the force and the distance from the fulcrum are large and their angle is 90°. We introduce a new physical quantity, called the torque $\tau$, which takes these factors into account:

$$\tau = r \cdot F \cdot \sin \phi \qquad [19]$$

The unit of torque is $N \cdot m = kg \cdot m^2/s^2$.

*The magnitude of torque is a measure of the strength of a rotation and is the product of the magnitude of the force and the perpendicular distance from its line of action to the fulcrum.*

Torque is a vector because the resulting motion occurs in a well-defined plane. Thus, the complete definition of torque includes Eq. [19] as its magnitude. The sine term in Eq. [19] serves as a hint for establishing the direction of torque when inspecting the Math Review on "Vector Multiplication" at the end of this chapter: we note that the magnitude of a vector resulting from a **vector product** carries a sine term of the angle between the two vectors used to calculate it. Applying the vector product is also suggested by identifying the mathematical character of the quantities on the right-hand side of Eq. [19]: both the position and force are vectors. Only one product of two vectors that results in a vector is defined: the *dot product* is the product of two vectors yielding a scalar, and the *vector product* is the product of two vectors yielding a vector. Thus, because our underlying assumption is correct that torque, force, and position are described by vectors, their relation is given as:

$$\boldsymbol{\tau} = \mathbf{r} \times \mathbf{F} \qquad [20]$$

We use vector products only to a limited extent in this textbook, e.g., in Concept Question 5.2. Thus, the component form of Eq. [20] is not discussed at this point (you will find it in the Math Review "Vector Multiplication" at the end of this chapter).

Eq. [20] adds a directional property to torque: it is directed perpendicular to the plane of the position vector and the force; i.e., it points along the direction of the axis of rotation. This becomes particularly evident as we introduce a choice consistently made in this textbook: the plane defined by the position vector and the force vector is defined as the $xy$-plane; i.e., $\mathbf{r} = (x, y, 0)$ and $\mathbf{F} = (F_x, F_y, 0)$. Physically, this means that the rotational motion of the point $\mathbf{r}$ at which the force $\mathbf{F}$ acts lies always in the $xy$-plane. In this case, the torque vector is $\boldsymbol{\tau} = (0, 0, \tau_z)$; i.e., it points along the $z$-axis. In Fig. 5.14, we illustrate Eq. [20] for the specific case in which the position vector points in the $x$-direction and the force points in the $y$-direction. This figure establishes the **right-hand rule**, which allows us to determine the direction of the third vector in Eq. [20]: stretch your thumb, index finger, and middle finger of the right hand such that they form pair-wise right angles with each other. The thumb represents the first vector of the vector product in Eq. [20], $\mathbf{r}$; the index finger points in the direction of the second vector, $\mathbf{F}$. The middle finger then represents the direction of the resulting vector in Eq. [20], $\boldsymbol{\tau}$. The shaded area in the figure represents the product in Eq. [19]; i.e., this area is equal to the magnitude $|\boldsymbol{\tau}|$.

## Concept Question 5.2

**(a) Someone writes Eq. [20] with the vectors r and F exchanged. What consequences does this error have? (b) Someone writes Eq. [20] but uses the left hand to identify the direction of $\tau$. What consequences does this error have?**

ANSWER TO PART (a): Using the right-hand rule with the wrong order of vectors yields a direction of the torque vector that is opposed to the correct direction. This means that the person concludes that the rotation occurs in the opposite direction than what is correct (clockwise versus counter-clockwise).

ANSWER TO PART (b): If the person works consistently with a left-hand rule, calculated results will be consistent with physical reality but the generally agreed upon conventions for torque have not been followed. When that person starts to communicate with others, hopeless confusion will result. Conventions are introduced in the scientific discussion only when needed to prevent such confusion; therefore, all conventions have to be followed consistently.

The definition of torque allows us also to emphasize once more why we focus in the current chapter on problems with a fixed axis of rotation: it allows us to familiarize ourselves with the torque concept while keeping the extent of mathematical complexity to a minimum. Using a fixed axis, the directional dependence of the torque can be reduced to the sign of its $z$-component, $\tau_z = +|\boldsymbol{\tau}|$ or $\tau_z = -|\boldsymbol{\tau}|$. This means that we can proceed with Eq. [19] to obtain quantitative results. The sign convention follows from Eq. [20]:

*If a force causes a counter-clockwise rotation, the torque $\tau$ is a positive term, $\tau > 0$. If a force causes a clockwise rotation, the torque is a negative term, $\tau < 0$.*

Fig. 5.15 summarizes the sign conventions for a bar with the fulcrum at its centre. If either $\mathbf{F}_1$ or $\mathbf{F}_3$ acts on the bar, a counter-clockwise rotation about the fulcrum occurs. The corresponding torque terms, $\tau_1$ and $\tau_3$, are therefore positive as indicated by a $+$ sign in a circle in the figure. If, in turn, either $\mathbf{F}_2$ or $\mathbf{F}_4$ acts on the bar, the resulting rotation is clockwise with negative torque terms $\tau_2$ and $\tau_4$ (indicated by $-$ signs in a circle in Fig. 5.15).

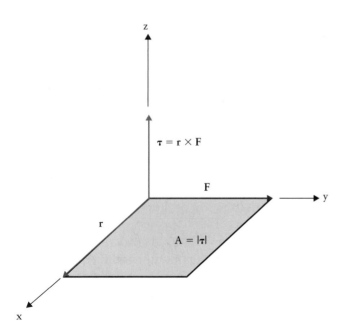

**FIGURE 5.14**

The torque vector $\boldsymbol{\tau}$ is orthogonal to the plane defined by the force $\mathbf{F}$ and the vector $\mathbf{r}$ that points from the fulcrum to the position on the rigid object at which $\mathbf{F}$ acts. The mathematical area defined by the vectors $\mathbf{F}$ and $\mathbf{r}$ equals the magnitude of the torque. The directions of the three vectors are related by the right-hand rule.

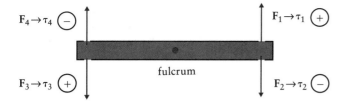

**FIGURE 5.15**

Conceptual sketch for the sign convention of the torque. Shown is a bar with the fulcrum at its centre. Any force acting on the bar and yielding a rotation can be thought of as one of the four forces shown in the sketch. For each force the resulting torque is labelled with a sign symbol in a circle that represents the sign of the respective torque contribution.

**Concept Question 5.3**

Fig. 5.16 shows the human head pivoted on the vertebral column. The upper branch of the trapezius muscle connects the head to the shoulder to compensate with force $F_{ext}$ for the action of the weight of the forehead, $W$. Based on Fig. 5.16, which negative torque term will be used in the calculations?

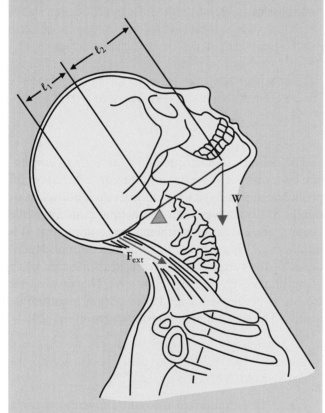

**FIGURE 5.16**

The head is pivoted on the vertebral column, defining the fulcrum (green triangle). The weight of the forehead pulls the head down in front of the fulcrum, while the upper branch of the trapezius muscle pulls the forehead up. To develop a mechanical model of the head we simplify it as a bar (red line). For calculations it is necessary to define the distances $l_1$ and $l_2$ from the fulcrum to the points at which the two forces act on the bar.

**ANSWER:** Fig. 5.16 illustrates how we can reduce the current problem to a bar on which the two forces $F_{ext}$ and $W$ act: we identify the pivot point of the vertebral column as the fulcrum (green triangle). Next, we draw a bar to connect the fulcrum with the two points at which the relevant forces act (red line). In the case of the trapezius force this is the point where the trapezius tendon is attached to the skull, and in the case of the weight of the forehead this is the centre of mass of the forehead. We will discuss the role of the centre of mass of the rigid object in more detail following this Concept Question.

Now we use Fig. 5.15 to determine the resulting rotation if the action of either force were not balanced. The bar would spin in a counter-clockwise direction if responding to $F_{ext}$, thus yielding a positive torque term $\tau_{F_{ext}} > 0$. In turn, the clockwise rotation the weight would cause leads to a negative torque term, $\tau_W < 0$.

When analyzing Concept Question 5.3 a bit further, three practical questions arise that will help us later when working on examples quantitatively:

• We learned in Chapter 3 to carefully ensure that no major forces are overlooked before proceeding with the problem solving in a mechanics-based problem. In Fig. 5.16 we seem to violate that approach because there must be a major force $F_0$ acting upward—otherwise, the head would accelerate downward. This observation leads to the question: Can we proceed with torque-related problems without including all major forces that act on the system? The answer is yes, even though we have to be cautious, as the neglected force may be required elsewhere in the solution. The type of force we can omit can be identified when looking at $F_0$ as it would enter Fig. 5.16. $F_0$ is a contact force between the head (system) and the top of the vertebral column (environment). This force acts on the system at the point we identified as the fulcrum. Thus, the distance between the fulcrum and the point at which $F_0$ acts is zero, which means that $r = 0$ in Eq. [19] and, therefore, the torque contribution of this force is zero, $\tau_{F_0} = 0$.

We can generalize this conclusion because Eq. [19] also contains the term $\sin \phi$. Even a force that acts on the system at a point other than the fulcrum can be neglected as long as it acts along a line through the fulcrum. In that case, the angle $\phi$ is 0° or 180°, which leads to $\tau = 0$ because $\sin 0° = \sin 180° = 0$.

*Forces that act on the system along a line through the fulcrum do not contribute to the net torque of the system.*

- Both forces in Fig. 5.16 act on the bar that represents the system at angles that are not 90°. What is the best way to deal with these angles? The answer is that different ways exist, and the choice is up to you. We can read the torque equation in two ways. One way is to interpret Eq. [19], in the form $\tau = r \cdot (F \sin \phi)$, i.e., as the length of the lever arm multiplied by the component of the force that is perpendicular to the lever arm causing the rotation. This view is illustrated in Fig. 5.17(a), and is the approach usually adopted in the discussions below. It allows us to simplify the formula for the torque if we choose the $x$-axis perpendicular to the lever arm, as illustrated in Fig. 5.18: we write the torque contribution of the force $F$ as $\tau = r \cdot F_x$. The force component $F_y$ can be neglected because it does not lead to a torque term based on the argument we made for forces that act along a line through the fulcrum.

  The second way to think about the torque definition of Eq. [19] is as $\tau = (r \sin \phi) \cdot F$, i.e., as the force multiplied by the component of the lever arm that is perpendicular to it, as shown in Fig. 5.17(b). This view is taken, e.g., in the definition of the torque as provided in the highlighted text following Eq. [19]. Of course, both ways of thinking give the same value for the torque $\tau$.

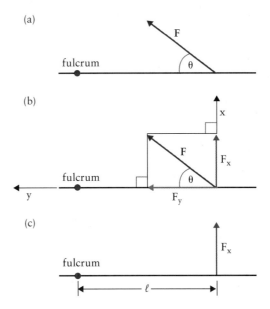

**FIGURE 5.18**

For practical purposes, it is convenient to simplify the application of Eq. [19] for each force acting on the bar by dividing it into components parallel and perpendicular to the bar. This is illustrated in (b) for the force **F**. Of the two force components, only the component perpendicular to the bar $F_x$ (shown in (c)) enters the torque equation.

- One of the forces acting on the head in Fig. 5.16 is a contact-free force. How do we decide where the weight of an object acts on it, and in particular where to draw the vector **W** in Fig. 5.16? This isn't a trivial issue, as the length $l_2$ from the fulcrum to the point of attack of the weight depends on it.

How we include the weight in the discussion of the rotational equilibrium of a rigid object is illustrated in Fig. 5.19, using the humerus as an example. In the figure the bone is shown at an angle with the negative $y$-axis. The fulcrum lies at the origin. The torque due to gravity is obtained by subdividing the humerus into a large number of segments. The size of the segments is chosen such that they are very small compared to the object; i.e., a well-defined position **r** can be assigned to each segment.

We evaluate the contribution to the torque for each segment individually, as demonstrated for the $i$-th segment highlighted in Fig. 5.19. An angle $\phi_i$ is formed between the line from the fulcrum to the segment and the negative $y$-axis. The weight of the segment, in turn, forms the angle $\psi_i$ with the line to the fulcrum. Using Eq. [19], we write the torque contribution for the $i$-th segment:

$$\tau_i = r_i \cdot m_i \cdot g \cdot \sin \psi_i \qquad [21]$$

Using the Z-rule for angles we find from Fig. 5.19 that $\phi_i = 180° - \psi_i$ and thus $\sin \phi_i = \sin \psi_i$. We note

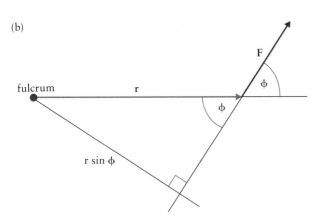

**FIGURE 5.17**

Two alternative graphical interpretations of the torque equation based on the choice of attributing the term sin $\phi$ to either (a) the force **F**, or (b) the vector from the fulcrum to the point at which the force acts on the rigid object, **r**.

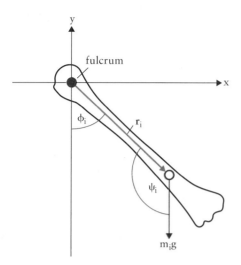

**FIGURE 5.19**

A single bone is used to illustrate the torque contribution due to its weight. First we place the origin at the fulcrum. Then the bone is subdivided into a large number of segments, each much smaller than the object itself. We find the torque contribution of the *i*-th segment (red circle). In the last step the torque contributions due to all segments are added.

also from the figure that $\sin \phi_i = x_i/r_i$, where $x_i$ is the *x*-component of the vector $\mathbf{r}_i$, and $r_i$ is its magnitude. Using this information, we write Eq. [21] in the form:

$$\tau_i = r_i \cdot m_i \cdot g \cdot \frac{x_i}{r_i} = m_i \cdot g \cdot x_i \qquad [22]$$

The total torque due to the object's weight, $\tau_{\text{weight}}$, is the sum of the contributions of all the segments into which we divided it:

$$\tau_{\text{weight}} = \sum_i m_i \cdot g \cdot x_i = g \sum_i m_i \cdot x_i \qquad [23]$$

Eq. [23] contains a large sum and must therefore be addressed further. Comparing Eq. [23] with the equation for the position of the centre of mass in Chapter 4 we note that the last sum is equal to the total mass of the object, $M$, times the horizontal *x*-component of the centre of mass, $x_{\text{c.m.}}$:

$$\tau_{\text{weight}} = x_{\text{c.m.}} \cdot M \cdot g \qquad [24]$$

*The torque due to the weight of an object is the product of the magnitude of its weight and the horizontal distance from the fulcrum to the centre of mass $x_{\text{c.m.}}$.*

More generally, we write:

$$\tau_{\text{weight}} = r_{\text{c.m.}} \cdot M \cdot g \cdot \sin \phi \qquad [25]$$

in which $\phi$ is the angle between the position vector of the centre of mass and the weight vector, and $r_{\text{c.m.}}$ is the length of that vector, $\mathbf{r}_{\text{c.m.}} = (x_{\text{c.m.}}, y_{\text{c.m.}}, z_{\text{c.m.}})$.

## Concept Question 5.4

We consider a horizontal, cylindrical bar of length $L$ and radius $r$ with uniform density $\rho$. Calculate the torque due to the weight of the bar if the bar is supported at one of its ends. Use this example to compare the concepts of **centre of mass** and **centre of gravity**, where the latter is defined as the point at which the entire weight of an object can be considered as concentrated so that if supported at this point the object remains in equilibrium against rotation. Note: Basic formulas for symmetric objects, such as cylinders, are summarized in the Math Review "Symmetric Objects" at the end of Chapter 3.

ANSWER: We first find the centre of mass for the bar. The respective definition in Chapter 4 need not be evaluated quantitatively due to the symmetry of the object: the centre of mass is the centre point of the circular cross-section at a distance L/2 from either end of the bar. Thus, the torque due to weight follows from Eq. [24] as:

$$\tau_{\text{weight}} = \frac{L}{2}\,\rho(r^2 \cdot \pi \cdot L)g = \frac{\pi}{2}\,\rho \cdot g(r \cdot L)^2 \qquad [26]$$

Note that the bracket in the second term, in which $r^2 \cdot \pi \cdot L$ is the volume of the cylindrical bar. The result in Eq. [26] might be a positive or negative contribution depending on the chosen geometry.

We note that the centre of mass is also the centre of gravity in this case, because supporting the bar at the centre of mass allows us to balance it. If we place the fulcrum at the geometric centre of the bar two torque contributions result, each for half the mass of the bar at a distance $L/4$ from the fulcrum. Because the contributions have opposite signs due to the sign convention and equal magnitude, the sum of the torque terms is zero. In turn, the centre of mass can be defined independent of the gravitational effect, e.g., for an object in outer space. Thus, centre of mass and centre of gravity are identical for objects on the surface of Earth where uniform gravity applies.

# Mechanical Equilibrium for a Rigid Object

We now introduce the concept of mechanical equilibrium for rigid objects. This equilibrium condition is a combination of the mechanical equilibrium for a point-like object as introduced in Chapter 3, and a condition that prevents the rigid object from rotating. Eq. [3.14] remains a part of the mechanical equilibrium condition of a rigid object. In addition, rotational accelerations are excluded by requiring that the sum of all torque contributions acting on the system must be zero. In general, this would require three equations, one each for the three Cartesian components of the torque vector. Since we limit our discussion to cases where the axis of rotation is fixed along the $z$-axis, only one torque component has to be considered, reducing the number of formulas needed to provide rotational equilibrium to just one. Therefore, the equilibrium condition for a rigid object with a fixed axis of rotation consists of a total of three equations:

condition 1: $\quad \sum_i F_{ix} = F_{net,x} = 0$

condition 2: $\quad \sum_i F_{iy} = F_{net,y} = 0 \qquad [27]$

condition 3: $\quad \sum_i \tau_i = \tau_{net} = 0$

In each case, the running index $i$ ensures that all forces contributing to the net force on the object, and all torque contributions, are included.

## Concept Question 5.5

Fig. 5.20 shows five ways in which a particular physical case of two forces acting on a bar at distance $d$ from the fulcrum at the bar's centre can be labelled. Which of these cases leads to the rotational equilibrium condition?

$$\sum_{i=1}^{2} \tau_i = \tau_{net} = 0$$
$$= F_1 \cdot d \cdot \sin \theta - F_2 \cdot d \cdot \cos \phi \quad [28]$$

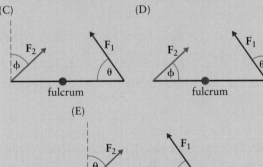

**FIGURE 5.20**

Five ways in which two forces, $\mathbf{F}_1$ and $\mathbf{F}_2$, may act on a bar with the fulcrum at its centre. Note also the variations in defining the angles $\theta$ and $\phi$.

ANSWER: Choice (C). Note that the definition of the torque includes the sine of the angle between the bar and the force. However, the trigonometric relations allow us to express the same term as the cosine of the angle between the force and the normal direction. The only other case close to the formulation in Eq. [28] is choice (A), which we have to dismiss based on the sign convention of torque.

## Concept Question 5.6

Fig. 5.21 shows five locations of the fulcrum along a red bar upon which five forces of any magnitude (blue arrows) act. Which of the five cases cannot be in rotational equilibrium?

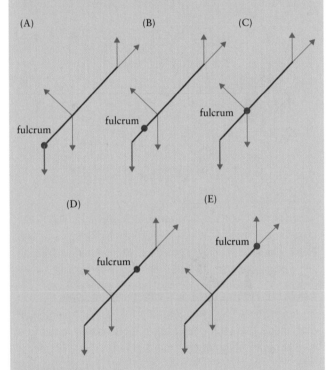

**FIGURE 5.21**

Five forces act on a red bar for which we consider five different fulcrum positions.

ANSWER: Case (C). In order to obtain rotational equilibrium, there must be at least one positive and one negative torque contribution (unless all five forces act along a line through the fulcrum). The two forces that act at the position of the fulcrum in case (C) qualify for this, ruling out the cases (A), (B), (D), and (E) because they contribute opposing torque terms in these four cases. To confirm that case (C) does not lead to a rotational equilibrium, we check the two forces at the bottom and top ends of the bar that do not act along a line through the fulcrum. Both indeed lead to counter-clockwise rotations, and thus do not compensate for each other's effect.

## Concept Question 5.7

Fig. 5.22(a) shows a standard man intending to do reverse pushdowns in the gym. In this exercise, the person stands facing the machine, holding the handle bar from below and flexing the elbows against the body. We identify the lower arm and hand as the system, with the ulna and hand bones defining the bar we use to address rotational equilibrium issues. Four forces act on this bar, as shown in Fig. 5.22(b): the force exerted by the triceps $F_1$, the force exerted by the humerus pushing into the elbow $F_2$, the weight of the system $W$, and the tension $T$ in the cable of the machine. Which of these forces can we neglect when addressing the rotational equilibrium in this case, and why?

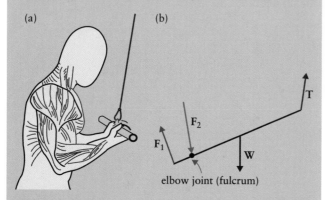

(a)        (b)

### FIGURE 5.22

A standard man does reverse pushdowns in the gym. We can identify four major forces acting on the lower arm: The triceps muscle exerts the force $F_1$, the humerus exerts force $F_2$ at the elbow, $W$ is the weight of the lower arm and hand, and $T$ is the tension in the string of the machine.

ANSWER: $F_2$. This force acts into the elbow. Note that we do not neglect this force, arguing that it has a negligible magnitude (which it does not), but because it leads to a torque contribution of zero due to $r = 0$ in Eq. [19].

## ● EXAMPLE 5.2

Fig. 5.23 shows a uniform horizontal bar of mass $m = 25$ kg and length $L = 4$ m that is attached to a vertical wall in a point about which the bar can rotate. The bar's far end is held by a massless string that makes an angle of $\theta = 40°$ with the horizontal. When an object of mass $M = 50$ kg is placed on the bar at a distance $l = 1.2$ m from the vertical wall, (a) find the magnitude of the tension in the string, and (b) find the horizontal and vertical components of the force exerted on the bar by the vertical wall.

*Solution:* We follow the problem-solving strategy as outlined in a Math Review at the end of

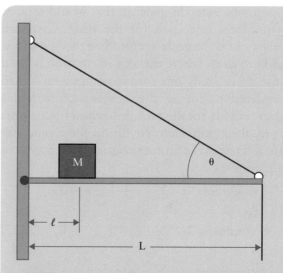

### FIGURE 5.23

A typical arrangement for an application of the torque concept: a uniform horizontal bar is attached to a wall at a point about which the bar may rotate. The bar's far end is supported by a massless string. An additional object is placed on the bar as shown.

Chapter 2 and highlight the additional operations concerning the rotational equilibrium of a rigid object. The bar is the system, since both parts of the question refer to forces acting on it. The object of mass $M$, the vertical wall, and the massless string are all part of the environment.

We identify all forces acting on the bar. Acting downward are its weight, $W_b$, and a contact force due to the weight of the object with mass $M$. We call this force $F$ and note $F = W_M$. The tension in the string, $T$, acts along the string. The force exerted by the vertical wall, $R$, has an initially unknown direction. Since the system is an extended rigid object, two sketches are required:

- a free-body diagram, shown in Fig. 5.24(a), and

- a new sketch, called the **balance of torque diagram**, shown in Fig. 5.24(b).

To develop the balance of torque diagram, we first draw a line to represent the bar with a dot that indicates the fulcrum. Next, all forces acting on the bar are added at their respective distance from the fulcrum. You may divide each force into two components, one that acts in the direction toward or away from the fulcrum, and one that acts perpendicular to the bar. This approach has been illustrated in Fig. 5.18. In the present example, the forces that are affected are $R$ with the components $R_x$ and $R_y$, and $T$ with $T \cdot \cos \theta$ and $T \cdot \sin \theta$. Note further that the weight of the bar is drawn at its centre of mass. This point lies at the geometrical centre of the bar due to its symmetry and uniform mass distribution.

The coordinate system for the free-body diagram is chosen in the same fashion as before. For the balance of torque diagram the x-axis is chosen along the bar and the y-axis is chosen perpendicular to the bar with the fulcrum at the origin.

From Fig. 5.24, three formulas are derived using Eq. [27]. The first two are applications of the first law of mechanics applied along the x- and the y-axes in the free-body diagram (Fig. 5.24(a)). The third formula is the balance of torque equation, from Fig. 5.24(b):

condition 1: $\qquad -T \cdot \cos\theta + R_x = 0$

condition 2: $\qquad T \cdot \sin\theta + R_y - F - W_b = 0$

condition 3: $\quad L \cdot T \cdot \sin\theta - \dfrac{L}{2}W_b - l \cdot F = 0$

$$[29]$$

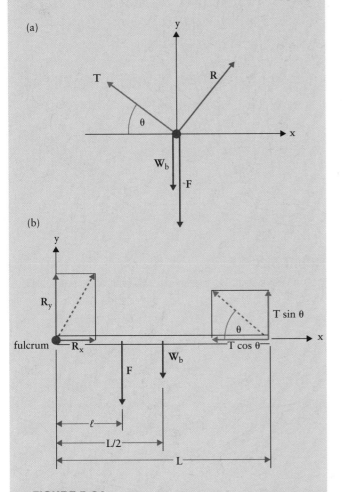

(a)

(b)

**FIGURE 5.24**

(a) Free-body diagram for the problem illustrated in Fig. 5.23. Four forces act on the bar: the weight of the bar, a contact force due to the weight of the additional object of mass M, the tension **T** in the string, and the force exerted by the wall. (b) The balance of torque diagram supplements the free-body diagram in part (a) with each force drawn to the actual point of contact.

We study condition 3 in more detail. First, note that several components of the forces do not enter the formula. Since torque is associated with forces that do not act in the direction toward or away from the fulcrum, the force components $R_x$, $R_y$, and $T \cdot \cos\theta$ do not contribute to the balance of torque in this case. Of the remaining three force components, two lead to negative terms and one leads to a positive term. This is due to the direction of rotation each of these force components causes if it were to act alone on the bar. $T \cdot \sin\theta$ would lead to a counter-clockwise rotation, and $F$ and $W_b$ would each cause a clockwise rotation. The signs of the three terms result from the torque sign convention defined in Fig. 5.15.

We now solve Eq. [29]. The torque formula is usually a good starting point because it doesn't contain all force components and therefore has the least number of unknown variables.

*Solution to part (a):* Isolating the magnitude of the tension **T** in the third formula of Eq. [29] provides:

$$T = \frac{\dfrac{L}{2}m \cdot g + l \cdot M \cdot g}{L \cdot \sin\theta}$$

$$= \frac{\left(\dfrac{L}{2}m + l \cdot M\right)g}{L \cdot \sin\theta} \qquad [30]$$

where we used $F = W_M = M \cdot g$.

Substituting into Eq. [30] the values given in the problem text, we find:

$$T = \frac{(2\,m)(25\,kg) + (1.2\,m)(50\,kg)}{(4\,m)\sin 40°}\,g = 419\,N$$

$$[31]$$

The magnitude of the tension in the string is 419 N.

*Solution to part (b):* The force exerted by the wall has two components, which are found when substituting the result of Eq. [31] in the first two formulas in Eq. [29]. For the x-component of the force **R**, we find:

$$R_x = T \cdot \cos\theta = (419\,N)\cos 40°$$

$$= 321\,N \qquad [32]$$

and for the y-component of the force **R**, we get:

$$R_y = F + W_b - T \cdot \sin\theta$$

$$= (M + m)g - T \cdot \sin\theta$$

$$= \{(25\,kg) + (50\,kg)\}g - (419\,N)\sin 40°$$

$$= 466\,N \qquad [33]$$

Again, $F = W_M = M \cdot g$ has been used. Thus, **R** is given as $(R_x, R_y) = (321\,N, 466\,N)$.

# Physiological Applications

It has become common practice to distinguish three classes of lever systems in anatomy based on the relative position of the fulcrum, and the weight and muscle force that act on the system. A **class I lever system** is shown in Fig. 5.25 for the head pivoted on the first cervical vertebra. The fulcrum is indicated by a green triangle. In this type of lever system, the weight acts on one side of the fulcrum and the muscle force that balances the weight acts on the opposite side of the fulcrum.

A **class II lever system** is illustrated in Fig. 5.26 for the foot. The fulcrum is at one end of the lever arm. The weight and the muscle force act on the same side of the fulcrum. These forces must act in opposite directions to obtain a rotational equilibrium. Note that the weight acts at a point closer to the fulcrum than the muscle force.

A **class III lever system** is shown in Fig. 5.27 for the lower arm. This case is similar to the second type in that the fulcrum is again at one end of the lever arm and the two forces establishing a rotational equilibrium act on the same side of the fulcrum. This time, though, the muscle force acts closer to the fulcrum than the weight.

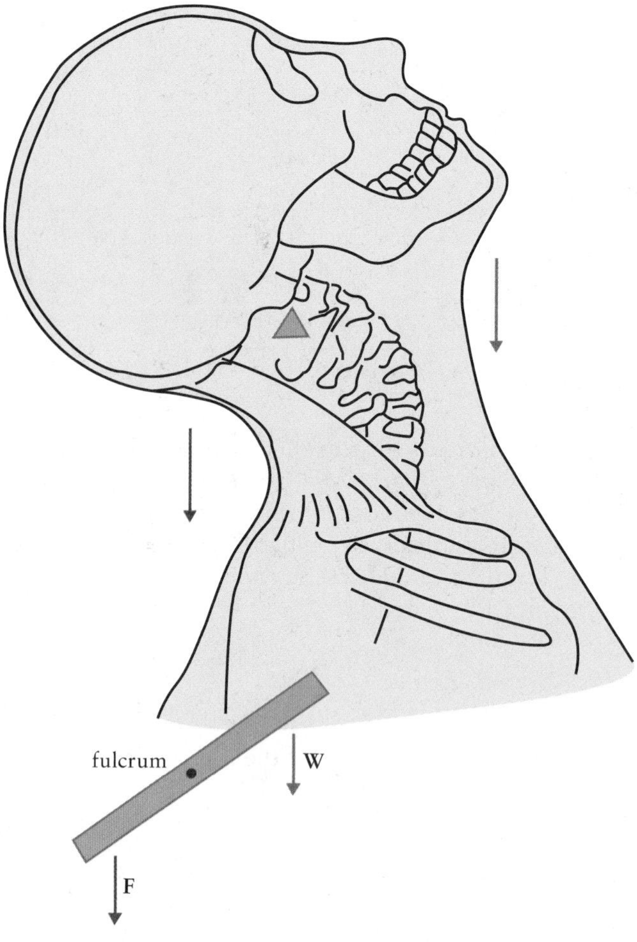

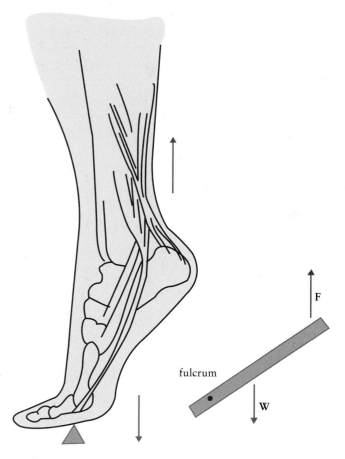

**FIGURE 5.26**

Class II lever system. The fulcrum is positioned near the end of the lever arm. The weight **W** acts on the lever arm closer to the fulcrum than the muscle force **F**.

**FIGURE 5.25**

Class I lever system. The fulcrum is located between the points at which the weight **W** and the muscle force **F** act.

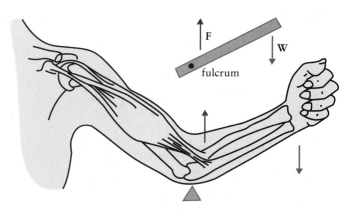

**FIGURE 5.27**

Class III lever system. The fulcrum is near the end of the lever arm. The muscle force **F** acts closer to the fulcrum on the lever arm than the weight **W**.

# The Achilles Tendon

## ● EXAMPLE 5.3

In Fig. 5.28 the anatomy of the foot is compared for a standard man standing on a flat surface (Fig. 5.28(a)) and standing backward on a diving board, intending to do a competitive backward dive into a pool (Fig. 5.28(b)). In Fig. 5.28(a), calculate (a) the magnitude of the two normal forces supporting the foot, and (b) the magnitude of the force acting in the Achilles tendon. In Fig. 5.28(b), calculate (c) the magnitude of the force in the Achilles tendon for the motionless athlete on the diving board in Fig. 5.28(b) and (d) the magnitude of $F_B$ and angle $\theta$. *Hint:* Neglect in all cases the weight of the foot. Use $x_1 = 6.2$ cm and $x_2 = 12.3$ cm, which are typical values for shoe size 11.

*Supplementary anatomical information:* Note that the athlete must adjust to standing on the diving board to obtain mechanical equilibrium because the supporting forces (normal forces) acting from below the foot have changed. You may convince yourself of this adjustment by trying to balance on the edge of a stair as shown in Fig. 5.28(b).

The Achilles tendon is shown in Fig. 5.28 as a string connected to the heel bone. We combine all the bones of the foot into a single rigid object, but allow tibia and fibula to rotate about the talus. The Achilles tendon can easily be detected by looking at your lower leg in a mirror sideways. The angle of the Achilles tendon with the vertical in Fig. 5.28(b) can be determined from photographs of athletes on a diving board. We use a value of $\phi = 8°$.

*Solution to part (a):* The system is the foot below the fibula and tibia, excluding the Achilles tendon. The Achilles tendon is treated as a massless string that connects the system to the calf muscle. Calf muscle, fibula, and tibia are part of the environment, with fibula and tibia exerting a contact force $F_{ext}$ on the system.

The free-body diagram is shown in Fig. 5.29(a). In this sketch, the foot is drawn as a dot. Three forces act on it: two normal forces at the support points, $N_1$ and $N_2$, and the force of the person's body pushing onto the talus, $F_{ext}$. We neglect the weight of the foot itself, as stated in the problem text.

The balance of torque diagram is shown in Fig. 5.29(b). Note that the system is now drawn as a bar to take its spatial extension into account. The diagram shows the same three forces as in the free-body diagram, but each is drawn at the appropriate position along the bar: the first normal force at the heel, the second normal force at the ball of the foot, and $F_{ext}$ at the talus. As the anatomy of the foot in Fig. 5.29 shows, the fulcrum is located at the talus. Note that $F_{ext}$ acts on the foot at the fulcrum.

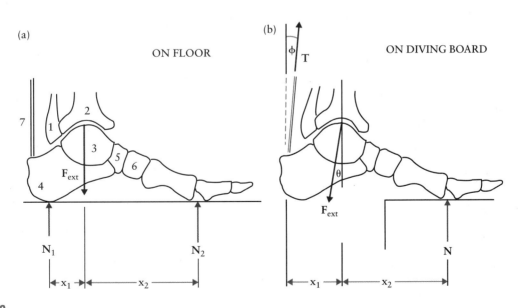

**FIGURE 5.28**

Anatomy of the foot of a standard man (a) resting on a flat surface, and (b) balancing backward on a diving board. Bones include the fibula (1), the tibia (2), the talus (3), the calcaneus (4), the navicular bone (5), and the medial cuneiform bone (6). Note that the Achilles tendon (7) is not vertical when balancing on the diving board. $F_{ext}$, the force due to the upper body pushing into the foot, and the tension $T$ in the Achilles tendon are very large forces. Note that $F_{ext}$ is not vertical in the right sketch and is not equal to the weight of the upper body resting on the foot since $T$ pulls the foot toward the leg, beyond the effect of the weight.

● **EXAMPLE 5.3** (*continued*)

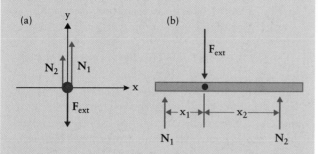

**FIGURE 5.29**

(a) The free-body diagram, and (b) the balance of torque diagram for the foot on the flat surface as shown in Fig. 5.28(a). Note that the two normal forces are drawn to different lengths and are labelled with different indices because we cannot assume they are equal in magnitude.

The choice of a coordinate system for the free-body diagram is straightforward because all three forces act along the vertical direction. For the balance of torque diagram the choice of coordinate system is determined by the direction of the bar representing the system.

The conditions of mechanical equilibrium are developed from the two diagrams in Fig. 5.29; because no force components act in the *x*-direction, only the two last conditions in Eq. [27] are needed:

condition 2:    $N_1 + N_2 - F_{ext} = 0$

condition 3:    $N_2 \cdot x_2 - N_1 \cdot x_1 = 0$    [34]

Condition 2 is the sum of the force components in the *y*-direction. For a relaxed person we note that the force acting downward in each leg is equal to half the person's weight, $F_{ext} = W/2$. Note that this is a simplifying assumption since the person may distribute the body weight unequally. Condition 3 in Eq. [34] is the balance of torque condition about the talus. It allows us to calculate the relative contributions of both normal forces. Using the given values $x_1 = 6.2$ cm and $x_2 = 12.3$ cm, we get approximately $N_1 = W/3 = 230$ N, and $N_2 = W/6 = 115$ N (with the standard man data from Table 3.3).

*Solution to part (b):* The calculations up to this point have not identified a tension acting in the Achilles tendon. Thus, the tension is zero, $T = 0$.

*Solution to part (c):* Now we consider the athlete on the board in Fig. 5.28(b). The free-body diagram and the balance of torque diagram are shown in Fig. 5.30. Note that the two anatomical sketches in Fig. 5.28 on one side, and the diagrams in Figs. 5.29 and 5.30 on the other side, each appear to display only minor differences. Despite the

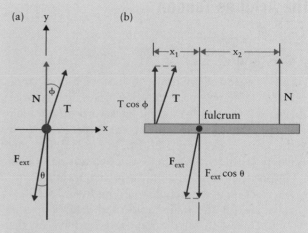

**FIGURE 5.30**

(a) The free-body diagram, and (b) the balance of torque diagram for the foot on the diving board as shown in Fig. 5.28(b).

similarities we will find surprisingly large forces in comparison to the situation when on flat ground.

Since one support point is removed from below the foot in Fig. 5.28(b), the upper body must tilt slightly forward to maintain balance, i.e., the athlete's centre of mass must now be positioned above the ball of the foot. This causes an angle $\phi$ between the Achilles tendon and the vertical, and an angle $\theta$ between the direction of force $\mathbf{F}_{ext}$ and the vertical. As a result, a tension $\mathbf{T}$ acts along the Achilles tendon, which must provide a balance for the *x*-component of $\mathbf{F}_{ext}$.

The three mechanical equilibrium conditions are written from Fig. 5.30:

condition 1:

$$T \cdot \sin \phi - F_{ext} \cdot \sin \theta = 0$$

condition 2:

$$T \cdot \cos \phi + N - F_{ext} \cdot \cos \theta = 0 \quad [35]$$

condition 3:

$$N \cdot x_2 - T \cdot \cos \phi \cdot x_1 = 0$$

We note that the magnitude of the normal force is equal to half the person's weight, $N = W/2$, because we assume that the athlete distributes the body weight equally over both legs.

We determine the magnitude of the tension $\mathbf{T}$ from the third condition in Eq. [35] and the standard man data in Table 3.3:

$$T = \frac{W \cdot x_2}{2 \cdot x_1 \cdot \cos \phi}$$

$$= \frac{(70 \, \text{kg})\left(9.8 \, \dfrac{\text{m}}{\text{s}^2}\right)(0.123 \, \text{m})}{2 \cdot (0.062 \, \text{m}) \cos 8°}$$

$$= 687 \, \text{N} \quad\quad\quad [36]$$

which is almost exactly the weight of the standard man. Thus, each Achilles tendon supports the equivalent of the entire weight of the athlete! This force is caused by the calf muscle, which provides the mechanical equilibrium in this rather awkward position. You feel this large force when you try to balance on a stair in the posture shown in Fig. 5.28(b).

*Solution to part (d):* We can determine two more variables from Eq. [35], as it contains three independent conditions. The other two variables are the angle $\theta$ and the magnitude of the force $\mathbf{F}_{ext}$. Using the result of Eq. [36], we divide the first condition by the second in Eq. [35]:

$$\frac{\sin \theta}{\cos \theta} = \tan \theta = \frac{W \cdot \sin \phi}{W \left( \cos \phi + \dfrac{1}{2} \right)}$$

$$= \frac{\sin 8°}{\cos 8° + 0.5} = 0.093 \qquad [37]$$

which yields:

$$\theta = 5.3° \qquad [38]$$

To find the magnitude of $\mathbf{F}_{ext}$, we substitute Eq. [38] into either the first or second formula of Eq. [35]. Choosing the first formula, we find:

$$F_{ext} = \frac{W \cdot \sin \phi}{\sin \theta}$$

$$= \frac{(70 \, \text{kg}) \left( 9.8 \dfrac{\text{m}}{\text{s}^2} \right) \sin 8°}{\sin 5.3°} = 1035 \, \text{N} \qquad [39]$$

which is 1.5 times the weight of the standard man. Thus, the large force in the tendon in Eq. [36] is primarily due to a large force pushing down onto the talus.

## The Mandible and the Masseter

### ● EXAMPLE 5.4

Fig. 5.31(a) shows the masseter, which is one of the strongest muscles in the human body. It connects the mandible (the lower jaw bone) to the skull. The mandible is pivoted about a socket just in front of the ear. Three forces act on the jaw bone, as shown in Fig. 5.31(b): $\mathbf{F}_{ext}$ is the external force exerted by the chewed food, $\mathbf{T}$ is the tension in the masseter tendon, and $\mathbf{R}$ is the force exerted on the mandible by the skull. We make the simplifying assumption that these three forces act perpendicularly to the lower part of the mandible as shown. Use $l_1 = 9$ cm and $l_2 = 5$ cm, and an

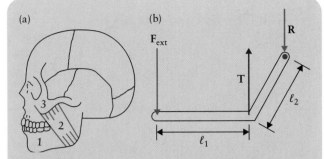

**FIGURE 5.31**

(a) Illustration of the attachment of the masseter (2) to the mandible (1) and the cheek bone (3). (b) Simplified arrangement of the forces acting on the mandible during chewing. The tension $\mathbf{T}$ is exerted by the masseter. The force $\mathbf{R}$ acts at the joint. The external force $\mathbf{F}_{ext}$ is due to the person's chewing. The mandible consists of two straight parts of lengths $l_1$ and $l_2$; the angle between these is 110°.

angle of 110° between the two parts of the mandible. Find (a) the magnitude of the tension $\mathbf{T}$ when the person bites down with a force of 40 N, and (b) the magnitude of the force $\mathbf{R}$ for the same bite.

*Supplementary physical information:* This problem is different from the previous examples because the mandible is bent. Therefore, the points at which the forces act on the system do not lie along a straight line.

We illustrate the approach to such cases in general terms first. Fig. 5.32 compares two balance of torque diagrams for a straight lever arm in Fig. 5.32(a) and for a bent lever arm in Fig. 5.32(b). In each case two forces, $\mathbf{F}_1$ and $\mathbf{F}_2$, act on the lever arm. For the straight lever arm these two forces are each divided into two force components in the same fashion as previously discussed. For the bent lever arm the two forces are divided into components in a different fashion: we first draw lines from the fulcrum to the points along the lever arm at which each force acts. Then each force is divided into components parallel and perpendicular to this line. The perpendicular force component and the distance between the fulcrum and the point of action of the force along the newly drawn line are then used in the balance of torque equation.

*Solution:* The mandible is the system; all relevant forces acting on it are shown in Fig. 5.31(b). The free-body diagram and the balance of torque diagram are shown in Fig. 5.33. Both the tension and the external force are divided into components parallel to and perpendicular to the line through the fulcrum. Of these components, the ones that are perpendicular to the line are needed for the balance of torque equation. We develop this diagram

● **EXAMPLE 5.4 (continued)**

(a)

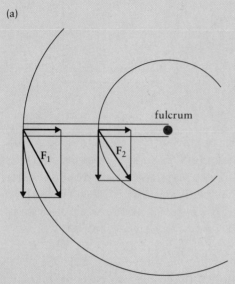

(b)

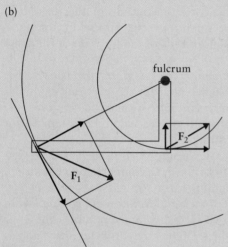

**FIGURE 5.32**

Conceptual sketch illustrating the difference between (a) a straight lever system and (b) a bent lever system. Two forces are considered acting on each lever arm: $F_2$ located in both cases between the fulcrum and the bend, and $F_1$ located at the far end of the lever arm. Both forces are divided into components. For $F_1$ in both cases and for $F_2$ in case (a) this is done in the same fashion as described in Fig. 5.18; for $F_1$ in case (b) the components are chosen parallel and perpendicular to the line through the fulcrum.

as shown in Fig. 5.33 because it is not possible to draw a single straight bar through the fulcrum and the two points at which the tension and the external force act on the mandible.

We choose the horizontal direction as the $x$-axis and the vertical direction as the $y$-axis in the free-body diagram. Thus, all forces are parallel and antiparallel to the $y$-axis. Since no force

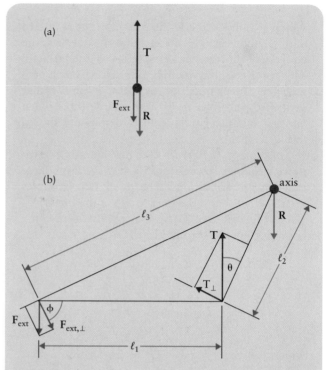

**FIGURE 5.33**

(a) Free-body diagram and (b) balance of torque diagram for the mandible system in Fig. 5.31. Note the application of the approach we developed in Fig. 5.32 for a bent lever arm.

components exist in the $x$-direction, only condition 2 is needed in Eq. [27]:

condition 2:   $-F_{\text{ext}} + T - R = 0$   [40]

Furthermore, to apply the torque equilibrium condition the angles $\theta$ and $\phi$ and the distances $l_2$ and $l_3$ have to be included from Fig. 5.33:

condition 3:

$$+F_{\text{ext}} \cdot l_3 \cdot \sin \phi - T \cdot l_2 \cdot \sin \theta = 0 \quad [41]$$

The components of the force $R$ do not appear in the balance of torque equation because $R$ acts at the fulcrum. Now we can answer the two parts of the question separately.

*Solution to part (a):* The magnitude of the tension is obtained from Eq. [41]:

$$T = F_{\text{ext}} \left( \frac{l_3 \cdot \sin \phi}{l_2 \cdot \sin \theta} \right) \quad [42]$$

In order to quantify the magnitude of $T$ in Eq. [42], we must first determine the values of $\theta$, $\phi$, and $l_3$. Since $T$ acts perpendicularly to the mandible and the angle between the two parts of the mandible is 110°, we know that $\theta = 110° - 90° = 20°$.

Determining $\phi$ is trickier. To do this we construct a right-angle triangle by extending the lower part of the mandible and drawing another

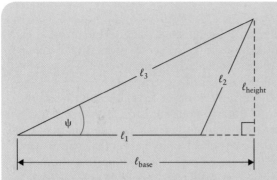

**FIGURE 5.34**
Geometrical sketch illustrating how the angles and side lengths of the triangle in Fig. 5.33 are related to each other.

line perpendicular to it running through the fulcrum. This is shown as dashed lines in Fig. 5.34. We use trigonometry to evaluate an angle when we have the lengths of two sides of a right triangle. The length of the base of the triangle in Fig. 5.34 is $l_{base} = l_1 + l_2 \cdot \cos 70° = 10.7$ cm. The length of the line perpendicular to the base in the figure is given as $l_{height} = l_2 \cdot \sin 70° = 4.7$ cm. The two lengths allow us to calculate the angle $\psi$ in Fig. 5.34: $\tan \psi = l_{height}/l_{base} = 4.7/10.7$, which yields $\psi = 23.7°$. The angle $\phi$ in Fig. 5.33 follows, then, as $\phi = 90° - \psi = 66.3°$. Using the Pythagorean theorem for the triangle constructed in Fig. 5.34 further yields:

$$l_3 = \sqrt{l_{base}^2 + l_{height}^2}$$

$$= \sqrt{(10.7)^2 + (4.7)^2} = 11.7 \text{ cm} \quad [43]$$

With these results from Fig. 5.34, we return to Eq. [42] to find:

$$T = 40\,\text{N} \frac{(11.7 \text{ cm})\sin 66.3°}{(5.0 \text{ cm})\sin 20°} = 250\,\text{N} \quad [44]$$

Note that you can get the correct answer in this case without converting the unit cm to m because the two quantities with unit cm cancel. Of course, you would also get the correct result if you do convert to standard unit m, and it is a good idea to get used to working with standard units to avoid forgetting to make the conversions when necessary.

*Solution to part (b):* The magnitude of the force **R** acting at the joint is found by substituting Eq. [44] into Eq. [40]:

$$R = T - F_{ext} = (250\,\text{N}) - (40\,\text{N})$$

$$= 210\,\text{N} \quad [45]$$

Calculations like the ones in this example are useful when we attempt reconstructions of fossil skulls to assess physiological properties of an extinct species. Applying this approach to hominids

from the past 5 million years provides a measure of strength of the masseter, which in turn is indicative of the diet of an individual. Calculating the required force for the same strength of bite allows us to judge whether the much more massive masseter of our ancestors like *Australopithecus robustus* represents a lesser adaptation due to the earlier stage of evolution or whether it indicates a diet that required a lot of biting or chewing.

Another application of mechanical calculations for the mandible is the evolutionary adaptation to burrowing among *caecilians*, which are worm-like amphibians. Burrowing is a very demanding task and advanced caecilians, such as *Microcaecilia rabei*, have developed a second set of muscles to supplement the masseter in jaw-closing.

## Concept Question 5.8

Fig. 5.35 shows three bent-lever arms with the fulcrum indicated by a dot and a single force **F** acting at the far end of the lever arm. Which of the three systems (a) is in mechanical equilibrium, and (b) does not rotate as a result of the force?

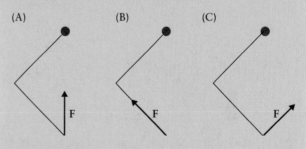

**FIGURE 5.35**
Three bent lever arm systems with fulcrum (dot) and the action of a single force **F** at the opposite end.

ANSWER TO PART (a): None. The mechanical equilibrium is defined by three conditions: a single force is always unbalanced and will cause an acceleration.

ANSWER TO PART (b): Choice (A). Do the following self-test to convince yourself: Relax your facial muscles, open your mouth slightly, and push gently on your chin almost straight up. This corresponds to case (C) in Fig. 5.35 and results in your teeth being pushed together. Next, push gently in a horizontal direction toward your throat; this corresponds to case (B) in Fig. 5.35. As a result, your mouth will open. Lastly, push in the direction of your ear (roughly the location of the fulcrum of the mandible). No rotation will occur.

## The Hip Joint

### ● EXAMPLE 5.5

Fig. 5.36 shows the anatomy and the main forces acting at the hip joint of a standard man (see data in Table 3.3) shifting from standing on both legs in Fig. 5.36(a) to balancing on one leg only in Fig. 5.36(b). Calculate for the person balancing on one leg (a) the magnitude of the tension in the abductor muscle's tendon, **T**, and (b) the components of the external force the pelvis exerts on the femur, $\mathbf{F}_{ext}$.

*Biological information:* Most of the time while walking, only one foot is on the ground. Seniors and some physically disabled people have to walk slowly, requiring them to establish a mechanical equilibrium during each step. This balance is achieved by shifting the centre of mass of the body over the foot currently on the ground. You can establish this in a self-experiment: Balance on one foot by lifting the other foot just slightly off the floor and observe your adjustments in posture in a mirror. We assume for the calculation that the centre of mass of the body lies on the central symmetry line, based on Concept Question 4.6. This line is the vertical dashed line in Fig. 5.36(b).

When only one foot is on the ground, the normal force pushing upward through the sole is equal in magnitude to the weight of the person, $N = W$. Due to the arrangement of the bones in the leg and the hip, we will find that large forces act on both sides of the head of the femur in Fig. 5.36(b).

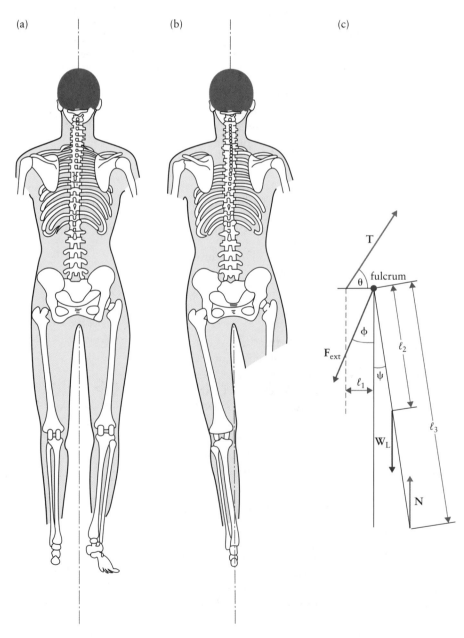

(a)          (b)          (c)

**FIGURE 5.36**

Posterior view of the hip joint (a) when the person stands on both feet, and (b) when the person balances on one leg. (c) The arrangement of the various forces considered in the example: **T** is the tension in the abductor muscle, $\mathbf{F}_{ext}$ is the force of the upper body exerted through the acetabulum, $\mathbf{W}_L$ is the weight of the leg, and **N** is the normal force exerted by the floor.

Nature accommodates these forces with a total of 14 muscles and ligaments connecting the pelvis to the femur. To simplify the situation, we combine these forces in a single tension assigned to the abductor muscle, which connects the pelvis to the *great trochanter,* the outer head of the femur. Fig. 5.36(c) is a sketch of the main forces that we include in the discussion. The figure serves also as the balance of torque diagram in this case. The inner head of the femur centres around the hip joint, fitting into the *acetabulum,* which is the socket in the pelvis. The tension forms an angle $\theta = 65°$ with the horizontal, and acts on the leg at a distance $l_1 = 8$ cm left of the fulcrum. The angle $\phi$ is formed between the vertical and the external force $\mathbf{F}_{ext}$.

The leg forms an angle of $\psi = 8°$ with the vertical, as shown in Fig. 5.36(b). Since the normal force and the weight of the leg act in the vertical direction, $\psi$ is also the angle between these two forces and the leg. Measuring the distances along the leg, the normal force acts at distance $l_3 = 90$ cm from the fulcrum and the weight of the leg acts at its centre of mass, which is $l_2 = 40$ cm from the fulcrum.

*Solution:* We identify the leg as the system. The environment includes the rest of the standard man, in particular the abductor muscle attached to the great trochanter. Thus, we consider a total of four forces that act on the leg:

- The tension in the abductor muscle $\mathbf{T}$, which acts on the great trochanter at an angle of $\theta = 65°$ with the positive $x$-axis that runs horizontally to the right.

- The external force due to the acetabulum $\mathbf{F}_{ext}$, which acts on the head of the femur. This force pushes in the direction of the hip joint.

- The normal force $\mathbf{N}$, exerted by the floor on the sole of the foot, with $N = W$ where $\mathbf{W}$ is the weight of the person.

- The weight of the leg $\mathbf{W}_L$, acting vertically downward at the centre of mass of the leg, which we discussed in Example 4.5 to be at $l_2 = (4/9) \cdot l_3$.

The free-body diagram is shown in Fig. 5.37, with the corresponding balance of torque diagram in Fig. 5.36(c). The distances along the leg are given for an average person as: $l_1 = 8$ cm, $l_2 = 40$ cm, $l_3 = 90$ cm. Note that the force $\mathbf{F}_{ext}$ and the force components $N \cdot \cos \psi$ and $W_L \cdot \cos \psi$ are not represented in the balance of torque equation since they all act in the direction of the fulcrum. Based on Figs. 5.36(c) and 5.37, the three conditions of mechanical equilibrium are written:

condition 1: $\qquad T \cdot \cos \theta - F_{ext,x} = 0$

condition 2: $\quad T \cdot \sin \theta - F_{ext,y} - W_L + N = 0$

condition 3: $\quad -l_1 \cdot T \cdot \sin \theta - l_2 \cdot W_L \cdot \sin \psi$
$$+ l_3 \cdot N \cdot \sin \psi = 0 \qquad [46]$$

*Solution to part (a):* We solve for the magnitude of the tension $\mathbf{T}$. Using condition 3, because it contains the least number of unknown variables, we substitute $N = W$ and $W_L = 0.15 \cdot W$ from Table 3.3:

$$T = \frac{\sin \psi \, (l_3 - 0.15 \cdot l_2)}{l_1 \cdot \sin \theta} W$$

$$= \frac{\sin 8°(90 \text{ cm} - 0.15 \cdot 40 \text{ cm})}{(8 \text{ cm})\sin 65°} (70 \text{ kg})\left(9.8 \frac{\text{m}}{\text{s}^2}\right)$$

$$= 1100 \text{ N} \qquad\qquad [47]$$

This means that the abductor muscle must provide a force that is about 1.6 times the weight of the standard man, a large force that may strain tendons connecting the muscle to the pelvis or the great trochanter. The largest contribution to this force is due to the torque of the normal force, because the joint is far off the body's symmetry line when the foot is vertically below the centre of mass. To circumvent such large forces the person may use a cane on the opposite side allowing the foot to be farther out, which greatly reduces the torque contribution due to the normal force.

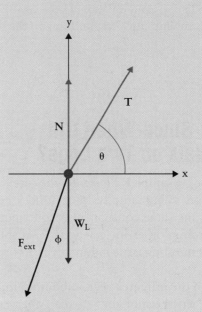

**FIGURE 5.37**
The free-body diagram of the leg in Fig. 5.36(b).

● **EXAMPLE 5.5** *(continued)*

*Solution to part (b):* Next, we solve for the two components of the external force $F_{ext}$. From condition 1 in Eq. [46], we find the *x*-component:

$$F_{ext,x} = T \cdot \cos \theta = (1100\,\text{N})\cos 65° = 465\,\text{N}$$
$$[48]$$

and from condition 2 in Eq. [46], we find the *y*-component:

$$F_{ext,y} = T \cdot \sin \theta + 0.85 \cdot W$$
$$= (1100\,\text{N})\sin 65° + 0.85 \cdot (70\,\text{kg})\left(9.8\,\frac{\text{m}}{\text{s}^2}\right)$$
$$= 1580\,\text{N}$$
$$[49]$$

Eqs. (48) and (49) are the Cartesian coordinates of the external force. Its magnitude is:

$$F_{ext} = \sqrt{F_{ext,x}^2 + F_{ext,y}^2}$$
$$= \sqrt{(465\,\text{N})^2 + (1580\,\text{N})^2}$$
$$= 1645\,\text{N} \qquad [50]$$

For the angle $\phi$, we find:

$$\tan \phi = \frac{F_{ext,x}}{F_{ext,y}} = \frac{465\,\text{N}}{1580\,\text{N}} = 0.294 \quad [51]$$

This yields $\phi = 16°$.

The external force is also very large, with a value of about 2.4 times the weight of the person. Our anatomy takes great care to ensure that this external force does not contribute to the torque at the hip joint. This is done by moving the head of the femur deep into the acetabulum of the pelvis.

# Case Study: Since When Did Hominids Walk on Two Legs?

The three previous examples illustrate the use of mechanical concepts in human physiology and kinesiology. However, the same concepts also contribute to scientific research in other life sciences. As a special example, an interesting issue in human evolution is presented here.

The evolution of the primates began about 45 million years ago, when the monkeys of the Americas and the monkeys of Africa and Eurasia split. The African group split again about 32 million years ago into *cercopithecids* and *hominoids*. The *cercopithecids* include today's baboons, while the *hominoids* branched four more times between 22 and 7 million years ago, with gibbon, orangutan, gorilla, chimpanzee, and ourselves as the contemporary representatives in each group. Of these, chimpanzees are our closest living relatives, with a DNA match exceeding 99%. The separation of their line occurred about half as long ago as the lines of fox and wolf split.

The evolution of the human branch during the past 5 to 7 million years is still not fully understood. The current section illustrates how physical reasoning in comparative anatomy and physiology can contribute to resolving new questions in this field.

We want to ask the question of whether humans began to walk upright to use tools, and whether walking upright is directly or indirectly linked to the increase in brain volume that isn't observed in any of the ape branches. The study is therefore based on a comparison of three species:

- the chimpanzee, which still moves on four legs when on flat ground,
- modern *Homo sapiens*, which is the only living bipedal mammal, and
- *Lucy*, an **Australopithecus afarensis**, which lived 3.2 million years ago in what is today Ethiopia. Lucy's skeleton is shown in Fig. 5.38 with paleoanthropologist Donald Johanson, its discoverer. We know Lucy's age from the potassium/argon dating method, which is based on nuclear physics concepts we will discuss in Chapter 23.

We first establish the major differences between chimpanzees and humans regarding the leg and the lower body anatomy. Then we use Lucy's fossil record to demonstrate that she was bipedal and, thus, that walking upright has been a feature of hominids for at least the past 3 million years. This is an important finding as it excludes the idea that the ability to walk upright was developed to allow humans to use tools with their hands. The use of tools actually emerged only about 2 million years ago, by which time the brain volume of hominids had sufficiently increased! Thus, modern research considers humans to be on an evolutionary track driven by the co-evolution of a complex hand, allowing the use of tools, and a large brain. The development of brain size as a function of time is illustrated in Fig. 5.39. The *Australopithecines* (1–4) showed a minor brain size increase relative to the modern-day chimpanzees, while about 2 million years ago the first member of the genus homo, *Homo habilis*, already displayed a brain size increase of almost 100% relative to the

**FIGURE 5.38**
Paleoanthropologist Donald Johanson and Lucy, a nearly complete *Australopithecus afarensis* skeleton found in Ethiopia.

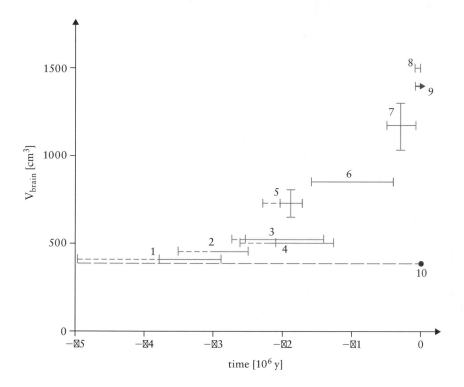

**FIGURE 5.39**

Development of the brain size in unit $cm^3$ as a function of time in million years before present for the members of the hominid branch. The first four species are *Australopithecines*, with (1) *Australopithecus afarensis*, (2) *Australopithecus africanus*, (3) *Australopithecus bosei*, and (4) *Australopithecus robustus*. The next five species are members of the genus *Homo*, with (5) *Homo habilis*, (6) *Homo erectus*, (7) *Homo sapiens* (archaic), (8) *Homo sapiens neanderthalensis*, and (9) *Homo sapiens sapiens* (modern man). For comparison, the brain size of a chimpanzee (10) is included. The solid error bars indicate confirmed data; dashed lines indicate possible extensions of the early period of existence of a species.

apes. *Homo habilis* was the first species known to have used hand-made tools.

Fig. 5.40 compares the major muscles of the leg and pelvis of (a) a modern human and (b) a chimpanzee. Dominating the muscle arrangement of the chimpanzee's upper leg are the small and medium gluteal muscles (called the abductor muscle in humans). These muscles stretch the ape at the hip joint, efficiently accelerating its body forward since the centre of mass lies in front of the hind legs. This means that pushing into the ground under a small angle

with the horizontal plane accelerates the chimpanzee in a similar fashion as the starting sprinter (see Example 3.9). In this context it is also beneficial that the ape has a comparably long upper body, which shifts the centre of mass far ahead of the pelvis. The long upper body is the result of the shape of the pelvis bones, shown in Fig. 5.41(a), with the hip bone stretched upward, and a rather narrow sacrum.

The upright posture of humans is associated with significant changes to the shape of the pelvis bones and to the function of the muscles of the legs.

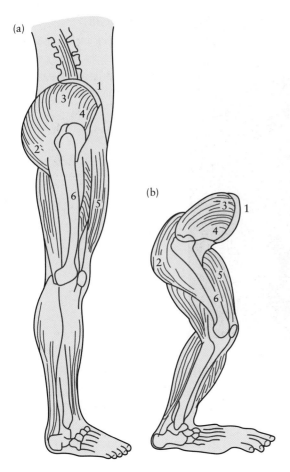

**FIGURE 5.40**

Comparison of the pelvis region and leg of (a) a modern human and (b) a chimpanzee. The figure emphasizes the difference in function of the upper leg muscles and the hip bone. The three gluteal muscles (large gluteal muscle (2), medium gluteal muscle (3), and small gluteal muscle (4)) are the major means of acceleration of a chimpanzee, causing a large, mostly horizontal force on the body when stretched. The gluteal muscle (2) and abductor muscles (3, 4) do not contribute to a forward acceleration for humans but are used to balance the upper body upright. This function is supported by a broader and flatter hip bone (1), lowering the centre of mass for the human body into the pelvis region and thus stabilizing the upright posture. Also labelled are the quadriceps femoris muscle (5) and the femur (6).

Contracting the abductor muscle or the large gluteal muscle, which dominates the muscle arrangements of the human upper leg, would accelerate the upper body only upward but not forward. Consequently, an entirely new mechanism for forward motion has been developed, and the muscles causing acceleration in the leg of the chimpanzee serve new purposes in human legs. The abductor muscle stabilizes the upright posture in the sideways direction, as discussed in Example 5.5, and the gluteal muscle keeps our upper body from falling forward while walking.

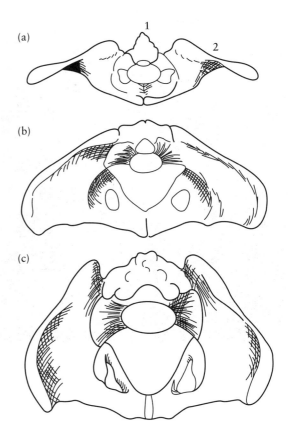

**FIGURE 5.41**

Comparison of the top view of the pelvis of three primates: (a) the chimpanzee with a narrow sacrum (1) and upward-directed wings of the hip bone (2), (b) Lucy, a 3-million-year-old *Australopithecine* with a noticeably broader sacrum and forward-turned wings of the hip bone, and (c) modern humans, where the arrangement of the pelvis bones is similar to those of the *Australopithecines* but resumes an overall more rounded shape.

This focus on balance rather than rapid acceleration also resulted in evolutionary changes to the pelvis, as shown in Fig. 5.41(c). The wings of the hip bone turned inward and the sacrum widened to accommodate the intestines, which lowered the centre of mass. This stabilizes the upright posture because the pelvis plane contains the axes about which our body tilts forward and sideways.

These differences between the quadrupedal chimpanzee and the bipedal modern human can now be used to study Lucy's fossil record. This is possible since her pelvis was found almost completely intact (Fig. 5.41(b)). The striking similarities between Lucy's hip bone and sacrum and those of modern humans indicate that she did indeed walk upright. This is further supported by marks on her pelvis that indicate where the tendons of the various leg muscles were once attached.

Studying Lucy's pelvis more quantitatively, we surprisingly find her even better adapted to an upright posture than modern humans! This is illustrated in Fig. 5.42, where the front view of Lucy's pelvis and the pelvis of modern humans as well as the respective abductor muscle arrangements are overlapped with a balance of torque diagram (dashed line). In both cases, the fulcrum is located in the head of the femur, as discussed in Example 5.5. When the upper body is balanced on one leg, the abductor muscle must compensate the torque about the hip joint. The longer the lever arm of the upper body, $L_{c.m.}$, and the shorter the distance between the abductor muscle and the head of the femur, $L_A$, the greater the strain in the tendons of the abductor muscle. Measuring these lengths in Fig. 5.42, we find:

$$\left(\frac{L_{c.m.}}{L_A}\right)_{Lucy} = 2.1 \qquad \left(\frac{L_{c.m.}}{L_A}\right)_{human} = 2.6$$

$$[52]$$

The larger the ratio in Eq. [52], the less favourable the lever arm arrangement of the pelvis region. Why, then, did the evolution of the genus *Homo* result in more poorly adapted individuals during the last 3 million years? A most likely explanation is based on a competing evolutionary process in modern humans: the development of a large brain. While Lucy was indeed well adapted to an upright posture, her pelvis had an elongated shape with an elliptic, narrow opening for the birth canal. She could never have given birth to the large-headed babies of modern humans. Nature had to compromise by reshaping the pelvis of modern humans to provide a rounder, larger birth canal at the expense of adaptation to the upright posture. Still, the large human brain and the corresponding head size of a baby at birth pose a challenge that required further adjustments. The brain size of a human at birth is 25% of the adult brain size, while a chimpanzee is born with 65% of its adult brain size. A significant fraction of the development of the human brain occurs after birth, which requires a long period of infancy and parental nurturing.

Considering all the problems associated with the upright posture, was it worthwhile for the hominid branch to opt for it? The answer is most likely that there was no other choice. About 20 million years ago, the Indian subcontinent collided with Asia, pushing the Himalayan mountains upward. This caused global climate changes, including a significantly drier landscape in Africa and Asia. Forests retreated in favour of open savannahs. While the lines of the great apes became confined to the dwindling tropical forests, our ancestors responded through adaptation to the new environment.

(a)

(b)

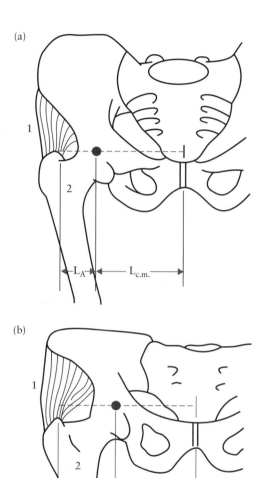

**FIGURE 5.42**

Comparison of the front view of the pelvis region with the abductor muscles (1) for (a) modern humans and (b) the *Australopithecine* Lucy. The *Australopithecines* were better adapted to upright walking as the head of their femur (2) is longer, providing a longer lever arm for the abductor muscle.

# MULTIPLE CHOICE AND CONCEPTUAL QUESTIONS

## A DIFFERENT APPROACH TO CONCEPT TESTING

**Q–5.1.** *Note:* In certain professional admission tests, some multiple choice questions are grouped with a common text called a *passage*. We illustrate this approach with the first four questions in this section.

*Passage:* We study a standard man bending forward to lift an object off the ground, as illustrated in Fig. 5.43(a). The fulcrum lies at the lower back, and the spinal column is the lever arm. We assume that the person is bending forward with the back horizontal and that the forearms are stretched downward. For this case we obtain the balance of torque diagram, shown in Fig. 5.43(b), with four forces acting on the spinal column:

(a)    (b)

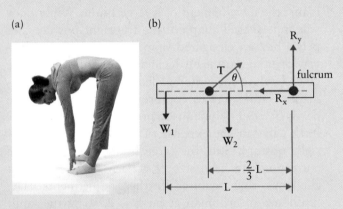

**FIGURE 5.43**

(a) A standard man bends down to lift an object off the ground. (b) The standard man's spine is shown as a bar with four major forces: the weight of the object and the arms, $W_1$; the weight of the trunk and head, $W_2$; the tension in the muscle that maintains the position of the back, $T$; and the force pushing the spine up at the hip, $R$.

- the weight of the torso, $W_2$, acting at the centre of mass located halfway between the two ends of the spinal column,
- the weight of the object that is lifted and combines with the weight of the arms and hands as $W_1$,
- the tension $T$ exerted on the spinal column by the back muscle responsible for the lifting. We assume this force is applied at a distance $d = 2 \cdot L/3$ from the fulcrum at an angle $\theta$ above the horizontal.
- A compressive force, $R$, exerted on the fulcrum in the lower back. Let $\beta$ be the angle between $R$ and the horizontal.

*Question (i):* An author reporting on this case may opt to exclude the force $R$ from Fig. 5.43(b). Why would the author have done so? (A) The author studies a problem of rotational equilibrium and anticipates that this force will not be required when writing the torque formula. (B) Different from a free-body diagram, we may eliminate up to all but one force from a diagram such as Fig. 5.43(b). (C) The physiological knowledge about the magnitude of the force $R$ and its angle $\beta$ is uncertain; thus, omitting the force in Fig. 5.43(b) would eliminate a possible source of error. (D) For the person in the posture shown in Fig. 5.43(a), the force $R$ indeed doesn't exist; i.e., $R = 0$. (E) Fig. 5.43(b) oversimplifies the problem: the force $R$ acts in a direction out of the plane of the paper.

*Question (ii):* Which of the following four formulas is the proper torque equation for the problem illustrated in Fig. 5.43? Note that the term "proper" includes the use of the generally accepted sign convention for torque as introduced in the textbook.

$$(A) \quad \tau_{net} = L \cdot W_1 + \frac{L}{2}W_2 + \frac{2}{3}L \cdot T \cdot \sin\theta = 0$$

$$(B) \quad \tau_{net} = L \cdot W_1 + \frac{L}{2}W_2 - \frac{2}{3}L \cdot T \cdot \sin\theta = 0$$

$$(C) \quad \tau_{net} = -L \cdot W_1 - \frac{L}{2}W_2 + \frac{2}{3}L \cdot T \cdot \sin\theta = 0$$

$$(D) \quad \tau_{net} = -L \cdot W_1 - \frac{L}{2}W_2 - \frac{2}{3}L \cdot T \cdot \sin\theta = 0$$

[53]

*Question (iii):* Assume that Fig. 5.43(a) were instead drawn such that the standard man is shown from the opposite side, i.e., bending down toward the right. Correspondingly, Fig. 5.43(b) would be drawn with the left and right ends flipped horizontally. For this modified display, which of the four choices in Eq. [53] would now be the proper torque equation?

*Question (iv):* If you answered the two previous questions choosing the same formula in Eq. [53], then skip this question. If you have chosen different answers for the two previous questions, then choose the statement below that best describes the consequences of your choices: (A) We need two different formulas because the two cases are physically different. (B) The two formulas we have chosen are mathematically equivalent (differ only due to the sign convention). This is correct because the two cases are physically the same. (C) The two cases should be the same, but the two formulas are indeed different. Thus, there must be something wrong with the introduced sign convention. (D) The two cases differ physically. That the two formulas are mathematically equivalent is accidental.

## TORQUE CONCEPT

**Q–5.2.** A steel band of a brace exerts an external force of magnitude $F_{ext} = 30$ N on a tooth. The tooth is shown in Fig. 5.44 with point B a distance 1.0 cm above point A, which is the fulcrum of the tooth. The angle between the normal with the tooth and the external force is $\theta = 45°$. Which of the following values is closest to the torque on the root of the tooth about point A? (A) 0.2 N · m; (B) 0.2 N; (C) 0.2 m; (D) 2.0 N · m; (E) 2.0 N.

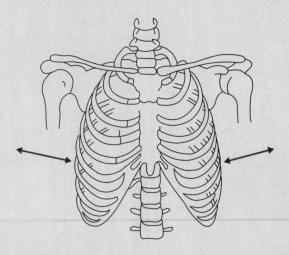

**FIGURE 5.45**

The thorax, with two arrows indicating the motion of the rib cage during breathing.

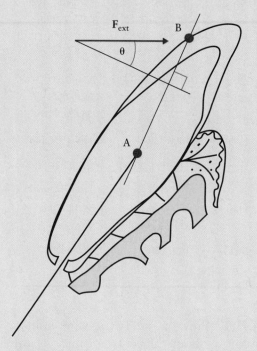

**FIGURE 5.44**

A horizontal force $\mathbf{F}_{ext}$ acts at point B on a tooth with the fulcrum at point A.

**Q–5.3.** The definition of torque contains the magnitude of the force **F** acting on a rigid object with a fixed axis, the magnitude of the vector **r** between the fulcrum and the point where the force is applied, and the angle $\phi$ between the force vector **F** and position vector **r**. Which of the following statements about torque is wrong? (A) Torque is linearly proportional to the magnitude of the force **F**. (B) Torque is linearly proportional to the magnitude of the vector **r**. (C) Torque is linearly proportional to the angle $\phi$. (D) Torque can be positive or negative depending on the angle $\phi$. (E) The force **F** can be applied to the rigid object such that the resulting torque is zero.

**Q–5.4.** Fig. 5.45 shows the motion of the thorax during breathing. Air is pulled into the lungs and pushed out of the lungs by the active change of their volume associated with the change in the volume within the rib cage. Two sets of intercostal muscles allow for the

increase and decrease of this volume. These muscles are shown in Fig. 5.46 and consist of the *intercostales interni muscles* (connecting points B' and C in the figure) and the *intercostales externi muscles* (connecting points B and C'). The fulcrum lies in the joint between the rib and the thoracic vertebrae. Determine from Fig. 5.46 which muscle contracts during inhalation (volume increase) and which muscle contracts during exhalation (volume decrease).

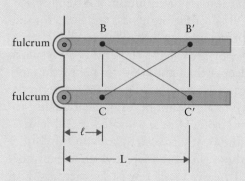

**FIGURE 5.46**

Muscle connections between two neighbouring ribs.

**Q–5.5.** A rod is 7 metres long and is pivoted at a point 2.0 m from the left end. A force of magnitude 50 N acts downward at the left end and a force of magnitude 200 N at the right end. At what distance from the pivot point must a third upward-directed force of magnitude 300 N be placed to establish rotational equilibrium? Neglect the weight of the rod. (A) 1.0 m; (B) 2.0 m; (C) 3.0 m; (D) 4.0 m; (E) None of the first four answers is correct.

**Q–5.6.** (a) Give an example in which the net force on an object is zero, but the net torque is not zero. (b) Give an example in which the net torque on an object is zero but not the net force.

## JOINTS AND LEVER SYSTEMS

**Q–5.7.** What is the major difference between (a) hinge and pivot joints, and (b) ellipsoid and saddle joints?

**Q–5.8.** What class of lever system is (a) the wing of the horsefly in Fig. 3.1 and (b) the pelvis and hip in Fig. 5.42?

## ROTATIONAL EQUILIBRIUM

**Q–5.9.** Why does holding a long pole help a tightrope walker stay balanced?

**Q–5.10.** Fig. 5.42 shows a comparison of the front view of the pelvis region with the abductor muscles for two bipedal species (a) and (b). The dot indicates the fulcrum located at the head of the femur. If we assume the same length of leg and weight of both individuals, but take into account that $L_A/L_{c.m.} = 0.38$ for individual (a) and $L_A/L_{c.m.} = 0.48$ for individual (b), then species (b) needs a greater strength (force) in the abductor muscle to balance its upper body on the shown leg. (A) True; (B) False; (C) We cannot determine whether this is true or false.

**Q–5.11.** A typical mass distribution of a tree is 60% for the trunk, 20% for the branches, and 20% for the root system. Despite the great heights to which trees can grow, most of them have shallow root systems not reaching deeper than about 60 cm below the surface. Considering once more Fig. 4.16, determine why the root system may not be a sufficient anchor to protect against strong winds, as noted in Table 5.1, which defines the Beaufort scale. Can you think of a reason why these shallow root systems evolved? Trees appeared in the fossil record as early as 370 million years ago, with most modern species emerging during the last 65 million years. Trees should therefore not display serious misadaptations.

**Q–5.12.** The Iceland scallop is a mollusk that protects its soft body with two shells. It moves by pulling the shells together, forcing out jets of water to push itself along. Discuss the advantages and disadvantages for the scallop of applying its force closer to or farther from the hinge between the shells.

### TABLE 5.1

**Beaufort scale of the force of winds, introduced in 1858 by Sir Francis Beaufort**

| Beaufort number | Wind speed (km/h) | Name | Effect on trees |
|---|---|---|---|
| 0–2 | 0–11 | Calm to light breeze | Leaves rustle |
| 3–4 | 12–28 | Gentle to moderate breeze | Leaves and small twigs in continuous motion, small branches move |
| 5–6 | 29–49 | Fresh to strong breeze | Small-leaved trees sway, large branches move |
| 7 | 50–61 | Moderate gale | Whole trees sway |
| 8–9 | 62–88 | Fresh to strong gale | Twigs break off |
| 10–11 | 89–117 | Storm to violent storm | Trees uprooted |
| 12 | >117 | Hurricane | Widespread damage |

**Q–5.13.** Fig. 5.47 shows a one-bottle wine holder. What do we know about the centre of mass of the system bottle and wine holder if it is in rotational equilibrium, i.e., doesn't fall over?

**FIGURE 5.47**

# ANALYTICAL PROBLEMS

## TORQUE

**P–5.1.** If the torque required to loosen a nut has a magnitude of $\tau = 40\ N \cdot m$, what minimum force must be exerted at the end of a 30-cm-long wrench?

**P–5.2.** A pendulum consists of an object of mass $m = 3.0$ kg that hangs at the end of a massless bar, a distance of 2.0 m from the pivot point. Calculate the magnitude of the torque due to gravity about the pivot point if the bar makes an angle of 5° with the vertical.

**P–5.3.** A steel band of a brace exerts an external force of magnitude $F_{ext} = 40$ N on a tooth. The tooth is shown in Fig. 5.44, with point B a distance 1.3 cm above point A, which is the fulcrum. The angle between the tooth and the external force is $\theta = 40°$. What is the torque on the root of the tooth about point A?

## ROTATIONAL EQUILIBRIUM

**P–5.4.** A standard man (see Table 3.3) stands on a scaffold supported by a vertical rope at each end. The scaffold has a mass of $m = 20.5$ kg and is 3.0 m long. What is the tension in each rope when the person stands 1.0 m from one end?

**P–5.5.** Fig. 5.48 shows a light of mass $m = 20$ kg supported at the end of a horizontal bar of negligible mass that is hinged to a pole. A cable at an angle of 30° with the bar helps to support the light. Find (a) the magnitude of the tension in the cable, and (b) the horizontal and vertical force components exerted on the bar by the pole.

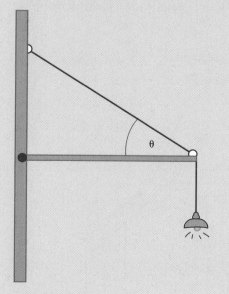

**FIGURE 5.48**

**P–5.6.** A ladder rests against a frictionless wall. It has a mass of 50 kg, a length of 15.0 m, and makes an angle of 60° with the ground. Find the horizontal and vertical force components exerted by the ground on the bottom of the ladder if a standard man stands on the ladder 4 m from the ground.

**P–5.7.** Fig. 5.49 shows a uniform boom of mass $m = 120$ kg supported by a cable perpendicular to the boom. The boom is hinged at the bottom, and an object of mass $M = 200$ kg hangs from its top. Find the tension in the massless cable and the components of the force exerted on the boom at the hinge.

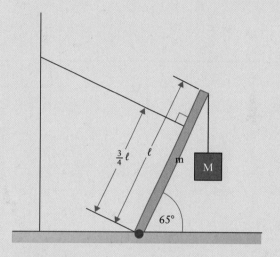

**FIGURE 5.49**

**P–5.8.** A standard man is doing push-ups, as shown in Fig. 5.50. The distances are $l_1 = 90$ cm and $l_2 = 55$ cm. (a) Calculate the vertical component of the normal force exerted by the floor on both hands, and (b) calculate the normal force exerted by the floor on both feet. Use Table 3.3 for the data of the standard man.

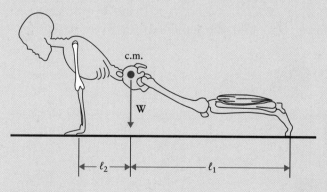

**FIGURE 5.50**

**P–5.9.** A standard man holds the upper arm vertical and the lower arm horizontal with an object of mass

$M = 6$ kg resting on the hand, as illustrated in Fig. 5.1. The mass of the lower arm and hand is one-half of the mass of the entire arm. Shown in Fig. 5.51 is the arrangement of the four forces acting on the lower arm that we include in the calculations: (I) the external force $\mathbf{F}_{ext}$, exerted by the bones and ligaments of the upper arm at the elbow (fulcrum), (II) the tension $\mathbf{T}$, exerted by the biceps, (III) a force $\mathbf{F}$ due to the weight $\mathbf{W}_M$ of the object of mass $M$, (IV) the weight $\mathbf{W}_F$ of the lower arm. The points along the lower arm, at which the forces act, are identified in Fig. 5.51: $l_1 = 4$ cm, $l_2 = 15$ cm, and $l_3 = 40$ cm. (a) Calculate the vertical component of the force $\mathbf{F}_{ext}$, and (b) calculate the vertical component of the tension $\mathbf{T}$.

(a) What is the magnitude of the vertical force exerted on the lower arm by the triceps muscle, and (b) what is the magnitude of the vertical force exerted on the lower arm by the humerus? *Hint:* The triceps muscle pulls vertically upward.

**P–5.11.** A standard man holds an object of mass $m = 2$ kg on the palm of the hand with the arm stretched, as shown in Fig. 5.53. Use the torque equilibrium equation to determine the magnitude of the force $\mathbf{F}$ that is exerted by the biceps muscle, when $a = 35$ cm, $b = 5$ cm, and the angle $\theta = 80°$. (a) Neglect the weight of the lower arm. (b) Is the assumption of a negligible mass of the lower arm in part (a) justified?

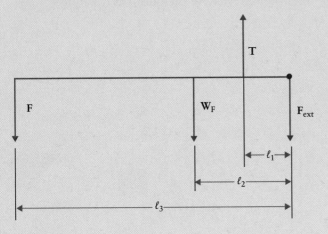

**FIGURE 5.51**

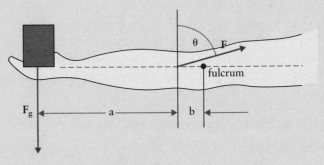

**FIGURE 5.53**

**P–5.10.** An object of mass $M = 10$ kg is lifted by a standard man with the aid of a pulley, as shown in Fig. 5.52. The upper arm is held vertical and the lower arm has an angle of $\theta = 35°$ with the horizontal. The label c.m. marks the centre of mass of the lower arm. Consider the force due to the weight of the object $M$, the weight of the lower arm and hand, the tension due to the triceps muscle, and the force due to the humerus. For the lengths we use the following values: $l_1 = 2$ cm, $l_2 = 15$ cm, $l_3 = 40$ cm. The lower arm and the hand have a mass of 2.3 kg.

**P–5.12.** The quadriceps femoris muscle, shown as (1) in Fig. 5.54(a), is a muscle in the upper leg that serves an analogous purpose to the triceps in the upper arm. Its tendon (2) is attached to the upper end of the tibia (3), as shown in the figure. This muscle exerts the major force of the upper leg on the lower leg when it is stretched. (a) We consider the weight of the lower leg, $\mathbf{W}_L$, the weight of the foot, $\mathbf{F}$, and the tension $\mathbf{T}$ of the quadriceps femoris muscle in Fig. 5.54(b). Find the magnitude of the tension $\mathbf{T}$

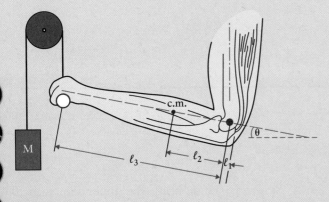

**FIGURE 5.52**

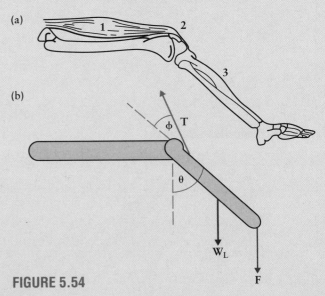

**FIGURE 5.54**

when the tendon is at an angle of $\phi = 30°$ with the tibia using the torque equilibrium. Assume that the lower leg has a mass of 3 kg and the mass of the foot is 1.2 kg. The leg is extended at an angle of $\theta = 35°$ with the vertical and the centre of mass of the lower leg is at its centre. The tendon attaches to the lower leg at a point $\frac{1}{3}$ of the way down the lower leg. (b) Establish whether the three forces shown in Fig. 5.54(b) are in mechanical equilibrium.

**P–5.13.** A standard man bends over as shown in Fig. 5.43(a) and lifts an object of mass $m = 15$ kg while keeping the back parallel with the floor. The muscle that attaches $\frac{2}{3}$ of the way up the spine maintains the position of the back. This muscle is called the back muscle or the *latissimus dorsi muscle*. The angle between the spine and the force **T** in this muscle is $\theta = 11°$. Use the balance of torque diagram in Fig. 5.43(b). The weight $\mathbf{W}_1$ includes the object and the arms; the weight $\mathbf{W}_2$ includes the trunk and head of the standard man (use data from Table 3.3). (a) Find the magnitude of the tension **T** in the back muscle, and (b) find the $x$-component of the compressive force **R** in the spine.

**P–5.14.** A standard man holds the arm stretched out horizontally. The major forces acting on the arm are shown in Fig. 5.55: $\mathbf{F}_{ext}$ is the force acting into the shoulder joint, **T** is the tension of the *deltoid muscle*, and **W** is the weight of the arm. Use the standard man data from Table 3.3, $\alpha = 15°$ for the angle, $l_1 = 13$ cm for the distance between the shoulder and the attachment point of the tendon of the *deltoid muscle*, and $l_2 = 35$ cm for the distance from the shoulder to the centre of mass of the arm. (a) Calculate the magnitude of the tension **T** in the tendon of the *deltoid muscle*, and (b) calculate the magnitude of the external force $\mathbf{F}_{ext}$ acting toward the shoulder.

**FIGURE 5.56**

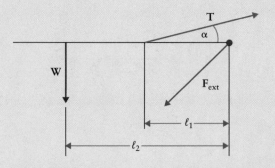

**FIGURE 5.55**

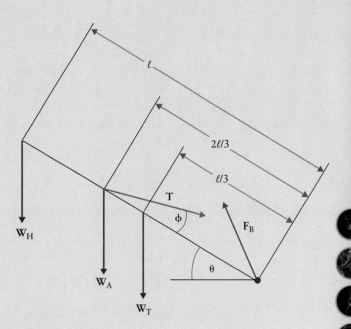

**FIGURE 5.57**

**P–5.15.** A standard man plays on the offence of a football team. Fig. 5.56 shows the quarterback and the centre. Before a play, the centre, the guards, and the tackles bend the upper body forward, forming about a $\theta = 45°$ angle with the horizontal, then remain motionless until the play starts. Fig. 5.57 shows the corresponding balance of torque diagram for the standard man's back. We consider the weight of the head H, the arms A, and the trunk T (see Table 3.3), as well as mass $m = 1.2$ kg for a typical helmet. Calculate (a) the magnitude of the tension T in the back muscle, and (b) the magnitude of the force $F_B$ acting on the fifth lumbar vertebra (fulcrum). *Note:* The figure indicates that the tension T forms an 11° angle with the spinal column.

## CHALLENGING PROBLEMS

**P–5.16.** A standard man is suspended from a high bar. The sketch in Fig. 5.58 shows the lower arm in a side view with the person facing right. Four forces act on the lower arm: the external force $F_{ext}$ exerted by the high bar, the weight of the lower arm $W_{la}$, the tension in the biceps tendon, T, and the force exerted by the humerus through the elbow, $F_{elbow}$. Assume that the forces exerted by the bar on the left and right hand are each equal in magnitude to $F_{ext}$ and directed parallel to each other. (a) Find the magnitude of the external force $F_{ext}$, (b) find the magnitude of the tension T, and (c) find the magnitude of $F_{elbow}$ and its angle with the lower arm, $\psi$. *Hint:* Include the weight of the lower arm $W_{la}$ with $m_{la} = 2.3$ kg, and assume that T and $F_{elbow}$ are the only forces exerted on the lower arm by the upper arm. Also use $l_1 = 40$ cm for the length from the hand to the elbow, $l_2 = 15$ cm for the length from the centre of mass of the lower arm to the elbow, and $l_3 = 4$ cm for the distance of the attachment point of the biceps tendon to the elbow. The two angles are $\theta = \phi = 8°$.

**P–5.17.** Fig. 5.59 shows a standard man wearing a cast supported by a sling, which exerts a vertical force F on the lower arm. The distance between the shoulder joint and the elbow is $l_1 = 35$ cm, and the mass of the cast is 3 kg. The sling supports the lower arm at the centre of mass $l_2 = 15$ cm from the elbow. Use one-half of the mass of the arm without cast for the mass of the lower arm, and $\theta = 70°$ for the angle of the arm at the elbow. Calculate the magnitude of force F. *Hint:* Other forces act on the arm, which we assume to act along a line through the shoulder joint. Thus, equating F with the weights of the upper and lower arm does not yield the correct result. Instead, the problem is solved with the balance of torque equation, in which the unknown forces at the shoulder joint are not included.

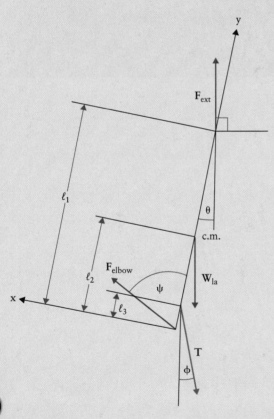

**FIGURE 5.58**

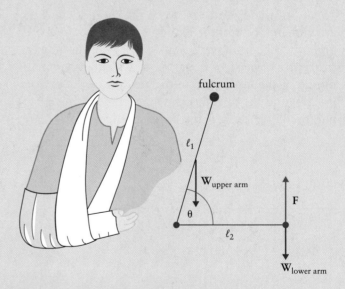

**FIGURE 5.59**

# MATH REVIEW

## VECTOR MULTIPLICATION: SCALAR PRODUCT

Two ways exist to multiply two vectors with each other. The scalar product or dot product leads to a scalar ($\mathbf{a} \cdot \mathbf{b} = r$), and the vector product or cross-product leads to a vector ($\mathbf{a} \times \mathbf{b} = \mathbf{r}$). Both products are discussed in this Math Review. Note that we use a large dot (•) to indicate a dot product. This distinguishes in print the multiplication of vectors from the (regular) multiplication of scalars (numbers), which we always indicate with a small dot (·).

Fig. 5.60 illustrates that the scalar product of two vectors is related to the product of the lengths of the two vectors after one vector has been projected onto the direction of the other:

$$\mathbf{a} \cdot \mathbf{b} = |\mathbf{a}| \cdot |\mathbf{b}| \cdot \cos \phi$$

Special cases are $\phi = 90°$ with $\mathbf{a} \cdot \mathbf{b} = 0$, $\phi = 0°$ with $\mathbf{a} \cdot \mathbf{b} = |\mathbf{a}| \cdot |\mathbf{b}|$, and $\mathbf{a} \cdot \mathbf{a} = |\mathbf{a}|^2$.

The scalar product is calculated using the components of the vectors:

$$\mathbf{a} \cdot \mathbf{b} = a_x \cdot b_x + a_y \cdot b_y \, (+ \, a_z \cdot b_z)$$

The benefit of using the Cartesian coordinate system with its orthogonal axes lies in the fact that the different components along the $x$-, $y$- and $z$-axes do not mix up in the last equation. Thus, vector algebra (with the exclusion of the vector product below) is rather simple, as any operation is equivalent to the same algebraic operation for numbers except that the operation is repeated for each component separately.

### Example 5.6

(a) Calculate the angle between any two CH bonds in the methane molecule, shown in Figs. 2.25 and 4.12.

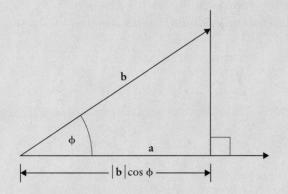

**FIGURE 5.60**

Illustration of the origin of the factor cos $\phi$ in the scalar product of vectors **a** and **b**.

This angle is called the tetrahedral angle for the $sp^3$-hybridization of carbon atoms in organic molecules. Hybridization is discussed in Chapter 22. (b) Using the length of 0.11 nm for a CH bond, determine the side length of the cube, $l$, and (c) the distance between any two hydrogen atoms.

*Solution to part (a):* First, we determine the vectors connecting the C atom with the hydrogen atoms $H_A$ and $H_B$ in Figure 4.12. These vectors are:

$$\mathbf{CH_A} = -\mathbf{C} + \mathbf{H_A}$$

written in component form:

$$x\text{-direction:} \quad -\frac{l}{2} + 0 = -\frac{l}{2}$$

$$y\text{-direction:} \quad -\frac{l}{2} + 0 = -\frac{l}{2}$$

$$z\text{-direction:} \quad -\frac{l}{2} + 0 = -\frac{l}{2}$$

and:

$$\mathbf{CH_B} = -\mathbf{C} + \mathbf{H_B}$$

written in component form:

$$x\text{-direction:} \quad -\frac{l}{2} + l = +\frac{l}{2}$$

$$y\text{-direction:} \quad -\frac{l}{2} + l = +\frac{l}{2}$$

$$z\text{-direction:} \quad -\frac{l}{2} + 0 = -\frac{l}{2}$$

i.e., to get from the carbon atom to the hydrogen atom $H_A$, you have first to travel the vector **C** backward to the origin, and then from the origin to the H atom forward along the vector $\mathbf{H_A}$. The angle $\theta$, between the vectors follows from the dot product:

$$\mathbf{CH_A} \cdot \mathbf{CH_B} = |\mathbf{CH_A}| \cdot |\mathbf{CH_B}| \cdot \cos \theta$$

The vector magnitudes on the right-hand side are:

$$|\mathbf{CH_A}| = |\mathbf{CH_B}| = \sqrt{\left(\frac{l}{2}\right)^2 + \left(\frac{l}{2}\right)^2 + \left(\frac{l}{2}\right)^2}$$

$$= \frac{\sqrt{3}}{2} l$$

and the dot product on the left-hand side is calculated from the basic definition of the dot product in component form:

$$\mathbf{CH_A} \cdot \mathbf{CH_B} = \left(-\frac{l}{2}\right) \cdot \frac{l}{2} + \left(-\frac{l}{2}\right) \cdot \frac{l}{2}$$
$$+ \left(-\frac{l}{2}\right) \cdot \left(-\frac{l}{2}\right)$$
$$= -2 \cdot \frac{l^2}{4} + \frac{l^2}{4} = -\frac{l^2}{4}$$

Thus, $\cos\theta = (-l^2/4)/(3l^2/4) = -\frac{1}{3}$ and $\theta = 109.47°$.

*Solution to part (b):* We calculated above that $|\mathbf{CH_B}| = \frac{1}{2}l\sqrt{3}$. With this length given as 0.11 nm, we find that $l = 2|\mathbf{CH_B}|/\sqrt{3} = 0.127$ nm.

*Solution to part (c):* Since the distance between any two hydrogen atoms is equal to the magnitude of the vector connecting the two H atoms, we find for the example of the hydrogen atoms labelled A and B that the distance $|\mathbf{H_A H_B}| = |-\mathbf{H_A} + \mathbf{H_B}| = (l^2 + l^2)^{1/2} = \sqrt{2} \cdot l = 0.180$ nm.

## VECTOR PRODUCT

The vector product is written in the form:

$$\mathbf{r} = \mathbf{a} \times \mathbf{b}$$

with $\mathbf{a}$ and $\mathbf{b}$ two non-parallel vectors and $\mathbf{r}$ the resulting vector. You apply it in its component form:

$x$-component: $r_x = a_y \cdot b_z - a_z \cdot b_y$

$y$-component: $r_y = a_z \cdot b_x - a_x \cdot b_z$

$z$-component: $r_z = a_x \cdot b_y - a_y \cdot b_x$

Note that the components of vectors $\mathbf{a}$ and $\mathbf{b}$ are no longer separated in the three component formulas. These equations determine the direction of the resulting vector: it is directed perpendicular to the plane defined by vectors $\mathbf{a}$ and $\mathbf{b}$. This is illustrated in Fig. 5.61, establishing the **right-hand rule**: stretch your thumb, index finger, and middle finger of the right hand such that they form pair-wise right angles with each other. The thumb represents the first vector of the vector product $\mathbf{a}$; the index finger points in the direction of the second vector $\mathbf{b}$. The middle finger then represents the direction of the resulting vector $\mathbf{r}$.

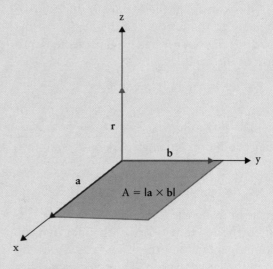

**FIGURE 5.61**

Relative directions of the vectors forming a vector product.

# SUMMARY

### DEFINITIONS

- If $\mathbf{F}$ is a force acting on a rigid object at distance $\mathbf{r}$ from the fixed axis of rotation, the torque $\tau$ is defined as:

$$\boldsymbol{\tau} = \mathbf{r} \times \mathbf{F}$$

- magnitude of torque:

$$\tau = r \cdot F \cdot \sin\phi$$

where $\phi$ is the angle between the vectors $\mathbf{F}$ and $\mathbf{r}$.

- magnitude of torque due to weight:

$$\tau_{\text{weight}} = r_{\text{c.m.}} \cdot M \cdot g \cdot \sin\phi$$

with $r_{\text{c.m.}}$ the distance of the fulcrum to the centre of mass, $M$ the mass of the system, and $\phi$ the angle between the weight vector and the lever arm.

- Sign-convention for the torque:

If the rotation is counter-clockwise, then $\tau > 0$; if the rotation is clockwise, then $\tau < 0$

### UNITS

Torque $\tau$: $N \cdot m = kg \cdot m^2/s^2$

### LAWS

- The mechanical equilibrium for a rigid object with a fixed axis along the $z$-direction is:

condition 1: $\sum_i F_{ix} = 0$

condition 2: $\sum_i F_{iy} = 0$

condition 3: $\sum_i \tau_i = 0$

# PART 2
# SEMPER IDEM

In the following group of four chapters the focus shifts from force to energy. This is necessary to prepare us to move beyond the realm of mechanics, i.e., beyond systems of a few distinguishable objects. The discussion still starts in mechanics, with the introduction of mechanical forms of energy. These alone, however, lead to problems in formulating a conservation law. At that point we leave mechanics behind and formulate the conservation law in its broadest form, called the first law of thermodynamics.

The ideal gas is introduced as a simple system that allows us to discuss thermal physics concepts, including the second law of thermodynamics. We move along this line of reasoning until we reach Gibbs free energy, which represents the interface with the traditional realm of chemistry. A particular topic at this boundary, the thermodynamics of mixed systems, is included because it plays a pivotal role in the understanding of physiologically relevant fluids.

The major theme of this part is **immutability**. When you enter a tropical rain forest, you find life buzzing all around you in boundless plenty and playful chaos. But if you look more carefully, you realize that it unfolds with detailed planning and purposeful budgeting of every move. Adherence to underlying immutable principles is absolute because—different from social economy—no option to run an energy deficit exists.

*Semper idem* means "always the same." It has been an idiom since Cicero, one of Rome's great orators and statesmen in the dying days of the Republic, introduced it as a reference to human activity. It certainly captures the meaning of the conservation laws we work with in the physical sciences.

# CHAPTER 6

# BIOENERGETICS
## Energy and Its Conservation

Living systems interact in three fundamental ways with their environment: (i) through the exchange of heat, (ii) through the performance of work, and (iii) through the exchange of matter. The first two interactions are quantified here.

Energy is the main concept in this chapter, but we need to define work first. We introduce work both for a mechanical object, where it is the product of an applied force and the resulting displacement of the object, and for a gas, where work is the negative product of gas pressure and volume change. This sign convention leads to a positive value of work when work is done on (received by) the system. Work done on or by the system in turn defines the change in energy of the system.

Energy can be stored in many ways in a system. Each form we introduce is quantified by allowing the system to undergo a specific change and measuring the amount of work exchanged with the environment. The only exception to this principle is thermal energy, which we define by the exchange of heat between system and environment. The thermal energy of a system is defined by its temperature; exclusive heat flow is related to a temperature change.

Energy obtains its central role in the physical sciences due to its conservation: the energy of an isolated system is constant, and the energy of a system in interaction with its environment varies exactly by the amount of work and heat exchanged.

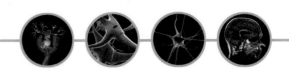

The term **bioenergetics** was created in 1912 to describe energy transformations and energy exchanges within and between living cells and their environment. It includes in particular the closely related concept of **metabolism,** which is the sum of all chemical changes in living cells by which energy is provided for vital processes. These processes can be divided into three types of work done by the cell:

- mechanical work in the context of locomotion,
- transport work in transferring matter across membranes, and
- chemical work to facilitate non-spontaneous reactions such as polymerizations.

Bioenergetics and metabolism are also studied at the macroscopic level to describe the energy budget of an organism.

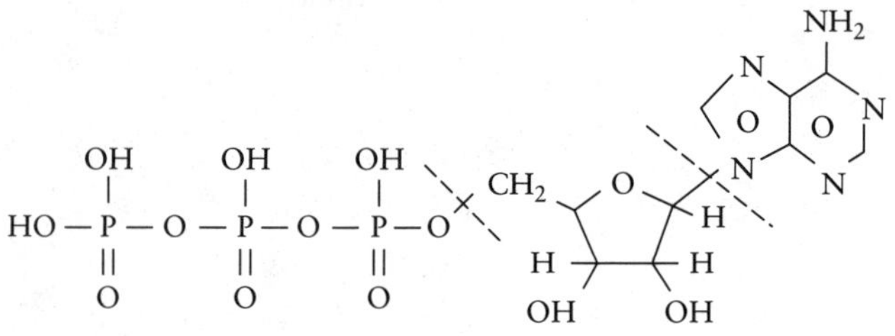

## Metabolism at the Cellular Level: The Role of ATP

In Chapter 3, Fig. 3.3 illustrates how a force is generated in muscle tissue by repetitively traversing the sliding filament mechanism, which consists of three basic steps: (i) the myosin–actin attachment, (ii) the muscle contraction during which the myosin heads tilt, and (iii) the regeneration. Every cycle of this process shortens each individual sarcomere by a very small distance; the simultaneous completion of these cycles by all sarcomeres in a muscle allows, then, for a macroscopic motion of a bone attached to the muscle.

We use the term *work* in our everyday language to describe what the muscle action accomplishes. Work cannot be done for free: we all have experienced the fatigue that results from prolonged use of our muscles, for example in sports. Thus, something must be stored in our body, or specifically in our muscles, that provides us with the capability to do the work. We define this thing as energy.

Fig. 3.3 allows us a glimpse into the way in which the muscle stores energy. You notice in the sketch of the resting muscle (top frame of the figure) a small circle labelled ATP. This represents a molecule with the chemical name **adenosine triphosphate**; it is shown in Fig. 6.1. ATP consists of three characteristic components, which are, from right to left, an adenine group, a pentose sugar group, and a chain of three phosphate groups. For the current discussion we focus on the last of the three phosphate groups at the left. If you follow the ATP molecule through the sliding filament mechanism of Fig. 3.3, you notice that it splits at the instant the myosin head tilts from

**FIGURE 6.1**

Chemical formula of an adenosine triphosphate (ATP) molecule. The molecule consists of three components frequently found in bio-molecules: A nitrogen-containing double-ring base (adenine, upper right part), a pentose sugar (ribose with an oxygen-containing ring at the centre), and three phosphate groups.

90° to 45°. This is the instant the sarcomere contributes to the muscle contraction. The release of the terminal phosphate group of the ATP molecule is a chemical reaction resulting in the formation of an adenosine diphosphate (ADP) molecule:

$$ATP + ROH \rightarrow ADP + R\text{—}OPO(OH)_2 \quad [1]$$

ROH is an alcohol molecule in which R means *rest molecule*. It is the ROH molecule to which the energy in the **ATP hydrolysis** of Eq. [1] is transferred. The involvement of energy in chemical reactions like the one in Eq. [1] is often highlighted in physical chemistry by rewriting the process in two partial reactions. We illustrate this for the synthesis of saccharose from glucose and fructose, which occurs in two steps:

| | |
|---|---|
| $ATP \rightarrow ADP + H_3PO_4$ | $+29\,kJ/mol$ |
| $Glucose + H_3PO_4 \rightarrow Glucose\text{–}Phosphate$ | $-12.5\,kJ/mol$ |
| $ATP + Glucose \rightarrow Glucose\text{–}Phosphate + ADP$ | $+16.5\,kJ/mol$ |

$$[2]$$

then the glucose–phosphate molecule reacts with fructose:

$$Glucose\text{–}Phosphate + Fructose \rightarrow Saccharose + H_3PO_4 \quad [3]$$

In summary,

$$ATP + Glucose + Fructose \rightarrow Saccharose + ADP + H_3PO_4 \quad [4]$$

i.e., a reaction that would not have occurred has been made possible by the transfer of energy released from the splitting of the ATP molecule and picked up by the glucose molecule by forming a reactive intermediate compound, glucose–phosphate. What these molecules transfer to each other is called **chemical energy**. Note that the amount of chemical energy released or taken up by the single steps in Eq. [2] can be added to quantify the overall reaction. However, the two energy values in Eq. [2] do not tell us the complete story of the processes involved in the saccharose synthesis. Thus, we need to study first what energy terms mean, such as those in Eq. [2], and then we need to investigate the details of the energy transfer mechanisms.

At any given time, the ATP concentration in muscle cells is relatively low and sufficient for only a few muscle contraction cycles. This means that the muscle must quickly find energy from somewhere else or it would become disabled before much is achieved. Since energy cannot be created out of nothing, only two options exist: transport ATP molecules through the cell membrane into the muscle cell, or produce new ATP molecules. The first option is not feasible because ATP molecules are too big to pass the cell membrane easily. Thus, the cell must recycle its ADP molecules; i.e., it must run the first reaction in Eq. [2] backward. This process is called **phosphorylation**. A problem is associated with this approach: since the ATP hydrolysis releases 29 kJ/mol of energy, the ADP phosphorylation requires the same amount of energy. Thus, the cell needs energy to exert a force (muscle action), but it also needs energy to re-synthesize the energy agent it uses.

The cell deals with this apparent dilemma in the following fashion: the ADP molecule formed in the muscle contraction step of Fig. 3.3 is removed and transported to a **mitochondrion** located within the muscle cell. During the regeneration step of the sarcomere, a new ATP molecule is attached to the myosin head. This ATP molecule in turn has been brought from the same or another mitochondrion in the cell. Thus, the mitochondria are the source of ATP molecules; i.e., the mitochondria are the intercellular power plants. The amount of energy that they have to provide to a cell varies vastly: a small microorganism may have just 10 mitochondria, while a human muscle cell requires on the order of 200 000 mitochondria to function properly.

Fig. 6.2 shows a scanning electron micrograph of a mitochondrion that is cut open to reveal its internal structure. A mitochondrion is about 1 μm long. It is enclosed by two membranes. The outer membrane is a smooth envelope; the inner membrane is heavily folded: this structure is called *cristae*. The cristae structure significantly increases the inner surface of the mitochondrion and thus increases the surface on which the ATP production takes place. Mitochondria absorb from the cytoplasm of the cell a compound called **pyruvic acid,** which is a primary product of the chemical breakdown of food in the cell. In a series of chemical reactions, single hydrogen atoms are isolated from the pyruvic acid. These

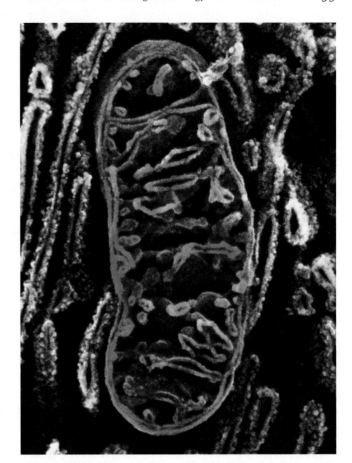

**FIGURE 6.2**

The mitochondrion is the power plant of the animal cell. This coloured high-resolution scanning electron micrograph (SEM) illustrates its internal structure. The mitochondrion is about 0.5 μm to 1.0 μm long and has two membranes, a smooth outer membrane and a folded inner membrane, called cristae. The folding increases the inner surface to allow for an increased rate of ADP phosphorylation to ATP. Mitochondria replicate independently during cell division. We believe therefore that they were originally bacteria that became incorporated into the eukaryotic cells by way of an intracellular symbiosis. When an egg is fertilized by a sperm, the mitochondria of the sperm do not enter the egg. Therefore, only the mother's mitochondria are inherited. This feature is used to trace maternal family trees, including evidence that all humans have descended from a woman who lived as long as 300 000 years ago in Africa. This woman is accordingly called Mitochondrial Eve.

hydrogen atoms combine with oxygen to form water. The energy released in this reaction is used in the phosphorylation of ADP.

Does the recycling of ADP molecules in the mitochondria solve the muscle cell's energy problem? Only for a short period: for the first 50 to 100 contraction cycles, which corresponds at most to a few seconds of muscle activity, the mitochondria have stored enough of an energy-rich molecule called keratin–phosphate to recover ATP from ADP molecules. Thereafter, for up to one minute, glycogen is used instead of keratin–phosphate. The chemical

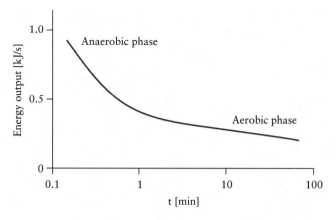

**FIGURE 6.3**

Energy dissipated per second by an average healthy adult on a bicycle. The logarithmic time scale highlights the change at shorter times during the anaerobic phase. The loss of power is slowed in the aerobic phase. The data representation of this figure shows in particular the transition from the anaerobic to the aerobic phase after about one minute.

reactions of both compounds have short response times because they are **anaerobic reactions**. Such reactions do not need the supply of oxygen from outside the cell and are called *lactic acid fermentations* because of the product formed in the process. Fig. 6.3 shows the typical energy output per second for an average healthy adult on a bicycle. The time axis of the figure is a logarithmic scale to highlight short times. As Fig. 6.3 illustrates, the energy output decreases fast initially, but after about one minute continues at a lower rate. This marks the transition to the **aerobic phase,** in which the muscle cells use oxygen acquired through the cell membrane.

The careful budgeting of energy is not limited to the processes occurring in the mitochondria. Most biochemical processes serve the purpose of transforming energy. These chemical processes, which are coordinated with each other throughout the organism, are described by the term *metabolism*. Metabolic processes are divided into two groups based on their energy balance:

- **anabolic processes,** which require energy and include the growth of new cells and the maintenance of body tissues, and

- **catabolic processes,** which involve the release of energy for external and internal physical activities.

Catabolism includes the maintenance of the body temperature and the degradation of chemical compounds into smaller substances that can be removed from the body via the skin, the lungs, the kidneys, or the intestines.

# Bioenergetics at the Organism Level

Why do life processes focus so much on energy? This is due to three important properties of energy we will establish in this chapter:

- energy cannot be created or destroyed, but

- energy can flow from one place to another, and

- energy can transfer between its different forms with some restrictions.

Let us highlight these three features with examples of the bioenergetics of bacteria and predatory dinosaurs.

## Case Study: The Bacterium *Escherichia coli* (*E. coli*)

*E. coli* is a **bacterium** responsible for several illnesses such as peritonitis, appendicitis, sepsis, sinusitis, otitis, diarrhea, and some forms of meningitis. *E. coli* are small with a volume of $2.25 \times 10^{-18}$ m$^3$ and a mass of about $2.5 \times 10^{-15}$ kg. Because they divide into two daughter bacteria every 20 minutes, their need for energy from ATP molecules is immense, as illustrated in Table 6.1: excluding the ATP molecules needed to replicate the bacterium's DNA, each *E. coli* produces more than 14 000 biomolecules per second. To accomplish this it consumes the energy of more than 2.3 million ATP molecules! Since *E. coli* bacteria do not photosynthesize, this energy must be absorbed as food from their environment.

**TABLE 6.1**

### Metabolism of *Escherichia coli*

| Compound | Weight fraction (%) | Molecules per bacterium | Molecules synthe-sized | ATP molecules needed |
|---|---|---|---|---|
| Protein | 70 | $1.7 \cdot 10^6$ | 1400 | $2.1 \cdot 10^6$ |
| Fat | 10 | $1.5 \cdot 10^7$ | 12 500 | $8.8 \cdot 10^4$ |
| Polysac-charides | 5 | $4.0 \cdot 10^4$ | 32 | $6.5 \cdot 10^4$ |
| RNA | 10 | $1.5 \cdot 10^4$ | 12 | $7.5 \cdot 10^4$ |

The values in the first column indicate the fraction of the total weight due to each type of compound; these values don't add up to 100% because the DNA contributes another 5%. The last two columns provide numbers of each type of molecule synthesized per second, and the number of ATP molecules needed for the synthesis per second.

# Case Study: The Predatory Dinosaurs

The question whether **dinosaurs** were cold-blooded or warm-blooded is one of the most contested issues in palaeontology, for three reasons:

- the terms *cold-blooded* and *warm-blooded* are ill-chosen for a scientific discussion, as the issue raised has nothing to do with the actual blood temperature,
- the underlying concepts of bioenergetics are complex even for living species, and
- considering the 160-million-year reign of the dinosaurs over our mammalian ancestors (from the late Triassic to the end of the Cretaceous), our prejudice sometimes stands in the way of proper analysis of the data.

Dinosaurs have been extinct for 65 million years, and we have little other than fossilized bones to reconstruct their anatomy and physiology. Fig. 6.4 illustrates some problems with the reconstruction of a typical predatory dinosaur, in this case Tyrannosaurus rex. The way this animal of the late Cretaceous is displayed in Fig. 6.4 is very likely correct with respect to the anatomical arrangement of the bones that are partially shown. However, the illustration of the animal as an aggressive and swift hunter can be correct only if a number of physiological assumptions are valid. For example, the elasticity of the leg bones must be such that they withstand bipedal running. This issue is discussed in detail in Chapter 16.

Here, we want to test whether the dinosaur in Fig. 6.4 was an **endotherm**, i.e., an animal with a constant body temperature maintained well above the environmental temperature. Only in that case is the swift-hunter assumption feasible. Was Tyrannosaurus an **ectotherm** with a body temperature fluctuating with the environmental temperature, rather, it would have been a scavenger walking slowly in search of carrion. Dinosaurs are related to both types of animals: they had a common ancestor (*Archosaurs*) with the ectothermic crocodiles until 250 million years ago in the early Triassic, and they are the ancestors of the endothermic birds, from which they split about 200 million years ago at the beginning of the Jurassic.

To establish a basis for this discussion, we compare modern endotherms (mammals and birds) and modern ectotherms (reptiles). With the differences established we review the dinosaur evidence and judge which group they fit in best. Fig. 6.5 shows the metabolic rate of living species, i.e., their energy consumption per second. The metabolic rate is measured in unit J/s, which is a unit for energy per time that we introduce later in the chapter. This plot is double-logarithmic, with the **resting metabolic rate** as the ordinate and the body mass as the abscissa. The metabolic rate of a non-growing endotherm at rest (with an empty stomach and experiencing no stress) is called the *basal metabolic rate*. The corresponding metabolic rate of an ectotherm at rest is called the *standard metabolic rate,* and must be given for a specified environmental temperature. The actual metabolic rate can significantly exceed the basal or standard metabolic rate, for humans by up to a factor of 50 for activities that last a few seconds, and by up to a factor of 5 for activities that last about an hour.

Fig. 6.5 indicates an important qualitative difference between ectotherms and endotherms: endotherms need about ten times more energy than ectotherms of the same size.

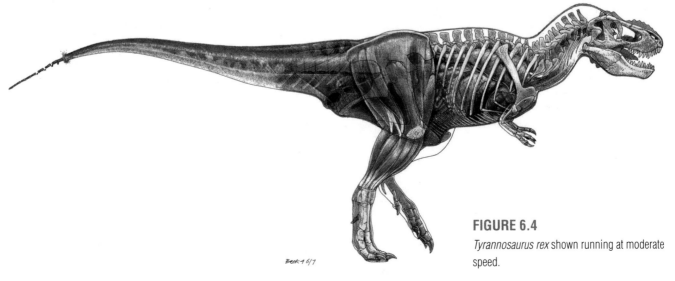

**FIGURE 6.4**

*Tyrannosaurus rex* shown running at moderate speed.

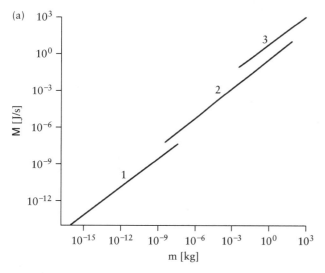
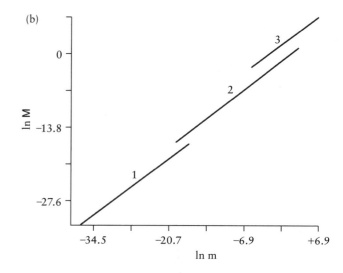

**FIGURE 6.5**

Double-logarithmic plot of the metabolic rate in unit J/s versus mass in unit kg for a wide range of species. Three straight lines represent data for (1) unicellular organisms at 20°C, (2) ectotherms at 20°C, and (3) endotherms at 39°C core body temperature. The three lines are parallel (same power law exponent) but differ in their respective prefactors. (a) The axes of the double-logarithmic plot are logarithmic with absolute values for mass and metabolic rate M. (b) The same plot with linear axes for ln $m$ and ln M.

● **EXAMPLE 6.1**

Three cases are shown in Fig. 6.5: (1) unicellular organisms at 20°C, (2) ectotherms at 20°C, and (3) endotherms at 39°C. Find the parameters $a$ and $b$ in the power-law relation $M = a \cdot m^b$, where M is the metabolic rate in unit J/s and $m$ is the mass in unit kg, for (a) ectotherms, and (b) endotherms.

*Solution:* The mathematical approach to analyzing double-logarithmic plots is discussed in the Math Review section "Graph Analysis Methods" at the end of Chapter 1. We begin by supplementing the logarithmic axes in Fig. 6.5(a) with linear axes ln $m$ and ln M, as shown in Fig. 6.5(b). Then we determine the two parameters $a$ and $b$ based on the linear relation:

$$\ln M = b \cdot \ln m + \ln a \qquad [5]$$

This procedure must be repeated for each animal group in Fig. 6.5.

*Solution to part (a):* For ectotherms, the straight line labelled 2 in Fig. 6.5 applies. Two data points from this line are listed in Table 6.2. Using Table 6.2, we write two linear formulas:

$$\begin{aligned} \text{(I)} \qquad -13.82 &= b(-16.02) + \ln a \\ \text{(II)} \qquad 0 &= b(1.93) + \ln a \end{aligned} \qquad [6]$$

$$\underline{\text{(II)} - \text{(I)} \quad 13.82 = b(17.95)}$$

This leads to $b = 0.77$ and $a = 0.22$.

**TABLE 6.2**

**Data sets for ectotherms from Fig. 6.5, line 2**

| M (J/s) | ln(M) | $m$ (kg) | ln $m$ |
|---|---|---|---|
| $10^{-6}$ | −13.82 | $1.1 \times 10^{-7}$ | −16.02 |
| 1 | 0 | 6.9 | 1.93 |

*Solution to part (b):* The data for endotherms are represented by the straight line labelled 3 in Fig. 6.5. Two data points from that line are listed in Table 6.3. Using Table 6.3, we write:

$$\begin{aligned} \text{(I)} \qquad -6.91 &= b(-11.33) + \ln a \\ \text{(II)} \qquad +6.91 &= b(+6.91) + \ln a \end{aligned} \qquad [7]$$

$$\underline{\text{(II)} - \text{(I)} \quad 13.82 = b(18.24)}$$

This leads to $b = 0.76$ and $a = 5.25$.

We note that all species have an exponent $b$ close to $\frac{3}{4}$. You can confirm the same power law

**TABLE 6.3**

**Data sets for endotherms from Fig. 6.5, line 3**

| M (J/s) | ln(M) | $m$ (kg) | ln $m$ |
|---|---|---|---|
| $10^{-3}$ | −6.908 | $1.2 \times 10^{-5}$ | −11.33 |
| $10^{+3}$ | +6.908 | $1.0 \times 10^{+3}$ | +6.908 |

coefficient for the unicellular organisms in Fig. 6.5 by repeating the approach in Example 6.1 for these organisms. The results are summarized for ectotherms and endotherms, with the metabolic rate given in unit kJ/day and the mass $m$ in kg:

$$\text{ectotherm:} \quad M = 20 \cdot m^{3/4}$$
$$\text{endotherm:} \quad M = 450 \cdot m^{3/4} \quad [8]$$

## Concept Question 6.1

**(a) What do we learn from the exponent $b$ in Eq. [8], and (b) what do we learn from the two prefactors in Eq. [8]?**

ANSWER TO PART (a): We note that the values for parameter $b$ are the same for the three groups of species, with $b = 3/4$. This suggests that all living organisms function at the fundamental metabolic level in the same fashion. Two simple models have been proposed to interpret Fig. 6.5:

MODEL 1: Each kilogram of tissue has the same metabolic requirements; i.e., the metabolic rate is proportional to the mass. This leads to a prediction of $b = 1$ because: $M \propto m^1$. This model does not match with the value derived in Example 6.1. Because this model is not correct, you have to be careful when you find metabolic rates in the literature (or in this textbook) reported per kilogram body mass. Such values apply only to a specific species. We also learn from P–6.2 that such values can be applied only to adults.

MODEL 2: The metabolic requirements are determined by the loss of heat to the environment through the skin. This leads to a prediction of $b = 2/3$ as derived in P–6.5. This model is also not consistent with the data found in Example 6.1. Even though the basal or standard metabolic rates are sometimes measured by placing an animal in a calorimeter (which is an instrument to measure the amount of energy released as heat), a careful averaging over a longer time period is needed in order to avoid determining wrong values based on the instant loss through the animal's surface.

ANSWER TO PART (b): The prefactors on the right-hand side of Eq. [8] differ significantly between endotherms and ectotherms. Maintaining a 5- to 20-times-higher energy throughput can be managed only with numerous anatomical, physiological, and behavioural adjustments. Some of these can be tested for extinct species as they enter the fossil record.

The **food consumption** $\mathcal{E}_{\text{food consumption}}$ of wet meat of predatory endotherms and ectotherms is given in unit kg/day as a function of the animal's mass $m$ in kg:

$$\text{ectotherm:} \quad \mathcal{E}_{\text{food consumption}} = 0.01 \cdot m^{3/4}$$
$$\text{endotherm:} \quad \mathcal{E}_{\text{food consumption}} = 0.11 \cdot m^{3/4} \quad [9]$$

To maintain a high metabolic rate, endotherms must consume about ten times as much food as ectotherms. Ectothermic predators therefore display a laid-back, non-confrontational style, while endothermic predators are always aggressive and compulsive about food. Note that this contrasts with our prejudice: it is much safer to swim toward a crocodile than to get within 100 metres of a polar bear.

An ecological difference caused by Eq. [9] is measured by the **predator/prey ratio** in a stable ecosystem. This ratio is quantified as the percentage of predator biomass relative to the biomass of the herbivores in the same area. Modern ecosystems are dominated by endothermic mammals. Because of the high amount of food these predators require, based on Eq. [9], a large number of prey are required to sustain the predator population. Consequently, predators represent only somewhere between 2 and 10% of the local biomass. Equivalent data for an ecosystem dominated by ectotherms exist only in the fossil record, because they stand no chance in competition with modern endotherms. However, the early reptiles at the transition from the Permian to the Triassic dominated the ecosystem of their time. The predator/prey ratio for the early reptiles was typically 40 to 100%; i.e., predators and prey shared the ecosystem in roughly equal numbers.

These data indicate that a range of significant differences exist between ectotherms and endotherms as a result of their tenfold difference in energy consumption. Since energy has to be budgeted at every level, the limited supply of energy ultimately controls the number of individuals of a certain species living in an ecosystem. Endothermic predators need much more food per individual than ectothermic predators and are therefore more rare in their ecosystem and occur more seldom in the fossil record. The predator/prey ratio of dinosaurs has been analyzed at 10 fossil beds; 9 of these show predator/prey ratios below 10%. Their presence in the ecosystem resembles that of mammals.

It was from these observations related to the energy consumption of animals that the suggestion of endothermic dinosaurs evolved in the 1970s. To appreciate the details of this discussion in the literature—and, more generally, to understand the limiting conditions for individual creatures—the governing principles of energy conservation, energy flow, and energy conversion must be established.

# Basic Concepts

One of the challenges of working with energy concepts is the diversity of processes we have to describe in this context. This diversity is the result of the three properties of energy we identified above: the conservation of energy, the ability of energy to flow from place to place, and the ability of energy to convert back and forth between different energy forms. We must stick to a set of definitions and conventions to avoid confusion in this discussion. We highlight in particular three issues at the beginning of this section:

- the distinction between equilibrium and non-equilibrium systems,
- the distinction between energy flow and energy conversion, and
- the distinction between the properties of a system and the properties of the system's environment.

## Equilibrium

We defined mechanical equilibrium using Newton's first and second laws. When reading the earlier chapters you may have noticed that the distinction between these two laws of mechanics appeared somewhat artificial, as the second law includes the first when we extend it to zero acceleration, $a = 0$. Why, then, did we keep these two laws separate? We did it because both laws are at the base of different branches of the natural sciences:

- *Newton's first law focuses on the equilibrium state of a system.* The equilibrium concept links mechanics to thermodynamics and later to stationary fluids and electrostatics.
- *Newton's second law deals with dynamic changes of the state of a system.* The dynamics concept links to chemical kinetics and non-equilibrium thermodynamic processes, as well as fluid dynamics and issues of electric currents.

The mechanical equilibrium is distinguished as a special state for an object in which all essential mechanical properties do not change with time: the net force on the object and its acceleration are zero, and its velocity and linear momentum are time-independent. This observation characterizes equilibria in general:

*A system is in **equilibrium** when all essential physical parameters that describe the system do not change with time.*

Note that this does not mean that all physical parameters are constant. For example, the position of an object in mechanical equilibrium changes continuously if the object is not at rest. However, for an isolated object the position is not an essential parameter since no possible physical observation such as those discussed in the previous chapters depends on the position.

The physical parameters that we consider to be essential vary with the physical concepts we study. For that reason, we must specify the context in which we refer to an equilibrium. This is done by using a descriptive adjective with the term "equilibrium." Examples of equilibria used in this textbook include:

- the **mechanical equilibrium** of a point-like or extended rigid object in Chapters 3 to 5;
- the **thermal equilibrium**, which we introduce together with the concept of temperature toward the end of this chapter;
- the **chemical equilibrium**, which is associated with chemical reactions like the process in Eq. [1], will be discussed in greater detail in Chapter 8;
- the **electric equilibrium**, which we introduce after defining electric charges in Chapter 13; and, as a case of combining such equilibria,
- the **electrochemical equilibrium**, which is used in Chapter 14 to study the microscopic processes at nerve membranes.

## Energy Flow and Energy Conversion

Although energy is conserved, energy can change in two ways: **energy can flow** from one place to another, and/or **energy can be converted** from one form into another. It is important that we distinguish these two processes throughout the subsequent discussion. To support the distinction we use different terms:

- we use the terms **heat** and **work** when energy flows in or out of a system, and
- we use the term **energy** with a descriptive adjective, e.g., *kinetic energy* or *thermal energy*, when energy converts from one form to another within a system. We label specific energy forms in this textbook $E$ and add a subscript to specify the particular form of energy. For example, $E_{kin}$ means kinetic energy.

Describing how energy moves or flows from one place to another requires a careful use of expressions from everyday language. For work, we usually say it is *done on* or *done by* an object. These expressions properly describe the direction of energy flow but do not express the fact that something is actually transferred from one object to another. For heat, terms such as *received* or *released* are usually used, which more clearly express both the transfer and direction of energy flow. We have chosen to use these standard notations in this book to allow the reader to relate easily to other literature. But we will also use the terms *received* and *released* in the context of work to emphasize the equivalence of work and heat as two forms of energy flow between a system and its environment.

## The System and Its Environment

In the discussion of muscle action we chose different systems for different purposes, for example a single myosin head, a single sarcomere, or an entire muscle cell. At each level we observed an exchange of matter between the system and its environment: the myosin head releases an ADP molecule and receives an ATP molecule in turn; the sarcomere trades ADP for new ATP molecules with the mitochondria; and the muscle cell acquires food from outside the cell to allow the mitochondria to run as cellular power plants. Thus, the environment plays a vital role in the processes we study at every level. As a result, a greater deal of attention has to be paid to the environment than in the previous chapters. In particular, an approach has to be developed to allow us to quantify the changes in the environment during its interaction with the system. For this purpose, an additional artificial boundary is drawn around the combination of system and environment such that both together are isolated from the rest of the world. This is then called an **isolated superstructure**.

To deal with the **system/environment interface** properly, we distinguish three types of systems based on their interactions as sketched in Fig. 6.6.

### ISOLATED SYSTEMS

Isolated systems (Fig. 6.6(a)) are systems that do not exchange energy or matter with their environment. We indicate this with two dashed lines surrounding the system, to show that the surface of the system cannot be penetrated by either energy or matter. Perfectly isolated systems are hard to establish experimentally but are of great relevance conceptually because they allow for the simplest mathematical formalism to quantify system parameters. Technical examples include the calorimeter, which is an instrument used to measure the energy content of chemical compounds, and closed Dewar containers, which are used to store liquid nitrogen.

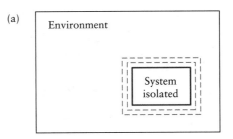

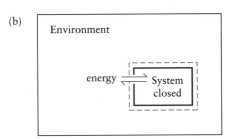

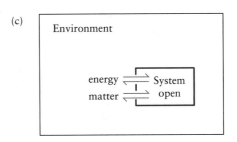

Isolated superstructure

**FIGURE 6.6**

An isolated superstructure contains a system and its environment. We distinguish three types of systems: (a) isolated systems that display no interaction with the environment, (b) closed systems that exchange energy (in the form of work and/or heat) with the environment but that exchange no matter, (c) open systems that exchange both energy and matter with their environment. The isolation of the superstructure ensures that the balance of energy and matter in the environment can be quantified.

*What we will introduce in this chapter*—The **conservation of energy** law: once all forms of energy of a system are identified, we calculate the total energy of the system by adding all individual contributions. The total energy is then called the **internal energy** of the system and is shown to be conserved in an isolated system.

If the isolated system is in equilibrium we know that its essential parameters are time-independent. Thus, for an isolated system in equilibrium each type of energy is separately constant. This represents the simplest situation we can study. We will therefore first define new system parameters, such as temperature, for isolated systems in equilibrium.

Non-equilibrium situations are best described by studying the interaction of a system with its environment. We distinguish two ways in which this can occur:

## CLOSED SYSTEMS

Closed systems (Fig. 6.6(b)) are systems that interact with their environment in a limited fashion, exchanging energy but not transferring matter. This is indicated by a single dashed line surrounding the system, to show that no matter can penetrate the system surface. Note that we now also require the isolated superstructure envelope, because otherwise we could not control the energy balance in the environment. A typical example is an organic chemistry experiment where the reaction takes place in some glassware with external oil-bath heating. Such a system is closed as long as no gas exchange with the external atmosphere occurs.

*What we will introduce in this chapter*—The **first law of thermodynamics**: the change of internal energy of the system between an initial and a final state is due to two contributions: (i) work released to or received from the environment, and (ii) heat that is exchanged with the environment. These two forms of energy flow are indicated by the arrows at the left side of the system across its surface. Note that the arrows point in both directions: heat and work can both leave and enter the system.

## OPEN SYSTEMS

Open systems (Fig. 6.6(c)) are systems that exchange matter and energy with their environment. This is indicated by two double-arrows at the left side of the system in the figure. Note that an exclusive exchange of matter without an exchange of energy is not possible because matter always carries energy. No dashed line surrounds the system, because it can be penetrated by both energy and matter.

*What we will introduce in this chapter*—Open systems are not discussed further: where possible, we avoid treating open systems quantitatively because the respective formalism leads to rather extensive equations. However, open systems must be considered when discussing non-equilibrium processes, such as diffusion in Chapter 10. We will then develop a different, phenomenological approach that allows us to introduce the physical concepts while limiting the needed mathematical formalism.

---

### Concept Question 6.2

**Identify a biological system that is (a) open, (b) closed, and (c) isolated.**

ANSWER TO PART (a): Practically all biological systems are open. For example, the live human body is an open system: we continuously lose heat to the environment, and we cycle matter through the respiratory and digestive systems.

ANSWER TO PART (b): A dormant virus is one of a very few cases of a closed system, as its interior is separated from the exterior space by a rigid membrane.

ANSWER TO PART (c): Essentially no isolated system exists. Even the entire biosphere undergoes energy and material exchange with outer space. We receive energy from the Sun, which varies from daily cycles to cycles that measure in the range of 100 000 years and are believed to have caused the ice ages. Matter reaches Earth in the form of cosmic radiation that interacts with the molecules in the atmosphere, forming, e.g., the $^{14}C$ isotopes of natural carbon that are used in carbon-dating techniques.

---

# Work

We referred in the previous section to the terms *work*, *heat*, and *energy*. The remainder of this chapter focusses on defining these terms quantitatively. We begin with work, as its flow in and out of a system allows us to define all but one form of energy. Only when these have been established do we turn to heat and thermal energy.

## Work in a Mechanical System

We base the definition of **work** on our everyday experience. Consider pushing this book across a table. We associate work with both the amount of force needed to move the book and the distance that it is moved. Note that we do not consider all forces acting on the book, but are concerned only with the specific force we exert on it. This distinguishes the discussion in this chapter from the discussion of Newton's laws, where we required the net force.

The simple experiment with the textbook allows us to write a first, though very general, formula for the work done by a force $\mathbf{F}$ to achieve a displacement $\Delta\mathbf{r}$ from an initial position $\mathbf{r}_{initial}$ to a final position $\mathbf{r}_{final}$, $\Delta\mathbf{r} = \mathbf{r}_{final} - \mathbf{r}_{initial}$:

$$W = f(\mathbf{F}, \Delta\mathbf{r}) \qquad [10]$$

This equation specifies that work $W$ is a function of (notation $f(\cdots)$) two vector parameters. Note that $W$ is not printed boldface, indicating that work is a non-directional quantity. Let's confirm that we agree with these features of Eq. [10] before continuing. We know already that force and displacement are vectors. Let's vary the directions of the displacement and force vectors without varying their magnitude: push the textbook in a different direction than before, but push it as far as you did in the first experiment. The effort you needed to invest is a measure of the work you did; it didn't change with the change in the direction. So, work is indeed not a vector; parameters that have no directional property are called **scalars**.

To specify Eq. [10] further, we repeat our experiment pushing the textbook across the table. Do it two more times, once pushing twice as far, and once after stacking a few more books on top. You find from these two experiments that the work is proportional to the displacement distance and the magnitude of the force. We propose, therefore, to write Eq. [10] in the form:

$$W = \mathbf{F} \cdot \Delta\mathbf{r} = \mathbf{F} \cdot (\mathbf{r}_{final} - \mathbf{r}_{initial}) \qquad [11]$$

The scalar product in Eq. [11] is introduced in the Math Review "Vector Multiplication" at the end of Chapter 5. Eq. [11] goes significantly beyond Eq. [10] in several ways: First, Eq. [11] specifies that work depends linearly on both the force and the displacement. Pulling with twice the force for the same distance, or pulling with the same force for twice the distance, doubles the work. Second, Eq. [11] does not contain a constant offset term, e.g., a term $W_0$ added on the right-hand side. Such an offset term is not present because either $\mathbf{F} = 0$ or $\Delta\mathbf{r} = 0$ must result in $W = 0$. This means that if we do not exert a force, or do not accomplish a displacement, then no work has been done. Third, no scalar prefactor is included in front of the dot product because we use Eq. [11] as a definition.

Eq. [11] also allows us to identify the unit of work. Recall that the unit of force is N and the unit of displacement is m. Thus the unit of work is N · m = kg · m$^2$/s$^2$. We define a derived SI unit for work, **joule** (J). 1 J is the work done when a force of 1 N moves an object a distance of 1 m with force and displacement parallel.

## Concept Question 6.3

**Someone looks at Eq. [11] and states that it must be wrong because it does not allow for the force to vary along the displacement; i.e., F = f(r) is excluded. Do you agree?**

ANSWER: Yes! Eq. [11] applies only if the force is constant along the displacement. We discuss cases with variable force later in this chapter, and will find then that Eq. [11] has to be replaced by a more complex mathematical formula.

This observation reminds us that we have to be vigilant when discussing physics: overlooking an essential assumption may cause major errors down the road. Note that Eq. [10] remains correct for variable forces, so the assumption of a constant force entered the discussion when we wrote Eq. [10] in the form of Eq. [11].

For applications with constant forces, Eq. [11] is used in either one of two forms:

- If we know or are interested in the magnitudes of displacement, $|\Delta\mathbf{r}|$, and force, $|\mathbf{F}|$, and the angle between the two vectors, $\theta = \sphericalangle(\mathbf{F}, \mathbf{r})$, we use Eq. [11] in the form:

$$W = |\mathbf{F}| \cdot |\Delta\mathbf{r}| \cdot \cos\theta \qquad [12]$$

- If we know or are interested in the components of the vectors in Eq. [11], we write it in component form:

$$W = F_x \cdot \Delta x + F_y \cdot \Delta y + F_z \cdot \Delta z \qquad [13]$$

in which the last term on the right-hand side can be neglected if the physical action takes place in the $xy$-plane, i.e., when we use the vectors $\mathbf{F}$ and $\mathbf{r}$ to define the $xy$-plane.

## Concept Question 6.4

**Someone reads Eq. [12] in the following way: "I better push an object at a large angle (i.e., a small term cos θ), because that means I need the least work to achieve a desired displacement." Do you agree?**

ANSWER: No. When read properly as a physical equation, Eq. [12] implies the opposite! To illustrate this we return to our experiment with the textbook. Push the book once with a force parallel to the table surface and once with a force at a steep angle. To achieve the same displacement the second force must be much larger than the first one, and you feel that you invested a greater effort to achieve the same outcome.

We understand this by studying Eq. [13]. For a given displacement in a particular experiment only the force component in the direction of the displacement contributes to the achieved work. At steeper angles a larger force is needed because its component perpendicular to the displacement does not contribute to the work. The misconception is compounded by the fact that we do not include all forces in the discussion, e.g., in the particular case frictional forces with the underlying surface.

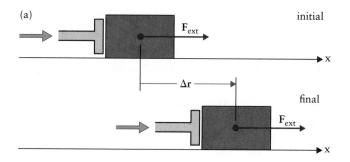

(a)

● **EXAMPLE 6.2**

Fig. 6.7 shows an object on an inclined plane that forms a 20° angle with the horizontal. An external force **F** of magnitude 10 N is applied on the object. The force **F** acts in a direction that forms a 60° angle with the horizontal. As a result of the force **F** the object moves a distance of 1 metre along the inclined plane. What work is done by the source of force **F**?

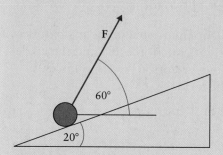

**FIGURE 6.7**

An object is pulled with a force **F** of given magnitude in a direction forming a 60° angle with the horizontal. As a result, the object is pulled a given distance along the underlying surface that forms a 20° angle with the horizontal.

*Solution:* We must first determine the angle between the displacement and the force as this angle enters Eq. [12]. This angle $\theta$ is obtained from the data given in the problem text: $\theta = 60° - 20° = 40°$. Now the given data can be substituted in Eq. [12]:

$$W = F \cdot \Delta r \cdot \cos \theta$$
$$= (10 \text{ N})(1 \text{ m})\cos 40° = 7.7 \text{ J} \quad [14]$$

**Concept Question 6.5**

**Using Eqs. [12] to [14], is it possible for work to be a negative number?**

ANSWER: Yes, for $90° < \theta < 270°$ we find that $\cos \theta < 0$. This range of angles means that force and displacement vectors are directed in opposite directions when we project them onto a common axis. As always in physics, a change in the sign has ramifications beyond the mathematical fact. This is explored below for Eq. [15].

Mathematically, Eq. [13] can be simplified in the special case when the force and the displacement vectors are parallel:

$$W = \pm F \cdot \Delta r \quad [15]$$

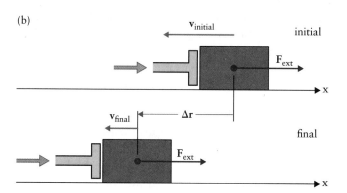

(b)

**FIGURE 6.8**

(a) A piston is used to displace an object by a distance $\Delta x$ along the $x$-axis. The experiment is conducted between an initial time (shown at top) and a final time (shown at bottom). To achieve the displacement an external force $\mathbf{F}_{ext}$ is needed. We assume that the external force acts collinear to the displacement. (b) For the same arrangement, a displacement of the object in the negative $x$-direction is possible if, for example, the object had an initial negative velocity component $v_{initial}$ and is slowed down to $v_{final}$ while moving toward the left. In this case the displacement and the external force act in anti-parallel directions.

$F$ is the magnitude of the force acting on the system and $\Delta r$ is the length of the displacement vector. The $\pm$ symbol in Eq. [15] indicates that work can be positive or negative: if $\theta = 0°$ in Eq. [13]—i.e., force and displacement are parallel—we find $W > 0$; if $\theta = 180°$—i.e., force and displacement are anti-parallel—we find $W < 0$. We illustrate this with two cases in Fig. 6.8 that explore the interaction of a piston pushing an object (green box) from the left. The piston exerts a constant force of magnitude $F_{ext}$ on the object. The figure can be seen as abstracting our earlier experiment if the object is the textbook on the table and the piston is your hand.

- **Fig. 6.8(a).** The displacement occurs in the same direction as $\mathbf{F}_{ext}$ acts. Depending on what we are interested in we may choose either the green box or the piston as the system.

  *The green box is the system.* The work is positive because $\mathbf{F}_{ext}$ and the displacement $\Delta \mathbf{r}$ point in the same direction regardless of our choice of co-ordinate system. We say in this case that **work is done on the system** by the environment (here, the piston).

*The piston is the system.* We must calculate the work from a force exerted on the piston. The force we need to study is the force that the green box exerts on the piston, i.e., the reaction force to $\mathbf{F}_{ext}$. Newton's third law states that this force is $-\mathbf{F}_{ext}$, i.e., that it has the same magnitude but acts in the opposite direction of $\mathbf{F}_{ext}$. Consequently, the work is negative because $-\mathbf{F}_{ext}$ and $\Delta\mathbf{r}$ point in opposite directions. We say in this case that **work is done by the system** on its environment (here, the green box).

- **Fig. 6.8(b).** Now the displacement occurs in the opposite direction of $\mathbf{F}_{ext}$. The piston still pushes against the green box, and the box still exerts a force on the piston due to Newton's third law. In Fig. 6.8(b), however, the box succeeds in pushing the piston to the left, causing a displacement to the left. This has consequences for the sign of the work.

*The green box is the system.* The work is now negative because $\mathbf{F}_{ext}$ and $-\Delta\mathbf{r}$ have opposite directions. The system does work on the environment.

*The piston is the system.* The work is positive because $-\mathbf{F}_{ext}$ and $-\Delta\mathbf{r}$ have the same direction. Work is done on the system.

In summary:

$$W > 0 \iff \text{system receives work} \\ \iff \text{work is done ON the system} \quad [16]$$

and

$$W < 0 \iff \text{system releases work} \\ \iff \text{work is done BY the system} \quad [17]$$

*The mathematical sign of work is positive when the system receives work, i.e., work is done on the system. The sign of work is negative when the system releases work, i.e., work is done by the system.*

This sign convention is easy to remember in the following way: identify yourself with the system; whatever you receive (here, work) is positive since you have more of it afterward; whatever you release is negative since you have less of it afterward.

## ● EXAMPLE 6.3

Determine the work done by a person when lowering an object of mass 1.0 kg by a distance of 1.0 m. The person applies a constant force $\mathbf{F}_{ext}$ such that the object moves with constant speed, i.e., without acceleration, as shown in Fig. 6.9.

*Solution:* It is worthwhile to re-emphasize the shift of focus in this chapter: while we combined all forces acting on a system as a net force in Newton's laws, we are now focussing on a specific interaction between the system and its environment. In Fig. 6.9, the object (a rectangular box of mass $m$) is the system and the person (not shown) is one interacting component of the environment. Another component of the environment interacting with the system is Earth as it exerts a gravitational pull on the object. Thus, the person, Earth, and the object together form an isolated superstructure with all interactions still identified as forces.

Two free-body diagrams are included in Fig. 6.9, each applied to the system in one of the two states we are interested in: the initial state at height $y_{initial}$, and the final state at height $y_{final}$. Note that mechanical equilibrium applies at both heights because the object does not accelerate; thus, the magnitude of the external force is equal to the weight of the object:

$$F_{ext} = m \cdot g \quad [18]$$

From the point of view of Newton's laws, no difference exists between the system at the initial and the final height. However, based on our discussion

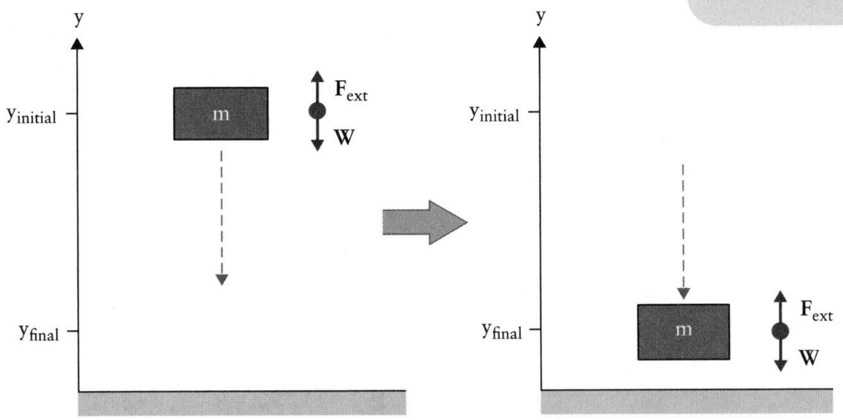

**FIGURE 6.9**

An object of mass $m$ is lowered from an initial height $y_{initial}$ (shown at left) to a final height $y_{final}$ (shown at right). The object moves from the initial to the final state with a constant speed if the magnitude of the external force $\mathbf{F}_{ext}$ is equal in magnitude to the weight $\mathbf{W}$ of the object.

● **EXAMPLE 6.3 (continued)**

in the current chapter, we can quantify as work the effort involved in the displacement of the system.

- Based on Eq. [15], we expect that the work is negative because both external force and displacement are collinear but point in opposite directions.

- This is confirmed by using Eq. [13], since both the external force and the displacement have only $y$-components and the external force is $F_{ext,y} > 0$ and the displacement is $\Delta y = (y_{final} - y_{initial}) < 0$.

The work is quantified as:

$$W = F_{ext} \cdot \Delta y = F_{ext}(y_{final} - y_{initial})$$
$$= m \cdot g(y_{final} - y_{initial}) \qquad [19]$$

Substituting the values given in the problem text, we find:

$$W = (1.0 \text{ kg})\left(9.8 \frac{m}{s^2}\right)(-1.0 \text{ m})$$
$$= -9.8 \text{ J} \qquad [20]$$

The negative result is interpreted with the sign convention in Eqs. [16] and [17]: the system has released work. Specifically, the person has not done work on the system, but received work from the system.

---

**Concept Question 6.6**

Fig. 6.10 shows three processes that unfold between an initial time $t_{initial}$ and a final time $t_{final}$. The first two processes are physically identical, but differ in the definition of the angle $\phi$ between the constant force acting on the object (green circle) and the displacement of length $\Delta s$. For which of the three cases is Eq. [12] suitable (with $\theta = \phi$)?

ANSWER: Cases (ii) and (iii), but not case (i). For case (i) the angle is not defined between force and displacement vectors, which is required to write Eq. [12] with the cosine term used. Case (iii) can be described by Eq. [12] since the case $\phi = 0°$ is covered with $\cos \phi = 1$.

---

**Power** $P$ is the rate at which work is done; the SI unit of power is **watt** (W, named for James Watt) with $1 \text{ W} = 1 \text{ J/s}$. Since work isn't completed instantaneously, the rate at which it is done may vary with time. Therefore, we define an average power by

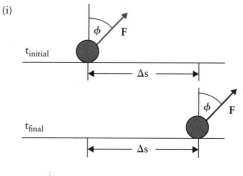
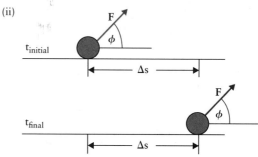
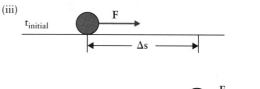
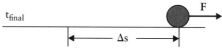

**FIGURE 6.10**

Three pairs of sketches showing an object at an initial (top) and final (bottom) instant. The displacement is labelled $\Delta s$. The force is not collinear with the displacement in the first two cases. Note that the angle labelled $\phi$ changes between case (i) and case (ii).

dividing the entire work obtained or released, $W$, by the time interval it takes to complete the work, $\Delta t$:

$$P = \frac{W}{\Delta t} \qquad [21]$$

Power is also related to the force $F$ that causes the work $W$ in turn:

$$P = \frac{W}{\Delta t} = \frac{F \cdot \Delta r}{\Delta t} = F \cdot v \qquad [22]$$

In the last step of Eq. [22] we assumed that the force is constant, i.e., that it does not change with time. Thus, power can be expressed as the dot product of a force acting on an object and the velocity of that object. A particular process does work at a higher rate (larger power) if it exerts a higher force or achieves a displacement in a shorter time, i.e., with a higher speed.

Replacing the unit J/s with the unit W is commonly done; however, the term *power* is more typically used in engineering applications. In the life sciences we usually instead use terms like *energy consumption rate* or *metabolic rate,* as in Fig. 6.5. Historically, there was an overlap in the 19th century between systems of biological and engineering interest in agriculture, which led to a non-SI unit of power called **horsepower** (hp), with 1 hp = 746 W.

## Pressure of a Gas

Before we can effectively proceed with the discussion of work, heat, and energy, we need to expand on the number of model systems we use to define physical concepts. The mechanical models we have used so far, from point-like to expanded rigid objects, are not particularly suitable for introducing key concepts in thermal physics. For these, we need a **gas model**. The most frequently used arrangement for the gas model is shown in Fig. 6.11: the gas is sealed off in a container with a mobile piston. We imagine the gas as a very large number of very small point-like particles that fill the container in a random fashion. The container wall is ideal; i.e., it isolates the system from its environment. We assume further that the piston is an ideal piston, which means that it can move without friction back and forth along the inside surface of the

**FIGURE 6.11**

A piston seals a gas in an isolated container. The piston is mobile along the *x*-axis. The motion of the piston is modelled without friction.

container. When the piston moves in the positive *x*-direction the gas is compressed, and when the piston moves in the negative *x*-direction the gas expands. Thus, the piston represents the means of interacting with the gas system. The source of the external force pushing the piston is part of the environment and is not shown in the figure.

For the gas system it is more difficult to describe how the force acts on the gas. When the piston is pushed in Fig. 6.11, some gas particles are pushed away, others not. Also, the displacement of the system is not well defined: some gas particles get displaced, others do not. Thus, we need to replace force and displacement with parameters better applicable to a gas: its volume and pressure. The **gas pressure** is defined in this section; we then return to the discussion of work for a gas in the next section.

We begin with the air pressure in the room you are in. This is a measure of the effect of the air on any surface, including your skin. Were that pressure to decrease (astronauts in outer space) or increase (deep-sea diving) a pressurized suit would be needed to protect you from the changed pressure in the surrounding medium. However, the pressure has no direction: it is a scalar.

From Fig. 6.11 we note that the gas pressure depends on the force **F** exerted by the gas on the piston and the area *A* of the piston:

$$p = f(\mathbf{F}, A) \qquad [24]$$

You can do the following experiment yourself to specify the mathematical form of Eq. [24]. Use two syringes with different piston sizes. Keep the syringe closed. First push the piston of one syringe with variable force, then push the pistons of both syringes with the same force. Varying the two parameters in Eq. [24] this way leads to the sealed gas pushing back on the piston more strongly

- when we increase the external force $\mathbf{F}_{ext}$ exerted on the piston, and

- when we decrease the piston area *A* at constant external force.

Thus, we might suggest writing Eq. [24] in the form $p = \mathbf{F}/A$. However, this is not correct! You can convince yourself by pushing the piston in Fig. 6.11 at an angle. Only the component perpendicular to the piston surface, $F_\perp$, contributes to the pressure; the component parallel to the surface does not affect the piston. Thus, we write:

$$p = \frac{F_\perp}{A} \qquad [25]$$

Because we will use pressure often we establish a derived unit, replacing the unit N/m$^2$ with the unit **pascal** (Pa), named for Blaise Pascal. Note that you frequently find pressures reported in kPa; e.g., the standard atmospheric pressure is 101.3 kPa.

While Eq. [25] makes physical sense, you should wonder about its mathematical meaning. We want to get a scalar from a mathematical operation that combines a vector and another scalar! The use of the normal component of force in Eq. [25] in particular confirms that the force **F** enters as a vector. So, we still puzzle over that equation. To resolve this issue, let's study the parameter $A$ more closely. Think of the palm of your open hand as the surface you are interested in. Its area remains the same, but its orientation changes as you rotate your hand. Thus, the area of a surface is a vector parameter. We define it by its magnitude $A$ in unit m$^2$ and by a vector of length 1, **n**, that is oriented perpendicular to the surface, as illustrated in Fig. 6.12:

$$\mathbf{A} = A \cdot \mathbf{n} \qquad [26]$$

Thus, the pressure in Eq. [24] is indeed the result of two vectors. Only one vector operation with two vectors results in a scalar, the scalar product. Note that in particular a division by a vector is not defined; i.e., we cannot write $p = \mathbf{F}/\mathbf{A}$! Refer to the Math Reviews "Vectors and Basic Vector Algebra" in Chapter 2 and "Vector Multiplication" in Chapter 5 for the mathematical background of this reasoning. The proper way to write Eq. [25] in vector notation is:

$$p = \frac{1}{A^2}\mathbf{F} \cdot \mathbf{A} = \frac{1}{A}\mathbf{F} \cdot \mathbf{n} \qquad [27]$$

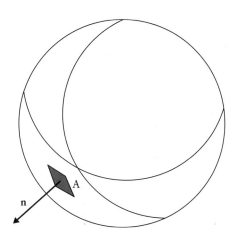

**FIGURE 6.12**

Representation of a surface segment in vector notation. The surface element is characterized by its area and by the direction of a vector of unit length that is oriented perpendicular to the surface.

---

### Concept Question 6.8

**Assume that no external force is applied to the piston in Fig. 6.11. Can you predict in which direction the piston accelerates?**

ANSWER: Not without further information. Note that the gas exerts a pressure $p$ on the inner surface of the piston. Based on Eq. [25], this results in a force of magnitude $F = p \cdot A$ pushing the piston to the left. However, the entire arrangement in the figure is in air (since not stated otherwise). Thus, a force also is acting on the piston toward the right, $F_{air} = p_{air} \cdot A$. The piston is in mechanical equilibrium if $p = p_{air}$; it will accelerate toward the left if $p > p_{air}$ and it will accelerate toward the right if $p < p_{air}$.

---

### ● EXAMPLE 6.4

In 1650, Otto von Guericke invented the vacuum pump. To secure continuous research funding, he demonstrated his new device at the Imperial Diet at Regensburg, Germany, in 1654. Historical sources report that he used two hollow bronze hemispheres of 42 cm diameter sealed together with a rubber gasket, as sketched in Fig. 6.13(a). Two teams of eight horses on each side could not pull the evacuated cavity apart. Do you believe the historical account?

*Solution:* No. Let's take the cavity as the system. Three forces act on it: (i) a tension caused by the team of horses on the right side, (ii) a tension caused by the team of horses on the left side, and (iii) a force due to the air pressure acting on the outer surface of the cavity. This force is not compensated by a force acting on the inner surface, since the cavity is evacuated. The arrows pointing toward the cavity in Fig. 6.13(a) illustrate the varying directions of the force $\mathbf{F}_{air}$. They are all directed toward the centre of the sphere, as this is the direction perpendicular to the cavity's surface, as needed in Eq. [25].

First we simplify the problem, using the symmetry of the experimental arrangement in Fig. 6.13(a). Of the two teams of horses, one is needed to keep the cavity in its place; were only one team present, the cavity would accelerate like a carriage. We can, however, replace one team, the attached string, and one-half of the cavity by a wall, as shown in Fig. 6.13(b), because such a wall can provide for mechanical equilibrium. To quantify this simplified version of the problem, we have to identify the force the horses have to overcome to pull the half-cavity away from the wall.

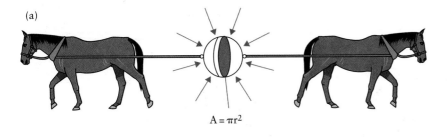

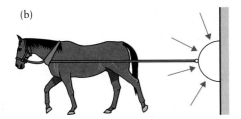

**FIGURE 6.13**

(a) Sketch of Otto von Guericke's experiment. Two teams of horses try to pull an evacuated cavity apart. The cross-sectional area of the cavity is $A = \pi \cdot r^2$ (green area) with $r$ the radius. The arrows indicate the direction of the force exerted by the atmosphere on the surface of the cavity. (b) Equivalent approach with one-half of the arrangement, one team of horses, and half the cavity replaced by a smooth wall to which the cavity is sealed.

The problem is not a simple application of the mechanics concepts we developed in Chapter 3 since the force $\mathbf{F}_{air}$ acts from variable directions across an extended surface. How can we quantify the force against which the horses try to pull the half-cavity away from the wall? The proper approach is to find the horizontal component of the net force caused by the air pressure on the hemisphere. This is mathematically difficult. However, we can circumvent this problem with some reasoning: note that the wall in Fig. 6.13(b) forms the circular base of a hemisphere that is equivalent to the green area in Fig. 6.13(a). All forces on the outer surface of the hemisphere must be equal to the force exerted by the wall because the cavity stays stationary after evacuation and before the horses pull. The net force acting on the flat circular area is much easier to calculate. If we label the radius of the sphere $r$, then $A = \pi \cdot r^2$ is the wall area covered by the cavity. Using for the atmospheric pressure $p_{atm} = 1.01 \times 10^5$ Pa, we find from Eq. [25] for the horizontal component of the net force due to the air pressure:

$$F_{air} = p_{atm} \cdot \pi r^2 = (1.01 \times 10^5 \, \text{Pa})\pi(0.21 \, \text{m})^2$$
$$= 1.4 \times 10^4 \, \text{N} \qquad [28]$$

Eight horses can overcome that force. To see this, note that a force of 14 kN is equivalent to lifting an object with a mass of 14 kN/9.8 m/s² = 1400 kg, i.e., 175 kg per horse. Von Guericke surely used fewer horses than the historical record claims.

## Work on or by a Gas

With the definition of pressure established in Eqs. [25] and [27], we evaluate the work done when the piston in Fig. 6.14(a) is pushed by an external force

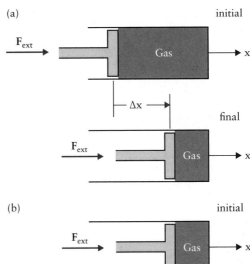

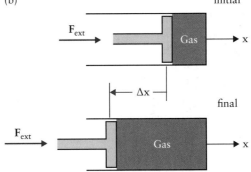

**FIGURE 6.14**

(a) A piston is pushed along the x-axis from an initial to a final state by an external force $\mathbf{F}_{ext}$. This causes the piston to move a distance $\Delta x$ toward the right, which leads to a compression of the gas. (b) Alternatively, the gas may expand and push the piston against an external force in the direction of the negative x-axis toward the left.

resulting in a displacement $\Delta x$. Note that we assume for all piston arrangements in this textbook that the external force acts parallel to the displacement of the piston. Thus, vector notation is unnecessary and the work done on the system reads:

$$W = F_{ext} \cdot \Delta x = \frac{F_{ext}}{A}(A \cdot \Delta x) \qquad [29]$$

which is rewritten with the definitions of pressure and volume in the form:

$$W = -p \cdot \Delta V \qquad [30]$$

It is important to note the origin of the negative sign in Eq. [30]. Using the first step in Eq. [29], the work done on the system gas is positive because the force $F_{ext}$ acting on the gas and the displacement of the gas point in the same direction. You may think of the displacement of the gas to be a shift to the right of its centre of mass. The subsequent multiplication with $A/A = 1$ in Eq. [29] has no effect on the sign. Proceeding from Eq. [29] to Eq. [30], we replace $F_{ext}/A = p$, which is the gas pressure when the system is in mechanical equilibrium. All absolute pressure values are positive. We also replace $A \cdot \Delta x = -\Delta V$, which is the volume change. The volume change introduces a negative sign because $A \cdot \Delta x$ in Fig. 6.14(a) is positive but $\Delta V$ is negative as the gas is compressed. The work for a **compression of a gas** is positive because work is done on the gas.

In Fig. 6.14(b), an **expansion of a gas** is studied. The external force and the displacement of the gas point in this case in opposite directions and the work is negative. This is consistent with Eq. [30], in which $p$ and $\Delta V$ are positive for Fig. 6.14(b). The work then is negative due to the additional negative sign on the right-hand side of Eq. [30].

## Work for Systems with Variable Force or Pressure

The work definitions for a mechanical object in Eq. [15] and for a gas in Eq. [30] have to be revised when the force varies during the displacement or the pressure varies during a compression or expansion. We need to include such cases because gas pressure often depends on the volume, and the force on an object attached to a spring depends on the expansion of the spring (see Chapter 16).

To get an idea how to modify Eq. [15], we first take another look at the case where the force is constant during displacement. This is shown in Fig. 6.15 with $F = F_0$, a constant value for all positions $x$, including the range from the position $x_1$ to the position $x_2$ of the displacement $\Delta x$. The equation for the work in this case is $W = F_0 \cdot \Delta x$. Reading this formula as a geometric equation means that the purple area represents the absolute value of the work, because the area of a rectangle is given by the product of its length and width. This observation holds generally:

*The absolute value of work is the area under the curve of the force as a function of position, $F(x)$, between the initial and the final position of the displacement.*

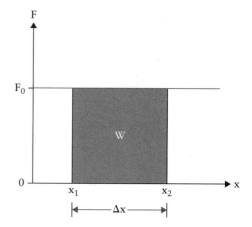

**FIGURE 6.15**

A graphical interpretation of the work for a system with collinear force and displacement, such as shown in Fig. 6.8, is based on a plot of the force $F$ as a function of position $x$. As a first case we study a constant force $F_0$, and a displacement from an initial position $x_1$ to a final position $x_2$ with $\Delta x = x_2 - x_1$. From Eq. [15] we find $W = F_0 \cdot \Delta x$, which corresponds to the purple area in the figure. Thus, the work is quantified by the area under the curve of the force as a function of position between the initial and final states of the system.

If the area is determined from a graph it is also important to note that the lower end of the area must be taken at $F = 0$.

Note that we have to deal with the sign of the work separately if it is determined from a graph. We have two possibilities:

- we treat $F_0$ as the magnitude of the force and use the sign convention discussed in Fig. 6.8 separately to determine the sign of $W$, or

- we treat $F_0$ as the component of the force in the direction of the displacement; i.e., it has to be a negative value if anti-parallel to the displacement.

With these observations we can now quantify the work for a position-dependent force as illustrated in Fig. 6.16. Fig. 6.16(a) shows the physical process of an object moved along a displacement $\Delta x = x_{final} - x_{initial}$. We do not obtain a simple rectangular area under the curve because the force varies with the position $x$. Various methods are available to determine mathematically the area under the curve. If the function $F = f(x)$ is known, analytical or numerical methods can be used. Fig. 6.16(b) illustrates how algorithms work that determine the area under a curve.

We choose a successively increasing number of correspondingly shorter intervals $\Delta x$ to obtain better and better estimates for the area under the curve in the interval $x_{final} - x_{initial}$. The first estimate is based on a rectangular area with width $x_{final} - x_{initial}$ and height $F_0$ where $F_0$ is the force at the centre position of the interval $x_{final} - x_{initial}$, i.e., at $x = \frac{1}{2}(x_{final} + x_{initial})$. We call this estimate $W_0$:

$$W_0 = F_0 \cdot (x_{final} - x_{initial}) \qquad [31]$$

This estimate is equivalent to the calculation we made to determine the work in Fig. 6.15. While it led to an exact result then, for the variable force case it is only a rough estimate as the rectangular area defined by Eq. [31] only remotely resembles the area under the curve in Fig. 6.16(a).

Better estimates are based on summation of the areas of an increasing number of shorter intervals. For example, in Fig. 6.16(b) the case is illustrated where the interval $x_{final} - x_{initial}$ is divided into $n = 6$ segments of width $\delta x$ each. The estimate of the area under the curve is obtained as:

$$W = \sum_{i=1}^{6} F_i \cdot \delta x \qquad [32]$$

in which the value $F_i$ is the force at the centre of each segment of length $\delta x$, labelled $x_i$ in the figure. Comparing the six areas with just one in Eq. [31] shows that this approach leads to estimates for the area under the curve that increasingly improve toward the actual value. Obviously, the best estimate follows when we divide the interval $x_{final} - x_{initial}$ such that we have an infinite number of segments of length $\delta x = 0$. This approach is mathematically feasible by finding the limit $n \to \infty$ for:

$$W = \lim_{n \to \infty} \sum_{i=1}^{n} F_i \cdot \frac{x_{final} - x_{initial}}{n} \qquad [33]$$

Eq. [33] can be evaluated analytically for some simpler functions $F(x)$, but is most frequently applied numerically with fast-converging computer algorithms. In Example 6.5 and Concept Question 6.9 we illustrate two intermediate approaches that avoid both the use of computers and the need for advanced mathematical methods.

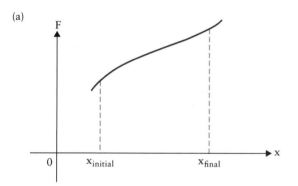

(a)

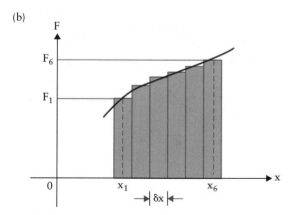

(b)

**FIGURE 6.16**

(a) An object is displaced from an initial position at $x_{initial}$ to a final position at $x_{final}$. The required force varies during the displacement; i.e., $F = f(x)$. (b) Numerical approach to determining the work for a variable force. The interval $x_{final} - x_{initial}$ is successively divided into an increasing number of small intervals; shown is the case with six sections of length $\Delta x$. The graph illustrates how the use of an increasing number of sections allows us to estimate the actual work better and better.

● **EXAMPLE 6.5**

(a) Assume that an object is moved from the origin $x_{initial} = 0$ to a final position $x_{final} > 0$. The force required to achieve the displacement is proportional to the displacement; i.e., $F(x) = a \cdot x + b$ with $a > 0$, $b = 0$. How does the work depend on the displacement? (b) How does the result change if $F(x) = F_0 - ax$ and a displacement along the positive $x$-axis starts at position $x_{initial} > 0$?

*Solution to part (a):* With the function $F(x)$ mathematically simple, we expect that Eq. [33] leads to a simple form. Figs. 6.17(a) and (b) show the approach we take. Each graph represents the force as a function of $x$. To evaluate Eq. [33], we choose in Fig. 6.17(a) an arbitrary position $x_0$. The contribution to the area under the curve at this position requires an interval of width $\delta x$ that we assume is later in the calculation narrowed in the extrapolation for $n \to \infty$. The purple area in Fig. 6.17(a) is $x_0 \cdot \delta x$, which does not change with the width $\delta x$ as long as the interval is chosen symmetrically around $x_0$.

This observation allows us to simplify Eq. [33] in the current case: If the formula for the area does not depend on the interval width $\delta x$, then we can choose for $\delta x$ the entire interval of interest, from the initial to the final position of the displacement. This is illustrated in Fig. 6.17(b). Note that we choose the initial position as the origin and the final position arbitrarily. We do not enter

## ● EXAMPLE 6.5 (*continued*)

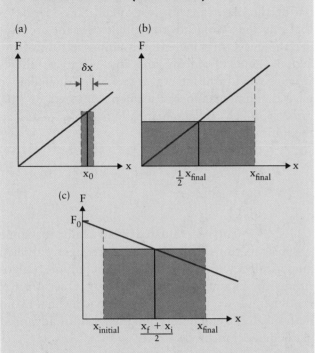

**FIGURE 6.17**

Three plots illustrating the calculation of work for a force that depends linearly on position. (a) Analyzing Eq. [33] requires us to find the purple area spanned by an interval of width $\delta x$ near the position $x_0$ where the force has a value $F(x_0)$. If the interval is symmetric to position $x_0$, the area is determined exactly as $F(x_0) \cdot \delta x$, independent of the width of the interval. (b) Thus, the area under the curve can be determined in one step by choosing the force value at the centre of the interval from initial to final position, multiplied by the full displacement: $F(x_{\text{final}}/2) \cdot x_{\text{final}}$. (c) The same procedure is applied when using a linear force function that does not pass through the origin.

a particular value for $x_{\text{final}}$, but want to drop the subscript "final" later and treat the final position of the displacement as variable.

The area of the triangle under the curve represents the work required to move the object from the origin to the final position. This area is equal to the purple rectangle with the function value $F(x)$ taken at the midway point, $F_{\text{midway}} = a \cdot x_{\text{final}}/2$. Thus:

$$W = \left( a \cdot \frac{x_{\text{final}}}{2} \right) x_{\text{final}} \qquad [34]$$

with the last term the entire interval length. The work depends quadratically on the distance from the origin to the final displacement. $W > 0$ follows whether $x_{\text{final}}$ is positive or negative; i.e., work is

received by (done on) the object. Dropping the subscript "final," we note that $W = a \cdot x^2/2$.

*Solution to part (b):* We study now a slightly more general case that will further highlight the origin of the various terms in the work formula. We start with Fig. 6.17(c). The displacement is from an initial to a final position with the final position again chosen arbitrarily and intended to be kept variable. Due to geometry, the area under the curve is equivalent to the purple rectangle, leading for the force $F(x) = F_0 - a \cdot x$ to the formula:

$$W = \left( F_0 - a \frac{x_{\text{final}} + x_{\text{initial}}}{2} \right)(x_{\text{final}} - x_{\text{initial}})$$

$$= -\frac{a}{2} x_{\text{final}}^2 + F_0 \cdot x_{\text{final}} - \frac{a}{2} x_{\text{initial}}^2 + F_0 \cdot x_{\text{initial}}$$

$$[35]$$

Dropping the subscript "final" in Eq. [35] leads to a negative quadratic term and a positive linear term in the work.

For many biological or physiological applications—including respiration, which we discuss at the beginning of the next chapter—the dependence of the force on the position is not known as an explicit mathematical formula. In such cases, the scientific approach to determine the work is based on experimentally measuring the force as a function of the position and then using graphical methods to determine the area under the curve. One possible albeit cumbersome approach is shown in Concept Question 6.9.

## Concept Question 6.9

**Determine the work done on an object that is brought from an initial position $x_1 = 1$ m to a final position $x_2 = 4$ m, requiring at each position the external force shown in Fig. 6.18(a).**

SOLUTION: We briefly study a method that allows us to quantify the work without a computer. We superimpose on Fig. 6.18(a) a narrow-spaced grid, as shown in Fig. 6.18(b). In this particular case, the distance between any two horizontal lines is 0.1 N and the distance between any two vertical lines is 0.1 m. From the chosen grid, we determine that the area of each small square is:

$$W_{\text{grid}} = \Delta F \cdot \Delta x = (0.1\,\text{N}) \cdot (0.1\,\text{m}) = 0.01 \text{ J} \quad [36]$$

This is a work term, since it is associated with an area in a force-versus-position graph. Now we count the small

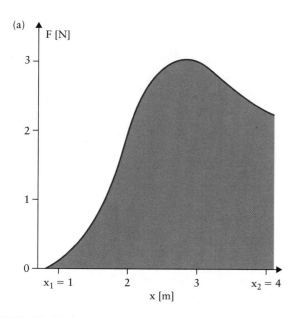

(a)

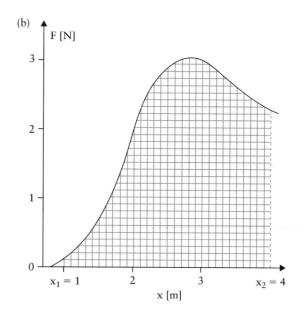

(b)

**FIGURE 6.18**

(a) An example of a variable force acting on an object. The force varies from 0 N to 3 N between positions $x_1$ and $x_2$. The work done on/by the object can be determined from measuring the area under the curve of this plot between the initial and final positions. (b) A simple graphical method to determine the area under the curve in part (a) is illustrated. We overlay the figure with a fine grid of lines that are spaced 0.1 m horizontally and 0.1 N vertically. Each rectangle corresponds to a work contribution of 0.01 J; the total area is determined by counting the number of rectangles.

rectangles below the curve in Fig. 6.18(b). This number is $N = 610$. The work in Fig. 6.18(a) therefore equals the work due to each small rectangle, multiplied by the number of rectangles under the curve:

$$W = N \cdot W_{grid} = 610 \cdot (0.01\,J) = 6.1\,J \quad [37]$$

Recall that this is an absolute value, as we didn't distinguish the directions of the force or the displacement. We must apply Eqs. [16] and [17] to determine the sign of work in this case. Since the question states that the work is done on the object, we find $W = +6.1$ J.

The same considerations apply to the case of a gas sealed by a piston: the work is the area under the function $p(V)$, as illustrated in Fig. 6.19. If the pressure does not depend on the volume, the area in the figure becomes a rectangle that is represented by the product of the pressure and the change in volume, as written in Eq. [30]. In Fig. 6.19, the purple area represents the absolute value of the work whether the gas is expanded or compressed.

The only difference between analyzing mechanical work and work on a gas is an additional negative sign for the gas case from Eq. [30] as illustrated in Fig. 6.20.

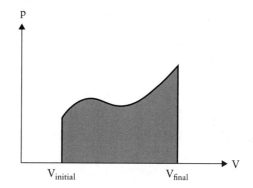

**FIGURE 6.19**

Sketch of the area under a curve for a process in which the pressure varies with volume between an initial value $V_{initial}$ and a final value $V_{final}$. The figure indicates that Eq. [30] can be treated in the same fashion as Eq. [15].

$$W = -\lim_{n\to\infty} \sum_{i=1}^{n} p_i \cdot \frac{V_{final} - V_{initial}}{n} \quad [38]$$

We need to distinguish two cases:

- the gas undergoes an **expansion** (volume increase indicated by arrow 1 in Fig. 6.20):
  $V_{initial} < V_{final} \Rightarrow W < 0$, or
- the gas undergoes a **compression** (volume decrease indicated by arrow 2 in Fig. 6.20):
  $V_{initial} > V_{final} \Rightarrow W > 0$.

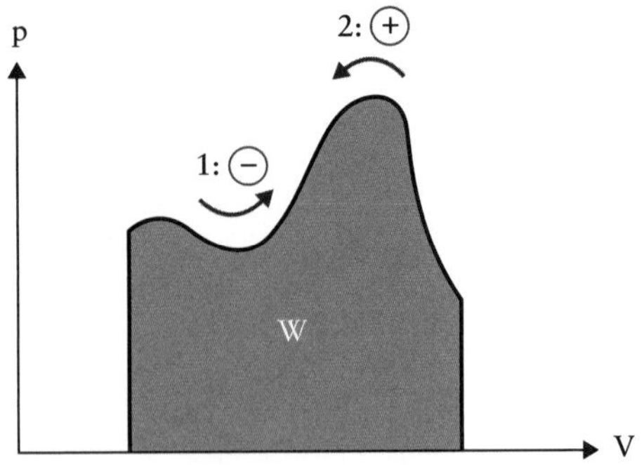

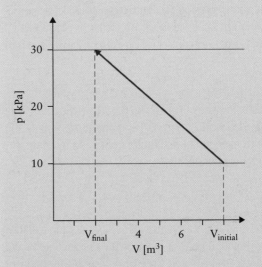

**FIGURE 6.20**

Sketch illustrating the two possible directions in which a process in a pressure versus volume diagram may occur. Path 1 is an expansion with a positive value for $\Delta V$. Because pressure values are always positive, the sign in Eq. [38] leads to a negative value of work $W$. Path 2 is a compression with a negative value for $\Delta V$. Combined with a positive pressure this leads to a positive $W$ value.

---

**Concept Question 6.10**

**We consider the gas in Fig. 6.19 to be the system. In the process shown, is the work positive or negative?**

ANSWER: Fig. 6.19 shows a volume expansion, since the volume $V_{initial}$ is smaller than the volume $V_{final}$. Therefore, based on Eq. [38] or Fig. 6.20, the work is negative, $W < 0$. This means that the gas does work on the piston during an expansion.

---

**Concept Question 6.11**

**Fig. 6.21 shows three processes during which the volume of a gas expands from an initial volume $V_{initial}$ to a final volume $V_{final}$. Rank the work in each of the three cases labelled (i), (ii), and (iii), starting with the highest value. Hint: −5 J < −2 J, but +5 J > +2 J.**

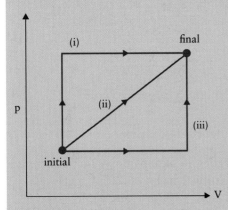

**FIGURE 6.21**

Three paths for an expansion of a gas system from an initial to a final volume. The paths are identified as (i), (ii), and (iii).

---

SOLUTION: The work is measured by the area under the curve, as indicated in Fig. 6.20. Note that path 1 of Fig. 6.20 matches qualitatively with each of the three processes in Fig. 6.21, because all of these processes are expansions. Thus, all four work terms are negative and, based on the area under each curve, we find:

$$0 > W_{(iii)} > W_{(ii)} > W_{(i)} \qquad [39]$$

---

● **EXAMPLE 6.6**

A gas is compressed from an initial volume of 8 m³ to a final volume of 2 m³. If the pressure depends specifically on the volume as shown in Fig. 6.22, what is the work required to complete the compression?

*Solution:* We first determine the absolute value of the work. This value is obtained from the area under the curve in Fig. 6.22. Analyzing the area is straightforward because of the linear pressure increase. We add the area of the lower rectangle and the area of the top triangle:

$$W = (10 \text{ kPa})(8 \text{ m}^3 - 2 \text{ m}^3)$$
$$+ \frac{1}{2}(30 \text{ kPa} - 10 \text{ kPa})(8 \text{ m}^3 - 2 \text{ m}^3)$$
$$= 1.2 \times 10^5 \text{ J} \qquad [40]$$

**FIGURE 6.22**

$p$–$V$ diagram for a gas that is compressed from an initial volume of 8 m³ to a final volume of 2 m³. The pressure increases linearly during the compression from 10 kPa to 30 kPa. This is an example of a system with varying pressure to which Eq. [30] cannot be applied.

Note that the area of the lower rectangle must be included, because the area under the curve includes every part down to the line $p = 0$.

In the second step we determine the sign of the work. In a compression, the volume change is negative. Eq. [38] leads to a positive work $W > 0$. This means the gas receives $W = +1.2 \times 10^5$ J; in other words, this amount of work is done on the gas.

# Energy

Even though a system may be capable of doing work, that work need not be done immediately. A system can store the capability to do work; what is stored is called *energy*.

*When a system interacts with its environment, its exchange of work represents a change in the amount of energy in the system.*

Energy can be stored in systems in several different ways. The following list includes the major forms of energy we discuss in this textbook:

- **Kinetic energy** is work stored in the speed of an object.

  *Example:* Blood ejected by the heart carries a high kinetic energy into the aorta. This energy must be reduced in the aortic arch because blood has to flow more steadily through the remaining cardiovascular system.

- **Potential energy** is work stored in the position of an object relative to other objects. We discuss:

  - *Gravitational potential energy*, which is the energy of an object due to its position relative to the surface of Earth.

    *Example:* The gravitational potential energy of blood varies in the feet, the heart, and the head when standing upright. We will see in Chapter 11 that this has consequences for the blood pressure.

  - *Electric potential energy*, which is the energy of an electrically charged object due to its position relative to other electric charges. It is discussed in Chapter 13.

    *Example:* Electric energy governs the transport of impulses in nerves.

  - *Elastic potential energy*, which is the energy due to the relative position of two objects that are connected through an elastic medium, most typically a spring. It is discussed in Chapter 16.

  *Example:* Elastic energy allows us to characterize molecular vibrations between the different parts in ATP in Fig. 6.1.

- **Thermal energy** is stored in the irregular motion of particles. The temperature of the system is a measure of this energy.

  *Example:* Thermal energy is generated and released when endotherms maintain a constant core body temperature.

- **Chemical energy** is work stored in chemical bonds of molecules.

  *Example:* Chemical energy is transferred during the ATP hydrolysis shown in Eq. [1].

- **Latent heat** is work stored in the phase of matter, such as the liquid, gaseous, or solid state.

  *Example:* Latent heat is dissipated during perspiration because perspiration is associated with the evaporation of water from the skin surface.

One consequence of the relation between work and the various forms of energy is that each form of energy has the same unit J as work. Only the kinetic, gravitational potential, and elastic potential energies can be defined for a mechanical object. They are therefore called mechanical energies. Since we have discussed mechanics extensively to this point, we introduce mechanical energies first.

## Kinetic Energy

To define kinetic energy, we study a system for which only its **speed** changes, but no other parameters. Such a system is shown in Fig. 6.23: an isolated object is allowed to interact for a well-defined time interval $\Delta t$ with its environment. The interaction leads to an acceleration of the system. For simplicity we choose the net force, which causes the acceleration to be constant and directed along the horizontal $x$-axis. Newton's second law, $F_{net} = m \cdot a$, then leads to $a = $ const during $\Delta t$. The acceleration changes the speed of the system from $v_{initial}$ to $v_{final}$.

We use the acceleration step to quantify kinetic energy from the work done on the object, $W = F_{net} \cdot \Delta x$. Fig. 6.23 illustrates which kinematic properties we have to include in the calculation: the speed of the object and its acceleration and displacement, but not the time. We use the third kinematic relation, derived in Eq. [2.25]. Substituting the acceleration from that equation into Newton's equation of motion, $F = m \cdot a$, yields:

$$F = m \cdot a = \frac{m}{2 \cdot \Delta x} (v_{final}^2 - v_{initial}^2) \quad [41]$$

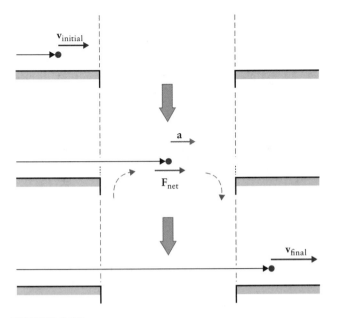

**FIGURE 6.23**

To define kinetic energy we choose to compare two states of a system in mechanical equilibrium that differ only in the speed of the object (blue circle). The initial state is shown at the top with speed $v_{initial}$ and the final state is shown at the bottom with $v_{final} > v_{initial}$. To quantify the relation between both equilibrium states the object is accelerated with a constant force acting while the object passes from the left end to the right end of an interaction zone, shown in the middle section of the sketch between the dashed lines.

The work is obtained by multiplying both sides of this equation by the displacement $\Delta x$:

$$W = F \cdot \Delta x = \frac{m}{2}(v_{final}^2 - v_{initial}^2) \qquad [42]$$

This is the work done on the object during the time interval $\Delta t$, when the external force acts on the system. The terms relating to the initial and final conditions can be separated:

$$W = \frac{m}{2}v_{final}^2 - \frac{m}{2}v_{initial}^2 \qquad [43]$$

Eq. [43] contains an interesting feature: the work is expressed as the difference of two terms:

- the second term contains only system parameters at the initial instant when the external force begins to act, and
- the first term contains only system parameters at the final instant when the external force ceases to act.

Otherwise, the two terms are mathematically the same and allow us to define a new function $E_{kin}$ (kinetic energy), in the form:

$$E_{kin} = \frac{1}{2}m \cdot v^2 \qquad [44]$$

With this definition, we rewrite Eq. [43] in the form called the **work–kinetic energy theorem**:

$$W = E_{kin,final} - E_{kin,initial} \qquad [45]$$

*When work is done on an object causing exclusively a change in its speed, that work is equal to the change in kinetic energy of the object.*

When the object does work on the environment, it becomes slower and the kinetic energy decreases, reflecting the amount of energy needed to do the work. If work is done on the object, it accelerates and then stores a larger amount of kinetic energy. There is a maximum amount of work a moving object can do, which is equal to the kinetic energy it loses by slowing down to rest, $v_{final} = 0$. In summary:

$$W > 0 \quad \Leftrightarrow \quad E_{kin,final} > E_{kin,initial}$$
$$\Leftrightarrow \quad \text{System receives work}$$
$$W < 0 \quad \Leftrightarrow \quad E_{kin,final} < E_{kin,initial} \qquad [46]$$
$$\Leftrightarrow \quad \text{System releases work}$$

**Concept Question 6.12**

**Fig. 6.24 shows five plots of the kinetic energy as a function of the velocity of an object. Which one correctly describes the kinetic energy of the object?**

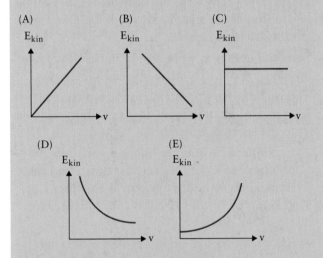

**FIGURE 6.24**

Five graphs of the kinetic energy as a function of velocity. The origin for each axis lies at the point where they intersect.

ANSWER: None. The first three plots are linear, but we require a quadratic dependence to represent Eq. [44]. Plot (D) implies that the kinetic energy decreases with speed, contrary to Eq. [44]. Plot (E) is incorrect, as it shows a non-zero value for $v = 0$.

● **EXAMPLE 6.7**

An object of mass $m = 0.5$ kg moves with initial speed $v_{initial} = 5.0$ m/s, then interacts with its environment, releasing 5.0 J of work. What is the speed of the object after the interaction is completed?

*Solution:* We use Eq. [45]:

$$W = E_{final} - E_{initial}$$
$$= \frac{1}{2}m \cdot v_{final}^2 - \frac{1}{2}m \cdot v_{initial}^2 \qquad [47]$$

Next, we isolate the final speed of the object:

$$\frac{1}{2}m \cdot v_{final}^2 = W + \frac{1}{2}m \cdot v_{initial}^2 \qquad [48]$$

which leads to:

$$v_{final} = \sqrt{\frac{2 \cdot W}{m} + v_{initial}^2} \qquad [49]$$

Applying the convention of Eqs. [16] and [17], we note that work released by the system has to be entered into Eq. [49] negative, $W = -5.0$ J. This leads to:

$$v_{final} = \sqrt{\frac{2 \cdot (-5.0 \text{ J})}{0.5 \text{ kg}} + \left(5.0 \frac{m}{s}\right)^2} = 2.23 \frac{m}{s}$$
$$[50]$$

It is important to understand whether work is released or received by the system to determine the sign of $W$. Using $W = +5.0$ J instead of $W = -5.0$ J in Eq. [50] leads to a wrong result.

## Velocity Detectors of the Human Body: Meissner's Corpuscles and Hair

We discussed acceleration detectors in the human body in Chapters 2 and 3: the Pacinian corpuscles and the semicircular canals in the vestibular organ. The argument for their existence is that acceleration is an important parameter in nature as it occurs explicitly in some fundamental natural laws (Newton's laws). Our body must measure its acceleration to be in a position to properly respond to its natural environment. In the previous section we found that speed is also relevant to physical phenomena as it is connected to kinetic energy. Does our body therefore also have **velocity detectors**? The answer is yes. We possess two independent detection systems, in the form of Meissner's corpuscles below the skin (about half a million corpuscles, with the highest concentration in the skin of the fingertips), and hair.

## MEISSNER'S CORPUSCLES

Fig. 3.10 shows a sketch of the cross-section of the outer layers of our palm, including **Meissner's corpuscles** just below the epidermis. Notice how much closer to the surface Meissner's corpuscles are located than Pacinian corpuscles. This is an important feature for the functional role of Meissner's corpuscles as velocity detectors. We further note that they are located near the steepest slope of the ridge–valley pattern in the fingertips.

Meissner's corpuscles measure the speed of objects that come into contact with the skin and consequently increase the tension on the skin. The microscopic structure of a Meissner's corpuscle in a human fingertip is shown in a light micrograph in Fig. 6.25. Each corpuscle consists of a stack of cells in the shape of an ellipsoid, with the more rigid cell nuclei located on alternating sides from cell to cell. Dendrites are intertwined between these cells.

The mechanism of the velocity detection of a Meissner's corpuscle is illustrated in Fig. 6.26. Shown is a piston just before and while pressing the skin of the finger. The corpuscle gets squeezed together, which leads to a change in the stacking structure of the cells. As a consequence the intertwined dendrite is bent, causing nerve impulses to the brain. The impulse rate, which is the number of impulses sent per second, is higher when the dendrite is bent faster.

We use graphs to establish this relationship between the velocity and the impulse rate: Fig. 6.27(a) shows a linear plot, and Fig. 6.27(b) is a double-logarithmic representation of the same data.

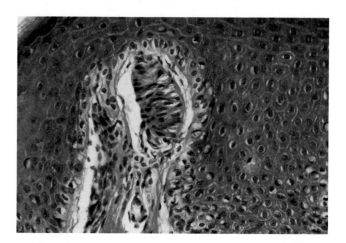

**FIGURE 6.25**

Light micrograph of a Meissner's corpuscle in the skin of a human fingertip. Shown is an oval-shaped corpuscle of approximately 100 $\mu$m length with cells stacked in an alternating arrangement of the cell nuclei. The dendrite is intertwined between the cells. The corpuscle is surrounded by numerous densely stained epidermal cells.

## FIGURE 6.26

Mechanism of Meissner's corpuscles. At left a piston is shown at time zero approaching the skin surface with velocity **v**. At right the same area is shown after the piston has pushed the skin a certain distance down. The piston is assumed to move with constant speed. Meissner's corpuscles get deformed in the process.

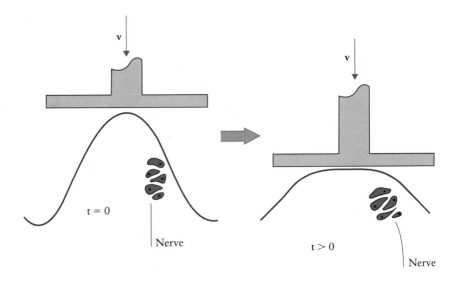

### Concept Question 6.13

**What can you conclude from (a) the linear plot, and (b) the double-logarithmic plot in Fig. 6.27?**

ANSWER TO PART (a): The linear plot highlights absolute values and variations in the steepness of the curve. Thus, the linear graph is suitable to pinpoint greatest sensitivity, corresponding to the interval of greatest steepness. The greatest sensitivity of Meissner's corpuscles occurs at very small speeds up to $v = 1$ cm/s. They are suitable to distinguish forms of gentle touching—not to measure the speed of an incoming baseball! Can you think of a reason why this is so?

ANSWER TO PART (b): The double-logarithmic plot allows us to distinguish whether one or more mechanisms are involved in a process because it shows straight line segments for each power law. The mathematical aspects of double-logarithmic plots are discussed in the Math Review at the end of Chapter 1. In the specific case of Fig. 6.27(b), the power law for the nerve impulse rate, $P$, is written in the form

$$P = a \cdot v^b \qquad [51]$$

in which $v$ is the speed of the object making contact with the skin. If the prefactor $a$ or the exponent $b$ in this power law is not constant, deviations from a straight line in the double-logarithmic plot occur. Any deviation from a straight line is, therefore, an indication that additional physical explanations are needed. In the present case, however, no such deviations occur, and thus the single mechanism illustrated in Fig. 6.26 is sufficient to explain Meissner's corpuscles based on the experimental data in Fig. 6.27.

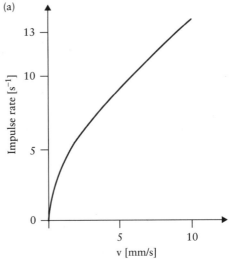

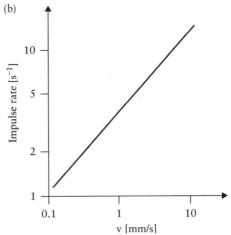

## FIGURE 6.27

The nerve impulse rate for Meissner's corpuscles as a function of the speed of an approaching object. The impulse rate is given in unit impulses per second and the speed is given in unit mm/s. (a) A linear plot of the data showing the greatest sensitivity to speeds of 5 mm/s. (b) In the double-logarithmic plot the same data follow a straight line segment. This means that a single power law describes the data and, therefore, that a single mechanism explains the operation of the corpuscle.

## HAIR

Fig. 3.10 shows a sketch of a cross-section of the human **skin containing hair** at the left. In comparison to hair-free skin, no Meissner's corpuscles are present. Pacinian corpuscles are still found in the deeper layers, and Merkel's corpuscles are still present below the epidermis. This selective absence of Meissner's corpuscles is explained by the hair replacing them as velocity detectors.

Unlike Meissner's corpuscles, hair can detect the velocity of objects not yet in contact with the skin; i.e., they represent a rudimentary remote sensing device. Their mechanism is illustrated in Fig. 6.28. Shown is a piston that moves parallel to the skin in near proximity to the surface. When the piston pushes the hair to the side, a force is exerted on the root sheath. This force is sensed by the dendrites coiling around the root of the hair. As in the case of Meissner's corpuscles, the rate of nerve impulses is a function of the speed of the piston.

## Potential Energy

Next we study cases in which the work is stored in the relative position of objects, particularly the work stored in the position of an object relative to the surface of Earth. This potential energy is properly referred to as **gravitational potential energy** to distinguish it from other potential energy forms; however, the adjective "gravitational" is usually dropped unless the various potential energies could be confused. Since we discuss only the gravitational potential energy in this chapter, the adjective is consistently omitted. To quantify this form of energy, we have to develop a proper experimental arrangement. The

system cannot be an isolated object, as for the definition of kinetic energy in Fig. 6.23. For the gravitational interaction Earth becomes part of the environment. An isolated superstructure consisting of Earth as the environment and the object as the system is still insufficient because then there would be only one force acting on the object (gravity). This does not allow us to establish a mechanical equilibrium. We need to add a second force with its source in the environment such that the system is in mechanical equilibrium. This source is a person holding the system. Note that we introduced this experiment previously in Fig. 6.9.

*The definition of a potential energy is based on the external force that is required to establish at least two different equilibrium states for the system.*

The two different equilibrium states that enable us to define potential energy are the same ones we used in Fig. 6.9:

- the system of mass $m$ held at rest at height $y_{initial}$ at an initial time, and
- the system held at rest at height $y_{final}$ at a later, final time.

We further choose $y_{final}$ to be lower than $y_{initial}$, as done in Fig. 6.9. The transfer between these two equilibrium states of the system can be accomplished in several ways. Dropping the system and catching it at the lower height is one possibility. This represents a more complicated transfer because non-equilibrium processes are involved, such as the slowing of the object near its final equilibrium state. The simplest transfer in Fig. 6.9 is to lower the system very slowly from the initial to the final height, moving it with a constant speed. In this case, the system is always in mechanical equilibrium and we know that $F_{ext} - W = 0$; i.e., $F_{ext} = m \cdot g$ during the transfer. Thus, the work due to the external force—which by definition establishes the mechanical equilibrium for the system—is calculated as:

$$W = F_{ext} \cdot \Delta y = m \cdot g(y_{final} - y_{initial}) \quad [52]$$

The work for the process in Fig. 6.9 is negative, because the expression in parentheses $(y_{final} - y_{initial})$ is negative while the external force is positive.

Postulating in analogy to Eq. [45] that the work is a measure of the change of the potential energy of the system from the initial to the final equilibrium state, we write:

$$W = E_{pot,final} - E_{pot,initial} \quad [53]$$

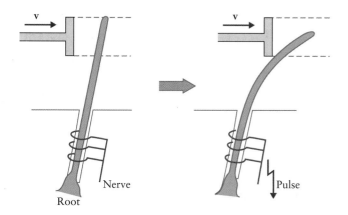

## FIGURE 6.28

Illustration of a hair as a velocity detector. A piston moves with velocity **v** parallel to the skin in close proximity. The bending of the hair causes the nerves at the root to send a signal to the brain.

Comparing Eqs. [52] and [53], we find:

$$E_{pot,initial} = m \cdot g \cdot y_{initial}$$
$$E_{pot,final} = m \cdot g \cdot y_{final}$$

[54]

Therefore, we define the potential energy in the form:

$$E_{pot} = m \cdot g \cdot y$$

[55]

*The potential energy depends linearly on the distance of the system from the surface of Earth. This statement is correct as long as we remain close to the surface of Earth, in particular up to heights reached by birds in flight (upper end of biosphere).*

Note that reporting absolute potential energy values is meaningless because values calculated from Eq. [55] depend on the choice of origin for the *y*-axis. Thus, only differences between potential energies, $\Delta E_{pot}$, play a role in physical processes—e.g., as work—as shown in Eq. [53].

## Concept Question 6.14

**Can you name an animal that shows a quantitative sense for potential energy?**

ANSWER: Several types of birds, for example. In parts of southern Europe, golden eagles feed mainly on tortoises, although their talons are no match for an animal tucked resolutely inside its shell. The eagle's solution is recorded in Greek mythology: An oracle warned Aeschylus that he would die by a house falling on his head. He wisely ensured he stood in the open on the fateful day, worried an earthquake might collapse any building he were to enter. He still met his untimely death, when an eagle fulfilled the prophecy by dropping a tortoise on him. Similar strategies are applied by Egyptian vultures to open ostrich eggs, and by crows feeding on gastropod mollusks along the Canadian Pacific coast.

The specific approach of the crows allows us to discuss physics a bit further. They fly with the mollusk to a certain height and drop their prey onto the rocky beach below. For each attempt, the bird must do work proportional to the height, as shown in Eq. [52]. Interestingly, the crows do not rise to a height from which they would be assured the mollusk would crack on the first attempt, but rather to an intermediate height from which they need to drop the mollusk several times to crack it open. For this behaviour to make sense, the crow must have found a height at which the total lifting work per mollusk is a minimum. This observation rules out the suggestion that the probability

*P* of the mollusk cracking open is proportional to its linear momentum at impact, $P \propto m \cdot v$. We illustrate this quantitatively in Example 6.9 using conservation of energy.

This discussion shows that even more complex scientific relations can be learned by experience. In humans, we would call similar behaviour intuition. We go beyond this in scientific reasoning when we apply abstraction, generalization, and associative thinking.

## Concept Question 6.15

**A person states that an object of mass $m = 1$ kg has a potential energy of 0 J. Where is the object located relative to the surface of Earth?**

ANSWER: We can't tell. What we know is that the object is located at the origin of the *y*-axis as chosen by the person. However, that person may choose $y = 0$ on the surface of a table, or at any other height. Additional information is needed to render the given energy information useful.

We add two further comments on Eqs. [52] and [53]:

- The derivation of Eq. [52] is based on a special case in which the external force is constant. We can generalize this for forces that vary with position by breaking the displacement down into *n* steps of length $\delta y$, with *n* then driven toward infinity:

$$W = \lim_{n \to \infty} \sum_{i=1}^{n} F_i \cdot \delta y$$

[56]

in which $\delta y = (y_{final} - y_{initial})/n$. We need Eq. [56] in order to determine the electric potential energy in Chapter 13 and the elastic potential energy in Chapter 16.

- A potential energy cannot be defined for all forces, leading in the literature to a distinction between **conservative forces** (with a potential energy) and **dissipative forces** (without a potential energy). We avoid a discussion of this issue by omitting dissipative forces until we introduce thermal physics. At that point we are no longer trying to describe physical laws with mechanical concepts, and the distinction between conservative and dissipative forces is no longer necessary.

# Conservation of Mechanical Energy

## An Object Falls Without Air Resistance

In equilibrium, both the kinetic and potential energies are independently constant. In this section, we want to find out how these energy forms depend on time for a system that is not in mechanical equilibrium but that does not exchange work with its environment.

The specific experiment we study is shown in Fig. 6.29: an object is released at an initial height and drops. The final observation is taken at a height where the object is still above the point of impact on the ground. During the time that elapses while the object moves from its initial to its final height, $\Delta t = t_2 - t_1$, only the speed and the height above the ground change. This means that we take a sufficient approach when considering only the kinetic energy and the potential energy. The system is the object: in this case, the isolated superstructure also contains Earth. No other object (such as a person) interacts with the system. For the system in this isolated superstructure, we quantify the energy changes during the process of falling.

We start with the relation between the parameters of the falling object. The displacement $y_{final} - y_{initial}$ along the vertical $y$-direction in Fig. 6.29 and the $y$-component of the acceleration $a_y = -g$ are substituted in the third kinematic equation, Eq. [2.25]:

$$v_{final}^2 - v_{initial}^2 = -2 \cdot g(y_{final} - y_{initial}) \quad [57]$$

We multiply this equation on both sides by the mass of the object and divide by 2:

$$\frac{1}{2}m \cdot v_{final}^2 - \frac{1}{2}m \cdot v_{initial}^2 = -m \cdot g(y_{final} - y_{initial}) \quad [58]$$

which yields after separation of the terms related to the initial and final stages, respectively:

$$\frac{1}{2}m \cdot v_{initial}^2 + m \cdot g \cdot y_{initial} = \frac{1}{2}m \cdot v_{final}^2 + m \cdot g \cdot y_{final} \quad [59]$$

We found that the sum of the potential and kinetic energy is the same at the initial and the final positions for the object in Fig. 6.29:

$$E_{kin,initial} + E_{pot,initial} = E_{kin,final} + E_{pot,final} \quad [60]$$

We generalize this result for any initial and final positions in two ways:

- The sum of kinetic and potential energy is constant at every position of the object or at any instant of the process in Fig. 6.29:

$$E_{kin} + E_{pot} = const \quad [61]$$

- The time change of the sum of the kinetic and potential energy of the object is zero.

---

**Concept Question 6.16**

Fig. 6.30 shows five graphs of energy versus vertical position for an object falling straight down from a given initial height. Which graph represents (a) the potential energy of the object, and (b) its total mechanical (kinetic and potential) energy? We neglect air resistance.

ANSWER TO PART (a): The potential energy is given in Eq. [55], with $E_{pot} \propto y$. This corresponds to graph (E). Note that graph (D) corresponds to $E \propto -y$, which would be the correct choice if the $y$-axis pointed downward.

---

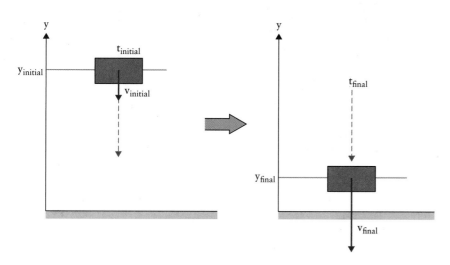

**FIGURE 6.29**

An object is released at time $t_1$ (at left) and falls toward the surface of Earth. The final observation of the object is done at time $t_2$, when the object has not yet hit the ground (at right). Note that this experiment is similar to the one shown in Fig. 6.9. However, the person holding the object in Fig. 6.9 is no longer part of the isolated superstructure because no interaction between a person and the object is required.

## Concept Question 6.16 (continued)

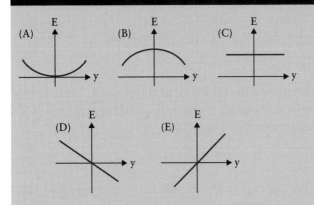

**FIGURE 6.30**

Five plots of energy $E$ as a function of vertical position $y$.

ANSWER TO PART (b): The total mechanical energy is conserved for a falling object. We write this in the form $E_{tot} \neq f(y)$, which means that the total energy is not a function of $y$. This corresponds to graph (C).

## ● EXAMPLE 6.8

An object of 0.2 kg moves initially at a speed of 30.0 m/s vertically upward. (a) What is the kinetic energy of the object at the highest point of its trajectory? (b) What is the potential energy of the object at the highest point? (c) How far is the highest point above the initial position of the object?

*Solution to part (a):* At the highest point, the downward-directed gravitational acceleration has eliminated the initially upward-directed speed component in the $y$-direction. Thus:

$$v_{at\ top} = 0 \qquad [62]$$

which yields:

$$E_{kin,at\ top} = \frac{1}{2} m \cdot v_{at\ top}^2 = 0\ J \qquad [63]$$

*Solution to part (b):* We first calculate the total mechanical energy of the system. Since energy is conserved, we can do this at any instant of the experiment. For convenience we choose the initial instant, because we know all system data at that time. We further arbitrarily choose the initial height as the origin, $y_{initial} = 0$; i.e., $E_{pot,initial} = 0$. This is done without loss of generality and does not affect the result! As a consequence, the total energy of the object initially has only a kinetic energy component $E_{kin,initial} = \frac{1}{2} m \cdot v^2 = 90\ J$. This

is, therefore, also the total energy of the system; in turn, the potential energy at the highest point, $m \cdot g \cdot y_{at\ top} = 90\ J$, where the kinetic energy is zero.

*Solution to part (c):* We substitute the result from part (b) in Eq. [55] to obtain the maximum height $y_{at\ top}$:

$$y_{at\ top} = \frac{E_{pot}}{m \cdot g} = \frac{90\ J}{(0.2\ kg)\left(9.8\ \dfrac{m}{s^2}\right)} = 46\ m \qquad [64]$$

## ● EXAMPLE 6.9

We discussed in Concept Question 6.14 how Pacific coast crows crack open the shells of mollusks. The behaviour of the crows indicates that an optimum height exists for dropping mollusks such that the lifting energy required per mollusk is a minimum. Is this observation consistent with the assumption that the probability $P$ for a mollusk shell to crack is proportional to its linear momentum at impact? *Hint:* Write the probability to crack open a shell in the form:

$$P = \gamma \cdot m_{mollusk} \cdot v_{ground} \qquad [65]$$

in which $v_{ground}$ is the speed with which the mollusk hits the ground, $m_{mollusk} \cdot v_{ground}$ is the momentum of the mollusk at impact, and $\gamma$ is a constant proportionality factor.

*Solution:* The total lifting work a crow has to do per mollusk is

$$W_{total} = N \cdot (m_{mollusk} + m_{crow}) g \cdot h \qquad [66]$$

in which $N$ is the number of drops needed to crack from height $h$. The last term is the potential energy difference at the release height because the crow has to transport the mollusk and itself to that height each time. $N$ is inversely proportional to the probability $P$ of cracking a mollusk open: $N = 1/P$. For example, if $P = 50\%$ then we need $N = 1/0.5 = 2$ attempts, and if $P = 25\%$ then we need $N = 1/0.25 = 4$ attempts. Thus:

$$W_{total} = \frac{1}{P} \cdot (m_{mollusk} + m_{crow}) g \cdot h \qquad [67]$$

The conservation of energy allows us to relate the velocity at impact, $v_{ground}$, and the height of release, $h$:

$$m_{mollusk} \cdot g \cdot h = \frac{1}{2} m_{mollusk} \cdot v_{ground}^2 \qquad [68]$$

which yields:

$$v_{\text{ground}} = \sqrt{2 \cdot g \cdot h} \qquad [69]$$

Eqs. [65] and [69] are now substituted in Eq. [67]:

$$W_{\text{total}} = \frac{m_{\text{mollusk}} + m_{\text{crow}}}{\sqrt{2} \cdot \gamma \cdot m_{\text{mollusk}}} \sqrt{g \cdot h} \qquad [70]$$

We find that the work is proportional to the square root of the height, $W_{\text{total}} \propto h^{1/2}$. This function has no minimum at a finite value for $h$. Thus, the assumption that the probability $P$ to crack open is proportional to the momentum of the mollusk at impact is not correct and a more complex relation must hold between these two parameters of interest to the crow.

## Elastic Collisions

Note carefully what we actually showed in the previous section: we found that the sum of kinetic and potential energy is conserved for the particular experiment shown in Fig. 6.29. For this to be of further interest, other experiments should lead to the same conclusion:

(i)   if the conservation result is consistently found in all experiments, a conservation law is formulated;

(ii)  if the conservation result is found often in experiments, a conservation rule may be formulated once proper restrictions are identified;

(iii) if the conservation result is found infrequently, the suggestion of a conservation law or rule would be dismissed.

In this section, we first use the perfectly inelastic collisions we discussed in Example 4.1 to prove that exceptions to the conservation of mechanical energy (kinetic and potential energy) exist; i.e., we cannot proceed as proposed in option (i). We then introduce elastic collisions to illustrate a wide range of phenomena that obey the conservation of mechanical energy, ruling out the idea to dismiss the usefulness of a conservation law as proposed in option (iii). We conclude the discussion in this section by evaluating option (ii).

### PERFECTLY INELASTIC COLLISIONS VIOLATE THE CONSERVATION OF MECHANICAL ENERGY

To test the conservation of energy in the case of a **perfectly inelastic collision**, we start with the conservation of momentum equation when an object 1 with mass $m_1$ and speed $v_{1,\text{initial}}$ collides with object 2 with mass $m_2$ that is initially at rest:

$$m_1 \cdot v_{1,\text{initial}} = (m_1 + m_2)v_{\text{final}} \qquad [71]$$

With no change in the potential energy during the collision, the conservation of mechanical energy would require $E_{\text{kin,initial}} = E_{\text{kin,final}}$. We test this formula with the parameters for the perfectly inelastic collision:

$$E_{\text{kin,initial}} = \frac{1}{2}m_1 \cdot v_{1,\text{initial}}^2$$

$$E_{\text{kin,final}} = \frac{1}{2}(m_1 + m_2)v_{\text{final}}^2 \qquad [72]$$

The second formula in Eq. [72] is rewritten using Eq. [71]:

$$E_{\text{kin,final}} = \frac{1}{2}(m_1 + m_2)\left(\frac{m_1}{m_1 + m_2}v_{1,\text{initial}}\right)^2$$

$$= \frac{1}{2}\frac{m_1^2}{m_1 + m_2}v_{1,\text{initial}}^2 \qquad [73]$$

The energy calculated in Eq. [73] is equal to that in the first formula in Eq. [72] only if:

$$\frac{m_1^2}{m_1 + m_2} = m_1 \quad \Rightarrow \quad \frac{m_1}{m_1 + m_2} = 1 \qquad [74]$$

i.e., $m_2 = 0$, which is a physically meaningless case. Thus, perfectly inelastic collisions always violate the conservation of mechanical energy. The conservation of mechanical energy cannot be a universal law!

### ELASTIC COLLISIONS ARE CONSISTENT WITH THE CONSERVATION OF MECHANICAL ENERGY

To test whether the conservation of energy is at all applicable to collisions we study a general collision, such as the one illustrated in Fig. 6.31. Note that Fig. 6.31 does not include the case of a perfectly inelastic collision because the two colliding objects remain separated after the collision. We quantify the case in Fig. 6.31 with two requirements:

• the **conservation of momentum**, which is universally applicable as we established in Chapter 4, and

• the **conservation of mechanical energy**, which we impose with the understanding that the resulting

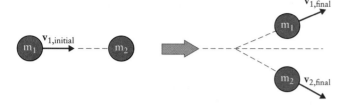

**FIGURE 6.31**

Collision of two objects of masses $m_1$ and $m_2$. Object 1 moves with velocity $\mathbf{v}_{1,\text{initial}}$ toward object 2, which is initially at rest. We define the *xy*-plane such that the two objects move in this plane after the collision at the right.

formalism may not apply to all collisions, and in the worst case may not apply to any collision at all.

We find below that there are indeed collisions that can be described by these two requirements. These collisions are called **elastic collisions**. Thus, for a horizontal elastic collision we write two conditions:

conservation of momentum:

$$m_1 \cdot \mathbf{v}_{1,\text{initial}} + m_2 \cdot \mathbf{v}_{2,\text{initial}} = m_1 \cdot \mathbf{v}_{1,\text{final}} + m_2 \cdot \mathbf{v}_{2,\text{final}}$$

conservation of energy:

$$\frac{m_1}{2} v_{1,\text{initial}}^2 + \frac{m_2}{2} v_{2,\text{initial}}^2 = \frac{m_1}{2} v_{1,\text{final}}^2 + \frac{m_2}{2} v_{2,\text{final}}^2$$

[75]

Eq. [75] is mathematically extensive, as it contains in 4 formulas 12 velocity components and 4 speeds. In applications, we can often reduce the number of parameters by using additional conditions for the system. For example, in Fig. 6.31 we assume that object 2 is initially at rest. This allows us to further define the plane in which the two objects move after the collision as the *xy*-plane. This allows us to rewrite Eq. [75] in the form:

momentum, *x*-direction:

$$m_1 \cdot v_{1x,\text{initial}} = m_1 \cdot v_{1x,\text{final}} + m_2 \cdot v_{2x,\text{final}}$$

momentum, *y*-direction:

$$m_1 \cdot v_{1y,\text{initial}} = m_1 \cdot v_{1y,\text{final}} + m_2 \cdot v_{2y,\text{final}} \quad [76]$$

energy:

$$\frac{m_1}{2} v_{1,\text{initial}}^2 = \frac{m_1}{2} v_{1,\text{final}}^2 + \frac{m_2}{2} v_{2,\text{final}}^2$$

i.e., we now deal with three formulas with 6 velocity components and 3 speeds. Eq. [76] has been used successfully to explain a large number of molecular, atomic, and sub-atomic collisions. We use its predictions for molecular or atomic gas particles that are

moving in a container in Concept Question 6.17 below. Sub-atomic collisions are mostly of interest in astrophysics, nuclear physics, and high-energy physics; we encounter some of these collisions in Chapter 23. For macroscopic processes both perfectly inelastic and elastic collisions are idealizations. However, collisions of hard spheres, such as billiard balls, or a hard sphere with a rigid wall, such as a steel sphere on a glass plate, come close. Mathematically, perfectly inelastic and elastic collisions are the only two cases that can be solved without detailed further knowledge of the system.

---

## Concept Question 6.17

We develop a mechanical model for a gas in Chapter 7 called the kinetic gas theory. In that model we are interested particularly in two elastic collision cases: (a) the collision of two identical objects with $m_1 = m_2$, and (b) the collision of an object with a much heavier wall. *Hint:* Discuss these cases for a one-dimensional elastic collision, because otherwise Eq. [76] leads to an extensive algebraic effort. The basic collision properties we are interested in can be established by confining the motion to one dimension (i.e., a head-on collision).

ANSWER: We rewrite Eq. [76] for the one-dimensional case. The conservation of momentum simplifies to a single formula:

$$m_1 \cdot v_{1,\text{initial}} = m_1 \cdot v_{1,\text{final}} + m_2 \cdot v_{2,\text{final}} \quad [77]$$

in which the final speed the object of mass $m_1$ is called $v_{1,\text{final}}$ and the final speed of the object of mass $m_2$ is $v_{2,\text{final}}$. The conservation of energy remains unchanged from Eq. [76]:

$$\frac{1}{2} m_1 \cdot v_{1,\text{initial}}^2 = \frac{1}{2} m_1 \cdot v_{1,\text{final}}^2 + \frac{1}{2} m_2 \cdot v_{2,\text{final}}^2 \quad [78]$$

To combine Eqs. [77] and [78], we first isolate $v_{2,\text{final}}$ in Eq. [77]:

$$v_{2,\text{final}} = \frac{m_1}{m_2}(v_{1,\text{initial}} - v_{1,\text{final}}) \quad [79]$$

and then substitute it in Eq. [78]:

$$m_1 \cdot v_{1,\text{initial}}^2 = m_1 \cdot v_{1,\text{final}}^2 + m_2 \frac{m_1^2}{m_2^2}(v_{1,\text{initial}} - v_{1,\text{final}})^2$$

[80]

Eq. [80] is a quadratic equation. See Math Review "Binomials and Quadratic Equations" at the end of this chapter. We sort the various $v_{1,\text{final}}$ terms:

$$v_{1,\text{final}}^2 \left[ m_1 \left( 1 + \frac{m_1}{m_2} \right) \right] - v_{1,\text{final}} \left[ 2 \cdot v_{1,\text{initial}} \frac{m_1^2}{m_2} \right]$$

$$+ v_{1,\text{initial}}^2 \cdot m_1 \left( \frac{m_1}{m_2} - 1 \right) = 0 \qquad [81]$$

This equation can be solved for $v_{1,\text{final}}$. We focus on the cases that relate to the question text.

ANSWER TO PART (a): A one-dimensional elastic collision of two objects of equal mass, $m_1 = m_2 = m$, leads to:

$$m \cdot v_{1,\text{final}}^2 - 2 \cdot m \cdot v_{1,\text{final}} \cdot v_{1,\text{initial}} = 0 \qquad [82]$$

which has two solutions:

$$v_{1,\text{final}} = 0 \quad \text{or} \quad v_{1,\text{final}} = v_{1,\text{initial}} \qquad [83]$$

Either the object of mass $m_1$ passes through the object of mass $m_2$ without interaction (physically not possible), or the object of mass $m_1$ transfers its entire speed to the object of mass $m_2$ and comes to rest. This is a suitable model for a head-on collision of equal gas particles, even though none of the particles is typically at rest. We therefore expect that elastic collisions in a gas cause a redistribution of the velocities, but that the sum of the kinetic energies of the colliding particles remains unchanged. In the kinetic gas theory both of these observations will be addressed: the conservation of the kinetic energy of the two particles allows us to neglect individual collisions in the formalism, and the redistribution of velocities requires us to allow for a velocity distribution of the gas particles.

ANSWER TO PART (b): A much heavier object hits a much lighter object at rest. An example is the collision between a fast car and a small, airborne pebble that bounces off the windshield without damaging it. In this case we use $m_1 \gg m_2$. From Eq. [81] we find:

$$v_{1,\text{final}}^2 \frac{m_1^2}{m_2} - 2 \cdot v_{1,\text{final}} \cdot v_{1,\text{initial}} \frac{m_1^2}{m_2} + v_{1,\text{initial}}^2 \frac{m_1^2}{m_2} = 0 \qquad [84]$$

which simplifies to:

$$(v_{1,\text{final}} - v_{1,\text{initial}})^2 = 0 \qquad [85]$$

Eq. [85] has only one solution:

$$v_{1,\text{final}} = v_{1,\text{initial}} \qquad [86]$$

i.e., the heavier object pushes the lighter object away without being affected.

Alternatively, a much lighter object hits a heavy object at rest. In this case, $m_1 \ll m_2$ and Eq. [81] simplifies to:

$$m_1 \cdot v_{1,\text{final}}^2 - m_1 \cdot v_{1,\text{initial}}^2 = 0 \qquad [87]$$

Eq. [87] has two solutions:

$$v_{1,\text{final}} = \pm v_{1,\text{initial}} \qquad [88]$$

i.e., either the incoming object passes through the heavy object without interaction (physically impossible), or it is reflected with the same speed, moving after the collision in the opposite direction compared to before the collision. This case is suitable for the elastic collision of a gas particle with a container wall, as required in the kinetic gas theory.

Most real collisions lie somewhere between perfectly inelastic and elastic. For example, **glaucoma testing** in ophthalmology is done with an instrument called a **tonometer**. Glaucoma is an eye disease in which the pressure inside the eyeball builds up and leads ultimately to blindness by damaging the cells in the retina. The tonometer is used to measure the pressure in the eyeball. It is a contact-free device that blows a puff of air against the surface of the open eye. The speed of the reflected air is a function of the stiffness of the eyeball: a healthy eye is soft, reflecting the air nearly inelastically, i.e., at slow speed. A glaucomic eye has a more rigid surface, causing the air reflection to be more elastic with a higher air speed.

## FORMULATION OF A RESTRICTED CONSERVATION OF ENERGY RULE

We found elastic collisions exist that obey the conservation of mechanical energy, but perfectly inelastic collisions violate this rule. Thus, the discussion at the beginning of this section would suggest that we formulate a *conservation of mechanical energy rule with restrictions*. Even though this seems to be a highly undesirable approach, it is frequently done in traditional physics textbooks. The only justification would be a situation where a more fundamental formulation has not yet been found and learning about the restrictions may enable future scientists to remedy this situation. In reality, though, long before such a restricted rule was introduced in those textbooks, scientists had already discovered the shortcomings of an attempt to formulate a rule for the conservation of mechanical energy: we do not live in a purely mechanical world and, therefore, natural phenomena can essentially never be limited to a purely mechanical view.

The most important form of energy missing in the discussion so far is thermal energy. Thermal energy is unavoidably set free in the form of heat even in the most careful mechanical experiments. For example, a falling raindrop quickly reaches a terminal speed. As it continues to fall, its potential energy decreases steadily but its kinetic energy remains unchanged. The loss of energy occurs in the form of frictional heating of the air through which the raindrop moves.

In summary, at this point we dismiss attempts to formulate a conservation law exclusively for mechanical energy forms. We postpone the formulation of a general energy conservation law until after we introduce the basic concepts of thermal physics. We will then be rewarded by finding an energy conservation law that is as universal as the conservation of momentum, i.e., free of artificial restrictions.

# First Law of Thermodynamics

In include thermal energy we leave mechanics and enter a new field of physics: the study of heat and thermal energy is called **thermodynamics** or **thermal physics**. We won't need a new model system for this discussion, because we have already introduced the gas system. However, we need to establish the temperature as a new parameter for a gas before we can introduce the concept of thermal energy.

## Temperature

In Newton's time, experimental inclusion of thermal energy was impossible since temperature had not been defined. There was a qualitative understanding that the temperature is high when something feels warm and that the temperature is low when something feels cold, but no instrument to measure temperatures was available.

This changed 60 years later, when Anders Celsius observed that the height of a liquid in a hollow glass cylinder varies with temperature. He postulated in 1742 that the expansion of common liquids, such as water, alcohol, and mercury (Hg, the only elemental metal that is liquid at room temperature), is linear with **temperature**. Choosing mercury, we define the temperature:

$$T = T_0 + \frac{1}{\alpha_{Hg}} \cdot \left( \frac{h - h_0}{h_0} \right)_{Hg} \qquad [89]$$

in which $T_0$ is an arbitrary reference temperature, usually $T_0 = 0°C$ or the temperature at which the thermometer is filled with mercury. The term in parentheses on the right-hand side of Eq. [89] is the fraction of the height change of the mercury column

during a temperature change; $\alpha_{Hg}$ is the **coefficient of linear expansion** of mercury, with a value of $\alpha_{Hg} = 1.82 \times 10^{-4} \; 1/°C$. This coefficient quantifies the proportionality between the length of the mercury column and the temperature. Both values $T_0$ and $\alpha_{Hg}$ are needed in order for us to use Eq. [89] to measure temperatures. These two parameters are determined by choosing two reference points. Celsius chose the melting point of ice, which he designated as 0 degrees, and the boiling point of water, which he designated as 100 degrees. In Celsius's honour, we call the resulting temperature scale the **Celsius scale** with the temperature unit °C.

The two reference points Celsius chose are easily reproducible in experiments because the thermometer reading for a slowly heated ice block stops at these two temperatures. This concept is illustrated in Fig. 6.32. We start by heating an ice block that is initially at $-25°C$. The temperature increases steadily except at the phase transition temperatures, when heat supplied to the system is used to complete the phase transition of the material. This heat is called the **latent heat**. At 0°C we add the latent heat of melting and at 100°C we add the latent heat of evaporation.

Note that the definition of temperature implies practically and conceptually the existence of a **thermal equilibrium**. The thermal equilibrium is subject of the **zeroth law of thermodynamics**.

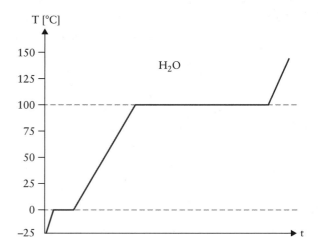

**FIGURE 6.32**

Graph of the temperature versus time for a continuously heated beaker of water, starting with ice of $-25°C$. The temperature rises to 0°C, then remains unchanged while the ice melts. After the phase transition the temperature rises steadily to 100°C. The water begins to boil and the temperature remains constant until the entire amount of water has turned into vapour. After the second phase transition the vapour temperature rises steadily, shown up to about 140°C.

*In a thermal equilibrium every part of the system has the same temperature. More specifically, if objects A and B are separately in thermal equilibrium with a third object (e.g., a thermometer), then objects A and B are in thermal equilibrium with each other (zeroth law of thermodynamics).*

Why is this statement a physical law, and why is it numbered out of normal sequence (i.e., zeroth)? It is a law because it generalizes a few experimental observations and states that the observation applies universally. It is important because the possibility of measuring temperatures relies on it; were the law not correct, we would never be sure what the reading of a thermometer means for the investigated system (i.e., the parameter "temperature" would be rendered useless). It is numbered out of sequence because it was initially not recognized as a prerequisite for the first and second laws of thermodynamics, which were named earlier.

In turn, if various parts of an object are at different temperatures we cannot define a meaningful single temperature for the object, and it is not in thermal equilibrium. If two systems in contact are not in thermal equilibrium, then heat flows from the hotter to the colder system until their temperatures are equal. We discuss such non-equilibrium cases in Chapter 10.

Due to the complex nature of the liquid state of matter, the Celsius thermometer is scientifically unsatisfactory. However, it was sufficient to get studies on thermal physics started, and because of its simple design it continues to be used to measure moderate temperature changes, e.g., for fever. We must return to the definition of temperature later for two reasons: to obtain a more precise definition to measure exact values, and to develop a better fundamental idea of what temperature physically tells us about the system.

## Temperature Detection in the Human Body

Temperature is also an important physiological parameter. Birds and mammals are endotherms, with a core body temperature in the range of 39°C to 42°C for birds and 36°C to 38°C for mammals. Individuals of a given species maintain their core body temperature within a very narrow window: 37.0 ± 0.5°C, in the case of humans. To exercise this control, continuous temperature measurements in the core part of the body and at the interface with the environment (at the skin) are required. All temperature information gathered by the body is centrally analyzed in the hypothalamus, which is located at

the lower end of the brain. Our body then employs complex regulation mechanisms to maintain the core temperature. We discuss homeostasis and some of the major regulation mechanisms it requires in Chapter 10. Here we focus on only the temperature measurement.

Animal testing suggests that temperature is measured in all core body parts, but the anatomical structure of the sensors is still unknown. **Temperature sensors** in the skin detect the peripheral temperature of the body, which is also a semi-quantitative measure of the temperature of the environment. It is only semi-quantitative because the near-skin temperature profile depends on not only the temperature of a touched object but also its heat conduction. You can convince yourself that this is correct: touch a piece of wood and a piece of metal that have been close to each other for a considerable time (i.e., they are in thermal equilibrium with each other). The two objects have the same temperature, but you perceive the metal object as colder than the wooden object. We explain this observation with heat conduction, which is a non-equilibrium phenomenon we discuss in Chapter 10.

The peripheral **thermoreceptors** are not associated with distinguishable corpuscles, but consist of a locally confined network of dendrites that terminate at the lower end of the epidermis. The temperature dependence of the number of nerve impulses sent to the brain allows us to distinguish two basic types of thermoreceptors in Fig. 6.33. **Cold spots** are most sensitive to temperatures between 25°C and 40°C. In comparison to about 250 000 cold spots, only about

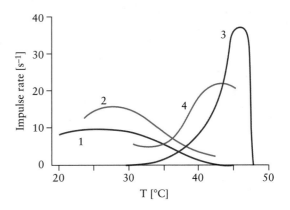

**FIGURE 6.33**

The nerve impulse rate of cold and warm spots as a function of the temperature in the human skin (red lines), and in the spinal cord (blue lines): (1) the cold spot response in the skin, (2) the cold spot response in the spinal cord, (3) the warm spot response in the skin, and (4) the warm spot response in the spinal cord. The sensitivity interval is defined as the temperature interval in which the impulse rate varies significantly, e.g., from 25°C to about 40°C for the cold spots and from 35°C to about 45°C for the warm spots.

30 000 **warm spots** are scattered across our skin. The warm spots are primarily sensitive to temperatures in the range of 35°C to 45°C. Fig. 6.33 also provides a comparison between thermoreceptors in the skin and in the spinal cord. We note that each pair—curves 1 and 2 for the cold spots, and curves 3 and 4 for the warm spots—follow a similar sensitivity pattern.

Thermoreceptors measure not absolute temperatures, but temperature changes. As a consequence, the nerve impulse transmission to the hypothalamus ceases when the temperature remains constant (receptor adaptation). You can test this by immersing your hand in water of 25°C; the water is perceived as cold only initially. Extreme temperatures are, however, continuously sensed as too hot or too cold. This is associated with separate **pain receptors**, called **nocireceptors**, which respond in a similar fashion as other sensors but become sensitized by repeated stimulation.

## Joule's Experiments

Anders Celsius's temperature scale made a proper definition of thermal energy possible. In 1798, Benjamin Thompson (Count Rumford) concluded from cannon drilling experiments that mechanical work leads to heating that in turn represents an increase in the thermal energy of the system. In 1842, Julius Robert von Mayer studied human blood in a tropical environment and found a correlation between the thermal energy and work obtained from chemical energy. In 1843, James Prescott Joule defined both terms, thermal energy and heat, and connected them quantitatively to the concepts of work and mechanical energy. His arguments are based on two experiments shown in Fig. 6.34: the experiment in Fig. 6.34(a) is used to define heat, and the one in Fig. 6.34(b) relates thermal and potential energy.

Joule used the first experiment to define heat $Q$: if heat is added to a system that consists of a beaker with water and a thermometer, a change of the system temperature occurs that is directly proportional to the heat, $Q \propto \Delta T$. He used the amount of propane gas burned as a measure of heat added to the beaker. Joule further noted that the heat needed to achieve a particular temperature increase is directly proportional to the amount of water in the beaker, $Q \propto m(H_2O)$. Finally, the heat needed for a given temperature increase of a fixed amount of liquid varies from liquid to liquid. This means that a materials-specific constant is needed. These observations allowed Joule to write the following **definition of heat**:

$$Q = c \cdot m \cdot \Delta T \qquad [90]$$

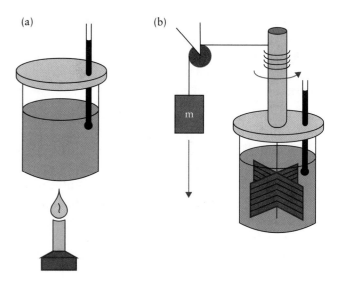

**FIGURE 6.34**

Conceptual sketches of the two experiments done by Joule. (a) In the first experiment heat is quantified by measuring the amount of gas burned. (b) The second experiment illustrates conceptually the equivalence of mechanical and thermal energy. The mechanical energy, released by the falling object at the left, is used to heat the water by operating a stirrer.

**TABLE 6.4**

**Specific heat capacity values at atmospheric pressure**

| Material | Specific heat capacity (J/kg · °C) |
|----------|-----------------------------------|
| Water | 4186 |
| Ice | 2090 |
| Steam | 2010 |
| Aluminium | 900 |
| Iron | 448 |
| Glass | 837 |
| Copper | 387 |
| Mercury | 138 |
| Gold | 129 |

in which the material constant $c$ is called the **specific heat capacity**. Table 6.4 provides a list of values for $c$. The heat flowing into the beaker is then identified as the change in the thermal energy of the system:

$$Q = \Delta E_{thermal} = E_{thermal,final} - E_{thermal,initial} \quad [91]$$

Historically, the unit **calorie** (cal) was introduced for heat, and the unit **Calorie** (Cal) for the energy content in food, with 1 Cal = 1000 cal. You should always convert these units to the SI unit joule. We note further that J/(kg · °C) is the unit of the specific heat capacity. *Heat capacity* is the proper term because a large heat capacity means that the material can absorb more heat than a material with a small specific heat capacity before the temperature rises by a given amount. However, treating the specific heat capacity as dependent only on the material is a simplification, as illustrated in Fig. 6.35. The figure shows that the heat capacity for water is not strictly constant, but varies by about 1% between the melting point and the boiling point. We neglect this minor variation in the following discussion.

For many applications, Eq. [90] is rewritten to replace the mass of the liquid by the amount of material in unit mol. For this step we define the number of moles $n$ as:

$$n = \frac{m}{M} \qquad [92]$$

in which $m$ is the mass of the material and $M$ is its molar mass. This leads to:

$$Q = C \cdot n \cdot \Delta T \qquad [93]$$

with $C$ the **molar heat capacity**, which is a material constant with unit J/(mol · °C). Values for both heat capacities are tabulated; when you find such values in the literature, always confirm the units used and then use either Eq. [90] or [93].

Eqs. [90] and [93] allow for an exchange of energy in two directions: heat can flow into or out of a system. This is consistent with our observation for work: a system can do work on a piston or the piston can do work on the system. Thus, we need to adhere to a strict sign convention for both work and heat.

*Any amount of heat flowing into the system or any work done on the system are positive as they increase the total energy of the system. The opposite processes are negative as they lead to a reduction of the total energy of the system.*

When checking a calculation, always identify yourself with the system; whatever you receive is positive, whatever you give away is negative.

We want to emphasize once more the difference between heat and thermal energy in a physiological context. The temperature detectors in the bodies of endotherms that we discussed above obviously are not needed in ectotherms, as their body temperature adjusts to the environmental temperature automatically. Thus, ectotherms are usually not able to measure the thermal energy content in their body. However, some ectotherms are able to measure heat arriving from the environment. They do this in a different manner and for a different purpose: vipers such as the one shown in the chapter-opening photograph are nocturnal hunters that possess **heat detectors** between their eyes and nostrils to allow them to find their endothermic prey without visual contact.

## General Form of the Conservation of Energy

Next, we examine Joule's second experiment in Fig. 6.34(b). The idea behind this experiment is that the object on the left falls, moving the stirrer through the water. Because the water resists the motion of the stirrer, their frictional interaction heats the water. Note that Joule chose a dissipative force to achieve a non-mechanical energy conversion. He was motivated by the observation that friction is responsible for the sensation of warmth when you rub your hands against each other.

To allow us to quantify the conversion of potential to thermal energy, we need to ensure it is not converted into kinetic energy of the falling object; i.e., we must ensure the object falls with a constant speed. Experiments such as the one sketched in Fig. 6.34(b) show that thermal energy and mechanical energy are equivalent. In Joule's case, the lost potential energy $\Delta E_{pot}$ is quantitatively converted into thermal energy $\Delta E_{thermal}$:

$$-m_{block} \cdot g \cdot \Delta y = c_{H_2O} \cdot m_{H_2O} \cdot \Delta T \qquad [94]$$

which is generalized to:

$$E_{pot} + E_{thermal} = \text{const} \qquad [95]$$

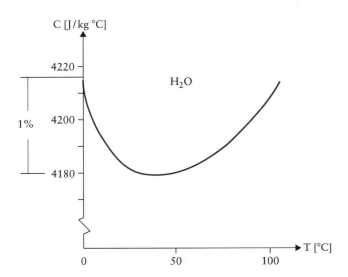

**FIGURE 6.35**

The specific heat capacity for water between 0°C and 100°C. The variation in this temperature interval corresponds to about 1% of the absolute amount.

## Concept Question 6.18

In using the experiment in Fig. 6.34(b) to prove the equivalence of thermal and mechanical energy, what should not happen or should not be done? (A) The liquid becomes warmer; (B) The object suspended from the string approaches the ground; (C) A liquid other than water is used; (D) The stirrer axis spins faster and faster; (E) The ambient pressure rises above the normal air pressure.

ANSWER: (D). The first two choices must happen for the experiment to work; the third and final choices are not excluded in Eq. [94] if we properly exchange the specific heat of water for that of the liquid used, $c_{liquid}$. In the case of (D) we convert potential into kinetic energy; i.e., we do not convert mechanical to thermal energy.

## Concept Question 6.19

(a) Do you believe that Joule actually did the experiment as shown in Fig. 6.34(b) to prove that Eq. [94] is valid? (b) If you do not, how do you think Joule convinced himself that Eq. [94] is correct? In particular, can you think of an experimental arrangement he might have assembled instead of Fig. 6.34(b)? *Hint:* Joule owned a brewery with a stable full of brewery horses, much like we still see today in beer commercials.

ANSWER TO PART (a): Joule didn't do the experiment in the form shown in Fig. 6.34(b). This is a conceptual sketch abstracting from the technical details necessary to make the experiment actually work. If you are not convinced, set it up yourself in, for example, your chemistry or physics lab: you need a sufficiently large mass of the falling object to start with enough mechanical energy to convert. In order to have the stirrer not accelerate you need a large stirrer in a big beaker of water for the stirrer to encounter enough resistance. The more water you use, the smaller the effect in Eq. [94]. By the time you have ensured no energy loss due to acceleration of the falling object, the deposited thermal energy is so small you will no longer be able to measure a temperature increase.

ANSWER TO PART (b): Joule increased the chances of seeing an effect by providing a much larger amount of mechanical energy to the system. He replaced the falling mass with a team of brewery horses that he harnessed to the stirrer and had walk around the beaker for several hours.

## ● EXAMPLE 6.10

(a) Calculate the work that an object with $m = 400$ g can do as a result of falling a distance of 3 m. (b) Assume that the object falls into 10 L (litres) of water in an isolated beaker. If the entire kinetic energy of the object is converted to thermal energy, by how much does the water temperature rise? *Hint:* For the specific heat capacity of water use the value at 0°C from Fig. 6.35, and neglect the heat the object can absorb itself.

*Solution to part (a):* By dropping the object 3 m, its potential energy has been reduced by:

$$\Delta E_{pot} = m \cdot g(h_{final} - h_{initial})$$

$$= (0.4 \text{ kg})\left(9.8 \frac{\text{m}}{\text{s}^2}\right)(-3.0 \text{ m}) = -11.8 \text{ J}$$

[96]

*Solution to part (b):* When the object is released and falls toward Earth, it is converting potential to kinetic energy. When it comes to rest in the isolated beaker its kinetic energy must convert to thermal energy. Eq. [96] requires $\Delta E_{thermal} = +11.8$ J. This value is positive since the released mechanical energy is added as thermal energy to the system water. We use Eq. [90] in the form:

$$\Delta E_{thermal} = c_{H_2O} \cdot m_{H_2O} \cdot \Delta T \quad [97]$$

to determine the associated change in the water temperature, $\Delta T$:

$$\Delta T = \frac{\Delta E_{thermal}}{\rho_{H_2O} \cdot V_{H_2O} \cdot c_{H_2O}} \quad [98]$$

in which $\rho_{H_2O}$ is the density of water: $\rho_{H_2O} = 1.0$ g/cm$^3$. The value $c_{H_2O} = 4.22$ kJ/(°C · kg) in the denominator is taken from Fig. 6.35. This leads to:

$$\Delta T = \frac{11.8 \text{ J}}{\left(1.0 \frac{\text{kg}}{\text{L}}\right)(10 \text{ L})\left(4.22 \frac{\text{kJ}}{\text{°C} \cdot \text{kg}}\right)}$$

$$= 2.8 \times 10^{-4} \text{°C} \quad [99]$$

We find only a negligible temperature change!

## Formulation of the First Law of Thermodynamics

Joule's experiment in Fig. 6.34(b) can be interpreted in two ways:

- we consider the falling object, the stirrer, the beaker, and the water together as an isolated system, or

- we consider the water in the beaker as the system and the stirrer and the falling object as the environment.

We use the above discussion of Fig. 6.34(b) to interpret the implications for the total energy of the isolated superstructure, for the conversion of energy between different forms, and for the flow of energy between system and environment.

## A FIRST VIEW OF FIG. 6.34(b)

We first consider all components in the figure as the system. In this case, Eq. [95] states that energy conservation applies also when non-mechanical energies, such as thermal energy, are involved. In 1874, Hermann von Helmholtz generalized this finding and formulated the **first law of thermodynamics for an isolated system**:

*Conservation of energy: the sum of all energy forms in an isolated system is constant.*

The sum of all energy forms in the system is called the **internal energy of the system**. It is labelled $U$. Thus, the energy conservation for an isolated system is written as:

$$\Delta U_{\text{isolated system}} = 0 \qquad [100]$$

This is a law since it predicts the outcome of future experiments. It even correctly predicts the outcome of experiments that Joule and Helmholtz could not have imagined in their day such as Enrico Fermi's 1942 nuclear fission experiment that led to the development of modern nuclear power technology. The first law of thermodynamics is not limited to mechanical systems and therefore surpasses the range of applicability of Newton's laws.

## A SECOND VIEW OF FIG. 6.34(b)

Now we consider only the water as the system. That means the left-hand side in Eq. [94] is a work term because it represents energy that flows into the system. We combine this observation with Fig. 6.34(a), in which heat is flowing into a system. In both cases the energy flowing leads to the same change in internal energy. This allows us to formulate the **first law of thermodynamics for a closed system**:

*The sum of all energy forms in a closed system changes by the amounts of heat and work that flow between system and environment.*

This is written as:

$$\Delta U_{\text{closed system}} = Q + W \qquad [101]$$

In Eq. [101], neither the order in which the exchange of energy with the environment occurs nor its form (heat or work) matter for the change of the internal energy as the system goes from an initial to a final state. A system property that depends not on its detailed history but only on its current state is called a **variable of the state**. Thus, the internal energy is a variable of the state of the system, like temperature, pressure, and volume. The change of a variable of the state is zero for any sequence of processes that returns the system to its original state. Such processes are called cyclic processes and are the subject of the next chapter.

## ● EXAMPLE 6.11

A standard man performs the standard ergometric test illustrated in Fig. 6.36. The test consists of a 6-metre horizontal run followed by running upward on a staircase by at least nine steps. For our calculations we focus only on the second part of the test, in which the person moves upward by $h = 1.05$ m from the third to the ninth step. For this part of the test the person requires an amount of 0.8 kcal of stored (food) energy. How much heat must the body of the person dissipate as the result of this part of the ergometric test?

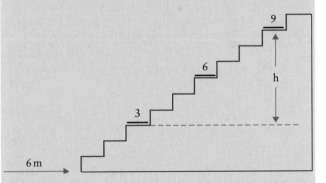

**FIGURE 6.36**

Standard ergometer test. The person must run 6 metres toward a staircase and then move upward at least 10 stairs. Contact mats on the third, sixth, and ninth stair record the motion. The height difference between the third and the ninth step is $h = 1.05$ m.

*Supplementary physiological information:* The step-test in Fig. 6.36 is usually supplemented by contact mats on every third step to allow a measure of the time the patient needs to complete the test. It was considered the standard ergometric test until stationary devices such as bicycle ergometers or the

## ● EXAMPLE 6.11 (*continued*)

treadmill came into use. A stationary bicycle ergometer is shown in Fig. 6.37. It is used for Exercise ECGs, where several vital parameters are measured on the patient during the test. To test athletes for fitness, coaches use measurements of oxygen consumption, impulse frequency, and lactose levels in the blood of the athlete to predict performance in track and field events.

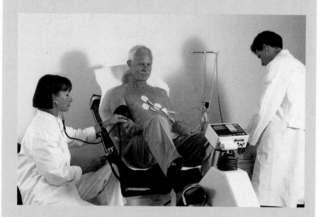

**FIGURE 6.37**

Bicycle ergometer used in sports physiology and for Exercise ECGs. The arrangement allows for continuous stationary recording of the person's vital parameters. The attending physician can vary the resistance of a frictional belt slowing the encased flywheel.

*Solution:* The problem is solved using the conservation of energy for the person moving between the initial position on the third step and the final position on the ninth step. Treating the person as an isolated system in this experiment, the formula for the conservation of energy (Eq. [100]) can be written in the form:

$$\sum_i E_i = \text{const}$$

$$= E_{pot} + E_{kin} + E_{thermal} + E_{chemical} \quad [102]$$

The food energy is labelled $E_{chemical}$. The kinetic energy in the equation can be neglected when assuming that the person's speed between the third and ninth step does not change. For the other three forms of energy, we use Eq. [102] in the form:

$$E_{pot,initial} + E_{thermal,initial} + E_{chemical,initial}$$
$$= E_{pot,final} + E_{thermal,final} + E_{chemical,final} \quad [103]$$

which is written as:

$$\Delta E_{pot} + \Delta E_{thermal} + \Delta E_{chemical} = 0 \quad [104]$$

Each term represents the difference between the final and initial amount of energy in the system. The thermal energy difference, $\Delta E_{thermal}$, is sought in the problem; the other two terms in Eq. [104] are:

$$\Delta E_{pot} = m \cdot g(h_{final} - h_{initial})$$

$$= (70 \text{ kg})\left(9.8 \frac{m}{s^2}\right)(1.05 \text{ m}) = +720 \text{ J}$$
$$[105]$$

and

$$\Delta E_{chemical} = -800 \text{ cal} = -3350 \text{ J} \quad [106]$$

The potential energy difference is positive because the final potential energy is higher than the initial potential energy of the body. The food energy is negative because the body stores this amount less at the end of the test. Substituting these values in Eq. [104] yields:

$$\Delta E_{thermal} = 3350 \text{ J} - 720 \text{ J} = +2630 \text{ J} \quad [107]$$

The thermal energy released in the process is about 2.6 kJ. It must be dissipated by the body in the form of heat, as it would otherwise contribute to a permanent temperature increase.

# MULTIPLE CHOICE AND CONCEPTUAL QUESTIONS

### WORK

**Q–6.1.** (a) Which is the standard unit for energy? (A) N, (B) J/s, (C) N · m, (D) Pa, (E) N/J. (b) Which is the standard unit for pressure? (A) N/s, (B) J/s, (C) kg/(m · s²), (D) N · m, (E) Pa · m³. (c) Work is measured in the same unit as (A) force, (B) energy, (C) pressure, (D) momentum, (E) power.

**Q–6.2.** The rate of change of work with time is: (A) energy, (B) power, (C) momentum, (D) force, (E) heat.

**Q–6.3.** A force of 5 N causes the displacement of an object by 3 m in the direction of the force. What work did the object do/has been done on the object? (A) $W = +1.5$ J, (B) $W = -1.5$ J, (C) $W = +15.0$ J, (D) $W = -15.0$ J, (E) none of the above.

**Q–6.4.** An object is pulled with a force **F** of magnitude 10 N upward by a distance of 3.0 m along an inclined plane, which forms an angle of 30° with the horizontal. Which of the following choices comes closest to the result for the work done on the object by the force **F** if **F** is directed parallel to the surface of the inclined plane? (A) $W = -15$ N, (B) $W = +15$ J, (C) $W = +26$ N, (D) $W = +26$ J, (E) $W = +30$ N, (F) $W = +30$ J.

**Q–6.5.** A person pushes an object off a seat and then tries to lift it with an external force **F** upward into an overhead bin. However, the person is too weak and the object drops to the floor under its own weight **W**, pulling the person along a distance $\Delta y$. Which of the following statements is correct? (A) Because the person did not succeed, no work is done in this experiment. (B) The person has done work on the object; the absolute value of the work is $W = |F| \cdot \Delta y$. (C) The person has done work on the object; the absolute value of the work is $W = |W| \cdot \Delta y$. (D) The object has done work on the person; the absolute value of the work is $W = |W| \cdot \Delta y$. (E) The object has done work on the person; the absolute value of the work is $W = |F| \cdot \Delta y$.

**Q–6.6.** You want to push an object up a ramp onto a platform. Do you need to do less work if you lengthen the ramp, as this lowers the angle of the ramp with the horizontal?

**Q–6.7.** Air, initially at 100 kPa, is sealed in a container by a mobile piston of cross-sectional area 10.0 cm². Now we push the piston with an additional force of $F = 100$ N to compress the air. What is the final pressure $p$ of the sealed air when the piston reaches mechanical equilibrium? (A) $p = 2 \times 10^4$ Pa, (B) $p = 1.0001 \times 10^5$ Pa, (C) $p = 2 \times 10^5$ Pa, (D) $p = 1 \times 10^6$ Pa, (E) none of the above.

**Q–6.8.** A gas sealed in a container by a mobile piston expands. The following statement is correct: (A) The piston does work on the gas. (B) No work is done in the process. (C) The gas does work on the piston. (D) The gas and the piston exchange heat only. (E) None of the above.

**Q–6.9.** A gas is compressed from 5 L to 1 L with its pressure held constant at 4000 Pa. To achieve this compression, the following work (absolute value only) is needed: (A) $W = 20$ kJ, (B) $W = 16$ kJ, (C) $W = 20$ J, (D) $W = 16$ J, (E) none of the above.

**Q–6.10.** Fig. 6.38 shows a $p$–$V$ diagram for a gas. Three processes (labelled a, b, and c) are investigated that bring the gas from an initial volume to a final volume. Which path yields the largest value for work? *Hint:* 5 J > 2 J, but −5 J < −2 J.

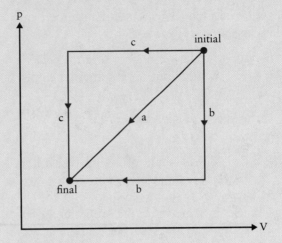

**FIGURE 6.38**

Three paths for the compression of a gas system from an initial to a smaller final volume. The paths are labelled a, b, and c.

## ENERGY AND ENERGY CONSERVATION

**Q–6.11.** How does the kinetic energy of an object change when its speed is reduced to 50% of its initial value? (A) The kinetic energy remains unchanged. (B) The kinetic energy becomes 50% of the initial value. (C) The kinetic energy becomes 25% of the initial value. (D) The kinetic energy doubles. (E) The kinetic energy increases fourfold.

**Q–6.12.** When the ATP molecule splits, forming an ADP molecule, the following physical change happens: (A) The ATP molecule takes up energy. (B) The ATP molecule exerts a force. (C) The ATP molecule does work. (D) The ATP molecule releases energy. (E) The pressure in the ATP-containing cell increases.

**Q–6.13.** How does the potential energy of an object change when its speed is doubled? (A) The potential energy is halved. (B) The potential energy becomes $\frac{1}{4}$ of the initial value. (C) The potential energy doubles. (D) The potential energy increases by a factor of four. (E) The information given is insufficient to choose one of the above answers.

**Q–6.14.** Labelling the kinetic energy $E_{kin}$ and the gravitational potential energy $E_{pot}$, the conservation of energy can be written as $E_{kin} + E_{pot} = $ const if: (A) $E_{kin} = $ const, (B) $E_{pot} = $ const, (C) the thermal energy of the system stays unchanged, (D) none of the internal energy of the system is converted into kinetic energy, (E) all energy forms other than $E_{kin}$ and $E_{pot}$ are unchanged.

**Q–6.15.** In a mechanical experiment with an isolated object, only the values of $E_{kin}$ and $E_{pot}$ can vary. If the object accelerates from 5 m/s to 10 m/s, its potential energy has: (A) not changed, (B) decreased by a factor of 2, (C) decreased by a factor of 4,

(D) decreased by a factor we cannot determine from the problem as stated, (E) increased.

**Q–6.16.** (a) Can the kinetic energy of an object be negative? (b) Can the (gravitational) potential energy be negative?

**Q–6.17.** If the speed of a particle is doubled, what happens to its kinetic energy?

**Q–6.18.** We consider a whale of 18 m length and mass $m$ = 4000 kg. It leaps straight out of the water such that half its body is above the surface. If the entire upward surge is achieved by its speed at the instant when breaking the water surface, how fast was it going at that moment? Choose the closest answer. (A) 5 m/s, (B) 15 m/s, (C) 20 m/s, (D) 200 m/s.

**Q–6.19.** In pole vault, several forms of energy play a role: kinetic energy of the runner, elastic potential energy of the pole (discussed in Chapter 16), the gravitational potential energy, and the internal energy of the vaulter, which is associated with muscles, tendons, and ligaments. For this question, however, we simplify the discussion by neglecting all but the kinetic and gravitational potential energy. We want to estimate what the highest possible pole vault is if the centre of mass of the athlete is 1.1 m above the ground and the maximum speed of approach is 11 m/s. Using the conservation of energy to estimate this height, choose the closest value. (A) 6.2 m, (B) 7.3 m, (C) 11.0 m, (D) 14.6 m.

**Q–6.20.** During a stress test of the cardiovascular system, a patient walks and runs on a treadmill. (a) Is the energy dissipated by the patient equivalent to the energy dissipated by walking or running on the ground? (b) If the treadmill is tilted upward, what effect does this have?

## TEMPERATURE

**Q–6.21.** Which of the following formulas describes the reading of a temperature $T$ (in degrees Celsius) when measured with an expanding mercury column as proposed by Celsius? In these formulas, $h$ is the height of the mercury column and $H$ is the height of the mercury column at a chosen reference temperature. $\alpha$ and $\beta$ are positive constants, with $\alpha$ the reference temperature at which the column height is $h = H$.

(A) $\quad T = \alpha - \beta\left(\dfrac{h - H}{H}\right)$

(B) $\quad T = \alpha + \beta\left(\dfrac{h - H}{H}\right)$

(C) $\quad T = \alpha - \beta\left(\dfrac{h + H}{H}\right)$

(D) $\quad T = \alpha + \beta\left(\dfrac{h + H}{H}\right)$

(E) $\quad T = \alpha - \beta\left(\dfrac{h + H}{H}\right)^2$ [108]

**Q–6.22.** Which of the following reasons did not contribute to Celsius's choice of the melting point of water (at 0°C) and the boiling point of water (at 100°C) as the two reference points on his newly developed thermometer? (A) Reproducibility of a reference system at these two temperatures. (B) Easy accessibility of water as the system providing the two reference temperatures. (C) Technical simplicity of obtaining a water system at all three states of matter: solid, liquid, and vapour. (D) Temperature independence of the heat capacity of water between 0°C and 100°C.

**Q–6.23.** In the next chapter a new temperature scale (Kelvin scale with unit K) is introduced, with $T$ (K) = $T$ (°C) + 273.15°. In an astronomy class, the temperature at the core of a star is reported as $1.5 \times 10^7$ degrees. Does it make sense to ask whether the temperature scale used is in units °C or K?

## THERMAL ENERGY

**Q–6.24.** An object of mass $m$ = 5 kg is dropped from a height of 10 metres. Just before reaching the ground, the thermal energy of the object is (use $g$ = 10 m/s$^2$): (A) unchanged, (B) $E$ = 50 J, (C) $E$ = 500 J, (D) $E$ = 5 kJ, (E) none of the above.

**Q–6.25.** Which of the following things cannot happen in a closed system? (A) Heat is transferred to the environment. (B) Work is done on the system by an object in the environment. (C) Matter flows into the system. (D) The temperature of the system increases. (E) The internal energy of the system remains unchanged.

**Q–6.26.** The specific heat for material A is greater than that for material B. If equal amounts of heat are added to both materials, the one reaching a higher temperature will be (assume that no phase transitions in either material occur): (A) material A, (B) material B, (C) they reach the same temperature, (D) it could be either material A or B.

**Q–6.27.** Early Europeans arriving in North America stored fruit and vegetables in underground cellars. In winter they also included a large open barrel with water. Why did they do this?

**Q–6.28.** Concrete has a higher specific heat than soil. Can this help us to explain why a city usually has a higher temperature than the surrounding countryside?

**Q–6.29.** The air temperature above coastal areas is significantly affected by the large specific heat of water. Estimate the amount of air for which the temperature can rise 1 degree if 1 m$^3$ of water cools by 1 degree. The specific heat of air is 1.0 kJ/(kg · °C); for its density use 1.3 kg/m$^3$.

**Q–6.30.** Ethyl alcohol has about 50% of the specific heat of water. If equal amounts of alcohol and water in separate beakers are supplied with the same amount of heat, which liquid will show the larger increase in temperature?

**Q–6.31.** What is wrong with stating that, of any two objects, the one with the higher temperature contains more thermal energy?

# ANALYTICAL PROBLEMS

## DOUBLE-LOGARITHMIC PLOTS AND METABOLISM

**P–6.1.** Fig. 6.27(b) shows in double-logarithmic representation the nerve impulse rate $P$ as a function of the speed of an approaching object for a Meissner's corpuscle. Using the power law relation $P = a \cdot v^b$, determine the constants $a$ and $b$.

**P–6.2.** Fig. 6.39 shows the height $h$ in mm versus mass $m$ in kg (red line) and the active metabolic rate $E$ in kcal/day versus height (blue line) for growing children. Determine the three exponents $b$ in (a) $h = a_1 \cdot m^{b_1}$ for $m < 15$ kg (curve I), (b) $h = a_2 \cdot m^{b_2}$ for $m > 15$ kg (curve II), and (c) $E = a_3 \cdot m^{b_3}$ for $m < 40$ kg (curve III). *For those interested:* (d) Find pictures of children and adults and compare the body proportions to see what causes the differences in the exponents.

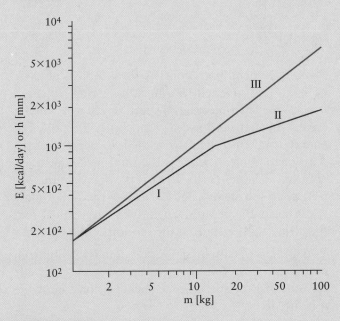

**FIGURE 6.39**

**P–6.3.** In the mid-Cretaceous (110 to 100 million years ago), dinosaurs lived near the poles, e.g., at 80°N for fossils in North Alaska and the Yukon, and at 80°S for fossils near Melbourne, Australia. The polar regions of the Cretaceous were densely forested with only occasional light freezes in the winter, but non-hibernating ectotherms cannot tolerate prolonged periods without sunlight. Indeed, the most northern fossil find of a large ectotherm is a giant crocodile (*Phobosuchids*) at 55°N. The energy cost for long-distance migration across land is given in unit J/m as a function of the animal's body mass $m$ in kg:

$$E_{\text{migration}} = 14 \cdot m^{3/4} \qquad [109]$$

(a) Using Eqs. [8] and [109], evaluate the hypothesis that ectothermic southern polar dinosaurs migrated annually between 80°S and 55°S latitudes for (I) Leaellynasaura, which was a 10-kg herbivore, (II) Dwarf Allosaur, which was a 500-kg carnivore, and (III) Muttaburrasaurus, which was a 4-tonne herbivore. Note in this context that caribou in the Canadian North migrate 4000 km annually. (b) Using the energy consumption for migration in Eq. [109] and the potential energy, compare the benefits of living in plains versus mountainous terrain for small and large endotherms.

**P–6.4.** Confirm that the prefactors given in Eq. [8] are consistent with the values we calculated for $a$ in Example 6.1.

**P–6.5.** We considered in Concept Question 6.1 a model in which an animal's metabolic requirements are determined by the loss of heat through the skin. Why does this lead to $b = 2/3$ as the exponent in M $\propto m^b$ with $m$ the mass of the animal and M the metabolic rate?

## WORK AND ENERGY FOR MECHANICAL OBJECTS

**P–6.6.** We found $\mathscr{F} \propto v^2$ for the drag force in Chapter 4. Derive this velocity dependence from the power required to accelerate the displaced medium to the speed of the moving object, and then use Eq. [22] to determine the drag force.

**P–6.7.** (a) The highest head-first dive is performed by professional divers near Acapulco, Mexico, from a height of 35 metres (see Fig. 6.40). With what speed does a diver (standard man) enter the water if leaving the platform from rest? (b) Draw the speed, the kinetic energy, and the potential energy as a function of height for the diver. *Hint:* Neglect air resistance.

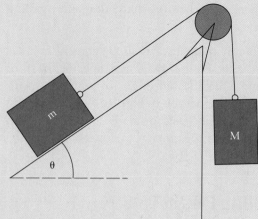

**FIGURE 6.41**

Fig. 6.42. The horizontal surface is frictionless and the system is released from rest. Using energy concepts, find the speed of $m_3$ after it has moved down 0.4 m.

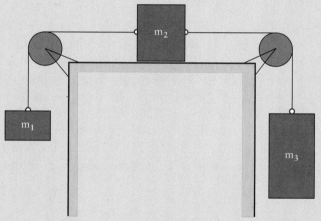

**FIGURE 6.42**

**FIGURE 6.40**

**P–6.8.** Two objects are connected by a massless string, as shown in Fig. 6.41. The pulley is massless and rotates without friction. The object of smaller mass $m = 1.2$ kg slides without friction on an inclined plane that makes an angle of $\theta = 35°$ with the horizontal. The mass of the larger object is given as $M = 2.5$ kg and hangs on the string. If the two objects are released from rest with the string taut, what is their total kinetic energy when the object of mass $M$ has fallen 30 cm?

**P–6.9.** Three objects with masses $m_1 = 5.0$ kg, $m_2 = 10.0$ kg, and $m_3 = 15.0$ kg are attached by massless strings over two frictionless pulleys, as shown in

**P–6.10.** A pendulum consists of an object of mass $m = 1.5$ kg attached to a massless string of length $l = 3.0$ m. The object has a speed of 2.0 m/s when it passes through its lowest point. (a) If the potential energy is taken to be zero at the lowest point of the path of the object, what is the total mechanical energy of the system? (b) What is the speed of the object when the string is at 75° below the horizontal? (c) What is the greatest angle with the vertical that the string reaches during the motion of the object?

**P–6.11.** If a person lifts a bucket of mass 20 kg from a well and does 6.0 kJ work, how deep is the well? Assume that the speed of the bucket is constant while it is lifted.

**P–6.12.** An outfielder in American baseball throws a baseball of mass 0.15 kg at a speed of 40 m/s at an initial angle of 30° with the horizontal. What is the kinetic energy of the baseball at its highest point of motion?

**P–6.13.** A standard man executes a pole vault. The approach is at 10 m/s and the speed moving above the bar is 1.0 m/s. Neglecting air resistance and energy absorbed by the pole, determine the maximum height of the bar.

**P–6.14.** A child and sled with a combined mass of 50 kg slide down a frictionless hill. If the sled starts from rest and has a speed of 3.0 m/s at the bottom, what is the height of the hill?

## WORK AND ENERGY FOR GENERAL SYSTEMS

**P–6.15.** A gas expands from a volume of 1.0 L to 5.0 L, as shown in the p–V diagram of Fig. 6.43. How much work does the gas perform on the piston?

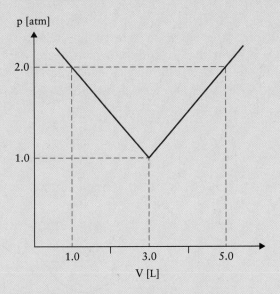

**FIGURE 6.43**

**P–6.16.** When people run, they dissipate about 0.6 J of mechanical energy per step and per kilogram of body mass. If a standard man dissipates 80 J of energy per second while running, how fast is the person running? Assume that the steps taken are 1.6 m long.

**P–6.17.** Table 6.5 shows the metabolic rate for given activities of the adult human body and Table 6.6 gives the energy content of the three most important components of food. (a) How much energy is expended by a standard man who walks for one hour every morning? (b) If the body of the person consumes body fat reserves to produce this energy, how much mass will be lost per day?

**P–6.18.** A standard man climbs 10 m up a vertical rope. How much energy in calories is dissipated as heat in a single climb if 20% of the total energy required is used to do the work?

### TABLE 6.5

| Activity | Metabolic rate (cal/(s · kg)) |
| --- | --- |
| Sleeping | 0.263 |
| Sitting | 0.358 |
| Standing | 0.621 |
| Walking | 1.0 |
| Biking | 1.81 |
| Swimming | 2.63 |
| Running | 4.3 |

### TABLE 6.6

| Food | Energy content (cal/g) |
| --- | --- |
| Carbohydrate | 4100 |
| Protein | 4200 |
| Fat | 9300 |

**P–6.19.** Assume that Joule's brewery horses each did $P = 750$ J/s of work per second (this corresponds roughly to the definition of horsepower). If Joule had four horses moving in a circle for 1 hour to operate a stirrer in a well-isolated container filled with 1 m$^3$ water at an initial temperature of 25°C, to what final value did the water temperature rise? Use Fig. 6.35 for the specific heat of water at 25°C.

**P–6.20.** When a raindrop of mass 30 milligrams (mg) hits the ground, by how much does the temperature increase if we assume that its kinetic energy is completely converted into thermal energy? *Hint:* Use the specific heat capacity of water at 0°C from Fig. 6.35.

**P–6.21.** The energy extracted from burning sugar is used in the mitochondria to synthesize ATP from ADP. Consider glucose, which releases 675 kcal/mol during cellular respiration (formation of $CO_2$). What fraction of this energy is used in the ATP formation if 38 molecules of ATP are formed for each molecule of glucose? Why is this value not 100%?

**P–6.22.** (a) How much chemical energy does an *E. coli* bacterium consume during its lifetime in the form of ATP (excluding the amount needed to replicate its DNA)? (b) Using the specific heat capacity of water, how hot would a thermally isolated *E. coli* get during its life if it formed at 37°C in a person's intestines? Note that about 60% of the consumed energy is released as thermal energy.

**P–6.23.** Water at the top of Niagara Falls has a temperature of $+10.0°C$. It falls a distance of 50 m. Assuming that all of its potential energy is converted into thermal energy, calculate the temperature of the water at the bottom of the falls.

**P–6.24.** A piece of iron has a mass of 0.4 kg and is initially at 500°C. It is lowered into a beaker with 20 L of water at 22°C. What is the final equilibrium temperature? Neglect heat loss to the environment.

The specific heat capacities of iron and water are found in Table 6.4.

## COLLISIONS

**P–6.25.** High-speed stroboscopic photographs show that the head of a golf club of mass 200 g is travelling at 55 m/s as it strikes a golf ball of mass of 46 g. At the collision the golf ball is at rest on the tee. After the collision, the club head travels in the same direction at 40 m/s. Find the speed of the golf ball just after impact.

# MATH REVIEW

## BINOMIALS AND QUADRATIC EQUATIONS

The following algebraic relations are used frequently:

$$(a + b)^2 = a^2 + 2ab + b^2$$
$$(a - b)^2 = a^2 - 2ab + b^2$$
$$a^2 - b^2 = (a + b)(a - b)$$
$$a^3 - b^3 = (a - b)(a^2 + ab + b^2)$$

For a quadratic equation written in the form $ax^2 + bx + c = 0$ with $a$, $b$, and $c$ constant, there are a maximum of two real solutions, labelled $x_1$ and $x_2$:

$$x_{1,2} = \frac{-b \pm \sqrt{b^2 - 4 \cdot a \cdot c}}{2 \cdot a}$$

# SUMMARY

## DEFINITIONS

- Isolated system: no exchange between system and environment.
- Closed system: no exchange of matter between system and environment, only exchange of work and/or heat.
- Open system: exchange of matter and energy between system and environment.
- Pressure
  - absolute value:

$$p = \frac{F_\perp}{A}$$

where $F_\perp$ is the force acting perpendicular to the area $A$.
  - in vector notation:

$$p = \frac{1}{A^2} \mathbf{F} \cdot \mathbf{A} = \frac{1}{A} \mathbf{F} \cdot \mathbf{n}$$

where $\mathbf{F}$ is the force acting on the surface of area $\mathbf{A} = A \cdot \mathbf{n}$ with $\mathbf{n}$ a vector of length 1 (unit vector) normal to the surface.
- Work $W$
  - force and displacement of object not collinear, force constant during displacement, dot product form:

$$W = \mathbf{F} \cdot \Delta \mathbf{r} = \mathbf{F} \cdot (\mathbf{r}_{final} - \mathbf{r}_{initial})$$

  - force and displacement of object not collinear, force constant during displacement, magnitude form:

$$W = |F| \cdot |\Delta r| \cdot \cos \theta$$

  - force and displacement of object not collinear, force constant during displacement, component form:

$$W = F_x \cdot \Delta x + F_y \cdot \Delta y + F_z \cdot \Delta z$$

- force and displacement of object collinear, force constant during displacement:

$$W = \pm F \cdot \Delta r$$

- sign convention for force-related work: $W > 0$ when force and displacement occur in same direction, $W < 0$ when force and displacement occur in opposite directions.
- for a gas in a container, pressure constant during volume change:

$$W = -p \cdot \Delta V$$

- sign convention for pressure-related work (gas processes): when the gas undergoes an expansion, $V_{initial} < V_{final}$, we use $W < 0$; when the gas undergoes a compression, $V_{initial} > V_{final}$, we use $W > 0$.
- Heat $Q$
  - for a liquid or solid system of mass $m$ given in unit kg:

$$Q = c \cdot m \cdot \Delta T$$

in which $c$ is the specific heat capacity.

  - for a liquid or solid system of amount $n$ in unit mol:

$$Q = C \cdot n \cdot \Delta T$$

in which $C$ is the molar heat capacity.

  - sign convention for heat: heat flowing into the system is positive, heat leaving the system is negative.
- Energy $E$ of a system in equilibrium
  - for any type of energy except thermal energy:

$$\Delta E = E_{final} - E_{initial} = W$$

for kinetic energy; this is called work–kinetic energy theorem.

- for thermal energy:

$$\Delta E_{thermal} = E_{thermal,final} - E_{thermal,initial} = Q$$

- Examples of various mechanical forms of energy:
  - kinetic energy: $E_{kin} = \frac{1}{2} m \cdot v^2$
  - potential energy: $E_{pot} = m \cdot g \cdot h$, in which $h$ is the height of the object relative to a pre-set height $h = 0$.

## UNITS

Work $W$, heat $Q$, energy $E$: $J = N \cdot m = kg \cdot m^2/s^2$

Temperature $T$: °C (a new unit is introduced in Chapter 7)

Pressure $p$: $Pa = N/m^2$

Specific heat capacity $c$: $J/(kg \cdot °C)$

Molar heat capacity $C$: $J/(mol \cdot °C)$

## LAWS

- Conservation of energy when applicable in a mechanical system:

$$E_{kin} + E_{pot} = const$$

- First law of thermodynamics for an isolated system (conservation of energy):

$$\Delta U_{isolated} = U_{final} - U_{initial} = 0$$

in which $U$ is the internal energy, i.e., the total energy of a system.

- First law of thermodynamics for a closed system:

$$\Delta U_{closed} = U_{final} - U_{initial} = W + Q$$

# CHAPTER 7

# RESPIRATION
## The Properties of Gases and Cyclic Processes

A systematic study of thermodynamics requires a model system with well-defined but simple relations among its basic parameters. The ideal gas is introduced as such a model system. Experimental observations by Boyle and Charles reveal that its pressure is inversely proportional to its volume at constant temperature ($p \propto 1/V$), and that its volume is directly proportional to its temperature at constant pressure ($V \propto T$). The combination of these observations yields the relation $p \cdot V/T =$ constant for the possible states of the gas. In this formula the constant term on the right-hand side depends only on the amount of ideal gas.

The ideal gas is further characterized microscopically using a mechanical model, called kinetic gas theory. In this model the gas is represented by a large number of particles (point-like objects) that collide elastically with the container walls and each other. The combination of the experimental and microscopic models leads to the internal energy of the ideal gas: it depends linearly on temperature, but is independent of the volume and pressure of the gas.

The ideal gas law allows us to identify four fundamental thermodynamic processes: the isochoric process (processes at constant volume), the isothermal process (processes at constant temperature), the isobaric process (processes at constant pressure), and the adiabatic process (processes that do not allow for exchange of heat between the system and the environment). All practical processes of interest can be derived from these four, including the important cyclic processes in respiration and blood circulation. The Carnot process is introduced as a model cyclic process; it is used in the following chapter to define entropy and to reach a formulation of the second law of thermodynamics.

Joule's basic experiments allowed us in the previous chapter to relate work, heat, and internal energy for isolated and closed systems. However, the formulations of the conservation of energy and the first law of thermodynamics remained very general because we did not identify a specific system for our studies. In the current chapter we develop the ideal gas model, because it is the simplest possible system that allows us to introduce all the basic thermodynamic properties of matter. It is also suitable as a model for the air we breathe and therefore allows us to develop a physical insight into the respiratory system, which is one of the key physiological systems of our body. Using the basic thermodynamics concept developed for the ideal gas, the dynamics of breathing and its work and energy requirements are quantified.

## Dynamic Breathing

Cells in the human body obtain most of their energy from internal chemical processes requiring oxygen. Sufficient amounts of oxygen must be provided to the cell from the ambient atmosphere in a timely fashion. Passive diffusive transport from the skin surface would suffice only to a depth of about 100 $\mu$m, i.e., for the outermost layers of cells. This supply problem has been solved in animals with the development of a four-step respiratory system: oxygen reaches the lungs within 1 to 2 seconds as part of the inhaled air; from the lungs it passes in less than 1 second to the red blood cells in the bloodstream; the cardiovascular system carries the oxygen in 30 seconds or less to the various organs; in each organ, $O_2$ is distributed in the capillary bed to the cell tissue. It diffuses out of the capillary to its final destination, again in less than 1 second.

To understand this four-step process quantitatively requires a large number of physical concepts and laws. We therefore divide its discussion into several chapters: in the current chapter the air exchange between the ambient atmosphere and the lungs is described—the different chemical components of air are not yet distinguished. We focus on the transfer of oxygen from lungs to blood capillaries in Chapter 10 when we discuss diffusion processes. The role of the physiologically active air components—oxygen, nitrogen, and carbon dioxide—is explored in Chapter 9. The concepts of blood flow in the cardiovascular system are developed in Chapter 12.

## Volume of the Lungs

The **spirometer** is the instrument that allows us to measure the gas volume in the lungs. This instrument

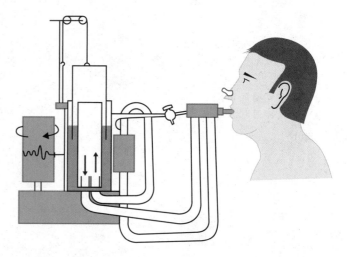

**FIGURE 7.1**

Conceptual sketch of a spirometer. The instrument consists of a fixed air volume into which the patient breathes through a mouthpiece. The top part of the container is a freely moving inverted cylinder jar. The open end of the jar is immersed in water to seal off the air in the instrument. The changing amount of air in the sealed volume causes the jar to move up and down. This vertical motion is recorded on a plotter at the left.

is shown schematically in Fig. 7.1. The person breathes through a mouthpiece and a pipe into the instrument, which measures volume changes in the lungs in the form of the elevation of an inverted jar. This inverted jar floats between two beakers fixed to the bottom plate of the instrument, which hold water to seal the interior volume against outside air. The vertical motion of the inverted jar is a measure of the total volume of the sealed air space and is connected to a recording device (the cylinder drum at the left end of the instrument).

The spirometer allows us to identify several breathing patterns, as illustrated in Fig. 7.2. Fig. 7.2(a) shows the time variation of the volume during regular breathing. A person inhales and exhales about 0.5 L; this volume is called the **tidal volume** (2). The unit L (litre) is a frequently used non-standard unit in the context of respiration. We convert with 1 L = 1 × 10⁻³ m³. We choose the lung volume after regular exhalation as the reference point $V = 0$. Based on 15 inhalations per minute, a typical person exchanges 7.5 L of air per minute. During strenuous activity we breathe deeper, as shown in Fig. 7.2(b), with an **inspiratory reserve volume** (1) of 2.5 L and an **expiratory reserve volume** (3) of 1.5 L. The two reserve volumes allow for a short-term, additional air exchange when a larger oxygen intake is required. Even after a deep exhalation the lungs are not empty. The remaining gas volume is called the **residual volume** (4) and is about 1.5 L. The residual volume cannot be measured with a spirometer, but

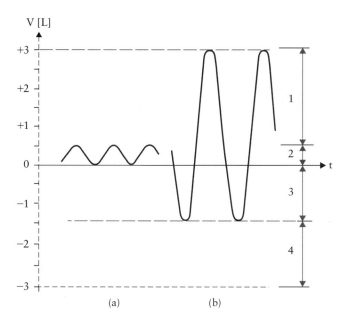

**FIGURE 7.2**

Typical data output of a spirometer. (a) A person breathing at rest, (b) a person breathing during heavy exercise. The data identify various contributions to the human lung volume: (1) the inspiratory reserve volume, (2) the tidal volume (regular breath volume), and (3) the expiratory reserve volume. These three volumes combined are called the person's vital capacity. The instrument cannot measure the residual volume (4).

must be determined indirectly by other methods. The most precise method is based on using an inert tracer gas, e.g., an air/helium mixture of known ratio. This method is illustrated in Example 7.1.

Combining the various volumes from Fig. 7.2 leads to a volume of 3.5 L after inhalation and 3.0 L after exhalation for the lungs of a standard man (refer to Table 3.3).

## ● EXAMPLE 7.1

A spirometer of volume $V_{spirometer} = 5.0$ L is filled with air at atmospheric pressure and room temperature. A fraction of $f_{initial} = 10$ vol% of that air has been replaced by helium gas (Fig. 7.3(a); the helium is indicated by red circles). A standard man is connected to the spirometer via a mouthpiece. After a single inhalation and exhalation in Fig. 7.3(b), a valve in the mouthpiece is closed and the gas mixture in the spirometer is analyzed. The fraction of helium is found to be $f_{final} = 6.25$ vol%. Calculate the lung volume $V_{lungs}$.

*Additional information:* When reporting fractions of matter, we use either volume–percent (vol%) or weight–percent (wt%) values. Gas and liquid mixtures are usually described in vol%. A given component with 5 vol% represents 5% of the total volume occupied by the system. Solid mixtures are often characterized by wt%, with 5 wt% referring to 5% of the total mass of the system.

*Solution:* A homogeneous mixture of the air in the spirometer and the gas in the lungs is established after breathing; i.e., the helium gas is then diluted across the entire volume of lungs and spirometer. This is indicated by the uniform distribution of dots in the gas space in Fig. 7.3(b). To quantify the lung volume, we calculate the total volume of helium gas contained in the combined volume before and after the breathing cycle.

Before the standard man breathes, helium is exclusively in the spirometer:

$$V_{He} = f_{initial} \cdot V_{spirometer} = 0.10 \cdot (5.0\,L) = 0.5\,L$$
$$[1]$$

i.e., the spirometer volume occupied by helium gas is 0.5 L.

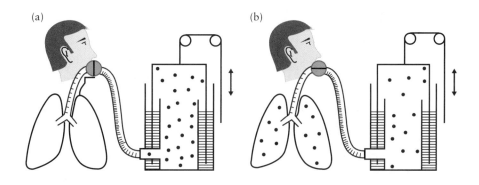

**FIGURE 7.3**

Experimental procedure to determine the lung volume: (a) a known air/helium mixture fills a spirometer at atmospheric pressure. The helium component is illustrated by dots in the gas space. The test person is asked to inhale then exhale once, which brings us from frame (a) to frame (b). The breathing cycle leads to a uniform distribution of helium in the combined space of lungs and spirometer. The fraction of helium in the spirometer after the respiratory cycle is a measure of the lung volume.

● **EXAMPLE 7.1** (*continued*)

After completing the breathing cycle, the same amount of helium is distributed in the combined volume with a uniform fraction $f_{final}$:

$$V_{He} = f_{final}(V_{spirometer} + V_{lungs}) \qquad [2]$$

Since the total amount of helium has not changed during the experiment, the left-hand sides of Eqs. [1] and [2] are equal. This leads to:

$$f_{initial} \cdot V_{spirometer} = f_{final}(V_{spirometer} + V_{lungs}) \qquad [3]$$

We isolate the sought volume of the lungs in Eq. [3]:

$$V_{lungs} = V_{spirometer}\left(\frac{f_{initial}}{f_{final}} - 1\right) \qquad [4]$$

Substituting the numerical values from the example text yields:

$$V_{lungs} = (5.0\ L)\left(\frac{0.10}{0.0625} - 1\right) = 3.0\ L \quad [5]$$

The volume in the lungs is therefore 3.0 L before inhalation.

Is it indeed that simple? Not quite. Before we accept a result, any assumptions we made must be evaluated. We need to check two issues in particular: the unknown initial pressure and temperature of the gas in the lungs, and the changes in chemical composition of the exhaled air.

First, we discuss the unknown pressure and temperature in the lungs. If either one of these parameters initially differs between the lungs and the spirometer, then we initially have a nonequilibrium situation. If that is the case, we may need to introduce a correction factor in Eq. [5] for an accurate value of $V_{lungs}$. This is due to the fact that $V = f(p, T)$; i.e., the volume of a gas depends on its pressure and temperature. The relation $V = f(p, T)$ is developed for a gas in the current chapter for this reason.

In the current example, the pressure values initially in the lungs and in the spirometer turn out to be the same; however, the temperature is different (core body temperature in the lungs of 37°C and room temperature in the spirometer). Thus, a correction of the result indeed has to take place. We introduce this correction in Example 7.4(a).

Second, we consider the compositional changes of the inhaled air during the breathing cycle. Two major changes take place: an exchange of some oxygen for carbon dioxide, and a water-vapour saturation of the incoming air in the nasal cavity and the trachea. The $O_2/CO_2$ exchange has only negligible effects on the pressure of the gas, as we will see in Example 7.4(b), but the saturation with water vapour adds more significantly to the absolute pressure of the gas. A second, more elaborate method to determine the total volume of the lungs is called the plethysmographic technique and is discussed in Example 7.5.

We usually neglect gas composition effects in the current chapter; however, it is useful to note that three different reference states of air are distinguished in the physiological literature:

- **BTPS = body temperature pressure saturated.** For this reference state the gas temperature is 37°C, the absolute pressure of the gas is $1.013 \times 10^5$ Pa (= 1 atm), and the partial pressure of water vapour is 6.3 kPa. Partial pressure of a gas component in a gas mixture is defined in Chapter 9 as the pressure that would be measured if all other gas components were removed from the studied container.

- **ATPS = ambient temperature pressure saturated.** This means that the gas temperature is the temperature in the spirometer, the absolute pressure of the gas is $1.013 \times 10^5$ Pa (= 1 atm), and the partial pressure of water vapour is the saturation pressure of water vapour at the temperature of the spirometer. At room temperature, this pressure is 2.3 kPa. The saturation pressure of a gas component is its partial pressure when in thermal equilibrium with the liquid phase.

- **STPD = standard temperature pressure dry.** In this reference state the gas temperature is 0°C, the absolute pressure of the gas is $1.013 \times 10^5$ Pa (= 1 atm), and the partial pressure of water vapour is zero.

Physical parameters of interest may easily vary by 10% when switching among these three reference states.

The four volumes we defined in Fig. 7.2 are based on anatomical considerations. **Anatomy** deals with the structural makeup of an organism or its parts; **physiology** addresses the functions and activities of organisms with respect to the physical and chemical phenomena involved. This distinction therefore often leads to two ways of dividing a system: physiologists usually divide the air space into an active and a **dead space**. Air that remains in the dead space of the respiratory system after inhalation does not change, while air in the active space undergoes an oxygen–carbon dioxide exchange before leaving the body. Oxygen exchange takes place only in the alveoli at the end of the bronchial tree, deep in the lungs. Thus, we expect air from the dead space in the trachea and the mouth to leave first during exhalation, while the last part of the exhaled volume represents the gas from the active space. This observation is used to quantify the two physiological volumes: a spirometer is used to collect a small sample of gas at the very end of an exhalation. The composition of air at the various stages of the breathing cycle is well-established for a healthy standard man: Fig. 7.4(a) shows the composition in vol% of dry air, Fig. 7.4(b) identifies the composition in the lungs (alveolar space), and Fig. 7.4(c) shows the composition of exhaled air. We use these data to estimate the dead space of respiration in Example 7.2.

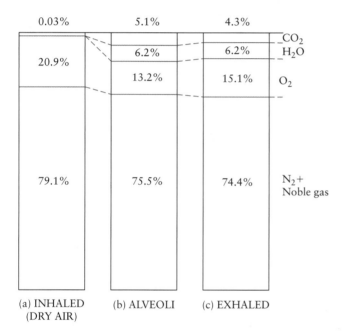

(a) INHALED (DRY AIR)  (b) ALVEOLI  (c) EXHALED

**FIGURE 7.4**

(a) The composition of air before inhaling, (b) the air in the alveoli, and (c) the exhaled air composition. Note the increase of the water fraction due to humidifying the air in the trachea.

● **EXAMPLE 7.2**

(a) Determine **Bohr's formula of the dead space in respiration**. In this formula, the ratio of the dead space volume to the total volume is expressed as a function of the volume fraction of oxygen in the inhaled, exhaled, and alveolar gases. (b) Use the formula derived in part (a) to quantify the fraction of space in the human respiratory system that is dead space.

*Solution to part (a):* In respiration studies we have to be careful when labelling parameters, as

there are many in the calculations and they are often similar. In this book, we use non-abbreviated subscripts to prevent confusion, even though this is not always done in the literature because it requires more writing.

We define three gas fractions for oxygen: $f_{\text{inhaled}} = 0.209$ is the fraction of oxygen in dry air as inhaled by the standard man (Fig. 7.4(a)); $f_{\text{alveoli}} = 0.132$ is the fraction of oxygen in the gas in the lungs (alveolar gas, Fig. 7.4(b)); and $f_{\text{exhaled}} = 0.151$ is the fraction of oxygen in the exhaled gas (Fig. 7.4(c)). We also define variables for the two physiological volumes: $V_{\text{dead space}}$ is the volume of the dead space, and $V_{\text{total}}$ is the total volume of the standard man's respiratory system filled with air, including the mouth and nose cavities, the trachea, and the lungs. The active space need not be labelled separately because it is equal to $V_{\text{total}} - V_{\text{dead space}}$.

We assume that the standard man inhales and then exhales. The exhaled air is described in a summary fashion by Fig. 7.4(c), but it can also be modelled by two fractions: one that is exhaled from the dead space and therefore has the same composition as the inhaled air, and one from the lungs that has the composition of the alveolar gas:

$$f_{\text{exhaled}} \cdot V_{\text{total}} = f_{\text{inhaled}} \cdot V_{\text{dead space}} + f_{\text{alveoli}}(V_{\text{total}} - V_{\text{dead space}}) \quad [6]$$

For Bohr's formula we need to isolate the two volumes and then determine their ratio. Separating the terms for the dead space and the total volume in Eq. [6], we find:

$$(f_{\text{exhaled}} - f_{\text{alveoli}}) V_{\text{total}} = (f_{\text{inhaled}} - f_{\text{alveoli}}) V_{\text{dead space}} \quad [7]$$

which we write as a ratio:

$$\frac{V_{\text{dead space}}}{V_{\text{total}}} = \frac{f_{\text{exhaled}} - f_{\text{alveoli}}}{f_{\text{inhaled}} - f_{\text{alveoli}}} \quad [8]$$

This is Bohr's formula for the dead space in respiration.

*Solution to part (b):* This part requires only a straightforward substitution of the given values in Eq. [8]. For a resting person, the total volume inhaled and exhaled is the tidal volume, $V_{\text{total}} = 0.5$ L. Thus:

$$V_{\text{dead space}} = V_{\text{total}} \frac{f_{\text{exhaled}} - f_{\text{alveoli}}}{f_{\text{inhaled}} - f_{\text{alveoli}}}$$

$$= (0.5 \text{ L}) \frac{0.151 - 0.132}{0.209 - 0.132}$$

$$= 0.125 \text{ L} \quad [9]$$

i.e., about one-quarter of the inhaled air never moves beyond the physiological dead space.

# Pressure in the Lungs

The discussion in the previous section indicates that the gas pressure is an important parameter that must be measured in physiological studies of the respiratory system. A more detailed look at the anatomy of the human chest indicates that we indeed need two pressure measurements. As illustrated in Fig. 7.5(a), each lung (1) is surrounded by a double-layered membrane called the **pleura** (2). The layer in contact with the lungs is called the visceral layer, and the outer layer is the parietal layer, which is attached to the inside of the rib cage (3). A small amount of fluid in the pleura allows frictionless movements of the lungs against the rib cage and prevents the harder ribs from puncturing the soft lung tissue. The pleura completely envelops the lungs, except for the entrance of blood vessels and the bronchus (primary bronchial branches (4) of the trachea (5)). Fig. 7.5(b) shows a corresponding anatomical view of the lungs.

Active breathing is achieved by several sets of muscles acting on the parietal layer: the diaphragm is a muscular layer that separates the chest cavity from the abdominal cavity. It is attached to the spine at the back, to the lower ribs along the side of the chest, and to the sternum at the front. The diaphragm pulls the lungs downward during inhalation and pushes them upward during exhalation. Muscles located between neighbouring ribs open the chest upward and sideways during inhalation and contract the rib cage during exhalation. These muscles are called intercostal muscles; their antagonistic action is described in Q–5.4.

Thus, we need to record the following two pressures during respiration: (i) The **pressure inside the lungs**, $p_{\text{lungs}}$. It is obtained from a pressure gauge in the spirometer tube on the mouth side of a valve, which allows the test person to be disconnected from the spirometer. (ii) The **pressure in the pleura**, specifically, the pressure in the gap between the visceral and parietal layers of the pleura, $p_{\text{gap}}$. This pressure can be estimated with a non-intrusive pressure gauge lowered into the lower one-third of the esophagus, which is the muscular passage from the pharynx to the stomach.

With volume and pressure measured, and by applying the gas laws we will develop in the current chapter, the respiratory processes in the lungs can be understood. A brief overview of the key observations will guide us through the development of the basic physics concepts. We saw in Chapter 6 that work and energy are key parameters in characterizing physical and biological systems. When gases are involved, the work is determined from a $p$–$V$ diagram of the process. Thus, representing respiration in a $p$–$V$ diagram

(a)

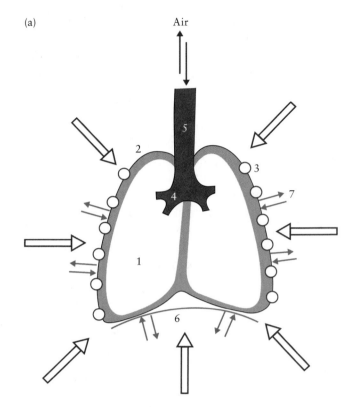

(b)

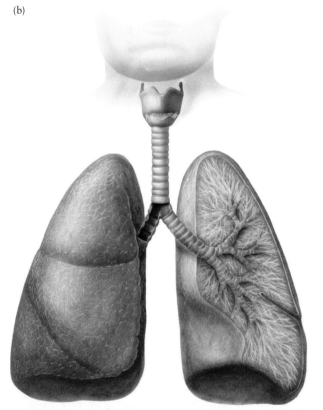

## FIGURE 7.5

(a) Sketch of the human thorax/lungs system, showing the lungs (1); the double-layered membrane enclosing the lungs (pleura, (2)); the rib cage (3); the trachea (5), which branches into the primary bronchi (4); the diaphragm and the abdominal muscle (6); and the intercostal muscles (indicated through their action, (7)). The large arrows indicate the effect of the external air pressure on the chest. (b) Artist's anatomical model of the lungs.

is the first step toward a quantitative discussion. Since the respiratory system is more complex than a simple piston-sealed container, this is not quite as straightforward as it sounds. We noted above that two relevant pressure measurements exist; in addition, the experiment can be conducted in several different ways. This leads to a number of possible $p$–$V$ diagrams for respiration. Of these, the most important ones are shown in Figs. 7.6, 7.7, and 7.8. Each of these diagrams contains three pressure curves:

- the curve labelled $p_{alveoli}$ represents the **gauge pressure inside the lungs,**
- the curve labelled $p_{pleura}$ represents the **gauge pressure in the pleura,** and
- the curve labelled $p_{alveoli} - p_{pleura}$ represents the pressure difference between lungs and pleura, called the **transmural pressure** (*trans* means "across" and *murus* means "wall" in Latin).

Note that both pressures $p_{alveoli}$ and $p_{pleura}$ are called **gauge pressures.** A gauge pressure is a pressure value relative to atmospheric pressure. Labelling the absolute pressure in the lungs $p_{lungs}$ and the absolute pressure in the gap between the visceral and the parietal layers of the pleura $p_{gap}$, we write:

$$p_{pleura} = p_{gap} - p_{atm}$$
$$p_{alveoli} = p_{lungs} - p_{atm} \qquad [10]$$

While absolute pressures are always positive, gauge pressures can be positive or negative. For example, the alveolar pressure is negative for lung volumes smaller than 3.0 L in Fig. 7.6. This means that the pressure inside the lungs is less than the atmospheric pressure for small lung volumes.

## THE $p$–$V$ DIAGRAM IN FIG. 7.6

This diagram represents the respiratory system at rest. The three curves were obtained as follows: the test person inhales a certain amount of air from the spirometer. Then the valve to the spirometer is closed and the test person relaxes his/her respiratory muscles. The pressure gauge on the mouthpiece records the alveolar pressure $p_{alveoli}$, because the test person's epiglottis remains open.

The respiratory equilibrium is defined at a lung volume of 3.0 L because the alveolar gauge pressure is zero at that lung capacity (large open circle in Fig. 7.6). Nothing would happen if the test person removed the mouthpiece of the spirometer at this stage.

When the test person inhales a large amount of air (to a lung volume larger than 4.5 L), both the alveolar pressure and the pleural pressure become positive, the latter because the lungs push the pleura outward against the ribcage. In turn, both the

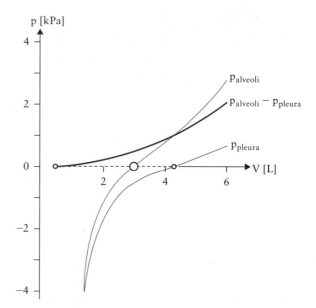

**FIGURE 7.6**

$p$–$V$ diagram of the respiratory system at rest with relaxed breathing muscles. The three curves show the alveolar pressure $p_{alveoli}$ (gauge pressure in the lungs, green curve), the pleural pressure $p_{pleura}$ (gauge pressure in the pleural gap, blue curve), and the transmural pressure difference between lungs and thorax $p_{alveoli} - p_{pleura}$ (gauge pressure difference of lungs and pleural gap, red line). The transmural pressure difference is positive at all lung volumes, to hold the lungs open. The pressure in the lungs exceeds atmospheric pressure for all volumes above 3.0 L (large open circle, lung volume at rest). The pressure in the pleural gap exceeds atmospheric pressure for lung volumes above 4.5 L. The horizontal dashed line indicates the consequences of a punctured lung: the lungs and the pleural gap collapse toward the small open circles; i.e., the lungs shrink to a volume of less than 1.0 L (at which the transmural pressure becomes zero) and the pleural gap widens toward the thorax (to a volume corresponding to a lung volume of 4.5 L).

alveolar and the pleural pressures are negative when the test person exhales to a lung volume below 3.0 L. The transmural pressure difference between the lungs and the pleura remains positive under all conditions because otherwise the lungs would collapse like a balloon from which the air has escaped. The curves in Fig. 7.6 are drawn between lung capacities of 1.5 L and 6.0 L, representing the maximum range of volume values accessible in breathing (compare with Fig. 7.2).

---

**Concept Question 7.1**

Fig. 7.6 is used in physiology to define the compliance of the lungs, the thorax, and the entire human breathing apparatus. Compliance measures the ability of a system to yield elastically when a force or a pressure is

## Concept Question 7.1 (continued)

applied. The three compliances in respiration are defined as the slope of the curves in Fig. 7.6:

$$C_{\text{lung tissue}} = \frac{\Delta V}{\Delta p_{\text{transmural}}}$$

$$C_{\text{thorax}} = \frac{\Delta V}{\Delta p_{\text{pleura}}} \qquad [11]$$

$$C_{\text{breathing apparatus}} = \frac{\Delta V}{\Delta p_{\text{alveoli}}}$$

**The pressure intervals chosen have to be as small as possible near the value of interest because the curves in Fig. 7.6 are not linear. (a) At which volume is each of the three compliances a maximum, and (b) how are the three compliances related to each other?**

ANSWER TO PART (a): Note that the definition of compliance in Eq. [11] is based on the slope $\Delta V/\Delta p$, which represents the steepness of a curve in a $V$–$p$ diagram. However, our discussions have been based on $p$–$V$ diagrams, such as Fig. 7.6. We note that:

$$C = \frac{\Delta V}{\Delta p} = \frac{1}{\dfrac{\Delta p}{\Delta V}} = \left(\frac{\Delta p}{\Delta V}\right)^{-1}$$

$$[12]$$

$$\Rightarrow \frac{\Delta p}{\Delta V} = \frac{1}{C}$$

A maximum compliance occurs in a $p$–$V$ diagram at the volume where the smallest steepness of the curve is recorded. This occurs between 3.0 L and 4.5 L for the entire breathing apparatus (based on curve $p_{\text{alveoli}}$), at minimum volumes for the lung tissue (based on the transmural pressure curve) and at maximum volumes for the thorax (based on curve $p_{\text{pleura}}$).

Let's see whether this agrees with what we expect intuitively: a large compliance means a soft response of the tissue; a small compliance means a stiff response of the tissue. Thus, the breathing apparatus response is particularly soft in the range of regular breathing, but stiffer at larger or smaller volumes. When you undertake a deep exhale or inhale, you notice that these require much more effort than tidal-volume breathing. The increasing stiffness serves the purpose of limiting you from inhaling or exhaling beyond the design limits of your chest.

ANSWER TO PART (b): The three compliances in Eq. [11] are obviously not related linearly to each other. However, consider the inverse compliances based on Eq. [12]:

$$C_{\text{lung tissue}}^{-1} = \frac{\Delta(p_{\text{alveoli}} - p_{\text{pleura}})}{\Delta V} = \frac{\Delta p_{\text{transmural}}}{\Delta V}$$

$$C_{\text{thorax}}^{-1} = \frac{\Delta p_{\text{pleura}}}{\Delta V} \qquad [13]$$

$$C_{\text{breathing apparatus}}^{-1} = \frac{\Delta p_{\text{alveoli}}}{\Delta V}$$

In this form, it is evident that the three inverse compliances are additive:

$$C_{\text{lung tissue}}^{-1} + C_{\text{thorax}}^{-1} = \frac{\Delta(p_{\text{alveoli}} - p_{\text{pleura}})}{\Delta V} + \frac{\Delta p_{\text{pleura}}}{\Delta V}$$

$$= \frac{\Delta p_{\text{alveoli}}}{\Delta V} = C_{\text{breathing apparatus}}^{-1}$$

$$[14]$$

This provides an additional insight into the concept of compliance: the stiffness of the breathing apparatus at small and large volumes that we noted above has different causes; at small volumes the stiffness of the thorax limits the breathing apparatus, while the lung tissue plays this role at large volumes.

## THE $p$–$V$ DIAGRAM IN FIG. 7.7

This diagram represents the respiratory system with very slow breathing, i.e., a case where the flow resistance in the air passageways is negligible. Note that this diagram covers only the volume range from 3.0 L to 4.0 L, as the assumption of such slow breathing does not allow a test person to reach larger or smaller lung volumes. This $p$–$V$ diagram looks distinctively different from the one in Fig. 7.6: the alveolar pressure is given at all lung volumes as zero. This is true because the test person breathes with open air passageways, i.e., with the lungs open to the external air pressure. The curve for the transmural pressure difference, $p_{\text{alveoli}} - p_{\text{pleura}}$, is the same as in Fig. 7.6, indicating that this pressure difference at any lung volume is independent of the type of breathing. Consequently, the pleural pressure varies in Fig. 7.7 in the opposite way from that in Fig. 7.6: $p_{\text{pleura}}$ decreases with lung volume for slow breathing, while it increases with lung volume when the thorax is at rest and the respiratory muscles are relaxed.

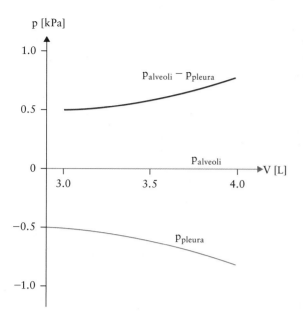

**FIGURE 7.7**

*p–V* diagram for a person breathing very slowly, i.e., without air flow resistance in the airways. The figure shows the same three pressure curves as Fig. 7.6 for the volume range from 3.0 L to 4.0 L. The pressure in the lungs (green curve) remains at atmospheric pressure because the test person's mouth is open and provides an open passage between the lungs and the outside air throughout the breathing cycle. The transmural pressure difference (red curve) has the same values as in Fig. 7.6 because it is only a function of the lung volume and does not depend on the details of the breathing process. Thus, the pleural pressure is negative across the regular breathing range (blue curve).

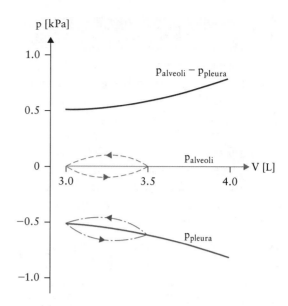

**FIGURE 7.8**

*p–V* diagram for a person breathing regularly. Two of the pressure curves in Fig. 7.7 are modified between 3.0 L and 3.5 L (tidal volume): the pressure in the lungs is larger than atmospheric pressure during exhalation (upper dashed curve with arrow to the left) and it is smaller than atmospheric pressure during inhalation (lower dashed curve with arrow to the right). These pressure variations are needed to push or pull the air through the airways. The same changes occur for the pleural pressure (dash-dotted lines). The transmural pressure difference (red curve) is not affected because the transmural pressure difference depends only on the lung volume.

## THE *p–V* DIAGRAM IN FIG. 7.8

This diagram represents the dynamic breathing we do continuously. The three pressure curves are based on Fig. 7.7, except that the alveolar and pleural pressures are modified between 3.0 L (exhaled) and 3.5 L (inhaled). In regular breathing, air is inhaled and exhaled fast enough that flow resistance in the air passageways has to be taken into account. Viscous flow of air in a tube is discussed in Chapter 12, where we learn that a pressure difference along the tube is needed to achieve gas flow through the tube. Thus, the pressure in the lungs is smaller than atmospheric pressure during inhalation ($p_{alveoli} < 0$) and is larger than atmospheric pressure during exhalation ($p_{alveoli} > 0$). This is illustrated in Fig. 7.9 for the alveolar pressure as a function of time for a complete breathing cycle. Dynamic breathing requires excess pressures of up to 100 Pa. Note again that dynamic breathing does not affect the transmural pressure difference in Fig. 7.8, as both alveolar and pleural pressure are modified in the same fashion.

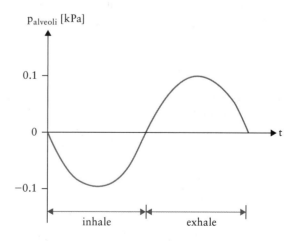

**FIGURE 7.9**

The alveolar pressure $p_{alveoli}$ as a function of time. The pressure in the lungs drops to 100 Pa below atmospheric pressure during inhalation, and exceeds the atmospheric pressure by up to 100 Pa during exhalation. These pressure variations allow the air to flow through the airways against the flow resistance.

**Concept Question 7.2**

Which of the following statements about Fig. 7.8 is correct? (A) The diagram does not allow us to calculate work done during respiration because the units kPa and L do not combine to the unit J. (B) The absolute pressure in the lungs becomes negative during the breathing cycle. (C) The transmural pressure increases faster during inhalation than it decreases during exhalation. (D) The pressure in the pleural gap displays two different values at a given lung volume, one during inhalation and another one during exhalation.

CORRECT: Choice (D). (A) is wrong because 1 kPa · 1 L = 1 J. (B) is wrong because the figure shows gauge pressures; absolute pressures anywhere in your body are always close to atmospheric pressure, which is 101.3 kPa. The maximum deviation from atmospheric pressure of any of the three curves in Fig. 7.8 is 0.7 kPa, or less than 0.7% of atmospheric pressure. (C) is wrong because the top curve in Fig. 7.8, which shows the transmural pressure, has only one value at all volumes. (D) is correct as the figure shows. Note that the pressure in the pleural gap varies even though it is not open to the lungs. You can vary the pressure in a closed container by squeezing it from outside.

What else can we learn from Figs. 7.6, 7.7, and 7.8? Can we calculate the work required for respiration from these figures? What role does the gas in the lungs play—or, more precisely, how do the physical parameters of the inhaled air influence the physiological processes? To answer these questions, below we develop a detailed understanding of the system gas.

# The Empirical Gas Laws

We introduce the ideal gas as the model system of thermal physics, since it will turn out to be simple but still sufficient to describe all the important features. We will see that the versatility of this model stems from the fact that both a macroscopic and a microscopic approach to the ideal gas exist. The macroscopic model is empirical because it is based on experimental observations; it is discussed first. The microscopic model is an extension of the mechanical concepts we developed in Chapters 3 and 4 and will be introduced in the next section.

We base the empirical gas model on two key experiments, the first one done by Robert Boyle in 1664 and the second one done by Jacques Alexandre Charles in 1787. The interpretation of the results of these two experiments then leads to a quantitative

formulation of the ideal gas law. Studying Boyle's and Charles's experiments in detail illustrates not only how the properties of gases are developed from an analogy to mechanical systems, but also how the experimental findings reach beyond mechanics.

## Boyle's Law

**Boyle's experiment** is illustrated in Fig. 7.10. A U-shaped glass tube has been filled with mercury in Fig. 7.10(a). The liquid metal reaches a mechanical equilibrium when its surfaces no longer move up or down. This mechanical equilibrium is indicated by a free-body diagram for the mercury surface in the left column: the normal force due to the mercury beneath the surface pushes the surface up, and the weight of the air column above the metal pushes it down. In equilibrium, the mercury surfaces in both tubes are at the same height because the same air pressure, $p_{atm}$, acts on both sides.

In the next step, shown in Fig. 7.10(b), the left glass tube is sealed. Since this step as such does not change the air pressure in the sealed volume, no other changes occur. Note that the sealed volume is now identified by the height of the air column above the mercury, $h_{initial,air}$.

Boyle then added mercury through the open column, as illustrated in Fig. 7.10(c). The weight of the additional mercury pushes the mercury column down, which means that it pushes the mercury surface upward in the left column. This upward push compresses the sealed gas—i.e., increases its pressure—until a new mechanical equilibrium is reached. Boyle measured the excess height of mercury between the two columns, $h_{Hg}$, and the height of the air in the sealed volume, $h_{final,air}$. When mercury was added repeatedly, he noticed that these measurements are related in the form:

$$h_{final,air} \propto \frac{1}{h_{Hg}} \quad [15]$$

To interpret Eq. [15] further, we replace both parameters with volume and pressure terms:

- $h_{final,air}$ relates to the volume of air in the sealed space, $V_{air}$, by multiplying it with the cross-sectional area $A$ of the glass tube:

$$V_{air} = h_{final,air} \cdot A \quad [16]$$

- $h_{Hg}$ relates to the pressure of the enclosed air in the following fashion: we use Newton's first law for the mercury surface in the left column as the system. We identify three forces acting on this surface: (i) the weight of the excess mercury in

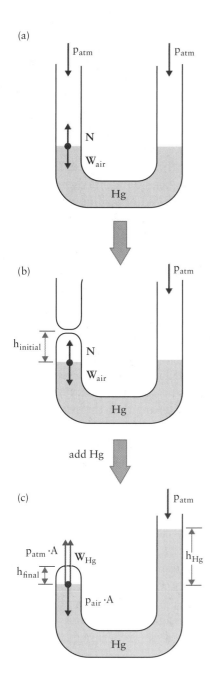

**FIGURE 7.10**

Boyle's experiment. (a) A U-shaped, hollow glass cylinder is filled with mercury and (b) the left glass column is sealed. (c) Adding mercury to the open column compresses the air in the sealed column. The free-body diagram included at the left mercury surface in (b) indicates a mechanical equilibrium. This free-body diagram changes in (c) due to the addition of mercury through the right column. The three forces that act on the mercury surface are balanced: the weight of the excess mercury and the air pressure above the open column push the mercury surface upward and the pressure of the sealed gas pushes the mercury surface downward.

the right column, $W_{Hg}$, pushes the mercury below in the right column downward. Correspondingly, this force pushes the mercury in the horizontal part of the tube to the left, and pushes the mercury in the left column upward. Thus, $W_{Hg}$ is

a force pushing the left mercury surface toward the sealed air at the top of the left column. (ii) The open air column above the right mercury surface pushes the right surface downward. It therefore contributes a second force pushing the left mercury surface upward, $p_{atm} \cdot A$. (iii) Acting in the opposite direction on the mercury surface is the gas pressure in the sealed air volume. It exerts a force $p_{air} \cdot A$ downward. The condition of mechanical equilibrium for these three forces reads:

$$p_{atm} \cdot A + |\mathbf{W}_{Hg}| = p_{air} \cdot A \qquad [17]$$

In the weight term, the mass of mercury is replaced by the product of its volume and density:

$$|\mathbf{W}_{Hg}| = m_{Hg} \cdot g = \rho_{Hg} \cdot V_{Hg} \cdot g \qquad [18]$$

in which the mercury volume is $V_{Hg} = A \cdot h_{Hg}$. Substituting Eq. [18] in Eq. [17], we find:

$$p_{atm} \cdot A + \rho_{Hg} \cdot A \cdot h_{Hg} \cdot g = p_{air} \cdot A \qquad [19]$$

Dividing both sides by the area $A$ leads to:

$$\rho_{Hg} \cdot h_{Hg} \cdot g + p_{atm} = p_{air} \qquad [20]$$

Thus, the pressure in the sealed air volume, $p_{air}$, is proportional to the height of the excess mercury column, $h_{Hg}$. Note that $p_{air} \propto h_{Hg}$ is correct because $p_{atm}$ in Eq. [20] is constant.

Boyle's result in Eq. [15] is therefore interpreted as:

$$V_{air} \propto \frac{1}{p_{air}} \qquad [21]$$

which we generalize by omitting the subscripts:

$$V \propto \frac{1}{p} \quad \Rightarrow \quad p \cdot V = \text{const} \qquad [22]$$

This relation is called **Boyle's law**. The dependence of the gas pressure on the gas volume in Boyle's law is shown in Fig. 7.11: the pressure and the volume are inversely proportional to each other in Eq. [22]. The product $p \cdot V$ has the standard unit Pa $\cdot$ m$^3$. In the physicochemical literature the equivalent unit of kPa $\cdot$ L is often used alternatively. Boyle's law is applied in a second form when we compare an initial and a final state of the gas:

$$p_{initial} \cdot V_{initial} = p_{final} \cdot V_{final} \qquad [23]$$

The constant term on the right-hand side of Eq. [22] is not a universal constant; it is only independent of the parameters $p$ and $V$. In particular, a strong dependence on the temperature is observed. Thus, Boyle's law applies only to *isothermal processes*, i.e., processes during which the temperature does not

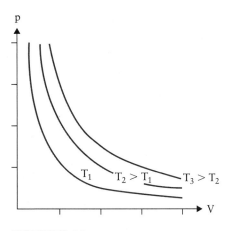

**FIGURE 7.11**

Boyle's pressure-versus-volume data for three different temperatures. Note that Boyle's law does not lead to a linear relation between pressure and volume but to an inverse relation of the form $p \propto 1/V$.

change. This is illustrated in Fig. 7.11 by displaying three separate curves for temperatures $T_1$, $T_2$, and $T_3$ where the temperatures increase from $T_1$ to $T_3$.

> *Boyle's law: The product of pressure and volume of a gas at constant temperature is constant.*

## Concept Question 7.3

**Which of the four graphs in Fig. 7.12 is consistent with Boyle's 1664 experiment that led to Boyle's law?**

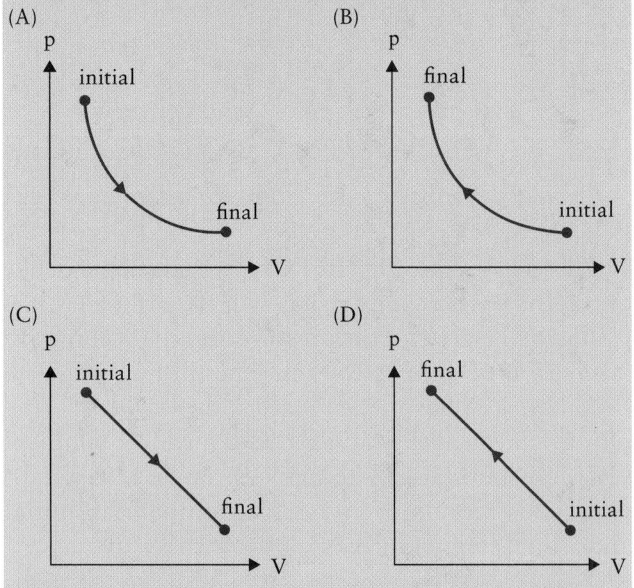

(A)

(B)

(C)

(D)

**FIGURE 7.12**

Four processes in a *p–V* diagram.

ANSWER: Choice (B). Note that the relation of *p* and *V* is not linear. Also, Boyle *added* mercury; i.e., he recorded his results while increasingly compressing the sealed gas.

## Charles's Law

We want to overcome the restriction to isothermal processes in Boyle's law to obtain a generally applicable law. Boyle could not do this, since Celsius only invented the thermometer 78 years after Boyle's studies. Charles was the first scientist to use a thermometer for studies of gases when he revisited Boyle's experiments in 1787. To investigate the temperature dependence of a gas, he modified the experiment as shown in Fig. 7.13. After sealing an air volume of height $h_{\text{initial,air}}$ in the same fashion Boyle had done, the glass tube with the mercury was immersed in water at an initial temperature $T_1$ (room temperature), as shown in Fig. 7.13(a). Then the temperature of the arrangement was raised to a temperature $T_2$, with $T_2 > T_1$, and held at that temperature as indicated in Fig. 7.13(b). **Charles's experiment** showed that the volume of the sealed air increased, pushing some of the mercury to the column at the right side. In the last step, shown in Fig. 7.13(c), mercury was removed with a syringe until both mercury columns were levelled again. This meant that the pressure of the confined air column at the left returned to its initial value since excess mercury no longer caused a compression. The final height of the air on the sealed side, $h_{\text{final,air}}$, was recorded. Charles found:

$$h_{\text{final,air}} \propto T_{\text{air}} \qquad [24]$$

in which $T_{\text{air}}$ is the temperature of the water bath and everything immersed in it: $T_{\text{air}} = T_2$ (according to the zeroth law of thermodynamics).

To interpret his results, Charles used Eq. [16] to convert the height $h_{\text{final,air}}$ in Fig. 7.13(c) to the air volume $V_{\text{air}}$. Generalizing again by omitting the subscripts, we formulate Charles's experimental results in the form:

$$V \propto T \qquad [25]$$

You can easily convince yourself that a gas expands as a result of a temperature increase: thoroughly rinse with boiling water the outside of an open, empty plastic bottle. Then close the cap so that the bottle is airtight. Place the bottle in the refrigerator and let it cool down. It will crumple under the external air pressure as the cooling air inside requires less and less volume.

Fig. 7.14 shows a graphical representation of Charles's data. In his experiments, Charles was able to vary the temperature between 0°C and 300°C by using an oil bath. Thus, we draw the results as solid lines between these two temperatures. The graph shows two experimental curves, one at atmospheric pressure $p_1 = 1$ atm, and one at elevated pressure

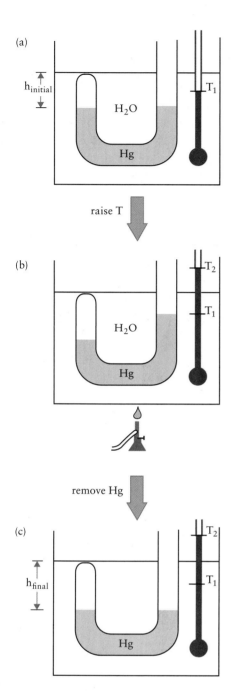

**FIGURE 7.13**

Charles's experiment. (a) A U-shaped, hollow glass cylinder is filled with mercury. (b) The left column is sealed and the arrangement is immersed in a bath at fixed temperature $T_1$. (c) Heating the bath to a higher temperature $T_2$ causes the sealed air volume to increase. Mercury is then removed with a syringe to level the two mercury columns.

using a fixed excess height of mercury in the right glass tube of Fig. 7.13(c). When we extrapolate the two curves in Fig. 7.14 toward lower temperatures (shown as dashed lines), we find that the curves meet at a common point: $T = -273.15°C$ and $V = 0$. In 1848, William Thomson Baron Kelvin of Largs (Lord Kelvin) concluded that there is a physical meaning to this observation and that the temperature of

$-273.15°C$ is the lowest possible temperature we can achieve in any experiment. This allows us to eliminate negative temperature values by introducing the **Kelvin temperature scale,** which is calibrated with a new zero point at $-273.15°C = 0$ K:

$$T_{Kelvin} = T_{Celsius} + 273.15 \qquad [26]$$

The Kelvin scale is closely related to the Celsius scale because the difference between the melting and boiling temperatures of water is 100 degrees in both cases. The Kelvin scale, however, has a great advantage over the Celsius scale: all scientific laws that depend on the temperature can be written much more simply. This is illustrated here with **Charles's law.** If we quantify the experimental data of Fig. 7.14 for one of the given pressure values and with the temperature measured in degrees Celsius, we have to write:

$$V = V_0 + \text{const} \cdot T$$
$$\Rightarrow \quad \frac{V}{T + 273.15} = \text{const} \qquad [27]$$

in which the constant term $V_0$ requires an additional volume measurement at $0°C$. For the temperature measured in degrees Kelvin, we find instead:

$$V = \text{const} \cdot T$$
$$\Rightarrow \quad \frac{V}{T} = \text{const} \qquad [28]$$

Comparing Eqs. [27] and [28], it is obvious that the formulation in Eq. [28] is simpler and thus preferable. Charles's law is applied in a second form that compares an initial and a final state of a gas:

$$\frac{V_{initial}}{T_{initial}} = \frac{V_{final}}{T_{final}} \qquad [29]$$

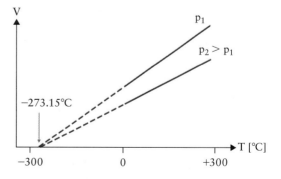

**FIGURE 7.14**

Charles's volume-versus-temperature data for two different pressures (combination of air pressure and excess mercury pressure). The solid part of the lines indicates the temperature range experimentally accessible at Charles's time. The dashed part of the lines is a linear extrapolation of the experimental data.

From the existence of curves with different slopes in Fig. 7.14, we conclude that the proportionality factor in Eq. [28] is not a universal constant but varies with pressure. Thus, Charles's law applies only to experiments done at constant pressure. Such experiments are called *isobaric experiments*.

*Charles's law: The quotient of the volume and the temperature of a gas at a given pressure is constant.*

## Formulation of the Ideal Gas Law

In the next step, Charles's and Boyle's laws are combined to formulate the ideal gas law. We want to follow this step carefully for two reasons. First, we learn how two earlier but more restricted laws are combined to yield a law that is much more widely applicable—a typical way that new insights emerge in the natural sciences. Second, the mathematical steps involved in the transition from Boyle's and Charles's laws to the ideal gas law illustrate how we can deal with **multi-variable functions**.

The derivation of the ideal gas law is illustrated in Fig. 7.15. We discuss this figure frame by frame. Fig. 7.15(a) shows the complete parameter space for a fixed mass of gas: from Charles's and Boyle's experiments we know that the three parameters pressure $p$, volume $V$, and temperature $T$ are variable. If these three parameters were independent of each other, we would not need any further discussion: any value in a $p$–$V$–$T$ diagram would describe an independent state of the gas. However, Boyle's and Charles's experiments show that $p$, $V$, and $T$ cannot be chosen independently. Instead, we need a relation in the form:

$$V = f(p, T) \quad \text{or} \quad p = f(V, T) \quad \text{or} \quad T = f(p, V)$$

$$[30]$$

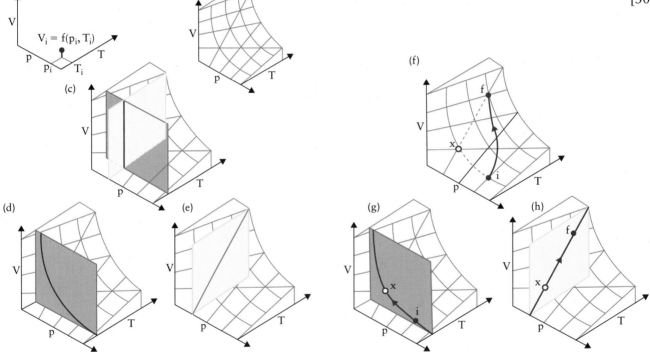

**FIGURE 7.15**

Graphical display of the ideal gas law in a $p$–$V$–$T$ diagram. (a) The diagram is constructed by measuring the volume for a given mass of an ideal gas for each pair of independent parameters: $p_i$ and $T_i$. The corresponding state of the system $i$ has the volume $V_i$, which is entered into the graph. (b) The graph combines the volume values for all parameter pairs $(p_i, T_i)$, leading to a two-dimensional surface that represents all possible states of the ideal gas. (c) Vertical planes can be positioned in the diagram to represent all states with a given temperature or a given pressure, respectively. These planes are perpendicular to each other. (d) A plane for constant temperature intersects the plane of possible states of the system. The resulting curve shows all possible states of the gas at that fixed temperature (isothermal condition). (e) A plane for constant pressure intersects the plane of possible states of the system. The resulting curve shows all possible states of the gas at that fixed pressure (isobaric condition). (f) An arbitrary process (red line with arrow) that guides the system from an initial state (labelled i) to a final state (labelled f). The dashed line shows an alternate possible path from the initial to the final state through an intermediate state (labelled x). The alternate path in part (f) consists of two steps we have discussed previously: (g) an isothermal process leads from the initial state to the intermediate state (Boyle's law), and (h) an isobaric process leads from the intermediate to the final state (Charles's law).

Which of the three forms in Eq. [30] is used depends on the specific purpose for which a given system is studied; in the remainder of this section, we use $V = f(p, T)$; i.e., we assume that the pressure and the temperature are independent variables and the volume is the dependent variable.

Mathematically, a function of two variables like $V = f(p, T)$ represents a two-dimensional surface in the three-dimensional $p$–$V$–$T$ diagram. To illustrate this point, we consider Figs. 7.15(a) and 7.15(b). In Fig. 7.15(a) we find a particular volume, $V_i$, after choosing the pressure and temperature parameters $p_i$ and $T_i$. This volume is found experimentally by measuring the volume for a fixed amount of gas once the desired pressure and temperature values are reached. Note that the subscript $i$ indicates a particular state of the gas, which is characterized by the three parameters $V_i, p_i, T_i$. Later, we choose this state as the initial state for a process in which the state of the gas is changed.

The volume measurement in Fig. 7.15(a) can be repeated for other combinations of pressure and temperature. In each case a point in the $p$–$V$–$T$ diagram is found that identifies the corresponding state of the gas. Instead of independent dots, we combine them in Fig. 7.15(b) as a surface. The points on this surface represent all possible states of the gas; points that are not on the surface cannot be states of the gas. Finding this surface is important when we plan to discuss a process for the gas: such a process must start at a possible state on the surface and reach a final state that must again lie on it. The process must further move through a sequence of possible intermediate states, i.e., along a line that lies fully in the surface we found in Fig. 7.15(b).

We do not necessarily expect a simple mathematical formula to describe the surface in Fig. 7.15(b). However, we already know two mathematical statements that must hold: Boyle's law in Eq. [22] for constant temperature, and Charles's law in Eq. [28] for constant pressure. Requiring a constant temperature means that we allow only states that lie on a vertical green plane as illustrated in Fig. 7.15(c); requiring a constant pressure leads to the yellow plane shown in the same figure. Note that these two planes are perpendicular to each other in the $p$–$V$–$T$ diagram.

We study the green plane with $T = $ const in Fig. 7.15(d) first. The possible states of the gas in this plane are highlighted as a red line along the intersection with the surface we developed in Fig. 7.15(b). This curve follows the same relation as the curves shown in Fig. 7.11, each representing Boyle's law. Fig. 7.15(e)

illustrates in the same fashion the yellow plane with $p = $ const. The intersection of this plane with the surface of possible gas states leads to a straight red line, representing Charles's law in Fig. 7.14.

We now turn our attention to an **arbitrary process** between an initial state (with subscript i in Fig. 7.15) and a final state (with subscript f in the figure). This process is shown in Fig. 7.15(f). We develop Fig. 7.15 further to establish how the initial gas parameters $V_{\text{initial}}, p_{\text{initial}}, T_{\text{initial}}$ are related to $V_{\text{final}}, p_{\text{final}}, T_{\text{final}}$. We use two perpendicular vertical planes with the initial state in a constant-temperature plane and the final state in a constant-pressure plane. The intersection line of these two planes contains an intermediate state of the gas. We label the intermediate state with subscript $x$ and show it as an open red circle.

Fig. 7.15(g) and 7.15(h) provide a new path from the initial to the final state of the gas through intermediate states that lie on either one of the two vertical planes. The first part of this process runs from the initial to the intermediate state in Fig. 7.15(g) as an isothermal process:

$$p_{\text{initial}}, V_{\text{initial}}, T_{\text{initial}} \quad \Rightarrow \quad p_{\text{final}}, V_x, T_{\text{initial}}$$

$$\text{apply Boyle's law:} \quad V_x = V_{\text{initial}} \frac{p_{\text{initial}}}{p_{\text{final}}} \qquad [31]$$

i.e., the system reaches its final pressure while the temperature is still at the initial value.

The process from the intermediate state to the final state, shown in Fig. 7.15(h), is then an isobaric process:

$$p_{\text{final}}, V_x, T_{\text{initial}} \quad \Rightarrow \quad p_{\text{final}}, V_{\text{final}}, T_{\text{final}}$$

$$\text{apply Charles's law:} \quad V_{\text{final}} = V_x \cdot \frac{T_{\text{final}}}{T_{\text{initial}}} \qquad [32]$$

We eliminate the intermediate volume $V_x$ by substituting Eq. [31] into Eq. [32]:

$$V_{\text{final}} = \left( V_{\text{initial}} \frac{p_{\text{initial}}}{p_{\text{final}}} \right) \frac{T_{\text{final}}}{T_{\text{initial}}} \qquad [33]$$

Finally, the variables describing the initial and final states are separated:

$$\frac{p_{\text{initial}} \cdot V_{\text{initial}}}{T_{\text{initial}}} = \frac{p_{\text{final}} \cdot V_{\text{final}}}{T_{\text{final}}} \qquad [34]$$

Note that Eq. [34] no longer contains any parameter of the intermediate state we chose in Fig. 7.15. The equation contains only initial and final parameters of the gas for the process of interest. Thus, Eq. [34] is valid independent of the path chosen between the initial and final states; i.e., the path in Fig. 7.15(f) must yield the same result as the path in frames (g) and (h) of Fig. 7.15. Eq. [34] can be generalized in the form:

$$\frac{p \cdot V}{T} = \text{const} \quad [35]$$

Thus, Boyle's and Charles's laws represent special processes that are possible for an ideal gas, but Eq. [35] represents all possible processes for the ideal gas.

The constant in Eq. [35] depends only on the mass of the gas and is, thus, a more fundamental constant than the two constants that appear in Eqs. [22] and [28]. In 1811, Amedeo Avogadro showed that to quantify the amount of gas as its mass (unit kg) is not the best approach. If we do this, the constant in Eq. [35] depends on the identity of the gas; i.e., it would become a materials constant. Instead, Avogadro expressed the amount of gas in unit mol, introducing the parameter $n$ for the amount of gas with $n = m/M$ in which $M$ is its molar mass. For a given material, the value of the molar mass is obtained from the Periodic Table and is given in unit kg/mol; e.g., the molar mass of carbon is $M = 12.01$ g/mol, and the molar mass of methane ($CH_4$) is $M = 12.01 + 4 \times 1.008 = 16.04$ g/mol. This convention for the molar mass defines 1 mol as a macroscopic amount of matter. One mol of ideal gas contains $6.02 \times 10^{23}$ atoms or molecules; this number is called the **Avogadro number**.

When the amount of gas in mol is separated from the constant in Eq. [35], we find const $= n \cdot R$ with $R = 8.314$ J/(K $\cdot$ mol)—a fundamental constant called the **universal gas constant**. The universal gas constant is independent of any other parameter, including the identity of the gas. Thus, the **ideal gas law** reads:

$$p \cdot V = n \cdot R \cdot T \quad [36]$$

*Ideal gas law: The product of pressure and volume of a gas is proportional to the product of its amount in unit mol and the temperature in unit Kelvin. The proportionality constant is the universal gas constant.*

The observation that 1 mol always fills the same volume of $V = 22.414$ L for any gas at 0°C and at 1.0 atm pressure (STPD conditions; see the definition after Example 7.1) led to **Avogadro's hypothesis of the molecular nature of gases**. This was one of the earliest hints of an atomic structure of matter—it was, however, not explored further until much later during the 19th century.

---

## Concept Question 7.4

**While you're doing some back-of-the-envelope calculations in a chemistry laboratory, you notice you forgot the standard unit of the universal gas constant. How can you recover the unit of $R$ without needing to consult the literature?**

ANSWER: We use the ideal gas law in Eq. [36]. Isolate the universal gas constant, then substitute all parameters with their respective units:

$$R = \frac{p \cdot V}{n \cdot T} \quad \Rightarrow \quad \frac{Pa \cdot m^3}{mol \cdot K} = \frac{J}{mol \cdot K} \quad [37]$$

This example illustrates how best to recover the units of constants if you recall a physical law in which the constant occurs.

---

## Concept Question 7.5

**Fig. 7.16 shows five processes by which a given amount of an ideal gas is brought from an initial to a final state. Which process occurs at constant temperature?**

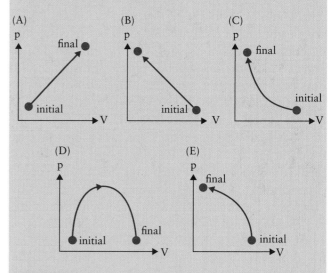

**FIGURE 7.16**

Five processes for an ideal gas.

ANSWER: Choice (C). We set the temperature constant in the ideal gas law, $T = T_0$:

$$p \cdot V = n \cdot R \cdot T_0 = \text{const} \quad [38]$$

Since $n$, $R$, and $T_0$ are all constant, they are best combined in a single constant as done in Eq. [38]. Eq. [38] is equivalent to Boyle's law; i.e., we have recovered Boyle's law from the ideal gas law at constant temperature. Boyle's law follows $p \propto 1/V$.

## Concept Question 7.6

The first manned free flight took place on November 21, 1783, in Paris, France. Two passengers travelled in a hot-air balloon for 25 minutes to a maximum height of about 900 m. The balloon had a rigid envelope with a large hole at the bottom and did not carry a burner; the hot air was generated by a fire below the balloon before take-off. Which of the following statements is not correct when comparing the air in the balloon before the fire was started and when the ropes were cut for take-off? (A) The amount of air (in mol) in the balloon had changed. (B) The air temperature in the balloon had changed. (C) The air pressure of the gas in the balloon had changed. (D) The air volume in the balloon remained unchanged. (E) The product of pressure and volume in the ideal gas equation, $p \cdot V$, remained unchanged.

ANSWER: Choice (C). The volume of the balloon remained unchanged, $V = V_0$, due to the rigid envelope. The pressure remained unchanged, $p = p_0$, due to the large opening in the envelope through which the air inside the envelope was heated. Thus, the ideal gas law reads:

$$p_0 \cdot V_0 = n \cdot R \cdot T \quad \Rightarrow \quad n \propto \frac{1}{T} \qquad [39]$$

i.e., the molar amount of gas in a hot-air balloon is reduced due to the increase in the gas temperature. Does this mean that doubling the gas temperature from 25°C to 50°C drives 50% of the gas out of the balloon envelope? No! This temperature increase is not a doubling of the temperature, because it rises from 298 K to 323 K; i.e., it increases by only about 8%. Never use Celsius units when making quantitative physical statements about absolute temperatures.

## ● EXAMPLE 7.3

(a) Using $\rho = m/V$ for the density definition and $n = m/M$ for the amount of gas in unit mol, show that the ideal gas equation can be written as:

$$M = \frac{\rho}{p} R \cdot T \qquad [40]$$

(b) Consider an ideal gas at 20°C and 2.0 atm with a density of 2.5 kg/m³. What is the molar mass of this gas? (c) Table 7.1 shows density measurements for $CO_2$ gas at 10°C as a function of pressure. Using Eq. [40] and graphical methods, determine the molar mass of $CO_2$.

### TABLE 7.1

**Density versus pressure data for carbon dioxide**

| Pressure (torr) | Density (g/cm³) |
|---|---|
| 515 | 0.0013 |
| 2065 | 0.0053 |
| 6185 | 0.0163 |

*Solution to part (a):* We start by substituting $n = m/M$ in the ideal gas law:

$$p \cdot V = \frac{m}{M} R \cdot T \qquad [41]$$

Next, we isolate the molar mass and group the parameters for the ratio $m/V$:

$$M = \frac{m}{V} \frac{R \cdot T}{p} = \rho \frac{R \cdot T}{p} \qquad [42]$$

This is the formula sought in the problem.

*Solution to part (b):* Using Eq. [42] with $T = 20°C = 293$ K and the data given in the example text, we find:

$$M = \frac{2.5 \frac{\text{kg}}{\text{m}^3}}{2.026 \times 10^5 \, \text{Pa}} \left( 8.314 \frac{\text{J}}{\text{K} \cdot \text{mol}} \right) (293 \text{ K})$$

$$= 0.030 \frac{\text{kg}}{\text{mol}} = 30 \frac{\text{g}}{\text{mol}} \qquad [43]$$

*Solution to part (c):* The data given in Table 7.1 are plotted in Fig. 7.17 (red circles). Note that the pressure axis has been converted to the standard

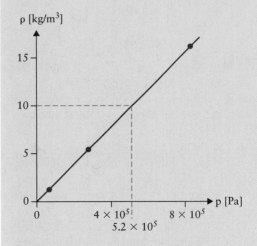

**FIGURE 7.17**

Plot of the density of carbon dioxide ($CO_2$) as a function of pressure.

## ● EXAMPLE 7.3 (continued)

unit Pa. To analyze this plot to obtain the molar mass of carbon dioxide, we rewrite Eq. [42] in the form:

$$\rho = \frac{M}{R \cdot T} p \qquad [44]$$

which shows that $\rho \propto p$ and explains why the data in Fig. 7.17 follow a straight line.

We calculate the slope of that line, $\Delta\rho/\Delta p$, to find the slope of Fig. 7.17:

$$\frac{\Delta\rho}{\Delta p} = \frac{M}{R \cdot T} \qquad [45]$$

The slope contains the molar mass. Using the origin and the data point indicated by the dashed lines in Fig. 7.17, we find:

$$\frac{\Delta\rho}{\Delta p} = \frac{10.0 \, \frac{kg}{m^3}}{5.2 \times 10^5 \, Pa} = 1.92 \times 10^{-5} \, \frac{s^2}{m^2} \qquad [46]$$

A single data point is sufficient in this case because the straight line in Fig. 7.17 passes through the origin; i.e., in the general equation for a linear function, $y = a \cdot x + b$, the constant $b$ is zero. Using the value from Eq. [46] and $T = 10°C = 283 \, K$, we calculate the molar mass:

$$M = R \cdot T \frac{\Delta\rho}{\Delta p}$$

$$= \left( 8.314 \, \frac{J}{K \cdot mol} \right) (283 \, K) \left( 1.92 \times 10^{-5} \, \frac{s^2}{m^2} \right)$$

$$= 0.0452 \, \frac{kg}{mol} = 45.2 \, \frac{g}{mol} \qquad [47]$$

## ● EXAMPLE 7.4

Inhaled air reaches body temperature while travelling through the nasal cavities and the trachea, i.e., before it reaches the lungs. Is this required to prevent thermally expanding air from exerting excessive force in the lungs? Specifically, (a) express the change in lung volume per inhalation if air at STPD conditions ($T_{air} = 0°C$ and $p_{air} = 1 \, atm$) reaches the lungs, and (b) compare the volume change in part (a) to the volume change due to oxygen/carbon dioxide exchange in the inhaled air. *Hint:* Assume that the processes in the lungs occur under isobaric conditions. (c) If you are

interested: Can you think of another reason why air at 0°C should not reach the lungs?

*Additional physiological information:* A resting standard man inhales 7.5 L air per minute, for which 15 inhalation cycles are required. Of the inhaled air, an amount of 0.26 L/min $O_2$ is absorbed into the blood system and 0.208 L/min $CO_2$ is released from the blood (standard man data are given in Table 3.3).

*Solution to part (a):* We calculate first the temperature-related change in the tidal volume from the given physiological information:

$$V_{tidal} = \frac{7.5 \, \frac{L}{min}}{15 \, \frac{inhalation}{min}} = 0.5 \, \frac{L}{inhalation} \qquad [48]$$

The calculation is done only for the tidal volume because the remaining lung volume of 3.0 L is filled with air that had been inhaled earlier and, therefore, is already at body temperature. Charles's law is used in this example because we assume that the processes in the lungs are isobaric, i.e., done at constant pressure. Charles's law is written in the form:

$$\frac{V_{tidal}}{T_{outside}} = \frac{V_{in \, lungs}}{T_{in \, lungs}} \qquad [49]$$

We substitute the standard man data and the given external temperature in this equation:

$$V_{in \, lungs} = V_{tidal} \frac{T_{in \, lungs}}{T_{outside}} = (0.5 \, L)\frac{310 \, K}{273 \, K} = 0.57 \, L \qquad [50]$$

Thus, 0.5 L dry air at 0°C becomes 0.57 L at core body temperature.

The calculated volume difference is now expressed as a fraction of the volume of the lungs after inhalation; i.e., $V_{inhaled} = 3.5 \, L$ from Fig. 7.2. The volume change $\Delta V = V_{in \, lungs} - V_{tidal} = 0.07 \, L$ represents

$$\frac{\Delta V}{V_{inhaled}} = \frac{0.07 \, L}{3.5 \, L} = 0.02 \qquad [51]$$

i.e., a volume change of 2%. Accommodating a 2% volume expansion would not be a problem for the lungs; the reason for the warming of air before it enters the lungs must be a different one.

*Solution to part (b):* The loss of oxygen from the tidal volume is calculated from the absorption rate of oxygen (0.26 L/min) and the given breathing rate of 15 inhalations per minute:

$$V_{loss}(O_2) = \frac{0.26 \, \dfrac{L}{min}}{15 \, \dfrac{inhalation}{min}} = 0.017 \, \frac{L}{inhalation} \qquad [52]$$

i.e., an amount of 0.017 L oxygen is absorbed into the blood system from each breath. In turn, $CO_2$ is released into the gas volume. The gain from release of $CO_2$ is 80% of the volume calculated in Eq. [52], because:

$$\frac{V_{gain}(CO_2)}{V_{loss}(O_2)} = \frac{0.208 \, \dfrac{L}{min}}{0.26 \, \dfrac{L}{min}} = 0.80 \qquad [53]$$

80% of 0.017 L is 0.014 L. Thus, 0.014 L $CO_2$ is added to the inhaled air per breath. Thus, the net loss of gas from the tidal volume is 0.003 L, which is the difference between the removed $O_2$ and the added $CO_2$. This corresponds to 0.6% of the tidal volume, or less than 0.1% of the total volume of the lungs after inhalation. Thus, the gas exchange can be neglected when studying the physical processes in our respiratory system.

*Solution to part (c):* The gas exchange between lungs and blood capillaries requires fast oxygen diffusion, which is facilitated by very thin membranes enveloping the air sacs at the end of the bronchial tree, called alveoli. The protection of these membranes at maximum efficiency of the diffusion process requires constant conditions, including a constant temperature ($T = 37°C$) and a constant humidity of the air in the lungs. For this reason, air not only is warmed to core body temperature in the trachea, but also becomes water vapour–saturated. Protection of the lungs against cooling is also the reason why dogs pant as opposed to taking deep breaths when in danger of overheating.

## ● EXAMPLE 7.5

A **plethysmograph** is an airtight box that allows us to measure the volume change of a patient's body inside the box by recording the pressure in the box (Boyle's law). The residual volume in the human lungs is determined with a plethysmograph in the following fashion: at the end of a normal exhalation through a mouthpiece, which is connected to the atmosphere outside of the plethysmograph, the air pressure in the lungs equals the atmospheric pressure (refer to Fig. 7.8). A shutter then closes off the mouthpiece. The patient is requested to continue breathing against the closed shutter. During the next inhalation, the patient's chest enlarges, creating a new lung volume by decompression; i.e., the original volume $V_{lungs}$ becomes $V_{lungs} + \Delta V$. At this point two parameters are measured:

- $\Delta V$ is determined from the pressure change in the plethysmograph, and
- the final gas pressure in the lungs is measured between the shutter and the patient.

For this method, determine a formula for the lung volume $V_{lungs}$.

*Solution:* We call the state of the patient after the exhalation the initial state and the state after the inhalation against the closed shutter the final state. Thus, the initial gas pressure in the lungs is $p_{initial} = p_{atm}$ and the final gas pressure is $p_{final}$ with $p_{final} < p_{initial}$. Both are measured in the experiment. The initial lung volume is $V_{initial} = V_{lungs}$; the final lung volume is $V_{final} = V_{lungs} + \Delta V$. $\Delta V$ is measured indirectly by recording the change in pressure in the plethysmograph and applying Boyle's law. Thus, we determine the lung volume $V_{lungs}$ as:

$$p_{initial} \cdot V_{initial} = p_{atm} \cdot V_{lungs} = p_{final} \cdot V_{final}$$
$$= p_{final}(V_{lungs} + \Delta V) \qquad [54]$$

which leads to:

$$V_{lungs} = \frac{p_{final} \cdot \Delta V}{(p_{atm} - p_{final})} \qquad [55]$$

$V_{lungs}$ includes the residual volume defined in Fig. 7.2.

# Mechanical Model of the Ideal Gas

The discussion of the ideal gas law in the previous section has raised several new questions: Why is there a minimum temperature of $-273.15°C$ below which matter cannot be cooled? Why is the gas defined in Eq. [36] called ideal? Which gases' behaviour is "ideal"? These questions are answered in this section as we obtain a deeper insight into the properties of the ideal gas by introducing a microscopic description. This approach was first proposed by Ludwig Boltzmann, James Clerk Maxwell, and Rudolf Clausius in the 1880s and is called the **kinetic gas theory**. Its most important application is to allow us to quantify the internal energy of the ideal gas.

# Four Postulates that Define a Gas as a Mechanical System

The kinetic gas theory is based on a **mechanical model of the gas**. The gas itself is characterized by identical microscopic objects called **particles**. Particles are a model for the real atoms or molecules in the gas, but represent a simplification because we treat them as point-like objects that can interact only in the most rudimentary fashion with each other or container walls. We exclude in particular most molecular properties, such as vibrations and rotations. Four properties are postulated for these particles in a macroscopic container:

(i) *The individual volumes of the particles are negligible.* This is an acceptable assumption as long as the total volume of the particles is small compared to the volume of the container.

(ii) *The gas consists of a very large number of identical particles.* This adds a further restriction on the applicability: when we combine the first two postulates, we note that the actual size of the particles must also be much smaller than the inter-particle distance.

(iii) *The particles are in continuous random motion.* This means that the motion of any particular particle is independent of the motion of all neighbouring particles (irregular motion).

(iv) *The only form of interaction between the particles or between particles and the container walls are elastic collisions.* All other intermolecular interactions are neglected.

## ● EXAMPLE 7.6

Test the validity of the first two postulates of the kinetic gas theory for air at STPD conditions. Specifically, find a lower limit for the ratio of the inter-particle distance to the particle radius. Use the value $\rho = 1.2$ kg/m$^3$ for the density of air at STPD. Estimate the size of particles for liquid water of density $\rho = 1.0$ g/cm$^3$. For this we assume that water particles are spheres and fill the space in liquid water such that neighbouring particles touch each other.

*Solution:* The volume per particle in water is calculated from the density and Avogadro's number. In the first step, the density is converted to a molar density:

$$\rho = \frac{m}{V} = \frac{n \cdot M}{V} \quad \Rightarrow \quad \frac{n}{V} = \frac{\rho}{M} \qquad [56]$$

With $M = 18$ g/mol, we find:

$$\left(\frac{n}{V}\right)_{H_2O} = \frac{1000\,\frac{kg}{m^3}}{0.018\,\frac{kg}{mol}} = 5.6 \times 10^4\,\frac{mol}{m^3} \qquad [57]$$

The inverse of this result, $(n/V)^{-1}$, is the volume per mol of water. With Avogadro's number, this is converted into a volume per particle:

$$\frac{1}{N_A}\left(\frac{n}{V}\right)^{-1}_{H_2O} = 3.0 \times 10^{-29}\,m^3 \qquad [58]$$

We estimate the diameter of the water particle, $d_{H_2O}$, by drawing the third root from this value: $d_{H_2O} = 3.1 \times 10^{-10}$ m $= 0.31$ nm, in which the last value is given in unit nanometre (nm).

Repeating the same calculation for air yields the centre-to-centre distance between the particles in the gas. We find for the molar density:

$$\frac{n}{V} = \frac{1.2\,\frac{kg}{m^3}}{0.029\,\frac{kg}{mol}} = 40\,\frac{mol}{m^3} \qquad [59]$$

in which we used $M = 29$ g/mol as an average molecular mass for air. This yields for the space occupied by a single particle:

$$\frac{1}{N_A}\left(\frac{n}{V}\right)^{-1}_{air} = 4.2 \times 10^{-26}\,m^3 \qquad [60]$$

which yields for the average distance between air particles $d_{air} = 3.5 \times 10^{-9}$ m $= 3.5$ nm. Using the result in Eq. [58] as the typical particle size, we illustrate the implications of Eqs. [58] and [60] in Fig. 7.18. The average distance between air particles is larger than the diameter of individual particles. We quantify this with the data calculated above:

$$\frac{d_{air}}{d_{H_2O}} = \frac{3.5\,nm}{0.31\,nm} = 11 \qquad [61]$$

i.e., the inter-particle distance in a gas at STPD is about 10 times larger than the size of the individual particles.

This calculation resulted in a lower limit for the ratio in Eq. [61] because the diameter of an actual water molecule is smaller than the value we calculated in Eq. [58].

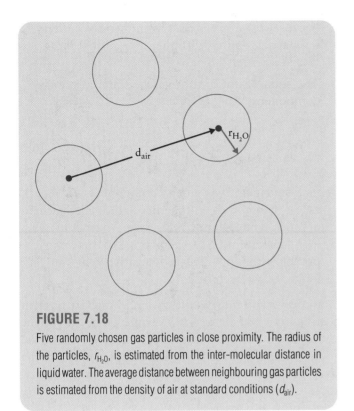

**FIGURE 7.18**

Five randomly chosen gas particles in close proximity. The radius of the particles, $r_{H_2O}$, is estimated from the inter-molecular distance in liquid water. The average distance between neighbouring gas particles is estimated from the density of air at standard conditions ($d_{air}$).

# Pressure Exerted by a Single Particle in a Box

We use the four postulates of the kinetic gas theory to develop a microscopic model of a gas. We begin with a single particle in a container as shown in Fig. 7.19. The container is a cube of side length $l$ and the particle initially has velocity **v**.

The first parameter we calculate in this model is the pressure the particle causes in the container. We are interested in the pressure because it allows us later to relate this model to the ideal gas law. We determine the pressure from the force exerted by the particle on the container walls. To simplify the calculation, we focus initially on the yellow wall in Fig. 7.19. This wall is oriented perpendicular to the $x$-axis. We include therefore only the $x$-component of the net force because the definition of pressure, $p = F_\perp/A$, requires the force component perpendicular to the surface. We start with Newton's second law in the $x$-direction:

$$F_{net,x} = m \cdot a_x = m \cdot \frac{\Delta v_x}{\Delta t} = \frac{\Delta p_x}{\Delta t} \qquad [62]$$

i.e., the force component on the yellow wall is equal to the change of the $x$-component of the momentum of the particle $p_x$ with time. Note that we need to use the instantaneous velocity; i.e., we would have to consider the limit for $\Delta t \to 0$ if the velocity or momen-

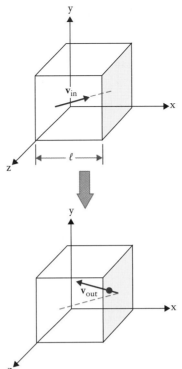

**FIGURE 7.19**

Model system for the kinetic gas theory. The system consists of a single particle that moves with velocity **v** in a cubic box of side length $l$. The interaction of the particle with the shaded wall is studied to relate pressure and volume of the gas to its microscopic properties. We assume that the particle collides with the wall elastically: the velocity components of the particle perpendicular to the wall before and after collision are related as $v_{x,in} = -v_{x,out}$.

tum varied continuously with time. However, the momentum of the particle changes only at the instant it hits a wall. Thus, the change of the $x$-component of the momentum per second can be written as the product of two time-independent terms:

$$\frac{\Delta p_x}{\Delta t} = \Delta p_{x,collision} \cdot \frac{N_{collision}}{\Delta t} \qquad [63]$$

- $\Delta p_{x,collision}$ *is the change of the $x$-component of the momentum per collision.* For an elastic collision, we know from Concept Question 6.17(b) that:

$$\Delta p_{x,collision} = 2 \cdot m \cdot v_x \qquad [64]$$

The value is twice the momentum component of the incoming particle because it approaches with a positive velocity component, $+v_x$, and leaves the wall with a negative velocity component, $-v_x$.

- $N_{collision}/\Delta t$ *is the number of collisions per second with the yellow wall.* We calculate this value from the $x$-component of the velocity of the particle, $v_x = 2 \cdot l/\tau$, in which $2 \cdot l$ is the distance the particle travels between two collisions with the yellow wall, and $\tau$ is the time of flight between two such collisions. Note that $1/\tau$ is the number of collisions per second:

$$\frac{l}{\tau} = \frac{N_{collision}}{\Delta t} = \frac{v_x}{2 \cdot l} \qquad [65]$$

Next, Eqs. [63] to [65] are substituted in Eq. [62]:

$$F_{net,x} = (2 \cdot m \cdot v_x)\left(\frac{v_x}{2 \cdot l}\right) = \frac{m \cdot v_x^2}{l} \qquad [66]$$

To obtain the pressure from Eq. [66], the force component perpendicular to the surface must be divided by the area on which the force acts. The surface is the yellow wall with area $A = l^2$ in Fig. 7.19:

$$p = \frac{F_x}{l^2} = \frac{m \cdot v_x^2}{l^3} = \frac{m \cdot v_x^2}{V} \qquad [67]$$

in which $l^3 = V$ is the volume of the cubic container in the figure.

## The Gas as a Very Large Number of Particles in a Box

To describe a gas we need not one but a very large number of particles in the box. As we add more and more particles, they start to hit each other. This is of no concern to our calculation, because these collisions are elastic and therefore kinetic energy and linear momentum are conserved. Both are just redistributed among the particles, as discussed for momentum in Concept Question 6.17(a). However, both the speed and the $x$-component of the velocity of individual particles vary. To avoid following each of the particles individually, we use an average velocity of the particles instead of the individual velocity. An average velocity can be determined in two ways, one based on the momentum and one based on the kinetic energy. We discuss both and choose the more suitable one for further discussion:

- The average $x$-component of the velocity $\langle v_x \rangle$ is defined as:

$$\langle v_x \rangle = \frac{1}{N} \sum_{i=1}^{N} v_{x,i} \qquad [68]$$

i.e., we add the $x$-components of $N$ particles and then divide by their number. The notation $\langle \cdots \rangle$ indicates that an average is taken. (The summation symbol in Eq. [68] is introduced in a Math Review at the end of Chapter 3.) The average $x$-component is not suitable for our purpose,

because $\langle v_x \rangle = 0$ for the gas in the box. Individual particles move with the same probability toward either left or right.

- **The square root of the average squared velocity component** $\sqrt{\langle v_x^2 \rangle}$ is defined as:

$$\sqrt{\langle v_x^2 \rangle} = \sqrt{\frac{1}{N} \sum_{i=1}^{N} v_{x,i}^2} \qquad [69]$$

i.e., we square the velocity components of $N$ particles, then add them together and divide by their number. The square root is taken to obtain a velocity in unit m/s. The advantage of this approach is that positive and negative values no longer offset each other.

However, we may wonder what physical argument justifies the use of Eq. [69]. Check Eq. [67] once more. We note that it contains the square of the velocity component $v_x$. Thus, it makes sense to use the average square of the $x$-component of the velocity, $\langle v_x^2 \rangle$, to replace the speed term in Eq. [67] for a box containing $N$ particles:

$$p = N \frac{m \cdot \langle v_x^2 \rangle}{V} \qquad [70]$$

The pressure for $N$ particles in a box differs from the pressure due to a single particle by (i) using an average velocity, and (ii) in that it is proportional to the number of particles, $N$.

Until now, we have focussed on the yellow wall in Fig. 7.19. However, we expect the pressure to be independent of any particular direction such as the $x$-direction because pressure is a scalar property. The only quantity in Eq. [70] that is direction-dependent is the speed term. From our everyday experience, we know that no distinction exists between the $x$-, $y$-, and $z$-directions in a gas. Take the air in the room you are in as an example. You do not sense a higher air pressure from any particular direction onto your skin. Thus the average of the square of the speed components must be equal in all directions:

$$\langle v_x^2 \rangle = \langle v_y^2 \rangle = \langle v_z^2 \rangle \qquad [71]$$

Applying the Pythagorean theorem in three dimensions yields:

$$\langle v^2 \rangle = \langle v_x^2 \rangle + \langle v_y^2 \rangle + \langle v_z^2 \rangle$$
$$= 3 \cdot \langle v_x^2 \rangle \qquad [72]$$

in which $\langle v^2 \rangle$ is the average of the squares of the speed of the particles. Substituting this result in Eq. [70]

leads to the main quantitative prediction of the kinetic gas theory:

$$p \cdot V = \frac{1}{3} N \cdot m \cdot \langle v^2 \rangle \qquad [73]$$

*Kinetic gas theory: The product of pressure and volume of a gas is proportional to two of its microscopic properties, the mass and the average of the squared speed of the particles. It is also proportional to the number of particles in the container.*

# Energy of the Ideal Gas

The result of the kinetic gas theory is used to determine the energy of an ideal gas.

## The Kinetic Energy of the Gas Particles

We recognize the similarity of the term $m \cdot \langle v^2 \rangle$ on the right-hand side of Eq. [73] to the kinetic energy. Indeed, $\frac{1}{2} m \cdot \langle v^2 \rangle$ is the average kinetic energy of a single particle in the gas, and $N \cdot \frac{1}{2} m \cdot \langle v^2 \rangle$ is the kinetic energy of all $N$ particles in the container. Thus, Eq. [73] relates the pressure and volume of an ideal gas to its kinetic energy:

$$p \cdot V = \frac{2}{3} \left( \frac{1}{2} N \cdot m \cdot \langle v^2 \rangle \right) = \frac{2}{3} E_{\text{kin}} \qquad [74]$$

The product $p \cdot V$ for the gas is equivalent to $\frac{2}{3}$ of the total kinetic energy stored in the gas.

## The Internal Energy of the Ideal Gas

Eq. [73] is now compared with the experimentally derived ideal gas law, $p \cdot V = n \cdot R \cdot T$. Because the product $p \cdot V$ is the same in both equations, we write:

$$\frac{2}{3} E_{\text{kin}} = n \cdot R \cdot T \qquad [75]$$

Recall that the kinetic gas theory defines the particle in the gas as a mechanical point-like object. This allows variations only in its kinetic and potential energy. The potential energy can be neglected because it does not play a role in the physical processes we observe. Otherwise, the gas would have to sink to the bottom of the container (sedimentation). This means the kinetic energy of the particles in the box is equal to their total energy $U$, $E_{\text{kin}} = U$. Replacing the kinetic energy with the internal energy of the gas in Eq. [75], we write:

$$U = \frac{3}{2} n \cdot R \cdot T \qquad [76]$$

*The internal energy of an ideal gas depends only on the amount of the gas (in unit mol) and temperature. It is independent of the pressure and the volume of the gas.*

# Conclusions from the Mechanical Model of the Ideal Gas and Its Internal Energy

The main ramifications of Eqs. [73] and [76] are discussed in this section.

## The Smallest Possible Temperature Is Zero Kelvin

Eq. [76] explains the existence of a minimum temperature as postulated by Lord Kelvin based on Fig. 7.14. At $T = 0$ K, the internal energy vanishes, $U = 0$ J. Thus, the entire kinetic energy is removed from the system at 0 K and $\langle v^2 \rangle = 0$ m/s. With no motion left, all particles collapse and fill a zero volume, $V = 0$ m$^3$. Thus, this prediction by Charles's law makes sense. In reality, however, atoms and molecules have a finite volume and the extrapolation of Charles's law cannot be made as indicated in Fig. 7.14. For that reason, the low-temperature ends of the lines in the figure are only dashed; we expect deviations from the ideal behaviour to be most notable at low temperatures.

## A Physiological Example: The Internal Energy of the Air in the Lungs

Eq. [76] is written with macroscopic amounts of gas in mind. However, the successful introduction of the kinetic gas theory suggests that it is also applicable at the microscopic scale of gas molecules. To rewrite the equation per particle, it is first written for 1 mol ($n = 1$):

$$U = \frac{3}{2} R \cdot T = \frac{1}{2} M \cdot \langle v^2 \rangle \qquad [77]$$

in which $M$ is the molar mass in unit kg/mol. In the next step we divide by Avogadro's number $N_A$, with $M = m \cdot N_A$ and $m$ the mass of a single particle in unit kg/particle:

$$\varepsilon = \frac{3}{2} \frac{R}{N_A} T = \frac{3}{2} k \cdot T \qquad [78]$$

$\varepsilon$ is the internal energy per particle and $k$ is the Boltzmann constant, $k = R/N_A = 1.38 \times 10^{-23}$ J/K. Note that we cannot attribute this energy to a particular particle in a gas because the value is based on averaging over a large number of particles.

## Concept Question 7.7

**What is the internal energy per mol and per molecule for an ideal gas at room temperature?**

ANSWER: Room temperature means $T = 298$ K. Note that we need no other information about the ideal gas to analyze Eqs. [77] and [78]. Per mol of gas, we find:

$$U = \frac{3}{2} R \cdot T = \frac{3}{2} \left( 8.314 \ \frac{J}{K \cdot mol} \right) (298 \ K)$$

$$= 3.72 \ \frac{kJ}{mol} \qquad [79]$$

Per molecule, the corresponding value is:

$$\varepsilon = \frac{3}{2} k \cdot T = \frac{3}{2} \left( 1.38 \times 10^{-23} \ \frac{J}{K} \right) (298 \ K)$$

$$= 6.2 \times 10^{-21} \ \frac{J}{particle} \qquad [80]$$

## ● EXAMPLE 7.7

For the air in the lungs after a regular exhalation, calculate (a) the amount in unit mol, and (b) the internal energy. *Hint:* For this calculation, we treat air as an ideal gas with molar mass $M = 29$ g/mol.

*Solution to part (a):* We know from the spirometer data in Fig. 7.2 that the gas volume of the lungs after exhalation is 3.0 L. Fig. 7.6 shows that the gas pressure in the lungs matches atmospheric pressure at $p_{atm} = 1.013 \times 10^5$ Pa after exhalation. The temperature of the gas in the lungs is then at the human core body temperature of $310 \ K = 37°C$. With these data we use the ideal gas law to determine the amount of air in the lungs:

$$n = \frac{p \cdot V}{R \cdot T} = \frac{(1.013 \times 10^5 \ Pa)(3 \times 10^{-3} \ m^3)}{\left( 8.314 \ \frac{J}{K \cdot mol} \right)(310 \ K)}$$

$$= 0.12 \ mol \qquad [81]$$

*Solution to part (b):* From Eq. [76], we determine the internal energy of the gas in the lungs assuming that air is an ideal gas. With the data from the problem text and part (a), we find:

$$U = \frac{3}{2} n \cdot R \cdot T$$

$$= \frac{3}{2} (0.12 \ mol) \left( 8.314 \ \frac{J}{K \cdot mol} \right)(310 \ K)$$

$$= 464 \ J \qquad [82]$$

It is interesting to compare this result to the work values we find later in the chapter for the cyclic respiration process: a single inhalation requires about 50 J of work, which is slightly more than 10% of the total internal energy of the gas in the lungs. It is therefore not possible that the energy for the inhalation is taken from the internal energy of the gas. The following calculation illustrates this: Eq. [76] predicts the temperature change in the lungs if the energy for the inhalation were taken from the gas:

$$\Delta U = \frac{3}{2} n \cdot R (T_{final} - T_{initial}) \qquad [83]$$

which yields for the final temperature:

$$T_{final} = T_{initial} + \frac{2 \cdot \Delta U}{3 \cdot n \cdot R} \qquad [84]$$

Using the numerical values given above, the right-hand side of Eq. [84] becomes:

$$310 \ K + \frac{2(-50 \ J)}{3(0.12 \ mol) \left( 8.314 \ \frac{J}{K \cdot mol} \right)} \qquad [85]$$

which yields $T_{final} = 277$ K.

Thus, the temperature in our lungs would sink close to the freezing point to accomplish just a single inhalation. Even though energy would flow fast into the lungs to maintain their temperature, during physical activities we are breathing at an accelerated rate and equilibration of the temperature would soon fall behind. Instead, the energy for the respiration work is provided in part by the various active components (muscles and diaphragm) and in part by the elastic action of the thorax.

## The Root-Mean-Square Speed of Gas Particles

We calculate the mean speed of the particles in an ideal gas from Eqs. [77] and [78]. This speed is called the **root-mean-square speed**, $v_{rms}$, and is given in the following form:

$$v_{rms} = \sqrt{\langle v^2 \rangle} = \sqrt{\frac{3 \cdot R \cdot T}{M}} = \sqrt{\frac{3 \cdot k \cdot T}{m}} \qquad [86]$$

The second-last term follows from Eq. [77] and expresses the root-mean-square speed as a function of two macroscopic parameters, the gas constant and the molecular mass. The last term in Eq. [86] follows from Eq. [78], expressing the root-mean-square speed as a function of two microscopic parameters: the Boltzmann constant and the mass of a molecule.

*The root-mean-square speed of a gas particle is proportional to the square root of the temperature and inversely proportional to the square root of the molar or molecular mass. It does not depend on the pressure or the volume of the gas.*

## EXAMPLE 7.8

(a) What is the speed of a typical nitrogen molecule at room temperature ($T = 298$ K)? (b) How much faster does a typical nitrogen molecule get when inhaled? *Hint:* Base your answers on the root-mean-square speed of the nitrogen component of the air, which is treated as an ideal gas.

*Solution to part (a):* The molar mass of nitrogen is $M(N_2) = 28$ g/mol. This quantity has to be converted into the standard unit kg/mol. We find:

$$v_{rms} = \sqrt{\frac{3\left(8.314\ \frac{J}{K \cdot mol}\right)(298\ K)}{0.028\ \frac{kg}{mol}}} = 515\ \frac{m}{s} \quad [87]$$

At first, this may appear to be a very high speed; 1850 km/h far exceeds the speed of most macroscopic objects we observe. It may also seem to be a high speed when you realize that this is the speed of billions and billions of particles hitting your skin right now. Can we put this result in some perspective? The speed in Eq. [87] can be related to the speed of sound, because nitrogen is a major component of air and sound is carried by air. The speed of sound is about 330 m/s; thus, the speed of 515 m/s for the typical nitrogen molecule appears to be of the right order of magnitude. A detailed discussion of the speed of sound in gases is provided in Chapter 17.

*Solution to part (b):* To solve this part, we could simply substitute the core body temperature into Eq. [87]. However, it is more useful to compare both speeds:

$$\frac{v_{rms}(T_2 = 310\ K)}{v_{rms}(T_1 = 298\ K)} = \frac{\sqrt{\dfrac{3 \cdot R \cdot T_2}{M}}}{\sqrt{\dfrac{3 \cdot R \cdot T_1}{M}}} = \sqrt{\frac{T_2}{T_1}}$$

$$= \sqrt{\frac{310\ K}{298\ K}} = \sqrt{1.04}$$

$$= 1.02 \quad [88]$$

The nitrogen molecules become 2% faster, leading to a root-mean-square speed of nitrogen in the lungs of 525 m/s.

## Maxwell–Boltzmann Velocity Distribution

There is a wide range of individual speeds in a box filled with gas particles. The root-mean-square velocity is only one velocity representative of a broad distribution of speeds. Fig. 7.20(c) shows the actual probability distribution of velocities for nitrogen molecules at 298 K and 1500 K. This plot is called the **Maxwell–Boltzmann velocity distribution**. Because it is a probability distribution it has to be interpreted differently from other graphs. The first two parts of the figure illustrate why.

We start with a velocity axis in Fig. 7.20(a). At a given instant in time, each particle in the box has a particular velocity and is shown as a dot at that velocity in the graph. Note that we have chosen only a very short segment of the velocity axis, indicated by the broken line before and after the range we study. The speed of nine particles fell in the displayed interval. Fig. 7.20(a) is not a useful graphical representation of the result because we get only a large number of dots along an axis. To turn this into a graph an interval of given length is chosen, all particles within this interval are counted, and this number is shown at the centre value of the interval. Specifically, we choose for Fig. 7.20 an interval length $2 \cdot \delta$. The histogram in Fig. 7.20(b) then shows that five particles lie in the velocity interval from $v_1 - \delta$ to $v_1 + \delta$, and four particles lie in the adjacent interval from $v_2 - \delta$ to $v_2 + \delta$. The vertical axis in Fig. 7.20(b) is the number of particles, $\Delta N$, in an interval of length $2 \cdot \delta$ at the speed $v$. Dividing this number by the total number of particles in the box, $\Delta N/N$, is the first step toward a probability axis. However, we also have to include the interval length $\delta$ because $\Delta N$ depends on it: thus, $\Delta N/(N \cdot 2 \cdot \delta)$ is the fraction of particles in an interval of length $2 \cdot \delta$ around speed $v$.

Fig. 7.20(c) shows smooth curves instead of a histogram. This is the result of choosing $\delta$ much smaller than the typical velocities of the particles in the gas. Thus, the vertical axis on Fig. 7.20(c) is $\Delta N/(\delta \cdot N)$ in unit s/m.

*The Maxwell–Boltzmann velocity distribution shows as a function of speed v the fraction of molecules in a gas that lie in an interval of width δ.*

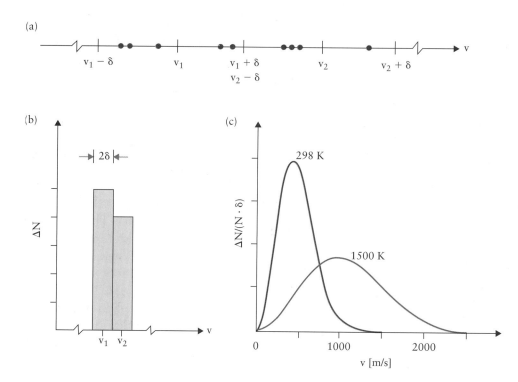

**FIGURE 7.20**

The Maxwell–Boltzmann velocity distribution of an ideal gas in thermal equilibrium. (a) We start with a single velocity axis along which all particles are placed at their respective speeds. (b) To develop from (a) a velocity distribution, the velocity axis is divided into bins of equal size $2 \cdot \delta$. We group the particles based on their individual velocities in the respective bins. (c) A smooth velocity distribution is obtained when the bin size is much smaller than the entire velocity range we study. This leads to the shown velocity distributions of nitrogen molecules at room temperature (solid line) and 1500 K (dashed line). The horizontal axis is the velocity of the gas particles in unit m/s. The vertical axis is called a probability density because it provides the fraction of particles, $\Delta N/N$, for each $2 \cdot \delta$ bin around the respective velocity $v$.

We saw in Example 7.8 that the root-mean-square speed of nitrogen at 298 K is 515 m/s. Finding this speed on the solid curve in Fig. 7.20(c), we see that the root-mean-square speed lies above the most probable speed at 450 m/s (speed at the peak of the curve). The root-mean-square speed and the most probable speed are different because the curves in Fig. 7.20 are not symmetric. The tail toward high speeds causes a higher root-mean-square speed, as large speeds contribute more dominantly to an average when it is calculated for square values.

molecules have the same temperature and the same average velocity. *Hint:* Use $M(O_2) = 32$ g/mol and $M(N_2) = 28$ g/mol.

ANSWER: Choice (D). The two gas components of air are in thermal equilibrium, which is usually established between two mixed gas components in a very short time. However, Eq. [86] shows that $v_{rms} \propto M^{-1/2}$ at a given temperature. Thus, the heavier oxygen molecules move slightly slower on average.

## Concept Question 7.8

We compare oxygen and nitrogen molecules in the air of your room. Which statement is true? (A) The oxygen molecules are slightly hotter than the nitrogen molecules. (B) The oxygen molecules are slightly cooler than the nitrogen molecules. (C) The oxygen molecules are on average slightly faster than the nitrogen molecules. (D) The oxygen molecules are on average slightly slower than the nitrogen molecules. (E) Both types of

## A Second Look at the Thermal Equilibrium

Both the internal energy and the temperature of a system are defined only when the system is in thermal equilibrium. A thermal equilibrium is established for a gas when the speed distribution of the particles in the gas matches the Maxwell–Boltzmann distribution shown in Fig. 7.20. Note that the bell-shaped curve flattens and shifts to larger speeds as the temperature increases to 1500 K (dashed curve in

Fig. 7.20(c)), indicating that at higher temperatures more gas particles are moving at higher speeds. This distribution plays a key role in the physical sciences: the definition of temperature, as introduced in the previous chapter, relies on the concept of thermal equilibrium. A thermal equilibrium can be defined only when enough particles in the system exist to determine a velocity distribution that can be compared to the Maxwell–Boltzmann distribution. Thus, **temperature is a collective property**; i.e., it is meaningless to talk about the temperature of a single particle or just a few.

> ANSWER: The Maxwell–Boltzmann velocity distribution identifies the probability of finding a particle in a narrow velocity interval. We cannot use this distribution to comment on the exact speed of a particle. This has been illustrated in Fig. 7.20.

## Real Gases

Simplifying models such as the ideal gas model are utilized throughout the sciences. While we can learn a lot from such models, we always need to be cautious about the limits of their applicability. The use of the ideal gas law to model the air we breathe is a good example for such a test.

The ideal gas law connects three parameters for a closed gas system: pressure, volume, and temperature. If the system were open, the amount of gas in mol would have to be included. Due to the number of parameters, real gases can be compared to the ideal gas law in several ways.

One approach is based on Fig. 7.15(d) and 7.15(e): we test the validity of Boyle's law at constant temperature, or Charles's law at constant pressure. Fig. 7.22 illustrates an experimental attempt to verify Boyle's law for several gases. Recall that Boyle's law states that the product $p \cdot V$ is constant for an isothermal process of the ideal gas. Even though Boyle derived his law from experiments, we need to take a second look with greater precision, evaluating a larger number of gases and a wider range of parameter values than he could have more than 300 years ago. Fig. 7.22 shows that the product $p \cdot V$ is actually not constant when the pressure varies isothermally, not even when the test is confined to small pressure intervals (graph at the left), and not for a noble gas with minimal inter-atomic interactions, such as neon.

> ### Concept Question 7.9
>
> **Fig. 7.21 shows an experimentally recorded velocity distribution for a given gas system. What can you conclude from the figure? (A) The gas has a hotter and a colder component. (B) The gas is not in thermal equilibrium. (C) The gas has a velocity distribution similar to the Maxwell–Boltzmann velocity distribution. (D) Most gas particles have a speed close to the average gas particle speed. (E) The gas has a particularly high temperature.**
>
>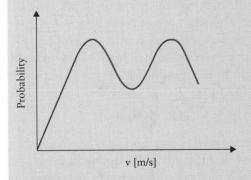
>
> **FIGURE 7.21**
> Velocity distribution measured in a particular experiment for a given gas system.
>
> ANSWER: Choice (B). Statements such as (A) and (E) cannot be made as we cannot define a temperature for a system that is not in thermal equilibrium.

> ### Concept Question 7.10
>
> **In the air in your room, how many gas particles are moving right now at exactly 300 m/s?**

> ### Concept Question 7.11
>
> **Using Fig. 7.22, quantify the deviation from ideal behaviour in isothermal experiments at 0°C for the air components (a) oxygen and (b) carbon dioxide. Use the gas composition in the lungs.**
>
> SUPPLEMENTARY INFORMATION: Air consists of a mixture of gases, including nitrogen, oxygen, carbon dioxide, and water vapour, as shown in Fig. 7.4. The air composition and its role in respiration are discussed in greater detail in Chapter 9. The concept of partial pressure is

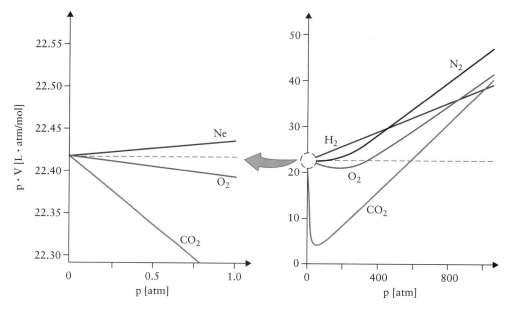

## FIGURE 7.22

Comparison of real gases with the ideal gas at 0°C, using measurements of the product $p \cdot V$. The figure at the right shows $p \cdot V$ data for 1.0 mol of oxygen ($O_2$), carbon dioxide ($CO_2$), hydrogen ($H_2$), and nitrogen ($N_2$) in the pressure range from 1.0 atm to 1000 atm. The horizontal dashed line corresponds to the prediction for the ideal gas (Boyle's law). In the figure at the left we focus on the narrower pressure range between 0.0 atm and 1.0 atm (dashed circle in figure on the right) for 1.0 mol of the same gases and neon (Ne). Note that the product $p \cdot V$ is given in the non–SI unit L · atm/mol.

### Concept Question 7.11 (continued)

introduced in that chapter, with partial pressures representing the pressure of each individual gas component. When discussing the properties of a particular component, the partial pressure is used. In the alveoli, the following partial pressures apply for oxygen and carbon dioxide: $p(O_2) = 13.3$ kPa = 0.13 atm and $p(CO_2) = 5.2$ kPa = 0.05 atm (see Fig. 7.4 and Table 9.3).

ANSWER TO PART (a): The ideal gas value in Fig. 7.22 is $p \cdot V = 22.418$ L · atm/mol. For oxygen at its partial pressure of $p = 0.13$ atm the value for $p \cdot V$ is 22.415 L · atm/mol; this corresponds to a deviation of slightly more than 0.01%.

ANSWER TO PART (b): For $CO_2$ at partial pressure $p = 0.05$ atm, $p \cdot V$ in Fig. 7.22 is 22.411 L · atm/mol; this corresponds to a deviation of slightly more than 0.03%. Thus, both gases essentially act like ideal gases at 0°C. The same applies in the lungs at 37°C, as gases become more ideal at increased temperatures.

Studying the plot at the right side of Fig. 7.22 indicates significant deviations from ideal behaviour when the pressure varies widely, e.g., between 0 atm and 1000 atm. In 1873, Johannes Diderik van der Waals concluded that two assumptions in the kinetic gas theory are too restrictive: (i) real gas molecules have a finite volume, and (ii) real gas molecules interact inelastically. He therefore made two modifications to the ideal gas equation.

- *Particle volume correction*: Van der Waals introduced an effective volume per mol of gas, labelled $b$ in unit m³, which represents the space in the container excluded for gas particles to travel as they cannot penetrate each other. This is taken into account in the modified ideal gas equation in the following form:

$$p(V - n \cdot b) = n \cdot R \cdot T \qquad [89]$$

- *Particle interaction correction*: Van der Waals then argued that the attractive interaction between the gas molecules leads to the measurement of an apparent pressure that is smaller than the actual pressure: every time a gas molecule approaches the container wall, it is pulled back by the other gas molecules and therefore exerts a reduced force on the wall during the collision. The effect on the pressure is proportional to $(n/V)^2$, with $n/V$ the molar density of the gas. One $(n/V)$ term represents the pressure contribution due to the number of particles colliding with the container wall per second; the second $(n/V)$ term represents the pressure reduction that is proportional to all other gas particles pulling back those that approach the container wall. Van der Waals introduced a second proportionality factor $a$ and implemented the pressure correction in Eq. [89]:

$$\left[ p + a\left( \frac{n}{V} \right)^2 \right](V - n \cdot b) = n \cdot R \cdot T \qquad [90]$$

Eq. [90] is called the **van der Waals equation**. It is a better description of real gases than the ideal gas law, but represents a mathematically and experimentally more complex formula. Its experimental drawback is the need to determine two new materials constants, *a* and *b*. Its mathematical drawback is that all the formulas we have derived so far and will derive later using the ideal gas law become more complicated for the van der Waals gas model. In particular, the internal energy can no longer be written in the form of Eq. [76], and one finds that the total energy for a van der Waals gas also depends on the pressure.

When do we use Eq. [90] and when do we retain the simpler ideal gas law? Concept Question 7.11 illustrates a case in which the additional effort required with the van der Waals equation is usually not justified. When the ideal gas law is consistent with experimental observations to within a percent, no further corrections are needed. Thus, the gases playing a major role in respiration can be treated as ideal gases with one exception: water vapour does not behave in an ideal way. Indeed, water vapour deviates from the ideal gas law so much at BTPS conditions that even the van der Waals equation is insufficient to describe it—water at BTPS conditions has reached the saturation level; i.e., it is at the transition point between the gaseous and the liquid state.

Van der Waals's idea is most frequently used in conceptual arguments. Here are two examples of relevance in our later discussions:

- *The internal energy of a real gas is pressure-dependent:* If you lower the pressure in a gas and therefore increase the average distance between gas molecules in the container, energy is required to separate the molecules because of inter-molecular attractive forces. Thus, energy is stored in the relative position of the gas particles; this is a form of potential energy contributing to the internal energy, something we did not allow for the ideal gas.

- *Real gases condense at low temperatures:* When the thermal energy in the gas can no longer overcome the attractive inter-molecular forces, the gas collapses and forms a dense liquid state. This is likely to occur at higher pressures, because the gas particles are closer to each other in such a gas. It is also likely to occur at low temperatures, because the particles have less kinetic energy to counter the attractive forces.

## Basic Thermodynamic Processes

Fig. 7.23 summarizes the features of our thermodynamic gas model: an isolated container with an ideal gas includes a mobile ideal piston that allows us to vary the pressure of the gas. The container/piston arrangement and its immediate environment form an isolated superstructure that allows us to account for work transfer $W$ between the gas and the source of a force operating the piston. However, considering the first law of thermodynamics for the internal energy change $\Delta U$ of a closed system,

$$\Delta U = U_{final} - U_{initial} = Q + W \qquad [91]$$

we note that the arrangement in Fig. 7.23 is not sufficient to allow for all thermodynamic processes because it doesn't specify how heat $Q$ flows into or out of the gas. Fig. 7.24 illustrates how the arrangement

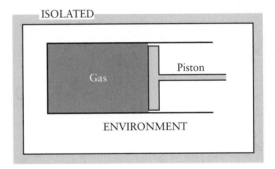

**FIGURE 7.23**

Gas model studied to this point in the discussion. An isolated box contains an ideal gas. A mobile ideal piston allows us to vary the gas pressure. The box with piston and its immediate environment form an isolated superstructure.

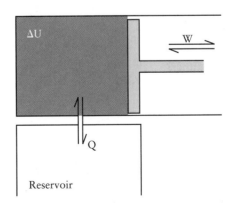

**FIGURE 7.24**

Conceptual sketch of an extended gas model that allows us to study all processes that are possible due to the first law of thermodynamics. The gas is sealed in a container (closed system with internal energy $U$). Work $W$ is exchanged with the environment via motion of a frictionless piston. Heat $Q$ is exchanged with a heat reservoir in the environment. The heat reservoir is ideal; i.e., its temperature remains unchanged during heat transfer.

of Fig. 7.23 is extended to account for heat exchange processes: a heat source has to be included that allows the gas to exchange heat with the environment. We will consider two devices for this purpose below:

- a simple Bunsen burner is depicted when we allow for heating of the system with a source at a temperature higher than the system. This leads to what we define in Chapter 8 as an irreversible heating under thermal non-equilibrium conditions.

- an **ideal heat reservoir** allows heat to flow into or out of the system when brought in thermal contact with the gas under equilibrium conditions, i.e., with equal temperatures of the system and the reservoir. The reservoir is ideal because it maintains a given temperature even during heat exchange. From a practical point of view, a reservoir much larger than the system comes close.

What are the **fundamental thermodynamic processes** the system in Fig. 7.24 makes possible? Fundamental for a thermodynamic process means several things: (i) the process must be important enough that we benefit from studying it, but (ii) it must also be sufficiently simple that its properties are easily applied in a wide range of practical cases. A good candidate for the latter requirement is a process that is sufficiently easy to handle mathematically. Eq. [91] suggests that the mathematical treatment of a process is minimal when any one of the three terms in that formula is zero. Alternatively, we expect simpler calculations for processes where at least one major system parameter in the ideal gas equation does not change. The following four sections identify such processes.

While you read through these sections, carefully observe at what point in each discussion we require properties of the ideal gas: formulas derived *before* that point apply to gases in general; formulas derived *after* that point apply only to the ideal gas!

## Isochoric Processes

An **isochoric process** is a process that takes place at **constant volume**; such a process is illustrated in Fig. 7.25. The top frames in the figure show the system before and after an **isochoric heating**. We expect the temperature and the internal energy of the system to increase in this process. The sketch in the large dashed circle at the bottom shows what happens during the process: a propane flame provides heat to the gas. Isochoric processes require rigid containers such as steel vessels. Rigid confinement is unusual in living

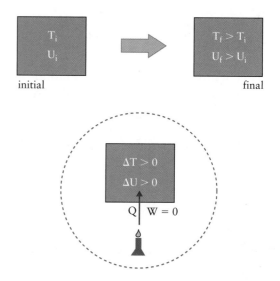

**FIGURE 7.25**

Sketch of an isochoric heating process. Isochoric processes are processes at constant volume. The top two frames show the system before and after the heating process, indicating the temperature and internal energy of the system. The frame in the large dashed circle illustrates the heating process itself. The container has fixed walls. Heat is supplied to the system from a hotter source, e.g., a Bunsen burner. The work done in the process is zero and the internal energy increases with the temperature. Note that the heat source must at least have temperature $T_{final}$.

systems; thus, isochoric conditions usually are not applicable. In physics, such conditions are typically found in high-pressure or high-vacuum experiments. High-pressure experiments are used to simulate conditions below Earth's crust (geophysics), and vacuum experiments are often used in surface and thin film physics.

The work for the isochoric process is $W = 0$ because the volume does not change and therefore the area under the curve between $V_{initial}$ and $V_{final}$ is zero. From the first law of thermodynamics it follows that $\Delta U = Q$: heat taken up or released in an isochoric process is completely taken up from or released into the internal energy of the gas. The heat exchange is quantified with Joule's definition, $Q = n \cdot C_V \cdot \Delta T$, in which $n$ is the amount of gas in mol, $\Delta T$ is the temperature change, and the index $V$ indicates that $C_V$ is **the molar heat capacity of a gas at constant volume**.

*Summary: Isochoric process of gases in general:*

$$W = 0$$
$$Q = n \cdot C_V(T_{final} - T_{initial}) \qquad [92]$$
$$\Delta U = Q$$

We combine the last two formulas in Eq. [92] to eliminate the heat: $\Delta U = n \cdot C_V \cdot \Delta T$. This relation defines a constant change of the internal energy with temperature, $\Delta U/\Delta T = n \cdot C_V$.

*The molar heat capacity $C_V$ is the change of the internal energy with temperature at constant volume for 1 mol of an ideal gas.*

Now we focus on the specific case of an ideal gas. Fig. 7.26 shows the $p$–$V$ diagram for an isochoric heating process. The two red lines in the figure represent the $p$–$V$ relation for an ideal gas for two different temperatures $T_{low}$ and $T_{high}$. The green arrow indicates the specific path the system takes in the $p$–$V$ diagram during the process in Fig. 7.25: both pressure and temperature increase but the volume remains unchanged.

For the ideal gas, we have a second formula addressing the change of the internal energy; the kinetic gas theory led to Eq. [76], $\Delta U = \frac{3}{2} \cdot n \cdot R \cdot \Delta T$. Comparing Eq. [76] with $\Delta U = n \cdot C_V \cdot \Delta T$ provides us with a value for the molar heat capacity of an ideal gas at constant volume:

$$C_V = \frac{3}{2} R \qquad [93]$$

*Summary: Isochoric process of an ideal gas:*

$$W = 0$$

$$\Delta U = \frac{3}{2} n \cdot R (T_{final} - T_{initial}) \qquad [94]$$

$$Q = \Delta U$$

Note that Eq. [76] applies to ideal gases regardless of whether the process is isochoric; however, $W = 0$ and $Q = \Delta U$ apply only for an isochoric process.

From $Q = \Delta U$ we conclude that an ideal gas system absorbs heat from the environment to increase its internal energy during isochoric heating. During

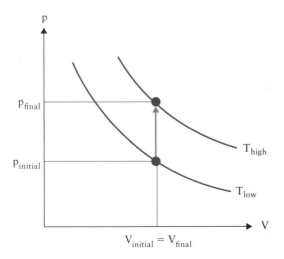

**FIGURE 7.26**

*$p$–$V$ diagram for isochoric heating of an ideal gas. The green arrow indicates the change of the temperature from $T_{low}$ to $T_{high}$ during the process. The arrow is vertical, as this corresponds to a constant volume process with $V_{initial} = V_{final}$.*

isochoric cooling—the inverse process—heat is removed from the system, which leads to a lowering of its internal energy.

**Concept Question 7.12**

Fig. 7.27 shows a *T–V* diagram (not a *p–V* diagram!) with four processes for an ideal gas. Which of the processes is an isochoric process?

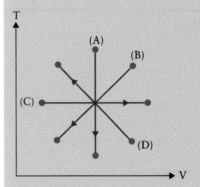

**FIGURE 7.27**

*T–V diagram with four processes for an ideal gas.*

ANSWER: Process (A).

## Isothermal Processes

**Isothermal processes** are processes that take place at **constant temperature.** An isothermal process is illustrated in Fig. 7.28. The top frames show the system before and after an isothermal expansion. The frame in the large dashed circle at the bottom of the figure shows what happens during an isothermal expansion: heat flows into the system and work is done by the system on a piston. Boyle's experiment is an example of an isothermal process.

We quantify the isothermal process for an ideal gas using a $p$–$V$ diagram. Fig. 7.29 shows the $p$–$V$ diagram for an ideal gas undergoing an isothermal expansion, in which the pressure decreases from $p_{initial}$ to $p_{final}$ and the volume increases from $V_{initial}$ to $V_{final}$.

For an isothermal process, Eq. [76] leads to:

$$\Delta U = \frac{3}{2} n \cdot R \cdot \Delta T = 0 \qquad [95]$$

Thus, the first law of thermodynamics connects heat and work of an ideal gas for an isothermal process in the form $Q + W = 0$; i.e., $Q = -W$. The work

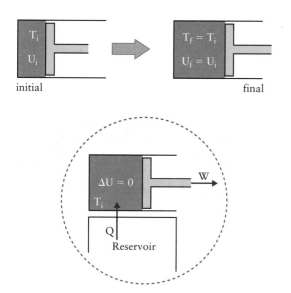

initial                                    final

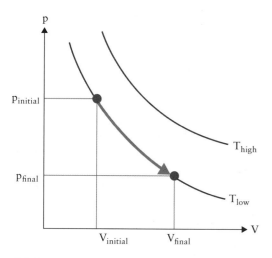

**FIGURE 7.28**

Sketch of an isothermal expansion. Isothermal processes are processes at constant temperature. The top two frames show the system before and after the expansion, indicating the temperature and internal energy of the system. The frame in the large dashed circle illustrates the expansion process itself. Heat $Q$ is absorbed by the gas from a heat reservoir, which is at the same temperature as the system. This heat does not change the temperature or the internal energy of the gas, but transfers through the system and is released as work to the piston.

**FIGURE 7.29**

$p$–$V$ diagram of an isothermal expansion of an ideal gas. The green arrow shows an isothermal expansion at temperature $T_{low}$ from an initial volume $V_{initial}$ to a final volume $V_{final}$.

is determined from the area under the curve in Fig. 7.29. We state without calculation that:

$$W = -n \cdot R \cdot T \cdot \ln\left(\frac{V_{final}}{V_{initial}}\right) \qquad [96]$$

in which $\ln(\cdots)$ is the natural logarithm. (Logarithms are reviewed in a Math Review at the end of Chapter 1.) The work is negative for an isothermal expansion

because the final volume is greater than the initial volume (see Fig. 7.28). This means that the system releases work to the piston. The energy to do this work does not come from the internal energy of the gas, as the internal energy remains unchanged in an isothermal process. Instead, the energy is passed through the system and originates in a heat reservoir that is in thermal contact with the system.

*Summary: Isothermal process of an ideal gas:*

$$W = -n \cdot R \cdot T \cdot \ln\left(\frac{V_{final}}{V_{initial}}\right)$$
$$Q = -W \qquad [97]$$
$$\Delta U = 0$$

## Concept Question 7.13

**Someone wants to report the result in Eq. [96] but writes:**

$$W = n \cdot R \cdot T \cdot \ln\left(\frac{V_{initial}}{V_{final}}\right) \qquad [98]$$

Do you accept this formula?

ANSWER: Yes. You have to familiarize yourself with the basic properties of the logarithm function, because it occurs frequently in physical applications of the life sciences. Note that we already used $\ln a - \ln b = \ln(a/b)$. Here we use $\ln(a/b) = -\ln(b/a)$, which is essentially the same statement because you can write:

$$\ln\left(\frac{a}{b}\right) = \ln a - \ln b = -(\ln b - \ln a)$$
$$= -\ln\left(\frac{b}{a}\right) \qquad [99]$$

## ● EXAMPLE 7.9

Find the work for an isothermal expansion from $p_{initial} = 1.0$ atm to $p_{final} = 0.1$ atm for 10 mol of an ideal gas at temperature 0°C.

*Solution:* Because the expansion is done isothermally, we use Eq. [97]. Boyle's law in the form $p_{initial} \cdot V_{initial} = p_{final} \cdot V_{final}$ is used to substitute the volume for pressure terms as independent variables:

$$W = -n \cdot R \cdot T \cdot \ln\left(\frac{V_{final}}{V_{initial}}\right)$$
$$= -n \cdot R \cdot T \cdot \ln\left(\frac{p_{initial}}{p_{final}}\right) \qquad [100]$$

Substituting the given values, we find:

$$W = -(10 \text{ mol})\left(8.314 \frac{J}{K \cdot mol}\right)(273 \text{ K})\ln\left(\frac{1.0}{0.1}\right)$$

$$= -52.3 \text{ kJ} \qquad [101]$$

This work is negative, which indicates that the gas does work on the environment, e.g., by pushing a piston.

## Isobaric Processes

**Isobaric processes** are processes that take place at **constant pressure**. An isobaric process is illustrated in Fig. 7.30. The top frames show the system before and after an isobaric expansion. The frame in the large dashed circle at the bottom of the figure shows what happens during an isobaric expansion: heat from a heat source flows into the system and work is done by the system on a piston. In addition, the internal energy of the gas increases. We discussed

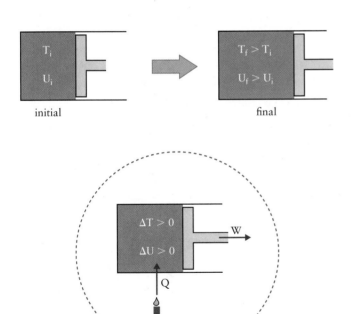

**FIGURE 7.30**

Sketch of an isobaric expansion. Isobaric processes are processes at constant pressure. The top two frames show the system before and after the expansion, indicating the temperature and internal energy of the system. The frame in the large dashed circle illustrates the expansion process itself. Heat $Q$ is absorbed by the gas from a Bunsen burner with a flame at least as hot as the highest temperature of the gas system. The added heat does increase the temperature and the internal energy of the gas, even though the gas also does work during the expansion.

Charles's experiment in Fig. 7.13, which is an example of an isobaric process. The work associated with an isobaric process is:

$$W = -p\left(V_{\text{final}} - V_{\text{initial}}\right) \qquad [102]$$

because the pressure $p$ is constant. The calculation of other quantities for isobaric processes is, however, slightly more complicated because none of the variables in the first law of thermodynamics vanish in this case: $\Delta U \neq 0$ and $Q \neq 0$ since $\Delta T \neq 0$. Still, isobaric processes are important because any experiment conducted in a system that is open to air (i.e., most experiments in chemistry, and all in biochemistry and molecular biology) takes place at constant pressure.

Physical chemists in the 19th century chose a particular approach to address this situation. Since this approach is now universally accepted, we follow their reasoning. When you read through the earlier discussion of the isochoric process you may have noted that it remained mathematically simple because the work term in $\Delta U = Q + W$ was zero. This, then, simplified the discussion further since we were able to eliminate the heat in favour of the change of the internal energy, which is a variable of the state, $\Delta U = Q$. As we switch from the case of constant volume to constant pressure, we can no longer neglect the work term, as shown in Eq. [102]. To recover the mathematical simplicity of the isochoric case we "absorb" the work term in the internal energy change, introducing a new variable $H$, which we call **enthalpy**:

$$\Delta H = Q \quad \text{for } p = \text{const}$$

$$\text{equivalent to:} \quad \Delta U = Q \quad \text{for } V = \text{const} \qquad [103]$$

This allows us in particular to rewrite Joule's definition of heat:

$$\Delta H = Q = n \cdot C_p \cdot \Delta T \quad \text{for } p = \text{const}$$

$$\text{equivalent to:} \quad \Delta U = n \cdot C_V \cdot \Delta T \quad \text{for } V = \text{const} \qquad [104]$$

with $C_p$ the **molar heat capacity at constant pressure**. This means that the simplicity of the isochoric case is not limited to that case, with its vanishing work term. It can be extended to the important isobaric case if we replace the internal energy $U$ with the enthalpy $H$ and the molar heat capacity for a gas at constant volume with the molar heat capacity at constant pressure. Before we accept this approach we must confirm two properties of the newly introduced functions: (i) the enthalpy must be a function of the state of the gas, and (ii) $C_p$ must be a materials constant like $C_V$.

Both points are tested by relating the new parameters, $H$ and $C_p$, to the respective parameters in the

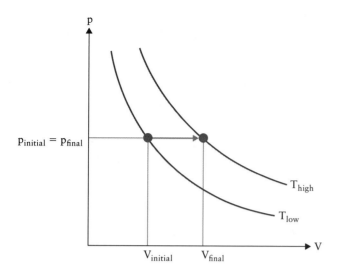

**FIGURE 7.31**

*p–V* diagram of an isobaric expansion of an ideal gas. The green arrow indicates an expansion from an initial volume $V_{initial}$ to a final volume $V_{final}$. The temperature increases concurrently from $T_{low}$ to $T_{high}$. The arrow is horizontal because this ensures $p_{initial} = p_{final}$.

isochoric case. We start with the enthalpy. Using the work term for the isobaric case, Eq. [102], we write for the first law:

$$\Delta U = Q - p \cdot \Delta V \implies Q = \Delta U + p \cdot \Delta V \quad [105]$$

The right-hand side equals the enthalpy change for the isobaric case, as stated in Eq. [103]:

$$\Delta H = \Delta U + p \cdot \Delta V \quad [106]$$

Since $U$, $p$, and $V$ are all variables of the state, so is the enthalpy. The **enthalpy** $H(U, p, V)$ is found from Eq. [106]:

$$H = U + p \cdot V \quad [107]$$

Note that we have not used the ideal gas law to this point. Thus, the enthalpy is a useful system parameter for all gases and even for liquid and solid materials, for which $H = U$, because pressure and volume changes are usually negligible for non-gaseous matter.

*Summary: Isobaric processes of gases in general:*

$$W = -p(V_{final} - V_{initial})$$
$$Q = n \cdot C_p(T_{final} - T_{initial}) \quad [108]$$
$$\Delta H = Q$$

Fig. 7.31 shows the *p–V* diagram for an ideal gas undergoing an isobaric process. The specific process shown in the figure is an isobaric expansion, in which the volume increases from $V_{initial}$ to $V_{final}$ and the temperature increases from $T_{low}$ to $T_{high}$.

For isobaric processes of the ideal gas, like the process in Fig. 7.31, the two molar heat capacities can be related to each other. In Eq. (106) we substitute

$\Delta H$ and $\Delta U$ from Eq. [104] and use the ideal gas law to replace $p \cdot \Delta V$ with $n \cdot R \cdot \Delta T$:

$$n \cdot C_p \cdot \Delta T = n \cdot C_V \cdot \Delta T + n \cdot R \cdot \Delta T \quad [109]$$

which yields:

$$C_p = C_V + R = \frac{5}{2}R \quad [110]$$

Thus, $C_p$ is a materials constant in the same fashion as the molar heat capacity at constant volume. Note that for the ideal gas we distinguish two molar heat capacities, $C_V$ and $C_p$, but that we introduced only one molar heat capacity when we studied Joule's definition of heat in Chapter 6. This is because we used liquid water as our system in the discussion in Chapter 6. The conditions of constant volume and constant pressure need not be distinguished when studying solids or liquids.

## Concept Question 7.14

Fig. 7.32 shows a process for a gas in a *V–T* diagram. The initial and final stages of the gas are indicated. Which of the following statements is correct? (A) The process is an isobaric compression of an ideal gas. (B) The process as shown is physically impossible. (C) The process is an isothermal process. (D) The process is an isobaric expansion of an ideal gas. (E) The process is an isochoric process.

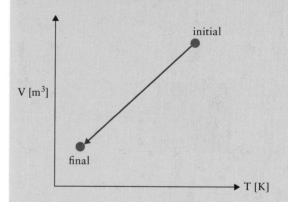

**FIGURE 7.32**

*V–T* diagram for a gas with the initial and final state indicated.

ANSWER: Choice (A). Note that the sketch is a *V–T* diagram. The ideal gas law leads to a linear relation between volume and temperature at constant pressure $p_0$: $p_0 V = n \cdot R \cdot T$; i.e., $V \propto T$. The arrow of the process in Fig. 7.32 shows that the process leads from a larger to a smaller volume; i.e., the process is a compression. The correct answer is therefore an isobaric compression.

# Adiabatic Processes

So far we have found that the first law of thermodynamics is easiest to apply when one of its variables is zero: for isothermal processes of the ideal gas $\Delta U = 0$, and for all isochoric processes $W = 0$. This leads us to wonder whether processes also exist with $Q = 0$, and whether these are limited to the ideal gas. **Processes with no heat exchange** with the environment do exist and are called **adiabatic processes**. Fig. 7.33 depicts an adiabatic expansion.

The lower part of Fig. 7.33 illustrates the system changes during the adiabatic expansion. Note that an adiabatic process requires that all heat reservoirs are disconnected from the system; this is indicated by the dashed line between the heat reservoir and the gas container.

For adiabatic processes, we determine from the first law of thermodynamics that:

$$\Delta U = W \qquad [111]$$

which applies to all systems. Thus, the energy for pushing the piston during the adiabatic expansion in the bottom part of Fig. 7.33 ($W < 0$) must be taken out of the internal energy of the system ($\Delta U < 0$).

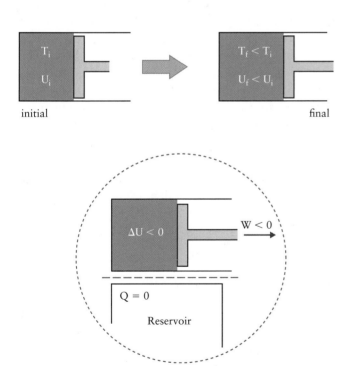

initial                                      final

**FIGURE 7.33**

Sketch of an adiabatic expansion. In an adiabatic process the system does not exchange heat with the environment. The top two frames show the system before and after the expansion, indicating the temperature and internal energy of the system. The frame in the large dashed circle illustrates the expansion process itself. The dashed line between the reservoir and the system indicates that they are isolated from each other.

Quantitative ramifications of Eq. [111] are discussed specifically for the ideal gas. We use Eq. [76] for the change of its internal energy,

$$\Delta U = \frac{3}{2}\,n \cdot R \cdot \Delta T \qquad [112]$$

and $W = -p \cdot \Delta V$ for the work. We substitute both terms in Eq. [111]:

$$\frac{3}{2}\,n \cdot R \cdot \Delta T = -\frac{n \cdot R \cdot T}{V}\,\Delta V \qquad [113]$$

which is correct for small changes $\Delta T$ and $\Delta V$ for any adiabatic process. We state without calculation that Eq. [113] yields:

$$V_{\text{initial}} \cdot T_{\text{initial}}^{3/2} = V_{\text{final}} \cdot T_{\text{final}}^{3/2} \qquad [114]$$

It turns out that Eq. [114] is also useful when describing gas systems other than the ideal gas if we replace the exponent 3/2 by $C_V/R$ from Eq. [93]:

$$V_{\text{initial}} \cdot T_{\text{initial}}^{C_V/R} = V_{\text{final}} \cdot T_{\text{final}}^{C_V/R} \qquad [115]$$

This formula is called **Poisson's equation**. Alternatively, we can replace the temperature in Eq. [115] by using the ideal gas law in the form $T = p \cdot V/(n \cdot R)$. We further use $C_V = C_p - R$ for the relation between the two molar heat capacities for the ideal gas. This leads to a second formulation for the adiabatic process in the form:

$$p_{\text{initial}} \cdot V_{\text{initial}}^{\kappa} = p_{\text{final}} \cdot V_{\text{final}}^{\kappa} \qquad [116]$$

$\kappa = C_p/C_V$ is called the **adiabatic coefficient** with a value $\kappa = 5/3$ for the ideal gas.

Fig. 7.34 compares an isothermal and an adiabatic expansion from 10 atm to 1.0 atm pressure for an ideal gas initially at 20°C. The comparison shows that the adiabatic expansion in volume is smaller but that a significant drop in temperature from 293 K to 116.6 K occurs. Since $\kappa > 1$, the solid adiabatic curve in Fig. 7.34 is steeper than the dashed isothermal curve, which follows $p \cdot V = $ const.

The difference between the two curves in Fig. 7.34 results from the differences in the physical processes of both expansions. In the isothermal case, the work done by the gas during the expansion is supplied by a heat reservoir, allowing the internal energy and therefore the temperature to remain constant. In the adiabatic case, the same amount of energy is required, but it is removed from the internal energy of the gas, which consequently cools down.

When reading physical chemistry texts, you will find a range of values reported for $\kappa$ for real gases. This implies that Eqs. [115] and [116] are good approximations of the behaviour of the real gas. However, $\kappa$-values differ significantly from $5/3 = 1.667$;

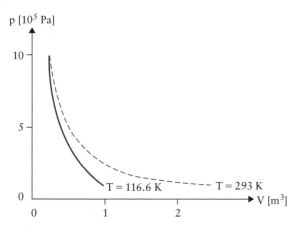

**FIGURE 7.34**

Comparison of an adiabatic expansion (solid line) and an isothermal expansion (dashed line) for 1 mol of an ideal gas in a p–V diagram. Both processes start from the same state of the gas, with $p = 1.0 \times 10^6$ Pa and $T = 293$ K. The final pressure is $\frac{1}{10}$ of the initial pressure, with $p = 1.0 \times 10^5$ Pa. During the isothermal expansion heat from a heat reservoir maintains the temperature of the ideal gas, while its temperature drops to 116.6 K during the adiabatic expansion, which occurs at the expense of the internal energy.

for example, $\kappa = 1.4$ for nitrogen ($N_2$). These deviations are related to properties of the molecules, since they are not point-like objects.

*Summary: Adiabatic processes of ideal gases:*

$$W = \Delta U$$
$$Q = 0 \qquad [117]$$
$$\Delta U = n \cdot C_V (T_{final} - T_{initial})$$

● **EXAMPLE 7.10**

1.0 mol of an ideal gas undergoes an adiabatic expansion from an initial volume of $V_{initial} = 1.0$ m$^3$ to twice that volume. The initial temperature is $T_{initial} = 270$ K. (a) What is the initial pressure, and (b) what is the final pressure?

*Solution to part (a):* The initial pressure is obtained from the ideal gas law:

$$p_{initial} = \frac{n \cdot R \cdot T_{initial}}{V_{initial}}$$

$$= \frac{(1.0 \text{ mol})\left(8.31 \frac{J}{K \cdot mol}\right)(270 \text{ K})}{1.0 \text{ m}^3}$$

$$= 2245 \text{ Pa} \qquad [118]$$

*Solution to part (b):* We use the formula for the adiabatic expansion, Eq. [114], to determine the final temperature of the gas:

$$T_{final}^{3/2} = \left(\frac{V_{initial}}{V_{final}}\right) T_{initial}^{3/2} \qquad [119]$$

Bringing both sides to the 2/3 power leads to:

$$T_{final} = \left(\frac{V_{initial}}{V_{final}}\right)^{2/3} T_{initial} \qquad [120]$$

We substitute the given values:

$$T_{final} = \left(\frac{1}{2}\right)^{2/3} (270 \text{ K}) = 170 \text{ K} \qquad [121]$$

In the next step, the ideal gas law is used to determine the final pressure:

$$p_{final} = \frac{n \cdot R \cdot T_{final}}{V_{final}}$$

$$= \frac{(1.0 \text{ mol})\left(8.31 \frac{J}{K \cdot mol}\right)(170 \text{ K})}{2.0 \text{ m}^3}$$

$$= 707 \text{ Pa} \qquad [122]$$

# Cyclic Processes

A major application of the thermodynamic processes discussed in this chapter are **cyclic processes**. These processes begin and end at the same point in a p–V diagram; i.e., they start and end at the same state of the system. They are important because cycles can continuously be repeated. A general form of a cyclic process is shown in Fig. 7.35(a). These processes have widespread applications in physiology and biology, including respiration in Fig. 7.35(b), which we discuss quantitatively below, or blood circulation in Fig. 7.35(c), which is addressed in P–7.27.

One cyclic process is of particular importance for the development of thermal physics and serves as a reference process for all other cyclic processes: the Carnot cycle.

## The Carnot Process

In 1824, Nicolas Léonard Sadi Carnot studied the cyclic process shown in Fig. 7.36. The system is an ideal gas, which is sealed in a container with a frictionless piston. This piston and two heat reservoirs, one at a higher temperature $T_{high}$ and one at a lower temperature $T_{low}$, are part of the environment. The superstructure, consisting of the system and the environment, is not in equilibrium since the two heat reservoirs are at different temperatures. However, Carnot's careful choice of the steps of the cyclic process enables us to describe the process using exclusively the first law of thermodynamics. We start with the gas at the temperature $T_{high}$, the pressure at $p_1$,

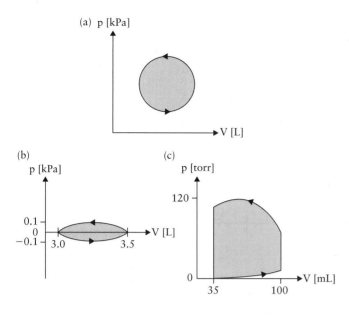

**FIGURE 7.35**

Conceptual sketch and key applications of cyclic processes. (a) A cyclic process is a process that returns to its initial state. Thus, it follows a closed curve in a *p–V* diagram. The grey area enclosed by the curve indicates the amount of work required or released per cycle. In the case shown the work is positive; i.e., the system receives work from the environment. (b) Respiration is a cyclic process discussed in detail in this chapter. The curve shows the alveolar pressure during regular breathing (compare Fig. 7.8). (c) The repetitive action of the heart is another cyclic process important in physiology. The system in this cycle is the blood. It is discussed in Q–7.34 and P–7.27 (compare Fig. 7.41).

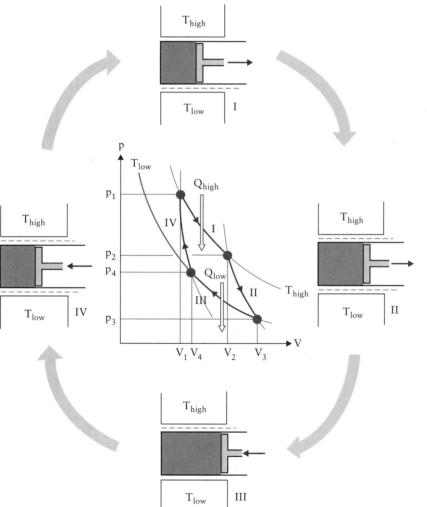

**FIGURE 7.36**

Sketch and *p–V* diagram for the Carnot process. An ideal gas is sealed in a chamber by a mobile piston. Two heat reservoirs at temperatures $T_{high}$ and $T_{low}$ are part of the environment. It is divided into four steps: (I) an isothermal expansion, (II) an adiabatic expansion, (III) an isothermal compression, and (IV) an adiabatic compression. The Carnot process is a cyclic process because the four steps return the system to its initial state. The *p–V* diagram is shown at the centre of the figure. The two isothermal curves are extended to both sides as thin blue lines. Heat is taken up from the high-temperature heat reservoir in step I and is released to the low-temperature heat reservoir in step III.

and the volume at $V_1$. The cyclic process consists of four steps:

• *Step I—Isothermal expansion:* The system is in thermal contact with the heat reservoir at temperature $T_{high}$. The dashed line between the heat

reservoir at temperature $T_{low}$ and the system indicates that the low-temperature heat reservoir is currently isolated from the system. The pressure and volume at the end of the first step are $p_2$ and $V_2$. Heat $Q_1 = Q_{high}$ is required to maintain the

## TABLE 7.2

**Summary of work, heat, and internal energy change during each step of the Carnot cycle**

| Step | I | II | III | IV |
|---|---|---|---|---|
| Process | Isothermal expansion | Adiabatic expansion | Isothermal compression | Adiabatic compression |
| Work $W$ | $-R \cdot T_{high} \cdot \ln(V_2/V_1)$ | $\Delta U_2$ | $-R \cdot T_{low} \cdot \ln(V_4/V_3)$ | $\Delta U_4$ |
| Heat $Q$ | $-W_1$ | 0 | $-W_3$ | 0 |
| Internal energy change $\Delta U$ | 0 | $C_V(T_{low} - T_{high})$ | 0 | $C_V(T_{high} - T_{low})$ |

temperature of the system. The gas does work on the piston.

- *Step II—Adiabatic expansion:* The high-temperature heat reservoir is disconnected from the system. The gas continues to expand, but now adiabatically, to a pressure $p_3$ and a volume $V_3$. During the adiabatic expansion the temperature decreases from $T_{high}$ to $T_{low}$. At the end of this step, the gas has expanded to its largest volume and lowest pressure. The gas continues to do work on the piston.

- *Step III—Isothermal compression:* The low-temperature heat reservoir at temperature $T_{low}$ is brought in thermal contact with the system. The gas is compressed to pressure $p_4$ and volume $V_4$. Heat $Q_3 = Q_{low}$ is released to the reservoir in order to maintain the temperature of the system. The piston does work on the gas.

- *Step IV—Adiabatic compression:* When the pressure reaches $p_4$ and the volume reaches $V_4$, the heat reservoir is disconnected from the system. The gas is still compressed, but adiabatically, which raises the temperature of the gas and brings the system back to its initial state at temperature $T_{high}$, pressure $p_1$, and volume $V_1$. In this last step the piston has again done work on the gas.

Then the process repeats, forming a continuous sequence of four-step cycles. The $p$–$V$ diagram for the Carnot process is shown at the centre of Fig. 7.36. The figure is based on two isothermal lines at temperatures $T_{high}$ and $T_{low}$. The four steps of the Carnot process are labelled with roman numerals I, II, III, and IV. The flow of heat is also indicated, with $Q_{high}$ received by the gas to maintain its temperature during the isothermal expansion, and $Q_{low}$ released by the system to keep its temperature from rising above $T_{low}$ during the isothermal compression.

We have already quantified heat, work, and internal energy for each of the single steps in the Carnot

cycle. The relevant energy terms are summarized in Table 7.2 for 1.0 mol of an ideal gas as the system.

Using Table 7.2, we determine the work done by the gas, the heat exchange with the heat reservoirs, and the change of the internal energy for one full cycle. Noting that $W_2 = -W_4$ from the table, the total work is calculated as:

$$\sum_{i=1}^{4} W_i = -R \cdot T_{high} \cdot \ln\left(\frac{V_2}{V_1}\right) - R \cdot T_{low} \cdot \ln\left(\frac{V_4}{V_3}\right)$$

$$[123]$$

To simplify this formula, we notice that the four volume terms are not independent of each other. After completing the first two steps, the isothermal compression has to lead to a specific value $V_4$, which connects back to $V_1$ in the final adiabatic step. To quantify the relation between the four volume terms we first write Eq. [115] for each of the two adiabatic steps in the Carnot process (step II and step IV):

Step II:  $T_{high}^{C_V/R} \cdot V_2 = T_{low}^{C_V/R} \cdot V_3$

Step IV:  $T_{high}^{C_V/R} \cdot V_1 = T_{low}^{C_V/R} \cdot V_4$  $[124]$

The two formulas in this equation are divided by each other:

$$\frac{V_2}{V_1} = \frac{V_3}{V_4} \qquad [125]$$

Substituting Eq. [125] in Eq. [123] yields for the total work per full cycle of the Carnot process:

$$W_{total} = -R(T_{high} - T_{low})\ln\left(\frac{V_2}{V_1}\right) \quad [126]$$

Next, we determine the heat exchange with the heat reservoirs using Table 7.2:

$$\sum_{i=1}^{4} Q_i = Q_{high} + Q_{low} = -W_1 - W_3 = -W_{total}$$

$$[127]$$

From the two results in Eqs. [126] and [127], the total change of internal energy for the Carnot cycle is calculated:

$$\sum_{i=1}^{4} \Delta U_i = 0 \qquad [128]$$

This result is not surprising, since the gas returns to its initial state after each cycle of the Carnot process. The internal energy describes that state, and thus must have the same value whenever the gas returns to this state. Comparing Eqs. [126], [127], and [128], we note once more the difference between a variable of state, such as the internal energy $U$, and quantities that depend on the history of the system, such as work $W$ and heat $Q$: only the variable of state returns to its original value after completion of a cyclic process.

*Summary: Carnot process per cycle with an ideal gas:*

$$W = -R(T_{high} - T_{low})\ln\left(\frac{V_2}{V_1}\right)$$
$$Q = -W \qquad [129]$$
$$\Delta U = 0$$

A second, more applied way to characterize cyclic processes is based on the introduction of an efficiency coefficient. The motivation stems from an economic interpretation of the Carnot process: the heat input in step I represents an investment, while the total work output represents a gain. Thus, we define the **efficiency coefficient** $\eta$ for a cyclic process as the ratio of the net work to the heat input per cycle, with the heat input given by the heat that is taken up by the system from the high-temperature heat reservoir:

$$\eta = \frac{|\text{net work}|}{\text{heat input}} = \frac{|W_1 + W_3|}{Q_{high}} \qquad [130]$$

The work and heat terms in this equation can be substituted from Table 7.2:

$$\eta = \frac{T_{high} - T_{low}}{T_{high}} \qquad [131]$$

Thus, the efficiency coefficient $\eta$ is always smaller than unity because it is technically and conceptually impossible to operate a cycle with the low-temperature heat reservoir at $T_{low} = 0$ K. The work obtained from a Carnot process never matches the energy invested into the system in the form of heat. The work obtained from a Carnot cycle is the maximum work we can extract from any cyclic process. Real cyclic processes are never as ideal as the Carnot process; i.e., the net work is always less than the net work calculated for the Carnot process.

The efficiency coefficient satisfies the interest of engineers in determining the cost efficiency of engines. For example, a 19th-century steam engine operated with steam at 120°C and its cooling water at 20°C. Thus, the maximum efficiency coefficient predicted by Eq. [131] is:

$$\eta = \frac{(393 \text{ K}) - (293 \text{ K})}{393 \text{ K}} = 0.25 \qquad [132]$$

i.e., the efficiency coefficient is 25%. At that time, no actual steam engine had an efficiency coefficient exceeding 10%! Natural cyclic processes, such as the ATP recycling in the mitochondria, come close to the efficiency of the Carnot process as written in Eq. [130]—man-made processes usually fall significantly short.

## Respiration Cycle

We need a model for the thorax/lungs system to study respiration as a cyclic process. This model has to be consistent with the $p$–$V$ diagrams we introduced in Figs. 7.6, 7.7, and 7.8 at the beginning of the chapter.

The best way to introduce this model is to look at the anatomical sketch of the thorax/lungs system in Fig. 7.5 and establish the important components in steps. We begin with the lungs. The figure indicates that no active muscle forces act directly on the lungs. The only direct interaction occurs with the air inside at pressure $p_{alveoli}$ and with the pleura at pressure $p_{pleura}$. Recall from our discussion at the beginning of this chapter that $p_{alveoli}$ and $p_{pleura}$ are gauge pressures, i.e., pressure values relative to atmospheric pressure. The suitable physical model we develop for the lungs is shown in the three parts of Fig. 7.37.

### FIG. 7.37(a): THE LUNGS AS A BALLOON WITH A PISTON

In the figure, the lungs are modelled by a balloon with a flexible outer membrane. The balloon has an internal pressure $p_{alveoli}$ and an absolute outside pressure of atmospheric pressure. For such a balloon to remain inflated we require $p_{alveoli} > 0$. A piston is attached to the balloon, which allows us to vary an external force $F_{ext,1}$, which enables us in turn to vary $p_{alveoli}$. From our experience in inflating children's balloons we know that the volume of the balloon increases with $p_{alveoli}$ and that larger and larger pressure increases are needed to achieve a given size increase as the balloon becomes bigger. This observation matches with the curve labelled $p_{alveoli} - p_{pleura}$ in Fig. 7.6, which is the transmural pressure difference from lungs to pleura, but it is not consistent with the

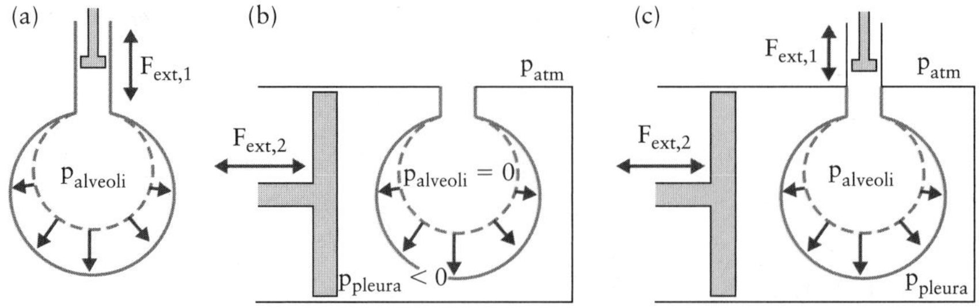

**FIGURE 7.37**

Three models used in the description of the respiratory system. (a) The lungs are represented by a balloon. The gas pressure in the balloon is varied by a piston (subscript 1). We define the gas pressure in the balloon as a gauge pressure (alveolar pressure $p_{\text{alveoli}}$). A pressure increase in the balloon causes an increase of its volume. Note that the pressure surrounding the balloon is atmospheric pressure. (b) The pleural gap is represented by a container that encloses the balloon. The balloon is open to the external atmospheric pressure. The container allows us to control the pressure surrounding the balloon (using the piston with subscript 2). The pressure surrounding the lungs is a gauge pressure, the pleural pressure $p_{\text{pleura}}$. (c) In the last model two pistons are introduced, one to control the alveolar pressure and one to control the pleural pressure.

curve labelled $p_{\text{alveoli}}$ in that figure. Thus, Fig. 7.37(a) is not a useful model for the lungs. Missing in the model is the pleura and the fact that the pleural pressure can differ from atmospheric pressure; i.e., $p_{\text{pleura}} \neq 0$ is possible.

## FIG. 7.37(b): THE PLEURA AS A CONTAINER WITH PISTON SURROUNDING THE LUNGS

To improve the proposed model, the pleura is added as a container that encloses the balloon. This container is sealed by a second piston (shown at the left), with which we can exert a second external force, $F_{\text{ext},2}$. Varying the piston's position allows us to change $p_{\text{pleura}}$. In this first extension of our original model the first piston has been removed and the balloon is open to the outside air. This means that $p_{\text{alveoli}} = 0$, and the balloon can be inflated only when $p_{\text{pleura}} < 0$.

Comparing Fig. 7.37(a) and 7.37(b) illustrates that it is neither one of the absolute pressures nor one of the gauge pressures that ultimately matters for the volume of the balloon: when we increase $p_{\text{alveoli}}$ in Fig. 7.37(a) and decrease $p_{\text{pleura}}$ in Fig. 7.37(b) such that the balloon has the same volume in both cases, we find $+p_{\text{alveoli}}$ in part (a) equals $-p_{\text{pleura}}$ in part (b). Thus, the volume of the balloon depends on the pressure difference across the balloon's membrane. Note that this pressure difference is not a gauge pressure, as we will see when discussing the model in Fig. 7.37(c), where both $p_{\text{alveoli}} \neq 0$ and $p_{\text{pleura}} \neq 0$.

## FIG. 7.37(c): CONTAINER AND ENCLOSED BALLOON ARE SEALED BY A PISTON

This model for the lung/pleura system is slightly more complex. The additional complexity comes from varying both $p_{\text{alveoli}}$ and $p_{\text{pleura}}$, which is possible because the model has two pistons, one attached to

the balloon to exert the force $F_{\text{ext},1}$ and one attached to the container surrounding the balloon to exert the force $F_{\text{ext},2}$. It is important to introduce this model because we need both pistons when describing the various curves in Figs. 7.6, 7.7, and 7.8: the model in Fig. 7.37(c) is used to characterize static properties of the respiratory system, i.e., when the test person is asked to inhale or exhale a certain amount of air, then stop (mouthpiece valve closed to spirometer) and relax the breathing muscles. The model in Fig. 7.37(b) in turn is used when studying very slow (air flow resistance–free) breathing with an open mouth. The open mouth guarantees that the pressure in the lungs is always equal to atmospheric pressure.

We first discuss in detail how the model in Fig. 7.37(c) explains the data shown in Fig. 7.6. The force $F_{\text{ext},1}$ is required to obtain $p_{\text{alveoli}} \neq 0$. The force $F_{\text{ext},1}$ can be exerted by two sources: (i) the streaming of air in or out of the lungs, and (ii) the propensity toward elastic collapse of the balloon-like lungs. When neither of these sources acts on the system, e.g., when you open your mouth and relax, then $p_{\text{alveoli}} = 0$ and the respiratory system is in mechanical equilibrium. In a simple self-experiment you can confirm that this state is reached after regular exhalation at a lung volume of 3.0 L: concentrate on your chest as you breathe very slowly. Hold your breath after a regular inhalation and after a regular exhalation. You notice that you are most relaxed after exhalation because the forces on the lungs are balanced and do not need support through muscle action.

The air flow–related force contribution to $F_{\text{ext},1}$ is excluded in Fig. 7.6 because this p–V diagram represents a static view of the respiratory system. Indeed, air flow–related issues enter the discussion only when we discuss Fig. 7.8. This leaves the elastic force of the lungs—i.e., their propensity toward an elastic collapse—as the only force contributing to $F_{ext,1}$ in Fig. 7.6.

The force $F_{ext,2}$ is needed to allow variations of the pleural pressure, i.e., $p_{pleura} \neq 0$ for the pressure in the container surrounding the balloon. Again, two different sources can provide this force: (i) the active muscle forces exerted by the diaphragm and the intercostal muscles between the ribs, and (ii) the elastic propensity of the thorax to collapse (outward toward the rib cage).

The active muscle forces are not included in the force $F_{ext,2}$ in Fig. 7.6 because the curves in that p–V diagram are drawn for a relaxed chest. Thus, the piston exerting the force $F_{ext,2}$ in Fig. 7.6 addresses the tendency of the thorax to change toward its elastic equilibrium position. We conclude that both pistons in Fig. 7.37(c) model elastic forces when interpreting Fig. 7.6: one associated with the propensity toward elastic collapse of the balloon-like lungs, and the other associated with the propensity of the thorax to move toward its equilibrium position. For the healthy person, these two forces are not independent because a fixed amount of fluid in the pleural gap provides for a strong adhesion between the visceral layer of the pleura on the lung surface and the parietal layer on the inside of the thorax. We can observe the action of both elastic forces independently for a patient with a punctured pleura. The injury allows air to enter the gap between lungs and thorax, and each relaxes to its equilibrium shape at zero gauge pressures $p_{alveoli}$ and $p_{pleura}$ (along the dashed horizontal line in Fig. 7.6): the lungs collapse to a minimum volume of less than 1.0 L and the thorax widens to a size corresponding to a 4.5-L capacity of the lungs.

For the healthy person, the curve labelled $p_{alveoli} - p_{pleura}$ in Fig. 7.6 indicates the elastic response of the lungs to the transmural pressure difference; this pressure difference is always positive since otherwise the lungs could not stay inflated. In the range of normal breathing (breathing of the tidal volume between lung capacities of 3.0 L and 3.5 L) the transmural pressure difference varies between 500 Pa and 600 Pa. For lung volumes above 3.0 L, $p_{alveoli}$ is positive; i.e., upon opening the mouth air will stream out of the lungs. In turn, for lung volumes below 3.0 L (after a deep exhalation), $p_{alveoli}$ is negative; i.e., opening the mouth will cause air to stream into the lungs.

The pleural pressure $p_{pleura}$ always lies below the alveolar pressure $p_{alveoli}$, but crosses from negative to positive values at about 4.5-L lung capacity. At that point, the direction of stress in the thorax is inverted: for smaller volumes the thorax wants to expand, and for larger volumes it wants to contract. This is the reason why it is particularly hard for a test person to hold more than 4.5 L of air in the lungs.

In the next step toward understanding the actual processes during breathing we evaluate the p–V diagram in Fig. 7.7, for which the model in Fig. 7.37(b) applies. Note that the piston allowing for the force $F_{ext,1}$ is not present in that figure. Instead, the balloon-like lungs are open to the external air pressure and $p_{alveoli} = 0$ at all lung volumes. We still neglect effects due to air flow resistance, for which the second piston would be required. In Fig. 7.37(b) the pressure $p_{pleura}$ can still vary; the pleural pressure is changing now due to the action of both possible forces: the active muscle forces and the elastic force of the thorax. The need for an active muscle force is evident from Fig. 7.6: if $p_{alveoli} = 0$ and $p_{pleura}$ were adjusted only by elastic forces in the thorax, then the only possible lung volume would be $V = 3.0$ L. However, we cannot breathe at a fixed lung volume. Thus, an active mechanism to vary the lung volume is required.

Breathing is modelled in Fig. 7.37(b) by the back-and-forth motion of the piston. During that motion the gauge pressure $p_{pleura}$ changes and with it the pressure difference $p_{alveoli} - p_{pleura} = -p_{pleura}$ (because $p_{alveoli} = 0$). The variation of these pressure values corresponds to different lung volume values in Fig. 7.7. We decrease the pleural pressure during very slow inhalation by expanding the thorax because the lungs expand faster. The effect is reversed during slow exhalation.

Note that the curve of the lung volume versus the pressure difference $p_{alveoli} - p_{pleura}$ is the same in Figs. 7.6 and 7.7: the volume of the lungs depends exclusively on the transmural pressure difference, as we have already concluded from comparing Figs. 7.37(a) and 7.37(b).

We want to calculate the work done during very slow breathing using the p–V diagram in Fig. 7.7. We do this in the form of an example.

## ● EXAMPLE 7.11

Calculate the work for very slow breathing from the p–V diagram in Fig. 7.7 for (a) a single inhalation, (b) a single exhalation, and (c) a full breathing cycle. (d) The work done by muscles during breathing at rest is reported as 0.7 J/s in the physiological literature. How do you explain your results in parts (a) and (c) when compared with this value? *Hint:* To simplify the calculations, approximate the pleural pressure curve in Fig. 7.7 as a straight line. This is shown in Fig. 7.38.

● **EXAMPLE 7.11** (*continued*)

(a)

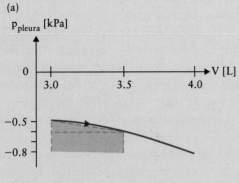

(b)

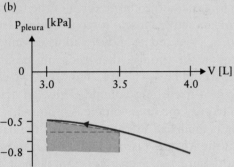

**FIGURE 7.38**

Geometric sketch of the area under the pleural pressure curve representing slow breathing between lung volumes of 3.0 L and 3.5 L (taken from Fig. 7.7).

*Solution to part (a):* We calculate the work required from the curve $p_{pleura}$ versus lung volume in Fig. 7.7 because the active muscles act on the pleura and therefore most directly affect the pleural pressure. Fig. 7.38(a) shows the curve $p_{pleura}$ versus lung volume for slow inhalation. Recall that the tidal volume is 0.5 L; i.e., a resting person inhales from a lung volume of $V_{exhaled} = 3.0$ L to a lung volume of $V_{inhaled} = 3.5$ L. Thus, the work required is the area under the curve between $V_{exhaled}$ and $V_{inhaled}$. This area is grey in Fig. 7.38(a).

The area under the curve in Fig. 7.38(a) is divided into two parts: a triangle and a rectangle located below the triangle. The rectangle must be included because the work calculation requires the area under the curve down to absolute pressure zero. The area of the triangle is:

$$A_\triangle = \frac{1}{2}(0.5\,\text{L})(0.1\,\text{kPa}) = 0.025\,\text{J} \qquad [133]$$

To calculate the area of the rectangle, the absolute pressure at the horizontal dashed line is needed:

$$p_{pleura,\text{top of }\square} = p_{atm} - 0.6\,\text{kPa}$$
$$= 1.013 \times 10^5\,\text{Pa} - 0.6 \times 10^3\,\text{Pa}$$
$$= 1.007 \times 10^5\,\text{Pa}$$
$$[134]$$

Thus, the rectangular area is:

$$A_\square = (0.5\,\text{L})(1.007 \times 10^5\,\text{Pa}) = 50.35\,\text{J}$$
$$[135]$$

The work per inhalation is the sum of these two areas: $W_{inhale} = -50.375$ J.

The negative sign brings us back to the question of what we identify as the system and what we identify as the environment. Naively, we would have argued that the gas in the lungs is the system, as this gas expands from $V_{exhaled}$ to $V_{inhaled}$. However, the gas in the lungs does not do the work we calculated. The only way the gas could do the work would be at the expense of its internal energy or at the expense of energy the gas absorbs from its environment. But neither of these processes occurs in the lungs, as we discussed earlier in this chapter. Instead, as suggested in Fig. 7.37(b), the work originates in the muscles acting on the pleura. Thus, the environment receiving the work consists of the elastic tissues of the pleura and the lungs; the work is done by the active muscles (on behalf of the gas in the lungs). We will discuss this process in further detail in part (d).

*Solution to part (b):* Next we calculate the work associated with a single exhalation, as illustrated in Fig. 7.38(b). This figure again shows the curve $p_{pleura}$ versus lung volume, with the work we want to calculate highlighted as the grey area under the curve between $V_{exhaled}$ and $V_{inhaled}$. The area under the curve in Fig. 7.38(b) is the same as in Fig. 7.38(a): the work per exhalation is $W_{exhale} = +50.375$ J. This value is positive because work is done on the system by its environment. Based on the same arguments we used in part (a), this result is interpreted in the following way: the work $W_{exhale}$ originates from the elastic tissues of the pleura and the lungs; this work is done on the gas and the active muscles.

*Solution to part (c):* The work for a full breathing cycle is the sum of the work for a single inhalation and the work for a single exhalation. Using the two values we found in parts (a) and (b), we determine that:

$$W_{cycle} = -50.375\,\text{J} + 50.375\,\text{J} = 0\,\text{J} \qquad [136]$$

No net work has been done per cycle. From experience we know that this is not true; as the question in part (d) states, work is required during breathing. Thus, the assumptions we made to find the result in Eq. [136] must be revisited. We will do this by studying Fig. 7.8 in greater detail in Example 7.12. That figure then applies to actual breathing as opposed to very slow breathing, which is an assumption that obviously oversimplifies the issue.

*Solution to part (d):* Before we turn our attention to the actual breathing process, we can still learn more from the current example. In this example we assumed idealized, very slow breathing. For this we found in part (a) that the initial inhalation requires an effort that we quantified as slightly more than $-50$ J of work. Then we determined that the same amount of work is recovered during the subsequent exhalation, leading to no net effort for the entire cycle. This can be true only if the work done during the inhalation is indeed recovered by the system that did the work in the first step. Otherwise, per breathing cycle, work equivalent of 50 J has to be done and 50 J of energy would then be dissipated during the exhalation, leading to a net total work of $-50$ J per cycle.

To clarify this issue, we begin with the actual, experimental value of the work done by the breathing muscles. This value is stated in the example text. Using 15 breathing cycles per minute for a resting person, 0.7 J/s corresponds to:

$$W_{cycle} = \frac{\left(0.7 \, \dfrac{J}{s}\right)\left(60 \, \dfrac{s}{min}\right)}{15 \, \dfrac{cycles}{min}}$$

$$= 2.8 \, \frac{J}{cycle} \qquad [137]$$

This is only about 5% of the work we calculated as required for a single inhalation. Thus, in real breathing our muscles need to do only a small fraction of the work that has to be done during an inhalation. Consequently, something else must be doing the lion's share of that work. But what is that? Remember that we already ruled out the gas in the lungs.

The answer for the inhalation is the same as for the exhalation: the work is provided by the elastic action of stretched tissue, the lungs expanding and collapsing inside the pleura leading to an opposite collapsing and expanding of the pleural tissue. Recall that the dashed horizontal line in Fig. 7.6 indicates the response of pleura and lungs when the lungs are punctured: both tissues collapse, the lungs to a small volume and the pleura outward. Thus, both tissues are stretched in opposite

directions. During inhalation the lungs expand and the pleura partially collapses. Then, during the following exhalation, the lungs partially collapse and the pleura expands. Thus, elastic energy is shifting back and forth between the lung tissue and the pleura tissue; only a small fraction of the work has to be done by the breathing muscles, accounting for energy losses during the energy transfer between lung tissue and pleural tissue.

Lastly, we study Fig. 7.8, for which we use the model shown in Fig. 7.37(c). The larger piston allows us to vary the pressure in the pleura surrounding the lungs, and the smaller piston allows us to vary the pressure inside the lungs. We need both abilities: the processes we just discussed for slow breathing continue to dominate the regular breathing process, including the alternating expansion and collapse of lungs and pleura to conserve the elastic energy. In addition, we need to account for the observation that air has to be pulled actively through the trachea into the lungs during inhalation, and that air has to be pushed actively out of the lungs during exhalation. The small piston in Fig. 7.37(c) allows for this to occur: during inhalation the pressure in the lungs is lowered by up to 100 Pa, and during exhalation the pressure in the lungs is increased by up to 100 Pa. This is illustrated in Fig. 7.9. These pressure differences have to be added to the slow breathing that we assumed in Fig. 7.7. Affected are only the pleural pressure and the pressure in the lungs; the transmural pressure remains unchanged because that pressure difference exclusively governs the size (volume) of the lungs. From Fig. 7.8 the fraction of work associated with the flow resistance of air in the trachea can be calculated for a full breathing cycle. This is shown in the example below.

### ● EXAMPLE 7.12

Calculate the work for a regular breathing cycle due to the air resistance during breathing. *Hint:* This work is given as the difference in work calculated for Figs. 7.7 and 7.8. To simplify the calculation, estimate this work from the four grey triangles illustrated in Fig. 7.39.

*Solution:* In the first step, the combined area of the four triangles in Fig. 7.39 is determined. Note that these triangles are identical, with each displaying a base of 0.25 L (e.g., the top left triangle has a base stretching from 3.0 L to 3.25 L), and

● EXAMPLE 7.12 (*continued*)

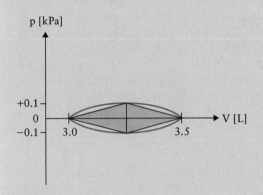

**FIGURE 7.39**
Geometric sketch of the area enclosed by the alveolar pressure (green line) during a tidal breathing cycle (compare Fig. 7.8).

a height of 0.1 kPa. Thus, their combined area is four times the area of each triangle:

$$A_{total} = 4 \cdot \frac{1}{2}(0.25 \text{ L})(0.1 \text{ kPa}) = 0.05 \text{ J} \quad [138]$$

The work in the cyclic process is positive; i.e., $W_{cycle} = +0.05$ J. Work has been done on the gas. This work is included in the work we calculated from experimental data in Eq. [137]. We note that less than 2% of the respiratory work is required for forcing the air into and out of the lungs; the flow resistance of the gas is comparably small. A fish requires much more work to obtain the required flow of water through its gills, because water is liquid and therefore has a much greater flow resistance than air.

# MULTIPLE CHOICE AND CONCEPTUAL QUESTIONS

## IDEAL GAS

**Q-7.1.** In Boyle's experiment, the volume of the sealed gas decreases as additional mercury is added to the open column. This effect is due to the fact that: (A) the volume of the gas decreases; (B) pressure and volume are linearly proportional to each other; (C) pressure and volume are proportional to each other; (D) pressure and volume are inversely proportional to each other; (E) pressure and volume are unrelated.

**Q-7.2.** Charles's law can be written as $V/T = \text{const}$ if (A) $V$ is reported in non-standard unit cm³; (B) $T$ is reported in non-standard unit degrees Celsius (°C); (C) the pressure varies moderately; (D) the gas is a noble gas; (E) none of the above.

**Q-7.3.** We study the ideal gas equation. The gas constant can be given in different units; however, this unit is wrong: (A) J/(K · mol), (B) (atm · m³)/(K · mol), (C) (Pa · cm²)/(K · mol), (D) cal/(K · mol), (E) none of the above; all are suitable for the gas constant $R$.

**Q-7.4.** Evaluate the following four statements about an ideal gas in a closed container ($n = \text{const}$): (i) if the pressure doubles during an isothermal compression, the volume doubles as well; (ii) if the pressure and the volume of the gas double, the temperature of the gas must increase; (iii) if the volume doubles during an isobaric expansion, the temperature stays un-

changed; (iv) if the temperature doubles, at least one of the parameters volume and pressure must increase. Which combination of these statements is correct: (A) i and ii, (B) i and iv, (C) ii and iii, (D) ii and iv, (E) iii and iv?

**Q-7.5.** When food has been cooked in a pressure cooker it is very important to cool the container with cold water before removing the lid. Why?

**Q-7.6.** Small air bubbles trapped between two sheets of plastic are often used to cushion breakable goods for shipping. Is this protection more effective on a warm or a cold day?

**Q-7.7.** Organisms in the deep sea are subjected to very high pressures, as we will discuss in the context of Pascal's law in Chapter 11. Why are these organisms destroyed when they are pulled up to the surface? *Note:* An animal living at those depths is the giant squid. Nobody has yet seen a live specimen of this species!

**Q-7.8.** Two identical cylinders at the same temperature contain the same gas. If cylinder A contains three times as much gas as cylinder B, what are the relative pressures of the two cylinders?

## KINETIC GAS THEORY

**Q-7.9.** In the kinetic gas theory developed by Boltzmann, Maxwell, and Clausius, which of the following is a result, not an assumption made to develop the model? (A) The gas consists of a very big number of particles with a combined volume that is negligible compared to the size of the container. (B) The internal energy of an ideal gas depends linearly on the temperature (in degrees Kelvin). (C) The molecule size is much smaller than the inter-particle distance. (D) The molecules are in continuous random motion, travelling along straight lines while not colliding with other particles or the walls. (E) Collisions with each other and the walls of the box are elastic, which excludes intermolecular interactions.

**Q–7.10.** One mol of hydrogen gas, which we treat as an ideal gas of molecular mass $M = 2$ g/mol, is held at 50°C. Which of the following values is closest to the root-mean-square speed of the molecules in this gas? (A) 2007 m/s, (B) 63.5 m/s, (C) 4 028 100 m/s, (D) 790 m/s, (E) 25.0 m/s.

**Q–7.11.** Which of the following statements about the temperature of a system is *not* correct? (A) The temperature of a single gas particle is determined by its velocity. (B) The temperature measurement in Fig. 6.32 is correct during the transition from liquid water to water vapour because the continuous addition of heat does not lead to a temperature change. (C) Temperature is a parameter that characterizes a system only when the system is in thermal equilibrium. (D) The temperature measurement with a Celsius thermometer is correct only when the expanding liquid in the thermometer and the system have the same temperature. (E) The temperature of the human body is usually higher than the air temperature in the immediate environment. Therefore, the human body and the surrounding air are not in thermal equilibrium.

**Q–7.12.** The Maxwell–Boltzmann velocity distribution of an ideal gas in thermal equilibrium does *not* allow us to predict the following property: (A) the temperature of the gas; (B) the root-mean-square speed of the gas molecules; (C) the most common speed of gas molecules in the gas; (D) the speed of a single gas particle we let escape from the gas container.

**Q–7.13.** Why is heat required to boil a liquid even though the molecules in the liquid and the vapour share the same temperature?

**Q–7.14.** The molar mass of He is $4 \times 10^{-3}$ kg/mol and for water it is $18 \times 10^{-3}$ kg/mol. What is the approximate ratio of the root-mean-square speed of He to that of water-vapour molecules at room temperature? (A) 2 : 1, (B) 1 : 2, (C) 4.5 : 1, (D) 1 : 4.5, (E) none of these.

**Q–7.15.** Which of the following assumptions is *not* made in developing the kinetic gas theory? (A) The number of molecules is small. (B) The molecules obey Newton's law of motion. (C) Collisions between molecules are elastic. (D) The gas is a pure substance, not a mixture. (E) The average separation between molecules is large compared to their size.

**Q–7.16.** Suppose that at some given instant molecules hitting a container wall from inside collide not elastically but perfectly inelastically with the wall. How would the pressure change at that instant (and for a brief time afterward)? (A) The pressure would be zero. (B) The pressure would be halved. (C) The pressure would be unchanged. (D) The pressure would be doubled.

**Q–7.17.** Small planets like Mercury and Mars have very thin or no atmospheres. Why?

**Q–7.18.** Although the average speed of gas molecules in thermal equilibrium at a given temperature is always greater than zero, the average velocity is zero. Why?

**Q–7.19.** One container is filled with helium gas, another with argon gas. If both containers are at the same temperature, which molecules have the higher root-mean-square speed?

## INTERNAL ENERGY OF GASES

**Q–7.20.** If a gas has an internal energy $U = 0$ J, we conclude: (A) None of the particles in the gas moves faster than the speed of sound; (B) The kinetic energy of all gas particles is proportional to their root-mean-square speed; (C) The temperature of the gas is 0 K; (D) The kinetic energy per particle is $\frac{3}{2}k \cdot T$; (E) The gas cannot be heated.

**Q–7.21.** A standard man inhales a tidal volume of air at 20°C. When the air arrives in the lungs, it has a temperature of 37°C. Treating air as an ideal gas, the change in internal energy is: (A) $\Delta U = 0$ J; (B) about an 85% increase over the initial value; (C) about a 5% increase over the initial value; (D) unknown, because the amount of air is not specified; (E) proportional to the change in the pressure of the air.

**Q–7.22.** We study 10 mol of an ideal gas at $-10$°C. The internal energy of that gas is (choose the value closest to the true value): (A) $U < 0$ J; (B) U = 0 J; (C) $0$ J $< U < 1$ kJ; (D) 1 kJ $< U < 100$ kJ; (E) $U >$ 100 kJ.

**Q–7.23.** Fig. 6.21 shows a $p–V$ diagram with three paths that a gas can take from an initial to a final state. Rank the paths in decreasing order according to (a) the change of internal energy $\Delta U$, and (b) the amount of heat transfer $Q$ between the system and the environment.

## THERMODYNAMIC PROCESSES

**Q–7.24.** We study the process shown in Fig. 7.40, which is a plot of pressure versus temperature following the relation $p \propto T$. Which of the following five statements is true? (A) The process in Fig. 7.40 is an isobaric compression of an ideal gas. (B) The process in Fig. 7.40 is an isothermal expansion of an ideal gas. (C) The process in Fig. 7.40 is an isobaric expansion of an ideal gas. (D) The process in Fig. 7.40 is an isothermal compression of an ideal gas. (E) The ideal gas must be heated during the process shown in Fig. 7.40.

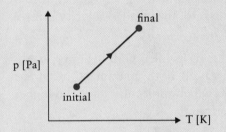

**FIGURE 7.40**

Graph of the pressure versus the temperature for a gas that follows the relation $p \propto T$.

**Q–7.25.** We plot the following processes for 1 mol of an ideal gas in a $p$–$V$ diagram. Which one leads to a linear plot, i.e., a plot that can be described by the linear formula $p = a + b \cdot V$? (A) an isothermal expansion, (B) an isobaric heating, (C) an adiabatic cooling.

**Q–7.26.** In which of the following processes does the volume of the system not change? (A) isothermal expansion, (B) isothermal compression, (C) isobaric heating, (D) isobaric cooling, (E) isochoric heating.

**Q–7.27.** A process is an isochoric process when: (A) the temperature remains constant and the pressure changes; (B) no work is done; (C) no heat is exchanged with the environment; (D) the internal energy remains constant; (E) the pressure remains constant and the temperature changes.

**Q–7.28.** We consider 1 mol of an ideal gas under isothermal conditions. If the pressure is doubled, (A) the volume remains unchanged; (B) the volume doubles as well; (C) the volume is halved; (D) the

volume increases by a factor of 4; (E) the volume decreases to 25% of its original value.

**Q–7.29.** A process is called adiabatic if: (A) the temperature remains constant; (B) no work is done; (C) no heat is exchanged with the environment; (D) the internal energy remains constant; (E) the volume remains constant.

**Q–7.30.** The internal energy of an ideal gas in an isothermal process does not change. Assume that the gas does work $W$ during this process. How much energy was transferred as heat?

**Q–7.31.** A standard man performs a strenuous exercise, e.g., lifting a weight or riding a bicycle. The standard man does work in this exercise and dissipates heat. Would the first law of thermodynamics not require that the internal energy, and therefore the temperature, of the standard man decrease?

**Q–7.32.** (a) If a process starts at pressure $p_0$ and volume $V_0$ and leads to a doubling of the volume, which of the following processes involves the most work: (A) an adiabatic process, (B) an isothermal process, (C) an isobaric process, (D) no answer is always correct. (b) Why would the choice "isochoric process" make no sense if offered as an answer?

**Q–7.33.** 2.0 mol of an ideal gas is maintained at constant volume in a container of 4 L. If 100 J of heat is added to the gas, what is the change in its internal energy? (A) zero, (B) 50 J, (C) 67 J, (D) 100 J, (E) none of these values is correct.

## LIFE SCIENCES APPLICATIONS

**Q–7.34.** Fig. 7.41 (heart cycle) shows the $p$–$V$ relationship in the left ventricle of the human heart. The curve is traversed counter-clockwise with increasing time. The stroke volume is 100 mL − 35 mL = 65 mL. The systolic pressure is 118 torr (equal to 15.7 kPa) and the diastolic pressure is 70 torr (equal to 9.3 kPa). The ventricular pressure drops below the diastolic pressure, while the pressure in the arteries remains about 70 torr because the aortic valve has closed and prevents backflow. To simplify calculations the dashed straight lines in the diagram allow us to replace the curved segments. Which of the following statements about the $p$–$V$ diagram in Fig. 7.41 is correct? (A) The diagram shows the data in standard units. (B) The maximum pressure variation during the heart cycle exceeds the atmospheric pressure value. (C) The work done in a single cycle can be

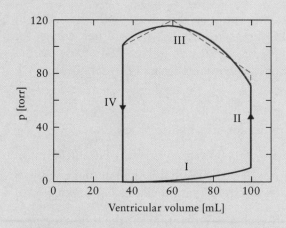

**FIGURE 7.41**

*p–V* diagram for the left ventricle of the human heart. The blood pressure initially increases slowly as blood flows into the ventricle from the left atrium (through the mitral valve, step I), but then jumps to about 75 torr during the contraction of the heart muscle (step II). This pressure causes the aortic valve to open. The blood pressure continues to rise, but the volume of the ventricular chamber decreases concurrently as blood is ejected from the heart (step III). The aortic valve closes when the muscle contraction is complete, leaving the ventricle at a fixed volume of 35 mL during step IV, until the mitral valve opens again for the next filling step.

determined from the area enclosed by the solid line in Fig. 7.41. (D) The system is the blood in the ventricle. This system is an isolated system.

**Q–7.35.** We consider one breathing cycle, starting with an inhalation and then followed by an exhalation. The net work for such a cycle is (A) positive ($W > 0$), (B) zero ($W = 0$), or (C) negative ($W < 0$). *Note:* The gas in the lungs is the system.

**Q–7.36.** A child wants to pretend to have a fever. The child notices that air breathed onto an arm feels warmer than the arm itself and reasons that breathing on a thermometer should effectively drive up the mercury column. Will this trick deceive the parents?

**Q–7.37.** (a) We consider 1.0 litre of an ideal gas at STPD conditions. Describe a state into which this gas cannot be transferred. (b) If you still need an ideal gas at the conditions you have chosen in part (a), how can you get it?

# ANALYTICAL PROBLEMS

## IDEAL GAS AND KINETIC GAS THEORY

**P–7.1.** (a) Draw a graph for the volume of 1.0 mol of an ideal gas as a function of temperature in the range from 0 K to 400 K at constant gas pressures of, first, 0.2 atm and, second, 5 atm. (b) Draw a graph for the pressure of 1.0 mol of an ideal gas as a function of volume between 0 L and 20 L at constant temperatures of 150 K and 300 K.

**P–7.2.** A container of volume $V = 10.0$ cm$^3$ is initially filled with air. The container is then evacuated at 20°C to a pressure of $5.0 \times 10^{-6}$ mmHg. How many molecules are in the container after evacuation if we assume that air is an ideal gas?

**P–7.3.** A container of volume $V = 400$ cm$^3$ has a mass of 244.5500 g when evacuated. When the container is filled with air of pressure $p = 1$ atm at temperature $T = 20°C$, the mass of the system increases to 245.0307 g. Assuming that air behaves like an ideal gas, calculate from these data the average molar mass of air.

**P–7.4.** 1.0 mol oxygen gas is initially at a pressure of 6.0 atm and a temperature of 300 K. (a) If the gas is heated at constant volume until the pressure has

tripled, what is the final temperature? (b) If the gas is heated such that both pressure and volume are doubled, what is the final temperature?

**P–7.5.** The pressure of an ideal gas is reduced by 50%, resulting in a decrease in temperature to 75% of the initial value. Calculate the ratio of final to initial volumes of the gas.

**P–7.6.** In the set-up shown in Fig. 7.23, the ideal gas is initially at temperature 300 K, volume 1.5 m$^3$, and pressure $2.0 \times 10^4$ Pa. What is its final temperature if it is compressed to a volume of 0.7 m$^3$ and the final pressure is $8.0 \times 10^4$ Pa?

**P–7.7.** An ideal gas is confined in a container at a pressure of 10.0 atm and at a temperature of 15°C. If 50% of the gas leaks from the container and the temperature of the remaining gas rises to 65°C, what is the final pressure in the container?

**P–7.8.** In a container of fixed volume is 0.4 mol of oxygen gas, which we treat as an ideal gas. Determine the mass of gas in unit kg that must be withdrawn in an isothermal fashion from the container to lower the pressure from 40 atm to 25 atm.

**P–7.9.** A spherical weather balloon is designed to inflate to a maximum diameter of 40 m at its working altitude, where the air pressure is 0.3 atm and the temperature is 200 K. If the balloon is filled at atmospheric pressure and temperature 300 K, what is its radius at lift-off? Treat the gas as an ideal gas.

**P–7.10.** Use Avogadro's number to find the mass of a helium atom.

**P–7.11.** The temperature in the upper regions of the atmosphere of Venus is 240 K. (a) Find the root-mean-square speed of hydrogen molecules ($H_2$) and carbon dioxide ($CO_2$) in that region. (b) A result of planetary science is that a gas eventually is lost from a planet's atmosphere into outer space if its root-mean-square is one-sixth of the escape velocity, which can be calculated from gravity. Using an escape velocity of 10.3 km/s for Venus, does either of the two gases in part (a) escape from that planet?

**P–7.12.** A 10.0-L container holds $2.0 \times 10^{23}$ oxygen gas molecules ($O_2$). If the pressure of the gas is 300 mmHg, what is (a) the temperature, and (b) the root-mean-square speed of the molecules? *Hint:* Treat oxygen as an ideal gas with a molecular mass of $M(O_2) = 32.0$ g/mol.

## THERMODYNAMIC PROCESSES

**P–7.13.** 1.0 mol of an ideal gas isothermally expands from an initial pressure of 20 atm to a final pressure of 5 atm. Calculate separately for two temperatures, 0°C and 25°C, (a) the work done by the gas, (b) the change of internal energy of the gas, and (c) the amount of heat taken from the environment.

**P–7.14.** (a) How much heat is needed to increase the temperature of 100 g argon gas (Ar) in a 1-m³ container from $-10$°C to $+10$°C? Treat Ar as an ideal gas and use $M(Ar) = 39.95$ g/mol. (b) By how many percent does $\langle v^2 \rangle$ of the argon atoms in the gas increase in this process? *Hint:* Part (b) does not ask for $v_{rms}$.

**P–7.15.** Show that Poisson's equation leads to $p \cdot V^\kappa = $ const when using the operations specified in the text.

**P–7.16.** 1.0 mol of an ideal gas that starts at 1.0 atm and 25°C does 1.0 kJ of work during an adiabatic expansion. (a) What is the final temperature of the gas? (b) What is the final volume of the gas?

**P–7.17.** In the text we stated that $C_p = C_V + R$ holds for an ideal gas. Derive this result for an isobaric expansion of 1.0 mol of ideal gas without using the

enthalpy concept. For this, start with the work in Eq. [102] and the change of internal energy in Eq. [76] for the expansion in Fig. 7.31. Then use the first law of thermodynamics and the definition

$$Q = n \cdot C_p \cdot \Delta T \qquad [139]$$

which applies for an isobaric process.

**P–7.18.** A container with $V = 0.4$ m³ holds 3.0 mol of argon gas at 303 K. What is the internal energy of this gas if we assume that it behaves like an ideal gas?

**P–7.19.** Sketch a $p$–$V$ diagram for the following processes: (a) An ideal gas expands at constant pressure $p_1$ from volume $V_1$ to volume $V_2$, and is then kept at constant volume while the pressure is reduced to $p_2$. (b) An ideal gas is reduced in pressure from $p_1$ to $p_2$ while its volume is held constant at $V_1$. It is then expanded at constant pressure to a final volume $V_2$. (c) In which process is more work done?

**P–7.20.** An ideal gas is in a container at pressure 1.5 atm and volume 4.0 m³. What is the work done by/on the gas if (a) it expands at constant pressure to twice its initial volume, or (b) it is compressed at constant pressure to one-quarter of its initial volume?

**P–7.21.** 1.0 mol of an ideal gas is initially at 0°C. It undergoes an isobaric expansion at $p = 1.0$ atm to four times its initial volume. (a) Calculate the final temperature of the gas, $T_{final}$. (b) Calculate the work done by/on the gas during the expansion.

**P–7.22.** An ideal gas undergoes a process in which its pressure is doubled from $p_0$ to $2 \cdot p_0$ while the volume doubles from $V_0$ to $2 \cdot V_0$. The pressure increases linearly with the volume in this process. How much heat does the gas exchange with its environment during this process?

## CYCLIC PROCESSES AND SPECIFIC LIFE SCIENCES APPLICATIONS

**P–7.23.** Compare the efficiency coefficient for a Carnot machine operating between a low-temperature heat reservoir at room temperature (25°C) and a high-temperature heat reservoir at the boiling point of water at two different pressures: (a) 5 atm with $T_{boil} = 152$°C, and (b) 100 atm with $T_{boil} = 312$°C.

**P–7.24.** A Carnot process is operated with 1.0 mol of an ideal gas of heat capacity $C_V = 3 \cdot R/2$. The pressure of the gas is 20 atm and the temperature is 500 K in the most compressed state. From there, an isothermal expansion leads to a pressure 2.0 atm.

The lower process temperature is 250 K. (a) Calculate for each step of this Carnot process the work and heat exchange with the environment. (b) What is the efficiency coefficient of this machine? (c) Draw this Carnot process as a $p$–$V$ diagram, then sketch it as a $p$–$T$ diagram, a $V$–$T$ diagram, and a $U$–$T$ diagram.

**P–7.25.** The cyclic process in Fig. 7.42 consists of (i) an isothermal expansion, (ii) an isochoric cooling, and (iii) an adiabatic compression. If the process is done with $n = 1.0$ mol of an ideal gas, what is (a) the total work done by the gas, (b) the heat exchanged with the environment, and (c) the change of the internal energy for one cycle? (d) Sketch the cyclic process of Fig. 7.42 as $p$–$T$, $V$–$T$, and $U$–$T$ diagrams.

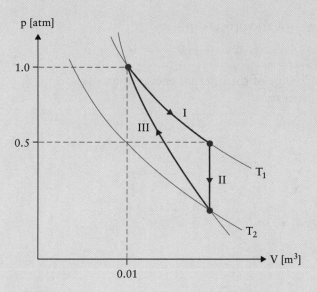

**FIGURE 7.42**

**P–7.26.** An ideal gas is taken through a cyclic process as shown in Fig. 7.43. (a) Find the net heat transferred between the system and its environment during one complete cycle. (b) What is the net heat transfer if the cycle is reversed, i.e., it follows the path ACBA?

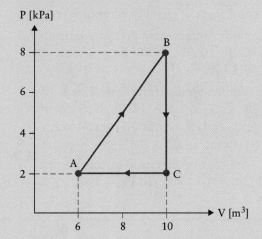

**FIGURE 7.43**

**P–7.27.** Fig. 7.41 shows the $p$–$V$ relationship in the left ventricle of the human heart. The curve is traversed counter-clockwise with increasing time. Using the stroke volume and pressure data from Q–7.34, determine graphically the amount of work done in a single cycle. *Hint:* Simplify the calculation by using the dashed straight lines in the $p$–$V$ diagram instead of curved segments.

**P–7.28.** We study a tidal volume (0.5 L) of dry air at two frequently used reference states. With index 1 we refer to the gas at STPD conditions ($p_1 = 101.3$ kPa, $T_1 = 0°C$, $V_1 = 0.5$ L), and with index 2 we refer to the gas at BTPS conditions but excluding the water-vapour component added during inhalation ($p_2 = 95.0$ kPa, $T_2 = 37°C$, $V_2 = 0.605$ L). (a) Why is $V_2$ not also given as 0.5 L? (b) We transfer the gas from state 1 to state 2. Assuming that we first adjust the pressure in an isothermal step and then the temperature in an isobaric step, what fraction of the total volume change occurs in the isothermal step? (c) Assuming that we invert the order of the two steps in part (b)—i.e., we start with an isobaric step followed by an isothermal step—is the fraction of the total volume change after the first step the same as in part (b)? (d) Can the process from STPD to BTPS conditions also be achieved with an initial isochoric step followed by an isobaric step?

# SUMMARY

## DEFINITIONS

- Heat $Q$ for:
  - isochoric process for an ideal gas:
  $$Q = C_V \cdot n \cdot \Delta T$$
  $C_V$ in unit J/(mol · K) is the molar heat capacity at constant volume, $C_V = 3 \cdot R/2$ for the ideal gas.

- isobaric process for an ideal gas:
  $$Q = C_p \cdot n \cdot \Delta T$$
  $C_p$ in unit J/(mol · K) is the molar heat capacity at constant pressure, $C_p = 5 \cdot R/2$ for the ideal gas.

- Standard conditions of gases in physiology:
  - BTPS = body temperature pressure saturated. $T = 37°C$, $p = 1.013 \times 10^5$ Pa = 1 atm, $p_{water} = 6.3$ kPa.
  - ATPS = ambient temperature pressure saturated. $T = T_{spirometer}$, $p = 1.013 \times 10^5$ Pa = 1 atm, $p_{water}$ equals saturation pressure of water vapour at $T_{spirometer}$.
  - STPD = standard temperature pressure dry. $T = 0°C$, $p = 1.013 \times 10^5$ Pa = 1 atm, $p_{water} = 0$.

## LAWS

- Ideal gas law:

$$p \cdot V = n \cdot R \cdot T$$

  with $R$ the gas constant.
- Internal energy of an ideal gas:
  - For 1 mol of gas ($U$ in unit J/mol):

$$U = \frac{3}{2} R \cdot T = \frac{1}{2} M \cdot \langle v^2 \rangle$$

  - per particle in the gas ($\varepsilon$ in unit J/particle):

$$\varepsilon = \frac{3}{2} \frac{R}{N_A} T = \frac{3}{2} k \cdot T$$

$N_A$ is the Avogadro number, $k$ is the Boltzmann constant

- Root-mean-square speed of gas particles, $v_{rms} = (\langle v^2 \rangle)^{1/2}$:

$$v_{rms} = \sqrt{\frac{3 \cdot R \cdot T}{M}} = \sqrt{\frac{3 \cdot k \cdot T}{m}}$$

$m$ is the mass of a single gas particle.
- Work: for an ideal gas with frictionless piston
  - isochoric process ($V$ = const):

$$W = 0$$

  - isothermal process ($T$ = const):

$$W = -n \cdot R \cdot T \cdot \ln\left(\frac{V_{final}}{V_{initial}}\right)$$

  - isobaric process ($p$ = const):

$$W = -p(V_{final} - V_{initial})$$

- Change of the internal energy for a cyclic process:

$$\Delta U_{cycle} = 0$$

# CHAPTER 8

# MOLECULAR BIOLOGY
## Basic Physics for Biochemistry

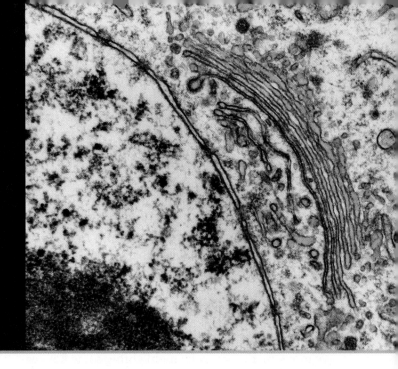

The first law of thermodynamics is insufficient to fully characterize systems that undergo dynamic processes such as chemical reactions. It distinguishes possible and impossible processes based on the conservation of energy, but it does not allow us to identify the spontaneous direction of a possible process. The second and third laws of thermodynamics fill this gap: the second law establishes the entropy as a parameter of the state of a system that remains constant in an isolated system with reversible processes (processes that proceed exclusively via equilibrium states) but increases for spontaneous irreversible processes. Based on a statistical interpretation, entropy is a measure of the disorder of a system; a fully ordered system at $T = 0$ K has an entropy of $S = 0$ J/K (third law of thermodynamics).

In a closed or open system at constant pressure, the Gibbs free energy $G$ combines the enthalpy and entropy to predict the dynamics of the system: $G$ remains constant if the process occurs between two states that are in equilibrium with each other (e.g., $\Delta G = 0$ for liquid water and ice at 0°C) and $G$ approaches a minimum value during a spontaneous irreversible process (e.g., $\Delta G < 0$ for the reaction of oxygen and hydrogen to form water).

We noted in the introduction to this book that the life sciences are rooted at the lowest level of complexity in the molecular structure of matter. For example, in Figs. 3.2 and 3.3 we highlight the molecular origin of muscle action, and at the beginning of Chapter 6 we note the chemical processes of the ATP molecule during cellular metabolism. The number of links that emerge between activities of living organisms and the underlying biochemical causes has significantly increased in recent decades. This has led to the identification of *molecular biology,* and more specifically *molecular genetics,* as separate fields of study in the life sciences. These fields focus on the physicochemical organization of living matter and especially the molecular basis of inheritance and protein synthesis. In the current chapter we review the basic physics required to describe biochemical reactions. We motivate this study by highlighting some key features of the chemical processes that constitute the cellular synthesis of proteins.

## Protein Synthesis as a Chemical Process at the Cellular Level

In 1665 Robert Hooke was the first to observe dead cells in cork, but it was only in the 1830s that Matthias von Schleiden and Theodor Schwann realized that all living organisms consist of cells. With the term **living cell** we mean a physiological entity that displays (i) metabolism and growth, (ii) irritability and mobility, and (iii) reproducibility. Fig. 8.1 is an artist's sketch of a typical human cell. It is preprogrammed to perform its functions. The necessary

know-how is contained in the cell nucleus (at the centre of Fig. 8.1) in the form of a variable number of **chromosomes**. Human cells in particular contain 46 chromosomes, which carry the blueprint for about 35 000 genes that are in turn construction plans for proteins. Each chromosome consists of a roughly 7-cm-long string of **deoxyribonucleic acid (DNA)**. James Dewey Watson and Francis Harry Crick recognized in 1953 that DNA is folded into a 10-$\mu$m-long structure resembling a twisted ladder (double-helix) that contains a pair of bases for every 0.34 nm of length. The sequence of four bases—adenine, thymine, cytosine, and guanine—on the DNA contains the genetic information in essentially the same fashion as a binary code contains the information stored in a computer.

In the cell nucleus, the genetic code is continuously copied (transcription process) onto m̲essenger-RNA (ribonucleic acid); m-RNA is then transferred out of the cell nucleus through pores in the nuclear membrane and into the cytoplasm of the cell. There, m-RNA reaches the ribosomal apparatus, which is the *rough endoplasmic reticulum* (labyrinth structure in Fig. 8.1) where the protein synthesis occurs. This spatial separation of DNA copying and protein synthesis is required because of the physicochemical properties of the underlying chemical reactions.

In the mid-1950s Marshall Warren Nirenberg identified the method by which the living cell decodes the information stored in the m-RNA. At the ribosomal apparatus, t̲ransfer-RNA molecules supply 20 different amino acids, each connected to a triplet of bases, called **codons**. By matching the codons of a t-RNA to the sequence of bases on the m-RNA, the

## FIGURE 8.1

An artist's conception of the three-dimensional organization of a eukaryotic cell. All cellular organisms are formed by eukaryotic cells with the exception of bacteria, which have a much simpler cell structure called a prokaryotic cell. Visible are the nucleus, with its porous membrane at the centre, first observed in 1831; the ribosomal apparatus (with a connected maze of tunnels stretching across the entire cell); the mitochondria, e.g., at the lower left; and the cell membrane (plasma membrane), which is about 10 nm thick. See also the chapter-opening micrograph.

## TABLE 8.1

### Genetic code

| 1 | 2<br>3 | U | C | A | G |
|---|---|---|---|---|---|
| U | U | Phe | Ser | Tyr | Cys |
|   | C | Phe | Ser | Tyr | Cys |
|   | A | Leu | Ser | **Stop** | **Stop** |
|   | G | Leu | Ser | **Stop** | Trp |
| C | U | Leu | Pro | His | Arg |
|   | C | Leu | Pro | His | Arg |
|   | A | Leu | Pro | Gln | Arg |
|   | G | Leu | Pro | Gln | Arg |
| A | U | Ile | Thr | Asn | Ser |
|   | C | Ile | Thr | Asn | Ser |
|   | A | Ile | Thr | Lys | Arg |
|   | G | **Start** | Thr | Lys | Arg |
| G | U | Val | Ala | Asp | Gly |
|   | C | Val | Ala | Asp | Gly |
|   | A | Val | Ala | Asp | Gly |
|   | G | Val | Ala | Asp | Gly |

Numbers 1, 2, and 3 identify the position of each base in the codon triplet; e.g., the triplet containing at first position a uracil (U) and an adenine (A) at positions 2 and 3 leads to the termination of the amino-synthesis ("stop"). Note that a genetic code based on duplets could encode only $4^2 = 16$ amino acids with no redundance.

RNA bases: A = adenine, C = cytosine, G = guanine, and U = uracil
*Amino acids (essential acids underlined):*

| | | | |
|---|---|---|---|
| 1 Ala = alanine | 2 Arg = arginine | 3 Asn = asparagine | 4 Asp = aspartic acid |
| 5 Cys = cysteine | 6 Gln = glutamine | 7 Gly = glycine | 8 His = histidine |
| 9 *Ile = isoleucine* | 10 *Leu = leucine* | 11 *Lys = lysine* | 12 *Phe = phenylalanine* |
| 13 Pro = proline | 14 Ser = serine | 15 *Start = methionine* | 16 Stop = glutamic acid |
| 17 *Thr = threonine* | 18 *Trp = tryptophan* | 19 Tyr = tyrosine | 20 *Val = valine* |

Lysosomes are lipoid containers that enclose the complete macromolecule at the ribosomal apparatus and/or at the Golgi apparatus (named after Camillo Golgi). This spatial separation is again required to protect against chemical degradation. As illustrated in Fig. 8.2(a), lysosomes travel to the outer cell membrane and release their content into the extracellular space. Fig. 8.2(b) shows a micrograph of lysosomes in a renal cell.

Protein synthesis is therefore a **uni-directional process**, starting with a transcription process in the cell

(a)

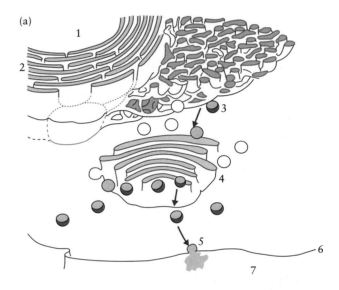

(b)

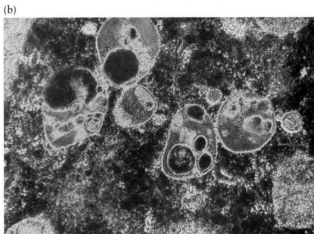

### FIGURE 8.2

Intra-cellular transport mechanisms with lysosomes. (a) In the cell nucleus (1), the genetic code is continuously transcribed to messenger-RNA that subsequently transfers out of the nucleus. It reaches the rough endoplasmic reticulum (2) where protein synthesis takes place. The synthesized peptides and proteins are packaged in lysosomes (3). They are either transferred to the Golgi apparatus (4) or directly out of the cell (5). At the cell membrane (6) the lysosome envelope integrates in the lipid layer, releasing its content to the extracellular fluid (7). (b) Colourized transmission electron micrograph (TEM) of a renal cell.

genetic code is translated into an amino acid sequence (see Table 8.1). Such amino acid chains are called **peptides** if the molecule contains fewer than 100 amino acids, and are called **proteins** when they contain more than 100 amino acids. Peptides and proteins are polymers and usually have specific structural and/or catalytic properties that enable them to serve a unique biological purpose. These peptides and proteins are called **enzymes**. For example, haemoglobin molecules possess a delicate structural arrangement capable of accommodating loosely adsorbed oxygen.

In the last step, the synthesized peptides and proteins are transported out of the cell in **lysosomes**.

nucleus and completed with the release of the protein from the cell. This uni-directional character has two components: the spatial separation of successive synthesis steps and the irreversibility of each single step. It is obviously not possible to develop such complex processes with single steps that run preferentially in the opposite direction: the entire protein synthesis mechanism would be rendered useless if, let's say, the underlying chemical process of attaching amino acids to a polymer sequence were to favour instead the decomposition of the polymer to monomers.

How do we know in which direction a chemical reaction occurs spontaneously? And can we influence the outcome? No answer can be given based on the physical principles we have introduced in the previous chapters. For example, the first law of thermodynamics allows us to distinguish processes that are possible from processes that would violate the conservation of energy. However, the reverse process to any process identified as possible by that law is also possible; thus, the first law does not allow us to distinguish the direction in which chemical processes unfold spontaneously. The current chapter addresses the issue of directionality of physical processes based on the introduction of the second law of thermodynamics. In preparation for that law, we must first introduce the concept of reversibility of a process.

# Reversibility

To develop a deeper understanding of thermodynamics a closer look at physical processes is necessary, where we no longer limit our interest to a comparison of the initial and final states but follow the system parameters along the path between these states. A fundamental distinction of processes follows when we study an arbitrary Process I that leads from an initial state A to a final state B, and its reverse Process II from state B to state A. Process I is called **reversible** if all associated parameter changes of the system and its environment are completely reversed during Process II. This is possible only if Process I travels from state A to state B through a continuous sequence of equilibrium states. The biological processes discussed throughout this textbook are not reversible; we therefore call them **irreversible**.

## Concept Question 8.1

**(a) You put a room-temperature glass of water in a microwave oven and heat it to 50°C. Then you place it back on the table and let it cool down to room temperature.**

Neglecting a slightly increased rate of evaporation, did you perform a reversible process when heating the water in the microwave oven? (b) If your answer is no, can you name another process you can perform that is perfectly reversible? If you can't name such a process, why do we introduce the concept?

ANSWER TO PART (a): The process is irreversible. The fact that you recovered the system in its original state (a room-temperature glass of water on your table) does not prove reversibility of the heating process because the cooling process has not restored all the parameters of the environment of your system: electric energy available to do work before the experiment has been lost as thermal energy to the air and the table beneath the glass.

ANSWER TO PART (b): There are no reversible processes you can actually perform. We have introduced idealized concepts before in this textbook with no real applications, such as (point-like) particles and the ideal gas. This is justified in each case because such idealizations allow us to model a physical situation or process under simplified conditions, which minimizes the mathematical complexity while preserving the key physical properties. In the current case, idealized reversible processes can be described with the equilibrium thermodynamics concepts we introduced earlier.

Reversible processes and all previously introduced laws are **time invariant**; i.e., the predictions remain unchanged whether time moves from the past to the future or whether it were to move from the future toward the past. The first law of thermodynamics serves as an example. For a closed system it is given in the form:

$$\Delta U = U_{\text{final}} - U_{\text{initial}} = Q + W \qquad [1]$$

Reversing the time in this equation means that the initial state of the system becomes the final state, and vice versa. Thus, the term $U_{\text{final}} - U_{\text{initial}}$ becomes $U_{\text{initial}} - U_{\text{final}}$, which is the same numerical value but carries the opposite sign. On the right-hand side of Eq. [1] the heat term changes under time reversal from $Q$ to $-Q$ (the heat flows in the opposite direction) and the work term changes from $W$ to $-W$ (work is undone). Thus, Eq. [1] looks exactly the same; we cannot distinguish the direction of time (past to future or future to past) using that law.

## Concept Question 8.2

**Assume we watch a movie that is run in reverse. Parts of this movie will look funny, such as people running backward. What sequence of the movie would appear equally acceptable whether run forward or in reverse?**

ANSWER: Static scenes, such as the camera sweeping across a room to show the setting prior to any action taking place. In this part of the movie, no time-dependent processes occur; i.e., all parameters are constant. The recording of cyclic processes on film would appear proper when shown backward, e.g., the breathing of a person otherwise at rest in a chair, or a medical doctor listening to the heartbeat of a patient. However, in these cases a full display of the vital signs of the person shown would clearly demonstrate the impossibility of the events shown in the reverse-running film.

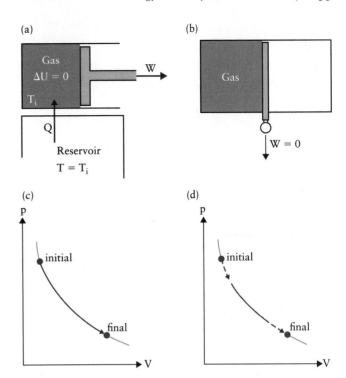

**FIGURE 8.3**

Comparison of a reversible and an irreversible isothermal expansion. (a) and (b) In the reversible case, heat flows to the gas from a heat reservoir at the same temperature as the gas. The piston moves without friction, representing the work released by the system. The process follows a continuous line in a *p–V* diagram. (c) and (d) In the irreversible case, a shutter is removed, allowing the gas to expand into a part of the container that was previously evacuated. No work is done in this case, and re-inserting the shutter does not recover the initial state of the system. The process cannot be represented in a *p–V* diagram because it is irreversible.

We choose in Fig. 8.3 a thermal expansion of an ideal gas to quantify the differences between reversible and irreversible processes. The reversible expansion is illustrated in part (a): heat transferred from the heat reservoir is transported through the system and deposited as work in the piston. The bottom frame indicates that this process is reversible: each successive state of the system is an equilibrium state along an isothermal curve in the *p–V* diagram. The process is done slowly enough to allow the pressure in the gas to remain uniform throughout the expanding gas. At every instant, the velocity distribution of the gas particles matches the Maxwell–Boltzmann distribution illustrated in Fig. 7.20(c). We can further prove the reversibility by following the expansion with an isothermal compression in which all parameter changes are exactly reversed: e.g., work is done by the piston and returns therefore as energy to the gas while an equivalent amount of heat flows from the gas to the heat reservoir. At the end of the reversed process the gas and its environment are in exactly the same state as they were before the expansion started. This is an idealization, as both an ideal heat reservoir with a fixed temperature and an ideal piston moving without friction are assumed.

Fig. 8.3(b) shows an irreversible isothermal expansion. The gas is initially sealed in a fraction of the container at the left, separated by a shutter from the remaining volume in which vacuum conditions will apply. When the shutter is allowed to drop down, the gas expands isothermally to fill the whole container.

The *p–V* diagram below the sketch shows that the initial and final states of the gas are the same as for the isothermal expansion in Fig. 8.3(a), but that the process between these states cannot be depicted in this diagram because every point in the *p–V* diagram represents an equilibrium state of the gas. Thus, the irreversible process does not follow the isothermal curve, as shown in Fig. 8.3(a); the gas parameters vary in an uncontrolled fashion between the initial and final equilibrium states. Pushing the shutter back in an attempt to reverse the process does not recover the initial state of the system, as the gas remains expanded. Even if we use other means to force the gas back into its initial state, permanent changes in the environment have taken place that can no longer be reversed. The major difference between both processes is that in Fig. 8.3(b) we allowed a change that suddenly converted the initial equilibrium state into a non-equilibrium state.

## ● EXAMPLE 8.1

Calculate the work done for the reversible and irreversible isothermal expansions in Fig. 8.3.

*Solution:* We determined the work for the reversible process already in Chapter 7. We found that the reversible isothermal expansion allowed us to obtain work from the system. In turn, the irreversible process in Fig. 8.3 does not release any useful work. Thus, we write:

$$W_{reversible} = -n \cdot R \cdot T \cdot \ln\left(\frac{V_{final}}{V_{initial}}\right) \quad [2]$$

$$W_{irreversible} = 0$$

We can generalize the result of Example 8.1:

*Reversible processes are processes in which a maximum amount of work is involved.*

This statement can be extended to cyclic processes: **reversible cyclic processes** are those with the greatest efficiency coefficient. In particular, the efficiency coefficient calculated for the Carnot process (in Eqs. [130] and [131] in Chapter 7) is the maximum possible efficiency coefficient for any cyclical process because the Carnot process is done in a reversible fashion.

We conclude from Fig. 8.3 and the result in Eq. [2] that work and heat exchange cannot be determined for a process by just specifying the initial and final states. In addition, a detailed knowledge of the history of the system is needed, e.g., whether it undergoes reversible or irreversible processes.

### Concept Question 8.3

**Consider Figs. 7.25 and 7.26. Are these two figures drawn appropriately based on our discussion of reversibility?**

ANSWER: No. The continuous vertical line in Fig. 7.26 implies that we conduct the isochoric heating in a reversible fashion. However, the illustration of the isochoric heating in the bottom frame of Fig. 7.25 uses a propane flame (Bunsen burner) for heating. For this approach to yield a final state at $T_{high}$, the propane flame must be hotter than the gas. Creating contact between a system and a component of its environment that are at different temperatures means that the isolated superstructure is not in thermal equilibrium. Processes that involve non-equilibrium states are not reversible.

We make two comments in defence of Figs. 7.25 and 7.26: (i) Conducting an isochoric process as reversible or irreversible does not make a difference as both approaches yield $W = 0$. (ii) Drawing Fig. 7.25 reversible is cumbersome. The way to do it would be to use an infinite number of heat reservoirs with infinitesimally small temperature differences $\Delta T$ (all of them part of the system's environment) and bringing one after the other into contact with the system to raise its temperature ever so slowly. If you insist on that level of precision, a corresponding revision of Fig. 7.31 for the isobaric process should also be made.

# The Second Law of Thermodynamics

With the definition of reversibility, we are now in a position to go beyond the first law of thermodynamics. Remember that the first law compares equilibrium states of a system. Thus, we were able to formulate the conservation of energy concept without details of the process by which the system transfers from the initial to the final state. We cheated a bit in this respect when we calculated work and heat transfer because we made the assumption of a reversible process without stating it. The second law of thermodynamics now builds on those calculations, but focusses on the history of the actual process, i.e., the heat and work terms that occur during the process. The starting point is the **Carnot process** because

- it is reversible; i.e., we were able to quantify it using the first law of thermodynamics, but

- it contains fundamental features about heat and work that have not yet been exploited completely.

## Formulation of the Second Law

The Carnot cycle consists of an isothermal expansion followed by an adiabatic expansion, an isothermal compression, and a final adiabatic compression. In Chapter 7 the efficiency coefficient for this process is defined as the ratio of the useful work to the heat input per cycle:

$$\eta = \frac{|\text{useful work}|}{\text{heat input}} = \frac{|W_1 + W_3|}{Q_{high}}$$
$$= \frac{T_{high} - T_{low}}{T_{high}} \quad [3]$$

In Eq. [3] the two work contributions result from the two isothermal steps, and the heat term in the denominator is the heat supplied during the first isothermal step by the higher-temperature heat reservoir.

As a result of the last term in Eq. [3], we find that no cyclic process can convert heat completely into work ($\eta < 1$) because it is impossible to operate with a low-temperature heat reservoir at 0 K. This implies that thermal energy is different from all other energy forms because these can be converted freely. We saw this for the kinetic and potential energy when a ball is thrown straight upward. The ball initially has kinetic energy based on its speed. At the instant the ball reaches its highest point it comes momentarily to rest and the entire mechanical energy of the ball is in the form of potential energy. As the ball falls down, the potential energy is converted back into kinetic energy.

Following Carnot's work, it became evident that his findings are applicable not only to the specific cyclic process he studied. Rudolf Clausius and Lord Kelvin generalized in 1850 the implications of the Carnot process to formulate the second law of thermodynamics. In the form as stated by Lord Kelvin, it reads:

*In a cyclic process it is impossible to take heat from a reservoir and change it into work without releasing a fraction of the heat to a second reservoir at lower temperature.*

It is useful to keep in mind that a system with two heat reservoirs at different temperatures is intrinsically a non-equilibrium system. The Carnot process is idealized insofar as its reversible character allows us to treat it conceptually as an equilibrium process.

## Concept Question 8.4

The reversibility of the Carnot process means that it could be operated in the opposite direction, i.e., with an isothermal compression while in contact with the high-temperature heat reservoir and with an isothermal expansion while in contact with the low-temperature heat reservoir. (a) Can you identify a process for which this inverse Carnot process is an idealization? (b) Try to formulate the second law of thermodynamics in analogy to Lord Kelvin's statement but based on the inverse Carnot process.

ANSWER TO PART (a): Comparing with Fig. 7.36, we find that the inverse Carnot process removes heat from the low-temperature heat reservoir and deposits heat in the high-temperature heat reservoir. For this process net work has to be done on the system; this work is converted into heat and is also deposited in the high-temperature heat reservoir. If we allow the low-temperature heat reservoir to change its temperature, then a lowering of its temperature occurs. If we allow the low-temperature

heat reservoir to pick up heat from its environment, then the inverse Carnot process is suitable to maintain the low temperature of the reservoir. Thus, the inverse Carnot process is a model of a **refrigeration** device.

ANSWER TO PART (b): In a cyclic process it is impossible to exclusively transfer heat from a low-temperature heat reservoir to one at a higher temperature. This is the formulation of the second law as introduced by Clausius.

## Definition of Entropy

For applications, we need to find a way to express the second law of thermodynamics quantitatively. To do this, we re-examine the efficiency coefficient $\eta$ of the Carnot process. For this we start with the last part of Eq. [3]. The two work terms in the numerator can be exchanged for the two corresponding heat terms of the isothermal steps used in Chapter 7 to quantify the Carnot process (Table 7.2):

$$\eta = \frac{|W|}{Q_{high}} = \frac{Q_{low} + Q_{high}}{Q_{high}} = \frac{T_{high} - T_{low}}{T_{high}} \quad [4]$$

Next, we sort the terms based on the subscripts "high" and "low"; i.e., we separate the terms associated with the temperature based on the high- and low-temperature heat reservoirs, respectively:

$$\frac{Q_{low}}{T_{low}} + \frac{Q_{high}}{T_{high}} = 0 \quad [5]$$

Eq. [5] is an interesting result because it states that the sum of the ratios of heat to temperature for a cyclic process is zero. Before we discuss the implications further, we want to confirm that the result in Eq. [5] applies to any reversible cyclic process, not just the Carnot process for which it was derived. This is shown in Fig. 8.4 for an arbitrary cyclic process in a $p$–$V$ diagram. By drawing a continuous line in a $p$–$V$ diagram we assume that the cycle is reversible. Next, a net of closely spaced isothermal and adiabatic lines is superimposed on the cycle. The more shallow lines are isothermal lines and the steeper lines are adiabatic lines, like those drawn in Fig. 7.34. This net of lines divides the arbitrary cycle into a large number of small Carnot processes, each with a very small temperature difference between the high- and low-temperature heat reservoirs. One such Carnot cycle created by the net of thin lines is highlighted near the centre for illustration. Following each small Carnot cycle we notice that its four contributing steps are shared with neighbouring Carnot cycles, except for the segments that run along the outer line, which constitutes the large arbitrary cycle. Thus, the sum

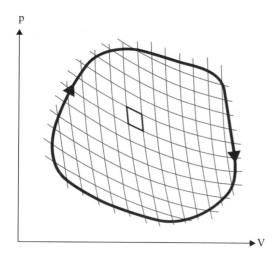

**FIGURE 8.4**

A *p–V* diagram for an arbitrary cyclic process. To quantify the properties of such a process it is divided into a very large number of Carnot processes, which are operated in adjacent cycles with very small temperature differences between the two heat reservoirs (thin lines). One such Carnot process is highlighted near the centre of the figure. The approach taken in the figure allows us to quantify the entropy change in the process.

over all $Q/T$ terms for all Carnot cycles in Fig. 8.4 provides a value corresponding to Eq. [5] for the arbitrary reversible cycle:

$$\sum_i \frac{Q_i}{T_i} = 0 \qquad [6]$$

We find that the sum of all quotients of heat transfer and temperature during a cyclic process is zero. The sum in Eq. [6] behaves in the same way as changes of the internal energy: whenever the system returns to its initial state, these values return to the same value they had before the cycle. Thus, the physical property underlying Eq. [6] has a fixed value for a given state of the system, in the same way a fixed value of internal energy is assigned to each possible equilibrium state of a system. Any parameter that has a well-defined value for each equilibrium state of a system—i.e., a value independent of the history of the system—is called a **variable of the state** of the system. Thus, the ratio $Q$ over $T$ is a variable of the state, while $Q$ separately is not a variable of the state. To fully describe a system, such variables of the state have to be measured. A complete description of the state of a system therefore includes temperature, volume, pressure, and the amount of material in unit mol or kg, as well as the internal energy and the newly introduced ratio of heat transfer and temperature. With this importance attached to the new quantity it was given a name, **entropy** $S$ with unit J/K. The name *entropy* is taken from the Classical Greek language and means "change" or "transformation." Further discussion will show why the parameter received this name.

To capture the quantitative definition of entropy we start with Eq. [6], which represents the change of the entropy for a cyclic process. If an arbitrary process does not return to the initial state, then an entropy change $\Delta S$ occurs where $\Delta S$ is the difference in entropy between its initial and final states:

$$\Delta S = S_{\text{final}} - S_{\text{initial}} = \sum_i \frac{Q_i}{T_i} \qquad [7]$$

This definition is useful as it also provides for a method to measure entropy: the system is brought into a "standard" initial state, for which the entropy is known. Then the state of the system is changed to the final state, for which the entropy value is sought. Measuring the heat transfer at each temperature during the change of state allows us to quantify the change in entropy between the two states. This procedure is discussed in detail later in this chapter.

● **EXAMPLE 8.2**

Two mol of air is initially confined to the left side of the container shown in Fig. 8.5. Assume that the air volume is doubled when the valve is opened and that the air temperature is held constant. (a) Is the expansion process reversible or irreversible? If it is irreversible, what is the corresponding reversible process? (b) Show that the entropy change for this process is:

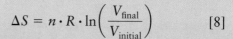

$$\Delta S = n \cdot R \cdot \ln\left(\frac{V_{\text{final}}}{V_{\text{initial}}}\right) \qquad [8]$$

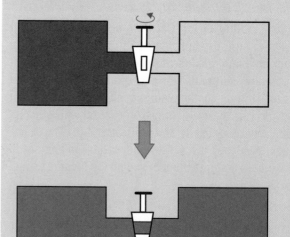

**FIGURE 8.5**

Expansion of 2 mol of air, which is initially confined to the half-space at the left. The expansion becomes possible when a valve between the two half-chambers is opened.

(c) Quantify $\Delta S$ for the case of Fig. 8.5. (d) Does the formula in part (b) depend on whether the process is reversible or irreversible?

*Solution to part (a):* The process is irreversible since it cannot be reversed. Closing the valve will not drive the air back into the chamber where it was at the beginning of the experiment. The corresponding reversible process is an air expansion with a mobile frictionless piston (Fig. 8.3(a)).

*Solution to part (b):* The heat added to an ideal gas when it expands isothermally was derived in Chapter 7. To quantify the process, we have to assume that air is an ideal gas; however, we note that the irreversibility of the process has no bearing on this question, as discussed in part (d). Thus:

$$Q = n \cdot R \cdot T \cdot \ln\left(\frac{V_{\text{final}}}{V_{\text{initial}}}\right) \qquad [9]$$

and with the definition of the entropy in Eq. [7], we find for the entropy change for an isothermal process:

$$\Delta S = \frac{Q}{T} = n \cdot R \cdot \ln\left(\frac{V_{\text{final}}}{V_{\text{initial}}}\right) \qquad [10]$$

*Solution to part (c):* We use $n = 2$ mol with a ratio of final to initial volume of $V_{\text{final}}/V_{\text{initial}} = 2$:

$$\Delta S = (2.0 \, \text{mol})\left(8.314 \, \frac{\text{J}}{\text{K} \cdot \text{mol}}\right) \ln 2$$

$$= +11.5 \, \frac{\text{J}}{\text{K}} \qquad [11]$$

*Solution to part (d):* When switching from a reversible to an irreversible process, the amount of heat exchange is not affected, but the maximum work (as calculated for the reversible process) is not obtainable in the irreversible process. The calculation in part (b) does not include a work term and therefore is not affected by the fashion in which the process is conducted.

## Concept Question 8.5

**Fig. 7.39 shows the *p–V* diagram for dynamic breathing. (a) Is dynamic breathing a reversible process? (b) What is the entropy change per cycle based on Fig. 7.39?**

ANSWER TO PART (a): Dynamic breathing is a real physiological process and is therefore irreversible. However, Fig. 7.39 shows continuous lines for a full breathing cycle, which implies that Fig. 7.39 illustrates an idealized reversible version of breathing.

ANSWER TO PART (b): We noted in Example 8.2 that the reversibility of a process does not affect the numerical value of the change of entropy of the system as no work term is included in the calculation of entropy. Thus, the entropy change for a cyclic process, whether it is reversible or irreversible, is the same, and is zero because the entropy is a variable of the state. If the cyclic process is irreversible it will cause an increase of entropy in the environment, as discussed quantitatively in the next section.

The following three sections focus on key properties of entropy that we will use later in the textbook and that you often will find references to in biophysical or biochemical studies.

## Entropy and Work

Based on the discussion of the Carnot process we note that the entropy is associated with the fraction of heat that cannot be utilized as work during a cyclic process, i.e., the heat lost to a low-temperature part of the environment. This is one interpretation of the entropy concept. We will expand on this interpretation when we introduce the Gibbs free energy later in this chapter: the total energy of a system can be diminished by the entropy-related useless energy to determine the energy available from the process to do work (to which the term *free energy* then refers).

## Entropy and Reversibility

We want to compare the values of the change of entropy $\Delta S$ for reversible and irreversible spontaneous processes, where **spontaneous process** refers to a process that progresses on its own. The explosive formation of water from oxygen and hydrogen gases is such a spontaneous process, while the opposite process, the splitting of water to obtain hydrogen and oxygen gases, is not spontaneous as it never happens without external effort.

Fig. 8.6 shows idealized reversible and irreversible processes for equilibrating the temperature of two identical bodies (1 and 2) that differ only in temperatures $T_1$ and $T_2$, with $T_1 > T_2$. The top sketch shows the reversible approach, and the bottom sketch shows an irreversible approach.

In the simpler, irreversible case, the two bodies are brought into direct thermal contact. As a result, an amount of heat $Q$ flows from the hotter to the colder body until both have the same temperature. This process is irreversible as no work is extracted and stored in the isolated superstructure to reverse the process,

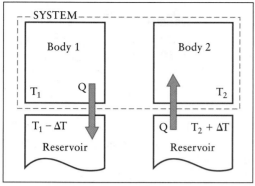

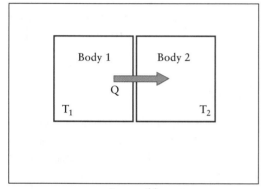

**FIGURE 8.6**

Comparison between a reversible (top) and an irreversible (bottom) experiment to equilibrate the temperature of two bodies B1 and B2. For the irreversible case the two objects are brought into direct thermal contact. For the reversible process heat reservoirs R1 and R2 have to be used to adjust the temperature of each part of the system in very small steps until the temperature difference is eliminated.

i.e., to re-establish different temperatures for both bodies after the temperature equilibrium has been established.

The reversible approach is more complex. The two bodies are not brought into direct contact; instead, each is brought into thermal contact with a heat reservoir that is minimally warmer in the case of body 2 and minimally colder in the case of body 1 than the respective body itself. The slight temperature differences of the body parts and the respective heat reservoirs are labelled $\Delta T$. We assume that the temperature difference $\Delta T$ is the same in both cases. Heat exchange with the heat reservoirs occurs. For simplicity, we assume that the initial temperatures of the two bodies also differ only by $T_1 - T_2 = \Delta T$. Otherwise, a very large number of heat reservoirs would have to be lined up for each body, with each one having a temperature smaller or higher than the previous heat reservoir by a difference of $\Delta T$. Even though such a reversible approach is obviously not practical

for achieving a notable temperature change, we use it for the sake of argument.

We carefully distinguish the *system*, which consists of the two bodies 1 and 2, and the *environment*, which consists of the two heat reservoirs 1 and 2 within the isolated superstructure of Fig. 8.6. For the respective changes of entropy in the reversible case, we find from Eq. [7]:

$$\Delta S_{\text{system}} = \Delta S_{\text{B1}} + \Delta S_{\text{B2}} = -\frac{Q}{T_1} + \frac{Q}{T_2} > 0$$

$$\Delta S_{\text{environment}} = \Delta S_{\text{R1}} + \Delta S_{\text{R2}} = \frac{Q}{T_1} - \frac{Q}{T_2} < 0$$

[12]

Eq. [12] yields for the isolated superstructure:

$$\Delta S_{\text{isolated superstructure}} = \Delta S_{\text{system}} + \Delta S_{\text{environment}} = 0$$

[13]

A **reversible process** is characterized by a zero change in entropy for the isolated superstructure. This allows for a decrease in the entropy of the system if the entropy of the environment is raised concurrently. Note that no entropy is created or destroyed in this case, but entropy flows across the interface between system and environment. The observations we made for the top frame of Fig. 8.6 characterize reversible processes in general—including systems that are in equilibrium, as these undergo no processes: the entropy remains constant, $\Delta S = 0$.

*$\Delta S = 0$ applies to isolated superstructures with reversible processes or systems that are continuously in an equilibrium state.*

Next, we study the irreversible process shown in the bottom frame of Fig. 8.6. In this case, the isolated superstructure contains only the system, which again consists of the two bodies 1 and 2. No heat reservoirs are needed as no heat exchange with the environment occurs. The entropy change of the system is the same as in the reversible case as the same amount of heat flows out of body 1 and into body 2. However, no entropy change occurs in the environment as no interaction with the environment takes place:

$$\Delta S_{\text{system}} = -\frac{Q}{T_1} + \frac{Q}{T_2} > 0$$

$$\Delta S_{\text{environment}} = 0$$

[14]

Eq. [14] yields for the isolated superstructure:

$$\Delta S_{\text{isolated superstructure}} = \Delta S_{\text{system}} + \Delta S_{\text{environment}} > 0$$

[15]

This result is different from the result of the reversible case in Eq. [13]: in a **spontaneous irreversible**

**process** the entropy of an isolated system increases. Entropy is created in the system! Interpreting the results in Eqs. [13] and [15], we note that an isolated system not in equilibrium will undergo spontaneous irreversible processes that increase its entropy. Such processes cease when the system reaches equilibrium. At that point the entropy does not increase any further.

*The entropy reaches a maximum value for a system in equilibrium:* $S_{eq}$ *= maximum.*

Two interesting consequences are noted:

- *Heat death of the universe:* Because the entire universe is an isolated superstructure with irreversible processes, it has an ever-increasing entropy. Since entropy is linked to the amount of useless heat, as discussed in the previous section, we conclude that the universe transfers heat continuously into reservoirs at lower temperatures. This can continue only until all energy has been transferred in this way and a final equilibrium is reached. For this final equilibrium state, the term **heat death of the universe** has been coined.

  It is important to keep in mind that Eq. [15] applies only to an isolated system. In the next section, we discuss how an open or closed system within an isolated superstructure can develop highly complex patterns without violating the second law of thermodynamics.

- *The difference between past and future:* The second law of thermodynamics is distinguished among all laws of physics as it is connected to the direction of time. **Future** is the direction of time in which the entropy of an isolated system increases, and **past** is the direction in which the entropy of an isolated system decreases. Therefore, one day we may be able to travel into the future—as H. G. Wells suggested in 1895 in his book *The Time Machine*—because this would not violate the second law of thermodynamics. But we will never be able to travel into the past!

## Concept Question 8.6

**We did not identify a heat transfer to the gas in the irreversible isothermal expansion in Fig. 8.3(b). Does the entropy of the gas change?**

ANSWER: Don't try to answer by looking at Fig. 8.3(b); the formulas we introduced require that we study an equivalent reversible process. In the reversible process of

Fig. 8.3(a), energy is required to push the piston; this energy is recovered as heat from a heat reservoir. The initial and final equilibrium states in Fig. 8.3(a) and (b) are identical, thus the entropy change in both cases is the same whether the process is done reversibly or irreversibly.

## Entropy and Order

The laws of thermodynamics can be derived in two ways. The approach we use in this textbook is called the **phenomenological approach** since it is based primarily on experimental evidence. The alternative approach is called **statistical physics** because the discussion begins with a large number of particles in a system and then describes their properties in a statistical fashion. This approach is cumbersome for describing the ideal gas and the first law of thermodynamics. It does, however, provide useful, additional insight into the concepts of temperature and entropy.

For temperature, it provides a broader basis for the equilibrium definition than the Maxwell–Boltzmann velocity distribution, because that distribution applies only to gases. Statistical physics reconfirms that temperature is a collective property of a large number of atoms or molecules and cannot be defined for a single or a few particles.

The greatest benefit of the statistical physics approach to thermodynamics is the interpretation of entropy. Ludwig Boltzmann showed that entropy is proportional to the number of accessible microscopic states of a system. The number of accessible states, though, is quite complicated to determine even for simple systems. Looking at, for example, the system we introduced in the kinetic gas theory, calculating the number of accessible states means that for each particle we must count the number of possible values for each of the three position components and for each of the three velocity components. The greater this sum for all the particles in the system, the greater the entropy.

While such calculations go beyond the scope of this book, we can use the concept qualitatively to judge whether processes are associated with an increase in entropy. Fig. 8.7 shows five processes, each associated with an increase of entropy when followed from the left to the right box:

(a) Adding particles (i.e., an open system with material influx) increases the entropy since each of the previously present particles has as many accessible states as before, but the new particles contribute additional states for the combined system.

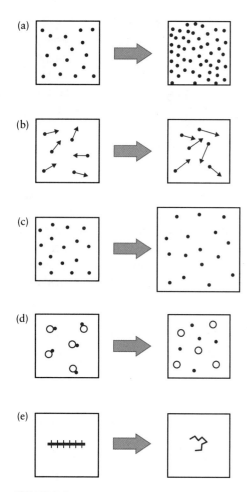

**FIGURE 8.7**

Processes with entropy increase: (a) increase of particle number, (b) increase of internal energy, (c) isothermal expansion, (d) dissociation of molecules, and (e) polymer relaxation.

(b) Adding energy to a closed system leads to an increase of the entropy. If the system is a gas, the molecules all gain speed; i.e., the range of accessible velocity components becomes larger. Note that no low-speed components are lost since, for example, a very fast particle can move mostly in the $xy$-plane and have still a small $z$-component of velocity.

(c) Increasing the volume can be done in two ways: by holding the internal energy constant (isothermal process) or by isolating the system (adiabatic process). An isothermal expansion increases the entropy since after the expansion the particles can resume all their previous positions but have access to additional positions with the number of accessible velocity components unchanged. Adiabatic expansions obey the entropy equation $\Delta S = 0$ since no heat exchange occurs, $Q = 0$. Therefore, adiabatic processes are also called **isentropic**. Why does the volume increase in this case not lead to an entropy increase? During an adiabatic expansion, each particle gains new accessible positions, but as the temperature drops sharply it loses the same number of accessible states linked to its velocity.

(d) A number of processes exist that we can qualitatively evaluate without a proper, often difficult, quantitative description. The last two examples in Fig. 8.7 illustrate such cases. The first one is the dissociation of molecules. If there are $N$ molecules initially, then the system has $6N$ free parameters (3 spatial and 3 velocity components per particle). In addition, the molecule may resume various states of rotation and various states of vibration. Dissociation is favoured because it doubles the number of free parameters to $12N$ since the number of independent particles doubles while the loss of vibrational and rotational states is much less.

(e) The last example is a polymer consisting of a large number of repetitive monomer units. If these units are connected with chemical bonds that can rotate, e.g., C—C single bonds, then the relaxation of the polymer represents an increase of entropy. This is due to the fact that a fully stretched polymer has only one relative orientation for adjacent monomers, while a very large number of relative positions of twisted repetitive units is possible for the relaxed polymer.

What the processes in Fig. 8.7 have in common is that the **degree of disorder** of the system increases as the entropy increases. Thus, entropy can be understood as a measure of the disorder in a system. Again, the second law does not prohibit a system from becoming ordered (e.g., crystals growing from solution or patterns developing in biological systems) unless it is an isolated system. If the system is open or closed, the total entropy or disorder of the isolated superstructure must increase in spontaneous processes but the entropy or disorder of the system itself can decrease.

**Concept Question 8.7**

**What is the most likely shape in which to find large biomolecules in the human body?**

ANSWER: Most polymers resume a folded equilibrium shape. Polymer relaxation is favoured by the entropy argument made with Fig. 8.7(e). We will see later in this chapter that the internal energy also plays a role because the system is not isolated; this contribution then favours a particular relaxed structure over random relaxation, i.e., supports the formation of the biochemically active structure. Neither entropy nor energy contributions favour a stretched polymer.

was not an isolated system. If the battery generating the discharges had been integrated with the arrangement to allow the combined system to be isolated, Miller's experiments would still have produced highly ordered molecules, at the expense of a net entropy increase due to irreversible processes in the discharging battery.

---

### Concept Question 8.8

**(a)** Sugar crystals form when a supersaturated sugar solution evaporates slowly. Crystals are a more ordered form of matter than a solution. Why does this observation not violate the second law of thermodynamics? **(b)** Stanley Miller achieved abiotic synthesis of organic compounds under "Early Earth" conditions in his famous 1953 experiment (Fig. 8.8 shows Miller and the apparatus). In a sealed container, electrical discharges in an atmosphere that consisted of water vapour, hydrogen, ammonia, and methane gases produced complex amino acids. Is this result consistent with the second law of thermodynamics?

**FIGURE 8.8**
Stanley Miller with the original equipment used in his 1953 experiments, which gave credence to the idea that organic molecules were created by conditions of the early Earth's atmosphere.

ANSWER TO PART (a): The system in this experiment is an open system that continuously loses solvent molecules to its environment. The second law of thermodynamics restricts ordering only for isolated systems.

ANSWER TO PART (b): Miller's experiment was done in a closed system (no exchange of matter with the environment). However, energy had to be supplied to the system to generate the electric discharges. Thus, again, the second law of thermodynamics does not restrict the complexity of compounds in Miller's arrangement since it

# Chemical Thermodynamics

Chemical reactions are non-equilibrium processes. However, it is possible to quantify some aspects of chemical reactions using equilibrium thermodynamics concepts. For example, chemists often are interested in whether or not a chemical reaction is possible as proposed, or which parameter ranges of temperature, pressure, and concentration favour the reaction. These questions can be answered with the concepts we have developed so far.

We need both the internal energy and the entropy to judge whether a chemical reaction is possible. The internal energy allows us to separate chemical reactions into **endothermic reactions**, which are reactions that require the supply of heat, and **exothermic reactions**, which are reactions that release heat. The entropy allows us to separate **spontaneous reactions** from reactions that have to be forced externally.

## Internal Energy and Enthalpy

We start with the role of the internal energy of a chemical process. Changes of the internal energy are measured with a **calorimeter,** which is an instrument that allows us to study a process in an isolated superstructure where the internal environment includes a heat reservoir that is capable of measuring the amount of heat released from the system. The heat reservoir may simply consist of a water-filled chamber surrounding the system; its temperature change is directly proportional to the amount of heat released. Such measurements are useful because the change of the internal energy is equal to the heat exchange of a system at constant volume. Fig. 8.9 shows a calorimeter that is set up specifically to study oxidation (combustion) processes at constant volume. Oxidation reactions include combustion of food components in metabolic processes. The chemical compound is placed in a small container pressurized with oxygen. The small container is immersed in a water bath, which is brought into thermal equilibrium with the small container after the chemical compound has been ignited and the oxidation has been completed.

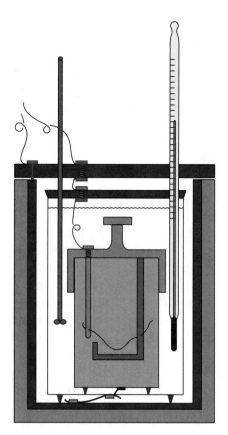

**FIGURE 8.9**

Sketch of a calorimeter used to determine the amount of heat released in a combustion process at constant volume. The probe material is placed in an inner steel container with a high-pressure oxygen atmosphere. The reaction is electrically ignited. The steel container is immersed in a water bath in which the temperature change is measured after the reaction is completed. The water bath in turn is isolated from the environment to prevent measurement errors due to heat loss through the outer wall.

---

**Concept Question 8.9**

Calorimeter arrangements like the one in Fig. 8.9 have been used in chemistry since the late 1700s. For example, in 1780 Antoine de Lavoisier and Pierre-Simon Laplace used ice for insulation in a calorimeter and measured the released heat by the amount of ice that melted during the process. In one experiment, they placed a guinea pig in the calorimeter and measured the heat dissipated by the animal as a function of the amount of oxygen it consumed. What idea did they test with this experiment?

ANSWER: They suggested that respiration is a form of combustion within the body of the animal, comparable to the combustion of carbon: $C + O_2 \rightarrow CO_2$. Comparing changes in the internal energies allowed them to quantify their model.

---

Most chemical processes, including biochemical processes, occur at constant pressure, i.e., at atmospheric pressure. We discussed in Chapter 7 that the enthalpy is better suited than the internal energy to describe the heat exchange, as it accounts properly for a possible volume change during a reaction at constant pressure. The volume change leads to a work term of the form $p_{atm} \cdot \Delta V$; this work is done *against* (expansion) or *by* (compression) the external atmosphere. The change of the internal energy of the system is a combination of this work and the heat that is exchanged between the system and the environment. The heat exchange at constant pressure then defines the enthalpy change $\Delta H$.

---

● **EXAMPLE 8.3**

We study the thermal decomposition of 1 mol $CaCO_3$ into $CaO$ and $CO_2$ at 900°C. A final $CO_2$ gas pressure of 1 atm is reached in this process. The system absorbs 175.7 kJ of heat. What is the change of the internal energy for 1 mol of $CaCO_3$? *Hint:* Neglect volume changes of the solid components $CaO$ and $CaCO_3$.

*Solution:* The internal energy is calculated from the measured enthalpy using the definition $H = U + p \cdot V$:

$$\Delta H = \Delta U + p \cdot \Delta V \quad \Rightarrow \quad \Delta U = \Delta H - p \cdot \Delta V \quad [16]$$

in which $p \cdot \Delta V$ is calculated from the ideal gas law for the only gaseous component in the decomposition ($CO_2$) with $p = p_{atm}$ and $T = 900°C = 1173$ K:

$$p \cdot \Delta V = n \cdot R \cdot T$$
$$= (1.0 \text{ mol}) \left(8.314 \frac{J}{K \cdot mol}\right)(1173 \text{ K})$$
$$= 9750 \text{ J} \quad [17]$$

in which $n = 1$ mol, because 1 mol of $CO_2$ is formed for every mol of $CaCO_3$. Further, we know from the heat required for this reaction that $\Delta H = +175.7$ kJ. Thus,

$$\Delta U = 175.7 \text{ kJ} - 9.75 \text{ kJ} = +166.0 \text{ kJ} \quad [18]$$

i.e., of the 175.7 kJ supplied to the system, 9.75 kJ is required for the volume expansion of the gaseous product. The balance of +166 kJ represents the increase of the internal energy of the system.

## Heat Capacity of Chemical Compounds

When heating a system, which need not be an ideal gas, the internal energy or enthalpy increases. To quantify the change in internal energy or enthalpy, the **heat capacity** is needed. If the system is a gas, we use either the molar heat capacity at constant volume, $C_V$, or the molar heat capacity at constant pressure, $C_p$. If the system is a liquid or a solid, $C_V = C_p$ and the subscript of the heat-capacity parameter can be dropped. We quantified $C_V$ and $C_p$ previously for the ideal gas: $C_V = 3 \cdot R/2$, with $R$ the universal gas constant and $C_p = C_V + R$. For any other system, we need to use tabulated values for the heat capacity. These values usually depend on the temperature. As an example, the molar heat capacity of solid and liquid water is listed as a function of temperature in Table 8.2.

### TABLE 8.2

**Molar heat capacity of liquid and solid water**

| State | Temperature | $C$ (J · mol$^{-1}$ · K$^{-1}$) |
|---|---|---|
| Solid | −34°C | 33.30 |
| Solid | −2.2°C | 37.78 |
| Liquid | 0°C | 75.86 |
| Liquid | 25°C | 75.23 |
| Liquid | 100°C | 75.90 |

Compare this table to the plot of the specific heat capacity of liquid water as shown in Fig. 6.35.

### ● EXAMPLE 8.4

We want to bring 1 kg water, initially at −10°C, to a final temperature of +10°C. What is the change in enthalpy for this process if the latent heat of melting is 6.0 kJ/mol? *Hint:* Use the heat-capacity value at −2.2°C from Table 8.2 for ice, and use the value at 0°C for liquid water. The molecular mass of water is $M = 18$ g/mol.

*Solution:* We divide the process into three steps: (I) heating ice from −10°C to the freezing point, (II) transforming ice to liquid water at that temperature, and (III) heating liquid water from the freezing point to +10°C. The amount of water is required for these calculations in unit mol:

$$n = \frac{1000\,\text{g}}{18\,\dfrac{\text{g}}{\text{mol}}} = 55.5\,\text{mol} \qquad [19]$$

Using $\Delta H = n \cdot C_p \cdot \Delta T$ from Chapter 7, we find:

(I) Heating ice by 10 degrees to the freezing point:

$$\Delta H = +(55.5\,\text{mol})\left(37.78\,\frac{\text{J}}{\text{K}\cdot\text{mol}}\right)(10\,\text{K})$$
$$= +21.0\,\text{kJ} \qquad [20]$$

(II) Melting ice, using the latent heat provided in the problem text:

$$\Delta H = +(55.5\,\text{mol})\left(6.0\,\frac{\text{kJ}}{\text{mol}}\right)$$
$$= +333.0\,\text{kJ} \qquad [21]$$

(III) Heating liquid water by 10 degrees:

$$\Delta H = +(55.5\,\text{mol})\left(75.86\,\frac{\text{J}}{\text{K}\cdot\text{mol}}\right)(10\,\text{K})$$
$$= +42.1\,\text{kJ} \qquad [22]$$

Thus, the total increase in enthalpy is $\Delta H = +396.1$ kJ.

## Standard Enthalpy of Formation

The result in Example 8.4 indicates that enthalpy values vary with several system parameters. For consistency in calculations, a **standard state** of the system is chosen at $T = 25°C = 298$ K and $p = 1$ atm. This standard state is then used to tabulate reference enthalpy values. Recall that absolute gravitational potential energy values are meaningless because we can freely choose a reference height for the system. The internal energy and enthalpy of a system are its total energy. Thus, absolute values for the internal energy or the enthalpy of a chemical system are similarly meaningless values. We use this fact to freely choose a reference point for these energies: the internal energy or enthalpy of an elementary system in its most stable form at standard conditions (25°C and 1 atm) is set equal to zero: $H = 0$ J. For any other system, we determine the enthalpy relative to this reference state. For example, $H = 0$ J for $O_2$ at standard conditions, while $H = +247.3$ kJ/mol for atomic oxygen under the same conditions.

Of particular use for such calculations is the **standard enthalpy of formation** of a compound, which is the energy needed to chemically form 1 mol of the compound from the elements at standard conditions. Standard enthalpy of formation values are tabulated and are usually labelled $\Delta H_f^0$, in which the subscript f stands for *formation* and the superscript 0 indicates the standard state.

Most standard enthalpy of formation values cannot be obtained experimentally. For example, it is impossible to mix carbon, oxygen, hydrogen, and nitrogen and hope to ignite the mixture to obtain isoleucine, which is a specific essential amino acid (see Table 8.1). In such cases the **theorem of Hess** is applied, which states that the enthalpy of formation is independent of the actual reaction by which the product is formed (because it is a variable of the state of the system). Thus, we can combine the enthalpies of several known processes, including chemical reactions, to obtain a value for a particular process we want to study. This is illustrated in Example 8.5 for the standard enthalpy of formation of carbon monoxide, CO.

**● EXAMPLE 8.5**

We want to determine the standard enthalpy of formation of CO. This value cannot be obtained experimentally, as oxidation of carbon always leads to the formation of (some) $CO_2$. However, the following processes yield experimentally accessible values:

$$C + O_2 \rightarrow CO_2 \quad \Delta H_f^0 = -393.5 \frac{kJ}{mol}$$
$$CO + \frac{1}{2} O_2 \rightarrow CO_2 \quad \Delta H_f^0 = -283.0 \frac{kJ}{mol} \quad [23]$$

Use Eq. [23] to find the standard enthalpy of formation of CO.

*Solution:* Using the theorem of Hess, the standard enthalpy of formation for $CO_2$ as given in the first formula of Eq. [23] remains unchanged whether carbon and oxygen react directly to carbon dioxide or whether CO is formed as an intermediate product:

$$C + O_2 \rightarrow CO + \frac{1}{2} O_2 \rightarrow CO_2 \quad [24]$$

For the process in Eq. [24], we know that $\Delta H_f^0$ for the entire reaction is $-393.5$ kJ/mol and that $\Delta H_f^0$ for the second reaction only is $-283.0$ kJ/mol. Thus, for the first reaction in Eq. [24] we find:

$$\Delta H_f^0 = -393.5 \frac{kJ}{mol} - \left(-283.0 \frac{kJ}{mol}\right)$$
$$= -110.5 \frac{kJ}{mol} \quad [25]$$

The formation of CO from the elements is an exothermic process (heat is released).

In chemical and biological processes, the energy stored in a molecule (e.g., a sugar molecule) may be used in two ways. First, it can be turned completely into heat. This is the case when a human body

**TABLE 8.3**

### Combustion heat* at 25°C for reactions of various compounds to $CO_2$ and $H_2O$

| Compound | $\Delta H$ (kJ/g) |
|---|---|
| Fat | −38.9 |
| Carbohydrates | −17.2 |
| Protein** | −17.2 |
| $C_nH_{2n+2}$, $1 \leq n \leq 7$ (Methane to heptane) | −55.7 to −48.1 |
| Ethanol | −29.7 |
| Benzene | −42.3 |
| Acetic acid | −14.5 |

*Combustion is a catabolic reaction, i.e., the breakdown of complex chemicals accompanied by the release of energy. The opposite case is called an anabolic reaction. These include all biosynthesis processes requiring energy.

**$\Delta H$ for reaction to urea since urea is the final combustion product of proteins in the human body.

responds to undercooling by shivering. For such cases, the knowledge of the change in internal energy in the reaction is sufficient (more precisely, the change of the enthalpy, since biological processes occur under isobaric rather than isochoric conditions). Table 8.3 compares enthalpy values for the combustion of the main components of food and some other organic compounds.

Second, the stored energy can be used as work. However, only part of the energy listed in Table 8.3 results in work, as calculated in Example 6.11. In that case the distinction between useful and useless energy matters, as the latter increases only the temperature of the body (as in the shivering case) but does not contribute to the work of muscle contraction. The enthalpy is not sufficient to describe such a process; the change in entropy needs to be taken into account.

## Standard Entropy

The enthalpy of formation of a chemical compound tells us nothing about the spontaneity of the process. The reason for this limitation is the fact that the internal energy and enthalpy are system properties obtained from the first law of thermodynamics. The conservation of energy does not reveal the direction in which a process evolves. Thus, we need to include one more parameter to completely describe a process: the entropy. It characterizes the state of a system and allows us to distinguish spontaneous from non-spontaneous processes. For the entropy, we established:

*$\Delta S > 0$: irreversible process, can occur spontaneously.*

*$\Delta S = 0$: reversible process, the system is continuously in equilibrium with its environment.*

*$\Delta S < 0$: process that requires a significant increase in the environmental entropy such that the entropy change of the superstructure is $\Delta S \geq 0$.*

Example 8.2 illustrates how entropy changes are calculated for physical processes. We are equally interested in the change of the entropy for chemical reactions, as these values indicate whether the chemical reaction is spontaneous. **Standard entropy** values at 25°C and 1 atm are tabulated for a wide range of chemical compounds. It is interesting to note that these values are obtained in a different fashion than the standard enthalpy of formation. In the case of the entropy, no compound or element has a zero-value at the standard state. This is due to the physical meaning of entropy as it relates to the degree of disorder in the system. Therefore, all absolute values of entropy are positive, or zero for a perfectly ordered system. Walther Nernst stated that perfectly ordered systems exist only at $T = 0$ K because the thermal energy of a system at $T > 0$ K causes at least some disorder. He therefore formulated the **third law of thermodynamics:**

*The entropy of a perfect crystal of a chemical element or compound at $T = 0$ K is zero, $S = 0$ J/K.*

Thus, the standard entropy at 25°C and 1 atm for 1 mol of any compound has a well-defined value. We find this value from Eq. [7], with the initial state at $T = 0$ K and the final state at $T = 25$°C. The right-hand side of Eq. [7] requires us to sum over all heat exchange contributions from 0 K to 298 K at atmospheric pressure, each divided by the respective temperature at which it occurs. These heat contributions in turn are written for 1 mol in the form $Q = C_p \cdot \Delta T$. Thus, we can determine the standard entropy from the area under the curve of $C_p/T$ versus $T$. An example is shown in Fig. 8.10, which illustrates the $C_p/T$ versus $T$ curve for $N_2$ from 0 K to 298 K. From the area under the curve we find $S^0_{N_2} = +191.2$ J/(K · mol). Standard entropy values are lower for pure crystals and higher for more complex solids (which allow for more disorder based on vibrations and rotations); this is illustrated by comparing diamond with the solid salts in Table 8.4. Standard entropy values also increase when we go from solid to liquid and again to the gaseous state, illustrated by comparing values along the subdivisions of Table 8.4.

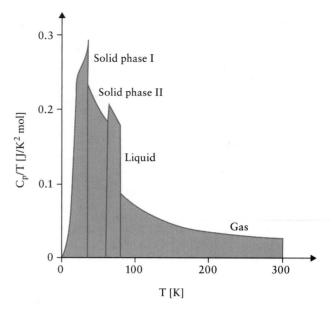

**FIGURE 8.10**

Plot of $C_p/T$ between 0 K and 298 K for nitrogen $N_2$. The area under the curve is the standard entropy for the compound $S^0_{N_2}$. In the temperature interval of interest nitrogen passes through two solid phases, melts at 63.14 K, and evaporates at 77.32 K. These phase transitions are noted in the figure as discontinuities of the heat-capacity function. At each phase transition, a term for the latent heat divided by the transition temperature must be added.

The standard entropy change for a given chemical reaction is then determined from values such as those in Table 8.4 by adding the entropy values of the products and subtracting the entropy values for the initial compounds. The stoichiometric factors have to be included in this calculation. In the same fashion, the **standard entropy of formation** of a chemical compound can be determined from the standard entropy of the compound minus the standard entropy of the elements.

## Gibbs Free Energy

The highlighted summary for entropy changes in the previous section is in principle sufficient to predict the outcome of any process we are interested in. However, for practical purposes, the entropy has the disadvantage that it requires a combined study of the system and its environment. As the statement for a process with $\Delta S < 0$ indicates, such processes can be achieved if appropriate processes occur concurrently in the environment. It would be more convenient to find a thermodynamic system parameter that allows us to make statements about the system and its propensity with respect to a certain process without considerations of the environment.

Initially, it was suggested to use the enthalpy for this purpose. However, spontaneous processes exist

## TABLE 8.4

### Standard entropy values (at 25°C, 1 atm) for various materials

| Material | Standard entropy $S^0$ ($J \cdot K^{-1} \cdot mol^{-1}$) |
|---|---|
| *1. Solids* | |
| Diamond (C) | 2.5 |
| Calcium (Ca) | 41.6 |
| CaO | 39.7 |
| $CaCO_3$ | 92.9 |
| NaCl | 72.4 |
| *2. Liquids* | |
| Mercury (Hg) | 76.0 |
| Water ($H_2O$) | 70.0 |
| Benzene ($C_6H_6$) | 175.3 |
| *3. Gases* | |
| Hydrogen ($H_2$) | 130.6 |
| Oxygen ($O_2$) | 205.0 |
| Nitrogen ($N_2$) | 191.2 |
| Water vapour ($H_2O$) | 188.9 |
| $CO_2$ | 213.8 |
| $NH_3$ | 192.6 |
| Ozone ($O_3$) | 237.7 |

Note an increase of the standard entropy with a decreasing order of the system: hard solids are more ordered than complex salts, solids are more ordered than liquids, and gases are the least ordered.

that are endothermic. Thus, even though most systems have a propensity toward a low energy state, this is not the sole driving force for chemical processes. Josiah Willard Gibbs resolved this issue in 1875 by introducing the **Gibbs free energy**:

$$G = H - T \cdot S$$
$$\Delta G = \Delta H - T \cdot \Delta S \qquad [26]$$

in which the second formula is used for the change of the state of a system or for a chemical reaction. The product $T \cdot S$ represents the amount of heat lost during the process. Thus, the Gibbs free energy represents the maximum obtainable work. The obtainable work is a maximum since a reversible process

is required to actually gain this amount of work. Eq. [26] allows us to summarize the properties of the Gibbs free energy for various processes:

*All natural phenomena are governed by the propensity of the system to lower its internal energy or enthalpy and, secondly, by the propensity of the system to increase its entropy.*
*$\Delta G < 0$: a spontaneous process.*
*$\Delta G = 0$: a process in which the initial and final states coexist in equilibrium.*
*$\Delta G > 0$: a process that occurs spontaneously in the reverse direction.*

Table 8.5 summarizes the basic processes that occur in physics and chemistry and the respective thermodynamic functions we need to study for a full characterization of the properties of the system during the process. For example, a process in an isolated system is fully described by studying the change in entropy because the internal energy of an isolated system is constant (first law of thermodynamics). On the other hand, a combination of isothermal and isobaric processes requires us to calculate the Gibbs free energy as both the enthalpy and the entropy may vary during the process. For most known organic and inorganic chemical processes, values of the standard Gibbs free energy are tabulated or can be calculated from tabulated values for the standard enthalpy and standard entropy.

The concept of maximum obtainable work as related to the Gibbs free energy further allows us to define the **chemical equilibrium**. If a system is in chemical equilibrium then the Gibbs free energy $G$ resumes a minimum value. If $G$ is not a minimum, then the system spontaneously decreases its Gibbs

## TABLE 8.5

### The fundamental physical and chemical processes and the respective thermodynamic functions needed to fully characterize the process

| Processes | Constant | Property to study |
|---|---|---|
| Isolated system | $U$ | Entropy $S$ |
| Isothermal/isochoric | $T, V$ | Free energy $F^*$ |
| Isothermal/isobaric | $T, p$ | Gibbs free energy $G$ |
| Adiabatic/isochoric | $S, V$ | Internal energy $U$ |
| Adiabatic/isobaric | $S, p$ | Enthalpy $H$ |

*The Helmholtz free energy has not been introduced since we do not further discuss isochoric processes.

free energy to the minimum value. If the process reducing the Gibbs free energy is reversible, then a maximum of work is obtained.

The parameters of state of a system $p$, $V$, $T$, $n$, $\Delta U$, $\Delta H$, $\Delta S$, and $\Delta G$ are all linked, with well-defined relations. We do not discuss all of these relations in the textbook; they are found in the physical chemistry literature when needed. Two examples are provided here because we need these relations later in this textbook:

- The dependence of the Gibbs free energy on the pressure for a process in which the temperature is held constant:

$$\Delta G = n \cdot R \cdot T \cdot \ln\left(\frac{p_{\text{final}}}{p_{\text{initial}}}\right) \quad [27]$$

This relation is used in Chapter 9 to define a chemical equilibrium between a solution and its vapour phase, and in Chapter 14 to discuss the electrochemical equilibrium across a nerve membrane.

- The dependence of the entropy on the temperature for a process in which the pressure is held constant:

$$\Delta S = n \cdot C_p \cdot \ln\left(\frac{T_{\text{final}}}{T_{\text{initial}}}\right) \quad [28]$$

This relation is used to solve problems at the end of the chapter.

## ● EXAMPLE 8.6

An instructive example of the role of the Gibbs free energy is the comparison of the formation of carbonates of group II elements from aqueous solutions. Table 8.6 provides the standard enthalpy and standard entropy for four carbonate formation reactions of the type

$$[X^{2+}]_{\text{aq}} + [CO_3^{2-}]_{\text{aq}} \rightarrow [XCO_3]_{\text{solid}} \quad [29]$$

What predictions can we make about the four processes?

*Solution:* We determine the Gibbs free energy for each of the four processes in Table 8.6: using $\Delta G = \Delta H - T \cdot \Delta S$ we find values ranging from $\Delta G = -46.0$ kJ/mol to $\Delta G = -50.2$ kJ/mol. Thus, all values are negative and quite similar: the four reactions occur spontaneously when the metal and carbonate ions meet in a solution.

However, the first three reactions have a positive $\Delta H^0$ value. This means that they are endothermic

### TABLE 8.6

**Standard enthalpy and entropy data for four carbonate formation reactions in aqueous solution under standard conditions**

| Element X | $\Delta H^0$ (kJ/mol) | $T \cdot \Delta S^0$ (kJ/mol) |
|---|---|---|
| Mg | +25.1 | +71.1 |
| Ca | +12.3 | +59.0 |
| Sr | +3.3 | +55.6 |
| Ba | −4.2 | +46.0 |

processes; i.e., the chemical reaction requires heat. This case is illustrated by the red curve in Fig. 8.11, which shows the enthalpy of a chemical reaction at constant pressure as a function of time. The reactants A and B form a transition state AB*, which leads to products C and D, which are either energetically less stable (case 1) or more stable (case 2) than the reactants. In case 1 the reaction is endothermic; in case 2 the reaction is exothermic.

Comparing the two columns in Table 8.6 shows that all four reactions are driven by the entropy term. The reason is the existence of a hydration shell around the ions that must be removed to form a solid precipitate. The elimination of the hydration shell allows the involved water molecules to move more freely; this represents a higher degree of disorder in the system.

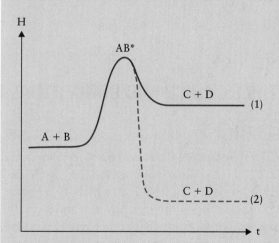

**FIGURE 8.11**

The enthalpy as a function of time for a chemical reaction. The reactants A and B form a transition state AB*, which then decomposes into the products C and D. Case 1 shows an endothermic process and case 2 an exothermic process.

## Concept Question 8.10

If mixing of components is always associated with an increase of entropy, why do water and oil not mix in Fig. 8.12?

**FIGURE 8.12**
Oil and water in a beaker.

ANSWER: Mixing is governed by the Gibbs free energy and not the entropy. In the case of oil and water, the enthalpy of mixing exceeds the gain from entropy, which is about 4 J/(K · mol). $\Delta H$ is large to provide for the formation of an increasing surface between oil and water droplets. (Surface energy is discussed in Chapter 11.) The result is different for mixing water and rock salt, where energy is gained when water molecules form a hydration shell around salt ions. (We discuss the formation of a hydration shell in Chapter 13.)

## Concept Question 8.11

The thermodynamic equilibrium between two states of a single component always lies entirely on one or the other side; e.g., at temperatures below the freezing point all water molecules are part of the solid state, and above the freezing point all water molecules are part of the liquid state. This situation is different for chemical reactions, where even for the most complete reactions a finite concentration of the reactants remains. What explains this difference?

ANSWER: The difference is due to the entropy of mixing. Its contribution is zero for a single component that undergoes a phase transition. The entropy of mixing contributes to the Gibbs free energy of a chemical reaction and always causes the concurrent presence of reactants and products, even though a large enthalpy variation can cause the equilibrium to lie very close to pure reactants or pure products.

# MULTIPLE CHOICE AND CONCEPTUAL QUESTIONS

### REVERSIBILITY

**Q–8.1.** 1 mol of an ideal gas is expanded from initial volume $V_{initial}$ to a final volume $V_{final}$, in each case starting at pressure $p_0$. (a) For which type of reversible process does the gas do the most work? (A) adiabatic expansion, (B) isothermal expansion, (C) isobaric expansion, (D) cannot be determined without further information. (b) For which type of irreversible process does the gas do the most work? (A) adiabatic expansion, (B) isothermal expansion, (C) isobaric expansion, (D) cannot be determined without further information. (c) If you chose one of the three processes in part (a), explain why the other two are still reversible despite the definition that a reversible process is the process that involves the most work.

**Q–8.2.** We use the arrangement of Fig. 8.5, but fill one chamber with oxygen and one chamber with nitrogen. (a) When you open the shutter, what process occurs? (b) Propose a modification to this experiment where the same process can be done reversibly.

**Q–8.3.** Marcellin Berthelot measured a large number of standard enthalpy of formation values. He justified that effort in an 1878 publication by saying that "every chemical process in an isolated system tends toward the products that release the most heat"; i.e., Berthelot believed his measurements reveal the **chemical affinity** of the reactants. Do you agree?

## ENTROPY

**Q–8.4.** We want to show that no engine (super-engine) can be more efficient than the Carnot process. For this we consider Fig. 8.13, which shows a proposed super-engine generating work and a reverse Carnot process restoring the heat extracted by the super-engine. Both engines operate between the same two heat reservoirs. (a) Is this process possible with respect to the first law of thermodynamics? (b) Is this process possible with respect to the second law of thermodynamics?

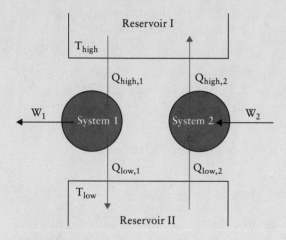

**FIGURE 8.13**

Two cyclic processes operating between two heat reservoirs. System 1 is a super-engine and system 2 is a Carnot process that operates in the reverse direction.

**Q–8.5.** The following statement about the entropy of a system is not correct: (A) It is a measure of the degree of order/disorder in the system. (B) It is a measure of the fraction of heat taken up by the system that is turned into work during a reversible cyclic process. (C) It determines whether an isolated system is in equilibrium or may undergo spontaneous processes. (D) It can be combined with the temperature and the enthalpy to determine the Gibbs free energy of the system. (E) The entropy difference between two states of the system is equal to the amount of heat exchanged with the environment during a process leading from one state to the other.

**Q–8.6.** Which of the following processes is associated with an increase in entropy? (A) A reversible expansion of a gas within an isolated superstructure. (B) An adiabatic expansion of a gas to twice its volume. (C) A complete Carnot cycle for an ideal gas. (D) Melting of a cube of ice in a beaker at room temperature. (E) Freezing of a litre of liquid water in a cold room at 5°C.

**Q–8.7.** A typical 1800s steam engine operated with steam of 125°C. Room-temperature air served as the low-temperature heat reservoir ($T = 25$°C). What was the maximum efficiency coefficient $\eta$ of that machine? (Choose the closest value.) (A) 100%, (B) 80%, (C) 34%, (D) 25%, (E) 10%.

**Q–8.8.** A cyclic Carnot process operates with a high-temperature heat reservoir at 500 K and a low-temperature heat reservoir at 300 K. To what temperature must the low-temperature heat reservoir be brought to increase the efficiency coefficient of the Carnot machine by a factor of 1.5? (Choose the closest value.) (A) 200 K, (B) 250 K, (C) 300 K, (D) 350 K, (E) 500 K.

**Q–8.9.** A machine operates within an isolated superstructure. Its operation causes an entropy increase of $\Delta S = 5$ J/K. What change $\Delta S^*$ is required in the machine's environment within the isolated superstructure to identify the machine as operating reversibly? (A) $\Delta S^* = 0$ J/K; (B) $\Delta S^* = +5$ J/K; (C) $\Delta S^* = -5$ J/K; (D) no value exists to answer the question; (E) the value of $\Delta S$ is different from those listed above.

**Q–8.10.** Which of the following processes has a negative change in entropy? (A) increase in the number of gas particles in a box; (B) increase of the internal energy of the particles in a box; (C) isothermal expansion; (D) formation of molecules from atoms, e.g., $2H \rightarrow H_2$; (E) relaxation of a stretched polymer.

**Q–8.11.** A piece of ice at temperature 0°C and 1.0 atm pressure has a mass of 1.0 kg. It then melts completely to water. What is its change in entropy? The latent heat of freezing of water is given as $3.34 \times 10^5$ J/kg. (A) 3340 J/K, (B) 2170 J/K, (C) 613 J/K, (D) 1220 J/K.

**Q–8.12.** Is it possible to build a heat engine that causes no thermal pollution?

**Q–8.13.** A thermodynamic process occurs in which the entropy of a system changes by $-8.0$ J/K. Based on the second law of thermodynamics, what can you state about the entropy change in the environment?

# ANALYTICAL PROBLEMS

## ENTROPY

**P–8.1.** We revisit the Carnot process discussed in P–7.24. This process is operated with 1.0 mol of an ideal gas of heat capacity $C_V = 3 \cdot R/2$. The pressure of the gas is 10.0 atm and the temperature is 600 K in the most compressed state. From there, an isothermal expansion leads to a pressure of 1.0 atm. The lower process temperature is 300 K. Draw this Carnot process in an $S–T$ diagram.

**P–8.2.** (a) We consider a reversible isothermal expansion of 1 mol of an ideal gas. Calculate the entropy change for a pressure decrease from 10 atm to 1 atm at 0°C. (b) What is the entropy change in the environment within the isolated superstructure? (c) What is the entropy change if the expansion is done adiabatically instead?

**P–8.3.** Calculate the entropy change during melting of 1.0 mol benzene. The melting point of benzene at atmospheric pressure is $T_m = 288.6$ K and its latent heat of melting is 30 kcal/kg.

**P–8.4.** Calculate the entropy of evaporation for 1 mol of the elements and compounds listed in Table 8.7.

### TABLE 8.7

**Boiling point $T_{boiling}$ and latent heat of evaporation for various materials**

| Material | $T_{boiling}$ (°C) | $\Delta H$ (kcal/mol) |
|---|---|---|
| Argon (Ar) | 87.5 | 1.88 |
| $CCl_4$ | 349.9 | 7.17 |
| $C_6H_6$ (benzene) | 353.3 | 7.35 |
| Mercury (Hg) | 629.8 | 15.50 |

**P–8.5.** We place 150 g ice at 0°C (latent heat of melting 1430 cal/mol) in a calorimeter with 250 g water at 80°C. Use 18.0 cal/(K · mol) for the molar heat capacity of liquid water and assume that this value is temperature-independent. (a) What is the final temperature of the water? (b) If the process is done reversibly, what is the entropy change of the combined system ice/water? (c) What is the entropy change in the environment for the reversible process? (d) What is the entropy change if the process is done irreversibly in an isolated beaker? *Hint:* Use Eq. [28] for the temperature dependence of the entropy.

**P–8.6.** Calculate the entropy of 1 mol oxygen gas ($O_2$) at atmospheric pressure and $T = 50$°C. Use for the molar heat capacity of oxygen its standard value at 25°C, i.e., $C_p = 29.4$ J/(K · mol).

**P–8.7.** Determine graphically the standard entropy of silver from the data given in Table 8.8.

**P–8.8.** We consider two phases of solid carbon: diamond and graphite, with $S^0_{diamond} = 2.44$ J/(K · mol) and $S^0_{graphite} = 2.3 \cdot S^0_{diamond}$. Which of the two carbon modifications is more stable if we establish a thermal equilibrium between them in an isolated system?

**P–8.9.** Derive Eq. [4] from Eq. [3].

## GIBBS FREE ENERGY

**P–8.10.** Assume that we found for a given chemical reaction $\Delta H = -100$ kJ and $\Delta S = -200$ J/K. Neglect the temperature dependence of these two values. What is the Gibbs free energy for the reaction at (a) room temperature and (b) 800°C?

**P–8.11.** Calculate $\Delta S$ and $\Delta G$ for the evaporation of 1 mol of water at $T = 100$°C and $p = 1$ atm. The latent heat of evaporation of water is 9.7 kcal/mol.

### TABLE 8.8

**Molar heat capacity $C_p$ for silver (Ag) at various temperatures**

| $T$ (°C) | $C_p$ (cal/(K · mol)) | $T$ (°C) | $C_p$ (cal/(K · mol)) | $T$ (°C) | $C_p$ (cal/(K · mol)) |
|---|---|---|---|---|---|
| −263 | 0.07 | −243 | 1.14 | −223 | 2.78 |
| −203 | 3.90 | −183 | 4.57 | −163 | 5.01 |
| −143 | 5.29 | −123 | 5.49 | −103 | 5.64 |
| −83 | 5.76 | −63 | 5.84 | −43 | 5.91 |
| −23 | 5.98 | −3 | 6.05 | +17 | 6.08 |

# SUMMARY

## DEFINITIONS

- Standard state for chemical processes (superscript 0): $p = 1$ atm, $T = 25°C = 298$ K
- Enthalpy: standard enthalpy of formation $\Delta H_f^0$: Difference between the enthalpy of a compound and the enthalpy of its elements.
- Entropy:
  - change of entropy with the state of a system:

$$\Delta S = S_{final} - S_{initial} = \sum_i \frac{Q_i}{T_i}$$

  - Standard entropy $\Delta S^0$ is the entropy of a chemical element or compound at the standard state.
- Gibbs free energy:

$$G = H - T \cdot S$$

## UNITS

- Entropy $S$: J/K
- Gibbs free energy $G$: J

## LAWS

- Second law of thermodynamics: In a cyclic process it is impossible to take heat from a reservoir and change it into work without releasing a fraction of the heat to a second reservoir at lower temperature.
- Third law of thermodynamics: The entropy of a perfect crystal of a chemical element/compound at $T = 0$ K is zero; $S = 0$ J/K.
- Entropy change for
  - reversible process: $\Delta S = 0$
  - spontaneous irreversible process (system and environment): $\Delta S > 0$
- Gibbs free energy change for
  - the transition between coexisting system components in equilibrium: $\Delta G = 0$
  - spontaneous processes $\Delta G < 0$

# CHAPTER 9

# BLOOD AND AIR
## Mixed Phases

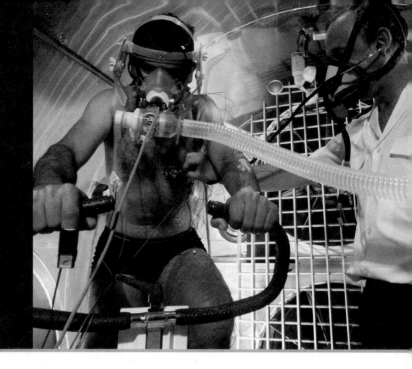

A mixed system in equilibrium is characterized by its composition. If the system is a gas, we define the partial pressure of each component as the pressure of this component as if it were alone in the container. Using the ideal gas law, Dalton demonstrated that the partial pressure is proportional to the molar fraction of the respective component.

If the mixed system is a liquid solution, we quantify its properties by studying the vapour phase, which is in thermodynamic equilibrium with the solution. The solution is called an ideal solution if no heat is released or required when mixing the components; thus, ideal solutions are conceptually equivalent to the ideal gas because intermolecular interactions are neglected in both systems.

Raoult showed that the partial pressure of a component in the vapour phase is proportional to the molar fraction of the same component in the ideal solution with which the vapour phase is in equilibrium. The thermal equilibrium between both phases is established when their respective Gibbs free energies are equal.

An important phenomenon in solutions is the osmotic effect. Osmosis is the movement of a solvent through a semipermeable membrane toward the side with the higher solute concentration. This effect tends to equalize the concentration of the solute on both sides of the membrane while causing a pressure difference across the membrane. This pressure difference is called the osmotic pressure.

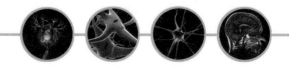

Blood and air are two important systems in human physiology. For this reason we discussed the ideal gas model in detail in Chapter 7, and we will devote Chapters 11 and 12 to the static and dynamic properties of fluids. In the current chapter the focus is on a particular aspect of these two systems: the properties of both air and blood depend on their composition of several chemically and physiologically distinct components.

John Mayow recognized the **multi-component gas composition** of air in the 17th century, stating that not all the components of air are essential for living organisms. It contains oxygen (first isolated by Joseph Priestley in 1774), which is its chemically most active component and which is essential for our metabolism. Antoine de Lavoisier identified nitrogen in 1776 as the main component in air. He also described carbon dioxide as a by-product of respiration.

Comparing the three panels in Fig. 7.4, we further note that the composition of air changes notably during respiration. The centre panel shows the composition of the air in the alveoli, which are the small hollow bubbles at the end of the bronchial tree where the gas exchange with the blood occurs. In the trachea the air is humidified (saturated with water). In the lungs the fraction of $CO_2$ has noticeably increased, mostly at the expense of the $O_2$ component. This is due to a diffusive exchange process discussed in the next chapter. The last panel then shows the composition of the exhaled air, which displays further changes due to the mixture of the gases in the active and dead spaces of the respiratory system during exhalation.

simplicity, we restrict our considerations to the oxygen and nitrogen components of dry air, and use $M_{O_2} = 32$ g/mol and $M_{N_2} = 28$ g/mol. Thus, the mass of 1 mol of air based on Fig. 7.4 is:

$$M_{air} = n_{O_2} \cdot M_{O_2} + n_{N_2} \cdot M_{N_2}$$

$$= 0.209 \text{ mol} \cdot 32 \frac{g}{mol} + 0.791 \text{ mol} \cdot 28 \frac{g}{mol}$$

$$= 28.836 \text{ g} \qquad [1]$$

and the weight contributions of its two components are:

$$f_{O_2} = \frac{m_{O_2}}{M_{air}} = \frac{n_{O_2} \cdot M_{O_2}}{M_{air}} = \frac{6.688 \text{ g}}{28.836 \text{ g}} = 23.2 \text{ wt\%}$$

$$f_{N_2} = \frac{m_{N_2}}{M_{air}} = \frac{n_{N_2} \cdot M_{N_2}}{M_{air}} = \frac{22.148 \text{ g}}{28.836 \text{ g}} = 76.8 \text{ wt\%}$$

$$[2]$$

We made the assumption that dry air can be modelled as an ideal gas. Note that it is not sufficient that this assumption applies separately to oxygen and nitrogen. We further require that the gas mixture acts ideal, i.e., that oxygen and nitrogen molecules do not interact with each other. This additional condition is discussed in the current chapter.

## Concept Question 9.1

**The values in Fig. 7.4 are given in vol%. Are the respective wt% the same? If not, how is dry air composed in wt%?** *Hint:* See the discussion of the terms *vol%* and *wt%* in Example 7.1.

ANSWER: These values are not the same, because the different components have different molecular mass. Vol% describes the fraction of space occupied by a component and is therefore given by the volume fraction occupied by particles (atoms or molecules) in the system. Weight percent (wt%) is the weight fraction of the system due to one of its components. Mass and weight in this context can be used alternatively as long as the experiment is done on the surface of Earth.

If we treat dry air as an ideal gas, 20.9 vol% oxygen means 0.209 mol of oxygen per mol of air. It contributes a mass of $0.209 \cdot M_{O_2}$ to the mass of 1 mol of air. For

## Blood as a Multi-Component Solution

Blood is a homogeneous mixture of liquids and liquid-like components. Fig. 9.1 shows the main components of human blood. The large blood cells can be separated in a centrifuge by a process called sedimentation. The volume fraction of blood cells is 46% for males and 41% for females. The remainder is called **blood plasma**. As shown in the lower part of Fig. 9.1, the plasma can be separated further. Water is the major component, but there are 70 to 80 g/L proteins, about 3.7 g/L cations (positively charged ions), and about 5.6 g/L anions (negatively charged ions) excluding protein ions. For the discussion in this chapter it is interesting to compare the concentrations of various ions in the plasma with those in cells and extracellular fluids. These data are provided in Table 9.1. Discrepancies between the concentrations in the cell and in the extracellular fluid (interstitium) will be discussed in Chapter 14, when we discuss how the mechanisms of nerve impulse transport depend on the differences between ion concentrations on the two sides of a cell membrane. In the

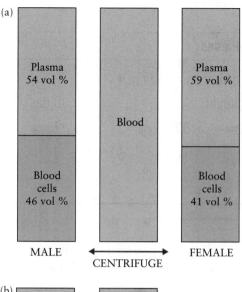

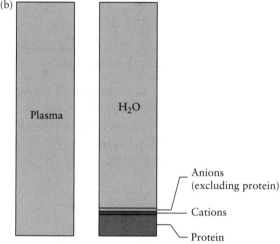

**FIGURE 9.1**

The components of human blood. (a) In a centrifuge plasma and blood cells are separated. The fractions vary slightly for males and females. The total amount of blood (5 L) contains on average $2.5 \times 10^{13}$ red blood cells (erythrocytes) and 2.5 to $5.0 \times 10^{10}$ leukocytes. (b) Separating the plasma further shows that it contains mostly water, with 70 to 80 g/L proteins, about 3.7 g/L positive ions, and about 5.6 g/L negative ions (excluding protein ions).

present chapter, the comparison of interest is between the columns labelled plasma and interstitium as each relates to osmotic effects in capillaries. The most important difference occurs in the concentration of proteins, which is four times higher in blood than in the interstitium.

## Mixed Phases

We start with a few definitions to clarify the nomenclature used in this chapter.

*A system that is homogeneous at the molecular level is called a **phase**. A phase consists of one or more **components**.*

Ice and snow are single phases. Homogeneously mixed chemicals, such as the alcohol and water in wine, are also single phases. Mixtures of gases always form single phases; liquid and solid mixtures may be one or several phases depending on their miscibility. Each type of molecule in a mixture is a component, e.g., sugar and water are the two components of an aqueous sugar solution, which is a single phase. However, if the chemical components are reactants and products of a chemical reaction, then they do not count as separate components. An example is singly and doubly charged phosphate ions in a solution, since they are related by a chemical equilibrium in the form $H_2PO_4^- \rightleftharpoons HPO_4^{2-} + H^+$.

*A system is called a **disperse system** when it consists of two or more phases but remains macroscopically homogeneous.*

A disperse system is a system that appears homogeneous when you look at it with the naked eye, but does not appear homogeneous when it is examined under a microscope. Different types of disperse systems are listed in Table 9.2; Fig. 9.2 shows a pumice stone. Not included as disperse systems are systems such as a water/oil mixture, since the two components in this system form two macroscopically separated phases.

---

**TABLE 9.1**

**Concentration of various positive and negative ions in blood plasma, extracellular fluids (interstitium), and cytoplasm (within cells)**

| Ion (mmol/L) | Na$^+$ | K$^+$ | Mg$^{2+}$ | Ca$^{2+}$ | Cl$^-$ | HCO$_3^-$ | Prot.$^-$ | HPO$_4^{2-}$ | SO$_4^{2-}$ |
|---|---|---|---|---|---|---|---|---|---|
| Plasma | 150 | 5 | 1 | 1.5 | 110 | 27 | 17 | 1 | 0.5 |
| Interstitium | 144 | 5 | 1 | 1.5 | 114 | 28 | 4 | 1 | 0.5 |
| Cells | 10 | 160 | 14 | — | 3 | 10 | 65 | 50 | 10 |

## TABLE 9.2

**Nomenclature for disperse systems. Examples are provided in parentheses**

| Phase 1 | | Dispersed in phase 2 (dispersion medium) | | |
| --- | --- | --- | --- | --- |
| | | In solid | In liquid | In gas |
| | Solid | Solid suspension (frosted glass) | Suspension (slaked lime) | Smoke |
| | Liquid | Solid emulsion (potter's clay) | Emulsion (milk) | Fog |
| | Gas | Solid foam (pumice stone) | Foam (soap foam) | — |

**FIGURE 9.2**
A pumice stone.

### Concept Question 9.2

**Identify examples for each of the disperse systems in Table 9.2.**

ANSWER: Examples are included in parentheses in Table 9.2.

## Dalton's Law

Gas mixtures such as air are the simplest case of mixed systems, as gases always mix and therefore always form a single phase. The physical behaviour of a gas mixture can be modelled with the ideal gas law. To describe gas mixtures we begin with the definition of the **partial pressure**. The partial pressure of a gas component is the pressure that would be measured if all other gas components were removed from the studied container. John Dalton studied a gas mixture of $n$ components with partial pressures $p_1, p_2, \ldots, p_n$,

and found in 1810 that the partial pressures add up to the total pressure measured for the mixture:

$$p_{\text{total}} = \sum_{i=1}^{n} p_i \qquad [3]$$

*Dalton's law states that the total pressure of a gas is equal to the sum of the partial pressures of its components.*

This means in particular that the partial pressure of a gas component does not depend on any of the other components; i.e., inter-molecular interactions are neglected. To interpret Eq. [3] further, we use the ideal gas law for each component:

$$p_{\text{total}} = \frac{n_1 \cdot R \cdot T}{V} + \cdots + \frac{n_n \cdot R \cdot T}{V} \qquad [4]$$

which is equivalent to:

$$p_{\text{total}} = \frac{R \cdot T}{V} \sum_{i=1}^{n} n_i \qquad [5]$$

Eqs. [4] and [5] state that the ideal gas law applies to an ideal gas mixture when the amounts of the individual gases $n_i$ in unit mol are added to obtain the total amount of the gas. This leads to the definition of the **molar fraction** $x_i$ of the $i$-th component:

$$\frac{n_i}{\sum_i n_i} = \frac{n_i}{n_{\text{total}}} = x_i \qquad [6]$$

With this definition, Eq. [5] is rewritten for each single component of the gas mixture:

$$\frac{p_i}{p_{\text{total}}} = x_i \qquad [7]$$

In this form, Dalton's law states that the ratio of the partial pressure of each component of a gas mixture to the total gas pressure is equal to the molar fraction of the same component. Historically, Dalton's discovery of the independent behaviour of gas components was one of the first significant indications that matter has a molecular structure.

Dalton's law can also be applied to gases dissolved in liquids if the solution is dilute, i.e., only a small concentration of a dissolved component is contained in the liquid. Several examples are presented in the following two sections to illustrate the importance of the partial pressure concept in physiological applications.

### Concept Question 9.3

**Under what conditions does Dalton's law not apply to a gas mixture?**

ANSWER: We used the ideal gas law for each gas component in Eq. [4]. This implies that two assumptions have been made:

- The individual gas components are ideal gases.
- The gas mixture is an ideal gas. This means that the various gas components don't interact with each other except for elastic collisions.

A case that obviously is excluded based on the second assumption is a chemically reacting gas mixture. But even a system that releases or requires heat during mixing is not ideal, because this heat exchange is a sign of intermolecular interactions.

## Applications of Dalton's Law in Diving

Two examples are discussed in this section.

### ● EXAMPLE 9.1

What is dangerous about diving while holding your breath? Specifically, study the case where a person hyperventilates first (to increase the fraction of oxygen in the lungs so that it is possible to dive longer) and then dives to a depth of 10 m, at which the total pressure in the lungs has doubled. Base the arguments on (i) the development of the partial pressures of oxygen and $CO_2$ in the lungs, and (ii) the partial pressures of both gases in the venous blood, as given in Table 9.3.

*Additional physiological information:* Table 9.3 provides the partial pressures of oxygen and carbon dioxide for a standard man in the alveoli and in the blood with respect to an air pressure of $p_{air} = 101.3$ kPa. The higher partial pressure of oxygen in the lungs causes oxygen to diffuse into the blood system. The opposite pressure difference pushes carbon dioxide from the venous blood into the

### TABLE 9.3

**Partial pressures of $CO_2$ and $O_2$ in the alveoli and the venous blood**

| Gas component | Alveoli | Venous blood |
|---|---|---|
| $O_2$ | 13.33 kPa | 5.33 kPa |
| $CO_2$ | 5.33 kPa | 6.13 kPa |

The values in the venous blood are obtained from Eq. [7] using the dissolved concentration of the gases.

lungs. Note that gas components always transfer from a space with higher partial pressure to a space with lower partial pressure. The pressure difference for $CO_2$ in Table 9.3 is lower since carbon dioxide penetrates the alveolar membrane more readily than oxygen and, therefore, does not need as high a driving force to pass through it. Diffusion concepts are discussed in the next chapter.

When a person is not breathing, the partial pressure of carbon dioxide in the blood increases as this gas cannot be removed through respiration. The increase in the partial pressure of $CO_2$ triggers the central chemoreceptor in the lowest section of the brain (medulla oblongata) to signal respiratory distress.

*Solution:* Fig. 9.3 illustrates the assumed diving attempt. The diver wants to extend the time to be spent under water and does this by initially hyperventilating (heavy breathing) to artificially decrease the carbon dioxide partial pressure in the blood. Hyperventilation allows the person to increase the partial pressure of oxygen in the alveoli, typically from 13.3 kPa to 15 kPa as shown in Fig. 9.3 (second curve from bottom, labelled $O_2$). The corresponding pressure scale is shown at the right side. The increase of the partial oxygen pressure is achieved by lowering the partial $CO_2$ pressure from 5.2 to 3.5 kPa (upper solid curve, labelled $CO_2$). The figure also includes a sketch of the alveolus/blood capillary system below the graphs, which shows at each stage of the dive the direction of gas exchange through the alveolar surface. The arrows indicate the dominant direction of gas transfer. During hyperventilation the partial pressure of nitrogen in the alveoli remains unchanged. Hyperventilation allows a healthy diver to stay below the surface for up to one minute.

Now the person dives to a depth of 10 metres. The depth profile of the dive is shown in Fig. 9.3 above the graphs of the partial pressures, defining the horizontal axis of the figure. As the diver

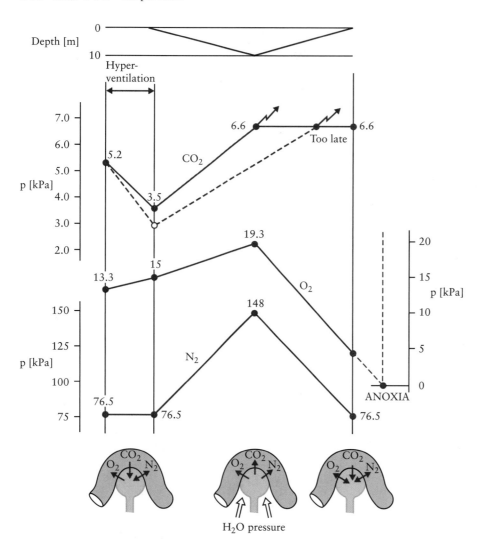

**FIGURE 9.3**

Sketch of a 10-m-deep dive after hyperventilation. The depth profile of the dive is shown at the top. Corresponding to the dive and the preceding hyperventilation, the changes of the partial pressures of nitrogen, oxygen, and carbon dioxide in the alveoli are recorded (solid lines). The dashed line corresponds to an even stronger initial hyperventilation, which causes the diver to resurface too late. In this case, anoxia-related unconsciousness may cause drowning. The curve for the partial pressure of $CO_2$ indicates that at 6.6 kPa a signal is triggered, forcing the person to resurface to breathe. The pressure scale for the partial alveolar pressure of carbon dioxide is shown at the upper left, for oxygen at the right, and for nitrogen at the lower left.

### ● EXAMPLE 9.1 (*continued*)

descends deeper and deeper below the surface, the pressure on the thorax increases significantly. We discuss this effect based on Pascal's law in Chapter 11, where we show quantitatively that the water pressure doubles at 10 m below the surface. This twofold increase of the external pressure on the thorax leads initially to a doubling of each partial pressure in the lungs due to Eq. [7]. However, as shown in the middle sketch at the bottom of Fig. 9.3, the increased pressure in the alveoli now pushes all gases into the blood system. $CO_2$ diffusion in particular is reversed when the $CO_2$ partial pressure in the lungs exceeds a value of 6.13 kPa, as shown in Table 9.3.

The validity of the changes in Fig. 9.3 for the $CO_2$ partial pressure in the alveoli and the blood capillaries is demonstrated with the following argument. When the external pressure on the human body rises, both the gas in the lungs and the blood in the arteries are subject to a pressure increase. The gas in the lungs responds like an ideal gas, allowing us to estimate the change in the concentration of $CO_2$ in the gas phase from the ideal gas law:

$$p_{CO_2} = \frac{n_{CO_2} \cdot R \cdot T}{V} = c_{CO_2} \cdot R \cdot T \qquad [8]$$

Thus, doubling the partial pressure doubles the concentration of the gas component.

On the other side of the membrane separating the alveolus and the blood capillary the liquid blood can be treated as an incompressible fluid, for which a pressure increase does not lead to a volume change. Consequently, no change in the concentration of dissolved components in the fluid results. Thus, a doubling of the pressure on the human body inverts the direction of the concentration step across the alveolar membrane.

During the dive shown in Fig. 9.3, the oxygen and carbon dioxide partial pressures in the alveoli rise by less than a factor of 2: $O_2$ to only 19.3 kPa, since it is continuously consumed by the body, and $CO_2$ to 6.6 kPa. The partial pressure of $CO_2$ cannot rise higher since the blood system can take up a large amount of $CO_2$. The value of 6.6 kPa partial pressure of $CO_2$ triggers the central chemoreceptor as described above; i.e., the diver now feels a strong urge to resurface.

A diver obeying this urge and approaching the surface from a depth of 10 m encounters a rapid decrease of the water pressure accompanied by noticeable changes in the partial pressures in the lungs. The nitrogen value comes down to its pre-dive value. The $CO_2$ partial pressure remains roughly constant as the blood pushes into the alveoli all excess $CO_2$ that it had to absorb due to the high external pressure. At this stage the change of the oxygen partial pressure is critical. It decreases during the resurfacing for three reasons: (I) a drop of the total gas pressure in the lungs, (II) a renewed ability of the blood to absorb oxygen to replace the leaving $CO_2$, and (III) continued oxygen consumption by the body's metabolism. In the case shown as solid lines for $CO_2$ and $O_2$ in Fig. 9.3, the final partial pressure of $O_2$ in the alveoli is 4.2 kPa.

However, the dashed line for $CO_2$ illustrates the dangers associated with diving for a person misjudging the physical laws of nature: excessive hyperventilation may lower the initial partial pressure of $CO_2$ below the value considered above. Thus, the person feels comfortable below the surface for a longer time, particularly at 10 m depth where the dangerous decrease of the partial pressure of oxygen in the lungs is not noticed because its partial pressure has increased due to the external water pressure. This time, following the dashed lines in Fig. 9.3, the signal to surface comes too late since the partial pressure of oxygen drops to 0.0 kPa during surfacing (anoxia). At that moment the diver loses consciousness and will drown if not rescued by others.

**FIGURE 9.4**

A diver with diving gear.

Water pressure at 60 m depth increases sevenfold. Thus, Eq. [9] states that a sevenfold increase also exists in the partial pressure of nitrogen in the alveoli. This increase, in turn, leads to about a sevenfold increase of the partial pressure of $N_2$ in the blood because gas diffuses across the membrane between the alveolus and the blood capillary as a result of the increased partial pressure in the lungs.

When the diver resurfaces too quickly, the blood cannot push the dissolved nitrogen back into the alveoli fast enough because diffusion is a slow process. The lower external pressure closer to the surface then causes nitrogen to exceed its solubility in blood and form bubbles. This effect is called **embolism**, **Caisson disease**, or **diver's paralysis**.

Even if the diver surfaces slowly, danger still looms during deep sea diving. At great depths, the partial pressure of oxygen in the blood has also risen to dangerous levels. A prolonged increase of the partial pressure of $O_2$ increases the risk of **hyperoxia**, which is the condition caused by excess oxygen in the blood, acting toxic for partial pressures above 40 kPa. A partial pressure for $O_2$ of 70 kPa for several days or 200 kPa for 3 to 6 hours causes the alveolar surface to shrink

## ● EXAMPLE 9.2

The diving gear shown in Fig. 9.4 allows diving to depths of about 60 m, since the gas cylinder automatically regulates the air supply so that the pressure of the inhaled air is always equal to the pressure of the surrounding water. Why is it dangerous to resurface from such a dive too quickly?

*Solution:* During the dive, the overall increase of the pressure leads also to an increase of the partial pressure of nitrogen in the lungs. This follows from Eq. [7] and a constant molar fraction of nitrogen:

$$p_{N_2} = x_{N_2} \cdot p_{total} \qquad [9]$$

## ● EXAMPLE 9.2 (*continued*)

irreversibly; an $O_2$ partial pressure of 220 kPa or higher results in cramping and unconsciousness. These conditions can occur when diving with compressed air/oxygen tanks at 100 m depth.

## Air Travel

## ● EXAMPLE 9.3

The atmospheric pressure decreases with height above sea level. The left column of Fig. 9.5 shows the total atmospheric pressure as a function of height from sea level to 20 km. (a) Above which height is it impossible to survive outside a pressurized aircraft? (b) Above which height is it deadly to breathe air? (c) Above which height is it no longer sufficient to breathe with an oxygen mask? (d) If great heights are so dangerous to us, how do birds manage to fly at high altitudes?

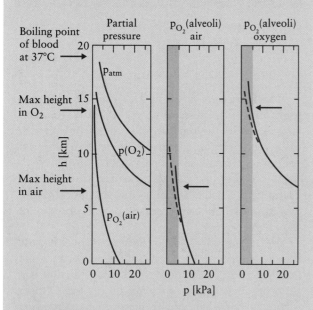

**FIGURE 9.5**

Total pressure and partial oxygen pressure in inhaled air (left column), partial oxygen pressure in the alveoli for air breathing (centre column), and partial pressure for oxygen-mask breathing (right column). Data include heights from ground to 20 km. The grey area represents partial oxygen pressures below 5 kPa, which prohibits breathing. The dashed curves indicate regular breathing; the solid curves correspond to oxygen-deficiency breathing.

*Solution to part (a):* At 19 km the air pressure has decreased to about 5 kPa, and blood starts to boil at 37°C. This was the cause of death of the

crew of the Russian *Soyuz II* mission, when returning from their 24-day *Salyut I* space station visit in June 1971 (the first successful USSR space station visit). When a seal of the space capsule broke during re-entry into Earth's atmosphere, the three cosmonauts, Georgi Dobrovolski, Vladislav Volkov, and Viktor Patsayev, died within seconds because they were not wearing pressurized space-suits.

At a reduced air pressure, boiling of a liquid occurs far below the temperature at which it boils in the laboratory under normal conditions. Fig. 9.6 illustrates how the boiling temperature of water depends on pressure. The reason for this observation lies in the thermal equilibrium between the liquid and its vapour at the boiling point. The partial pressure of water reaches the atmospheric pressure earlier when the atmospheric pressure is lowered. In *The Travels of Marco Polo* (written in 1299), the Venetian adventurer described how complicated the preparation of food was in 1272 when he camped in the Pamir (Himalayan mountains) more than 4000 m above sea level. At that height, water boils between 80°C and 90°C, as shown in Table 9.4. It is interesting to note that Marco Polo also reported their campfires provided much less warmth at that altitude.

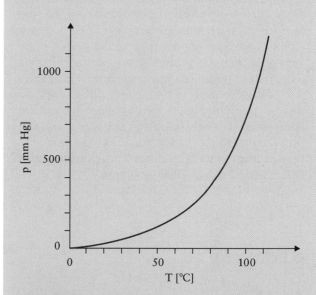

**FIGURE 9.6**

Pressure of water vapour in equilibrium with liquid water at temperatures between 0°C and 120°C. Water boils when the atmospheric pressure is equal to its vapour pressure.

*Solution to parts (b) and (c):* Nominal air pressure at sea level is 101.3 kPa. Given that oxygen makes up 21% of air, a partial pressure of oxygen of 21.3 kPa is calculated from Eq. [7]. When this

## TABLE 9.4

### Boiling point of water as a function of altitude

| Altitude (m) | Pressure (mmHg) | Boiling point H$_2$O (°C) |
|---|---|---|
| 0 | 760 | 100 |
| 1000 | 671 | 98 |
| 2000 | 592 | 94 |
| 3000 | 523 | 91 |
| 4000 | 461 | 88 |
| 5000 | 407 | 84 |
| 6000 | 359 | 80 |
| 7000 | 317 | 78 |
| 8000 | 280 | 75 |

air is inhaled, the partial oxygen pressure in the alveoli is sustained at 13.3 kPa, as shown in Table 9.3. This value is lower than the atmospheric value since (i) the inhaled air becomes saturated with water vapour in the trachea, and (ii) the continuous gas exchange in the alveoli increases the $CO_2$ component of the air at the expense of the oxygen component (see Fig. 7.4).

The dependence of the various pressure values relevant to breathing are shown in the first two columns of Fig. 9.5 as a function of altitude. The total pressure and the partial pressure of oxygen in air are shown as the top and bottom curve in the first column, and the corresponding partial pressure of oxygen in the alveoli is shown in the middle column (dashed line). As the plot indicates, the partial pressure curves are essentially parallel to the total air pressure since Eq. [7] applies.

**Hypoxia** is an acute respiratory distress disabling normal brain functions that occurs when the partial pressure of $O_2$ in the alveoli decreases below 4.7 kPa. At that point sufficient oxygen can no longer be absorbed by the blood to maintain a partial pressure of oxygen in the veins of 5.33 kPa (see Table 9.3). This limit is indicated by the shaded areas in the last two columns of Fig. 9.5.

*Solution to part (b):* The middle column of Fig. 9.5 shows that the minimum oxygen limit is reached at 4000 m height for a person breathing normally. Increased breathing involving the respiratory reserve volume (called **oxygen-deficiency breathing**) is triggered automatically by our body when needed. Increased breathing stretches the limit to a maximum height of 7000 m. A well-known accident caused by hypoxia was the 1999 death of U.S. golf champion Payne Stewart when a small aircraft suddenly lost cabin pressure at high altitude. Flying on autopilot between 7 km and 13 km altitude for several hours, the airplane carried the incapacitated passengers and crew until it ran out of fuel and crashed.

*Solution to part (c):* Above 7000 m, oxygen equipment must be used. For a person breathing 100% oxygen (e.g., in large airplanes) the centre curve in the left column of Fig. 9.5 shows the partial pressure of $O_2$ before it is inhaled and the last column shows the partial pressure of $O_2$ in the alveoli for oxygen breathing. Normal breathing with this equipment allows a person to maintain a partial pressure above 4.7 kPa to a height of 12 km, or, with oxygen-deficiency breathing, to 14 km. Thus, commercial airplanes stay below heights of 14 km, since above that height even oxygen masks would not save the lives of the passengers and crew in the case of accidental cabin pressure loss.

*Solution to part (d):* Birds have adapted to flight at high altitudes, as shown in Fig. 9.7. The figure highlights the avian respiratory system, which consists of lungs and several air sacs. Contraction and relaxation of the air sacs pushes the air through the lungs. We distinguish posterior sacs, through which the air flows before it reaches the lungs, and anterior sacs, which the air reaches after it passes through the lungs. During inhalation, both sets of

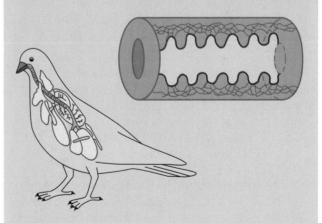

**FIGURE 9.7**

The respiratory system of birds. Air sacs in front of (posterior air sacs) and behind (anterior air sacs) the lungs ventilate the lungs. The inset shows a small bronchial tube (parabronchi) with alveoli and capillaries along the side walls. This arrangement allows the air to flow steadily through the parabronchi while gas exchange occurs at the membrane walls. During inhalation both sets of air sacs expand, and during exhalation both sets of air sacs deflate. Two cycles of inhalation and exhalation are required for the air to pass all the way through the bird's respiratory system.

## ● EXAMPLE 9.3 (*continued*)

air sacs expand. The posterior sacs fill with fresh air from the outside, and the anterior sacs fill with used air from the lungs. Later, during exhalation, both the air sacs deflate, pushing air from the posterior sacs into the lungs, and from the anterior sacs out through the bird's trachea. Two cycles of inhalation and exhalation are therefore required for the air to pass all the way through.

This system completely exchanges the air in the lungs for every breath; i.e., a lung oxygen concentration much higher than in mammals is maintained. This better use of the partial pressure of oxygen in the air is one reason why birds get away with flying at high altitudes. This adaptation is not a simple one, though. Besides the addition of air sacs, the alveoli had to be reconfigured from a dead-end system to a system allowing for continuous one-directional flow through tiny tubes, which are called **parabronchi**.

# Thermodynamics of Mixed Phases

We have introduced all of the required laws of thermodynamics to allow us to quantify processes that occur in mixed phases or during mixing. An example highlights their applications.

## ● EXAMPLE 9.4

Two gas containers are each thermally isolated. They are separated by a valve. Container I contains 1.5 L of ideal gas I at 0°C, and container II contains 2.5 L of ideal gas II at 25°C. The pressures in the two containers are initially the same at $p_{initial} = 1$ atm. Assume that the mixed gas is also ideal. (a) Express the amount of gas in each container in unit mol. (b) What are the final pressure and temperature after the valve has been opened? (c) What are the molar fraction and the partial pressure of ideal gas I? (d) What is the entropy change during mixing?

*Solution to part (a):* The gases are not yet mixed. Using the initial gas parameters, we find:

$$n_I = \frac{p_{initial} \cdot V_I}{R \cdot T_I}$$

$$= \frac{(1.013 \times 10^5 \, \text{Pa})(1.5 \times 10^{-3} \, \text{m}^3)}{\left(8.314 \, \frac{\text{J}}{\text{K} \cdot \text{mol}}\right)(273 \, \text{K})}$$

$$= 0.067 \, \text{mol}$$

$$n_{II} = \frac{p_{initial} \cdot V_{II}}{R \cdot T_{II}}$$

$$= \frac{(1.013 \times 10^5 \, \text{Pa})(2.5 \times 10^{-3} \, \text{m}^3)}{\left(8.314 \, \frac{\text{J}}{\text{K} \cdot \text{mol}}\right)(298 \, \text{K})}$$

$$= 0.102 \, \text{mol} \qquad [10]$$

*Solution to part (b):* Assuming that the gas mixture behaves ideally, we use Eq. [4] in the form:

$$p_{mix}(V_I + V_{II}) = (n_I + n_{II}) \cdot R \cdot T_{mix} \quad [11]$$

This equation cannot be solved without further input because both $p_{mix}$ and $T_{mix}$ are unknown. We know that the system does not exchange work or heat with the environment during mixing. Work is excluded because a valve is opened, and heat exchange is excluded since both containers are thermally isolated. Thus, the internal energy of the two gases must remain constant during mixing:

$$\Delta U_I + \Delta U_{II} = 0 \qquad [12]$$

This can be rewritten for the mixing process of ideal gases using $U = (3/2)n \cdot R \cdot T$:

$$n_I \cdot R(T_{mix} - T_I) + n_{II} \cdot R(T_{mix} - T_{II}) = 0 \quad [13]$$

which yields after division by the universal gas constant $R$:

$$(n_I + n_{II})T_{mix} = n_I \cdot T_I + n_{II} \cdot T_{II} \qquad [14]$$

We combine Eqs. [11] and [14] to obtain the final pressure:

$$p_{mix} = \frac{(n_I + n_{II})R \cdot T_{mix}}{V_I + V_{II}}$$

$$= \frac{n_I \cdot R \cdot T_I + n_{II} \cdot R \cdot T_{II}}{V_I + V_{II}} \qquad [15]$$

The two terms in the last numerator are rewritten with Eq. [10]:

$$p_{mix} = \frac{p_{initial} \cdot V_I + p_{initial} \cdot V_{II}}{V_I + V_{II}} = p_{initial} \quad [16]$$

The pressure in the system has not changed during mixing, as expected from Dalton's law for ideal gas components. The final temperature is then calculated from Eq. [11]:

$$T_{mix} = \frac{p_{initial}(V_I + V_{II})}{R(n_I + n_{II})}$$

$$= \frac{(1.013 \times 10^5 \text{ Pa})(1.5 \text{ L} + 2.5 \text{ L})}{\left(8.314 \frac{J}{K \cdot mol}\right)(0.067 \text{ mol} + 0.102 \text{ mol})}$$

$$= 288 \text{ K} \qquad [17]$$

which corresponds to +15°C.

*Solution to part (c):* The molar fraction is defined in Eq. [6] as:

$$x_I = \frac{n_I}{n_I + n_{II}} = \frac{0.067 \text{ mol}}{0.067 \text{ mol} + 0.102 \text{ mol}}$$

$$= 0.396 \qquad [18]$$

Note that this value is not equal to the ratio of 1.5 litres to 4.0 litres because the two gases are initially at different temperatures.

The partial pressure of ideal gas I in the mixed gas is determined from Eq. [4] or [5]:

$$p_I = \frac{R \cdot T_{mix}}{V_{total}} n_I$$

$$= \frac{\left(8.314 \frac{J}{K \cdot mol}\right)(288 \text{ K})}{4.0 \times 10^{-3} \text{ m}^3} 0.067 \text{ mol}$$

$$= 40.1 \text{ kPa} \qquad [19]$$

We obtain this result alternatively from the molar fraction of gas I in Eq. [7]:

$$p_I = x_I \cdot p_{mix} = 0.396 \cdot (1.013 \times 10^5 \text{ Pa})$$

$$= 40.1 \text{ kPa} \qquad [20]$$

*Solution to part (d):* If we study each gas component separately, the entropy of mixing has four contributions: each gas component changes its volume and, independently, its temperature. We assume that these contributions can be calculated separately, using Eq. [8.10] for the volume change and Eq. [8.28] for the temperature change. Recall that $C_p = 5 \cdot R/2$ for an ideal gas. Thus, we obtain for ideal gas I:

$$\Delta S_{\Delta V} = n_I \cdot R \cdot \ln\left(\frac{V_{final}}{V_{initial}}\right)$$

$$= (0.067 \text{ mol})\left(8.314 \frac{J}{K \cdot mol}\right)\ln\left(\frac{4.0 \text{ L}}{1.5 \text{ L}}\right)$$

$$= +0.546 \frac{J}{K}$$

$$\Delta S_{\Delta T} = n_I \cdot C_p \cdot \ln\left(\frac{T_{final}}{T_{initial}}\right)$$

$$= (0.067 \text{ mol})\left(20.78 \frac{J}{K \cdot mol}\right)\ln\left(\frac{288 \text{ K}}{273 \text{ K}}\right)$$

$$= +0.074 \frac{J}{K} \qquad [21]$$

and for ideal gas II:

$$\Delta S_{\Delta V} = n_{II} \cdot R \cdot \ln\left(\frac{V_{final}}{V_{initial}}\right)$$

$$= (0.102 \text{ mol})\left(8.314 \frac{J}{K \cdot mol}\right)\ln\left(\frac{4.0 \text{ L}}{2.5 \text{ L}}\right)$$

$$= +0.399 \frac{J}{K}$$

$$\Delta S_{\Delta T} = n_{II} \cdot C_p \cdot \ln\left(\frac{T_{final}}{T_{initial}}\right)$$

$$= (0.102 \text{ mol})\left(20.78 \frac{J}{K \cdot mol}\right)\ln\left(\frac{288 \text{ K}}{298 \text{ K}}\right)$$

$$= -0.072 \frac{J}{K} \qquad [22]$$

The total change in entropy during mixing is $\Delta S = +0.947$ J/K. The entropy of mixing is dominated by the volume contributions; the temperature effect is minor.

## Concept Question 9.4

**Is the mixing process in Example 9.4 reversible? If not, how can the mixing be modified so that it is done reversibly?**

ANSWER: The mixing process described in the example is irreversible because the process cannot be reversed by closing the valve at a later time. This is not surprising, because we did not store work from the initial process in the environment; usually such work has to be applied to the system when reversing the process.

Mixing can be performed reversibly. This is illustrated in Fig. 9.8: initially, two gases are separated by two pistons that are built with semipermeable membranes. The left membrane allows gas I molecules to pass, while it is not permeable for gas II molecules. The right membrane in turn allows gas II to pass while blocking gas I. Allowing each gas to expand by pushing away the respective piston that blocks it leads to mixing of the gases with a constant

## Concept Question 9.4 (*continued*)

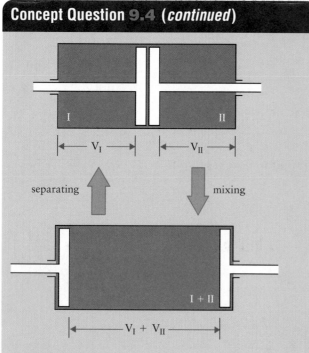

**FIGURE 9.8**

Reversible mixing of two ideal gases I and II. Two pistons are initially located face to face at the centre of the container. The spaces behind the pistons have volumes $V_I$ and $V_{II}$ and contain, respectively, the two separated gases. During mixing, each piston is pushed back by the gas that cannot penetrate it. The other gas passes through the piston, mixing in the centre space that opens up in the process. At the end of the mixing, the two gases share the centre space of volume $V_I + V_{II}$. The work done on each piston can be stored in the environment and can later be used to reverse the mixing process by pushing the pistons together to their initial positions.

volume. The process is reversible because the work done on the pistons can be used to push the pistons back to their initial position. The gases become separated as only one membrane can be passed by each gas.

## Liquid Solutions

As we turn our attention from gases to liquids, Dalton's law is no longer sufficient because it assumes ideal gas behaviour for each component of the mixture, which requires that intermolecular interactions can be neglected. This is an inappropriate assumption for a **solution** because intermolecular interactions are required to cause the gas to condense to become a liquid in the first place. Thus, we need other tools to describe liquid mixtures such as blood, extracellular fluids, and the cytoplasm in the cell.

A liquid in a beaker has a surface that separates the **condensed phase** from the **vapour phase**. It is useful to develop a description of liquid solutions starting at that interface. We know that the solution is in mechanical and chemical equilibrium with the vapour at the surface. It would have to accelerate upward or downward were there no mechanical equilibrium, and the amount of vapour would have to increase or decrease if there were no chemical equilibrium. This allows us to utilize the gas laws we have already established to characterize the vapour phase and thereby the condensed phase indirectly.

An important experimental observation is the fact that in equilibrium a well-defined, non-zero vapour pressure is present above a liquid at any temperature. The pressure of this vapour is called the **saturation vapour pressure**. If a gas comes in contact with a liquid and is undersaturated, evaporation occurs until saturation is reached. This is the mechanism by which the dry air that we inhale is saturated with water vapour in the trachea before it reaches the alveoli in the lungs.

## Ideal Solutions and Raoult's Law

Now that we have introduced the concept of a vapour pressure above a liquid, we can define and study ideal solutions.

*An **ideal solution** is a solution for which the enthalpy of the system is the same for the sum of the separated components and for the mixed system.*

This means that no heat is absorbed or released while mixing the components of an ideal solution, except for the energy needed to adjust the volume (due to the $p \cdot V$ term in the definition of the enthalpy $H$). This definition utilizes the same concept used in Dalton's definition of partial pressures in gas mixtures: ideal means that interactions between the various molecular species in the mixed state are negligible.

François Raoult made the following experimental observation for such a system, called **Raoult's law**:

$$p_i = x_i \cdot p_i^0 \qquad [23]$$

*Raoult's law states that the partial pressure $p_i$ of the i-th component in the vapour phase above the solution is proportional to the molar fraction $x_i$ of the i-th component in the solution. The proportionality factor is the vapour pressure of the i-th component above a pure liquid of the same component ($p_i^0$).*

This law is important for the description of solutions as it allows us to predict their properties from measurements in the vapour phase. The vapour pressure curves for an ideal solution of two components A and B are shown in Fig. 9.9. The vertical axis is the partial pressure of component A or B and the

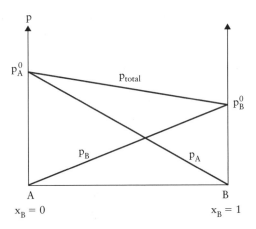

**FIGURE 9.9**

Sketch of a two-phase system illustrating Raoult's law. The partial pressures of the two components in the gas phase are linearly proportional to the molar fractions of the components in solution.

horizontal axis is the molar fraction of component B, ranging from $x_B = 0$ for pure liquid A, to $x_B = 1$ for pure liquid B.

Fig. 9.10 shows experimentally measured partial and total vapour pressure data for two real systems. Toluene and benzene, shown in Fig. 9.10(a), behave ideally since the data follow Raoult's law across the entire molar fraction range. This indicates that effectively no interaction occurs between the benzene and toluene molecules—in particular, no interaction that differs from the interactions between either a pair of toluene molecules or a pair of benzene molecules. Many other systems behave non-ideally. As an example, a system consisting of acetone and chloroform is shown in Fig. 9.10(b). The vapour pressure curves predicted by Raoult's law are shown as dashed lines. The solid lines are the experimental data and clearly deviate from Raoult's law.

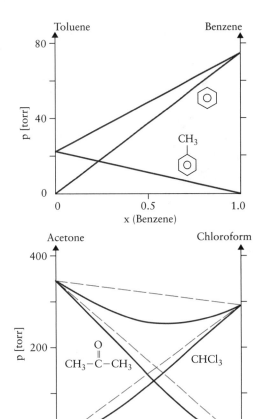

**FIGURE 9.10**

Experimental partial pressure curves over a liquid solution for (a) toluene and benzene, which is a nearly ideal solution that follows Raoult's law, and (b) acetone and chloroform, which is a non-ideal solution that follows Raoult's law only in the very dilute limit, i.e., near $x = 1$ and $x = 0$.

---

## Concept Question 9.5

**The system acetone/chloroform in Fig. 9.10 does not obey Raoult's law (dashed lines). Under what conditions would you still use Raoult's law for this system?**

ANSWER: The figure confirms that ideal behaviour is still a good approximation if the system is dilute ($\lim x_i \to 0$ or $\lim x_i \to 1$). Note that the solid curves and the dashed curves coincide reasonably well near $x(CHCl_3) = 0$ and $x(CHCl_3) = 1$.

---

Sometimes Raoult's law is confused with Henry's law. **Henry's law** states that the solubility of a gas in a liquid is proportional to its pressure above the

surface of the liquid. Henry's law therefore allows us to *control* the composition of a solution by adjusting parameters in the gas phase. Raoult's law in turn allows us to *measure* the composition of a solution using the gas phase.

## Gibbs Free Energy and the Chemical Potential

Our next objective is to apply the laws of thermodynamics to the vapour/solution systems discussed in this section. Since we are dealing with open systems in which an exchange of matter between the vapour phase and the solution is possible, we connect to our discussion of Gibbs free energy in Chapter 8. The studied system is sketched in Fig. 9.11, which shows a solution and a vapour phase with one component highlighted (solid dots). If the solution and the

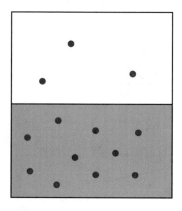

**FIGURE 9.11**

Sketch of a solution and its gas phase in equilibrium. The component of interest is represented by blue circles.

vapour phase are in equilibrium, the Gibbs free energies must be balanced:

$$G_{\text{mixed vapour}} = G_{\text{solution}} \quad [24]$$

If the Gibbs free energies for both system parts were not the same, evaporation or condensation would occur to establish a chemical equilibrium at the liquid surface. We study the Gibbs free energy because we focus on the pressure and the temperature as the primary system parameters. The solution and the vapour phase are two open systems. Consequently, we have to add one more variable to our consideration: the amount of the highlighted component in Fig. 9.11 on each side of the liquid surface in unit mol. This allows us to include the change in the energy of the system as a function of the change in the amount of material, $G = f(p, T, n)$. If $p$ and $T$ are held constant, we define a new variable, called the **chemical potential $\mu$**:

$$G_{\text{total}} = \sum_{i=1}^{n} \mu_i \cdot n_i \quad [25]$$

Thus, the chemical potential of the $i$-th component, $\mu_i$, is the Gibbs free energy per mol for that component in unit J/mol. Since the single components in an ideal solution do not interact with each other, the overall equation for the equilibrium of the system, Eq. [24], must apply to each component separately:

$$\mu_{i,\text{gas phase}} = \mu_{i,\text{solution}} \quad [26]$$

For the gas phase, the expression for the Gibbs free energy as a function of pressure in Eq. [8.27] applies when the temperature of the solution and the vapour phase are the same. Choosing $p^* = 1$ atm as the reference pressure for the standard state (indi-

cated by the *), the chemical potential of 1 mol of the $i$-th component in the vapour is written in the form:

$$\mu_{i,\text{gas}} = \mu_{i,\text{gas}}^* + R \cdot T \cdot \ln\left(\frac{p_{i,\text{gas}}}{p^*}\right) \quad [27]$$

This equation allows us to study the pressure-related contributions to the chemical potential explicitly. Next, we rewrite Eq. [27] to replace the pressure dependence with the molar fraction dependence, using Raoult's law in the form $p_{i,\text{gas}} = p_{i,\text{gas}}^0 \cdot x_i$ from Eq. [23]:

$$\mu_{i,\text{gas}} = \mu_{i,\text{gas}}^* + R \cdot T \cdot \ln\left(\frac{p_{i,\text{gas}}^0}{p^*}\right) + R \cdot T \cdot \ln(x_i) \quad [28]$$

Now we use Eq. [26]. The left-hand side is replaced with Eq. [28]. This leads to:

$$\mu_{i,\text{solution}} = \mu_i^0 + R \cdot T \cdot \ln(x_i) \quad [29]$$

in which $\mu_i^0$ is the chemical potential (Gibbs free energy per mol) of the vapour of the $i$-th component over the pure liquid of component $i$. Thus, Eq. [29] allows us to study the dependence of the chemical potential in the solution on the molar fraction of the $i$-th component in the vapour phase.

In particular, Eq. [29] allows us to derive a formula for the Gibbs free energy per mol for mixing. We write the Gibbs free energy based on Eq. [25], before and after mixing:

$$G_{\text{before mixing}} = \sum_{i=1}^{n} \mu_i^0 \cdot n_i$$

$$G_{\text{after mixing}} = \sum_{i=1}^{n} \mu_i \cdot n_i \quad [30]$$

$$= \sum_{i=1}^{n} \mu_i^0 \cdot n_i + R \cdot T \sum_{i=1}^{n} n_i \cdot \ln(x_i)$$

where we used Eq. [29] to rewrite the second formula. The difference between the two terms represents the Gibbs free energy of mixing:

$$\Delta G_{\text{mixing}} = R \cdot T \sum_{i=1}^{n} n_i \cdot \ln(x_i) \quad [31]$$

We divide this equation by $n_{\text{total}}$ to find the Gibbs free energy of mixing for 1 mol of the solution:

$$\Delta G_{\text{mixing}}\left(\frac{\text{J}}{\text{mol}}\right) = R \cdot T \sum_{i=1}^{n} x_i \cdot \ln(x_i) \quad [32]$$

● **EXAMPLE 9.5**

Calculate the Gibbs free energy of mixing (a) for 0.5 mol each of a two-component system at room temperature (25°C), (b) at body temperature (37°C), and (c) for the system discussed in

Example 9.4, neglecting the contribution due to the initial temperature difference.

*Solution to part (a):* Eq. [32] is written for two components:

$$\Delta G_{mixing}\left(\frac{J}{mol}\right) = R \cdot T(x_1 \cdot \ln(x_1) + x_2 \cdot \ln(x_2))$$

[33]

Substituting the given values yields:

$$\Delta G_{mixing} = \left(8.314 \frac{J}{K \cdot mol}\right)(298 \text{ K}) \cdot 2 \cdot \left(\frac{1}{2} \ln \frac{1}{2}\right)$$

$$= -1.7 \frac{kJ}{mol}$$

[34]

This value is negative because molar fractions are always smaller than one, and the logarithm of a number less than one is negative. Thus, mixing is a spontaneous process.

*Solution to part (b):* We use Eq. [34] but change the temperature to $T = 310$ K: $\Delta G_{mixing} = -1.79$ kJ/mol.

*Solution to part (c):* We mixed two ideal gases in Example 9.4 with a total amount of 0.169 mol. Thus, Eq. [31] is used:

$$\Delta G_{mixing} = R \cdot T(n_1 \cdot \ln(x_1) + n_2 \cdot \ln(x_2))$$ [35]

which is rewritten with the data found in Example 9.4:

$$\Delta G_{mixing} = \left(8.314 \frac{J}{K \cdot mol}\right)(288 \text{ K})$$

$$\times \left((0.067 \text{ mol}) \cdot \ln\left(\frac{0.067}{0.169}\right)\right.$$

$$\left. + (0.102 \text{ mol}) \cdot \ln\left(\frac{0.102}{0.169}\right)\right)$$

[36]

Eq. [36] yields $\Delta G_{mixing} = -270$ J.

Eq. [32] allows us further to determine the entropy of mixing for an ideal solution. The general relation between the thermodynamic functions of state of a mixed system is:

$$\Delta G_{mixing} = \Delta H_{mixing} - T \cdot \Delta S_{mixing}$$ [37]

which simplifies for an ideal solution due to $\Delta H_{mixing} = 0$:

$$\Delta S_{mixing} = -\frac{\Delta G_{mixing}}{T} = -R \sum_{i=1}^{n} n_i \cdot \ln(x_i)$$ [38]

## ● EXAMPLE 9.6

Calculate the entropy of mixing (a) for 0.5 mol each of a two-component system at room temperature (25°C) and (b) for the system at 288 K discussed in Examples 9.4 and 9.5, neglecting again the contribution due to the initial temperature difference.

*Solution to part (a):* With the Gibbs free energy for mixing already calculated in Example 9.5, the first formula in Eq. [38] is used:

$$\Delta S_{mixing} = -\frac{\Delta G_{mixing}}{T} = -\frac{-1.7 \frac{kJ}{mol}}{298 \text{ K}}$$

$$= +5.7 \frac{J}{K \cdot mol}$$

[39]

*Solution to part (b):* We again use the first formula in Eq. [38] and the data from the last part of Example 9.5:

$$\Delta S_{mixing} = -\frac{\Delta G_{mixing}}{T} = -\frac{-270 \text{ J}}{288 \text{ K}} = +0.94 \frac{J}{K}$$

[40]

This value corresponds to the result in Example 9.4(d).

Fig. 9.12 shows the three thermodynamic functions of state for mixing of 1 mol of an ideal solution at room temperature.

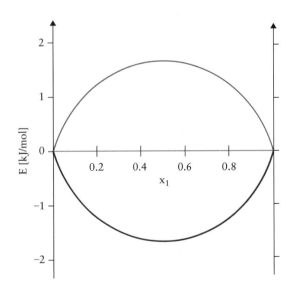

**FIGURE 9.12**

Gibbs free energy $\Delta G_{mixing}$ (red line), enthalpy $\Delta H_{mixing}$ (green line), and entropy multiplied by temperature $T \cdot \Delta S_{mixing}$ (blue line) for 1 mol of an ideal solution. The curves are shown as a function of the molar fraction $x_1$, with the molar fractions related as $x_2 = 1 - x_1$. The temperature is room temperature (25°C).

# Osmosis

An important physiological application of the physics of solutions is the process of **osmosis**. Osmosis occurs when some components in a solution cannot pass through an otherwise permeable membrane. This occurs, for example, in the blood filtration system in the glomerulus of the kidneys, in which the basement membrane blocks proteins and blood cells from leaving the blood system.

Osmosis can be observed in many biological systems. Various weeds are capable of breaking through asphalt surfaces. The plants develop the strength from osmotic transport of water from cell to cell, building up an internal water pressure comparable to the force a jackhammer can exert. The pressure in a cell due to water driven in by osmosis is called **turgor pressure**. It is this pressure that allows wood-free plants to stand upright.

## Osmotic Pressure

We quantify the osmotic effect for the system shown in Fig. 9.13. The figure shows two parts of a system separated by a membrane. The left part contains a pure liquid (component 1) and the right part contains the same liquid, which acts as a solvent for a second component (component 2, illustrated by blue circles). The solvent passes the membrane freely and therefore establishes a chemical equilibrium for component 1 between the two parts of the system. Component 2 cannot pass through the membrane—i.e., the membrane is semipermeable—and no equilibrium is established for component 2.

*Osmosis is the movement of a solvent through a semipermeable membrane into a solution of higher solute concentration. This effect tends toward equilibration of the concentration of the solute on the two sides of the membrane.*

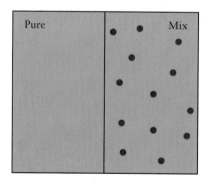

**FIGURE 9.13**

Sketch of a model to describe the osmotic effect. A solvent is free to pass through a semipermeable membrane (centre line), while a dilute component (blue circles) is blocked by the membrane.

The equilibrium condition for component 1 of the system in Fig. 9.13 requires its chemical potential to be the same on both sides of the membrane:

$$\mu_{1,\text{pure}} = \mu_{1,\text{mix}} \qquad [41]$$

Since the chemical potential is different for a pure liquid and the same liquid in a solution, some molecules of component 1 diffuse through the membrane, resulting in non-equal amounts of component 1 on the two sides. This leads to a difference in the pressure of component 1 across the membrane. This pressure difference is defined as the **osmotic pressure** $\Pi$ (capital letter $\pi$):

$$\Pi = p_{\text{mix}} - p_{\text{pure}} \qquad [42]$$

*The osmotic pressure is the excess pressure we must apply on the side of the solution to prevent the diffusion of solvent through the membrane.*

## Van 't Hoff's Law

Jacobus Henricus van 't Hoff determined the dependence of the osmotic pressure on the concentration of the non-permeable component: Consider a pure solvent, labelled 1, which is separated from a solution of component 2 in solvent 1 by a membrane permeable only to solvent 1. In equilibrium, an osmotic pressure $\Pi$ has developed, as defined in Eq. [42]. The condition for equilibrium is that the chemical potential of component 1 is the same on both sides of the membrane, as stated in Eq. [41]. Thus, in equilibrium, the value of $\mu_1$ in the solution must equal the value of $\mu_1$ in the pure solvent 1.

Two factors cause the value of $\mu_1$ in the solution to depart from that in pure solvent 1. These factors must therefore have exactly equal and opposite effects on $\mu_1$. The first is the change in $\mu_1$ produced by mixing with component 2 in the solution. This change causes a lowering of $\mu_1$ as quantified in Eq. [29]. Counteracting this is the increase in $\mu_1$ in the solution due to the imposed pressure $\Pi$. We note without deriving this result that the change of the chemical potential with pressure at constant temperature is equal to the molar volume of the respective chemical component. For simplicity, we assume that the molar volume of component 1, $V_1$, is independent of pressure; i.e., the solution is incompressible. We further assume that the solution is an ideal solution. Then we can write:

$$V_1 \cdot \Pi = R \cdot T \cdot \ln(x_1) \qquad [43]$$

Note that the logarithm function is included in the Math Review "Powers and Logarithms" at the end of

Chapter 1. The implications of Eq. [43] can be stated as follows: The osmotic pressure is the external pressure that must be applied to the solution to raise the vapour pressure of solvent 1 to that of the pure component 1.

Now we assume that we deal with a very dilute solution, i.e., a solution with a very small molar fraction of the non-permeating component. This allows us to make further simplifications to Eq. [43]. First we replace $x_1$ in Eq. [43] by $(1 - x_2)$ and use a common mathematical expansion (Taylor series) of the logarithm function in the form:

$$-\ln(1 - x) = x + \frac{1}{2}x^2 + \cdots \qquad [44]$$

If $x \ll 1$, only the first term on the right-hand side has to be considered. Second, the molar volume $V_i$ of the solvent in the solution is set equal to the molar volume of the respective pure liquid, $V_1^0$. This allows us to rewrite Eq. [43] for $x_2 \ll 1$ in the form:

$$V_1^0 \cdot \Pi = R \cdot T \cdot x_2 \qquad [45]$$

which is **van 't Hoff's law.** We isolate the osmotic pressure in Eq. [45]:

$$\Pi = \frac{R \cdot T}{V_1^0} x_2 \qquad [46]$$

*The osmotic pressure is directly proportional to the molar fraction (concentration) of the dilute dissolved component, $x_2$.*

Eq. [46] is used to illustrate the osmotic effect experimentally. A vertical tube filled with a sugar solution and sealed with a semipermeable membrane is placed in a beaker with water. The water, which is able to pass the membrane in both directions, is driven into the tube due to the lower water concentration in the tube. The liquid level in the tube rises until its hydrostatic pressure compensates the osmotic pressure from Eq. [46]. The same effect happens on a microscopic scale when cellular systems are immersed in water.

**FIGURE 9.14**

Ripe cherries.

ANSWER TO PART (a): If the stem of a dandelion is split into strips and the weed is placed in water, the strips roll up because the spongy cells inside the stem expand due to the osmotic uptake of water. In uncut stems, the strong outer layer of cells prevents this from happening.

ANSWER TO PART (b): The skins of ripe cherries burst when they are placed in water. The skin allows water to diffuse into the cherry while preventing the sugar juice from diffusing outward. The water pressure in the cherry cells is driven up by the osmotic effect until it causes the fruit to burst.

# Physiological and Medical Applications

## Homeostatic Control of the Osmolarity of Blood

The human body operates a careful budgeting of the intake and loss of water. The primary mechanisms of water loss are urine excretion (1.5 L/day, corresponding to 60%) and perspiration through skin and the lungs (0.9 L/day, corresponding to 36%). The water intake of an adult typically consists of 1.5 L/day as beverages and 0.7 L/day with solid food. Another 0.3 L/day results from the metabolic reactions in the body.

The water balance is measured by a centre in the hypothalamus. This centre doesn't measure the total amount of body water directly, but analyzes changes

---

> **Concept Question 9.6**
>
> Find examples of the osmotic effect in your environment. In particular, what happens when (a) the stem of a dandelion is split into long strips and the weed is placed in a glass of water, and (b) ripe cherries, such as the ones in Fig. 9.14, are placed in water?

in the concentration of various components dissolved in water. The measurement is based on the osmosis effect and takes place in the **osmoreceptors** of the hypothalamus. Eq. [46] establishes that the osmotic pressure is proportional to the concentration of the dilute components, which cannot permeate the membrane in the osmoreceptors. These components in the blood are said to be osmotically active. Their concentration is used to define the **osmolarity** with unit osm/L. The unit osm is related to the unit mol. For example, if we dissolve 1 mol glucose in water, we obtain a solution with 1 osm/L. If we dissolve 1 mol of NaCl (rock salt), we obtain a solution of 2 osm/L because the salt molecule dissolves into two separate ions, $Na^+$ and $Cl^-$.

Blood has an osmolarity of 290 mosm/L. A solution with this value is called **isotonic**, a solution with a smaller osmolarity is called **hypotonic**, and a solution with a larger osmolarity is called **hypertonic**. The osmoreceptors cause the release of ADH (antidiuretic hormone) when we observe variations in the osmolarity as small as 3 mosm/L (i.e., variations of about 1%). ADH triggers the kidneys to respond to hypertonic conditions with water retention or to hypotonic conditions with excess water excretion. A hypertonic osmolarity also causes a signal to the brain creating the perception of thirst.

This sensitive water concentration detection system has been developed by the body to protect itself against the rather severe consequences of a water imbalance. Water deficit can lead to diabetes insipidus and hypovolemic shock; excess water can cause intracellular edemas (e.g., brain swelling). Also, a too-fast intake of water (e.g., by a patient who is dehydrated) is dangerous as it may cause vomiting or even shock.

## Edemas

*Edema is an abnormal infiltration and excess accumulation of serous fluid in connective tissue.*

Solutions are found throughout the body. They are often separated by semipermeable membranes, leading to many applications of osmosis. In this section, the concepts introduced above are applied to the special case of edemas, such as the case shown in Fig. 9.15. An edema is a collection of liquids (serum) in body tissue (outside of cells and blood vessels). To establish the different factors that play a role in the occurrence of edemas, the osmotic properties of a healthy blood capillary are introduced first.

Fig. 9.16 shows a typical capillary system. An arteriole splits into several capillaries, which reunite in

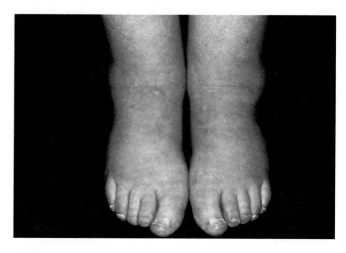

**FIGURE 9.15**

An example of edema in the legs of a person.

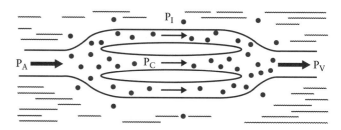

**FIGURE 9.16**

Arteriole (at left) splitting into several parallel capillaries that reunite downstream into a single venule (shown at right). The protein concentration (blue circles) is about four times higher in the blood than in the interstitium.

a venule after passing through organ tissue. The capillaries are surrounded by extracellular fluid since the blood vessel membrane is semipermeable, blocking proteins in the blood from leaving while permitting serum to diffuse in and out of the blood system. This semipermeable behaviour is reflected in Table 9.1, which compares the concentrations of different components in the interstitium and the blood plasma. Large protein molecules cannot pass through the membrane, while all other components can do so and establish equal concentrations on both sides.

Gauge pressures at different points in Fig. 9.16 are as follows (remember that gauge pressures are values relative to air pressure): $p_A = 3.3$ kPa at the arterial end of the capillaries, $p_V = 1.3$ kPa at the venous end of the capillaries, and $p_I = -0.8$ kPa in the interstitium. Due to the protein concentrations listed in Table 9.1, the osmotic pressure of the blood is given as $\Pi_C = \Pi_A = \Pi_V = 3.7$ kPa, and the osmotic pressure of the extracellular fluid is $\Pi_I = 0.8$ kPa.

Note that the capillary system varies from the simple model in Fig. 9.13 because non-zero protein concentrations are present on both sides of the membrane, which means that the osmotic pressure on both sides must be considered. We first check for consistency of the presented data, beginning with the ratio of the osmotic pressures by using van 't Hoff's law in the form:

$$\frac{\Pi_C}{\Pi_I} = \frac{x_C}{x_I} \qquad [47]$$

The ratio of concentrations of the osmotic active components (proteins) on both sides of the membrane is given in Table 9.1 in millimol per litre:

$$\frac{x_C}{x_I} = \frac{17 \pm 1 \text{ mmol/L}}{4 \pm 1 \text{ mmol/L}} = 4.3 \pm 1.1 \qquad [48]$$

The osmotic pressure data are given in this section:

$$\frac{\Pi_C}{\Pi_I} = \frac{3.7 \text{ kPa}}{0.8 \text{ kPa}} = 4.6 \qquad [49]$$

The values found in Eqs. [48] and [49] are consistent with Eq. [47] and therefore prove that the osmotic pressure data used in this section are consistent with the data in Table 9.1.

What are the consequences for the blood passing through a capillary? Fig. 9.17 illustrates the flow of serum in a healthy capillary. Shown is the pressure relative to atmospheric pressure along the capillary from the arterial end (left side) to the venous end (right side). The dashed curve at the top represents the pressure change in the capillary. Due to the high concentration of proteins in the blood, a large osmotic pressure must be taken into account. The apparent pressure in the capillary after correcting for the proteins is given by the curve $p_C - \Pi_C$, which decreases left to right from $-0.4$ kPa to $-2.4$ kPa.

The interstitium pressure is harder to measure, but has been estimated to be $-0.8$ kPa. Again, the calculation of the apparent pressure in the interstitium must include the correction for the osmotic pressure due to the protein concentration—which, however, is lower outside the blood vessel. The apparent pressure in the interstitium is constant at a value of $-1.6$ kPa, as the curve $p_I - \Pi_I$ in Fig. 9.17 illustrates.

Comparing the apparent pressures inside and outside the capillary membrane (two red lines in Fig. 9.17) allows us to predict the direction of serum flow. Serum flows in the direction toward the lower pressure; i.e., it is pushed away by the higher pressure. Since the two apparent pressure curves cross somewhere between the arterial and venous ends of the capillary, an initial outward flow of serum into the extracellular tissue is compensated by an inward flow from the tissue into the capillary slightly farther

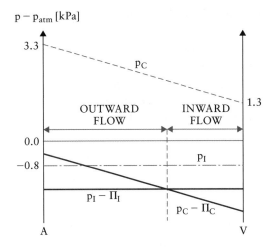

**FIGURE 9.17**

Pressure diagram along a healthy capillary from the arterial end (A) to the venous end (V). The measured pressures are given by the dashed line (in capillary) and dash-dotted lines (in interstitium). To determine the serum flow across the blood vessel membrane, these pressures have to be corrected for the osmotic pressure due to the presence of a non-permeating protein component. This leads to the red lines crossing at about the halfway point along the capillary. At this point the flow of serum reverses from vessel ⟹ interstitium to interstitium ⟹ vessel.

downstream (a typical capillary length is 0.85 mm). On balance, no increase of serum occurs in the tissue: 90% actually returns into the capillary immediately (resorption) and about 10% reaches the lymphs.

This delicate balance can be disturbed in several ways, leading to medical problems we can now illustrate by studying Fig. 9.17:

- The pressure on the venous end increases, leading to a continuous outflow of serum across the entire organ. This occurs, for example, when a patient has a **right heart failure**, i.e., when the pumping of blood in the right heart ventricle becomes ineffective. In this case, blood collects in the veins, resulting in a pressure increase. Liquid collects in the tissue of the lowest body parts (legs for a patient who is standing, and back for a patient who is lying down) until the pressure of the interstitium has built up enough to suppress this outward flow. A **left heart failure** causes the same effect in the pulmonary veins (the veins leading to the lungs). This results in a pulmonary edema, which causes the patient literally to drown.

- The osmotic pressure in the capillary decreases. The clinical term for this is **hypoproteinemia.** This condition often indicates that the patient is suffering from a *nephrotic syndrome*, i.e., protein loss due to the diffusion of protein into the urine in the kidneys, where the basement membrane has become permeable to proteins. A reduction in the blood concentration of proteins results in a decrease of the osmotic pressure in the entire cardiovascular system. This disturbs primarily the balance of in- and outward flow of serum in capillaries.

• The osmotic pressure of the capillaries and the osmotic pressure of the interstitium become equal due to local diffusion of proteins into the extra-cellular tissue. This is often caused by **inflammation**. Injured or burned tissue leads to dilation (widening) of capillaries to increase the blood supply as an increased number of immune-response components are needed locally, such as antibodies, macrophages (slow), or granulocytes (fast). Since these rather large units have to enter the tissue, other proteins and blood cells are also enabled to permeate the capillary walls. This secondary effect leads to a local levelling of the osmotic pressures in interstitium and blood vessels. Subsequently, serum is leaking into the tissue.

Osmotic effects also play a prominent role in the resorption processes in the nephrons of the kidneys. Water is not directly re-absorbed but follows actively re-absorbed components, such as sodium ions and $HCO_3^-$, due to the created osmotic pressure gradient toward the blood side of the membrane.

# MULTIPLE CHOICE AND CONCEPTUAL QUESTIONS

**Q–9.1.** Extracellular fluids and the cytoplasm of most human cells have a concentration of osmotically active components of 0.29 mol/kg, due to dissolved sugar or ions such as potassium, sodium, and chlorine. (a) If the body loses water (dehydration) or has a too-large intake of salt, both of which affect the extracellular fluid, what consequence does this have for the body cells? (b) What would happen if, instead, a human body were to lose too much salt from the extracellular fluid?

**Q–9.2.** Which is lighter under otherwise equal conditions (i.e., same pressure, temperature, volume): humid air or dry air?

**Q–9.3.** In 1965, a French team led by Jacques-Yves Cousteau lived for 28 days in the deep-sea station *Conshelf III* at 108 m below the sea surface. They breathed an oxygen/helium mixture (called helox) instead of air. (a) Would you agree with their claim that breathing this mixture is easier than breathing air? (b) Can you think of another reason why they used helox instead of air? *Note:* One member of the team reported that among other adverse effects this exercise irritated his tastebuds, and he could no longer distinguish caviar from chicken. This, of course, is a disastrous effect for a Frenchman!

**Q–9.4.** Both the freezing point and the boiling point of a solution are different from the respective pure solvent value. The freezing point of a dilute solution of component B in solvent A is lowered as:

$$\Delta T = T_{melt} - T_{melt,A} = -\frac{R \cdot T_{melt,A}^2}{\Delta H_{melt}} x_B \quad [50]$$

in which $T_{melt}$ is the melting point of the solution, $T_{melt,A}$ is the melting point of the solvent, $\Delta H_{melt}$ is the latent enthalpy of melting, and $x_B$ is the molar fraction of the solute.

The boiling point of a dilute solution of component B in solvent A in turn is raised as:

$$\Delta T = T_{boil} - T_{boil,A} = +\frac{R \cdot T_{boil,A}^2}{\Delta H_{evaporation}} x_B \quad [51]$$

in which $T_{boil}$ is the boiling point of the solution, $T_{boil,A}$ is the boiling point of the solvent, $\Delta H_{evaporation}$ is the latent enthalpy of evaporation, and $x_B$ is the molar fraction of the solute. Using the result in P–9.3, illustrate both effects in a $p$–$T$ diagram for the vapour pressure.

**Q–9.5.** (a) The osmolarity of a solution is measured with an osmometer. Does Q–9.4 provide a physical principle suitable for designing an osmometer? (b) The osmolarity in an aqueous solution is recorded as a value per litre water. If you measure osmolarity for blood plasma that contains 70 g/L proteins, or for cytoplasm in erythrocytes with 300 g/L haemoglobin, how large a correction factor do you need to include in the value you report?

# ANALYTICAL PROBLEMS

**P–9.1.** The osmotic effect is often used to determine the molar mass of macromolecules. Here, we illustrate how this is done. The apparatus used is shown in Fig. 9.18: it consists of two chambers that are separated by a semipermeable membrane. One tube is filled with a dilute solution of the macromolecules and the other tube is filled with pure solvent. Additional tubes are mounted vertically on each chamber to measure the osmotic pressure (using Pascal's law, as discussed in Chapter 11).

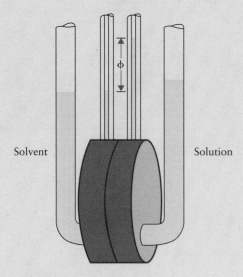

Solvent          Solution

**FIGURE 9.18**

Assume that the experiment is done at 25°C. We use van 't Hoff's law in the form:

$$\Pi = \frac{R \cdot T}{M} c \qquad [52]$$

where $c$ is the concentration of the macromolecule in the solution (in unit kg/m³), $M$ is the molar mass (in unit kg/mol) of the macromolecule, and $\Pi$ is the osmotic pressure, as measured with the apparatus in Fig. 9.18. Since van 't Hoff's law applies exactly only

for very dilute solutions, several measurements are taken for various dilute solutions (i.e., several different values of $c$) and are then extrapolated. For the extrapolation, we plot $\Pi/c$ vs. $c$ and obtain the value for $\Pi/c$ at $c = 0$ from the plot.

Using the data from Table 9.5 for the osmotic pressure of polyisobutylene in benzene and cyclohexane, (a) plot $\Pi/c$ versus $c$ for both solutions, (b) find the extrapolation value of $\Pi/c$ at $c = 0$ for each curve, and (c) use Eq. [52] to determine the molar mass of polyisobutylene.

## TABLE 9.5

**Polyisobutylene data for two solutions**

| Concentration (g/cm³) | Osmotic pressure $\Pi$ (atm) | |
|---|---|---|
| | In benzene | In cyclohexane |
| 0.02 | 0.0021 | 0.0122 |
| 0.015 | 0.00153 | 0.0068 |
| 0.01 | 0.001 | 0.0031 |
| 0.005 | 0.0005 | 0.0009 |

**P–9.2.** We mix 0.25 g oxygen gas ($O_2$) and 1.5 g nitrogen gas ($N_2$) in a container of 2.0 L at 20°C. Assuming that both gases behave ideally, what are (a) the partial pressure of oxygen, (b) the partial pressure of nitrogen, and (c) the total pressure in the container? *Hint:* For the molar mass of oxygen use 32 g/mol and for the molar mass of nitrogen use 28 g/mol.

**P–9.3.** Use Raoult's law to derive the **vapour pressure depression** for an ideal dilute solution. *Hint:* Consider a system with two components, solvent A and solute B, with $x_A \gg x_B$.

# SUMMARY

## DEFINITIONS

• Partial pressure of component $i$ is the pressure of the $i$-th component with all other components removed from the container.

• Molar fraction $x$:

$$\frac{n_i}{\Sigma_i n_i} = \frac{n_i}{n_{total}} = x_i$$

• Chemical potential: the chemical potential of the $i$-th component, $\mu_i$, is the Gibbs free energy per mol for that component:

$$G_{total} = \sum_{i=1}^{n} \mu_i \cdot n_i$$

• Osmotic pressure $\Pi$: We must apply excess pressure on the solution side to prevent diffusion of solvent through the membrane:

$$\Pi = p_{mix} - p_{pure}$$

## LAWS

- Dalton's law for partial gas pressures:

$$p_{\text{total}} = \sum_{i=1}^{n} p_i$$

This is equivalent to:

$$\frac{p_i}{p_{\text{total}}} = x_i$$

- Raoult's law for ideal solutions:

$$p_i = x_i \cdot p_i^0$$

where $p_i$ is the partial pressure in the vapour phase, $x_i$ is the molar fraction, and $p_i^0$ is the vapour pressure of the $i$-th component.

- Chemical potential of the $i$-th component in solution:

$$\mu_{i,\text{solution}} = \mu_i^0 + R \cdot T \cdot \ln(x_i)$$

where $\mu_i^0$ is the chemical potential of the vapour above the pure liquid of component $i$.

- van 't Hoff's law of osmosis:

$$\Pi = \frac{R \cdot T}{V_1^0} x_2$$

where $V_1^0$ is the molar volume of component 1 (solvent), and $x_2$ is the molar fraction of the dilute, non-permeating component.

# PART 3

# YIN AND YANG

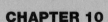

The following six chapters establish important concepts for major physical and physiological systems: membranes, fluids, and charged particles. This group of chapters follows the same approach we used in the first two parts: the introduction of static properties in equilibrium is followed by dynamic processes that result from imbalances introduced into the system. Thus, the universality of the **dichotomy** of the themes of the first two parts lies at the centre of Part III.

Electrically neutral membranes allow for energy transfer and/or transport of matter. A system outside the chemical or thermal equilibrium displays increasingly structured patterns as we move farther from the equilibrium. The same is observed for fluids. Their equilibrium properties follow directly from a mechanical model. However, dynamic aspects become more complex as we study first ideal dynamic fluids, then Newtonian fluids, and finally non-Newtonian systems. Explaining static electric phenomena requires only Coulomb's law. But when charged particles move, an analogy to the transport phenomena we establish at membranes must be included. When charges in an electric system move, the system also traverses into the realm of magnetism and electromagnetism. These phenomena are left to the next part of this book.

Yin and yang originated in ancient Chinese philosophy as two fundamentally opposed but complementary cosmic forces, such as water and fire. Taoism holds that all forces in nature have both yin and yang states, i.e., a receptively passive and a creatively active side. This concept captures nicely the dichotomy of ever-changing forces and immutable conservation laws.

# CHAPTER 10

## MEMBRANES
### Transport of Energy and Matter

Membranes separate systems. A semipermeable membrane enables two adjacent systems to interact through exchange of heat and/or matter. The exchange occurs if the two systems differ in one or more essential parameters: if they differ in temperature, heat flows toward the colder system (heat conduction), and if they differ in the concentration of a chemical component, matter flows toward the more dilute system (diffusion). The transport across the membrane is proportional to the cross-sectional area of the membrane and is inversely proportional to its length. The proportionality constants between heat flow and temperature difference (called the thermal conductivity coefficient) and between matter flow and concentration difference (called the diffusion coefficient) are materials constants.

Diffusion coefficients are strongly temperature-dependent. This is explained by a microscopic model of individual particles hopping between energetically favoured adjacent sites in the matrix. In the hopping process an activation energy must be overcome, utilizing the thermal energy of the diffusing particle (Arrhenius's model). Each particle jumps randomly to any of the available adjacent sites, including the site from which it came in the previous jump. Consequently, the particle traverses in $N$ jumps of length $a$ a total distance less than $N \cdot a$. Einstein found that the total distance, defined as the diffusion length, is proportional to $(D \cdot t)^{1/2}$ with $D$ the diffusion coefficient and $t$ the diffusion time.

Heat conduction and diffusion are non-equilibrium phenomena that we classify as transport phenomena. For these phenomena, a common formalism exists that is based on the entropy production in the irreversible process. Near the equilibrium (called the linear regime), the steady state is the only stable process because it has a minimum entropy production.

Life is about diversity. Life is about incredible complexity down to the microscopic level of the living cell. And life is about continuous change, from change the fossil record documents on a time scale of hundreds of millions of years to change that occurs on a time scale of minutes in which the life cycle of bacteria brings about a new generation. Structural complexity and change with time are key characteristics of life that set it apart from inanimate matter. The distinction between life and inanimate matter on the basis of these characteristics is so profound that many generations of scientists sought a unique ingredient of life: the vis vitalis.

# Beyond the Equilibrium

Even though the previous chapters of this textbook contain many useful applications of physics in the life sciences, you may wonder how the physical sciences can be expected to grasp the essence of life based on the concepts developed so far. Surveying our discussion for assumptions that may have been too restrictive, we find it is indeed the concept we relied most heavily upon throughout the earlier sections that appears to block access to the modelling of real-life processes: the equilibrium concept leads to uniform, structureless systems in which all essential parameters are time-independent; i.e., the equilibrium assumption favours system conditions that are opposite to what we expect from a model of life processes.

But how can we abandon the equilibrium concept as all other parameters we introduced, such as the temperature and the energy, are so closely linked to the equilibrium state? Do we not risk losing all we have learned when trying to move beyond the equilibrium? These are indeed non-trivial questions. It took the physical sciences more than 250 years, from the time René Descartes, Sir Isaac Newton, and others had opened the door to modern scientific inquiry, until we found ways to tackle the concerns caused by the equilibrium assumption. This long delay in characterizing non-equilibrium states was due to two prohibitive features:

- there are very few clues in the material discussed so far in this textbook that suggest where to start, and
- many of the equilibrium concepts we have developed need to be altered or abandoned as we proceed beyond equilibrium states.

The first point is not as bad as it seems. Indeed, one key reference in thermal physics points toward non-equilibrium processes: the entropy concept and its ability to characterize the direction of irreversible processes. Trying to start from the entropy concept, though, is not straightforward, as is evident when we take into account that the second law of thermodynamics was formulated in 1850, but that the ramifications for non-equilibrium processes were discovered only in the 1930s. Nevertheless, the far-reaching importance of non-equilibrium processes in the biological sciences justifies the effort to discuss these concepts at the end of the current chapter.

Scientists already wondered about the realm beyond the equilibrium long before these more rigorous concepts were developed. Important observations date back to the beginning of the 19th century. Useful phenomenological laws resulted from these early studies including a quantitative description of heat conduction and diffusion. In the current chapter, we familiarize ourselves with these particular non-equilibrium phenomena first.

# A New Model System

## Physical Membranes: An Idealized Concept

Throughout the sciences we depend on suitable models when developing new concepts. Membranes prove to be a simple but powerful model for introducing time-dependent, non-mechanical processes. To be able to quantify these processes, a simplified membrane is introduced. This model is called a **physical membrane**. It is a uniform barrier that is characterized by a very limited number of variables, primarily its width and a homogeneous chemical composition.

*A physical membrane is a barrier separating two uniform systems. Each system is in equilibrium. At least one parameter varies between the two systems, establishing a non-equilibrium across the membrane.*

The parameter varying across the membrane is either a physical parameter, such as pressure or temperature, or a chemical parameter, such as the concentration of molecules in solution. Often, more than one parameter varies across real membranes. In Chapter 14, for example, nerve membranes are discussed that separate different concentrations of positive and negative ions, leading to a combination of electric and chemical effects. Before studying such combinations of effects, however, we need to develop the basic concepts of interactions across a membrane. For our discussion we need to specify two properties of membranes:

## PERMEABILITY

The major physical property of a membrane is the degree of interaction it allows between the two systems it is separating. This degree of interaction is characterized by the permeability of the membrane.

A membrane can be **impermeable**, which means that it is completely blocking the interaction across the membrane. This case is of limited interest as it creates isolated systems on either side, each fully described by the concepts we already discussed in the context of thermal physics.

The opposite extreme is a membrane that is **fully permeable**; i.e., everything transfers freely in both directions across the membrane. Again, such a membrane is not particularly interesting as it does not alter the interactions within the system.

The type of membrane used to develop the concepts of this chapter is, therefore, the **semipermeable membrane**. In the biological literature, **selective permeability** is often used as an alternate notion. A semipermeable membrane allows some system components to pass but blocks others. Fig. 10.1 illustrates the most important system components in transport processes: energy in the form of heat, and matter in the form of atoms, ions, or molecules. The simplest type of semipermeable membrane is a membrane that allows only heat to pass but blocks matter. Such a membrane is used to introduce heat conduction. We later proceed to membranes that block only some chemical components while allowing others to pass. Semipermeable membranes of this type are used to develop the concept of diffusion.

## MEMBRANE WIDTH

The thickness of a membrane also plays a role in the extent of interactions allowed between the two adjacent systems. A semipermeable membrane may be impermeable in practice if it is too thick. We distinguish conceptually two types of membranes: a **zero-width membrane** and a **finite-width membrane**. If we want to study the consequences of interactions across the membrane focussing on the two adjacent systems, a zero-width membrane allows us to neglect the mechanisms of transport through the membrane. In other cases we want to focus on the transport mechanisms in the membrane itself. In these cases a membrane of finite width has to be taken into account. The variation of a system parameter across a finite-width membrane requires the introduction of the gradient as a new mathematical concept in this chapter.

The physical membrane is obviously a good description for physical barriers such as windows. Biological membranes are usually more complex. In our body, membranes are neither uniform in thickness nor chemically homogeneous and they often actively participate in the physiological processes rather than form a passive barrier. The concepts we develop for the physical membrane still apply to biological membranes and illustrate the role of basic transport processes in physiology.

## Complexity of Biological Membranes

Membranes were the focus of biological studies for most of the 19th century. A heated debate concerned first the presence of membranes encapsulating the cells (the so-called **plasma membrane**), then the membranes encapsulating the nucleus.

Particularly puzzling to biologists was that membranes not only serve as passive envelopes for biological units, but also are actively involved in the dynamic processes occurring in our body, e.g., serving as a filter in the kidneys (this will be described in Chapter 12), or regulating the metabolism of a cell using enzymes embedded in the membrane to gather various chemical molecules from the environment and dispose of them back into the environment.

Biological membranes come in many different forms. One chemically simpler example—but at the same time one of the great success stories of the evolutionary process—is the egg shell. Consisting mainly of calcium carbonate, it establishes a non-equilibrium between the egg inside and the environment outside. The egg shell allows air to infiltrate but does not allow water to escape. This feature allowed cotylosaurs about 300 million years ago to move to dry land for their entire life cycle. Their amphibian ancestors had to spend at least part of their life in

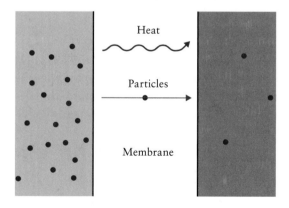

**FIGURE 10.1**

Sketch of the major transport mechanisms operating across a physical membrane (white area at centre): particles and/or energy may be transported. When energy flows independently of a material transport it is in the form of heat.

water since their eggs would desiccate on dry land. Cotylosaurs in turn were able to move far away from the coastline and eventually became the ancestor of all reptiles, birds, and mammals. You can verify the air exchange across the egg shell in a simple experiment. Place an egg in hot water. Air bubbles will form all over the egg shell. This is due to the thermal expansion of air inside the egg: the expansion pushes some of the air out.

Two other examples illustrate the complexity biological membranes may display: the membrane of a human cell (a eukaryotic cell), and the structure of the outer envelope of bacteria (a prokaryotic cell).

### A HUMAN CELL

Fig. 10.2 shows a schematic sketch of a human cell membrane (plasma membrane), which separates the cytoplasm inside from the interstitium outside. Membranes are an example of organic molecules organized into a higher level of complexity. The aggregation of phospholipids in an aqueous solution is driven by the molecule's **amphipathic** character: with one end of the molecule *hydrophobic* (water repelling) and the other end *hydrophilic* (water attracting), the hydrophilic ends will reach into the aqueous solution while the hydrophobic ends will merge together to exclude water. The result is a bilayer of phospholipids with the hydrophilic ends directed outward. These double-layer structures self-assemble into three-dimensional spherical forms called *protobionts*, which can maintain an internal aqueous environment different from the external environment.

The human cell is far more complex than a simple phospholipid bilayer. Various protein molecules are associated with the membrane, some stretching across the membrane layer and some attached only extrinsically. These proteins play a role in specific transport processes across the membrane.

### A BACTERIUM

Fig. 10.3 shows the cell membrane of a typical bacterium, with the interior at bottom and the exterior at top. The membrane consists of three layers that are needed to form the outer envelope to protect the bacterium from its environment. The central **murein layer** is a sturdy, uniform hetero-polymer. Penicillins are deadly for bacteria because they prevent the biosynthesis of the murein membrane. The other two layers of the bacterial membrane are highly structured. The inner layer (plasma membrane) resembles the membrane of human cells, as shown in Fig. 10.2. The outer membrane contains specialized components for chemical exchange and physical interaction with the bacterium's environment. Porine proteins

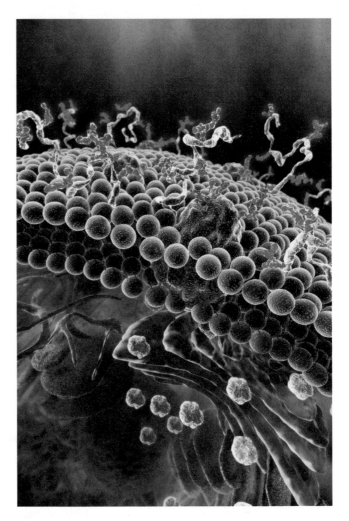

**FIGURE 10.2**

**Fluid mosaic model** of a human cell membrane. The lipid bilayer (green) consists of chain-like macromolecules with hydrophobic and hydrophilic ends. The hydrophilic ends are directed toward the external aqueous milieu. Proteins can be embedded in the membrane or pass completely through it (purple). They are able to diffuse laterally on or within the membrane. The protein mobility is the reason that the term fluid (versus rigid) is used to label this membrane model. Inside the cell, the Golgi apparatus (lower right) produces lysosomes (blue spheres).

stretch the entire membrane to facilitate diffusion processes across the membrane (green), while the lipo-polysaccharide chains (red) constitute the defence system of the bacterium due to their toxigenic properties.

## Heat Conduction

The physical membrane is sufficient to discuss the time-dependent transport of physical or chemical properties. These phenomena are grouped together under the term **transport phenomena** and include heat conduction, diffusion, viscosity, and electric current.

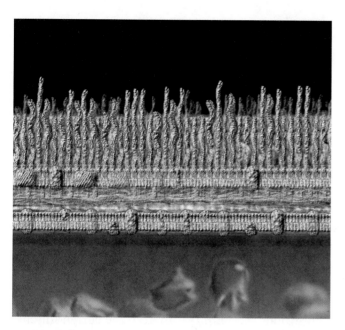

**FIGURE 10.3**

Sketch of the cell membrane of a bacterium. The membrane consists of three layers, the cytoplasm membrane (bottom), the rigid murein layer (centre), and an outer layer with porine-proteins and lipo-polysaccharide chains (top).

- *Heat conduction* is the flow of energy to eliminate temperature differences. We assume that the temperature difference occurs across a membrane that is impermeable to matter but allows the transfer of energy in the form of heat. An example is the continuous heat loss of our body through the skin at moderate temperatures. Heat conduction is discussed in the current section.

- *Diffusion* is the process by which molecules move from a region of higher concentration to one of lower concentration. The concentration difference occurs across a membrane that is semipermeable, permitting some chemical components to pass while others are blocked or significantly slowed down. Two important examples are (a) the transfer of oxygen and carbon dioxide between capillaries and the gas space in the lungs, and (b) the resorption of blood plasma components in the renal tubes of the kidney as discussed in Chapter 12. Diffusion is discussed in a later section of this chapter.

The other two transport phenomena are studied later in this textbook, viscosity in Chapter 12 and electric currents in Chapter 14.

## Fourier's Law

In 1822, Jean Baptiste Fourier set up an experiment suitable for investigating the flow of heat. The experiment is shown in Fig. 10.4(a) and in conceptualized form in Fig. 10.4(b). He quantified heat conduction in a rod connecting two heat reservoirs at different temperatures. For easy control of their temperatures, one is held at 0°C with an ice–water mixture, while the other is held at 100°C by boiling water. The rod is well insulated so that all heat transported through the rod is transferred from the high-temperature heat reservoir to the reservoir of lower temperature. The cylindrical rod has length $L$ and a cross-sectional area $A$. Fourier found an empirical relation for the heat flow by varying every parameter in Fig. 10.4. Increasing the temperature difference between the two heat reservoirs and increasing the cross-sectional area of the rod increased the rate of heat flow toward the low-temperature heat reservoir. Decreasing the length of the rod also increased the heat flow rate, indicating that the length of the rod is inversely proportional to that rate. Defining the flow of heat per time interval as $Q/t$ with unit J/s, Fourier wrote:

$$\frac{Q}{t} = \lambda \cdot A \frac{T_{high} - T_{low}}{L} \qquad [1]$$

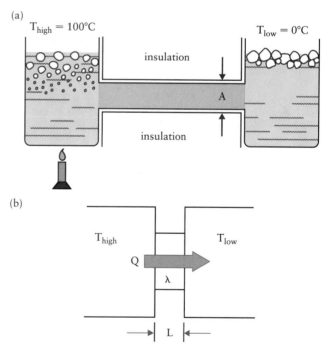

**FIGURE 10.4**

Fourier's experiment of heat conduction. (a) Experimental set-up. A steady-state heat flow across a rod of length $L$ and cross-sectional area $A$ is achieved by providing for a thermal contact to heat reservoirs at $T_{low} = 0$°C and $T_{high} = 100$°C at the two ends of the rod. The areas above and below the rod indicate thermal insulation of the rod to prevent lateral heat loss. (b) Conceptual sketch. Heat $Q$ flows from a high-temperature heat reservoir through the system with thermal conductivity $\lambda$ to a low-temperature heat reservoir.

Note that area $A$ is not the surface of the membrane. Only the cross-sectional area perpendicular to the transport direction of heat enters Fourier's law. The proportionality constant $\lambda$ is a materials constant because it depends on the composition of the rod; $\lambda$ is called the **thermal conductivity coefficient** and has unit $J/(m \cdot s \cdot K)$. Table 10.1 lists these coefficients for a range of materials. All values of $\lambda$ are positive; i.e., heat always flows from an area of higher temperature to one with lower temperature.

## TABLE 10.1

### Thermal conductivity coefficients at room temperature

| Material | Thermal conductivity $\lambda$ $(J \cdot m^{-1} \cdot s^{-1} \cdot K^{-1})$ |
|---|---|
| *1. Solid metals and alloys* | |
| Silver (Ag) | 420 |
| Copper (Cu) | 390 |
| Gold (Au) | 310 |
| Aluminium (Al) | 230 |
| Iron (Fe) | 80 |
| Steel | 50 |
| *2. Nonmetallic solids* | |
| Ice | 1.6 |
| Quartz glass ($SiO_2$) | 1.4 |
| Window glass | 0.8 |
| Fat | 0.24 |
| Rubber | 0.2 |
| Wood | 0.12−0.04 |
| Felt, silk | 0.04 |
| *3. Liquids* | |
| Mercury (Hg) | 8.3 |
| Water ($H_2O$) | 0.6 |
| Ethanol ($C_2H_5OH$) | 0.18 |
| *4. Gases* | |
| Air | 0.026 |

Note that the coefficients vary by less than 5 orders of magnitude. Compare this with the variations of diffusion coefficients in Table 10.5 and electric resistivities in Chapter 14.

Although Eq. [1] is written as if the thermal conductivity coefficient is temperature-independent, the values in Table 10.1 are given specifically at room temperature. It has been found experimentally that the thermal conductivity of most materials varies with temperature, e.g., by more than 20% for water and air between 0°C and 100°C. We neglect this temperature dependence in the current section but will address it in the Appendix at the end of this chapter.

The term $\Delta T/L$ represents the temperature step along the length $L$ of the rod. If the rod is oriented along the $x$-axis this term can be written as the change of the temperature with position along the rod, which is the slope $\Delta T/\Delta x$, in which $\Delta x$ is an interval along the rod. The term $\Delta T/\Delta x$ is called a **gradient**. The gradient itself can be a function of the position $x$, requiring more complicated mathematical expressions than Eq. [1]. To keep the current discussion simple we limit ourselves to cases in which the gradient has a constant value.

## Concept Question 10.1

Some admission tests for professional schools are structured such that a lead-off paragraph (passage) is followed by several questions related to the same topic. This concept question serves as an example: the lead-off paragraph would be an abbreviated form of the text in this section to this point. Then the following three questions follow:

(a) What did Fourier measure as a function of temperature difference, length, and cross-section of the rod? (A) the heat removed from the low-temperature heat reservoir, (B) the heat transfer through the rod per second, (C) the heat deposited in the high-temperature heat reservoir, (D) the work done on the low-temperature heat reservoir by dropping ice pellets into it, (E) the internal energy of the water in the low-temperature heat reservoir.

(b) In order to increase the effect Fourier observed, he could have done the following: (A) increase the length of the rod, (B) decrease the diameter of the rod (assumed to be of cylindrical shape), (C) increase the temperature of the low-temperature heat reservoir, (D) decrease the length of the rod, (E) decrease the temperature of the high-temperature heat reservoir.

(c) When Fourier changed the rod from aluminium to iron the following happened: (A) he had to increase the temperature of the low-temperature heat reservoir to obtain the same heat flow rate as before, (B) he had to increase the temperature of the high-temperature heat reservoir to obtain the same heat flow rate as before, (C) his observations did not change, (D) he could not do the experiment because it doesn't work with iron rods, (E) he had to lengthen the rod to obtain the same heat flow rate as before. *Hint:* Use Table 10.1.

ANSWERS: (a) B, (b) D, (c) B (use Eq. [1] for the last two answers).

## Concept Question 10.2

**In Fourier's experiment, heat is irreversibly transferred from a high- to a low-temperature heat reservoir. Can you suggest a reversible approach?**

ANSWER: We have discussed the idea of heat transfer between objects of different temperature before; in particular, reversible and irreversible conduction of these experiments was studied in Fig. 8.6. An elegant way to answer this question is to refer back to the Carnot process in Fig. 7.36 and consider only the first three steps: isothermal and adiabatic expansion and isothermal compression. During the isothermal reversible expansion in step I, heat $Q$ is taken from the high-temperature heat reservoir and is deposited as work in the piston. The adiabatic expansion then adjusts reversibly the temperature of the system to that of the low-temperature heat reservoir. The third step is an isothermal reversible compression where the work stored in the piston is turned into heat that is deposited in the low-temperature heat reservoir. In the Carnot process we stop the third process such that a subsequent adiabatic compression closes a cyclic process. In the current case the compression in the third step has to be done to a smaller volume to deposit the same amount of heat in the low-temperature heat reservoir as was removed from the high-temperature heat reservoir.

## Heat Loss of the Human Body

When we touch an object, it is its thermal conductivity—and not its actual temperature—that affects our impression of warmth or coldness. Conduct the following self-experiment: touch a piece of metal and a piece of wood that are both at room temperature. The metal feels cold and the wood feels warm. Since our hand in this experiment is warmer than the objects we touch, heat flows from our body into the

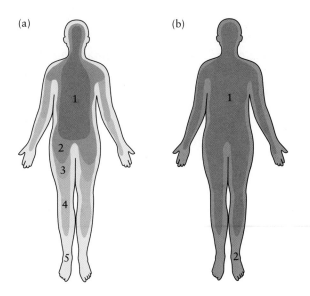

**FIGURE 10.5**

The temperature profile for a human body at ambient temperatures of (a) 20°C and (b) 35°C. Both sketches show a cross-section through the centre of the body. The different shades represent different temperatures. They are numbered as follows: (1) 37°C, (2) 36°C, (3) 34°C, (4) 31°C, and (5) 28°C.

object. The greater this flow of heat, the colder we perceive the object to be.

The same heat loss occurs continuously from the skin to the surrounding air. The air is not usually perceived as cold because the heat conductivity of gases is rather low (see Table 10.1), and thus the heat loss in room-temperature air is not large enough to be felt. Still, the thermal non-equilibrium between the body temperature of 37.0 ± 0.5°C and the air temperature is reflected in a gradual temperature drop in our bodies toward the surface. This is illustrated in Fig. 10.5 for two environmental temperatures. Fig. 10.5(a) shows a cross-sectional temperature profile in the body for an ambient temperature of 20°C, and Fig. 10.5(b) illustrates the same profile for an ambient temperature of 35°C. As the figure shows, the temperature profile is not a single temperature step from 37°C to the environmental temperature. Instead, the temperature decreases by as much as 9 degrees in the limbs in a room-temperature environment.

Three primary processes facilitate the continuous loss of heat to the environment: perspiration (evaporation of water from the skin), convection (heat carried away by air passing across the skin), and radiation. Table 10.2 summarizes the relative contributions to the heat loss of the human body at various environmental temperature conditions (dry air). Note that neither convection nor radiation contribute at 36°C and above.

## TABLE 10.2

### Mechanisms of heat loss from the human body as a function of the ambient temperature

| Temperature of environment | Total heat loss | Fraction of evaporation | Fraction of convection | Fraction of radiation |
|---|---|---|---|---|
| 20°C | 63 J/(m² · s) | 13% | 26% | 61% |
| 30°C | 38 J/(m² · s) | 27% | 27% | 46% |
| 36°C | 43 J/(m² · s) | 100% | — | — |

The total loss is given in the second column in unit J/(m² · s). The third, fourth, and fifth columns show how this amount is distributed among perspiration, convection, and radiation.

Heat conduction is an effective heat loss process when swimming in water, but contributes little in air. **Convection**, on the other hand, which is caused by the turbulent flow of air across the skin, can significantly enhance the heat loss in air. It is for this reason that bedouins in northern Africa wear black or dark blue robes; convection contributes more effectively to the cooling of the skin beneath dark cloth than beneath cloth of brighter colours.

Heat loss by **perspiration** is based on the phase transition of water from liquid to vapour on the skin. Sweat glands bring liquid water to the skin. The evaporation of water requires energy. This amount of energy is called the latent heat of evaporation. It is supplied from the body's thermal energy. The vapour leaves the skin, carrying the latent heat into the environment. This heat transfer is very effective, corresponding to a loss of 2428 kJ per litre of water evaporated. However, perspiration is effective only in dry air. If the air is humid (saturated with water vapour), temperatures of about 33°C become unbearable.

Heat loss by **radiation** is a totally different process for which we discuss the physical principles in Chapter 20. Radiative energy is not carried by the medium air like heat in heat conduction or convection. You notice this when you hold the palm of your hand facing the Sun and then turn it 90°. The Sun causes the sensation of warmth because heat from the Sun reaches the hand. This heat flow must be independent of a medium to transport the heat, because most of the distance between the Sun and your hand passes through vacuum. The experiment with the hand also illustrates that heat transport by radiation works well when a cooler surface lies in the line of sight of a hotter surface. Thus, a cold wall contributes to loss of heat by radiation even if the air in the room is warm.

## ● EXAMPLE 10.1

(a) Calculate the steady rate at which a standard man (see data in Table 3.3) with winter clothing loses body heat. Assume that the clothing is 1.5 cm thick, the average surface temperature of the standard man is 34°C, and the temperature of the outer surface of the clothing is 0°C. For the thermal conductivity of the clothing, use the value for felt in Table 10.1. (b) How does the answer to part (a) change if the clothes of the standard man get soaked with water?

*Solution to part (a):* We use Fourier's law as given in Eq. [1]. Substituting $A = 1.85$ m² from Table 3.3, $L = 0.015$ m, the temperature difference of $\Delta T = 34°C - 0°C = 34$ K, and the thermal conductivity for felt $\lambda = 0.04$ J/(m · s · K), we find:

$$\frac{Q}{t} = \frac{\lambda \cdot A \cdot \Delta T}{L}$$

$$= \frac{\left(0.04 \dfrac{\text{J}}{\text{m} \cdot \text{s} \cdot \text{K}}\right)(1.85 \,\text{m}^2)(34 \,\text{K})}{0.015 \,\text{m}}$$

$$= 168 \frac{\text{J}}{\text{s}} \qquad [2]$$

*Solution to part (b):* In this part we are asked to derive an answer relative to the answer in part (a). Instead of repeating the calculation as shown in the first part, we divide the respective left- and right-hand sides of Fourier's law for the "dry" and the "wet" case:

$$\frac{(Q/t)_{\text{dry}}}{(Q/t)_{\text{wet}}} = \frac{\dfrac{\lambda_{\text{dry}} \cdot A(T_{\text{high}} - T_{\text{low}})}{L}}{\dfrac{\lambda_{\text{wet}} \cdot A(T_{\text{high}} - T_{\text{low}})}{L}} = \frac{\lambda_{\text{dry}}}{\lambda_{\text{wet}}} \qquad [3]$$

Using the thermal conductivity of water from Table 10.1 for the soaked clothes Eq. [3] yields:

$$\left(\frac{Q}{t}\right)_{\text{wet}} = \left(\frac{Q}{t}\right)_{\text{dry}} \frac{\lambda_{\text{wet}}}{\lambda_{\text{dry}}}$$

$$= \left(168 \,\frac{J}{s}\right) \frac{0.6 \,\dfrac{J}{m \cdot s \cdot K}}{0.04 \,\dfrac{J}{m \cdot s \cdot K}} = 2520 \,\frac{J}{s} \tag{4}$$

Thus, the person loses heat 15 times faster when the clothes are wet! An interesting case in this context: Fritjof Nansen, a famous Norwegian polar explorer, tried to reach the North Pole with a second Norwegian in March of 1895. After leaving their ship at 84.4°N they failed in their quest for the Pole, drifting away from it faster than they could travel. They reached as far north as 86.14°N, which was a record at the time. Later they had to struggle through breaking ice on their way back. At one point all their supplies, which were stored in small boats, drifted away and Nansen had to swim after them. Before doing so, he stripped off his clothes. Eq. [3] demonstrates that this was an intelligent decision despite the freezing temperatures. It took Nansen only a few minutes to salvage the boats, but his colleague had to warm him up for several hours. Luckily, Nansen survived the incident. Had he jumped into the water with his warm clothes, they would not have protected him from the frigid water but would have dragged him down once soaked.

## Whales in the Arctic Ocean

### ● EXAMPLE 10.2

Whales are mammals that live in the sea. Their bodies generate heat at the rate given for endotherms in Eq. [6.8] by burning their food. Like humans, they must maintain a core body temperature of about 37°C. Some of these whales spend part or all of the year in the frigid Arctic Ocean near the edge of the pack ice (water temperature 0°C). These include large whales such as bowhead whales of 100 tonnes body mass, and small whales such as the narwhal with about 1.5 tonnes. Their only protection in the chilly water is a thick fat layer. Calculate the minimum thickness of that fat layer for these whales as a function of body size. *Hint:* Use a spherical shape for the whale's body.

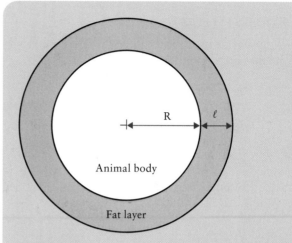

**FIGURE 10.6**

Simplified model of a whale consisting of an inner body of radius R, covered by a fat layer of uniform thickness l.

*Solution:* Fig. 10.6 shows the simplified model used for the whale in this problem: the spherical animal has an inner body of radius $R$ and a fat layer of uniform thickness $l$. The minimum thickness of the fat layer is determined by balancing the heat loss and the conversion of food to thermal energy (metabolic rate) in the whale's body.

For the heat loss, we use Fourier's law with the thermal conductivity coefficient of fat from Table 10.1. The higher temperature in Fourier's law is the core body temperature and the lower temperature is the temperature of the seawater, i.e., $\Delta T = 37$ K. The area across which the heat flows is the surface of the inner body of the whale, $A = 4 \cdot \pi \cdot R^2$ (which is the surface of a sphere of radius $R$). Thus:

$$\left(\frac{Q}{t}\right)_{\text{loss}} = \lambda \cdot 4 \cdot \pi \cdot R^2 \cdot \frac{\Delta T}{l}$$

$$= \left(110 \,\frac{J}{m \cdot s}\right) \cdot \frac{R^2}{l} \tag{5}$$

in which we left the radius of the whale, $R$, and the fat layer thickness, $l$, variable and combined all other parameters to a single prefactor of 110 J/(m · s). Thus, the heat loss is expressed in Eq. [5] as a function of the radius of the whale and the thickness of the fat layer. We keep these two parameters variable because we want to find their relation for whales of any size.

To offset the heat loss in Eq. [5], the whale's metabolism converts food energy into thermal energy as given in Eq. [6.8]. We rewrite Eq. [6.8] in standard units, defining the metabolic rate as

● **EXAMPLE 10.2** (*continued*)

$(Q/t)_{gain}$ in unit J/s, and expressing it as a function of the mass $m$ in unit kg:

$$\left(\frac{Q}{t}\right)_{gain} = 5.2 \cdot m^{3/4} \qquad [6]$$

To relate again to the radius $R$ of the whale, the mass of the animal is rewritten as its density and volume $V = 4 \cdot \pi \cdot R^3/3$ (this is the volume of a sphere of radius $R$). This leads to:

$$\left(\frac{Q}{t}\right)_{gain} = 5.2 \left(\rho \cdot \frac{4}{3} \cdot \pi \cdot R^3\right)^{3/4}$$

$$= 5.2 \left(\frac{4}{3} \cdot \pi \cdot \rho\right)^{3/4} \cdot R^{9/4} \qquad [7]$$

Since the whale is floating in seawater, the density of its body must be close to that of seawater. We use the value $\rho = 1020 \text{ kg/m}^3$ in Eq. [7] for the average density of seawater. With $Q/t$ in unit J/s and the radius $R$ in unit m we find:

$$\left(\frac{Q}{t}\right)_{gain} = 2750 \cdot R^{9/4} \qquad [8]$$

For calculating the minimum fat layer thickness the balance between the whale's heat loss and thermal energy gain must be found; i.e., Eqs. [5] and [8] are set equal:

$$\left(\frac{Q}{t}\right)_{loss} = \left(\frac{Q}{t}\right)_{gain} \qquad [9]$$

Substituting the equations we found above:

$$110\frac{R^2}{l} = 2750 \cdot R^{9/4} \qquad [10]$$

With both length $l$ and radius $R$ given in units m this leads to:

$$l = \frac{0.04}{R^{1/4}} \qquad [11]$$

Eq. [11] relates the fat layer thickness to the radius of the whale. The bigger the animal (i.e., the larger $R$) the thinner a sufficient fat layer (this is called the **bulk effect**). An animal of radius $R = 0.1 \text{ m} = 10 \text{ cm}$ (rat-sized) needs a fat layer thickness of about $l = 7 \text{ cm}$; for an animal of radius $R = 1 \text{ m}$ (sea lion–sized) a fat layer of 4 cm is needed, and for $R = 10 \text{ m}$ (whale-sized) a fat layer of 2.5 cm is sufficient. Obviously, a polar rat would be a clumsy creature, and therefore does

not exist. Sea lions and whales have no problem developing a sufficient fat layer that does not hinder them in their daily lives.

Indeed, real whales typically have fat layer thicknesses (blubber) of about 0.5 m; in the case of the right whale, as much as 40% of its body mass is blubber. Comparing with our calculation above, this means that the whale's fat layer is significantly oversized. This is due to the fact that the fat layer thickness cannot be adjusted on a short time scale—e.g., to accommodate day–night temperature changes or water temperature variations caused by currents. Thus, whales require another mechanism of temperature regulation. Nature's solution to the problem includes an oversized fat layer and a secondary mechanism to dissipate excess thermal energy through the fat layer–free tail. Thermal energy is carried by blood flow to the tail, where it is brought close to the skin (perfusion). The fluke has no fat layer and therefore allows for effective heat conduction into the surrounding water. The effectiveness of this mechanism is illustrated in Fig. 10.7 for a dolphin's fluke. The figure shows the temperature profile of the tail from an infrared photograph (**thermography**; equipment shown in Fig. 10.8). The various temperatures are shown in different shades: red is hottest and white is coldest. The

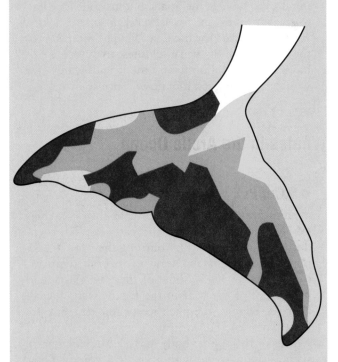

**FIGURE 10.7**

Sketch of an infrared photograph of a dolphin's fluke. The red area has the highest temperature, then, decreasing in order, orange, yellow, and white, indicating that the fluke radiates the most heat.

**FIGURE 10.8**

Thermogram taken of the legs and shoes of an athlete on a treadmill. A wind machine is replicating the conditions during running.

figure clearly illustrates that the fluke is used not only for motion but also serves as the body's temperature-control device.

Whaling was a major branch of the fishing industry in the mid-1800s when Herman Melville wrote the famous adventure story *Moby Dick*. At that time whales were little-understood creatures, and the described mechanism of heat dissipation was unknown. Thus, whalers often reported their amazement when they found temperatures in whale carcasses to be as high as 60°C and the whale meat half-cooked. This is due to the fact that the heart of a dying whale stops immediately, interrupting the blood flow to the fluke. However, thermal-energy-generating metabolic processes continue for a short time after death.

Is there an actual case in nature to which the direct balance of heat loss and gain in Eq. [9] applies? The family Megapodidae contains 22 bird species that are found in Australasia, including the Australian Brush-turkey, shown in Fig. 10.9. They have in common a unique nesting and incubation technique: they build a large mound of forest litter in which they bury their eggs after a strong rainfall. Heat in the mound is generated by decomposition (putrefaction). The parent birds must return frequently to the mound to adjust its thickness based on Eq. [9] because ambient temperatures vary but the incubation temperature must remain constant at $T_{\text{incubation}} = 35°C$ to $36°C$. A calculation of the dependence of the radius of the mound on the ambient temperature yields (the complete formula is derived in P–10.11):

$$R \propto \sqrt{T_{\text{incubation}} - T_{\text{ambient}}} \qquad [12]$$

With day/night temperature variations moderate in the habitat of these birds and the square-root dependence in Eq. [12] reducing the work to alter the size of the mounds, the Brush-turkeys manage their task of balancing heat loss and heat generation well.

**FIGURE 10.9**

Australian Brush-turkey.

## Concept Question 10.3

Not every problem in the sciences requires a full calculation; often, so-called back-of-the-envelope estimates are sufficient. These include cases where the actual formula for the physical process is derived through an educated guess. Educated guesses are frequently based on dimensionality considerations. The following is an instructive example:

Food that has a high concentration of fat has to be heated longer during **pasteurization**. For awhile this observation was explained as follows: In fatty food bacteria cover themselves with a fat layer that, for practical purposes, cannot be much thicker than the size of the bacteria. Heat cannot penetrate this layer as readily because heat conductivity is much lower in fat than in water, effectively protecting the bacteria against thermal destruction. Do you accept this explanation?

*Hint:* Determine the **thermal relaxation time** $\tau$, which we define as the time it takes for a sphere of radius $R$ to adjust its initial temperature $T_{initial}$ to the ambient temperature $T_{ambient}$ after immersion. *Note:* An analytical derivation of $\tau$ is provided in P–10.12.

ANSWER: If heat conduction governs this process, the physical formula for the relaxation time should contain the radius $R$ of the sphere, the density of the sphere $\rho$, the specific heat capacity of the sphere $c$, the initial temperature difference $\Delta T$, and the heat conductivity coefficient of

fat $\lambda$. Table 10.3 shows the units of these parameters in terms of the fundamental SI units.

We seek a combination of the five parameters $R$, $\rho$, $\Delta T$, $c$, and $\lambda$ to describe the parameter $\tau$ with unit s. We start with a combination of $c$ and $\lambda$. Since none of $R$, $\Delta T$, or $\rho$ contains the unit s, the combination of $c$ and $\lambda$ must result in a unit s. This is obtained with the ratio $c/\lambda$. This term also carries a unit $kg^{-1}$. Multiplication by the density compensates for this unit: $c\rho/\lambda$ has the unit $s/m^2$. Now we introduce a factor $R^2$ in the numerator to eliminate the unit $m$ in the denominator. Thus, we propose for the thermal relaxation time:

$$\tau \propto \frac{R^2 \cdot \rho \cdot c}{\lambda} \qquad [13]$$

Note that we did not need the initial temperature difference $\Delta T = T_{ambient} - T_{initial}$ in this formula. This makes sense because a larger temperature difference would require more heat to flow to the colder sphere, but the larger temperature difference would drive this heat into the sphere faster.

Assuming that Eq. [13] is a reasonable estimate (it is indeed correct to within a factor of 3, as shown in P–10.12), we quantify the various parameters, modelling the bacterium as a spherical droplet of water. The radius of a bacterium is about 10 $\mu$m, $\rho_{water} = 1000$ kg/m³, $c_{water} = 4210$ J/(kg · K) at 100°C from Fig. 6.35, and

## TABLE 10.3

### Dimensional analysis for thermal relaxation time in pasteurization

|  | Radius $R$ | Density $\rho$ | Heat capacity $c$ | Thermal conductivity $\lambda$ | Temperature K | Relaxation time $\tau$ |
|---|---|---|---|---|---|---|
| Length (m) | 1 | −3 | 2 | 1 | 0 | 0 |
| Mass (kg) | 0 | 1 | 0 | 1 | 0 | 0 |
| Time (s) | 0 | 0 | −2 | −3 | 0 | 1 |
| Temperature (K) | 0 | 0 | −1 | −1 | 1 | 0 |

Example: Density has unit kg/m³, which consists of factors metre with exponent −3 and kilogram with exponent +1.

$\lambda_{fat}$ = 0.24 J/(m · s · K) from Table 10.1. Substituting these values in Eq. [13] yields:

$$\tau = \frac{R^2 \cdot \rho \cdot c}{\lambda}$$

$$= \frac{(1 \times 10^{-5}\,\text{m})^2 \left(1000\,\dfrac{\text{kg}}{\text{m}^3}\right)\left(4210\,\dfrac{\text{J}}{\text{kg}\cdot\text{K}}\right)}{0.24\,\dfrac{\text{J}}{\text{m}\cdot\text{s}\cdot\text{K}}}$$

$$= 1.8 \times 10^{-3}\,\text{s} \qquad [14]$$

Thus, the bacterium with the assumed fat layer thermally equilibrates within a few milliseconds with its environment. The idea that the fat layer is a thermal protective layer has to be dismissed.

## Lord Kelvin's Age of Earth

### ● EXAMPLE 10.3

After publishing *The Origin of Species by Means of Natural Selection* in 1859, Charles Darwin had to endure some malicious criticism. On the other hand, there were only very few serious objections. The most credible one came from Lord Kelvin, who estimated the age of Earth to be 400 million years or less and the age of the Sun to be 100 million years or less. He later even corrected these numbers downward to as little as 20 million years.

We consider Lord Kelvin's argument for the **age of Earth**. It is based on the following data: from underground mining we know that the temperature below the surface increases by 3 K per 100 metres. This is called the **geothermal effect**. Assuming that Earth started as molten rock called the **Proto-Earth**, with a uniform temperature of $T = 3000°C$,

how long did it take to reach the current state? For the density of rock use $\rho = 3\ \text{g/cm}^3$, for the heat capacity of rock $c = 1470\ \text{J/(kg} \cdot \text{K)}$, and for its thermal conductivity coefficient $\lambda = 1.7\ \text{J/(m} \cdot \text{s} \cdot \text{K)}$.

*Solution:* Based on the geothermal effect, the current temperature profile of Earth is shown in Fig. 10.10. At the surface (the radius of Earth is taken as 6400 km), the temperature is about 0°C (not 0 K, due to the atmosphere). Based on the geothermal effect it rises to 3000°C at 100 km depth, i.e., 6300 km from the centre of Earth.

For our quantitative calculations, we consider a rectangular segment of 100 km depth and of surface area $A = 1\ \text{m}^2$ as illustrated in Fig. 10.11. The heat loss of this segment is determined using

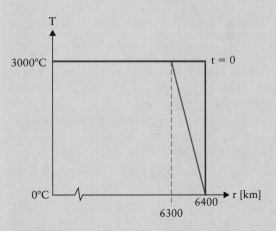

**FIGURE 10.10**

Temperature profile of Earth based on the geothermal effect (blue line). With the temperature increasing by one degree for each 30 m, the temperature increases for about 100 km until the temperature of molten rock (3000°C) is reached. Using 6400 km for the radius of Earth, molten rock is reached at $r = 6300$ km. The red line, labelled $t = 0$, indicates the temperature profile of the Proto-Earth, which was a liquid sphere throughout due to the *great bombardment* with space debris during the early solar system.

## ● EXAMPLE 10.3 (continued)

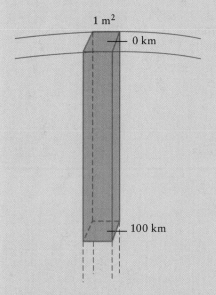

**FIGURE 10.11**

Segment of Earth's crust used for the calculation of the rate of heat loss.

Fourier's law as given in Eq. [1]. We write it in the form:

$$\frac{Q/t}{A} = \lambda \cdot \frac{\Delta T}{l} \qquad [15]$$

Substituting the given values yields:

$$\frac{Q/t}{A} = \left(1.7 \frac{J}{s \cdot m \cdot K}\right)\left(0.03 \frac{K}{m}\right) = 0.05 \frac{J}{s \cdot m^2} \qquad [16]$$

The term $(Q/t)/A$ is the rate of loss of heat per time interval through the area $A$. The term $\Delta T/l$ is the **geothermal temperature gradient.**

Next, using Joule's definition of heat we calculate the total heat lost since the times of the liquid Proto-Earth:

$$Q = m \cdot c_{rock} \cdot \Delta T = \rho \cdot V \cdot c_{rock} \cdot \Delta T \quad [17]$$

in which the mass of the rock slab of Fig. 10.11 has been rewritten as its density and volume. The volume can further be rewritten as the surface area $A$ times the depth $l$, leading to:

$$Q = \rho \cdot A \cdot l \cdot c_{rock} \cdot \Delta T \qquad [18]$$

We divide by the area to express the heat per unit surface area:

$$\frac{Q}{A} = \rho \cdot l \cdot c_{rock} \cdot \Delta T \qquad [19]$$

$Q/A$ is the total heat lost through the surface area $A$. Evaluating Eq. [19] must be done carefully since the temperature change, $\Delta T$, varies with depth as shown in the lower part of Fig. 10.12. The figure indicates that due to the direct proportionality between heat and temperature in Eq. [19], the total loss of heat corresponds to the triangle enclosed by the dashed lines and the line indicated with vertical arrows. Thus, the total amount of heat lost through the surface area $A$ is found from Fig. 10.12 graphically. The area of the triangle equals half the area of the rectangle with a temperature drop of 3000 degrees throughout. Thus, we substitute in Eq. [19] for $\Delta T$:

$$\frac{Q}{A} = \frac{1}{2}\left(3000 \frac{kg}{m^3}\right)(1.0 \times 10^5\,m)$$
$$\times \left(1470 \frac{J}{kg \cdot K}\right)(3000\,K)$$
$$= 6.6 \times 10^{14} \frac{J}{m^2} \qquad [20]$$

in which 3000 K is the difference between 0°C and 3000°C.

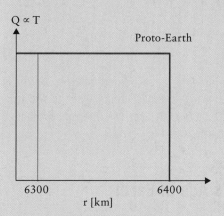

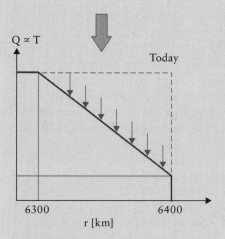

**FIGURE 10.12**

Illustration of the total amount of heat, $Q$, lost between the times of the Proto-Earth (top) and the current state (bottom).

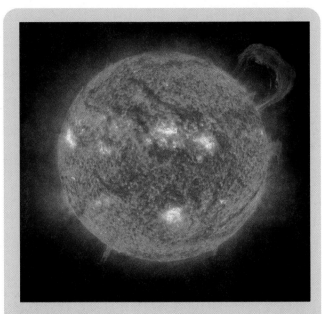

**FIGURE 10.13**
NASA image of the Sun.

Lord Kelvin then divided the total energy lost from the 100-km-deep segment in Eq. [20] by the rate of loss through area $A$ from Eq. [16]:

$$t_{Earth} = \frac{\frac{Q}{A}}{\frac{Q/t}{A}} = \frac{6.6 \times 10^{14} \frac{J}{m^2}}{0.05 \frac{J}{s \cdot m^2}}$$

$$= 1.3 \times 10^{16} s = 4 \times 10^8 \text{ years} \quad [21]$$

This is the predicted age of Earth since cooling began, $t_{Earth} = 400$ million years.

Lord Kelvin tried to confirm this estimate by comparing it with an estimate of the age of the Sun, shown in Fig. 10.13. The modern view of the solar system is that the Sun and the Proto-Earth formed at about the same time. Thus, since the Sun is still operating, Lord Kelvin was able to calculate an upper limit to the age of the Sun by determining how long the fuel of the Sun would last.

His first estimate of the Sun's age was based on the assumption that the Sun operates with chemical energy, i.e., energy obtained by burning energy-rich compounds like coal or hydrogen. This would allow the Sun to operate for only 1500 to 5000 years, depending on the type of fuel. A better estimate followed when Lord Kelvin added the energy released during a gravitational collapse of the Sun. This obviously requires that the Sun started with a much larger radius than it has today. Accepting that assumption, Lord Kelvin arrived at a value of $2 \times 10^7$ years. By taking into consideration the fact that the Sun's core is much denser than its outer shell, he was able to push the age of the Sun up to $1 \times 10^8$ years, which he judged sufficiently close to his estimate of the age of Earth to confirm the previous result.

Both estimates are much longer than the age predicted on the basis of a literal interpretation of the Bible, which inspired a 17th-century vice-chancellor of Cambridge University to claim that "man was created by the Trinity on October 23, 4004 BC, at nine o'clock in the morning." Why, then, was Lord Kelvin's result a problem for Charles Darwin? To answer that question, we take a look at our current knowledge of the history of life on Earth as shown in Table 10.4: given the slow pace of evolution, Lord Kelvin's age of Earth and the Sun would not provide enough time for the emergence of complex organisms such as human beings.

**TABLE 10.4**

**A brief history of life on Earth**

| Years ago | Event |
|---|---|
| $13 \times 10^9$ | Age of universe (**Big Bang**) |
| $4.7 \times 10^9$ | Formation of the solar system from an interstellar cloud of gas |
| $4.6 \times 10^9$ | Proto-Earth (great bombardment) |
| $4.03 \times 10^9$ | Oldest rock (Yellowknife, Canada) |
| $3.6-3.8 \times 10^9$ | First prokaryotes (stromatolithic bacteria) |
| $2.5 \times 10^9$ | First eukaryotes (algae) |
| $1.7 \times 10^9$ | Oxygen atmosphere |
| $1.0 \times 10^9$ | Sexual reproduction |
| $6.7 \times 10^8$ | Multicelled animal fossils found at many places on Earth |
| $5.8 \times 10^8$ | Animals with shells and skeleton |
| $4.8 \times 10^8$ | Plants expand from sea to land |
| $4.2 \times 10^8$ | Animals expand from sea to land |
| $2.4 \times 10^8$ | First mammals |
| $1-4 \times 10^8$ | *Kelvin's age of Earth and Sun* |
| $65 \times 10^6$ | End of dinosaurs |
| $4.0 \times 10^6$ | Early hominids (*Australopithecus*) |
| $2.5 \times 10^6$ | Genus *Homo* |
| $0.125 \times 10^6$ | Modern *Homo sapiens* |

## ● EXAMPLE 10.3 (*continued*)

Why were both of Lord Kelvin's estimates wrong by at least a factor of 10? For the estimate of the age of Earth, his model of a cooling Proto-Earth is inadequate. The current geothermal temperature profile is actually a steady-state profile; i.e., the temperature profile does not change with time. To offset the heat loss by heat conduction, heat is continuously generated by radioactive processes that occur in the core of Earth, and the convection in the liquid outer core, which converts gravitational energy into heat. Thus, the current temperature profile of Earth is not the result of the cooling mechanism assumed by Lord Kelvin.

For the Sun, Lord Kelvin's model of heat generation is incorrect. Neither chemical energy nor gravitational energy contributes significantly; rather, nuclear fusion in the core of the Sun generates the heat the Sun radiates. In Lord Kelvin's defence, it should be noted that in both cases the underlying physics had not yet been discovered at the time he criticized Charles Darwin's ideas.

## Countercurrent Flow

A circulatory adaptation to thermo-regulation in animals is based on an arrangement of blood vessels such that thermal energy is preserved in the body core. Most effective for this purpose is a countercurrent heat exchange where the arteries transporting blood to the skin are in close contact with the veins transporting blood back from the skin to the heart (body core). The following example and concept questions illustrate a few cases of such **heat-exchanger** systems.

## ● EXAMPLE 10.4

Heat exchangers require two adjacent tubes with good thermal contact. When fluids pass through the tubes, heat exchange occurs between the two fluids. Fig. 10.14 distinguishes two types of heat-exchanger designs: (i) a system with parallel flow in the tubes, and (ii) a countercurrent flow. In which of the two systems does the heat exchange occur more uniformly?

*Supplementary biological information:* Even though insects and fish are ectotherms, the application of countercurrent flow allows some species to maintain a core temperature exceeding the environmental temperature. Bluefin tuna can maintain

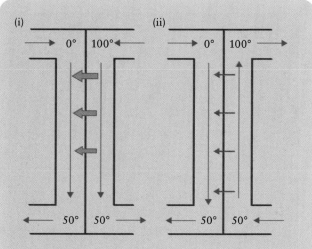

**FIGURE 10.14**

Two tubes with fluid flow in thermal contact. The fluid in the left tube enters at 0°C and the fluid in the right tube at 100°C. (i) Flow in both tubes occurs in the same direction. This leads to significant heat exchange near the initial contact zone of the tubes while little exchange occurs at the tail end of the flow. (ii) A countercurrent flow arrangement allows for the temperature difference between both tubes to be essentially the same along the entire contact length. This provides for a uniform and therefore more effective heat exchange.

a core temperature of 10 degrees above the water temperature despite the high heat conductivity of water compared to air. Winter-active moths use flight muscle action (flapping their wings without take-off) to generate heat that is preserved by a countercurrent heat exchanger in their thorax. These moths display core body temperatures up to 30°C in sub-freezing environments.

Countercurrent exchangers are also used for diffusive exchange when a concentration gradient exists across a separating, semipermeable membrane. An example is the liver, where bile and arterial blood pass each other in a countercurrent flow to absorb some components back into the blood system. This type of countercurrent exchange is discussed in the section on diffusion.

*Solution:* Fig. 10.15 compares the two heat-exchanger designs of Fig. 10.14 with a detailed inclusion of the temperatures along both tubes. If the hot and cold fluids enter from the same side at the top (sketch (i)), a high heat flux occurs at the top end of the arrangement since at that point a large temperature difference exists between the two adjacent tubes ($\Delta T = 80$ K). Only a small heat flow occurs at the bottom, where the temperature difference between both tubes is greatly diminished—in the figure, to a value of $\Delta T = 10$ K. If the hot and cold fluids enter from opposite sides, as shown in sketch (ii), then a uniform heat flow occurs across the interface since the temperature

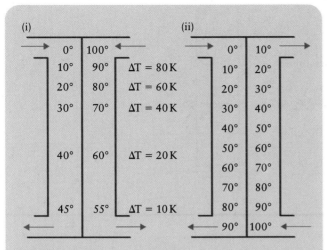

| (i) | | | (ii) | | |
|---|---|---|---|---|---|
| 0° | 100° | | 0° | 10° | |
| 10° | 90° | ΔT = 80 K | 10° | 20° | |
| 20° | 80° | ΔT = 60 K | 20° | 30° | |
| 30° | 70° | ΔT = 40 K | 30° | 40° | |
| | | | 40° | 50° | |
| | | | 50° | 60° | |
| 40° | 60° | ΔT = 20 K | 60° | 70° | |
| | | | 70° | 80° | |
| 45° | 55° | ΔT = 10 K | 80° | 90° | |
| | | | 90° | 100° | |

**FIGURE 10.15**

The same two tubes as shown in Fig. 10.14. Temperature values are provided along the tubes to illustrate the benefit of the countercurrent arrangement.

difference between both tubes is essentially constant along the entire exchange length, i.e., $\Delta T = 10$ K from top to bottom in the figure.

**FIGURE 10.17**
Arctic fox.

ANSWER TO PART (b): The Arctic fox in Fig. 10.17 lives in the tundra and prevents its feet from freezing with this approach. Venous blood is effectively warmed by the arterial blood before it leaves the legs, keeping low-temperature blood confined to the extremities. The fox has continuously cool feet, which helps to reduce the heat loss to the environment even further. During strong arctic breezes the fox further hunkers down and wraps its tail around its face like a scarf.

## Concept Question 10.4

**Fig. 10.16 shows a countercurrent flow heat exchanger with a loop. In a loop the same fluid passes through both tubes sequentially. (a) Why is such an arrangement of blood flow beneficial to a goose or a penguin standing on ice? (b) In which fox species do you expect to find heat-exchanger arrangements between arterial blood vessels flowing to the feet and venous blood vessels flowing back to the heart?**

ANSWER TO PART (a): The cold blood flowing upward from the feet of the penguin warms up quickly without large temperature differences occurring between neighbouring blood vessels in the bird's legs.

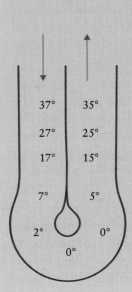

**FIGURE 10.16**
Countercurrent flow heat exchanger with a loop. This arrangement is useful for blood capillaries carrying blood toward and away from the skin (skin perfusion).

## Concept Question 10.5

**Fig. 10.18 shows a similar countercurrent blood flow for a loop in the human skin, with the incoming vessel a small artery and the outgoing vessel a small vein.**

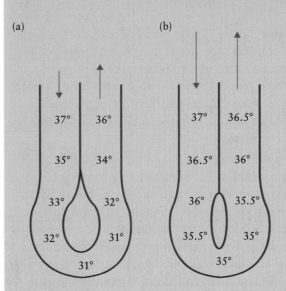

**FIGURE 10.18**
Effect of vessel diameter and blood flow speed on the efficiency of a countercurrent heat-exchange arrangement of capillaries in the human skin.

## Concept Question 10.5 (continued)

**Explain how the increase in the cross-section of the blood capillary from Fig. 10.18(a) to Fig. 10.18(b) leads to a higher dissipation of body heat into the environment.**

ANSWER: Whenever the core temperature of the human body exceeds the normal level of 37°C, an increase in heat dissipation into the environment is necessary. This is achieved by widening blood capillaries, allowing an increased blood flow to the skin. An increase of the blood volume passing below the skin per time unit corresponds to an increase in the heat transported to the skin surface. The efficiency of heat transport to the skin is further enhanced as the increased blood flow leads to a reduction in the heat exchange between the adjacent arterioles and venules (small blood vessels leading to and from the capillaries; blood flow rates in various blood vessels are discussed in Chapter 12). Thus, when the blood flow to the skin is increased, blood reaches the body surface at a higher temperature. A larger temperature difference between the blood and the surrounding air causes a larger heat loss per time.

# Diffusion

All membranes have in common the ability to maintain a non-equilibrium between the systems they separate. In addition, biological membranes participate actively in the exchange processes between the two systems they separate. For this role, cell membranes command a range of transport processes as illustrated in Fig. 10.19:

- *Passive diffusion*, sketched as an arrow through the uniform membrane material, allows small ions and molecules to penetrate the membrane in the direction of an existing concentration step. In the case of diffusion, the flow of material is in the direction from the higher to the lower concentration.

- *Facilitated diffusion* is an enhanced diffusion of specific molecules, supported by proteins. This type of diffusion is indicated in the figure by an arrow with the label "protein." These proteins are embedded in the cell membrane, as shown in Fig. 10.2. The diffusion process is the same as in passive diffusion. In biology, proteins that facilitate diffusion are called **gated channels** for the motion of the diffusing species.

- *Active ion transport*. Proteins and enzymes are also capable of transporting (mostly smaller) ions across the membrane against a concentration

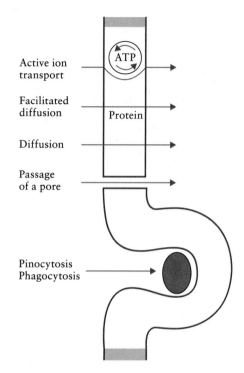

**FIGURE 10.19**

Conceptual sketch illustrating the main mechanisms of material transport across biological membranes. Diffusion along a concentration gradient is discussed in this chapter. Facilitated diffusion allows for chemically specific transport and is described by the same mechanisms we introduce for passive diffusion. Active ion transport against a concentration gradient is discussed in Chapter 14 for the potassium and sodium ion transport across nerve membranes. Passage of pores in a membrane is discussed in Chapter 12 as a fluid flow phenomenon. Pinocytosis and phagocytosis are more complex processes that include shape changes of the membrane.

step. This process is called active ion transport and requires energy, typically provided by ATP molecules as indicated in Fig. 10.19. Important examples include the transport of potassium and sodium across the membrane of nerve cells, as discussed in Chapter 14, and proton pumps in plants, fungi, and bacteria to remove $H^+$ from the cell.

- *Fluid flow*. Small-sized molecules pass through pores in the membrane. An example is the passage of blood plasma components through the basement membrane in the kidneys. This process is not considered a diffusion process in the context of this chapter but is treated as a flow process in Chapter 12.

- *Pinocytosis*. Very large molecules or bacteria are transported across the membrane in processes called **pinocytosis** (for molecules) or **phagocytosis** (for bacteria). These processes are complex encapsulations and are not included in the current discussion.

# Fick's Law

In 1855, the physician Adolf Fick described the transport of matter across a membrane in analogy to Fourier's law of heat transport. Fick observed empirically that the rate of a gas passing through a membrane of contact area $A$ and width $l$ is proportional to $A$, and the density difference on both sides of the membrane, $\rho_{high} - \rho_{low}$. The transport rate of a given component $i$ is also inversely proportional to the width of the membrane:

$$\frac{m_i}{t} = D \cdot A \frac{\rho_{i,high} - \rho_{i,low}}{l} \qquad [22]$$

This is **Fick's law**. The proportionality factor $D$ is called the **diffusion coefficient**, with SI unit $m^2/s$. The index $i$ in Eq. [22] indicates that Fick's law applies to components of a mixed phase as well. In biological systems, mixed systems occur frequently as membranes separate liquid solutions, such as cytoplasm from the extracellular fluid; or membranes separate gaseous and liquid solutions, such as blood and air in the lungs. For such systems the mass of the $i$-th component, $m_i$, is usually rewritten as the amount of the component $n_i$ in unit mol:

$$n_i(\text{mol}) = \frac{m_i\,(\text{kg})}{M\left(\dfrac{\text{kg}}{\text{mol}}\right)} \qquad [23]$$

and the density $\rho_i$ is rewritten as **concentration** $c_i$:

$$c_i\left(\frac{\text{mol}}{\text{m}^3}\right) = \frac{\rho_i\left(\dfrac{\text{kg}}{\text{m}^3}\right)}{M\left(\dfrac{\text{kg}}{\text{mol}}\right)} \qquad [24]$$

Using these definitions, Fick's law of diffusion can be given in a second form:

$$j_i = \frac{n_i}{t} = D \cdot A \frac{c_{i,high} - c_{i,low}}{l} \qquad [25]$$

in which $j_i$ is the **material flux** (the amount of matter that continuously passes a given location in unit mol/s). It is equal to the amount of component $i$, $n_i$, crossing the membrane from the side of higher concentration to the side of lower concentration during the time interval $t$.

The term $\Delta c/l$ is the concentration step from one side of the membrane to the other. This term can be generalized as the change of the concentration with position across the membrane, i.e., a **concentration gradient** $\Delta c/\Delta x$ when the direction perpendicular to the membrane is the $x$-axis. The concept of a concentration gradient is more useful when we do not want to refer to a particular membrane thickness. For example, concentration gradients of morphogens are thought to define the body axes in embryos (**gradient hypothesis in embryology**). In this case you are interested in the local change of a concentration, not a concentration step across the entire embryo. As with temperature gradients, concentration gradients need not be constant but can be a function of the position. In the current chapter, however, we continue to confine our discussion to constant gradients.

In analogy to Fourier's law, Fick's law of diffusion applies only when transport occurs in a steady state, which means that no essential parameter of the system varies with time. In particular, the concentration of component $i$ on both sides of the membrane must be constant and the profile of the diffusing component across the membrane must not change with time. A steady state therefore excludes any initial, transient period after the experiment has started. During the early transient period the concentration profile across the membrane varies, eventually approaching the steady-state profile. The steady state is an important state because the system will develop toward this state if it cannot develop toward an equilibrium state. As an example, the concentration difference across the membrane is always maintained in a human cell, preventing the cell from approaching a chemical equilibrium. The unique role of the steady state for non-equilibrium systems is discussed in more detail later in this chapter.

Since material flows continuously from one side to the other in a steady-state diffusion process, independent processes are required to ensure that the concentration of component $i$ does not decrease on the higher-concentration side of the membrane (continuous supply) and that it does not increase on the lower-concentration side of the membrane (continuous consumption). Thus, whenever a concentration gradient is maintained across a semipermeable biological membrane, additional physiological processes are involved. Examples include:

- *passive chemical processes*, such as the buffer effect regulating the acidity (pH value) of blood by using the chemical reaction $CO_2 + H_2O \rightleftharpoons HCO_3^- + H^+$,

- *active biosynthesis* of components such as immunoglobulin (antibodies in blood), or

- *active transport* across the membrane against the concentration gradient as discussed in Chapter 14 for nerve cells.

## ● EXAMPLE 10.5

We consider sucrose diffusing along a 10-cm-long tube filled with water. The cross-sectional area of the tube is 6.0 cm². The diffusion coefficient is $5.0 \times 10^{-10}$ m²/s and a total amount of sucrose of $8.0 \times 10^{-14}$ kg is transported in a steady state along the tube in 15 s. What is the difference in the density levels of sucrose at the two ends of the tube?

*Solution:* We use Fick's law in the form given in Eq. [22]. This equation is rewritten to isolate the unknown density difference:

$$\Delta\rho = \left(\frac{m}{t}\right)\frac{l}{D \cdot A} \qquad [26]$$

Now we substitute the given data into Eq. [26]:

$$\Delta\rho = \frac{(8 \times 10^{-14}\,\text{kg})(0.1\,\text{m})}{(15\,\text{s})\left(5 \times 10^{-10}\,\dfrac{\text{m}^2}{\text{s}}\right)(6 \times 10^{-4}\,\text{m}^2)}$$

$$= 1.8 \times 10^{-3}\,\frac{\text{kg}}{\text{m}^3} \qquad [27]$$

## Concept Question 10.6

**Anoxia is a lack of oxygen supply to cells, while hypoxia is a deficiency of oxygen supply. Which parameters in Fick's law play a possible role in anoxia or hypoxia?**

ANSWER: We use Eq. [25]. The oxygen flux $j_{O_2}$ into the receiving tissue is lowered when

- the concentration step is too small because the blood oxygen concentration $C_{O_2,high} = C_{O_2,in\ blood}$ is too low,
- the concentration gradient is too low because the membrane thickness $l$ is too large, or
- the diffusion coefficient is lowered.

Too-low oxygen levels in the blood can be the result of a diminished uptake of oxygen (at high altitudes; too-high pressure on the thorax while diving with a snorkel that is too long; sleep apnea), a too-low oxygen capacity of the blood (too-low erythrocyte count; haemoglobin deficiency, e.g., due to iron deficiency, sickle cell anaemia, or carbon monoxide poisoning), or a diminished flow of blood through the blood capillaries (too-low blood pressure, e.g., during heart failure or serious injury; local circulatory disorder due to embolism or thrombosis). Diffusion paths get too long during irregular tissue growth (see Concept Question 10.7). The diffusion coefficient cannot be altered directly; however, alterations in the cells can

diminish the rate of oxygen uptake, e.g. hydrocyanic acid poisoning where the oxygen reaction with food in the mitochondria is inhibited.

## Concept Question 10.7

**Each blood capillary is capable of supplying oxygen to a surrounding tissue cylinder with a radius of about 20 $\mu$m, called Krogh's cylinder. Which factors affect this radius?**

ANSWER: We start with Eq. [25]. The blood oxygen concentration or its partial pressure in the blood, and the oxygen permeability of the tissue, which is defined in physiology as the diffusion coefficient per length of membrane tissue, $D/l$, govern the oxygen flux per unit area of the capillary wall. Further, the oxygen consumption rate of the receiving tissue is a limiting factor.

## Countercurrent Exchange Processes in Diffusion

Heat exchangers are based on two adjacent tubes with good thermal contact. When fluids pass through the tubes, heat exchange between the two fluids occurs. In the same fashion, if we establish good diffusive contact between the two tubes, exchange of matter occurs if a concentration difference exists across the separating membrane. Such exchangers work most effectively in the countercurrent mode, as illustrated in the heat-exchange case.

Countercurrent exchange is often applied in nature. It allows, for example, seabirds such as the albatross to drink seawater. The birds use a pair of nasal glands that produce a fluid saltier than seawater. That fluid is then disposed of through the beak. In a countercurrent exchange, salt is removed from blood vessels into tubules that collect the salty fluid in the glands. Thus, the salt is removed from the bird's body without the need for fresh water.

A second example is highlighted in Fig. 10.20, which illustrates the respiratory action of fish. Fish extract oxygen from air dissolved in water. They continuously let water stream through their mouths and over the highlighted gill arches (parts (a) and (b)). Each gill arch has two rows of gill filaments, illustrated in part (b). These filaments are composed of flat plates called lamellae. The lamellae contain a mesh of blood capillaries that absorb oxygen from the water passing through the flat plates. The blood

(a)

(b)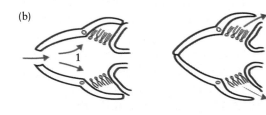

(c)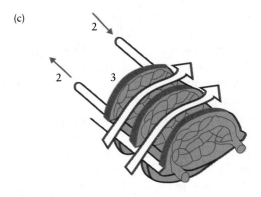

**FIGURE 10.20**

Illustration of the function of fish gills. Fish require a continuous flow of water over their gill arches (1). These arches contain blood vessels (2) that branch into capillaries absorbing oxygen from the water in the lamellae (3) of the gill filaments. To maximize the oxygen harvesting, blood flow and water flow are arranged in a countercurrent pattern, with oxygen-poor blood entering the lamellae upstream of the water flow and oxygen-rich blood leaving the lamellae downstream.

flow direction in the capillaries (noted with green arrows in Fig. 10.20(c)) is opposite to the flow direction of the passing water (red arrows). The countercurrent flow enhances the oxygen absorption from the flowing water. This elaborate countercurrent flow approach is necessary as the total amount of oxygen dissolved in water is much less than the fraction of oxygen in air. Thus, efficient methods of harvesting oxygen from water are necessary for aquatic animal life.

## Temperature Dependence of Diffusion

Table 10.5 shows several diffusion coefficients $D$ for biologically relevant systems at 20°C. The data indicate some interesting trends—for example, that the same molecule (e.g., oxygen) diffuses faster in less dense media, i.e., fastest in gases and slowest in solid tissue. The data also show that bigger particles

### TABLE 10.5

**Biologically relevant diffusion coefficients at $T = 20°C$**

| System | Diffusion coefficient |
|---|---|
| Oxygen ($O_2$) in air | $6.4 \times 10^{-5} \ m^2/s$ |
| Oxygen ($O_2$) in water | $1 \times 10^{-9} \ m^2/s$ |
| Oxygen ($O_2$) in tissue | $1 \times 10^{-11} \ m^2/s$ |
| Water in water | $2.4 \times 10^{-9} \ m^2/s$ |
| Sucrose in water | $5 \times 10^{-10} \ m^2/s$ |
| Haemoglobin in water | $7 \times 10^{-11} \ m^2/s$ |
| Tobacco mosaic virus in water | $5 \times 10^{-12} \ m^2/s$ |

The value for water self-diffusion applies at $T = 25°C$.

diffuse more slowly in a given medium—for example, sucrose diffuses faster than haemoglobin in water.

When wondering about such observations and the fact that they seem not to be predicted by Eq. [22], we need to keep in mind that Fick's law is a **phenomenological law**. This means that it is an adequate description of experimental observations of the relation between the flux of matter across a membrane and the corresponding concentration change, but it is not derived from the fundamental laws of physics, e.g., the three laws of thermodynamics or Newton's three laws of mechanics. Empirical laws usually contain constants, such as the diffusion coefficient in Fick's law, for which a fundamental origin is not revealed by the empirical law itself. Consequently, although we know the diffusion coefficients in Table 10.5, we cannot predict values for other diffusion coefficients based on our understanding of nature in general, nor can we explain the temperature dependence of $D$ in spite of our intuition that it should be significant.

To understand the temperature dependence of diffusion, a microscopic look at the membrane is necessary. Since diffusion is based on the motion of single atoms or molecules, the membrane model has to be developed at the atomic length scale. We used this approach before, when we developed the kinetic gas theory as an atomic scale model in Chapter 7 to link temperature and the root-mean-square speed of particles.

A microscopic model for the matrix in which diffusion is observed is illustrated in the top panels of Fig. 10.21: it consists of a regular array of atoms or molecules with fixed relative positions (open red circles). This is a good model for crystalline solids, but it is also suitable to describe diffusion in solids

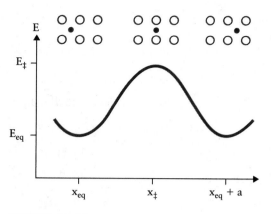

**FIGURE 10.21**

Top panel: three sequential sketches for the microscopic diffusion mechanism in an ordered matrix. The matrix particles are indicated by open circles. The diffusing foreign particle (solid dot) hops from one wide-open site within the matrix to another, passing through a zone in which the matrix particles are located in a denser array. The wide-open sites are equilibrium sites for the foreign particle in which it spends most of the time. Bottom panel: the corresponding plot of the potential energy of the foreign atom as it moves from its initial site at $x_{eq}$ to the final site of the jump at $x_{eq} + a$. At the equilibrium sites the energy of the atom is $E_{eq}$. The atom has a maximum energy $E_{\ddagger}$ in the transition state at position $x_{\ddagger}$.

without long-range order, e.g., amorphous solids, liquids, and most biological systems.

This microscopic model of diffusion was first introduced quantitatively by Svante August Arrhenius in 1889. Diffusion results when the foreign particle, shown as the solid dot in Fig. 10.21, travels from one open site in the matrix to the next by passing through a zone in which the matrix particles are more crowded. The plot in the lower panel of Fig. 10.21 shows the potential energy of the foreign atom as a function of its position. Sites that provide more space for the diffusing particle are associated with a smaller potential energy. Such sites are shown in the first and last panel at the top of the figure and correspond to positions $x_{eq}$ and $x_{eq} + a$ where $a$ is a typical spacing of adjacent open sites for a given matrix. Since the potential energy of the diffusing particle has a minimum value at $x_{eq}$, we call this an equilibrium position and label the corresponding energy $E_{eq}$.

The foreign particles are in thermal equilibrium with the matrix, which means that they will not have a sufficiently high total energy to move through the matrix like gas particles move in the kinetic gas theory model. Instead, the total energy of the particle is much smaller than the energy barrier between positions $x_{eq}$ and $x_{eq} + a$ in Fig. 10.21, and the particle is confined to the equilibrium position for most of the time.

When an atom moves, it must pass through an area of higher potential energy. The state where the foreign atom reaches the maximum potential energy is called the **transition state** and its potential energy is labelled $E_{\ddagger}$. $\Delta E = E_{\ddagger} - E_{eq}$ is then called the **activation energy** since this energy difference must be provided to the atom in order for it to be able to cross into a neighbouring equilibrium site. How can particles ever pass the energy barrier when the transition-state energy exceeds the total energy of the diffusing particle? The atom jumps successfully when its kinetic energy is higher than the activation energy at the instant it attempts to jump. For atoms at a given temperature the Maxwell–Boltzmann distribution from Fig. 7.20(c) allows us to determine the fraction of foreign atoms that have enough kinetic energy to pass the barrier. These will be the particles in the tail of the distribution at high speeds. It is apparent from Fig. 7.20(c) that more atoms have enough energy to overcome the activation energy barrier if the system is at a higher temperature. This explains why diffusion coefficients are larger at higher temperatures.

This qualitative prediction is tested in Fig. 10.22, which displays the diffusion data for many elements in silicon. The crystalline silicon matrix is chosen because by far the best-established diffusion data exist for that system. Shown in the figure are the diffusion coefficients as a function of temperature (the temperature scale is shown above the panel). We see that copper has the highest diffusion coefficient: it is the fastest-diffusing element in silicon; and silicon self-diffusion has the smallest diffusion coefficient, i.e., silicon diffuses more slowly than any other element in silicon. The wide range of diffusion coefficients in the silicon system is partially due to the existence of two different diffusion mechanisms. Fast diffusors like copper move in the fashion indicated in Fig. 10.21, which is called **interstitial diffusion**. Particles that diffuse more slowly—i.e., those located below the dashed line in Fig. 10.22—diffuse **substitutionally**: they move from lattice site to lattice site displacing silicon atoms. Arrhenius's model applies to both types of diffusion.

Based on the model in Fig. 10.21, Arrhenius predicted the following temperature dependence of the diffusion coefficient:

$$D = D_0 \cdot e^{-\Delta E/(k \cdot T)} = D_0 \cdot \exp\left(-\frac{\Delta E}{k \cdot T}\right) \quad [28]$$

in which $k$ is the Boltzmann constant and $D_0$ is called a pre-exponential factor with unit $m^2/s$. The letter $e$ indicates the exponential function, which is also often written as $\exp(\cdots)$. Thus, the diffusion coefficient depends on the temperature in a nonlinear fashion. As we have done with power law

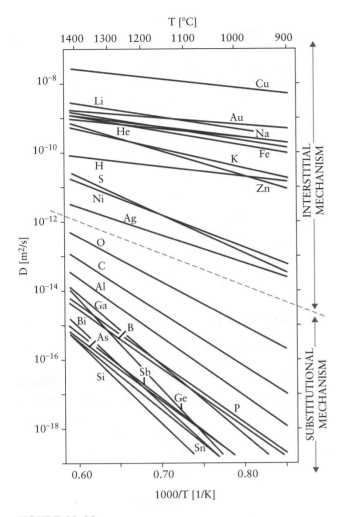

**FIGURE 10.22**

Arrhenius plot of diffusion coefficients (in unit m²/s) for various elements in silicon. Temperatures are given in unit °C at the top and inversely as $1000/T$ in unit 1/K at the bottom. Elements above the dashed line follow an interstitial diffusion mechanism, and elements below a substitutional diffusion mechanism. Both mechanisms are consistent with Arrhenius's equation for the diffusion coefficient as a function of temperature.

that the diffusion coefficient decreases as the ratio of the activation energy, $\Delta E$, to the term $k \cdot T$ increases; $k \cdot T$ is an energy term related to the temperature of the matrix. Therefore, diffusion coefficients become larger at higher temperatures. A more detailed evaluation of Arrhenius's theory also provides a physical explanation for the factor $D_0$ in Eq. [28]: $D_0$ is associated with the frequency of attempts by the particle to overcome the activation energy barrier and is therefore related to its vibration frequency.

---

**Concept Question 10.8**

In Arrhenius's model, the activation energy depends on: (A) the temperature, (B) the pre-exponential factor $D_0$, (C) the concentration of the diffusing atoms, (D) the concentration gradient (or concentration step) of the diffusing atoms across the matrix, (E) none of the above.

ANSWER: (E). The activation energy measures the energy barrier for a single hop of a diffusing particle from one possible site to an adjacent one. The temperature plays a role as part of the thermal energy available to the particle to overcome the barrier, but the barrier itself is predetermined by the arrangement of the matrix atoms.

---

relations before, we want to linearize Eq. [28]. This is done by taking the logarithm on both sides of the equation:

$$\ln(D) = \ln(D_0) - \frac{\Delta E}{k \cdot T} \qquad [29]$$

Eq. [29] states that plotting the logarithm of the diffusion coefficient, $\ln(D)$, versus $1/T$ yields a linear plot of the type $y = a + b \cdot x$. Here, $\ln(D_0)$ is the constant offset term $a$ and $\Delta E/k$ is the slope $b$. This is called an **Arrhenius plot**. Alternatively, the ordinate can be plotted as a logarithmic scale. This is done in Fig. 10.22 for the diffusion coefficients in silicon. Note that the abscissa in that figure is $1000/T$, not $1/T$.

Arrhenius's result provides a more detailed explanation of the diffusion coefficient. Eq. [28] shows

---

**● EXAMPLE 10.6**

Using Fig. 10.22, determine the activation energy $\Delta E$ and the pre-exponential factor $D_0$ for (a) the diffusion of germanium (Ge) in silicon, and (b) the diffusion of copper (Cu) in silicon.

*Solution:* The approach to analyzing logarithmic plots is discussed in detail in the Math Review "Graph Analysis Methods" at the end of Chapter 1. The simplest way to analyze a logarithmic plot such as Fig. 10.22 is to first replace the $D$-axis (ordinate) by a linear $\ln(D)$ axis. This is achieved by replacing each value along the axis by the logarithm of that number; e.g., the value $10^{-14}$ m²/s is assigned a new value of $-32.24$ and $10^{-8}$ m²/s is assigned a new value of $-18.42$. The new ordinate is linear with an increment of 2.303 for each decade of the original axis.

*Solution to part (a):* From this modified plot, two pairs of ordinate and abscissa values, $\ln(D)$ and $1/T$, are needed to determine the unknown parameters in Eq. [29]. Table 10.6 shows such data from the curve labelled germanium (Ge).

● EXAMPLE 10.6 (continued)

### TABLE 10.6

**Parameter sets for Ge diffusion in Si**

| ln($D$) | $1/T$ (1/K) |
|---------|-------------|
| $-44.74$ | $8.0 \times 10^{-4}$ |
| $-32.80$ | $6.0 \times 10^{-4}$ |

We substitute each data pair from Table 10.6 into Eq. [29]:

$$\text{(I)} \quad -44.74 = \ln(D_0) - \frac{\Delta E}{k} 8.0 \times 10^{-4}$$

$$\text{(II)} \quad -32.80 = \ln(D_0) - \frac{\Delta E}{k} 6.0 \times 10^{-4} \quad [30]$$

The two formulas in Eq. [30] are subtracted from each other to solve for the unknown variable $\Delta E/k$. We find:

$$\frac{\Delta E}{k} = 59\,700 \text{ K} \quad [31]$$

The activation energy is isolated by multiplying by the Boltzmann constant $k$:

$$\Delta E = 8.24 \times 10^{-19} \text{ J} \quad [32]$$

Activation energies for diffusion are often reported in another energy unit, the electron-volt (eV). The conversion is $1 \text{ eV} = 1.6 \times 10^{-19}$ J (for the physical motivation of this unit, see Chapter 13). With this conversion we find that the activation energy for diffusion of Ge in Si can be expressed as 5.1 eV. In comparison, the average thermal energy of a particle at room temperature is $k \cdot T = 0.025$ eV, i.e., 0.5% of the energy needed for a Ge atom to overcome the diffusion barrier between neighbouring sites in silicon.

A value for $\ln(D_0)$ is obtained from Eq. [30] by substituting $\Delta E = 8.24 \times 10^{-19}$ J into either one of the two formulas. This leads to $D_0 = 2 \times 10^1$ m²/s.

*Solution to part (b):* This part is solved in an analogous fashion to part (a). Table 10.7 shows the data pairs chosen from the curve labelled copper (Cu). The data pairs in Table 10.7 are again substituted into Eq. [29]:

$$\text{(I)} \quad -19.17 = \ln(D_0) - \frac{\Delta E}{k} 8.5 \times 10^{-4}$$

$$\text{(II)} \quad -17.71 = \ln(D_0) - \frac{\Delta E}{k} 6.0 \times 10^{-4} \quad [33]$$

### TABLE 10.7

**Parameter sets for Cu diffusion in Si**

| ln($D$) | $1/T$ (1/K) |
|---------|-------------|
| $-19.17$ | $8.5 \times 10^{-4}$ |
| $-17.71$ | $6.0 \times 10^{-4}$ |

Eq. [33] leads to $\Delta E = 8.06 \times 10^{-20}$ J $= 0.5$ eV. This is an energy barrier that is an order of magnitude smaller than the energy barrier in the case of germanium diffusion. We further find $D_0 = 6.8 \times 10^{-7}$ m²/s.

## Diffusion Length

Albert Einstein developed Arrhenius's model further, considering particles that make not one but many jumps. For each jump a particle selects randomly from its neighbouring equilibrium sites. This means, for example, that two consecutive jumps can bring the atom back to its initial position. Thus, the atom does not move a total distance of $N \cdot a$ after $N$ jumps of length $a$. From a statistical analysis of this problem, Einstein found instead a non-linear formula for the **diffusion length**. The diffusion length $\Lambda$ at a given temperature is defined as the average distance a diffusing particle moves during a time period $t$ (Einstein's formula for the diffusion length):

$$\Lambda = \sqrt{2 \cdot D \cdot t} \quad [34]$$

in which $D$ is the diffusion coefficient.

### Concept Question 10.9

**If time is the dependent variable, in which of the following forms is Einstein's diffusion equation written correctly?**

$$\text{(A)} \quad t = \frac{\Lambda^2}{2 \cdot D} \qquad \text{(B)} \quad t = \frac{\Lambda}{2 \cdot D^2}$$

$$\text{(C)} \quad t = \sqrt{\frac{\Lambda^2}{2 \cdot D}} \qquad \text{(D)} \quad t = \sqrt{\frac{\Lambda}{2 \cdot D^2}} \quad [35]$$

$$\text{(E)} \quad t = \frac{\Lambda}{2 \cdot D} \qquad \text{(F)} \quad t = \left(\frac{\Lambda}{2 \cdot D}\right)^{1/2}$$

ANSWER: Choice (A). This implies that the time required to diffuse a distance $\Lambda$ is proportional to $\Lambda^2$.

## ● EXAMPLE 10.7

Fig. 10.23 shows the alveolar sacs at the end of the bronchial tree. The alveoli are in direct contact with blood capillaries. In the alveoli, the inhaled air gets in closest contact to the red blood cells, which carry oxygen. Fig. 10.24(a) shows a scanning electron micrograph of red blood cells travelling through a capillary. Fig. 10.24(b) highlights the transport process barrier between the gas space of an individual alveolus and the adjacent blood capillary. The narrow capillary forces the erythrocyte to deform in order to tightly squeeze through. The membrane width is 1–2 $\mu$m. An erythrocyte passes through the contact zone in about 0.75 s. (a) How long do oxygen molecules need to diffuse from the gas phase to a passing erythrocyte? (b) How thick may the membrane tissue between alveolus and capillary become before the oxygen transfer is significantly reduced? This occurs when the oxygen cannot diffuse to the erythrocyte during the time period an erythrocyte passes the alveolus.

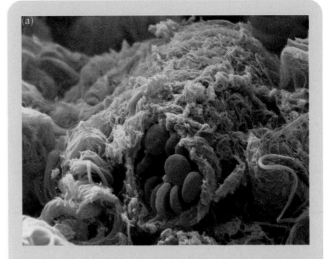

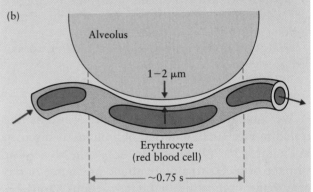

### FIGURE 10.24

(a) Coloured scanning electron micrograph (SEM) of a section through a human capillary with red blood cells (doughnut-shaped red discs). (b) Sketch of a blood capillary in contact with an alveolus across a 1- to 2-$\mu$m-wide membrane. An erythrocyte, which is about 7.5 $\mu$m wide and 1 $\mu$m to 2 $\mu$m thick, passes through the contact area in 0.75 s. A healthy red blood cell can deform to squeeze through the capillary because it does not contain a nucleus.

*Solution to part (a):* We use Eq. [34] with the diffusion coefficient for oxygen in tissue taken from Table 10.5. The diffusion length is the maximum distance in healthy tissue, which is 2 $\mu$m. Eq. [34] is rewritten with Concept Question 10.9 to express the time for diffusion:

$$t = \frac{\Lambda^2}{2 \cdot D} = \frac{(2 \times 10^{-6}\,\text{m})^2}{2 \cdot 1 \times 10^{-11}\,\frac{\text{m}^2}{\text{s}}} = 0.2\,\text{s} \quad [36]$$

Oxygen diffusion occurs without a problem across the membrane between alveolus and blood capillary in the allotted time.

*Solution to part (b):* We use the same diffusion coefficient as before and $t = 0.75$ s. This time,

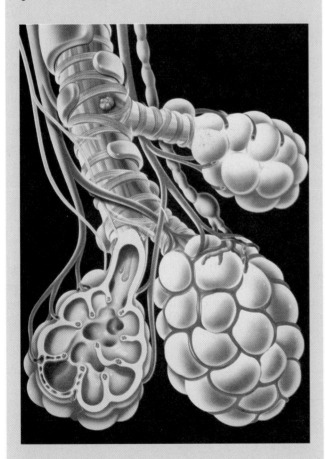

### FIGURE 10.23

At the end of each bronchial branch in the lungs, small sacs of about 0.3 mm diameter form an interface between the inhaled air and blood capillaries. These sacs are called alveoli. Oxygen transfer from air into blood occurs across the alveolar membrane.

## ● EXAMPLE 10.7 (continued)

Eq. [34] is used as written since the diffusion length is sought:

$$\Lambda = \sqrt{2 \cdot D \cdot t}$$

$$= \sqrt{2 \cdot \left(1 \times 10^{-11} \frac{m^2}{s}\right)(0.75\ s)}$$

$$= 3.9 \times 10^{-6}\ m \qquad [37]$$

Doubling of the membrane width between alveolus and blood capillary from 2 $\mu$m to 4 $\mu$m already shifts the diffusion barrier into a physiologically dangerous range. The medical term for alveolar membrane thickness increase is *pneumonosis*. It is usually caused by atypical pneumonia (which is caused by viruses) or pulmonary congestion. The resulting drop in the oxygen concentration in the arterial blood is referred to as *hypoxemia*.

We compare the respiratory effort of fish as illustrated in Fig. 10.20 and that of humans as discussed in Example 10.7. Breathing in air has the obvious advantage of access to a more abundant source of oxygen. Water in most fish habitats contains about 4−8 mL of $O_2$ per litre, while each litre of air contains 210 mL $O_2$. Because oxygen and $CO_2$ diffuse much faster in air than in water, ventilation of the internal surfaces of the alveoli for us is a much lesser concern. Indeed, a resting fish must actively pump water through its gills to not suffer from oxygen deprivation.

However, a problem with air breathing had to be addressed before life on land became possible: the humidity of air changes often, which would lead to varying degrees of water vapour inhalation. The inner surfaces of the alveoli would change (dry versus moist), causing significant variations in the physiological effectiveness of the respiration process. As a solution, the respiratory system of land-living animals always operates with completely water-saturated air. The humidity of the air is controlled by a turbulent flow of the inhaled air through the trachea, which has a moist inner surface. In this process moisture is picked up to the saturation level before the air reaches the lungs.

# Non-Equilibrium Thermodynamics

In the late 19th century, similarities were recognized among the four transport phenomena of diffusion, heat conduction, viscous flow, and electric conduction. In particular, scientists noted a striking similarity in the underlying formulas, Fick's law of diffusion, Fourier's law of heat conduction, the formula for viscosity we will discuss in Chapter 12, and Ohm's law for the electric current, which we introduce in Chapter 14. All four laws can be written in the same general form:

$$J = \frac{\Delta x_1}{\Delta t} = c \cdot A \cdot \frac{x_2}{l} \qquad [38]$$

in which $J$ is a **flux** (change of variable $x_1$ with time), and $x_2/l$ is a gradient, i.e., a change of variable $x_2$ across a membrane of length $l$. Also, $A$ is the cross-sectional area, and $c$ is a proportionality coefficient. The gradient creates the **non-equilibrium** in the system, and the flux is driven by the gradient. For this reason, the gradient is called a **driving force**. In each of the four laws the parameters $x_1$ and $x_2$ have different physical meaning, as outlined in Table 10.8. (In the table, viscosity and the electric flow are included even though we present the underlying physics only later in the textbook.)

Eq. [38] is a linear relation between flux and driving force. For each of the four transport phenomena in Table 10.8, thresholds exist toward regimes where other, more complex relations hold, i.e., where the flux is no longer linearly proportional to the driving

### TABLE 10.8

**Summary of the transport phenomena**

| Phenomenon | $x_1$ | $x_2$ | Coefficient $c$ |
|---|---|---|---|
| Heat conduction | Heat $Q$ | Temperature $T$ | Thermal conductivity $\lambda$ |
| Diffusion | Mol number $n$ | Concentration $c$ | Diffusion coefficient $D$ |
| Viscosity | Momentum **p** | Flow velocity **v** | Viscosity coefficient $\eta$ |
| Electric current | Charge $Q$ | Electric potential $V$ | Resistance $R$ |

Viscosity and electric current are discussed in Chapters 12 and 14, respectively.

force. In the case of heat conduction, the corresponding non-linear effect is convection. In the case of diffusion, the non-linear regime occurs when the diffusion coefficient becomes concentration-dependent.

Once these similarities were noticed, it also became evident that **chemical reactions** display many similarities to the transport phenomena. Although chemical reactions do not follow Eq. [38] because they do not have spatial gradients to act as a driving force, Arrhenius's transition-state model is successfully used to describe the kinetics of chemical reactions. Chemical reaction rates are therefore often displayed in Arrhenius plots.

In the first half of the 20th century it came to be understood that the four transport phenomena are dynamic processes near the equilibrium. Lars Onsager showed in 1931 that fluxes and driving forces near the equilibrium are always connected linearly with each other. In 1945, Ilya Prigogine and H. B. G. Casimir showed further that the **steady state** plays a particularly important role in this linear regime as it represents the state with minimum entropy production toward which all systems near the equilibrium develop.

Beyond this linear regime things become more complex. In 1954, Prigogine and Glansdorff proposed a first attempt at a model for systems far from the equilibrium (called **non-linear non-equilibrium thermodynamics**). They derived evolution criteria for systems that allow us to make some predictions. Despite the great interest in non-linear phenomena in biological processes we still do not have a complete formalism to describe all observations in this regime in a comprehensive fashion.

The remainder of this chapter, therefore, is divided into a brief but complete discussion of the linear regime and an example from the non-linear regime.

## Entropy in Non-Equilibrium Systems

To connect the non-equilibrium state of a system to the concept of entropy we must investigate further the irreversible character of heat conduction when two objects of different temperature are brought into thermal contact (as in the lower frame of Fig. 8.6). Fig. 10.25 shows the same system with a zero-width membrane and additional parameters of interest. The system consists of two homogeneous parts at each side of the membrane, labelled I and II, which are each uniform in all parameters but differ in temperature with $T_I < T_{II}$. The system (part I, part II, and membrane) is closed toward the environment (ENV); i.e., only heat exchange with the environment is allowed.

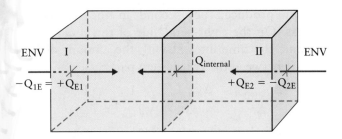

**FIGURE 10.25**

Model of a closed system with two parts separated by a zero-width membrane. Three heat fluxes are studied: heat exchange between either system part with the environment (ENV), and heat transfer between the two system parts.

Three heat fluxes must be considered as indicated by the arrows in Fig. 10.25: a heat flow between the system and the environment at part I shown at the left, labelled $Q_{E1}$; a heat flow between the system and the environment at part II shown at the right, labelled $Q_{E2}$; and a heat flow across the membrane toward the lower temperature part of the system, labelled $Q_{internal}$. The heat balance for each of the system parts I and II is given as:

$$Q_I = Q_{E1} + Q_{internal}$$
$$Q_{II} = Q_{E2} - Q_{internal}$$
[39]

Using Eq. [39], we write the entropy change of the combined system:

$$\Delta S_{system} = \Delta S_I + \Delta S_{II} = \frac{Q_I}{T_{low}} + \frac{Q_{II}}{T_{high}}$$

$$= \frac{Q_{E1}}{T_{low}} + \frac{Q_{E2}}{T_{high}} + Q_{internal}\left(\frac{1}{T_{low}} - \frac{1}{T_{high}}\right)$$
[40]

The right-hand side of Eq. [40] contains three terms. The first two each represent an **entropy flux** between the system and its environment. This flux is not of particular interest, because we showed already in Chapter 8 that entropy flux between the system and the environment occurs.

The last term in Eq. [40] represents an **entropy production** within the system due to a heat flow across the membrane. This is a term we have not seen before. It is zero when the temperatures are the same on both sides of the membrane. It resumes a non-zero value only for systems outside the equilibrium.

We introduce an explicit time dependence by dividing Eq. [40] on both sides by the time interval $\Delta t$, where $\Delta t$ is the time in which the entropy production $\Delta S$ takes place. This defines the entropy production rate as $\Delta S/\Delta t$ in unit J/(s · K), i.e., the amount of entropy produced per second in the irreversible process. On the right-hand side of the equation we combine the time interval with the amount of heat flowing between the two system parts:

$$\frac{\Delta S_{\text{internal}}}{\Delta t} = \frac{\Delta Q_{\text{internal}}}{\Delta t} \left( \frac{1}{T_{\text{low}}} - \frac{1}{T_{\text{high}}} \right) \quad [41]$$

The right-hand side of Eq. [41] is positive, thus the label *entropy production* as opposed to *entropy annihilation* is justified. We can further generalize this finding. Two factors contribute to the entropy production: the difference in inverse temperatures, which is identified as a driving force across the membrane (we use the variable $X$ for such driving forces), and the time change in the internal heat, which is identified as a flux (we use the variable $J$ for such fluxes). The flux always occurs in response to a non-vanishing driving force. The entropy production in Eq. [41] is therefore given in the form:

$$\frac{\Delta S_{\text{internal}}}{\Delta t} = J \cdot X \quad [42]$$

This formula explains why we found a similarity between the transport phenomena discussed earlier in this section, and why the forces and fluxes are combined in the way observed. Each driving force has a corresponding flux, such that the two together represent the entropy production of the system, as shown in Eq. [42].

An open system can be treated in an analogous fashion. For an open system the zero-width membrane is permeable for a chemical component, and internal fluxes for the heat and the permeating component have to be considered. Again, only the exchange across the membrane contributes to the production of entropy. For such a system it can be shown that Eq. [42] holds again, except that the flux $J$ and the driving force $X$ are now more complicated terms.

## Driving Force–Flux Relations near the Equilibrium

The second law of thermodynamics allows us to study the entropy function near the equilibrium. We know from Chapter 8 that $S$ has a maximum value at the equilibrium and thus must have a smaller value if any parameter describing the system is not at its equilibrium value. If the equilibrium is not yet reached, irreversible processes will take place and the entropy rises until the system is in equilibrium. When the system is in equilibrium, no further processes can occur.

Let us consider $\alpha$ to be a variable of the system we define such that $\alpha = 0$ when the system is in equilibrium. For example, $\alpha$ could be a temperature differ-

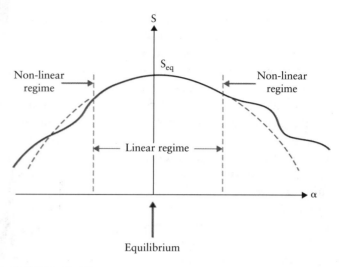

**FIGURE 10.26**

The dependence of the entropy on parameter $\alpha$ (e.g., the temperature), shown near the equilibrium. The parameter interval for which the dashed parabolic function fits the actual entropy function (red line) is called the linear regime (indicated by the two dashed vertical lines). Beyond this interval the parameter range is called the non-linear regime.

ence between the actual temperature and the equilibrium temperature, $\alpha = T - T_{\text{eq}}$. Fig. 10.26 shows, then, a sketch of the entropy as a function of this parameter, $S = f(\alpha)$. The entropy at the equilibrium is $S_{\text{eq}}$, which is the value we introduced in the context of the second law of thermodynamics. We know that the entropy is a maximum at $\alpha = 0$; thus the sketch in Fig. 10.26 shows properly that the entropy function bends downward both for $\alpha > 0$ and $\alpha < 0$.

We want to write a mathematical formula that describes the entropy function near $\alpha = 0$. Note that we do not know the entropy function outside the equilibrium; the downward bending is the only feature we know, due to the second law of thermodynamics. We want to use the simplest possible function that is sufficient to describe the curve in Fig. 10.26. For the part of the curve near the equilibrium—i.e., for small $\alpha$ values—a parabolic function opening downward is a good approximation. Introducing a coefficient $c_0$ to describe the curvature of the function, we write for the **entropy near the equilibrium**:

$$S = S_{\text{eq}} - \frac{1}{2} c_0 \cdot \alpha^2 \quad [43]$$

The interval of $\alpha$ values near the equilibrium in which this equation applies is called the **linear regime** (for the origin of this notion, see below). This regime is indicated by the blue vertical-dashed lines in Fig. 10.26. Note that this is the first time in thermal physics we make a statement that is true beyond the equilibrium but based on the fundamental laws of physics! All we have to do for a specific parameter $\alpha$ is to determine $c_0$ and we have derived a genuine non-equilibrium law.

To learn more about the coefficient $c_0$, Eq. [43] is connected to the previous discussion on entropy production. Without derivation, we note that the entropy changes with time in Eq. [43] as:

$$\frac{\Delta S_{\text{int}}}{\Delta t} = -c_0 \cdot \alpha \, \frac{\Delta \alpha}{\Delta t} \qquad [44]$$

in which we assumed a very short time interval $\Delta t$. The entropy production is proportional to the product of the variable $\alpha$ and the change of parameter $\alpha$ with time.

Comparing Eq. [44] with Eq. [42], we identify the first term as a driving force, $X = -c_0 \cdot \alpha$, and the second term as a flux, $J = \Delta \alpha / \Delta t$. Thus, near the equilibrium, the driving force and the flux are both linear in $\alpha$ and, therefore, are linked in a linear fashion with each other. This leads to **Onsager's equation**, in which $L$ is introduced as **Onsager's phenomenological coefficient**:

$$J = L \cdot X \qquad [45]$$

Eq. [45] can be compared with the transport phenomena equations, e.g., Fourier's law in Eq. [1] or Fick's law in Eq. [22]. As an example, the comparison with Fourier's law of heat conduction is discussed in the Appendix at the end of this chapter.

Onsager's equation is the central law in the discussion of non-equilibrium thermodynamics. In addition to unifying the four empirical transport phenomena, it allows us to define the conditions under which these empirical laws apply. It also allows us to classify some previously known observations as well as predict new phenomena. In the following discussion a few conclusions from Onsager's law are illustrated qualitatively as they are relevant to the biological sciences.

## Interference Effects

In real physical, chemical, and biological systems, more than one parameter of the system may deviate from the equilibrium value. For example, across the membrane of a cell, there can be concentration steps of different components capable of permeating the membrane. Or, during fast breathing at very low external temperatures, the air may not reach body temperature before reaching the alveoli, causing a combined thermal and concentration gradient across the membrane toward the blood capillaries. In this respect, Fig. 10.26 is only a special case, and a more general plot has to be drawn that allows for several parameters $\alpha_i, \alpha_k, \ldots$ of the system to have values outside of the equilibrium.

Such a plot for two parameters is shown in Fig. 10.27. The equilibrium of the system is given at $\alpha_i = \alpha_k = 0$ with $S = S_{\text{eq}}$ a maximum due to the second law of thermodynamics. We can repeat the same arguments we used in the discussion of Fig. 10.26. In particular, a linear regime occurs near the equilibrium in which the function $S = f(\alpha_i, \alpha_k)$ is a paraboloid that opens toward negative $S$ values. Further away from the equilibrium, that approximation does not hold and the entropy function deviates from the paraboloid shape.

Fig. 10.27 predicts the same behaviour of a system with two variables as Fig. 10.26 does for one variable: near the equilibrium Onsager's equation holds for both parameters; in other words, the system displays a linear relation between two driving forces and the corresponding fluxes:

$$\begin{array}{ll} \text{(I)} & J_i = L_{ii} \cdot X_i + L_{ik} \cdot X_k \\ \text{(II)} & J_k = L_{ki} \cdot X_i + L_{kk} \cdot X_k \end{array} \qquad [46]$$

For example, the index "$i$" could stand for a heat conduction process and the index "$k$" for a diffusion process. The terms with the coefficients $L_{ii}$ and $L_{kk}$ represent, then, the isolated transport phenomena as discussed earlier, while the two terms with coefficients $L_{ik}$ and $L_{ki}$ are cases in which transport phenomena interfere with each other. In 1931,

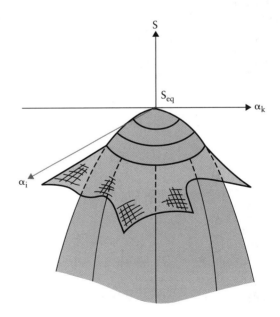

**FIGURE 10.27**

Entropy plot equivalent to Fig. 10.26, with the exception that more than one system parameter varies. In this particular plot we allow two parameters, $\alpha_i$ and $\alpha_k$, to vary. Linear and non-linear regimes for the parameters are defined in the same fashion as discussed for Fig. 10.26.

Onsager showed that a reciprocity applies to these coefficients: $L_{ki} = L_{ik}$. This helps to identify such interference processes, which usually are weaker than the primary transport phenomena.

One special case is illustrated here: the **thermomolecular pressure difference**, in which a heat flux through a closed system causes a pressure difference across the membrane, as shown in Fig. 10.28. At $t = 0$ a temperature difference of $T_1 - T_2 \neq 0$ is established across the membrane and is maintained by providing a continuous flow of heat through the system (indicated by the arrows on the left and right of the system). The bold arrow below the system indicates that the heat flux is the dominant transport effect in this case. Consequently, at $t > 0$ matter is pulled through the membrane in the same direction as the heat flows, decreasing the pressure on the left

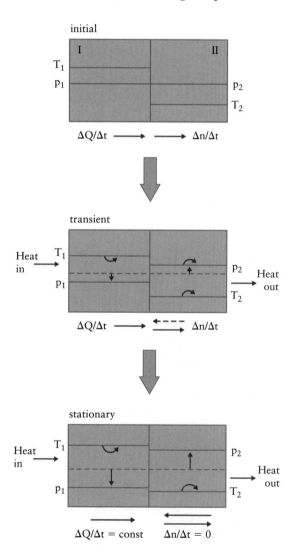

**FIGURE 10.28**

Thermomolecular pressure difference: an initial temperature difference between the two system parts is maintained by a continuous heat flow through the system. During a transient time a pressure difference between the two parts of the system builds up and becomes stationary in the steady state.

side and increasing the pressure on the right side. In this transient stage the pressure difference rises while the temperature difference is kept constant by externally regulating the heat flow. A small flow of matter ($\Delta n/\Delta t$) toward the right is observed. Eventually, the matter flow ceases as the pressure difference leads to an increasing diffusion-driven counterflow. At that point the pressure difference between the two system parts becomes stationary; that is, $p_1 - p_2 = $ const. Thus, a continuous heat flow leads to a pressure difference across the membrane.

## The Steady State

We have mentioned the stationary state or **steady state** several times in the discussion of non-equilibrium processes. So far, it was mostly used as a convenient simplification since all transport phenomena become time-independent when the steady state is reached; i.e., the mathematical formalism becomes easier to handle. For example, in the case of diffusion, only the first of two laws by Fick was introduced, the one applicable to the steady state. However, mathematical convenience is not a sufficient justification for focussing on a particular case.

The steady state is important for fundamental reasons. It plays the same role for open or closed systems near the equilibrium as the equilibrium plays for a homogeneous system. We found in our discussion of thermodynamics in Chapters 6 and 7 that the equilibrium state is unique in two respects: (i) that a system not in equilibrium approaches the equilibrium spontaneously, and (ii) that the equilibrium is a stable state; i.e., a system in equilibrium immediately returns to the equilibrium after a perturbation has occurred.

As early as 1922 in pioneering biological studies, and then since 1933 for physical systems, it was recognized that the steady state plays a very similar role outside the equilibrium as long as the system is close to the equilibrium, or, more specifically, in the linear regime. The steady state is the state toward which any system that is not yet in the steady state develops. The steady state is also a stable state of the system; i.e., the system always returns to the steady state in response to a perturbation. In 1945, Prigogine discovered the underlying property that drives this behaviour:

*The steady state is the state for which the entropy production is a minimum.*

Thus, outside the equilibrium this principle replaces the second law of thermodynamics, and the entropy production replaces the entropy as the property that determines the dynamics of the system. Prigogine's principle is the reason why the secondary flux in the interference effect example in the previous section ceases in the stationary case.

*In summary, the following statements apply to systems in the linear non-equilibrium regime (close to the equilibrium): (I) a system with no constraints reaches the equilibrium as this state has a zero entropy production, (II) a system with a driving force constraint (i.e., with a non-zero driving force maintained) goes to the steady state with minimum entropy production, and (III) a system that is either in equilibrium or in a steady state responds to a perturbation such that the perturbation is compensated (Henri* **Le Châtelier's principle of moderation***).*

## Homeostasis

**Homeostasis** *is the state of dynamic stability of the internal environment of a living body that is maintained by the ever-changing processes of feedback and regulation in response to external changes.*

The unique role of the steady state for biological systems was recognized by Claude Bernard when he distinguished the external environment of a living organism and its internal environment. He noted that many animals maintain quite constant internal conditions even when the conditions outside of the body change. This observation applies to several critical parameters in the human body: the body temperature is allowed to vary only by less than a degree around 37°C, the pH of blood and other interstitial fluids is held at a value of 7.4, and the sugar concentration in the blood is held at 0.1%. We refer to this state of the animal body as *homeostasis* (which translates as "steady state").

Homeostasis provides significant benefits in the animal body. Cells in an organism with stable temperature and/or chemical conditions operate in an unperturbed state. Individual chemical processes, such as enzyme syntheses, are performed at constant rates, and the entire cell works in a well-coordinated fashion. Cells for which such an environment is not established display fluctuating productivity that at times may idle other bodily functions for lack of supplies.

The benefits of maintaining steady-state conditions in the body are significant enough for the evolutionary development of coupled feedback mechanisms to control these conditions. These are sufficiently complex that modern biological research is still trying to piece the complete network of processes together. Part of this complexity stems from the fact that nature does not want to establish

a too-rigid steady state, but leaves open the option for non-linear processes we discuss in the next section. Allowing for change is necessary for a healthy development of individual organisms; e.g., the balance of hormones in the blood varies significantly during puberty or pregnancy.

## Non-Linear Non-Equilibrium Processes

Reading the previous section, we note that the linear regime of non-equilibrium phenomena is not sufficient to explain a large number of complex features of biological systems. In particular, what remains elusive is the formation of complex spatial patterns already at the cellular level. The most complex feature that can develop in an initially homogeneous system near the equilibrium—i.e., in the linear non-equilibrium regime—is a simple gradient, as discussed in the context of the thermomolecular pressure difference.

The inability of linear non-equilibrium concepts to explain biological processes is not too surprising since chemical reactions are dynamic non-equilibrium processes with no, or only a negligible, linear regime. Since chemical reactions are vital to the formation of biological systems, we have to study the non-linear regime far from the equilibrium to find the mechanisms that form more complex patterns. This field is still an area of intensive research, and we do not yet fully understand all the existing observations. Therefore, only an example is discussed to illustrate the types of observations and applications possible in this regime: the spatial pattern formation in hydrodynamic Bénard cells.

The top part of Fig. 10.29 shows Bénard's arrangement for a heat conduction experiment far from the equilibrium, which he conducted in 1900. A thin layer of thickness $l$ of a temperature-resistant oil is heated from below while its surface is cooled by air. This leads to a large temperature gradient $(T_2 - T_1)/l$, shifting the system far enough from the equilibrium that the entropy formulation in Eq. [43] has to be re-evaluated. Without knowing a mathematical form for the entropy formula in the non-linear regime far from the equilibrium, instead of Eq. [43] we write:

$$S = S_{eq} - \frac{1}{2} c_0 \cdot \alpha^2 + O(\alpha^3) \qquad [47]$$

This equation is equivalent to Eq. [43] for the linear regime except for a term $O(\alpha^3)$, which stands for "terms of at least the order of $\alpha^3$", i.e., terms with the third, fourth, and higher power of $\alpha$. When this term begins to dominate on the right-hand side of Eq. [47], the function is no longer a parabola. Calculating the entropy production from Eq. [47] no longer leads to a linear Onsager equation; i.e., fluxes and forces are no longer connected in the linear form of Eq. [45]. With Eq. [45] no longer applicable, new phenomena become possible, which we refer to as non-linear effects.

In the specific case of Bénard's experiment, the last term in Eq. [47] allows for an accelerated heat transport, which is necessary because oil cannot transport heat quickly via Fourier's heat conduction. The new heat conduction mechanism is called **convection**. Convection differs from Fourier's heat conduction in that the heat conducting medium itself moves, with hot oil going up and cooler oil going down. This is indicated by arrows in the top part of Fig. 10.29. Such convection flow of oil can be observed for cooking oil in a pan on your stove. Ordered Bénard patterns, however, cannot form in cooking oil as it cannot be heated strongly enough. Using silicon oil, Fig. 10.30 shows that the convection flow is circular. The most intriguing feature is shown in the bottom part of Fig. 10.29. In a top view of the thin oil film, a highly ordered hexagonal pattern is observed. The hexagons are called cells. The boundaries of the hexagonal

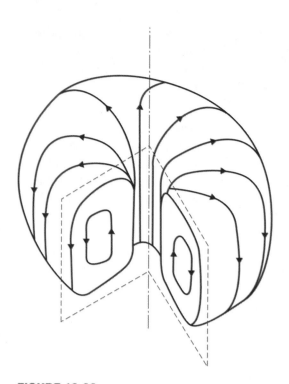

**FIGURE 10.30**

Side view of a single (honeycomb) convection cell indicating the flow pattern in Bénard's experiment.

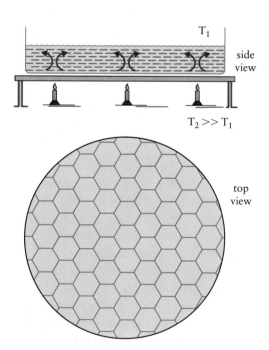

**FIGURE 10.29**

(top) Experimental set-up for Bénard's convection experiment. The side view shows a thin oil layer that is heated from below by a high-temperature heat source. The oil dissipates heat to the air above the oil layer. The heat transport occurs by convection. Convection requires the flow of oil, which leads to highly ordered honeycomb flow patterns when viewed from above (bottom sketch).

structure are coincident with the outer boundaries (dashed lines in Fig. 10.30) around each convection seed. Bénard cells were an early example of the transition from linear to non-linear behaviour, with Fourier's heat conduction the linear process and convection the non-linear process that leads to the highly complex patterns in Fig. 10.29.

Work on non-equilibrium thermodynamics by Prigogine and Glansdorff in the 1950s showed how difficult it is to describe these non-linear processes. It was found that even entropy is not a system property useful for characterizing the non-linear regime since no general rules apply. In particular, steady states are no longer stable; i.e., perturbations cause the system to leave such states and drift away. Even minor fluctuations in the parameters of a system can cause major effects. In some cases the entire dynamics of the system is driven by unpredictable random fluctuations.

# Appendix: Fourier's Law and Onsager's Equation

Eq. [41] is written for a zero-width membrane. To compare the driving force and flux from this formula with Fourier's law, we need to use Fig. 10.31 to rewrite Eq. [41] for a finite-width membrane (with width $\Delta x = l$). Fig. 10.31 shows essentially the same

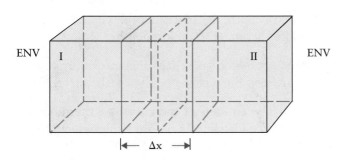

**FIGURE 10.31**

Model sketch used to extend a non-equilibrium, zero-width membrane model to describe systems with a finite membrane width.

system as Fig. 10.25, except that the zero-width membrane (indicated by the short-dashed lines) has been replaced by two interfaces, separated by a distance $\Delta x$.

The entropy production in Fig. 10.25, as quantified in Eq. [41], occurs entirely at the zero-width membrane because the temperature drop occurs at that point. For the system in Fig. 10.31 the entropy production is distributed across the entire length of the finite membrane. Thus, it is more useful to express an entropy production for a finite-width membrane as an **entropy production density**. This is done by dividing the entropy production by the volume in which it occurs:

$$\frac{1}{V}\left(\frac{\Delta S_{\text{internal}}}{\Delta t}\right) = \frac{1}{V}\frac{\Delta Q_{\text{internal}}}{\Delta t}\left(\frac{1}{T_{\text{low}}} - \frac{1}{T_{\text{high}}}\right) \quad [48]$$

The last term in this equation is then rewritten in the form $T_{\text{high}} = T + \frac{1}{2}\Delta T$ and $T_{\text{low}} = T - \frac{1}{2}\Delta T$, because we assume that the temperature difference between system parts I and II is not too large, i.e., $T \gg \Delta T$. Substituting these two temperatures in the last set of parentheses in Eq. [48] leads to:

$$\frac{1}{T_{\text{low}}} - \frac{1}{T_{\text{high}}} = \frac{T_{\text{high}} - T_{\text{low}}}{T_{\text{high}} \cdot T_{\text{low}}} \cong \frac{\Delta T}{T^2} \quad [49]$$

With Eq. [49], the entropy production density in Eq. [48] is rewritten in the form:

$$\frac{1}{V}\left(\frac{\Delta S_{\text{internal}}}{\Delta t}\right) = \frac{1}{A}\frac{\Delta Q_{\text{internal}}}{\Delta t} \cdot \frac{1}{T^2}\frac{\Delta T}{l} \quad [50]$$

in which $V = A \cdot l$ is used to split the volume of the membrane into the cross-section $A$ and the length $l$ on the right-hand side of the equation. Using Eqs. [44] and [45], we identify the driving force $X$:

$$X = \frac{1}{T^2}\frac{\Delta T}{l} \quad [51]$$

and the flux $J$:

$$J = \frac{1}{A}\frac{\Delta Q_{\text{internal}}}{\Delta t} \quad [52]$$

This allows us to compare Onsager's phenomenological coefficient $L$ from Eq. [45] and the thermal conductivity defined in Fourier's equation:

$$\text{Onsager:} \quad \frac{1}{A}\frac{\Delta Q_{\text{internal}}}{\Delta t} = L\left(\frac{1}{T^2}\frac{\Delta T}{l}\right)$$

$$\text{Fourier:} \quad \frac{Q}{t} = \lambda \cdot A\frac{T_{\text{high}} - T_{\text{low}}}{l} \quad [53]$$

which yields

$$L = \lambda \cdot T^2 \quad [54]$$

We find that Onsager's phenomenological coefficient and the thermal conductivity differ by a temperature-dependent factor. Because Onsager's coefficient is a constant due to Eq. [45], the thermal conductivity constant $\lambda$ in Fourier's law found phenomenologically is indeed not a constant, but temperature-dependent.

# MULTIPLE CHOICE AND CONCEPTUAL QUESTIONS

## HEAT CONDUCTION

**Q–10.1.** Which of the following statements is true? (A) Gold conducts heat better than copper. (B) Under otherwise equal conditions, about two times more heat transfers through gold than through iron per second. (C) If I conduct Fourier's experiment with a steel and an aluminium rod of the same shape, then I must use a longer rod for aluminium to obtain the same rate of heat transfer between beakers of freezing and boiling water. (D) The thermal conductivity in Table 10.1 is not given in SI units. (E) Table 10.1 shows that the thermal conductivity is a materials-independent constant.

**Q–10.2.** Lord Kelvin tried to show that Earth is much younger than Darwin required for the theory of evolution. In his calculations he studied the rock material of Earth's crust to a depth of 100 km and at one point wrote Eq. [21]. What does this equation contain? (A) The term $Q/A$ is the rate at which the entire Earth loses heat per second. (B) The term $(Q/t)/A$ is the rate at which the entire Earth loses heat per second. (C) The term $Q/A$ is the amount of heat Earth has lost since $t = 0$ (molten Proto-Earth state). (D) The term $(Q/t)/A$ is the amount of heat Earth has lost since $t = 0$ (molten Proto-Earth state). (E) The term $Q/A$ is the amount of heat Earth has lost since $t = 0$ (molten Proto-Earth state) through each square metre of its surface.

Q–10.3. The material of the rod in Fourier's experiment is changed such that its thermal conductivity decreases by 20%. What change allows us to best re-establish the previous flow rate of heat ($Q/t$): (A) decreasing the length of the rod by 10%, (B) increasing the length of the rod by 10%, (C) increasing the diameter of the rod by more than 20%, (D) increasing the diameter of the rod by 20%, (E) increasing the diameter of the rod by less than 20%.

Q–10.4. Use the thermal conductivity coefficient for window glass from Table 10.1 and for wood use $\lambda_{wood} = 0.08 \ J/(m \cdot s \cdot K)$. What happens if you replace a broken window by a wood panel of one-quarter the thickness of the glass? (A) The window opening with wood panel is thermally better insulated. (B) The window opening with wood panel is about as well insulated as before. (C) The window opening with wood panel allows an increased amount of heat to escape the room. (D) The stated data do not allow us to draw any of the previous three conclusions.

Q–10.5. When studying the heat loss of a sphere of radius $R$ we use the following term for the surface area $A$ through which heat flows in Fourier's law: (A) $A = \pi \cdot R$, (B) $A = \pi \cdot R^2$, (C) $A = 4 \cdot \pi \cdot R^2$, (D) $A = 4 \cdot \pi \cdot R^3$, (E) $A = 4 \cdot \pi \cdot R^3/3$.

Q–10.6. The following change in Fourier's experiment causes a doubling of the flow rate of heat: (A) doubling the diameter of the rod between the two heat reservoirs, (B) doubling the length of the rod connecting the two heat reservoirs, (C) cutting in half the length of the rod connecting the two heat reservoirs, (D) doubling the temperature of the high-temperature heat reservoir, (E) doubling the temperature of the low-temperature heat reservoir.

Q–10.7. The geothermal effect states that the temperature below Earth's surface increases by one degree Celsius for every 30 metres depth. Assuming a surface temperature of 0°C, which of the following statements is true: The temperature rises to 1000 K

at (A) 8 km depth, (B) 15 km depth, (C) 22 km depth, (D) 30 km depth, (E) 100 km depth.

Q–10.8. A tile floor may feel uncomfortably cold to your bare feet, but a carpeted floor feels warm. Why?

Q–10.9. The column of mercury in a thermometer initially descends slightly before rising when the instrument is placed in a hot liquid. Why?

## DIFFUSION

Q–10.10. Fig. 10.22 shows the temperature dependence of the diffusion coefficient for various elements in silicon. Which of the following statements is consistent with that data? (A) The activation energy for copper (Cu) is smaller than the activation energy for aluminium (Al). (B) The diffusion coefficient is linearly proportional to the temperature. (C) The diffusion coefficient is inversely proportional to the temperature. (D) The diffusion coefficient is a materials-independent constant. (E) The activation energies for elements at the upper end of the graph are higher than for those at the lower end of the graph.

Q–10.11. Use the diffusion coefficients for sucrose and tobacco mosaic virus in water from Table 10.5. To obtain the same rate of mass transfer for equal concentrations of sucrose and the virus on both sides of a water-filled cylindrical tube of fixed tube radius, the tube length has to be reduced for the virus by a factor of (choose the closest value): (A) 3.2, (B) 10, (C) 32, (D) 100, (E) 320.

Q–10.12. When an erythrocyte passes through a blood capillary adjacent to an alveolus, oxygen diffusion occurs because (A) a small temperature difference is established between both sides of the membrane; (B) the moving erythrocyte causes a drag effect pulling the oxygen through the membrane; (C) a concentration step for oxygen is established with the lower concentration at the erythrocyte's side; (D) there is no concentration gradient, but oxygen moves randomly in the membrane and ends up in the erythrocyte by chance.

Q–10.13. In two separate experiments the following two diffusion coefficients of a contaminant in tissue are found: experiment I: $D = 7 \times 10^{-11} \ m^2/s$, and experiment II: $D = 7 \times 10^{-9} \ cm^2/s$. Your laboratory head suggests further experiments to check whether the two contaminants are the same. What do you do? (A) Conduct the suggested experiments because the two diffusion coefficients are essentially the same.

(B) Repeat the previous experiments to see whether the new data are still so close to each other. (C) Ask another researcher to confirm the group head's conclusion because it isn't that easy to compare the two given diffusion coefficients. (D) Reject the laboratory head's suggestion and proceed with the conclusion that the two contaminants are different.

**Q–10.14.** If we double the membrane width of the membrane between the alveolar air space and an adjacent capillary from 2 $\mu$m to 4 $\mu$m, oxygen diffusion across the membrane at body temperature of 37°C will require (A) the same time, (B) half the previous time, (C) double the previous time, (D) one-quarter of the previous time, (E) four times as long.

**Q–10.15.** The diffusion length of a molecule in a solution is $\Lambda = 1$ cm after the experiment is run for $t = 1$ hour. When will the diffusion length double? (A) after an additional hour, (B) after an additional 2 hours, (C) after an additional 3 hours, (D) after an additional 4 hours.

**Q–10.16.** The diffusion length for a given system does not depend on the following parameter: (A) the temperature, (B) the pre-exponential factor $D_0$ of the diffusion system, (C) the diffusion coefficient, (D) the thickness of the sample in which the diffusion is observed, (E) the time duration of the experiment.

## TRANSPORT PHENOMENA IN GENERAL

**Q–10.17.** Which of the following statements about a system in steady state is correct? (A) The system is in an equilibrium state. (B) All system parameters change as a function of time. (C) The internal energy of the system increases continuously. (D) The entropy production in the system is a minimum. (E) The system reaches the equilibrium within a short time.

**Q–10.18.** Heat conduction and diffusion are called transport phenomena. What exactly is transported in heat conduction? (A) temperature, (B) thermal energy, (C) heat, (D) internal energy, (E) entropy.

# ANALYTICAL PROBLEMS

## HEAT CONDUCTION

**P–10.1.** We quantify Fourier's experiment, shown in Fig. 10.4, for a cylindrical copper rod of a length 1.2 m and a cross-sectional area 4.8 cm². The rod is insulated to prevent heat loss through its surface. A temperature difference of 100 K is maintained between the ends. Find the rate at which heat is conducted through the rod.

**P–10.2.** We focus on the geothermal effect in a slightly different fashion than in Example 10.3. We know that the average rate at which heat is conducted through the surface of the ground in North America is 55 mJ/(s · m²). Assuming a surface temperature in summer of 25°C, what is the temperature at a depth of 30 km (near the base of Earth's crust, which together with the brittle upper portion of the mantle forms the 100-km-deep lithosphere)? *Hint:* Ignore the heat generated by the presence of radioactive elements and use 1.7 J/(m · s · K) for the average thermal conductivity of the near-surface rocks. Start with Fourier's law.

**P–10.3.** For poor heat conductors the thermal resistance $R$ has been introduced. The thermal resistance of a piece of material of thermal conductivity $\lambda$ and thickness $l$ is defined as:

$$R = \frac{l}{\lambda} \quad [55]$$

(a) Show that Eq. [55] allows us to rewrite Fourier's law in the form:

$$\frac{Q}{t} = A \frac{T_{high} - T_{low}}{R} \quad [56]$$

in which $A$ is the cross-sectional area of the piece of material. (b) What is the SI unit of the thermal resistance $R$?

**P–10.4.** In a table you find for the thermal conductivity of quartz glass at 0°C a value of $\lambda = 3.4 \times 10^{-3}$ cal/ (cm · s · K). (a) Is this value consistent with the value given in Table 10.1? (b) What is the thermal resistance of a quartz glass sheet of thickness 1.0 cm?

**P–10.5.** In a cookbook, a poultry thawing chart states that a 10-kg whole turkey takes four days to defrost in a refrigerator. Estimate how long it would take to defrost a 2-tonne Siberian mammoth from the same initial temperature in an industrial refrigeration hall. *Hint:* Treat both animals as spherically shaped and use the same approach we applied in Example 10.3.

**P–10.6.** We want to measure the thermal conductivity of an unknown insulator material. For this we use the following set-up: A 4-mm-thick plate of the unknown material is placed between two iron plates of thickness 3 cm each. All three plates are 15 cm by 15 cm in size. The upper iron plate is heated to

350 K and the lower iron plate is kept at 290 K. Once a stationary temperature profile has developed across the insulator, the heater is removed from the upper iron plate. We observe that the temperature of the upper iron plate drops by 2.5 K after 100 seconds. Neglecting any loss of heat to the environment, what is the thermal conductivity coefficient $\lambda$ for the unknown insulator material? *Hint:* Approach this problem in the same fashion as we solved Example 10.3. The density of iron is $\rho = 7.9$ g/cm$^3$ and its specific heat capacity is given in Table 6.4.

**P–10.7.** Fig. 10.32 shows a block that consists of two materials with different thicknesses $l_1$ and $l_2$ and different thermal conductivities $\lambda_1$ and $\lambda_2$. The temperatures of the outer surfaces of the block are $T_{high}$ and $T_{low}$, as shown in the figure. Each face of the block has a cross-sectional area $A$. (a) Show that the formula

$$\frac{Q}{t} = \frac{A(T_{high} - T_{low})}{(l_1/\lambda_1) + (l_2/\lambda_2)} \qquad [57]$$

correctly expresses the steady-state rate of heat transfer. *Hint:* In the steady state, the heat transfer through any part of the block must be equal to the heat transfer through the other part of the block. Introduce a temperature $T_x$ at the interface of the two parts as shown in Fig. 10.32, and then express the rate of heat transfer for each part of the block separately. (b) Rewrite Eq. [57] using Eq. [55], which introduces $R_1$ and $R_2$ as the thermal resistances for the two parts of the block. By comparing the result with Eq. [56], determine how thermal resistances are combined for materials in sequence.

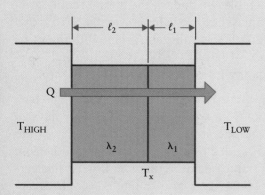

**FIGURE 10.32**

**P–10.8.** Show that the temperature $T_x$ at the interface of the block in Fig. 10.32 is given by:

$$T_x = \frac{R_1 \cdot T_{high} + R_2 \cdot T_{low}}{R_1 + R_2} \qquad [58]$$

**P–10.9.** We want to compare combinations of insulator materials in the case shown in Fig. 10.33. The figure shows a two-layer system with a total of four square pieces. Each piece has an area $A$, thus the two systems each cover an area of $2 \cdot A$. The two arrangements in Fig. 10.33 differ in the order of the two materials (labelled 1 and 2). Which arrangement, (a) or (b), allows for a greater heat flow?

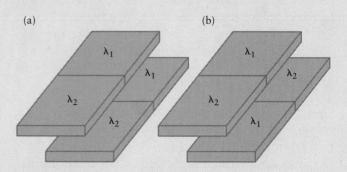

**FIGURE 10.33**

**P–10.10.** Two identical rectangular rods of metal are welded together as shown in Fig. 10.34(a), and 1 J of heat is conducted in a steady-state process through the combined rod in 1 minute. How long would it take for the same amount of heat to be conducted through the rods if they were welded end to end, as shown in Fig. 10.34(b)?

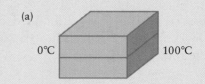

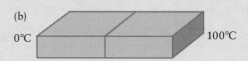

**FIGURE 10.34**

**P–10.11.** In the text we discussed the Australian Brush-turkey's approach to nesting. We noted that it must maintain the radius of a decomposing forest-litter mound in which its eggs incubate according to Eq. [12]. Confirm that this equation properly describes the relation between mound radius and its temperature profile.

**P–10.12.** In Concept Question 10.3, we used dimensional analysis to estimate the thermal relaxation time for a spherical bacterium in a fatty fluid. We derived Eq. [13] based on these arguments. Confirm this equation based on the total amount of heat needed to bring the bacterium up to ambient temperature using a reasonable estimate of the temperature gradient in the bacterium during the process.

**P–10.13.** Heat loss via convection occurs only when heat is carried by a moving fluid. For example, when heating water in a beaker from below, the increase of the water temperature at the bottom leads to a decrease of the water density and causes the warmer water to rise due to buoyancy. The rising water carries excess heat to the surface. (a) Compare bare skin to skin covered with clothes. Why is the heat loss of the body significantly reduced when wearing clothes? (b) At temperate lakes and ponds it is often observed that algae bloom for a short period during spring and autumn. Consider Fig. 10.35, which shows the stratification during summer (top) as well as the seasonal turnover in spring and autumn (bottom). How can the convection-driven turnover cause algal blooms?

**P–10.14.** A styrofoam box with surface area 0.8 m$^2$ and wall thickness of 20 mm has a temperature of +5°C on its inner surface and +25°C on the outer surface. Calculate the thermal conductivity of styrofoam if it takes 480 minutes for a 5.0-kg piece of ice to melt in the box. The latent heat of freezing of water is $3.33 \times 10^5$ J/kg.

## DIFFUSION

**P–10.15.** Determine the diffusion coefficient for glycerine in H$_2$O using the following observations: glycerine diffuses along a horizontal, water-filled column that has a cross-sectional area of 2.0 cm$^2$. The density step across $\Delta\rho/l$ is $3.0 \times 10^{-2}$ kg/m$^4$ and the steady-state diffusion rate is $5.7 \times 10^{-15}$ kg/s.

**P–10.16.** We want to test a statement we made in Chapter 9: carbon dioxide diffuses more easily than oxygen across the membrane between the alveoli and the blood capillaries. To show this, calculate the ratio of the diffusion coefficients of CO$_2$ and O$_2$ in tissue at 37°C. *Hint:* Start with Eq. [25]. Rewrite the concentration difference as a pressure difference using the ideal gas law. Apply this equation for both gases separately. For the pressure differences across the membranes in the lungs use the values $\Delta p(CO_2) = 0.8$ kPa and $\Delta p(O_2) = 8.0$ kPa. The amount of both gases diffusing across the interface alveoli/capillaries can be determined from the data given in Example 7.4.

**P–10.17.** Why can bacteria rely on passive diffusion for their oxygen supply but human beings cannot? *Hint:* Calculate from Eq. [34]: (a) the time it takes for oxygen to diffuse from the interface with the environment to the centre of a bacterium of radius $r = 1.0$ $\mu$m, and (b) the time it takes for oxygen to diffuse from the external air to an organ 10 cm below human skin. *Note:* For an upper limit use the diffusion coefficient of oxygen in water, and for a lower limit use the diffusion coefficient of oxygen in tissue from Table 10.5. These two values give you a good approximation since humans consist of roughly 10 L extracellular fluid and 30 L cells. (c) *If you are interested:* Why can many relatively large invertebrates such as hydras survive without a cardiovascular system?

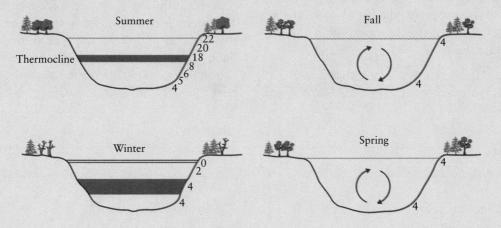

**FIGURE 10.35**

Lakes and ponds in temperate climates usually stratify by temperature and water density in winter and summer. In the summer, the warmer water is above the thermocline (water zone between 8°C and 18°C), with temperatures below the thermocline near 4°C (temperature of water at its highest density). In the winter, the water above the thermocline is cooler (between 0°C and 4°C) than the water below. The seasonal turnover occurs biannually as denser water sinks to the bottom of the lake.

## TABLE 10.9

**Diffusion coefficients in aqueous solution at 20°C and molecular mass for various biomolecules and viruses**

| Protein | $D$ (m²/s) | $M$ (kg/mol) |
|---|---|---|
| Tobacco mosaic virus | $5.3 \times 10^{-12}$ | 31 000 |
| Urease | $3.5 \times 10^{-11}$ | 470 |
| Catalase | $4.1 \times 10^{-11}$ | 250 |
| Haemoglobin | $6.3 \times 10^{-11}$ | 67 |
| Insulin | $8.2 \times 10^{-11}$ | 41 |

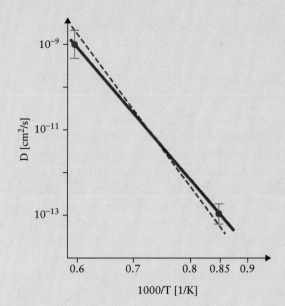

**FIGURE 10.36**

**P–10.18.** We want to determine the relation between the diffusion coefficient and the molecular mass of macromolecules. Use a double-logarithmic plot of the data listed in Table 10.9 to determine the coefficients $a$ and $b$ in

$$D = a \cdot M^b \qquad [59]$$

**P–10.19.** (a) How far does a tobacco mosaic virus move in water at 20°C in 1 hour? (b) Using the ratio of the diffusion coefficients for oxygen and carbon dioxide in tissue from P–10.16, what is the ratio of diffusion lengths for these molecules in tissue at 20°C?

**P–10.20.** Determining the pre-exponential factor $D_0$ in the manner shown in Example 10.6 leads to a large uncertainty of the value. To illustrate this, we choose the diffusion of carbon (C) in silicon. Fig. 10.36 shows the Arrhenius plot of the available data (note that silicon melts at about 1400°C). Use the solid and dashed lines to determine (a) the variation of the activation energy $\Delta E$, and (b) the variation of the pre-exponential factor $D_0$.

**P–10.21.** Fig. 10.37 shows a block that consists of two materials with different thicknesses $l_1$ and $l_2$ and

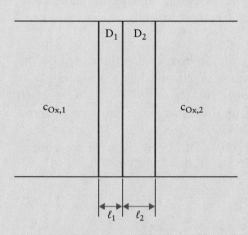

**FIGURE 10.37**

different diffusion coefficients for oxygen $D_1$ and $D_2$. The oxygen concentrations at the outer surfaces of the block are $c_{Ox,1}$ and $c_{Ox,2}$, as shown in the figure. Each face of the block has a cross-sectional area $A$. Determine a formula for the steady-state mass transport through the block in analogy to P–10.7.

## SUMMARY

### DEFINITIONS

- Amount in mol and concentration of the $i$-th component in solution:

$$n_i = \frac{m_i}{M}$$

$$c_i = \frac{\rho_i}{M}$$

### UNITS

Molar mass $M$: kg/mol

Amount of matter $n$: mol

Concentration $c$: mol/m³

Density $\rho$: kg/m³

## LAWS

- Fourier's law of steady-state heat conduction:

$$\frac{Q}{t} = \lambda \cdot A \, \frac{T_{high} - T_{low}}{l}$$

where $\lambda$ in unit J/(m · s · K) is the thermal conductivity coefficient, $l$ is the length of the membrane, and $A$ is its cross-sectional area.

- Fick's law of steady-state diffusion for the transport of

  - an amount of material in unit kg:

  $$\frac{m_i}{t} = D \cdot A \, \frac{\rho_{i,high} - \rho_{i,low}}{l}$$

  where $D$ in unit m²/s is the diffusion coefficient, and $\rho$ is the density.

  - an amount of material in unit mol:

  $$j_i = \frac{n_i}{t} = D \cdot A \, \frac{c_{i,high} - c_{i,low}}{l}$$

  where $j_i$ in unit mol/s is the material flux of the $i$-th component.

- Temperature dependence of the diffusion coefficient:

$$D = D_0 \cdot e^{-\Delta E/(k \cdot T)} = D_0 \cdot \exp\left(-\frac{\Delta E}{k \cdot T}\right)$$

where $k$ is the Boltzmann constant, and $\Delta E$ is the activation energy. This is equivalent to:

$$\ln(D) = \ln(D_0) - \frac{\Delta E}{k \cdot T}$$

- Einstein's formula for the diffusion length $\Lambda$:

$$\Lambda = \sqrt{2 \cdot D \cdot t}$$

- Steady state is a non-equilibrium process with minimum entropy production.

# CHAPTER 11

# LIQUID WATER AND AQUEOUS SOLUTIONS
## Static Fluids

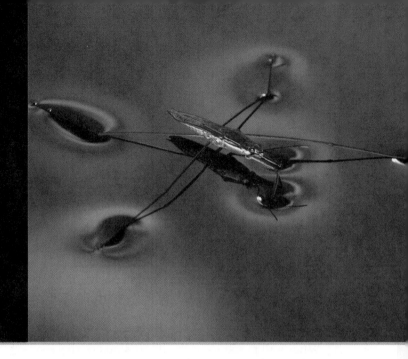

The term *fluid* includes liquids and gases. Fluids are deformable, which allows them to evolve toward a mechanical equilibrium in a given space. When intermolecular forces dominate, the fluid is found in the liquid state. When the thermal energy of the system dominates, the fluid is found in the gaseous state. Liquids occupy a well-defined volume, forming a surface when the size of the accessible space exceeds the liquid's volume.

The ideal fluid model assumes that the fluid is incompressible. If such a fluid is in mechanical equilibrium it is called an ideal stationary fluid. If the ideal stationary fluid is in the condensed liquid state, Pascal's law states that the pressure increases linearly with depth below the surface. The mechanical equilibrium at the surface requires the pressure at the liquid surface to be equal to the pressure in the adjacent gas space.

Fluids support immersed objects with a buoyant force. This force counteracts the weight of the object and is proportional to the volume of the object and the density of the displaced fluid.

The surface of a condensed ideal stationary fluid has properties that are distinct from those of the bulk material. This is due to an excess amount of energy required to form a surface, called surface tension or surface energy. Surface energy causes a pressure difference across a bubble or droplet surface that is inversely proportional to its radius.

Fluid surfaces facing a substance other than air or vacuum are called interfaces. Interfacial energies are conceptually similar to surface energies and are related to the wetting properties at the interface. A consequence of interfacial interactions is capillarity, which is the action by which the surface of a liquid is elevated or depressed in a tube based on its surface energy and the tube/liquid interfacial energy.

At this point we have reached an important milestone in the discussion of physics: thermal physics, which Albert Einstein once identified as its most unshakeable pillar, has allowed us to travel the entire distance from the simple equilibrium to complex pattern formation in living systems. We have developed many powerful concepts along the way, but we have done it with an incredibly simple model system: the ideal gas.

Now it is time to shift gears and use these tools to develop the properties of those physiological systems that play important roles in our body, e.g., liquids such as blood, elastic materials such as tissues, vibrating fluids such as the perilymph in the inner ear, electrically active solutions at the surfaces of nerves, and optical materials such as lenses in our eyes or rods and cones in the retina.

What will guide us in the discussions of these systems in the following chapters are the tools we have successfully developed using the ideal gas: starting with equilibrium properties and the first law of thermodynamics, we will establish dynamic properties by seeking linear near-equilibrium phenomena first and more complex non-linear properties last.

The current chapter is one of four chapters that focus on the most important biological system: **water**. We approach water from four different directions:

- the macroscopic properties of stationary water as an equilibrium system in the current chapter,

- the macroscopic phenomena of flowing water as a dynamic non-equilibrium system in Chapter 12,

- the microscopic structure of the water molecule as an electric dipole in Chapter 13, and

- water as a solvent and main constituent of mixed phases such as blood. We discussed this aspect already in Chapter 9; it will be useful to recapitulate that chapter after reading Chapters 11 through 13.

Life on Earth began in water and remained there exclusively for more than three billion years. Even life on dry land maintains close ties to water. The importance of water is evident from its abundance throughout the human body. The fraction of our body mass made up by water is about 75% for a baby, decreases to about 60% for young adults, and is as low as 50% for seniors. Two-thirds of the water in an adult's body is located in the cells, with the remaining one-third in extracellular fluids, including blood plasma.

# Model System: The Ideal Stationary Fluid

We discuss the macroscopic properties of water in this and the next chapter. However, we don't focus exclusively on water but study a more general model system that displays many of the same properties. This model system is called a **fluid**. Fluids are systems that yield to any force that attempts to alter their shape, causing the system to flow until it reaches a mechanical equilibrium in which the fluid then conforms to the shape of the container. Based on this definition, the term *fluid* refers to both liquids and gases, but distinguishes them from solids, which remain unchanged when placed in containers of different sizes.

There are, however, differences between liquids and gases we have to take into account. The molecules in a liquid are in a condensed state, i.e., they maintain a constant intermolecular distance. If the liquid is brought into a container with a volume larger than the volume the liquid occupies, the liquid forms a surface. In contrast, gases adjust their intermolecular distance and fill any provided space uniformly. Gases have no natural surfaces.

We focus first on fluids in mechanical equilibrium; in that state we call the fluid **stationary**. Remember that we defined the term *equilibrium* such that it refers to the state in which all essential parameters of the system are time-independent. What we mean by "essential parameters" in the current context is illustrated using a glass filled with water. Next time you have a drink, look at the liquid before you touch the glass. The liquid is in equilibrium: no obvious changes occur while you observe the system. However, as in a gas, a tremendous amount of motion of the particles exists at the microscopic level. Thus, the equilibrium of a macroscopic fluid does not include as an essential parameter the microscopic motion of the fluid molecules. The properties essential for an **ideal stationary fluid** are that:

- *The ideal stationary fluid is incompressible.* This means that both the volume of the fluid, $V$, and its density, $\rho = m/V$, are constant, i.e., they particularly do not depend on the pressure. This is a good approximation for liquids, but does not apply to gases. We have to retain the ideal gas model as introduced in the previous chapters for this reason.

- *The ideal stationary fluid is deformable* under the influence of forces and seeks a mechanical equilibrium. Only after the mechanical equilibrium is established does the fluid become stationary. This applies equally to liquids and gases. This condition is obviously very useful because we already know a great deal about the mechanical equilibrium.

Note that we did not include a condition for the type of interactions between the fluid molecules, or with the container walls. In particular, the limitation to elastic collisions we used for the ideal gas law is not used, as it would exclude concepts such as surface tension and capillarity we introduce later in the chapter.

## Pressure in an Ideal Stationary Fluid

We are well aware of pressure variations in the atmosphere. These are most notable after take-off in an airplane. Still, pressure variations in liquids are much more profound. Many diving-related accidents and the need for life-guards in all public pools are a clear sign that we are exposed to unexpectedly strong effects once we immerse our bodies in water. But how can we express this strong effect quantitatively? The idea goes back to Blaise Pascal and the year 1653, i.e., 34 years before Sir Isaac Newton laid the foundation of mechanics.

## Pascal's Law

Instead of following Pascal's original reasoning, we utilize the mechanical equilibrium introduced in Chapter 3 to study an ideal stationary fluid. The approach is illustrated in Fig. 11.1. The pressure dependence on depth in the fluid is established by selecting a small fluid element at a certain depth, as highlighted in Fig. 11.1 by a small box. The fluid element must be small compared to the size of the beaker, but must still contain a macroscopic amount of the fluid. The element is a rectangular prism with a horizontal surface of area $A$ and a height $\Delta y = y_{up} - y_{down}$, which we choose to be a small length because the pressure in the fluid varies in the vertical direction. The volume of the fluid element is then $V = A \cdot \Delta y$.

The sketch at the right side of Fig. 11.1 shows the vertical forces of the free-body diagram for this fluid element. Horizontal forces act on it, but cancel each other. The three vertical forces acting on the fluid element include:

- the weight of the fluid element **W**, which is directed downward;

- the contact force due to the fluid below the element, $\mathbf{F}_{up}$, which pushes the fluid element upward; and

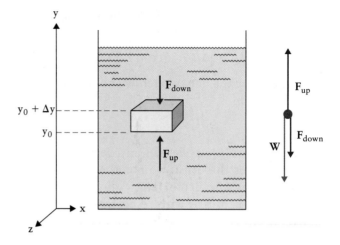

**FIGURE 11.1**

A small element of fluid is identified in a beaker. Three forces act on this element: two contact forces due to the remaining fluid, and the weight of the fluid element. The corresponding free-body diagram for the fluid segment is shown at the right. Note that such a fluid element is at rest in an ideal stationary fluid.

- the contact force due to the fluid above the element, $\mathbf{F}_{down}$, which pushes the fluid element downward.

The fluid element neither rises nor sinks, because it is in mechanical equilibrium. Newton's first law applies in the vertical direction:

$$F_{net,y} = 0 = F_{up} - W - F_{down} \qquad [1]$$

We use Eq. [1] to find a relation between pressure and depth. All three forces are rewritten, the weight to show density and volume, and the two contact forces to show the related pressure terms. Because density is mass divided by volume, the mass of the fluid element is given as:

$$m = \rho \cdot V = \rho \cdot A \cdot \Delta y \qquad [2]$$

in which $A$ is the horizontal surface area of the water element and $\rho$ is the density of the fluid. Thus, the weight of the fluid element in Fig. 11.1 is:

$$W = m \cdot g = \rho \cdot g \cdot A \cdot \Delta y \qquad [3]$$

The two contact forces in Eq. [1] are replaced by the respective pressure terms since the forces act on an extended object. For this, we first note that the fluid element stretches vertically from $y_0$ to $y_0 + \Delta y$. At the position $y_0$ the pressure is labelled $p$ and at $y_0 + \Delta y$ it is labelled $p + \Delta p$. This allows us to express the magnitudes of the forces acting on the two horizontal surfaces of the fluid element:

$$\left| \mathbf{F}_{up} \right| = p \cdot A$$
$$\left| \mathbf{F}_{down} \right| = (p + \Delta p) \cdot A \qquad [4]$$

Using Eqs. [3] and [4], we rewrite Eq. [1] in the form:

$$p \cdot A - (p + \Delta p)A - \rho \cdot g \cdot A \cdot \Delta y = 0 \quad [5]$$

After combining the first two terms and then dividing by $A$, we obtain:

$$\Delta p = -\rho \cdot g \cdot \Delta y \quad [6]$$

Note that Eq. [6] applies for any depth difference $\Delta y$ since neither the density $\rho$ nor the gravitational constant $g$ vary with depth. Thus, choosing two arbitrary depths $y_1$ and $y_2$ with respective pressures $p_1$ and $p_2$, Eq. [6] is written in the form of **Pascal's law**:

$$p_2 - p_1 = -\rho \cdot g(y_2 - y_1) \quad [7]$$

*Pascal's law states that the difference between the pressures at two different positions in a fluid is proportional to the vertical distance between these two positions. The proportionality factor is the product of the density of the fluid and the gravitational acceleration.*

Eq. [7] is the first of two formulations we introduce for Pascal's law. It is used in this general form when the surface of the fluid cannot be identified and thus cannot be used as a reference point. An important example is the blood in the cardiovascular system, because it is a closed system with no identifiable surface of blood toward air.

In systems with an identifiable surface of the fluid, e.g., for water in a glass, index 1 in Eq. [7] is chosen to refer to the surface of the liquid. Therefore, we set $y_1 = 0$ and $p_1 = p_{atm}$. The atmospheric pressure is the proper value for the pressure of the fluid surface since it is in mechanical equilibrium. The force pushing the surface upward equals the force caused by the air pressure pushing downward. Note that we used this argument before when we studied Boyle's experiment in Chapter 7.

It is, further, more convenient in this case to define the position axis downward, i.e., to define the depth below the surface as a positive distance. This changes the negative sign on the right-hand side of Eq. [6] into a positive sign. Writing $y_2 = d$, with $d$ the depth below the surface of the fluid in unit m, we get:

$$p = p_{atm} + \rho \cdot g \cdot d \quad [8]$$

Eq. [8] is a second, frequently used formulation of **Pascal's law**. It expresses the pressure at depth $d$ below the surface as a function of the pressure at the surface and the weight of the water column above depth $d$. The following comments on the two formulations of Pascal's law are useful:

- Pascal's law does not apply to the fluid **air**; i.e., Eq. [7] does not describe pressure variations in the atmosphere. This is illustrated by trying to calculate the height of the upper end (surface) of the atmosphere by substituting for the height $y_2 = y_{max}$, which is the maximum height of the atmosphere:

$$(p_{y_{max}} - p_{ground}) = -\rho \cdot g(y_{max} - y_{ground}) \quad [9]$$

At the maximum height the pressure drops to a value of $p_{y_{max}} = 0$ atm; i.e., $y_{max}$ is the height where the vacuum of outer space would begin. The ground-level values are $y_{ground} = 0$ m and the pressure $p_{ground} = p_{atm}$ with $\rho = 1.2$ kg/m$^3$ for the density of air at sea level. We find from Eq. [9]:

$$y_{max} = \frac{1.01 \times 10^5 \, \text{Pa}}{\left(1.2 \, \dfrac{\text{kg}}{\text{m}^3}\right)\left(9.8 \, \dfrac{\text{m}}{\text{s}^2}\right)} = 8614 \, \text{m} \quad [10]$$

The assumption of a constant density throughout the atmosphere is clearly inadequate, as the atmosphere would terminate at 8614 m height—234 m below the peak of Mount Everest! Thus, Pascal's law does not apply to gases because gases are compressible and their density depends on pressure. The dependence of the gas density on the pressure was discussed in detail for carbon dioxide in Example 7.3.

- Pascal's law does not contain any information about the shape of the container. Thus, regardless of the shape of the container, the pressure increases below the surface and results in a fixed value at a given depth. This is illustrated in Fig. 11.2, in which the fluid surface is located at the same height in each column above the connected bottom tube. Note that deviations from

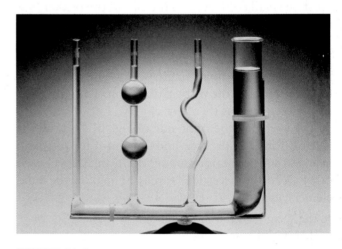

**FIGURE 11.2**

Experimental illustration of the result of Pascal's law (Eq. [8]) that the pressure at various depths in a fluid does not depend on the shape of the fluid container.

this observation occur for fluid containers with tiny diameters. We discuss these capillarity effects later in this chapter.

- Pressure data are often given in non-standard units. Blood pressure, for example, is usually recorded in unit mmHg. For calculations it is advisable to convert such units to standard units. The standard unit of pressure is Pa. Some pressure data, such as blood pressure, are reported relative to air pressure. A pressure value relative to air pressure is called a **gauge pressure**:

$$p_{gauge} = p_{absolute} - p_{air} \qquad [11]$$

which may have either a positive or a negative value. In particular, the term $\rho \cdot g \cdot d$ in Eq. [8] represents a gauge pressure.

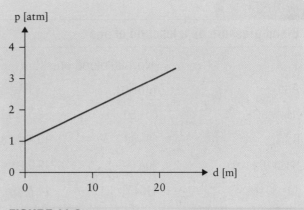

**FIGURE 11.3**

The water pressure as a function of depth.

below the water surface rises fast, doubling at just 10 m depth. In Fig. 11.3, Eq. [12] is used to illustrate the pressure in water as a function of depth. The fast pressure increase is a critical issue for diving, as we noted in Examples 9.1 and 9.2.

## Concept Question 11.1

We introduced Pascal's law in two forms in Eqs. [7] and [8]. Under what circumstances can only the form in Eq. [7] be used? (A) when the fluid is incompressible; (B) when the atmospheric pressure above the fluid surface is zero; (C) when the fluid is stationary; (D) when the fluid is in mechanical equilibrium; (E) when the fluid completely fills a closed system, such as blood in the cardiovascular system of the human body.

ANSWER: Choice (E). Eq. [7] is the general form of Pascal's law. We used a constant density and the mechanical equilibrium for its derivation. In addition, Eq. [8] requires that we can identify the surface of the fluid toward the ambient atmosphere or a vacuum ($p_{atm} = 0$).

## Blood Pressure

We distinguish high- and low-pressure sections of the cardiovascular system because the **blood pressure** varies significantly, as illustrated in Fig. 11.4. The high-pressure part includes the aorta, the arteries and arterioles, and the capillaries of the systemic circulation. The blood pressure in the arteries varies between 10.7 kPa (**diastolic pressure**, equal to 80 mmHg) and 16.0 kPa (**systolic pressure**, equal to 120 mmHg). The low-pressure part includes the veins and the pulmonary circulation; in this circulation the pressure

## ● EXAMPLE 11.1

What is the pressure in a lake 10 m below the surface?

*Solution:* The density of fresh water has a value of $\rho = 1.0\,g/cm^3 = 1.0\,kg/L = 1 \times 10^3\,kg/m^3$. We use $p_{atm} = 1\,atm = 1.01 \times 10^5\,Pa$, because we want to do the calculation in standard units. From Eq. [8], at 10 m depth we get:

$$p_{10\,m} = 1.01 \times 10^5\,Pa$$

$$+ \left(1000\,\frac{kg}{m^3}\right)\left(9.8\,\frac{m}{s^2}\right)(10\,m)$$

$$= 1.99 \times 10^5\,Pa \qquad [12]$$

We use the inverse pressure conversion from unit Pa to unit atm to find that the result of Eq. [12] is $p_{10\,m} = 1.97\,atm$; i.e., the pressure

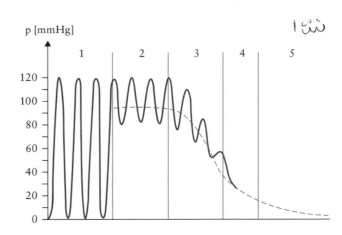

ﺷﻰ ﺍ

**FIGURE 11.4**

Blood pressure variations along the cardiovascular system: (1) left ventricle of heart, (2) large arteries, (3) arterioles, (4) capillaries, (5) venules and veins. Note that the pressure values are gauge pressures, i.e., values given relative to the atmospheric pressure.

## TABLE 11.1

### Blood pressure as a function of age

| | Normal blood pressure | |
|---|---|---|
| Age | (mmHg) | (kPa) |
| Newborn[†] | 60–80 | 8.0–10.7 |
| Baby[†] | 80–90 | 10.7–12.0 |
| Up to 10 years[‡] | 90/60 | 12.0/8.0 |
| 10–30 years[‡] | 110/75 | 14.7/10.0 |
| 30–40 years[‡] | 125/85 | 16.7/11.3 |
| 40–60 years[‡] | 140/90 | 18.7/12.0 |
| >60 years[‡] | 150/90 | 20.0/12.0 |

[†] Systolic blood pressure only.
[‡] Systolic/diastolic blood pressure.

varies only between 1.3 kPa and 3.3 kPa (10–25 mmHg). Since all blood pressure values in Fig. 11.4 are positive gauge pressure values, we conclude that the pressure in our cardiovascular system exceeds the ambient air pressure everywhere. This is, however, only correct while lying down; negative gauge pressures can occur while standing, as outlined in Example 11.2. The pressure in the high pressure part also changes with age, as illustrated in Table 11.1.

● **EXAMPLE 11.2**

Relative to the blood pressure in supine position, calculate the additional blood pressure difference between the brain and the feet in a standing standard man. Use $\rho = 1.06$ g/cm$^3$ for the density of blood.

*Supplementary physiological information:* The term **supine position** specifies that the person is lying down, as shown in Fig. 11.5(a). The blood pressure in supine position is fully described in Fig. 11.4, with a maximum variation of about 15% of atmospheric pressure. When the person stands, as shown in Fig. 11.5(b), an additional difference between the blood pressure in the feet and in the brain is due to the extra column of blood that rests on the blood in the feet. Recall that a standard man is 173 cm tall, as noted in Table 3.3.

*Solution:* To quantify the additional difference for the standing standard man, we use Pascal's law in the general form as given in Eq. [7] (because no blood surface exists):

$$p_{\text{brain}} - p_{\text{feet}} = -\rho_{\text{blood}} \cdot g \left( y_{\text{brain}} - y_{\text{feet}} \right) \quad [13]$$

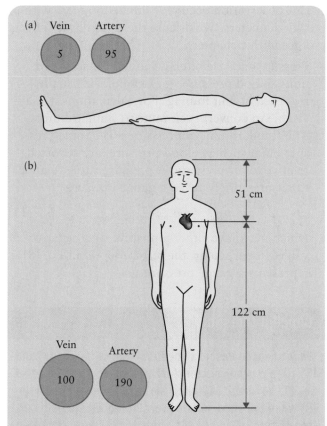

**FIGURE 11.5**

Blood pressures and blood vessel sizes in the feet of a person (a) in supine position and (b) standing upright. The vessel sizes are indicated by the areas of the circles shown. The numbers in the vessels are the respective blood pressures in unit mmHg.

Eq. [13] is rewritten with $\Delta p = p_{\text{feet}} - p_{\text{brain}}$ for the pressure difference and $\Delta h = y_{\text{brain}} - y_{\text{feet}}$ for the height of the person. This choice for $\Delta p$ eliminates the extra minus sign on the right-hand side of Eq. [13]:

$$\Delta p = \rho_{\text{blood}} \cdot g \cdot \Delta h \quad [14]$$

Substituting the given values in Eq. [14] yields:

$$\Delta p = \left( 1.06 \times 10^3 \, \frac{\text{kg}}{\text{m}^3} \right) \left( 9.8 \, \frac{\text{m}}{\text{s}^2} \right) (1.73 \text{ m})$$

$$= 1.80 \times 10^4 \, \text{Pa} = 18.0 \text{ kPa} \quad [15]$$

This difference is about 20% of the atmospheric pressure; i.e., it is of the same order of magnitude as the pressure variations within the cardiovascular system in supine position.

For physiological applications, it is more useful to refer to pressures that are measured relative to the pressure at the height of the heart. For a standing person of 1.73 m height, the heart is at a height of 1.22 m and the arterial and venous pressures in the feet are increased relative to the pressures at the height of the heart by:

$$\Delta p = \rho \cdot g \cdot \Delta h$$

$$= \left(1.06 \times 10^3 \frac{kg}{m^3}\right)\left(9.8 \frac{m}{s^2}\right)(1.22 \text{ m})$$

$$= 12.7 \text{ kPa} = 95 \text{ mmHg} \qquad [16]$$

The pressure is increased to an average arterial value of 190 mmHg and an average venous value of 100 mmHg. This is illustrated in Fig. 11.5. The figure shows two pairs of circles that indicate the relative sizes of veins and arteries in the feet. The numbers in the circles refer to blood pressures in the respective vessel in unit mmHg. In the scalp, the pressures decrease for a standing person by:

$$\Delta p = \left(1.06 \times 10^3 \frac{kg}{m^3}\right)\left(9.8 \frac{m}{s^2}\right)(-0.51 \text{ m})$$

$$= -5.3 \text{ kPa} = -40 \text{ mmHg} \qquad [17]$$

The average arterial pressure drops to a value of 55 mmHg and the average venous pressure becomes −35 mmHg. This low venous value does not lead to the closing of the veins in the skull, though, since the blood vessels in the brain are surrounded by cerebrospinal fluid and the pressure in that fluid also drops by a corresponding amount relative to the extracellular fluid in the chest when the person is standing upright.

**FIGURE 11.6**

A giraffe bending down to drink water.

Another group of animals that had similar issues to deal with were the large quadrupedal dinosaurs, such as Seismosaurus, a 40-metre-long herbivore that lived in North America during the late Jurassic period. With their upright gait and long necks (up to 10 metres long), cardiovascular adaptations were needed to compensate blood pressure variations as a function of body posture.

### Concept Question 11.2

**For which animals does the effect discussed in Example 11.2 pose the greatest challenge?**

ANSWER: In large land animals, this effect can be much more profound than in humans. The additional pressure required when blood must be pushed above the level of the heart can be generated only with the four-chambered heart of mammals. Of these, the pumping challenge is greatest for animals with long necks. A standing giraffe needs to pump blood as much as 2.5 m above the heart to the brain. That requires significantly more of an additional blood pressure in the left ventricle; the normal systolic pressure at the heart of a giraffe is therefore more than 250 mmHg. Such a systolic pressure would be extremely dangerous for humans. Special valves and a feedback mechanism reduce cardiac output when the giraffe bends its neck down to drink (see Fig. 11.6). In this position the brain is suddenly almost 2 m below the heart and would otherwise be exposed to a tremendous blood pressure due to the changed height difference.

### Concept Question 11.3

**An oceanographer chooses to report water pressure values below the ocean surface as gauge pressures. (a) What values do his reports contain when referring to surface water? (b) When are negative values reported?**

ANSWER TO PART (a): The gauge pressure in seawater near the surface is close to 0 Pa because the water surface is defined by the mechanical equilibrium between air pushing the surface down and water pushing the surface up.

ANSWER TO PART (b): No negative values will be reported because the water pressure never drops below atmospheric pressure.

## Key Properties of the Ideal Stationary Fluid

Ideal stationary fluids display a range of physical properties that are important for biological land physiological applications. We discuss buoyancy, surface tension, and capillarity in this section.

# Buoyancy (Archimedes Principle)

The density of an ideal stationary fluid into which an object is released has a profound effect on the resulting motion of the object: a piece of wood released above a table falls down onto the table, but floats up to the surface when released from a submerged position in a beaker of water. Even an object that accelerates downward in both air and water, such as a rock, displays a different apparent weight when suspended from a spring scale and held below the surface of water.

Fig. 11.7 illustrates how the effect due to the surrounding fluid is quantified. A beaker with a fluid and a block $B$, suspended above the fluid, are shown in the left sketch. A fluid element $F$ with the same shape and volume as the block $B$ is identified below the fluid surface. For the fluid element $F$, mechanical equilibrium conditions apply in the same fashion as discussed in Fig. 11.1. Choosing the positive $y$-axis to be directed upward, the mechanical equilibrium condition for the fluid element $F$ is written as:

$$F_{up} - F_{down} - W_F = 0 \qquad [18]$$

$\mathbf{F}_{up}$ is the contact force due to the fluid below the chosen fluid element, $\mathbf{F}_{down}$ is the contact force due to the fluid above the chosen fluid element, and $\mathbf{W}_F$ is the weight of the chosen fluid element itself. In the first step, we assume that the fluid element $F$ is removed from the beaker and placed in a small container, leaving an empty bubble of equal size in the beaker. We can simply think of this bubble to be air-filled with the mass of air in the bubble negligible. This bubble is not in mechanical equilibrium since its weight is significantly reduced compared to the removed fluid, but the two contact forces remain unaltered as the fluid around the bubble, which exerts these forces, has not changed:

$$F_{up} - F_{down} = W_F > 0 \qquad [19]$$

As a result of Newton's second law, an acceleration of the bubble to the surface is observed. Before this happens, the bubble is replaced by block $B$ with weight $\mathbf{W}_B$. This leads to the following net force acting on the block in the vertical direction:

$$F_{net} = F_{up} - F_{down} - W_B = W_F - W_B \qquad [20]$$

Eq. [20] illustrates which terms we need to study to describe the submerged block in Fig. 11.7: its weight $\mathbf{W}_B$ and the weight of the displaced fluid $\mathbf{W}_F$. Three cases are distinguished for Eq. [20]:

- $F_{net} > 0$. The weight of the block is less than the weight of the displaced fluid, and the block $B$ rises to the surface. Examples of this case are ice or wood in water. The wood fibres are denser than the displaced water, but wood contains a large fraction of enclosed air. Ice has a lower density than liquid water due to its peculiar structure in the solid state at atmospheric pressure.

- $F_{net} = 0$. The block floats at its current depth below the fluid surface. The weight of the block equals the weight of the displaced fluid. This case describes a fish, or a submerged diver with breathing equipment.

- $F_{net} < 0$. The weight of the block is larger than the weight of the displaced fluid and the block sinks to the bottom of the container.

These findings were first established by Archimedes in antiquity. Based on Eq. [20], the principle is usually stated in the following form:

**Archimedes principle:** *When an object is immersed in a fluid, the fluid exerts an upward force on the object equal to the weight of the fluid displaced by the object.*

We define the buoyant force as equal in magnitude to the weight of the displaced fluid. Thus, the magnitude of the **buoyant force** is:

$$F_{buoyant} = \rho_{fluid} \cdot V_{object} \cdot g \qquad [21]$$

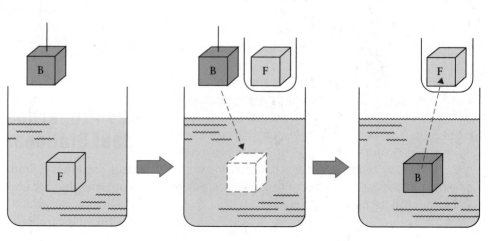

**FIGURE 11.7**

Illustration of the Archimedes principle. We consider two steps: in the first step, a fluid element with the same shape as the object is removed. In the second step, the object is placed in a void.

in which the density is the value for the displaced fluid and the volume is the value for the immersed object. The buoyant force is always directed upward, i.e., in the direction opposite to gravity. Comparing Eq. [21] to Eq. [20], we emphasize that $F_{\text{buoyant}}$ replaces $W_F$ and not $F_{\text{net}}$: the net force can in particular be zero, but the buoyant force is always non-zero unless the object of interest is placed in a vacuum.

Mechanical equilibrium applies in one of the three cases; the system accelerates toward a new equilibrium in the other two cases. When $F_{\text{net}} > 0$—i.e., the buoyant force exceeds the weight—the object floats to the surface of the fluid. When a sufficient fraction of the object rises above the fluid surface, the object's volume that displaces fluid is reduced and the weight of the displaced fluid becomes equal to the weight of the block. Note that for an object floating at the surface of a fluid, only the fraction of the volume below the surface of the fluid enters Eq. [21]. When $F_{\text{net}} < 0$, the object sinks. At the bottom of the beaker, a mechanical equilibrium is reached due to an additional normal force acting upward on the object.

Buoyant forces are observed in many contexts. In Example 3.12, we calculated the force on the central dendrite in a Pacinian corpuscle (shown in Fig. 3.40). That example illustrated how the buoyant force is taken into account in a mechanical problem involving a floating object. Buoyancy can also be illustrated in simple experiments you can do at home. For example, place a freshly cut piece of **lemon peel** in a bottle filled with water. Close the bottle and exert variable pressure on the plastic cap with your thumb. The lemon peel rises or sinks depending on the exerted pressure. The lemon peel floats in the first place due to very small air bubbles in its porous structure. When you squeeze the cap, variations in the water pressure occur. The size of the air bubbles varies significantly with pressure changes because air as a gas is highly compressible. As a result, the volume of the peel varies in Eq. [21].

## ● EXAMPLE 11.3

In 1936, the zeppelin LZ-129 *Hindenburg* successfully completed 17 round trips across the Atlantic Ocean. During the winter, 10 passenger cabins were added accommodating up to 22 additional passengers. On May 6, 1937, on its first flight to the United States, the *Hindenburg* exploded at Lakehurst Naval Air Station in New Jersey. Did the increased load due to additional passengers contribute to this famous accident?

*Supplementary historical information:* The *Hindenburg* was the largest aircraft ever to fly. At 245 metres in length it was longer than three Boeing 747s and almost as long as the *Titanic*. It had a capacity of 50 passengers (72 after the upgrade) and 61 crew. Its 16 gas cells had a combined volume of 210 000 $m^3$ and were initially designed to be filled with helium gas (density $\rho_{\text{He}} = 0.16$ kg/$m^3$). When helium remained unavailable due to an embargo, the Deutsche Zeppelin Reederei opted for hydrogen gas instead (density $\rho_{\text{H}_2} = 0.08$ kg/$m^3$). The *Hindenburg* had a mass of 130 tons without passengers, crew, and cargo.

With these data, calculate (a) the maximum payload (in kg) that the *Hindenburg* could carry as designed (i.e., with a helium filling). Then calculate (b) by how much the payload had increased with a hydrogen filling. *If you are interested:* (c) find out what factors led to the disaster at Lakehurst in 1937.

*Solution:* Buoyancy also occurs in gases such as air. In the case of hot air balloons, lighter hot air displaces heavier cold air in the balloon's envelope. Hot-air balloon operation is discussed in P-11.10. Alternatively, gases that are lighter than air can be employed. This is illustrated with the current example.

*Solution to part (a):* We use Eq. [20] with $F_{\text{net}} = 0$ to determine the maximum payload; i.e., we find the total mass of the zeppelin at which its weight and its buoyant force are balanced. The buoyant force is obtained from Eq. [21]. The weight has three contributions: the weight of the empty zeppelin, the weight of the payload (passengers, crew, and cargo), and the weight of the gas in the 16 gas cells:

$$F_{\text{net}} = 0 = \rho_{\text{air}} \cdot V_{\text{gas cells}} \cdot g - W_{\text{ship}}$$
$$- W_{\text{payload}} - \rho_{\text{He}} \cdot V_{\text{gas cells}} \cdot g \quad [22]$$

We divide Eq. [22] by the gravitational acceleration $g$, switching the various weight terms to the respective masses. We use for the air density at 1 atm a conservative (lower) estimate. Note that $\rho_{\text{air}} = 1.29$ kg/$m^3$ at 0°C and $\rho_{\text{air}} = 1.21$ kg/$m^3$ at 20°C. Thus, the value at 20°C is substituted in Eq. [22]. This yields for the payload of the Hindenburg's original design:

$$m_{\text{payload}} = (\rho_{\text{air}} - \rho_{\text{He}}) V_{\text{gas cells}} - m_{\text{ship}}$$
$$= \left(1.05 \, \frac{\text{kg}}{\text{m}^3}\right)(2.1 \times 10^5 \, \text{m}^3)$$
$$- 1.3 \times 10^5 \, \text{kg} \quad [23]$$

i.e., $m_{\text{payload}} = 9.6 \times 10^4$ kg = 96 tons. Note that this result corresponds to more than 600 standard

## ● EXAMPLE 11.3 (continued)

men (each with an additional 70 kg luggage). There were only 50 spaces for passengers on the *Hindenburg*, showing that it was never intended for modern mass tourism. During the two days of travel—at a maximum speed of 135 km/h—the passengers enjoyed luxury comparable to that on a modern cruise ship, including dining halls, reading rooms, a lounge, a music salon with piano, and even a smoking room!

*Solution to part (b):* Exchanging helium for hydrogen in Eq. [23] yields a payload of 107 tons, i.e., an increase of about 11%. An additional 11-ton lifting capacity is plenty for 22 additional passengers. Thus, they were not to blame for the accident. Indeed, prior to the trip to Lakehurst, the modified *Hindenburg* had already completed a round trip to Brazil to start off the 1937 season. On the doomed flight it carried only 36 passengers.

*Solution to part (c):* The generally accepted explanation is the static spark theory, which requires concepts we discuss in Chapter 13. The outer envelope of the airship was electrically isolated from its aluminium frame. When the *Hindenburg* flew through a weather front, both its outer skin and the mooring lines became wet, turning them into electrically conducting surfaces. The wet skin then accumulated electric charges, causing a significant electric potential relative to the ground. The mooring lines were anchored on the aluminium frame. When they were lowered to the ground the aluminium frame became electrically grounded. The high potential difference at close proximity between skin and metal frame probably caused sparking. Sparks wouldn't ignite hydrogen in the gas tanks; however, the *Hindenburg* was venting some hydrogen in preparation for landing. Hydrogen mixed with oxygen in the air formed a combustible mixture.

southern Mediterranean Sea loses more water through evaporation. It receives fresh water from only four major rivers: Po (Italy), Rhône (France), Ebro (Spain), and Nile (Egypt). Thus, the salt content in the Mediterranean Sea is high, at 38 g/L NaCl, which corresponds to a density of $\rho = 1.028$ g/cm$^3$. The Black Sea is smaller than the Mediterranean Sea, but receives fresh water from three major rivers: Danube (Romania), Dnieper (Ukraine), and Don (Russia). Thus, its salt content is lower at 16 g/L NaCl and its density is $\rho = 1.014$ g/cm$^3$.

The Archimedes principle predicts that the Mediterranean Sea can float 1.4% more weight than the Black Sea. Thus, an overloaded ship must reduce its cargo when travelling north through Istanbul Bogazi (Bosporus). Cargo ships travelling across the Atlantic and continuing along the St. Lawrence River to Montreal are affected in the same way.

Average seawater in Earth's oceans contains 25.5 g/L NaCl, with a density of $\rho = 1.02$ g/cm$^3$. With the molar mass of sodium $M = 23$ g/mol and chlorine $M = 35.5$ g/mol, the NaCl salt concentration of average seawater corresponds to 435 mmol/L. The extracellular fluid in our body has a NaCl concentration of 165 mmol/L; i.e., the NaCl concentration in the interstitium is 40% that of seawater.

The effect discussed in Concept Question 11.4 can be verified in a simple experiment. In your kitchen, fill a jar about halfway with water and dissolve a large amount of table salt in it. Then add more salt-free water, pouring it into the jar carefully such that the two liquids don't mix. If you place a chicken egg in the water, it will sink to the interface between both liquids. The reason for this is the same effect we just discussed for ships on the high seas: the egg displaces a fixed volume of water equal to its own volume; the weight of the displaced tap water is less than the weight of the egg, but the weight of the same volume of salt water is greater than the weight of the egg.

### Concept Question 11.4

Greek mythology reports the story of the Argonauts. Under Jason's leadership, they travelled to Aeëtes, king of Colchis, in their quest for the Golden Fleece. On the way they were forced to throw significant amounts of gold overboard to prevent their ship from sinking as they passed from the Mediterranean Sea into the Black Sea, near modern-day Istanbul in Turkey. Can this part of the myth be true?

ANSWER: A significant difference between the salt concentrations of these two bodies of water exists. The more

### Concept Question 11.5

In North America, the Lake Superior region currently rises by almost 1 cm per year. Can you explain this effect with the Archimedes principle?

ANSWER: Yes. Note that it is not the water level of the lake that rises but the land itself. The continental land mass (rigid lithosphere) floats like a boat on the hotter, more plastic zone of the upper mantle (asthenosphere). The area around Lake Superior carried a tremendous weight of ice during the last Ice Age. When the ice melted, the lithosphere beneath started to float upward like a ship that has cleared its cargo.

## Concept Question 11.6

In Britain and Germany, you find examples of waterways that cross each other. An example is the *Mindener Wasserstraßenkreuz*, which literally translates as "the water canal intersection at Minden." Ships can travel along both the lower and the upper canal. Imagine you were asked to design a water canal bridge. Which of the following would be your approach? (A) Anticipate the weight of the heaviest ship that may pass the canal and design the bridge to withstand its weight. (B) Anticipate the weight of the heaviest ship that may pass the canal, add the weight of the water on the bridge, and design the bridge to withstand the combined weight. (C) Design the bridge based only on the weight of the water on the bridge, which you determine from the density of water and the volume of the canal. (D) Reject the contract because you could never be sure there isn't a heavier ship coming one day and the bridge will collapse.

ANSWER: Boats using the canal float; i.e., they displace an amount of water corresponding to their own mass. The water level in the canal doesn't change as the boat travels because it displaces the same amount of water wherever it is along the canal, including during the passage of the bridge. A remote risk exists, though, that the boat may sink while on the bridge. Why would that cause concern?

## Buoyancy in Physiology

### ● EXAMPLE 11.4

The human brain is immersed in cerebrospinal fluid, of density 1.007 g/cm$^3$. This density is slightly less than the average density of the brain, which is 1.04 g/cm$^3$. Thus, most of the weight of the brain is supported by the buoyant force of the surrounding fluid. What fraction of the weight of the brain is not supported by this force?

*Solution:* This problem is an application of the Archimedes principle. The magnitude of the weight of the brain is:

$$W = \rho_{\text{brain}} \cdot V_{\text{brain}} \cdot g \qquad [24]$$

The buoyant force, in turn, for the brain fully immersed in the cerebrospinal fluid follows from Eq. [21]:

$$F_{\text{buoyant}} = \rho_{\text{cerebrospinal fluid}} \cdot V_{\text{brain}} \cdot g \qquad [25]$$

We know that these two forces do not balance each other because the brain is connected through the medulla oblongata to the spinal cord, which exerts an additional force on the brain. To determine the fraction of the weight of the brain that is not balanced by the buoyant force, we calculate:

$$
\frac{W - F_{\text{buoyant}}}{W} = \frac{\rho_{\text{brain}} - \rho_{\text{cerebrospinal fluid}}}{\rho_{\text{brain}}}
$$

$$
= \frac{\left(1.04 \, \dfrac{g}{cm^3}\right) - \left(1.007 \, \dfrac{g}{cm^3}\right)}{1.04 \, \dfrac{g}{cm^3}}
$$

$$
= 0.032 \qquad [26]
$$

Just 3.2% of the brain's weight is not balanced by the cerebrospinal fluid, requiring only a small force to be exerted by the spinal cord on the brain. You can calculate the actual brain mass not supported by using $m_{\text{brain}} = 1.5$ kg for the standard man (from Table 3.3). This yields 50 g.

Buoyancy is used by many marine animals to float, rise, or sink in seawater without effort. A famous example is **spirula**, shown in Fig. 11.8. Spirula is a cephalopod that was thought to have died out 50 million years ago but was then discovered by a scientific expedition of *H.M.S. Challenger* during its voyage around the world in 1873–1876. The animal swims head down because it has a buoyant, gas-filled shell at the posterior end.

Most bony fish possess a swim bladder to control buoyancy. The swim bladder is an air sac that allows gas exchange with the fish's blood. This gas exchange leads to a variation in size of the swim bladder, which in turn adjusts the density of the fish. Bony fish can therefore conserve energy by remaining motionless at a chosen depth in the water. Sharks don't have swim bladders and must swim all their life to prevent their body from sinking.

An interesting living fossil is the **nautilus** (see Fig. 11.9), a relative of the spiral-shelled ammonites. The nautilus's shell not only protects the soft-bodied mollusk, but also provides the animal with perfect control over its buoyancy. The mollusk inhabits only the last of a spiralling series of chambers inside the shell. Using osmosis it regulates the seawater fraction in its inner chambers, which contain a mixture of air

**FIGURE 11.8**

As described in the *Report on the Scientific Results of the Voyage of the* H.M.S. Challenger *During the Years 1873–1876,* one of the more remarkable events during the long voyage to chart the world's oceans was the discovery of the spirula, a cephalopod that was thought from fossil evidence to have died out 50 million years ago. The spirula has a squid-like body between 3.5 and 4.5 cm long. It has eight arms and two longer tentacles. The most distinctive feature is the buoyancy chamber, which is an internal shell that keeps the animal's body vertical.

**FIGURE 11.9**

The nautilus is a relative of the long-extinct spiral-shelled ammonites. Its shell (16 to 27 cm in diameter) not only protects the soft-bodied mollusk but also provides the animal with perfect control over its buoyancy. The mollusk inhabits the last chamber inside the shell, while the other chambers (up to 30 for an adult animal) are filled with a mixture of air and seawater to adjust its overall density. The nautilus's shell is coiled, calcareous, and lined with mother-of-pearl for pressure resistance (preventing implosion to a depth of 800 m).

and seawater, to adjust its overall density. Decreasing the density allows the nautilus to rise during its nightly migration from the depths of the Pacific Ocean to the surface. We discuss the nautilus's vertical migration quantitatively in P–11.14.

## Surface Tension

**Surface tension** is a fluid property associated with the presence of a surface toward air. The term **interfacial tension** is used to describe analogous phenomena for fluids having interfaces with solids or other liquids. Surfaces and interfaces have properties distinct from the bulk of the fluid as the symmetry of the interactions of molecules with their immediate neighbours is broken. This is shown in Fig. 11.10. Sufficiently far below the surface, each water molecule has attractive interactions in all directions with its nearest neighbours. The attractive forces cancel each other out and the molecule is in equilibrium. When such a water molecule comes to within one nanometre of the surface, the sphere of neighbouring molecules is no longer complete and a net force acts on the water molecule, pulling it back from the surface. This resulting force is greatest when the water molecule reaches the surface, because at this point half of its neighbours have vanished.

The resulting force pulls molecules away from the surface. However, molecules cannot leave the surface toward the bulk as the surface area cannot shrink. Since the molecules in the surface layer have to be brought to the surface against the net force shown in Fig. 11.10, there is an energy associated with the formation of a surface. We define the surface energy $\sigma$:

$$\sigma = \frac{\Delta E}{\Delta A} \qquad [27]$$

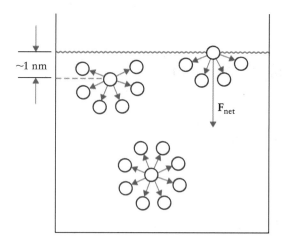

**FIGURE 11.10**

Three water molecules, shown as open circles, are illustrated with their respective neighbours. Any molecule that is 1 nm or farther below the surface has a symmetric cloud of other water molecules around it. Only molecules at the surface encounter a net force downward due to an incomplete cloud of attracting neighbours.

in which $\Delta E$ is the energy needed to increase the surface of a fluid by an area $\Delta A$. Thus, $\sigma$ is the energy required to form 1 m$^2$ of new surface and carries the unit J/m$^2$.

There is a second way to look at $\sigma$. For this approach, Eq. [27] is rewritten as:

$$W = \Delta E = \sigma \cdot \Delta A \qquad [28]$$

in which $W$ is the work required to increase the surface by $\Delta A$. As you recall from Chapter 6, work is connected to a force by $W = \mathbf{F} \cdot \mathbf{d}$, in which $\mathbf{d}$ is the displacement vector, attributed to the action of the force $\mathbf{F}$. We use the device shown in Fig. 11.11 to derive a relationship between the force $\mathbf{F}$ exerted on a surface and the surface energy $\sigma$. The device consists of a thin film, such as a soap film, spanned by a fixed U-shaped wire and a mobile straight wire. Attached to the straight wire is a handle that can be pulled with force $\mathbf{F}$ to enlarge the surface enclosed by the wire frame. We consider an increase in area $A$ from $A = l_x \cdot l_y$ to $A = l_x \cdot (l_y + \Delta l_y)$. The work needed to enlarge the area is $W = F \cdot \Delta l_y$. Note that the force and the displacement are parallel and vector notation is no longer needed. The resulting change in area is $\Delta A = l_x \cdot \Delta l_y$. These terms are substituted in Eq. [28]:

$$\sigma \cdot \Delta A = \sigma \cdot l_x \cdot \Delta l_y = W = F \cdot \Delta l_y \qquad [29]$$

Division by $\Delta l_y$ yields:

$$\sigma = \frac{F}{l_x} \qquad [30]$$

in which the right-hand side has the unit N/m, which is therefore also the unit of $\sigma$. $\sigma$ represents in Eq. [30] a tangential force needed to increase the surface per unit length. For this reason, $\sigma$ is also called **surface tension**. This double interpretation of $\sigma$ as energy to increase a surface or force to stretch a film is possible because the units for an energy per surface area and for a force per unit length are the same, J/m$^2$ = N/m.

Fig. 11.11 illustrates one practical way in which the surface of a fluid can be increased. This approach is particularly suitable for soap films due to their high cohesiveness. Surface tensions of other fluids such as water cannot be measured this way. For such fluids an alternative setup exists where the fluid surface area is initially reduced by bringing a flat solid surface of known area into contact with it. The surface tension is then determined from the force needed to lift the solid surface off the fluid.

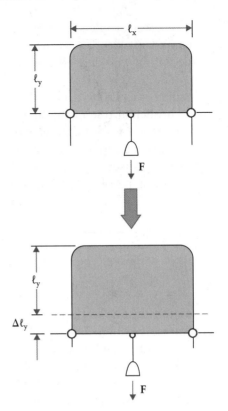

**FIGURE 11.11**

Sketch of a device to measure surface tension in the form of the force $\mathbf{F}$ acting per unit length on a film. The U-shaped wire and the mobile bar enclose the film. The mobile bar has length $l_x$ and in the lower frame is pulled from the dashed line down to the solid line by a distance $\Delta l_y$.

## Bubbles and Droplets

Two key consequences of the surface tension concept will be discussed in this section and the next: the equilibrium shape of bubbles and droplets, and the pressure in small bubbles, droplets, and cylindrical tubes.

We first study a free system—i.e., a fluid that is not confined by any external surface such as a container wall. An example is a raindrop. Since work has to be done to increase the surface of a liquid, the drop minimizes its surface to achieve its energetically most favourable shape. The equilibrium shape of the raindrop is the geometrical figure that has the least surface for a fixed volume; this is the sphere. If a drop is not spherical, it releases energy while reshaping toward a sphere. When the drop is spherical, external energy has to be provided to change its shape.

If we introduce additional boundary conditions, e.g., a droplet sitting on a flat surface, the shape with a minimum surface becomes more complex; however, some simpler cases can be noted. For any flat frame, as in Fig. 11.11, the minimum surface for a film is a flat layer, not a bent structure. For droplets on inert surfaces, such as water droplets on glass, a circular interface forms and the droplet assumes a partially spherical shape with a well-defined contact angle.

A physiological example is the 300 to 400 million alveoli at the end of the bronchial tree in the lungs. Each alveolus is a partial sphere with a diameter of about 0.3 mm, placed on top of a circular bronchial tube. However, before we can discuss physiological consequences of the bubble shape of the alveoli we need to find how the pressure in a bubble depends on its radius.

## Pressure in a Bubble: Laplace's Law

Use a children's soap solution from a toy store. Blow a few soap bubbles and observe them. Their spherical surface is stretched smoothly, suggesting that it is held open by the air inside. Even though the soap film forming these **bubbles** is less than a micrometre thick, it is able to retain compressed air inside. To illustrate that indeed an enhanced pressure exists inside a bubble, we need a traditional pipe or a pipe-like bubble blower from a toy store. Catch a soap bubble on the pipe bowl while covering the mouthpiece with your finger, as shown in Fig. 11.12. Then hold the mouthpiece close to the flame of a burning candle and remove your finger. The candle flame is blown to the side while the bubble shrinks and vanishes into the pipe bowl.

We want to quantify by how much the pressure inside a bubble exceeds atmospheric pressure. Fig. 11.13(a) shows a close-to-square-shaped segment selected on the spherical surface of a bubble. In Fig. 11.13(b) a coordinate system is chosen for this

segment. The z-axis is perpendicular to its surface. The x- and y-axes are parallel to the edges of the segment. They are chosen to intersect with the z-axis at the point where the z-axis intercepts the bubble surface. Thus, edges 1 and 3 of the segment lie in the yz-plane and edges 2 and 4 lie in the xz-plane. The four arrows in the figure indicate the directions in which the remaining bubble surface pulls to stretch the segment open. Since the segment bends downward from the origin, these four forces are all directed below the horizontal.

Fig. 11.13(c) shows the free-body diagram for the bubble segment. The four forces discussed above are identified as $\mathbf{F}_i$ with $i = 1$ to 4. Due to the symmetry of the surface segment in Fig. 11.13(b), the following relations among the components of the four forces $\mathbf{F}_i$ apply:

$$x\text{-direction:} \quad F_{1,x} = -F_{3,x} \quad F_{2,x} = F_{4,x} = 0$$
$$y\text{-direction:} \quad F_{2,y} = -F_{4,y} \quad F_{1,y} = F_{3,y} = 0$$
$$z\text{-direction:} \quad F_{1,z} = F_{2,z} = F_{3,z} = F_{4,z}$$
$$[31]$$

The force components in the x- and y-directions (first two lines in Eq. [31]) compensate each other. Only the z-components yield a non-vanishing net force.

If the four forces in Eq. [31] were the only forces acting on the bubble segment, then the segment would not be in mechanical equilibrium in the z-direction as a net force downward would result, which would cause the segment to accelerate. Thus, for a bubble in mechanical equilibrium additional forces must be present and be taken into account. These are contact forces due to air inside of the bubble with pressure $p_{inside}$, and air outside of the bubble with pressure $p_{outside}$. To express a force, each pressure is multiplied by A, where A is the area of the bubble segment shown in the figure. Newton's first law then describes the mechanical equilibrium of the bubble segment in the z-direction:

$$\sum_{i=1}^{6} F_{i,z} = 0 = 4 \cdot F_{1,z} + p_{inside} \cdot A - p_{outside} \cdot A \quad [32]$$

Eq. [30] is used to quantify $F_{1,z}$ in Eq. [32] further. If $l$ is the length of each edge of the segment, i.e., $l^2 = A$, then $|\mathbf{F}_1| = 2 \cdot \sigma \cdot l$. The factor 2 in this relation is due to the fact that the bubble has an inner and an outer surface. We use Fig. 11.14 to determine the z-component of this force. In the figure, r is the radius of the bubble and $\varphi$ is the opening angle of the segment of length $l/2$. The red line in Fig. 11.14 corresponds to a side view of the segment shown in

**FIGURE 11.12**

A soap bubble caught on the bowl of a toy pipe.

(a)

(b)

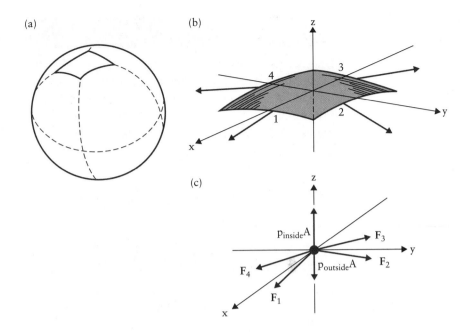

(c)

**FIGURE 11.13**

(a) A bubble with a highlighted near-square area close to the bubble's upper pole. (b) The same segment of the bubble is shown with sides 1 and 3 aligned in the $yz$-plane and sides 2 and 4 aligned in the $xz$-plane. (c) The corresponding free-body diagram for the bubble segment contains four contact forces that are due to the tangential pull of the remaining bubble membrane and two contact forces due to the gas pressure acting perpendicular to the segment's inner and outer surfaces.

Fig. 11.13(b). Applying trigonometric relations to express $\sin \varphi$ in Fig. 11.14, we find:

$$\sin \varphi = \frac{l/2}{r}$$

$$\sin \varphi = \frac{F_{1,z}}{|F_1|}$$

[33]

Eq. [33] contains two relations, because the angle $\varphi$ occurs twice in Fig. 11.14. We equate the right-hand sides of the two formulas in Eq. [33] to express $F_{1,z}$:

$$F_{1,z} = 2 \cdot \sigma \cdot l \frac{l/2}{r} = \sigma \frac{l^2}{r} = \frac{\sigma \cdot A}{r}$$

[34]

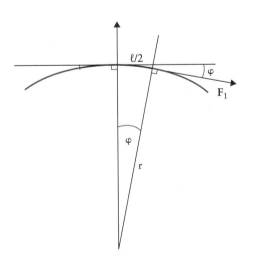

**FIGURE 11.14**

Geometric sketch of the $z$-components of the forces shown in Fig. 11.13. The red line represents the side view of the square segment highlighted in Fig. 11.13.

in which we replaced $l^2 = A$. Substituting the $z$-component of the force from Eq. [34] into the mechanical equilibrium condition of Eq. [32], we find:

$$\sum_{i=1}^{6} F_{i,z} = 0 = -\frac{4 \cdot \sigma \cdot A}{r} + A \cdot \Delta p$$

[35]

which leads to:

$$\Delta p = \frac{4 \cdot \sigma}{r}$$

[36]

Eq. [36] is **Laplace's law**. $\Delta p = p_{inside} - p_{outside}$ is called the **transmural pressure**. Thus, the internal pressure in a small bubble is found to be larger than the external pressure. This pressure difference maintains the curved surface of the soap bubbles you observed earlier.

Formulas equivalent to Eq. [36] can also be derived for homogeneous droplets or other curved shapes of hollow or homogeneous liquids. The derivation of such formulas follows the same steps we took with Fig. 11.13 and Eqs. [31] to [36]. Two factors vary between the different cases:

- Droplets and homogeneous cylinders display only one curved surface, while bubbles and hollow tubes have two curved surfaces, an outer and an inner surface.

- Cylinder symmetric systems, such as hollow and homogeneous tubes, display a finite curvature in only one direction across their surface while spherically symmetric systems, such as bubbles and droplets, have a finite curvature in two perpendicular directions across their surface. When drawing a figure equivalent to Fig. 11.13 for a cylinder only one curved edge of the surface segment will be present.

Either of these changes eliminates a factor of 2: for homogeneous systems a factor of 2 is eliminated from the magnitude of the force $\mathbf{F}_1$, i.e., $|\mathbf{F}_1| = \sigma \cdot l$; and for the cylinder symmetric systems only two instead of four $z$-components occur in the last line of Eq. [31]. These factors carry through the calculation to Eq. [36]. Thus, we find three formulations for Laplace's law:

bubble:

$$\Delta p = p_{\text{inside}} - p_{\text{outside}} = \frac{4 \cdot \sigma}{r}$$

droplet or hollow cylinder:

$$\Delta p = p_{\text{inside}} - p_{\text{outside}} = \frac{2 \cdot \sigma}{r} \qquad [37]$$

solid cylinder:

$$\Delta p = p_{\text{inside}} - p_{\text{outside}} = \frac{\sigma}{r}$$

*Laplace's law states that the pressure difference between the inside and outside of a fluid with a curved surface is inversely proportional to the radius of curvature of the curved surface. This means that a smaller bubble, droplet, or cylinder has a larger pressure difference $\Delta p$.*

Each of the formulas in Eq. [37] has physiological applications. We highlight blood vessels and alveoli in the lungs as examples in the remainder of this section. The formula for the homogeneous cylinder applies to blood vessels: their elastic tissue must be capable of sustaining the pressure difference in Eq. [37]. We compare blood capillaries and small arterioles to illustrate the consequences. The transmural pressure values between blood in a vessel and the surrounding tissue are essentially identical to the values in Fig. 11.4. From that figure we find that similar pressure differences apply for the smallest arterioles (near the right end of the interval labelled 3 in Fig. 11.4) and the capillaries (labelled 4 in Fig. 11.4). This leads to:

$$\Delta p_{\text{arteriole}} = \Delta p_{\text{capillary}} \quad \Rightarrow \quad \frac{\sigma_{\text{arteriole}}}{r_{\text{arteriole}}} = \frac{\sigma_{\text{capillary}}}{r_{\text{capillary}}} \qquad [38]$$

Therefore, the surface tension for a capillary of small radius must be smaller than the surface tension of an arteriole with a larger radius:

$$r_{\text{arteriole}} > r_{\text{capillary}} \quad \Rightarrow \quad \sigma_{\text{arteriole}} > \sigma_{\text{capillary}} \qquad [39]$$

Eq. [39] is physiologically important, because it allows the walls of the capillaries to be thinner; this in turn improves the efficiency of diffusive transport of small ions and oxygen from the blood into the surrounding tissue.

---

## Concept Question 11.7

If we use a surfactant that reduces to 50% the surface tension of a bubble membrane, we obtain the same transmural pressure if (A) the radius is increased by a factor of 4, (B) the radius is doubled, (C) the radius remains unaffected, (D) the radius is reduced to one-half of the previous value, (E) the radius is reduced to one-quarter of the previous value.

ANSWER: Choice (D) based on Eq. [37].

---

## Concept Question 11.8

A lung has collapsed when the alveoli have retracted so that their membranes stretch almost flat across the ends of the bronchial tubes, as shown in the second sketch from the left in Fig. 11.15. What happens when we try to inflate a collapsed lung?

ANSWER: When the alveoli are collapsed, the corresponding radius of the alveolar surface, $r_1$, is large and the transmural pressure in the alveolus is low due to the inverse relation between radius and pressure difference in Eq. [37]. When trying to inflate such a collapsed lung, a significant resistance must be overcome. Initially, the tissue resists the inflating of the lung, because pushing the alveoli out of the bronchial tubes reduces their radii significantly, $r_1 \gg r_2$. Thus, pressurizing the lung has initially very little effect until an external pressure has been reached that provides the transmural pressure needed for alveoli of radius $r_2$. When this radius is reached the external pressure must be lowered suddenly because inflating the alveoli from $r_2$ to $r_3$ in Fig. 11.15 requires a decreasing

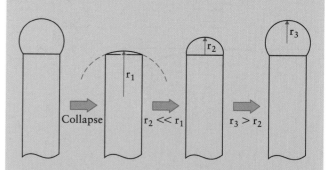

**FIGURE 11.15**

Left panel: healthy alveolus sealing the end of a bronchial tube. Three right panels: stages of the inflation of a collapsed lung. Initially (second panel) the lungs resist inflation until the alveoli reach an intermediate, smallest radius (third panel). Thereafter, the completion of the inflation does not require further pressurizing (last panel).

pressure based on Eq. [37] and $r_2 < r_3$. Thanks to the great elasticity of human tissues the risk of over-pressurizing and rupturing the lungs during inflation is not too high.

## ● EXAMPLE 11.5

We study two alveoli in competition at adjacent bronchial tubes as shown in Fig. 11.16. The actual size of any two adjacent alveoli will usually differ slightly. Why does this create a problem?

*Solution:* We choose the second formula from Eq. [37] for the alveoli because they have only one

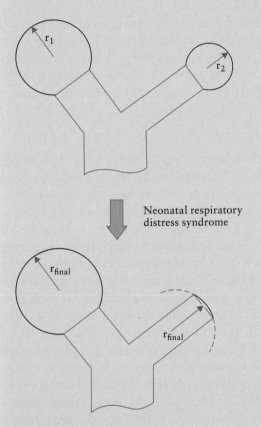

Neonatal respiratory distress syndrome

**FIGURE 11.16**

Sketch of two alveoli of different radii located near a bronchial branching point. The smaller alveolus requires a larger pressure difference; therefore, it should collapse in favour of the bigger alveolus. After collapsing, both alveoli have the same radius $r_{final}$, but the previously smaller alveolus is essentially completely retracted into the bronchial tube. A healthy lung has means of preventing this effect using pulmonary surfactants to modify the surface tension in the alveoli. However, prematurely born babies lack these surfactants, and the collapse of small alveoli is observed. This neonatal respiratory distress syndrome was in the past a major cause of death in prematurely born babies.

open surface inside, with the outside immersed in extracellular fluid (inverse droplet configuration):

$$\Delta p = p_{inside} - p_{outside} = \frac{2 \cdot \sigma}{r} \quad [40]$$

We assume two adjacent alveoli with different radii, $r_1 > r_2$. Since the external pressure $p_{outside}$ in the surrounding tissue is the same for both alveoli, the corresponding internal pressures of the two alveoli would have to vary due to Laplace's law:

$$r_1 > r_2 \quad \Rightarrow \quad \Delta p_1 = \frac{2 \cdot \sigma}{r_1} < \frac{2 \cdot \sigma}{r_2} = \Delta p_2 \quad [41]$$

However, the internal pressures cannot be different for adjacent alveoli because their air spaces are connected through the bronchial tree. Eq. [41] means that either one of the two alveoli cannot be in mechanical equilibrium for a given pulmonary pressure. In practice, the air pressure in the lungs would not sufficiently pressurize the smaller alveoli and they would collapse. We cannot allow this to happen, since the air exchange in the lungs is proportional to the contact area of the alveoli with the adjacent blood capillaries, i.e., small alveoli contribute more effectively than larger ones.

To prevent this problem, alveolar cells produce **pulmonary surfactants** that wet the alveolar surface to counterbalance the radius effect in Eq. [41] by lowering the surface tension $\sigma$ for smaller alveoli. Pulmonary surfactant is formed starting late in fetal life. For this reason, it is often the case in premature births that insufficient pulmonary surfactant is present, which causes **neonatal respiratory distress syndrome**. For a baby with this syndrome the lung is stiff, with some alveoli collapsed and others likely to be filled with fluid. Immediate medical attention is required at a neonatal hospital unit, as shown in Fig. 11.17.

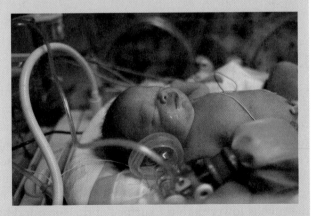

**FIGURE 11.17**
A newborn baby in a neonatal hospital unit.

## ● EXAMPLE 11.5 (*continued*)

By adding some soap to a bottle filled with water, you can easily demonstrate that the competitive effect between small and large bubbles discussed in this example does indeed exist. When water is poured out of the bottle, air streams in and bubbles form. You observe that the smaller bubbles arch into larger, more stable bubbles.

## ● EXAMPLE 11.6

An average alveolus in the human lungs has a radius of about 50 μm. (a) What is the predicted transmural pressure if we model the extracellular fluid outside of the alveolus as water with surface tension $\sigma = 0.073$ N/m? (b) Do you recall the actual value from our earlier discussions in this textbook?

*Solution to part (a):* We use Eq. [40] for the same reason outlined in Example 11.5. Substituting the given radius and value for $\sigma$, we get:

$$\Delta p = \frac{2 \cdot \sigma}{r} = \frac{2 \cdot \left(0.073 \, \frac{N}{m}\right)}{5.0 \times 10^{-5} \, m} = 2900 \, Pa \quad [42]$$

i.e., a value close to 3 kPa.

*Solution to part (b):* The transmural pressure in the lungs is defined as the difference between the alveolar and pleural pressures, $p_{alveoli} - p_{pleura}$. This pressure is included in Figs. 7.6 to 7.8, where we found that this value never exceeds 2 kPa and for regular breathing lies in the range of 0.5 to 0.7 kPa. Thus, pulmonary surfactants are needed in average-sized alveoli to allow for a transmural pressure smaller than the value in Eq. [42] by a factor of 4 to 6.

## Capillarity

**Capillarity** is closely related to surface tension. This effect is illustrated in Fig. 11.18, which compares the results of two experiments. A small, hollow glass tube is immersed in water (left sketch) or liquid mercury (right sketch). It is observed that the water rises in the tube and its surface bends up slightly at the water/glass/air interface. In turn, the mercury level in the tube is lower than the surface of the surrounding mercury and the mercury bends downward at the mercury/glass/air interface. This indicates that both the surface tension of the liquid and the interfacial

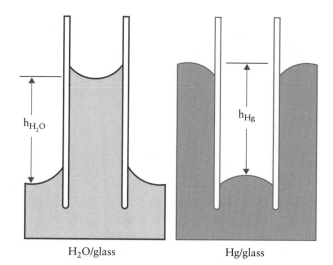

$H_2O$/glass          Hg/glass

## FIGURE 11.18

Comparison between the wetting of a hollow glass tube immersed in water (left panel) and immersed in mercury (right panel). The two final equilibrium states shown indicate that water wets glass, which leads to an upward force on the water in the tube. This effect is called capillarity (capillary action). Mercury does not wet glass, leading to a mercury level in the tube below the mercury surface in the remaining beaker.

tension at the water/glass or mercury/glass interfaces play a role in this experiment. Surface tension values are always positive since forming a surface toward air requires energy to reduce the number of attractive neighbouring molecules in the liquid, as indicated in Fig. 11.10. Interfacial tensions can be positive or negative since a solid or liquid surface contains a similar density of molecules for interaction as the studied liquid. The attractive interaction with equal molecules is replaced by a possibly stronger attractive interaction with the molecules on the other side of the interface. This is the case for water and glass. Consequently, water wets glass because forming this interface requires less energy than forming a surface with air. Mercury, in turn, does not wet glass as formation of the glass/mercury interface requires a large amount of energy.

A second experiment illustrating the effect of capillarity is shown in Fig. 11.19. Two tubes with different inner diameters are submerged in water. The height of the water level in a tube is greater when the tube diameter is smaller. This is due to the total energy required in each tube to form surfaces toward air and interfaces along the glass walls. Capillarity is an essential part of many life processes. In higher animals blood is pumped through arteries and veins but capillarity is important in the smallest blood vessels, which are therefore called capillaries. We address this issue in part (b) of Example 11.7.

**FIGURE 11.19**

The capillarity effect of water. Two glass tubes of varying diameter are submerged into water. The tube with the smaller diameter at left shows the greater capillarity effect because the interaction between water and the glass surface contributes more strongly to the water column's mechanical equilibrium, which allows the water to rise to higher levels.

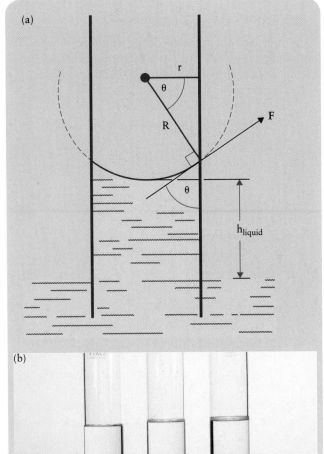

**FIGURE 11.20**

(a) Sketch of a liquid column rising in a narrow capillary of radius $r$ to a height $h_{liquid}$. The curvature of the meniscus of the liquid is defined by the radius of curvature, $R$, which leads to a contact angle $\theta$ of the liquid with the inner capillary wall. The force related to the surface tension is indicated. (b) Comparison of the water menisci of distilled water (left), tap water (centre), and seawater (right).

● **EXAMPLE 11.7**

(a) Using Fig. 11.20(a) for a liquid that has risen in a capillary to height $h_{liquid}$ and forms a contact angle $\theta$ with the inner surface of the capillary of radius $r$, show that the height of the liquid column in the capillary is given by **Jurin's law:**

$$h_{liquid} = \frac{2 \cdot \sigma_{liquid}}{\rho_{liquid} \cdot g} \cdot \frac{\cos \theta}{r} \qquad [43]$$

(b) For whole blood with a surface tension of $\sigma = 0.058$ N/m and a density of 1.06 g/cm³, calculate the maximum height to which it can rise in a capillary that has a diameter of 4.5 $\mu$m.

*Solution to part (a):* In Fig. 11.20(a) you notice that the meniscus of the liquid surface is not flat but curved like an inverse sphere. This is due to the capillarity effect in the tube and is quantified with Eq. [37]. We use the second formula in Eq. [37] with the proportionality factor 2 for the droplet because there is only one interface between liquid and air. The pressure difference between the liquid at the meniscus in the tube and the outside air is:

$$p_{liquid\ surface} - p_{atm} = -\frac{2 \cdot \sigma_{liquid}}{R} \qquad [44]$$

in which $R$ is the radius of curvature of the meniscus, as shown in Fig. 11.20(a). Eq. [44] has a negative sign on the right-hand side since the meniscus is curved upward (as opposed to the curvature of the bubbles in Figs. 11.15 and 11.16). The radius of curvature in Eq. [44] is related to the inner radius of the capillary and the contact angle $\theta$, as shown in Fig. 11.20(a):

$$R = \frac{r}{\cos \theta} \qquad [45]$$

Pascal's law enables us to write a second condition for the same pressure difference since we know that the surface pressure of water and the

● **EXAMPLE 11.7 (continued)**

air pressure are the same at the water/air interface outside of the tube, i.e., at a height $h_{liquid}$ below the meniscus in the capillary in Fig. 11.20(a). Thus, at the meniscus in the tube we find:

$$p_{\text{liquid surface}} - p_{\text{atm}} = -\rho_{\text{liquid}} \cdot g \cdot h_{\text{liquid}} \quad [46]$$

Equating the right-hand sides of Eqs. [44] and [46], and substituting Eq. [45] for $R$, leads to:

$$-\frac{2 \cdot \sigma_{\text{liquid}}}{r/\cos\theta} = -\rho_{\text{liquid}} \cdot g \cdot h_{\text{liquid}} \quad [47]$$

which is rearranged as Jurin's law:

$$\frac{2 \cdot \sigma_{\text{liquid}} \cdot \cos\theta}{r \cdot \rho_{\text{liquid}} \cdot g} = h_{\text{liquid}} \quad [48]$$

Fig. 11.20(b) shows that this effect already plays a role for the different types of water we deal with in this textbook: the three test tubes contain distilled water (left), tap water (centre), and seawater (right), illustrating the different menisci they form. This image illustrates that surface tension differences between these three types of water exist. Distilled (i.e., highly purified) water has a small meniscus height, and seawater with high ion concentrations has the highest meniscus. Dissolved salts increase the surface tension of seawater.

*Solution to part (b):* This part of the example is an application of Jurin's law. First, we need to interpret the term "maximum height" in the example text. Note that we do not identify the contact angle $\theta$. The range of possible contact angles between 0° and 180° allows for the range of cosine values $-1 \le \cos\theta \le +1$ in Eq. [43]. Thus, a maximum height is reached when $\cos\theta = 1$:

$$h_{\text{max,blood}} = \frac{2 \cdot \sigma_{\text{blood}}}{r \cdot \rho_{\text{blood}} \cdot g} \quad [49]$$

We substitute the values given in the example text and obtain $h_{\text{max, blood}} = 5.0$ m from:

$$\frac{2 \cdot \left(5.8 \times 10^{-2} \, \frac{\text{N}}{\text{m}}\right)}{\left(1.06 \times 10^3 \, \frac{\text{kg}}{\text{m}^3}\right)\left(9.8 \, \frac{\text{m}}{\text{s}^2}\right)(2.25 \times 10^{-6} \, \text{m})} \quad [50]$$

Significant amounts of water are transported upward in trees: a full-grown birch evaporates about 350 litres of water from its leaves per summer day. It is still a matter of research to what extent the effect shown in Fig. 11.19 plays a role in this transport of

water and sap in tall trees. In order to transport water by capillarity into the canopies of even the tallest trees, e.g., eucalyptus trees of 150 m height, capillary diameters of smaller than 0.1 $\mu$m would be required. However, the xylem fibres, in which water has been shown to rise in trees, typically have diameters of 20 $\mu$m to 300 $\mu$m. Xylem tissue of a leaf midrib is shown in a coloured scanning electron micrograph in Fig. 11.21. In the cross-section shown, the midvein runs through the centre. The layer surrounding it is large mesophyll cells, followed by a thin outer layer of epidermal cells. The midvein contains the larger, water-carrying xylem tubes bundled at the centre and surrounded by a ring of smaller phloem tubes that carry nutrients.

Clearly other effects play a role in the transport of water from the ground to the leaves. We study the wood anemone as an example. The wood anemone is a flower that stands erect and opens only when the sun shines. When a cloud covers the sun or when we create an artificial shade for the flower, the flower closes and the stem bends down. This is a sign of reduced water pressure in the stem. When the shade is removed, the flower resumes its erect posture as the water pressure in the stem increases again. In the anemone, the water pressure is regulated by chemical reactions that operate only under sunny and warm conditions.

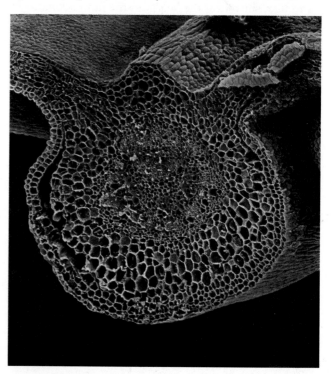

**FIGURE 11.21**

Leaf midrib as seen with coloured scanning electron microscopy (SEM). This is a cross-section through the midrib, the continuation of a leaf's stem along the centre of the leaf. The main vein, called the midvein, runs through the centre of the midrib.

# Wetting

Different liquids wet glass (or any other surface) differently, as Fig. 11.18 indicates. Some, like water on glass, like to form an interface and rise in the tube (with an upward-curved meniscus); others, like mercury, do not like to form an interface with glass. In that case the meniscus drops and is curved downward. Any liquid forming an upward-curved interface with glass, as shown in the left sketch in Fig. 11.18, is referred to as wetting the surface; any liquid forming a downward-sloped interface, as shown in the right sketch of Fig. 11.18, is referred to as non-wetting the surface.

**Wetting** versus **non-wetting** is an important issue, e.g., for the textile industry. Fluorinated clothes (Gore-Tex) cause a non-wetting condition for water; i.e., the clothes allow air to penetrate but keep water out. However, wetting is often not complete, leading to a range of contact angles of the liquid with the glass surface, with values between 0° (complete wetting) and 180° (complete non-wetting).

The forces acting at a point where the three materials meet—air, water, and glass—are illustrated for a partially wetting droplet on a surface in Fig. 11.22.

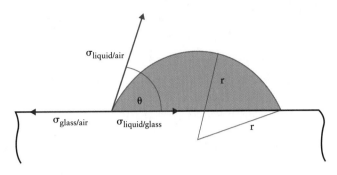

**FIGURE 11.22**

A partially spherical droplet of radius $r$ on a flat surface. The three surface and interface tensions indicated are connected by the Young–Dupré equation, which allows us to calculate the contact angle $\theta$.

A mechanical equilibrium between the three interfacial and surface tensions, which are forces per unit length of contact line, must exist along the surface, since the common point would accelerate otherwise along the surface (and the droplet would change its shape). We obtain the condition for mechanical equilibrium from Fig. 11.22 (called the **Young–Dupré equation**):

$$\sigma_{glass/air} = \sigma_{glass/liquid} + \sigma_{liquid/air} \cdot \cos\theta \qquad [51]$$

# MULTIPLE CHOICE AND CONCEPTUAL QUESTIONS

## FLUID PRESSURE AND DENSITY

**Q–11.1.** Which law is used to quantify the pressure at the bottom of a lake? (A) Arrhenius's law, (B) Pascal's law, (C) Newton's first law, (D) Laplace's law, (E) none of these.

**Q–11.2.** (a) The nautilus (see Fig. 11.9) rises to depth of 60 metres below the surface of the Pacific Ocean at night to feed on plankton. What is the water pressure at that depth using the rule from Example 11.1 that the pressure in water roughly increases by 1 atm per 10 metres depth? (A) 3 atm, (B) 4 atm, (C) 5 atm, (D) 6 atm, (E) 7 atm. (b) The nautilus is a temperature-sensitive animal, diving to greater depth during daytime to escape near-surface temperature increases due to solar heating. They have been found as deep as 400 metres below the surface. What pressure variation has its shell to tolerate during this daily vertical migration? Use the same rule as in part (a). (A) Less than 30 atm, (B) 32 atm, (C) 34 atm, (D) 36 atm, (E) 38 atm, (F) 40 atm, (G) more than 40 atm.

**Q–11.3.** Which of the following pressures can be negative? (A) The transmural pressure in the lungs, (B) the blood pressure in supine position, (C) the alveolar pressure, (D) the air pressure, (E) the water pressure below the surface of a lake.

**Q–11.4.** The vertical distance from feet to heart of a standing individual is 1.2 m. Using for the density of blood $\rho = 1.06$ g/cm$^3$, find the difference in blood pressure between the two levels (heart and feet). Choose the closest value. (A) 1270 Pa, (B) 1.06 kPa, (C) 12.5 kPa, (D) 1.0 atm.

**Q–11.5.** Pascal's law is applied to an unknown liquid in an open container. We observe that the pressure is 1.05 atm at 10 cm below the surface. At what depth in the liquid is the pressure 1.2 atm? (A) 0.2 m, (B) 0.4 m, (C) 0.8 m, (D) 1.2 m, (E) 2.5 m.

**Q–11.6.** Under what circumstances can air not be modelled as an ideal stationary fluid? (A) when applying Pascal's law, (B) when determining the buoyant force acting on an object, (C) when applying

Laplace's law, (D) when describing the pressure in a soap bubble.

**Q–11.7.** Exchanging one fluid for another in a given beaker, the density of the beaker's content increases if (A) the fluid mass decreases per unit volume, (B) the fluid volume decreases per unit mass, (C) both fluid mass and volume double, (D) both fluid mass and volume are halved.

**Q–11.8.** Vapour bubbles in a beaker of boiling water get larger as they approach the surface. Why?

## BUOYANCY

**Q–11.9.** We consider a motionless shark slowly sinking to the bottom of a lagoon. Which of the choices in Fig. 11.23 represents the proper free-body diagram for the shark of weight **W**? *Hint:* the arrows are not drawn proportional to magnitude of the respective force.

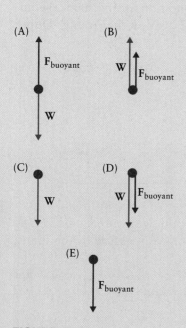

**FIGURE 11.23**

Five proposed free-body diagrams for a motionless shark in water.

**Q–11.10.** Most fish can float in water. What must be true for such fish? (A) Their density is larger than that of water. (B) Their density is equal to that of water. (C) Their density is smaller than that of water. (D) No conclusions about the fish's density can be drawn.

**Q–11.11.** Siamese fighting fish (see Fig. 11.24) have an unusual way of caring for their young. Males prepare a home for their future offspring by taking gulps of air and blowing saliva-coated bubbles that collect at the water's surface as a glistening froth. When a female arrives ready to mate, she swims under the bubble-nest where the male embraces her and fertilizes her eggs. Then, picking up the eggs in his mouth, he spits them, one by one, into the bubbles. The role of father continues for the male Siamese fighting fish as he conscientiously watches over the developing eggs. Any that slip from a bubble and start to sink are carefully retrieved and spat back into a bubble. Based on these observations, what statement can we make about the Siamese fighting fish's fertilized eggs? (A) They are heavy. (B) They have a small volume. (C) Their density is larger than that of water. (D) Their density is equal to that of water. (E) Their density is smaller than that of water.

**FIGURE 11.24**

A Siamese fighting fish.

**Q–11.12.** Fig. 11.25(a) shows a beaker on a scale. The beaker is filled to the rim with water. It is then taken from the scale and a piece of wood is lowered into the beaker. The beaker with wood is then placed back on the scale, as shown in Fig. 11.25(b). How has the reading of the scale changed from part (a) to part (b)?

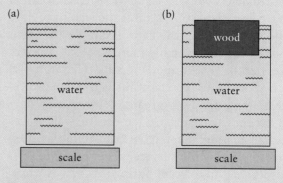

**FIGURE 11.25**

(a) A beaker filled with water to the rim is placed on a scale. (b) A piece of wood is lowered into the beaker and the beaker is placed again on the scale.

**Q–11.13.** Consider the *Hindenburg* zeppelin, which exploded in 1937 at Lakehurst, New Jersey. At the time of the accident, its tanks were filled with hydrogen gas. Had they been filled with the following gas, the airship could have carried more passengers: (A) helium, (B) methane, (C) carbon monoxide, (D) nitrogen, (E) none of these.

**Q–11.14.** The food label on a package of cheese starts with the line: "Nutrition facts per 3 cm dice (30 g)." If we take a piece of that cheese and throw it into seawater of density 1025 kg/m³, what happens? (A) The piece sinks. (B) The piece floats at the surface; i.e., part of the piece rises above the water surface. (C) The piece floats fully immersed in the water, i.e., with its entire volume below the water surface. (D) What happens depends on the size of the piece we throw into the water. (E) What happens depends on the mass of the piece we throw into the water.

**Q–11.15.** We study a solid steel sphere completely immersed in water (which we treat as an ideal stationary fluid). We use the variable $d$ to represent the depth below the water surface. Which sketch in Fig. 11.26

shows the dependence of the buoyant force acting on the solid sphere as a function of depth?

**Q–11.16.** The buoyant force acting on a seagull in level flight is equal to: (A) the density of the bird, (B) the mass of the bird, (C) the volume of the bird, (D) the weight of the bird, (E) the weight of the air displaced by the bird.

**Q–11.17.** We study Fig. 11.27. Part (a) shows a sphere with a radius $r = 10$ cm and density of $\rho_a = 1.8$ g/cm³ suspended in water. Part (b) shows a wooden sphere of diameter $d = 10$ cm (density $\rho_b = 0.95$ g/cm³) anchored under water with a string. Which of the four free-body diagrams shown in Fig. 11.28 correspond to the two cases in Fig. 11.27? *Note:* $\mathbf{T}$ is tension, $\mathbf{W}$ is weight, and $\mathbf{F}_{buoyant}$ is buoyant force. (A) The free-body diagram in sketch Fig. 11.28(A) belongs to the case in Fig. 11.27(a) and the free-body diagram in sketch Fig. 11.28(B) belongs to the case in Fig. 11.27(b). (B) The free-body diagram in sketch Fig. 11.28(B) belongs to the case in Fig. 11.27(a) and the free-body diagram in sketch Fig. 11.28(C) belongs to the case in Fig. 11.27(b). (C) The free-body diagram in sketch Fig. 11.28(C) belongs to the case in Fig. 11.27(a) and the free-body diagram in sketch Fig. 11.28(D) belongs to the case in Fig. 11.27(b). (D) The free-body diagram in sketch Fig. 11.28(C) belongs to the case in Fig. 11.27(a) and the free-body diagram in sketch Fig. 11.28(A) belongs to the case in Fig. 11.27(b). (E) The free-body diagram in sketch Fig. 11.28(B) belongs to the case in Fig. 11.27(b) and the free-body diagram in sketch Fig. 11.28(C) belongs to the case in Fig. 11.27(a).

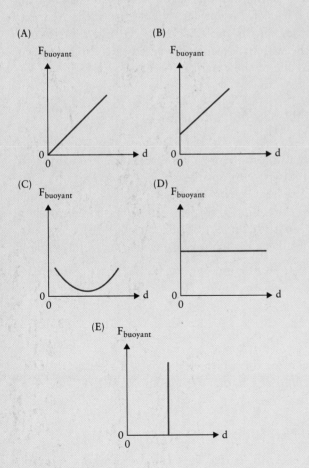

**FIGURE 11.26**

Five graphs proposing a dependence of the buoyant force acting on a solid sphere as a function of depth.

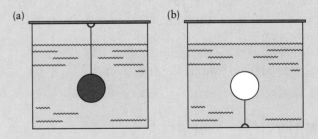

**FIGURE 11.27**

(a) A sphere of radius $r = 10$ cm and density $\rho_a = 1.8$ g/cm³ is suspended in water. (b) A wooden sphere of diameter $d = 10$ cm and density $\rho_b = 0.95$ g/cm³ is held under water by a string.

**SURFACE TENSION**

**Q–11.18.** Which is the standard unit of surface tension? (A) J, (B) Pa, (C) (kg · m)/s², (D) kg/s², (E) kg/(m · s²).

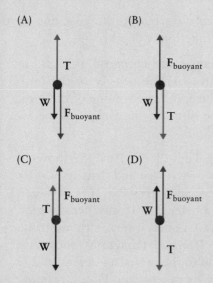

(A)

T

W

$F_{buoyant}$

(B)

$F_{buoyant}$

W

T

(C)

$F_{buoyant}$

T

W

(D)

$F_{buoyant}$

W

T

**FIGURE 11.28**

Four suggested free-body diagrams for the two arrangements in Fig. 11.27.

**Q–11.19.** Laplace's law describes the pressure in an alveolus in the lungs in the form $p_{inside} - p_{outside} = 2 \cdot \sigma/r$, in which $\sigma$ is the surface tension and $r$ is the radius of curvature of the alveolus. In healthy alveoli a surfactant is used to reduce the surface tension by coating parts of the surface. Which of the following statements is false? (A) The surfactant particularly must coat areas with a large radius of curvature. (B) The surfactant particularly must coat areas with a small radius of curvature. (C) A surfactant does not change the pressure in the bubble.

**Q–11.20.** Fig. 11.15 shows in three steps how a lung collapses and then is re-inflated under medical observation. We call the collapse "step 1," the step from alveolar radius $r_1$ to $r_2$ "step 2," and the final step from alveolar radius $r_2$ to $r_3$ "step 3." In which step must a health practitioner exert the greatest pressure from outside through the mouth? (A) during step 1, (B) during step 2, (C) during step 3, (D) after step 3 to keep the lung from collapsing again.

**Q–11.21.** Which law is used to quantify the pressure in a soap bubble? (A) Jurin's law, (B) Pascal's law, (C) Newton's third law, (D) Laplace's law, (E) none of these.

**Q–11.22.** You study a large and a small soap bubble. In which of the two is the air pressure higher? (A) neither; it's the same, (B) in the larger bubble, (C) in the smaller bubble, (D) that depends on the common outside pressure, (E) impossible to predict.

**Q–11.23.** A water-strider is an insect that can walk on water. Looking at one of the six legs of the water-strider resting on the water surface, the following is the case for the surface underneath the insect's foot: (A) it is perfectly flat, (B) it is bent upward due to the attractive force of the foot, (C) it is curved downward because the foot simulates an increased pressure from above the water surface, (D) it splits and the lower end of the foot dangles below the surface.

**Q–11.24.** In Fig. 11.10 a force is shown acting on a molecule in the water surface. Our knowledge of Newton's laws tells us that (A) the water molecule accelerates downward until it hits the bottom of the beaker, (B) the water molecule accelerates downward until it has left the surface, (C) at least one more force must act on the molecule to keep it at the surface, (D) the water molecule is ejected into the gas space above due to the reaction force to force F.

## A SMALL RESEARCH PROJECT

**Q–11.25.** A few lizards have developed specialized feet that allow them to climb smooth surfaces, such as windows, without the aid of claws. Examples include several gecko species, which can even walk across the ceiling in tropical homes. (a) How can they hold on to such a smooth surface? (b) How can they walk at reasonable pace up the window glass surface?

# ANALYTICAL PROBLEMS

## GEOMETRIC PROPERTIES OF OBJECTS

**P–11.1.** The sphere is the shape with the smallest surface for a given volume. To prove this statement properly requires variational analysis. Here we only want to confirm this result for a selection of highly symmetric shapes by calculating the ratio of surface and volume. Find these ratios for (a) sphere, (b) cylinder, (c) cube, (d) pyramid, (e) tetrahedron, and (f) cone. Does the statement hold for these six shapes? See the Math Review "Symmetric Objects" at the end of Chapter 3 for some required data.

## FLUID PRESSURE

**P–11.2.** A diver used to standard snorkel tubing of length 25 cm tries a self-made tube of length 7 m. During the attempt, what is the pressure difference between the external pressure on the diver's chest and the air pressure in the diver's lungs? *For those interested*: What happens to the diver as a result of the attempt?

**P–11.3.** A scuba diver takes a deep breath from an air-filled tank at depth $d$, then abandons the tank. During the subsequent ascent to the surface the diver fails to exhale. When reaching the surface, the pressure difference between the external pressure and the pressure in the lungs is 76 torr. At what depth did the diver abandon the tank? *For those interested*: What potentially lethal danger does the diver face?

**P–11.4.** What is the pressure increase in the fluid in a syringe when a force of 50 N is applied to its circular piston, which has a radius of 1.25 cm?

**P–11.5.** What minimum gauge pressure is needed to suck water up a straw to a height of 10 cm? Recall that the gauge pressure is defined as the pressure relative to atmospheric pressure, $p_{gauge} = p - p_{atm}$.

**P–11.6.** Collapsible plastic bags are used in hospitals for infusions. We want to use such a bag to infuse an electrolyte solution into the artery of a patient. For this we mount the bag at a height $h$ above the arm of the patient, as shown in Fig. 11.29. Assuming that the average gauge pressure in the artery is 13.3 kPa and the density of the electrolyte solution is 1.03 g/cm$^3$, what is the minimum height $h$ in order for the infusion to work?

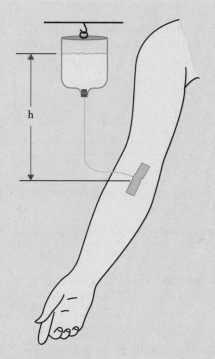

**FIGURE 11.29**

**P–11.7.** Water is pumped to the top of the 365-m-tall Empire State Building in New York City. What gauge pressure is needed in the water line at the base of the building to achieve this?

**P–11.8.** The U-shaped glass tube in Fig. 11.30 contains two liquids in mechanical equilibrium: water of density $\rho_w = 1.0$ kg/L, and an unknown liquid of density $\rho_l$. The unknown liquid is in the left tube, floating on top of the water with a clearly visible interface. Use $h_1 = 150$ mm and $h_2 = 15$ mm with the heights as labelled in Fig. 11.30. What is the density $\rho_l$?

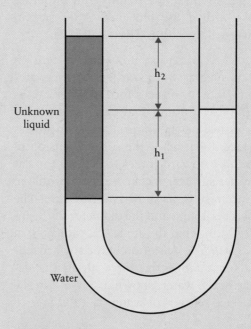

**FIGURE 11.30**

**P–11.9.** The density of ice is $\rho_{ice} = 920$ kg/m$^3$ and the average density of seawater is $\rho_w = 1.025$ g/cm$^3$. What fraction of the total volume of an iceberg is exposed?

**P–11.10.** We consider a hot air balloon of mass 250 kg (basket and envelope). The spherical envelope of the balloon has a diameter of 16 m when fully inflated. To what temperature must the enclosed air be heated for the balloon to carry four standard men? Assume that the surrounding air is at 20°C and is treated as an ideal gas. Use 29 g/mol for the molar mass of air.

**P–11.11.** (a) Fig. 11.27(b) shows a wooden sphere with a diameter of $d = 10$ cm (density $\rho = 0.9$ g/cm$^3$) held under water by a string. What is the tension in the string? (b) Fig. 11.27(a) shows a sphere of radius $r = 10$ cm and density of $\rho = 2.0$ g/cm$^3$ suspended in water. What is the tension in the string? *Note*: Draw the free-body diagram in each case.

## ADVANCED EXAMPLES FROM PHYSIOLOGY

**P–11.12.** Water is transported upward in plants through xylem tissue, which consists of cells of 1 mm length and a species-dependent diameter between 40 $\mu$m and 400 $\mu$m. The xylem cells are attached to each other to form a channel. To what maximum height can water rise in these xylem channels due to the capillarity effect? *Hint:* The surface tension of water is $\sigma = 0.073$ N/m at 20°C. *For those interested:* Confirm this result with a simple experiment: cut and split the stem of a flower with white petals (e.g., a dahlia or a carnation) and place one half of the stem in a glass with dilute red ink and the other half in a glass with dilute blue ink. After several hours the flower will be half red and half blue.

**P–11.13.** Fig. 11.31(a) shows how surface tension supports insects such as water-striders on the water surface. Assume that an insect's foot is spherical, as shown in Fig. 11.31(b), and that the insect stands with all of its six feet on the water. Each foot presses the water surface down while the surface tension of the water produces upward forces to restore the flat shape of the water surface. A characteristic profile of the water surface results, as shown in the figure. The mass of the insect is 15 mg and the diameter of the insect's foot is 250 $\mu$m. Find the angle $\theta$ as indicated in Fig. 11.31(b). *Hint:* The definition of the surface tension provides for a tangential force along the depressed surface of the water, shown as force **F** in the figure. The surface tension of water at 20°C is $\sigma = 0.073$ N/m.

**P–11.14.** To what depth below the Pacific Ocean's surface does the nautilus have control over its buoyancy based on osmotic pumping of water into its inner chambers? *Hint:* Determine the depth at which the osmotic and hydrostatic pressures are equal across the membrane that separates the animal's body from the inner chambers of the shell. The average salt content of seawater is 0.435 mol/L NaCl. Use Eq. [9.46] for the osmotic pressure.

(a)

(b)

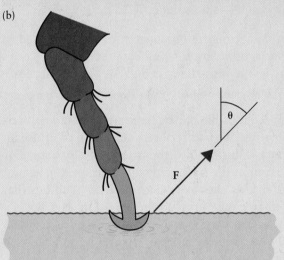

**FIGURE 11.31**

## SUMMARY

### DEFINITIONS

- Atmospheric pressure: $p_{atm} = 1.01 \times 10^5$ Pa.
- Gauge pressure: a pressure value relative to air pressure:

$$p_{gauge} = p_{absolute} - p_{air}$$

- Buoyant force:

$$F_{buoyant} = \rho_{fluid} \cdot V_{object} \cdot g$$

- Surface energy $\sigma$ is the energy required to form an area of 1 m² of new surface:

$$\sigma = \frac{\Delta E}{\Delta A}$$

- Surface tension (equivalent to surface energy):

$$\sigma = \frac{F}{l_x}$$

$l_x$ is the length along which the force acts tangentially to the surface.

## UNITS

Surface tension $\sigma$: $J/m^2 = N/m$

## LAWS

- Pascal's law (depth $d$ measured from surface downward):

$$p = p_{atm} + \rho \cdot g \cdot d$$

- The Archimedes principle:

$$F_{net} = F_{buoyant} - W_{object}$$

- Laplace's formula for pressure difference across the surface for ($r$ is radius)
  - hollow bubble: $\Delta p = 4 \cdot \sigma/r$
  - homogeneous droplet or hollow cylinder: $\Delta p = 2 \cdot \sigma/r$
  - homogeneous cylinder: $\Delta p = \sigma/r$
- Jurin's law for capillarity:

$$h_{liquid} = \frac{2 \cdot \sigma_{liquid}}{\rho_{liquid} \cdot g} \frac{\cos \theta}{r}$$

where $r$ is radius, and $\theta$ is contact angle of fluid with capillary wall.

# CHAPTER 12

# CARDIOVASCULAR SYSTEM
# Fluid Flow

A fluid that is not in mechanical equilibrium will flow. Different aspects of flow are described, with two models introduced for dynamic fluids: the ideal dynamic fluid and the Newtonian fluid. Both are idealized, as we assume that the fluid is incompressible and turbulence free. The flow under these conditions is called laminar flow.

In the ideal dynamic fluid, molecular interactions are limited to elastic collisions. This yields frictionless motion of the fluid at stationary walls. Two laws determine the properties of the resulting flow: the *equation of continuity* is an expression of the conservation of fluid mass, and *Bernoulli's law* represents the conservation of energy. These two laws predict that the flow through a tapering tube accelerates, and that the pressure in the fluid decreases with increasing speed.

In Newtonian fluid interaction, the container walls become important as fluid molecules transfer energy in inelastic collisions. The equation of continuity continues to apply, but Bernoulli's law is no longer sufficient to describe the pressure in the fluid. We develop the concept of viscosity to take into account flow resistance. In a Newtonian fluid two forces are present in the direction of the flow: a forward-acting force based on a pressure difference along the tube, and a resistance force that depends on the viscosity of the fluid. In steady state a parabolic velocity distribution results in a cylindrical tube and the volume flow rate is proportional to the fourth power of the radius of the tube (Poiseuille's law).

When the properties of a flowing fluid violate the assumptions made for a Newtonian fluid non-Newtonian behaviour is observed, most notably as deviations from Poiseuille's law. Examples include turbulent flow at high fluid speeds, and velocity-dependent interactions within the fluid if it is a mixed phase.

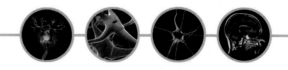

We focus on the human cardiovascular system because it is an important physiological application of fluid flow. The overview in Fig. 12.1 identifies its two circulations that are connected in series:

- In the **systemic circulation**, blood is pumped out of the left ventricle of the heart to the capillaries in the organs throughout the body, where it delivers oxygen and nutrients. Loaded with carbon dioxide, it then returns to the heart. From the right atrium it proceeds into the right ventricle, entering

- the **pulmonary circulation**. From the right ventricle blood is pumped to the capillary bed in the lungs, where carbon dioxide is replaced by oxygen. From the lungs blood then returns to the left atrium to complete a full cycle.

In the systemic circulation, organs are arranged in parallel to allow the body to prioritize oxygen supply based on the vital relevance of the organ and the current metabolic demand. For the major organs, Fig. 12.1 shows the fraction of the received blood flow, $I/I_0$. $I = \Delta V/\Delta t$ is the volume flow rate through an organ, and $I_0$ is the total volume flow rate of the systemic circulation. The term *volume flow rate* refers to a fluid volume $\Delta V$ that flows through a vessel per time interval $\Delta t$. $I_0$ can be determined from the amount of blood ejected into the aorta per heart beat, which is 70 mL. With the repetition rate of 70 heart beats per minute, a total volume flow rate of $I_0 = 5$ L/min results.

Fig. 12.1 also shows the fraction of oxygen consumed in each organ as a percentage value (labelled

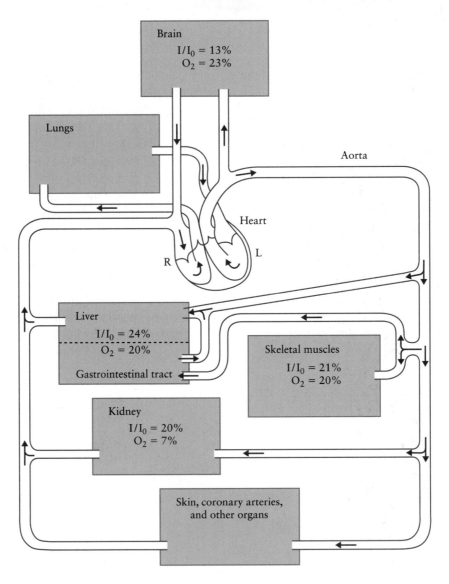

**FIGURE 12.1**

Quantitative overview of the flow diagram of the human cardiovascular system. Listed for each major organ are its fraction of the volume flow rate, $I/I_0$, and its fraction of oxygen consumed (labelled $O_2$).

$O_2$). The rate of oxygen uptake in the pulmonary circulation is 0.25 L/min. Sufficient blood supply to the brain has the highest priority, as the brain is very sensitive to oxygen deficiency (hypoxia). In turn, the brain is efficient in retrieving oxygen from the blood: it requires only 13% of the blood flow to consume 23% of the total oxygen. The same priority is given to the heart muscle, which receives about 5% of the blood, because survival requires continuous blood circulation.

A high priority is further given to the kidneys, which receive 20% to 25% of the blood even though their share is less than 0.5% of the body mass. This preferred supply is due to the filtration function of the kidneys, as discussed in an example later in the chapter. Supply to the skeletal muscles and the gastrointestinal tract with the liver varies significantly with demand. While physically active, up to two-thirds of the blood flow is distributed to the skeletal muscles. While digesting, a similarly high fraction of blood reaches the gastrointestinal tract. Thus, one shouldn't force both organ systems to work at the same time, e.g., by eating just before physical exercise!

Fig. 12.1 points to some of the physical concepts and parameters we need to discuss to understand the physiology of the cardiovascular system. We saw that blood circulates in two ways: it passes the systemic and the pulmonary circulations in series, but it flows through several organ systems in parallel. These two flow patterns have to be distinguished. To quantify blood flow along a single vessel, we have to study the dependence of the volume flow rate on blood velocity, blood pressure, and the cross-sectional area of the blood vessel. To correlate the total volume flow rate and the size and strength of the heart, the origin of flow resistance and its consequences for blood flow in various vessels have to be established. We further noted that blood supply can vary; an active regulation process is required for this. Two mechanisms have been proposed for the control of blood flow through organs: (i) a smooth muscle layer on the arterioles near the capillary bed; when these muscles contract, the blood vessel is constricted and blood flow is reduced, and (ii) rings of smooth muscles, called **precapillary sphincters**, have been suggested as a means of closing capillaries near the afferent arteriole (Fig. 12.2). As a result, blood flow bypasses the capillary bed and reaches a nearby venule directly from the arteriole via a single channel that always remains open.

Blood flow at bifurcations depends on the flow resistance of the two downstream tube systems. Due to this pivotal role of flow resistance, we devote an

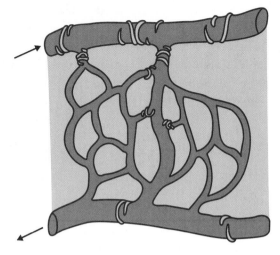

**FIGURE 12.2**

Regulation of blood flow in capillary beds. Rings of smooth muscles called sphincters are located at the afferent arteriole. When these muscles close, blood flow is limited to a throughfare channel to keep the circulatory system open.

entire section to the underlying physics based on the concept of viscosity.

The total blood volume of a standard man is 5.1 L (about 8% of the total body mass; see Table 3.3). Fig. 12.3(a) shows the volume distribution in the cardiovascular system. At any time, at least 80% of the blood is in veins, the right ventricle, and the pulmonary circulation. This part of the cardiovascular system is called the low-pressure system since the blood pressure is no greater than 2 kPa. Note that all blood pressure data are given relative to atmospheric pressure, which is about 101.3 kPa. The main purpose of the low-pressure system is the storage of blood. This part of the system can accommodate as much as 98% of the blood in the human body—e.g., when the total blood volume is increased during blood transfusion.

The main purpose of the high-pressure system is to supply the organs with oxygen. This requires a speedy delivery of blood to the capillaries, leading to the occurrence of more than 90% of the total flow resistance in the systemic circulation, as shown in Fig. 12.3(b). Note that the figure shows that the arterioles, and not the fragile capillaries, accommodate the biggest fraction of this effect. We will explain this observation later in the chapter.

Fig. 12.4 illustrates how the respective volumes in Fig. 12.3(a) are distributed along the systemic circulation. The numbers at the top indicate how many blood vessels of each type are found in a standard man. They

## FIGURE 12.3

(a) Blood volume distribution and (b) the contribution to the flow resistance for the main components of the systemic circulation. While the veins accommodate a major fraction of the blood, it is the small arteries and arterioles that accommodate the largest fraction of the flow resistance.

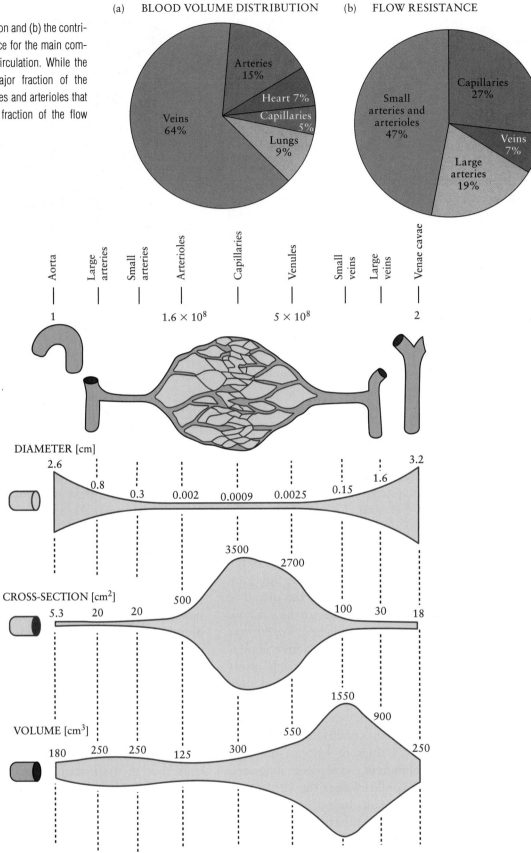

## FIGURE 12.4

Anatomical data for various types of vessels of the systemic circulation. The top row identifies the type of blood vessel. The second row gives numbers of blood vessels for some types. For each type, the *outer* diameter of a single vessel, the *outer* cross-sectional area, and the volume of all vessels of this type are illustrated. The numerical values are given in the indicated units.

vary from one aorta to 5 billion systemic capillaries. Below these numbers are three sketches for:

- the individual diameter of a vessel of a given type in unit cm,
- the total cross-section for all vessels of this type in unit cm$^2$, and
- the total capacity of all vessels of this type in unit cm$^3$.

Since the graph in Fig. 12.4 is not drawn to scale, values are included to permit its quantitative use. Note that we refer to Fig. 12.4 frequently when calculating the physical properties of the cardiovascular system.

Fig. 12.5 illustrates that the human cardiovascular system is the result of an extensive evolutionary development; it compares the generalized circulatory schemes of fish, amphibians, and mammals. Fish have a relatively simple two-chambered heart that provides blood to a single circulation. As life moved to dry land, the cardiovascular system became more complex. Amphibians have a three-chambered heart with two circulations, called the pulmocutaneous and the systemic systems. The systemic system delivers blood under high pressure to the systemic organs. The pulmocutaneous system delivers blood to the skin and to the lungs for oxygen uptake. Mammals have a **four-chambered heart** that represents, essentially, the two pumps of a double circulation system.

But how do we know that the changes from (a) to (c) in Fig. 12.5 that occurred in the past 420 million years are an example of evolutionary progress? We can judge this by how effectively each system is optimized within the framework of applicable physical laws; therefore, let's now discuss these laws.

# Flow of an Ideal Dynamic Fluid

The description of flow cannot be based on the stationary fluid model we introduced in the previous chapter, because it is a dynamic process that requires us to drop the requirement of a mechanical equilibrium. To develop a suitable model, in this chapter we ultimately modify two properties of the stationary fluid model. In this section, we introduce the ideal dynamic fluid model, which requires the fewest modifications to address the mechanical non-equilibrium of the fluid during flow. Later, then, we develop the Newtonian fluid model, which further allows an interaction between the fluid and the confining container walls.

## Ideal Dynamic Fluid Model

The ideal stationary fluid is incompressible and deformable. Both of these properties are retained in the dynamic case. The ideal stationary fluid further fills any given container such that it is in mechanical equilibrium. This condition has to be replaced: flow occurs specifically because the fluid has not yet achieved this mechanical equilibrium.

However, this alone does not define the ideal dynamic fluid, because additional effects can occur when a fluid flows. Thus, we have to make further assumptions that address the inclusion or exclusion of such phenomena. The **ideal dynamic fluid** is called ideal because it excludes the largest number possible of phenomena we observe in real fluids. Specifically, we require that:

(i) **no turbulences** (which are a departure from smooth flow as specified below) occur during flow,

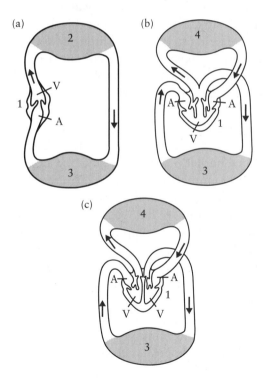

**FIGURE 12.5**

Comparison of the circulatory systems of various vertebrates. (a) Fish have a two-chambered heart (1) with a single circulation. Gills (2) and capillary beds in the rest of the body (3) are shaded. (b) Amphibians have a three-chambered heart with two circulatory systems. These are called the pulmocutaneous system and the systemic system. The systemic system is a high-pressure system. The lungs (4) are shaded. (c) Mammals have a four-chambered heart with two circulations: the systemic and the pulmonary circulations. The heart completely separates oxygen-rich blood from the lungs and oxygen-depleted blood emerging from the systemic circulation.

(ii) **no sound waves** (which require density fluctuations) develop in the flowing fluid, and

(iii) **no friction** occurs with walls, or other objects adjacent to the flowing fluid, that move at a different speed than the fluid. This requires that the interaction of the fluid particles is limited to **elastic collisions.**

What do these three assumptions imply? The first assumption rules out consideration of the actual flow of air through the trachea, which is usually turbulent. Including turbulence is mathematically challenging and in this textbook we touch the issue only briefly, later in this chapter when we introduce an empirical threshold speed above which flow becomes turbulent.

The second assumption is automatically applicable if the fluid is incompressible, since sound waves are the result of localized compressions in the fluid. However, sound propagation through a fluid is extremely important in physiology as it leads to acoustics. Thus, we will eventually drop this assumption (in Chapter 17).

Fluid flow that satisfies the first two assumptions is called **laminar flow**, and is illustrated in Fig. 12.6. The figure shows an amount of fluid entering the field of view through the green area at the left side. If we imagine the fluid divided into small fluid segments, then we can follow each segment as a function of time. Its path is called a **flow line** and can be envisaged to lie fully within an envelope we call a **flow tube**, as indicated for one flow line in the lower part of Fig. 12.6.

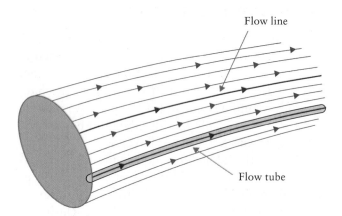

Flow line

Flow tube

**FIGURE 12.6**

Sketch of laminar flow through an arbitrarily chosen area. The path taken by each fluid segment is drawn as a flow line (highlighted in red). One of the lower flow lines in the sketch is enclosed in a flow tube (grey cylinder). Flow lines cannot cross each other during laminar flow. Laminar flow characterizes ideal dynamic fluids and Newtonian fluids.

*Laminar flow is established when (i) flow lines in the fluid never cross each other, and (ii) flow tubes never penetrate each other.*

Note that laminar flow and the ideal dynamic fluid are therefore not synonymous concepts. An ideal dynamic fluid must always flow laminar because it shares the same assumptions with the laminar flow concept. However, laminar flow can occur for fluids that violate the third assumption for the ideal dynamic fluid. For example, we will still discuss laminar flow after we include flow resistance in the second half of this chapter.

The third assumption for the ideal dynamic fluid has to be discussed a bit further as it can easily lead to misconceptions. First, it differs notably from the other two conditions in that it addresses objects beyond the fluid. This condition has to be formulated somewhat vaguely because we want to develop widely applicable laws that are not confined to particular containers. For example, we want to apply these laws to the flow of air past the wing of a bird, or to a stream of water falling from a water tap toward the kitchen sink. Deriving laws in this chapter is easier when referring to a fluid-confining container or tube; however, the existence of the container or its shape may not matter to the laws' applicability.

In the easiest case, the ideal dynamic fluid is an ideal gas. In this case, the third assumption is equivalent to the respective assumption in the kinetic gas theory we introduced in Chapter 7. Elastic collisions were studied in Chapter 6 with the results for a collision with a wall summarized in Fig. 12.7: the component of the velocity of the fluid particle parallel to the wall (∥-direction in Fig. 12.7) remains unchanged, while the velocity component perpendicular to the wall changes its sign (⊥-direction in Fig. 12.7). In the kinetic gas theory, a non-zero component parallel to the wall allows for collisions with variable angles; for a flowing ideal gas the component parallel to the wall also contains the velocity of the collective flow. Since this velocity component does not change as a result of an elastic collision, no additional effect occurs due to the particle–wall interaction that is not already covered in the discussion of the ideal gas. This means that wall interactions are frictionless and can be neglected in the discussion of flow of an ideal gas. Unfortunately, though, we saw in the previous chapter that the ideal gas is not a good example for a fluid because it is compressible.

If the ideal dynamic fluid is a liquid, neglecting inelastic collisions is problematic: in a dense liquid, the

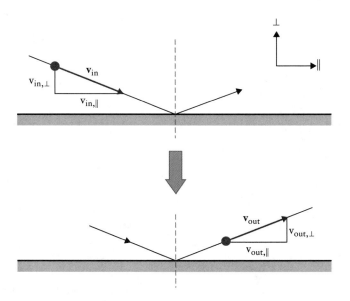

**FIGURE 12.7**

Elastic collisions of a fluid particle with a stationary wall. Its velocity component parallel to the wall (∥) remains unchanged; its velocity component perpendicular to the wall changes its sign (⊥) but not its magnitude.

fluid particles interact extensively with each other and the walls. We exclude inelastic collisions in the current section regardless, but will be forced to abandon this assumption when we introduce Newtonian fluids.

## Equation of Continuity

We now establish the laws governing flow of an ideal dynamic fluid. We start with Fig. 12.8, which shows a fluid flowing from left to right through a tube of varying cross-sectional area. The cross-sectional area of the tube changes from $A_1$ to $A_2$ with $A_1 > A_2$. From experience, we know that fluid is neither created nor lost along the tube. Thus, during any given time interval, the same mass of fluid that enters through cross-section $A_1$ (grey area in upper sketch) must leave through cross-section $A_2$ (grey area in lower sketch):

$$\frac{\Delta m_1}{\Delta t} = \frac{\Delta m_2}{\Delta t} \qquad [1]$$

Since the fluid is incompressible, the **conservation of fluid mass** is equivalent to a conservation of fluid volume. Using $\rho$ for the density of the fluid, Eq. [1] is written in the form:

$$\rho \frac{\Delta V_1}{\Delta t} = \rho \frac{\Delta V_2}{\Delta t} \qquad [2]$$

The term $\Delta m/\Delta t$ in Eq. [1] is called the **mass flow rate**, and $\Delta V/\Delta t$ in Eq. [2] is called the **volume flow rate**.

The volume of a fluid segment in Fig. 12.8 can be written as the product of the cross-sectional area of the tube and the segment's length in Eq. [2]:

$$\rho \cdot A_1 \frac{\Delta l_1}{\Delta t} = \rho \cdot A_2 \frac{\Delta l_2}{\Delta t} \qquad [3]$$

$\Delta l/\Delta t$ is now interpreted as a displacement of the fluid along the tube per time interval $\Delta t$. This is equivalent to the speed of the fluid in the tube. With $|v| = \Delta l/\Delta t$ Eq. [3] takes its final form:

$$A_1 \cdot |v_1| = A_2 \cdot |v_2| \qquad [4]$$

Because Eq. [4] applies between any two points 1 and 2 along the tube, we can write it in a generalized form:

$$A \cdot |v| = \text{const} \qquad [5]$$

This is the **equation of continuity**. Note that the reasoning that led from Eq. [2] to Eq. [5] also establishes a second useful equation for the volume flow rate:

$$\frac{\Delta V}{\Delta t} = A \cdot |v| \qquad [6]$$

which applies anywhere along the tube, including at the cross-sectional areas with index 1 and 2 in Fig. 12.8.

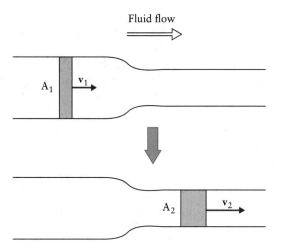

**FIGURE 12.8**

Model of a tapering tube that we use to derive the equation of continuity. Fluid flow occurs from left to right. (Top) The fluid segment is initially represented by the grey area at the left with cross-sectional area $A_1$ and fluid speed $v_1$. (Bottom) Later, the fluid segment is positioned in the grey area at the right with cross-sectional area $A_2$ and flow speed $v_2$.

*The equation of continuity is an expression of the conservation of mass or the conservation of volume of an incompressible fluid. It states that the volume flow rate is constant along a tube. The fluid flows faster when it passes through a section of the tube with a smaller cross-section.*

Let's check this law carefully. We still need to establish whether it applies to laminar flow and/or to an ideal dynamic fluid. The two differ in that the former does not include an assumption about the interactions within the fluid and with the container wall. If you read once more through the derivation of the equation of continuity, you note that the type of interaction plays no role: the mass of the fluid is conserved regardless. Thus, the equation of continuity applies to laminar flow whether the fluid is an ideal dynamic fluid or not.

---

### Concept Question 12.1

**A tube widens from a cross-sectional area $A_1$ to a cross-sectional area $A_2 = 3 \cdot A_1$. As a result the speed of an ideal dynamic fluid in the tube changes from $v_1$ to (A) $v_2 = v_1$, (B) $v_2 = v_1/3$, (C) $v_2 = 3 \cdot v_1$, (D) $v_2 = v_1/9$, (E) $v_2 = 9 \cdot v_1$.**

ANSWER: Choice (B). We use Eq. [4]:

$$\frac{v_1}{v_2} = \frac{A_2}{A_1} = \frac{3 \cdot A_1}{A_1} = 3 \qquad [7]$$

Thus, $v_1 = 3 \cdot v_2$, or $v_2 = v_1/3$.

---

### Concept Question 12.2

**We study the steady flow of water from a water tap, e.g., in your kitchen sink. The jet of water (A) broadens as it falls, (B) narrows as it falls, (C) does not change its cross-sectional shape, (D) slows before hitting the bottom of the sink. *Hint:* Neglect effects that could lead to the breakup of a continuous flow into droplet formation.**

ANSWER: (B). We ask ourselves first whether we can use the equation of continuity even though no flow-confining tube exists. This makes no difference for an ideal dynamic fluid since the third condition neglects interactions with such a wall. The mass of the fluid is conserved between the water tap and the sink, thus the volume flow rate $\Delta V/\Delta t$ out of the water tap is the same as the volume flow rate reaching the base of the sink. Water accelerates in between due to gravity. With the speed of the fluid increasing in Eq. [6] and the volume flow rate constant, the cross-section of the fluid must diminish.

---

## Speed of Blood in Capillaries

### ● EXAMPLE 12.1

The heart of a standard man (Table 3.3) pumps 5 litres of blood per minute into the aorta. (a) What is the volume flow rate in the cardiovascular system? (b) What is the speed of blood in the aorta? (c) If we assume that the blood passes through all systemic capillaries in our body in series, how fast would it have to flow through each capillary? Use data from Fig. 12.4. Would this result make sense? (d) What is the speed of blood in a capillary if we instead assume that the blood flows in parallel through the systemic capillaries in the human body?

*Solution to part (a):* The amount of blood flowing through the aorta per minute corresponds to a volume flow rate of:

$$\left(\frac{\Delta V}{\Delta t}\right)_{\text{aorta}} = \frac{5.0\,\text{L}}{60\,\text{s}} = 8.3 \times 10^{-5}\,\frac{\text{m}^3}{\text{s}} \qquad [8]$$

*Solution to part (b):* The diameter of the aorta is given in Fig. 12.4 as $d = 2.6$ cm, which leads to an outer cross-sectional area $A = \pi(d/2)^2 = 5.3$ cm$^2$ (also shown in the figure). The inner diameter defines the **lumen**, which is the open volume inside a blood vessel. To calculate the inner diameter of the blood vessel, the wall thickness has to be taken into account. The fraction of the total diameter attributed to the blood vessel wall lies between 15% and 20%; thus, a typical inner diameter of the aorta is $d_{\text{aorta}} = 2.2$ cm. This leads to the cross-sectional area of the lumen:

$$A_{\text{aorta}} = \pi\left(\frac{d_{\text{aorta}}}{2}\right)^2 = \pi\left(\frac{2.2\,\text{cm}}{2}\right)^2$$
$$= 3.8 \times 10^{-4}\,\text{m}^2 \qquad [9]$$

The speed of the blood in the aorta is obtained from its inner cross-sectional area and the volume passing per second. Using Eq. [6], we obtain:

$$|\mathbf{v}_{\text{aorta}}| = \frac{\left(\dfrac{\Delta V_{\text{aorta}}}{\Delta t}\right)}{A_{\text{aorta}}}$$

$$= \frac{8.3 \times 10^{-5}\,\dfrac{\text{m}^3}{\text{s}}}{3.8 \times 10^{-4}\,\text{m}^2} = 0.22\,\frac{\text{m}}{\text{s}} \qquad [10]$$

This is a frequently used result: blood flows through the aorta at an *average speed* of about 20 cm/s.

*Solution to part (c):* Let's assume that blood passes through each single systemic capillary at the rate found in part (a). For the outer diameter of a capillary we use 9 $\mu$m from Fig. 12.4. This value leads to an inner diameter of $d_{\text{capillary}} = 7\ \mu$m (capillary wall thickness is about 1 $\mu$m). The cross-sectional area of the capillary is:

$$A_{\text{capillary}} = \pi \left( \frac{d_{\text{capillary}}}{2} \right)^2 = \pi \left( \frac{7 \times 10^{-6}\,\text{m}}{2} \right)^2$$
$$= 3.8 \times 10^{-11}\,\text{m}^2 \qquad [11]$$

We use the equation of continuity to derive the speed for blood in the capillary, $|v_{\text{capillary}}|$:

$$|\mathbf{v}_{\text{capillary}}| = \frac{A_{\text{aorta}}\,|\mathbf{v}_{\text{aorta}}|}{A_{\text{capillary}}}$$
$$= \frac{8.3 \times 10^{-5}\,\dfrac{\text{m}^3}{\text{s}}}{3.8 \times 10^{-11}\,\text{m}^2} = 2200\,\frac{\text{km}}{\text{s}} \qquad [12]$$

Even if the capillaries could sustain blood rushing through at such speed, it would no longer be possible to exchange oxygen and nutrients with the surrounding tissue; i.e., the physiological purpose of the cardiovascular system would be lost.

*Solution to part (d):* A slow flow of blood in the systemic capillaries is achieved by arranging them parallel to each other with a combined cross-section that is larger than the cross-section of the aorta. Fig. 12.4 suggests that this is the case with 3500 cm$^2$ for the capillaries, compared to 5.3 cm$^2$ for the aorta. The equation of continuity allows us to determine the actual speed of blood in the capillaries once we have corrected the cross-sectional areas from Fig. 12.4 to represent the lumen. A correction factor $k$ is defined as the ratio of the lumen cross-sectional area to the outer cross-sectional area and is quantified with the inner and outer diameter for a typical capillary:

$$k = \frac{A_{\text{lumen}}}{A_{\text{outer}}} = \frac{(7\,\mu\text{m})^2}{(9\,\mu\text{m})^2} = 0.6 \qquad [13]$$

The two diameters are squared because the area is proportional to the square of the radius. With this factor we obtain for the cross-sectional area of the lumen of the capillaries $A_{\text{capillary}} = 0.6 \cdot 3500\,\text{cm}^2 = 2100\,\text{cm}^2$. Thus:

$$|\mathbf{v}_{\text{capillary}}| = \frac{\left( \dfrac{\Delta V}{\Delta t} \right)_{\text{aorta}}}{A_{\text{capillary}}}$$
$$= \frac{8.3 \times 10^{-5}\,\dfrac{\text{m}^3}{\text{s}}}{0.21\,\text{m}^2} = 4 \times 10^{-4}\,\frac{\text{m}}{\text{s}} \qquad [14]$$

Again, this is a frequently used value: blood flows very slowly through the capillaries, at less than 1 mm/s.

## Bernoulli's Law

The changes we observed in the speed of a flowing fluid due to changes in the cross-section of the tube also lead to changes in the pressure in the fluid. This can be illustrated experimentally with an instrument called a **Venturi meter**, which is shown in Fig. 12.9. The instrument consists of a tube with a constriction zone at its centre. A W-shaped tube connects at the left and right to the wide sections of the main tube; in the middle it is open to the constriction zone. The W-shaped tube is partially filled with a liquid to indicate the pressure in the section of the horizontal tube above each column. Initially, while the fluid in the main horizontal tube is at rest, the liquid in the W-shaped tube rises to the same level in all three columns, indicating that the pressure is the same. When the fluid flows through the main tube, a pressure difference is observed: the liquid in the middle column rises highest, indicating that the pressure in the constriction zone is lower than in the wider sections. Thus, the speed of the fluid, which is higher in the constricted section due to the equation of continuity, is inversely related to the pressure.

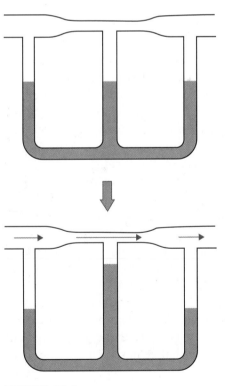

**FIGURE 12.9**

The Venturi meter is an instrument to measure the speed of a fluid in a horizontal tube. (Top) It indicates the same pressure in every section of the tube while the fluid is at rest. (Bottom) When the fluid flows as indicated by the arrows in the tube, pressure variations become evident: the pressure is higher where the speed of the fluid is slower.

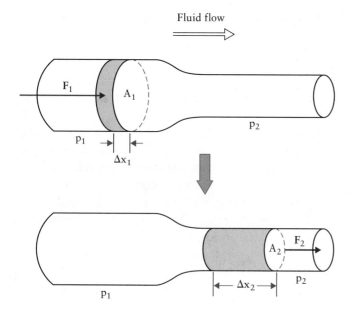

**FIGURE 12.10**

A sketch defining the parameters needed to derive Bernoulli's law. We study a fluid segment (grey) that initially occupies the volume $A_1 \cdot \Delta x_1$ (top) and later the volume $A_2 \cdot \Delta x_2$ (bottom). Fluid flow in the sketch occurs from left to right through a tapering tube. The fluid pressure varies from $p_1$ to $p_2$ at the constriction. The change in the speed of the fluid causes a change in the kinetic energy that is accounted for by a work term associated with the transfer of fluid into the constriction.

Daniel Bernoulli quantified this observation starting from Fig. 12.10. Shown is a horizontal tube that tapers from cross-section $A_1$ to $A_2$. We assign a pressure $p_1$ to the wider section of the tube and $p_2$ to the narrower section. With these definitions, the grey fluid segment is studied. We want to determine its kinetic energy at an initial and a final instant and then relate the change in the kinetic energy to the work needed to move it into the constricted section. We specifically choose the initial time (index 1) when the fluid segment occupies the grey volume shown in the top part of Fig. 12.10. At that instant the volume of the fluid segment is $\Delta V = A_1 \cdot \Delta x_1$. The final instant is shown in the bottom part of Fig. 12.10 (index 2). Now its volume is $\Delta V = A_2 \cdot \Delta x_2$.

The cross-sectional area and the speed of the fluid are related by the equation of continuity. A force $\mathbf{F}_1$ has to be applied to accelerate the fluid segment through the tube. The change in the kinetic energy of the fluid segment is:

$$\Delta E_{kin} = \frac{1}{2}\Delta m \cdot v_2^2 - \frac{1}{2}\Delta m \cdot v_1^2 \qquad [15]$$

in which $\Delta m$ is the mass of the fluid segment. With $\rho$ the density of the fluid, we rewrite the mass as $\Delta m = \rho \cdot \Delta V$:

$$\Delta E_{kin} = \frac{1}{2}\rho \left(v_2^2 - v_1^2\right)\Delta V \qquad [16]$$

Since the tube becomes narrower, the speed must increase and thus the kinetic energy of the fluid segment increases. To achieve this increase in kinetic energy, work must be done on the fluid segment. This work is required to transfer the fluid segment from its initial to its final position. We can split the work in two contributions: removing the fluid segment in the part of the tube with pressure $p_1$, and adding the fluid segment to the part of the tube with pressure $p_2$. Quantitatively, this means that the volume of the segment is changed from $\Delta V$ to 0 in the top part of Fig. 12.10, and, concurrently, its volume is changed from 0 to $\Delta V$ in the bottom part. The work is:

$$W = -p_2 \cdot \Delta V - p_1(-\Delta V)$$
$$= -(p_2 - p_1)\,\Delta V \qquad [17]$$

The conservation of energy for the fluid segment as a closed system requires that $\Delta U = W$, because no heat exchange takes place. The only form of energy that changes in Fig. 12.10 is the kinetic energy and, thus, $\Delta U = \Delta E_{kin}$:

$$-(p_2 - p_1)\,\Delta V = \frac{1}{2}\rho(v_2^2 - v_1^2)\,\Delta V \qquad [18]$$

We separate all the terms related to positions 1 and 2 in the equation and divide by $\Delta V$:

$$p_1 + \frac{1}{2}\rho \cdot v_1^2 = p_2 + \frac{1}{2}\rho \cdot v_2^2 \qquad [19]$$

Eq. [19] applies at any position along the tube:

$$p + \frac{1}{2}\rho \cdot v^2 = \text{const} \qquad [20]$$

This is **Bernoulli's law.**

*Bernoulli's law is an expression of the conservation of energy for a closed system. It states that an increase in the speed of an ideal dynamic fluid in a tube is accompanied by a drop in its pressure.*

Bernoulli's law indeed applies only to the ideal dynamic fluid. The third condition limiting the interactions of the fluid particles with the container wall to elastic collisions is necessary to apply the conservation of energy in the form used in Eq. [18]. When we revise this condition in the next section, we must revisit the calculation of the pressure in the flowing fluid.

Bernoulli's law is sometimes reported in the physics literature with an additional term that accommodates possible changes in the height of the tube. We do not introduce that term because Example 11.2 provides an alternative approach to include height differences via Pascal's law.

on the leaf and is the origin of the motion you observe. Note that we applied Bernoulli's law in this concept question to an ideal dynamic fluid outside a tube.

## Concept Question 12.3

**Can Bernoulli's law explain the quaking of the leaves of the aspen tree during summer or early fall? In a gentle breeze, the leaves move up and down, or left and right, depending on the direction of the wind.**

ANSWER: Yes. Fig. 12.11 shows aspen leaves. Notice that they are slightly arched. Wind blowing through the tree splits above and below the leaves. It has to travel different path lengths above and below the leaf. This causes different wind speeds. From Bernoulli's law we find that the difference in the speed of the wind causes a difference in the pressure above and below the leaf. This causes a net force

## Concept Question 12.4

**(a) In a person with advanced arteriosclerosis (artery constriction due to accumulated plaque on the inner walls, as shown in Fig. 12.12), Bernoulli's effect produces a symptom called vascular flutter. To maintain a constant volume flow rate in this situation, the blood must travel faster than normal through the constriction. At a sufficiently high blood speed, the artery collapses and immediately reopens, leading to a repeated temporary interruption of the blood flow that can be heard with a stethoscope. Why does vascular flutter occur? (b) An aneurysm is a weakened spot of an artery where the artery walls balloon outward; Fig. 12.13 shows an aneurysm of the aorta. Blood flows more slowly through this region, resulting in an increase in pressure at the aneurysm relative to the pressure in adjacent sections of the artery. This condition is dangerous because the increased pressure can cause the artery to rupture (see Chapter 16 for a detailed discussion of aneurysms). What slows blood flow in an aneurysm?**

**FIGURE 12.11**

The leaves of the aspen tree are slightly curved. A mild breeze blowing over the leaf causes a difference in wind speed above and below the leaf. This causes a variation in air pressure across the leaf, which causes in turn a force. This force sets the leaf in vibrating motion.

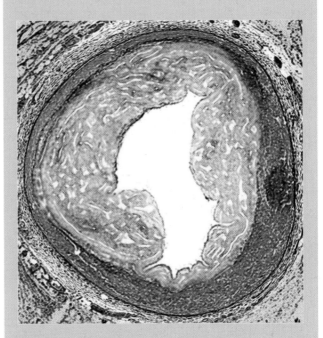

**FIGURE 12.12**

Advanced arteriosclerosis is an artery constriction due to accumulated plaque on the inner vessel walls. Shown is a coronary artery cross-section with atherosclerotic plaque (yellow) in the lumen.

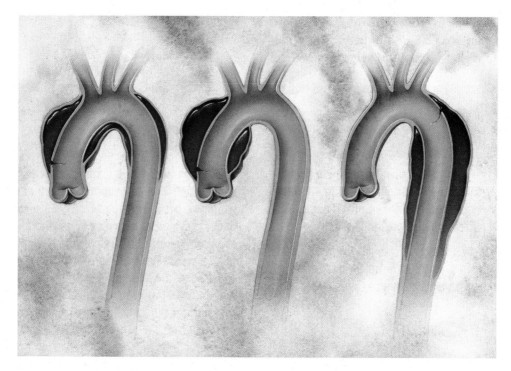

**FIGURE 12.13**

An artist's rendering of an aneurysm of the aorta. The inner layer of the aorta wall (pink) has ruptured. Blood (dark red) has pooled in the fissure of the wall, producing the visible bulge. Surgical repair of the aorta is required.

## Concept Question 12.4 (*continued*)

ANSWER TO PART (a): The artery collapses since the high speed of the blood inside the vessel lowers the pressure in the bloodstream relative to the pressure in the stationary extracellular fluid. This is due to Bernoulli's law: a high value for the speed, *v*, leads to a low value of the pressure, *p*. Once the pressure difference is large enough to close the artery, the blood flow stops momentarily. When this happens the blood upstream from the clogged vessel causes a pressure increase that is sufficient to reopen the artery. The closing and reopening of the artery then continues in a cyclic fashion.

ANSWER TO PART (b): The cross-sectional area of a blood vessel and the speed of blood in the vessel are related by the equation of continuity. Thus, the speed of blood flow decreases in a blood vessel when its cross-section increases in an aneurysm.

### ● EXAMPLE 12.2

Blood flows smoothly through the aorta as its cross-section tapers to 75% of its initial value, similar to the case illustrated in Fig. 12.10. What is the pressure difference $\Delta p$ between the wide and the narrow sections? *Hint:* Data we used before and require for this calculation are the volume flow rate $\Delta V/\Delta t = 83$ cm$^3$/s, the density of blood $\rho = 1.06$ g/cm$^3$, and the lumen cross-section of the aorta $A_{\text{aorta}} = 3.8$ cm$^2$ (see Eq. [9]).

*Solution:* We start with Bernoulli's law. Let index 1 in Eq. [19] refer to the wide section and index 2 to the narrow section of the aorta. From the equation of continuity we know that the flow is faster in the narrow section; i.e., $v_2 > v_1$. Inserting this inequality in Eq. [19] leads to $p_1 > p_2$. Thus, we predict that the pressure drops from section 1 to section 2. This must be taken into account when writing the pressure difference in the form $\Delta p = p_1 - p_2$. In this form, $\Delta p > 0$. Note that we could have chosen to define $\Delta p$ as $p_2 - p_1$, in which case $\Delta p$ would be a negative value.

Eq. [6] allows us to quantify the two speeds, $v_1$ and $v_2$, since we know how the two cross-sectional areas are related: $A_2 = 0.75 \cdot A_1$:

$$v_1 = \frac{\Delta V/\Delta t}{A_1} \qquad [21]$$

and

$$v_2 = \frac{\Delta V/\Delta t}{A_2} = \frac{4 \cdot \Delta V/\Delta t}{3 \cdot A_1} \qquad [22]$$

Substituting Eqs. [21] and [22] into Eq. [19], we find:

$$\Delta p = \frac{1}{2}\rho\left(\frac{16\,(\Delta V/\Delta t)^2}{9\cdot A_1^2} - \frac{(\Delta V/\Delta t)^2}{A_1^2}\right) \qquad [23]$$

which leads to:

$$\Delta p = \frac{7\cdot\rho(\Delta V/\Delta t)^2}{18\cdot A_1^2} \qquad [24]$$

The given values are substituted into Eq. [24]:

$$\Delta p = \frac{7\cdot\left(1060\,\dfrac{\text{kg}}{\text{m}^3}\right)\left(8.3\times10^{-5}\,\dfrac{\text{m}^3}{\text{s}}\right)^2}{18\cdot(3.8\times10^{-4}\,\text{m}^2)^2}$$
$$= 20\,\text{Pa} \qquad [25]$$

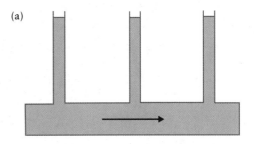

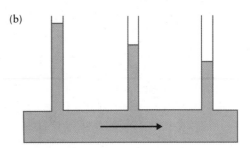

**FIGURE 12.14**

Comparison of (a) an ideal dynamic fluid and (b) a Newtonian fluid flowing through a horizontal tube. Flow resistance leads to a pressure drop along the tube, as indicated by the lower column height of the fluid above the tube at the right in part (b).

# Flow of a Newtonian Fluid

Up to this point, fluid flow was discussed for the ideal dynamic fluid. We established two laws: the equation of continuity and Bernoulli's law. We now test how closely predictions based on these laws correlate with experimental observations. The experiment we use is illustrated in Fig. 12.14: a liquid flows through a horizontal tube from left to right (direction of arrow). Three smaller, vertical columns are placed at different positions along the tube. The height to which the liquid rises in each of these columns depends on the pressure in the flowing liquid below. If that liquid can be modelled as an ideal dynamic fluid, all three columns have to be equally high, as shown in Fig. 12.14(a). This prediction results from the laws of the previous section: the equation of continuity states that the fluid speed does not change for a constant cross-section of the tube, then Bernoulli's law states that the pressure in the fluid does not change either.

The actual experimental result for a real liquid is shown in Fig. 12.14(b). The farther the liquid progresses along the tube, the shorter the vertical columns. Thus, the experimental result differs fundamentally from the prediction in Fig. 12.14(a): the liquid speed and/or the pressure along the tube must change; i.e., the equation of continuity and/or Bernoulli's law must be modified. The equation of continuity applies as long as fluid flow is laminar: the fluid speed cannot change because fluid would have to accumulate in or vanish from the tube. Therefore, an approach beyond Bernoulli's law is needed to quantify the fluid pressure.

# Newtonian Fluid Model

The **Newtonian fluid model** is developed to correctly describe the observation in Fig. 12.14(b). It is derived from the ideal dynamic fluid model by removing the assumption that was identified as too restrictive: a dense fluid such as a liquid cannot travel past a solid wall without extensive interactions. We noted these interactions already for the ideal stationary fluid in the last chapter, when we attributed the capillarity effect to a significant interface energy term.

How do we formulate a condition to replace the elastic collision restriction we used in the previous section? In the natural sciences we usually proceed by conducting experiments. In this particular case, the macroscopic observation of viscosity provides a promising approach even though it is not primarily a phenomenon describing the interaction between a fluid and a container wall.

# Viscosity

**Viscosity** is an interaction between neighbouring layers of a moving fluid in a direction perpendicular to the flow lines. This is illustrated in Fig. 12.15, in which two parallel fluid layers of area $A$ are highlighted. Let's assume that the lower layer is at rest. This could be, for example, due to close proximity to the resting walls of the tube. The upper layer, a distance $\Delta y$ away from the lower layer, moves with

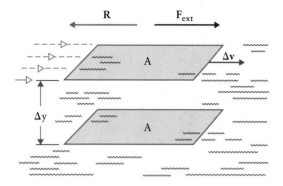

**FIGURE 12.15**

Experimental setup to measure viscosity coefficients. Two parallel plates are immersed in a fluid at a distance $\Delta y$ from each other. The lower plate is held at rest and the upper plate is pushed by an external force $\mathbf{F}_{ext}$. The resistance force of the fluid $\mathbf{R}$ balances the external force, leading to a constant velocity $\Delta\mathbf{v}$ of the plate toward the right.

velocity $\Delta\mathbf{v}$ toward the right. The moving layer encounters a resistance force $\mathbf{R}$ that tries to slow it down. To maintain a constant velocity, Newton's first law requires the presence of a second force, $\mathbf{F}_{ext}$, with which the upper layer of fluid is pushed forward. Thus, if a fluid encounters flow resistance, an external force must be applied to push the fluid through the tube. The magnitude of this external force is found empirically by submerging two parallel test plates into a resting fluid and moving one plate relative to the other, as Fig. 12.15 suggests. From such experiments the force $\mathbf{F}_{ext}$ is found to be proportional to (i) the area $A$ of the fluid layers that face each other, and (ii) the difference in speed of these layers, $|\Delta\mathbf{v}|$. The force is also inversely proportional to (iii) the distance $\Delta y$ between the two layers:

$$F_{ext} = \eta \cdot A \frac{|\Delta\mathbf{v}|}{\Delta y} \qquad [26]$$

Since the required external force further varies from fluid to fluid, with smaller forces typically needed in gases and larger forces in liquids, a materials constant is introduced that is called the **viscosity coefficient** $\eta$. Based on Eq. [26], the unit of $\eta$ is $N \cdot s/m^2$. Table 12.1 lists viscosity coefficients for several fluids.

Note that the third column in Table 12.1 gives the temperature at which the reported values apply, implying that these values change with temperature. Viscosity is one of the transport phenomena like diffusion and heat conduction, which we discussed in Chapter 10. A microscopic model is needed in addition to the phenomenological law of Eq. [26] to describe the temperature dependence of the viscosity coefficient. In the case of viscosity two different microscopic models apply, one for gases and one for liquids.

- The **viscosity coefficients of gases** in Table 12.1 increase with temperature. This can be explained with a model that combines a velocity gradient $\Delta\mathbf{v}/\Delta y$ with the ideal gas model. In this model, we choose the distance between the neighbouring layers in Fig. 12.15 to be at the average distance between consecutive collisions of gas molecules. After encountering a collision in one layer the gas particle has its next collision in the neighbouring layer. During each collision the particle equilibrates its momentum with the average momentum of its environment, thus accelerating other particles in a slower layer and slowing them in a faster layer. Gases become more viscous at higher temperature because the gas molecules become faster and penetrate neighbouring layers more rapidly. This interlocks neighbouring sections of the gas more effectively.

- The **viscosity coefficients of liquids** decrease with temperature in Table 12.1. The temperature dependence indicates that an energy barrier has to be overcome (compare with Arrhenius's diffusion model in Chapter 10). For the motion of two liquid layers the origin of this barrier is qualitatively

**TABLE 12.1**

**Viscosity coefficients of various fluids**

| Fluid | Viscosity coefficient $\eta$ (N · s/m²) | Temperature (°C) |
|---|---|---|
| *1. Gases* | | |
| $N_2$ | $1.78 \times 10^{-5}$ | 25 |
| $O_2$ | $2.08 \times 10^{-5}$ | 25 |
| Air | $1.71 \times 10^{-5}$ | 0 |
| $H_2$ | $9.0 \times 10^{-6}$ | 25 |
| $H_2$ | $8.4 \times 10^{-6}$ | 0 |
| $H_2O$ | $9.8 \times 10^{-6}$ | 25 |
| *2. Liquids* | | |
| $H_2O$ | $1.79 \times 10^{-3}$ | 0 |
| $H_2O$ | $1.01 \times 10^{-3}$ | 20 |
| $H_2O$ | $2.8 \times 10^{-4}$ | 100 |
| (Whole) blood | $2.3 - 2.7 \times 10^{-3}$ | 37 |
| Blood serum | $1.6 - 2.2 \times 10^{-3}$ | 20 |
| Ethanol | $1.19 \times 10^{-3}$ | 20 |
| Glycerin | 1.5 | 20 |

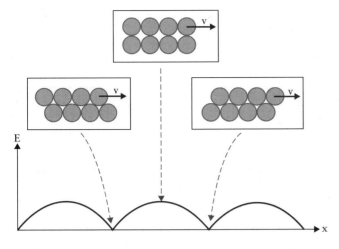

**FIGURE 12.16**

Microscopic model for viscous flow of a liquid. The three boxes in the upper part of the sketch illustrate how tightly packed spheres representing the molecules in the liquid move past each other. The corresponding potential energy profile of the motion is given below.

sketched in Fig. 12.16. In the sequence of three insets from left to right, we see that a liquid's molecules are tightly packed. Each row of molecules must therefore squeeze past adjacent layers if it is to move faster than that layer. To do so energy is required, as illustrated in the main plot, which shows the potential energy of the row of molecules as a function of its position relative to the layer beneath.

Eq. [26] establishes that viscosity is a dynamic effect that requires a velocity gradient perpendicular to the direction of the flow lines in the fluid, $\Delta v/\Delta y$. This means in turn that viscosity does not play a role in stationary fluids ($\mathbf{v} = 0$) or in ideal dynamic fluids ($\Delta v/\Delta y = 0$), even though the viscosity coefficient for all physiologically relevant fluids is $\eta > 0$. This means, further, that there is no fluid, not even the ideal gas, that doesn't behave as a Newtonian fluid once a velocity gradient is introduced.

*In a Newtonian fluid, the inelastic interaction with the fluid-confining walls causes velocity gradients. Viscosity replaces the assumption of elastic collisions required between the ideal dynamic fluid and its confining walls. In Newtonian fluids the flow is laminar and viscous.*

**● EXAMPLE 12.3**

A 1.0-mm-thick coating of glycerine is placed between two microscope slides of width 2 cm and length 7 cm each. Find the force required to move the microscope slides at a constant speed of 10 cm/s relative to each other. The viscosity coefficient of glycerine is found in Table 12.1.

*Solution:* This problem is solved with Eq. [26]. Each of the terms on the right-hand side of the equation is given in the example text. The area is:

$$A = 0.02 \text{ m} \cdot 0.07 \text{ m} = 1.4 \times 10^{-3} \text{ m}^2 \quad [27]$$

Note that $A$ isn't twice this value for the two faces of a slide because only the cross-sectional area enters Eq. [26]. The difference in speed is $\Delta v = 0.1$ m/s and the coating thickness is the distance $\Delta y = 1.0 \times 10^{-3}$ m. Using $\eta = 1.5$ N · s/m$^2$, we find:

$$F = \frac{\left(1.5 \frac{\text{N} \cdot \text{s}}{\text{m}^2}\right)(1.4 \times 10^{-3} \text{m}^2)\left(0.1 \frac{\text{m}}{\text{s}}\right)}{1.0 \times 10^{-3} \text{m}}$$
$$= 0.21 \text{ N} \quad [28]$$

This is a notable force, given the rather wide 1-mm separation between the slides. Imagine you reduce their separation to 1 $\mu$m. Now a force of $F = 210$ N is required; i.e., a mass of more than 20 kg has to be suspended from one of the slides to achieve the stated motion. This phenomenon was used in the development of adhesive tape.

## Fluid Velocity Profile in a Cylindrical Vessel

In a Newtonian fluid the inelastic interaction of fluid molecules with a stationary wall causes velocity gradients perpendicular to the flow lines. This leads to a non-uniform velocity profile across the fluid in the direction perpendicular to the stationary wall. The actual velocity profile depends on the shape of the stationary wall; we confine the discussion in this section to cylindrical tubes, which are physiologically important because they include blood vessels.

Eq. [26] is used to quantify the inclusion of inelastic collisions of the fluid particles with the stationary wall. Eq. [26] can be used only when the fluid flow has reached a steady state; thus, steady state is an additional assumption for quantitative predictions for the Newtonian fluid. This assumption is reasonable for blood flow in the cardiovascular system. A more general approach would require us to replace Eq. [26] with a formula that includes transient fluid accelerations. Recall that we excluded transient behaviour in transport phenomena before, e.g., when using Fick's law for diffusion.

In steady-state flow, two forces act on the fluid in the tube. In the direction of the motion of the fluid there is a force due to a pressure difference along the tube. This force pushes the fluid through the tube. The viscosity of the fluid causes a resistance force acting in the direction opposite to the direction of motion of the fluid. This force tries to slow the moving fluid. The mechanical equilibrium between these two forces varies with the position in the tube: near the stationary wall viscosity dominates and the fluid flows slowly (with the speed vanishing directly at the wall), whereas toward the centre of the tube the force pushing the fluid dominates and the fluid moves comparably fast. The **velocity profile** is written quantitatively in the form:

$$v = \frac{r_{tube}^2 - r^2}{4 \cdot \eta} \cdot \frac{\Delta p}{l} \qquad [29]$$

in which $r_{tube}$ is the radius of the tube and $\Delta p$ is the pressure difference along a segment of the tube of length $l$. $\eta$ is the viscosity coefficient of the fluid. The term $\Delta p/l$ is a constant pressure gradient along the tube. Eq. [29] provides a parabolic velocity distribution, as shown in Fig. 12.17. This velocity profile can be demonstrated with a slow-flowing fluid such as honey. If you open a jar of honey at room temperature

and turn it upside down, the honey travels fastest at the centre of the jar, while honey near the glass surface won't flow out.

### Concept Question 12.5

**In hospitals and in the food industry workers are required to wash their hands frequently and extensively. Why are elaborate hand-washing procedures required in these environments?**

ANSWER: Eq. [29] shows that fluid flow near a stationary surface vanishes ($v \rightarrow 0$ for $r \rightarrow r_{tube}$). Thus, allowing water to flow past your hands does not wash away pathogens and toxins that are attached to the skin, where the water flows slowly if at all. Only extensive rubbing with soap may loosen these. This always applies; however, hospitals are more directly concerned because of the larger number of pathogens and toxins their employees come in contact with.

## Poiseuille's Law

Jean Leonard Poiseuille used Eq. [29] to determine the volume flow rate through a cylindrical tube. We motivate his result with a simplified argument. Eq. [29] shows that an average velocity of the fluid is proportional to the square of the radius of the tube, $r_{tube}^2$, and the pressure gradient along the tube, $\Delta p/l$. It is also inversely proportional to the viscosity coefficient of the fluid, $\eta$. We can substitute this average velocity in the equation of continuity, which states that the volume flow rate $\Delta V/\Delta t$ is equal to the (average) speed of the fluid and the cross-sectional area of the tube, $A$, with $A \propto r_{tube}^2$. Thus, the volume flow rate must be proportional to the pressure gradient and inversely proportional to the viscosity coefficient. It also is proportional to the fourth power of the radius of the tube, $r_{tube}^4$:

$$\frac{\Delta V}{\Delta t} = \frac{\pi}{8 \cdot \eta} r_{tube}^4 \frac{\Delta p}{l} \qquad [30]$$

This is **Poiseuille's law,** with the proportionality factor $\pi/8$ that applies specifically to a cylindrical tube.

*Poiseuille's law states that the volume flow rate of a Newtonian fluid through a cylindrical tube is proportional to the fourth power of the radius of the tube.*

Thus, a narrower tube reduces the flow severely; e.g., when the diameter of a tube is reduced by a factor of 2, the flow through the tube is diminished by a factor of 16!

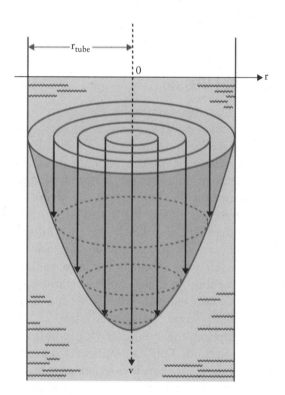

**FIGURE 12.17**

The steady-state velocity profile of a Newtonian fluid flowing through a cylindrical tube. The highest speed is reached at the centre of the tube (longest red arrows), while the fluid layer directly in contact with the wall does not move. Note that the figure shows a physical sketch of the system, which includes the walls of the tube, and a diagram with the velocity axis pointing downward and the position axis pointing to the right.

Eq. [30] can be generalized for arbitrarily shaped containers in the form of **Ohm's law:**

$$\Delta p = R \, \frac{\Delta V}{\Delta t} \qquad [31]$$

where $R$ is the **flow resistance** with unit $Pa \cdot s/m^3$.

*Ohm's law states that the volume flow rate of a Newtonian fluid is proportional to the pressure difference along the tube, and that the proportionality constant is the flow resistance.*

This relates to the everyday use of the word resistance since if the resistance is high a large pressure difference leads to only a small volume flow rate. In our discussion of the physics of the nervous system in Chapter 14 we will compare Eq. [31] to one of the laws of electricity, which is also called Ohm's law. We will see then that both laws are conceptually the same, except that we study viscous flow of fluids in the current chapter and then the flow of charges in a conductor.

For a cylindrical tube, the flow resistance is defined by Eq. [30]. It is directly proportional to the viscosity coefficient $\eta$ of the fluid:

$$R = \frac{8 \cdot l}{\pi \cdot r_{\text{tube}}^4} \, \eta \qquad [32]$$

It is important to note that Poiseuille's law cannot be extrapolated to the case $\eta = 0$. In particular, Eqs. [29] and [30] do not predict an infinite velocity or an infinite volume flow rate in this case. This interpretation would be inconsistent with many other laws of physics. Why is that so? Essentially, the answer is that $\eta > 0$ is an assumption in the derivation of Eq. [29]: we used mechanical equilibrium between a force pushing the fluid forward and a force holding it back. If $\eta = 0$, this equilibrium requires that the pressure gradient along the tube is also zero. Thus, substituting the conditions for an ideal dynamic fluid into Eqs. [29] and [30] leads to a division of zero by zero, which is mathematically undefined.

## Concept Question 12.6

A Newtonian fluid is forced through a tube to obtain a certain volume flow rate (experiment 1). If the same fluid is then forced through a tube of same cross-sectional area with double the length (experiment 2), how has the pressure difference $\Delta p_2$ along the tube changed from the previous value $\Delta p_1$ if we observe the same volume flow rate? (A) $\Delta p_2 = \Delta p_1$, (B) $\Delta p_2 = 2 \cdot \Delta p_1$, (C) $\Delta p_2 = 4 \cdot \Delta p_1$, (D) $\Delta p_2 = 8 \cdot \Delta p_1$, (E) $\Delta p_2 = 16 \cdot \Delta p_1$.

**ANSWER: Choice (B).** We use Poiseuille's law twice to write the ratio for the volume flow rates in both experiments (note that the radius of the tube is the same in both cases):

$$\frac{\left(\dfrac{\Delta V}{\Delta t}\right)_1}{\left(\dfrac{\Delta V}{\Delta t}\right)_2} = \frac{\dfrac{\pi}{8 \cdot \eta} \dfrac{r_{\text{tube}}^4}{l_1} \Delta p_1}{\dfrac{\pi}{8 \cdot \eta} \dfrac{r_{\text{tube}}^4}{l_2} \Delta p_2} = \frac{\Delta p_1 \cdot l_2}{\Delta p_2 \cdot l_1} \qquad [33]$$

Now we substitute $(\Delta V/\Delta t)_1 = (\Delta V/\Delta t)_2$ and $l_2 = 2 \cdot l_1$ in Eq. [33]:

$$1 = \frac{\Delta p_1 \cdot 2l_1}{\Delta p_2 \cdot l_1} = \frac{2 \cdot \Delta p_1}{\Delta p_2} \qquad [34]$$

which yields $\Delta p_2 = 2 \cdot \Delta p_1$.

## ● EXAMPLE 12.4

What is the pressure gradient (the drop of pressure per length unit) in the aorta? Assume that blood flows as a Newtonian fluid. The viscosity coefficient of blood is taken from Table 12.1 as $\eta_{\text{blood}} = 2.5 \times 10^{-3} \, N \cdot s/m^2$. Note this example differs from Example 12.2 because no change in the aortic cross-section is assumed.

*Solution:* The volume flow rate in the aorta is $\Delta V/\Delta t = 8.3 \times 10^{-5} \, m^3/s$ (see Example 12.1). The aorta is cylinder-shaped with an inner diameter of 2.2 cm. We apply Poiseuille's law to obtain the pressure gradient $\Delta p/l$:

$$\frac{\Delta p}{l} = \frac{\Delta V}{\Delta t} \cdot \frac{8\eta}{\pi} \cdot \frac{1}{r_{\text{tube}}^4} \qquad [35]$$

This yields:

$$\frac{\Delta p}{l} = \frac{8 \cdot \left(8.3 \times 10^{-5} \, \dfrac{m^3}{s}\right) \left(2.5 \times 10^{-3} \, \dfrac{N \cdot s}{m^2}\right)}{\pi \, (1.1 \times 10^{-2} \, m)^4}$$

$$= 36 \, \frac{Pa}{m} \qquad [36]$$

## Newtonian Fluid Flow with Variable Tube Size

Fig. 12.14(b) illustrates why the equation of continuity must apply to Newtonian fluids: with or without flow resistance, no place exists for either excess fluid to collect or fluid to disappear along the tube. Thus, Eqs. [1] to [6] apply to Newtonian fluids. Fig. 12.18 shows which role Bernoulli's law plays in Newtonian fluids. Part (a) of the figure shows the laminar flow

(a)

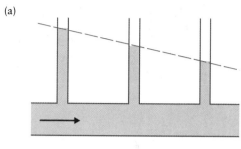

(b)

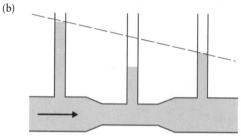

**FIGURE 12.18**

Role of Bernoulli's law for Newtonian fluids. (a) Laminar flow through a tube of fixed diameter. (b) The tube diameter varies. Bernoulli's law predicts the pressure relative to the value at the same location if the tube diameter had not changed (dashed line).

through a tube of fixed diameter. A constant pressure gradient applies; the volume flow rate is governed by Poiseuille's law. Fig. 12.18(b) highlights the changes that occur if the tube diameter varies: Bernoulli's law allows us to determine, at any given point along the tube, the pressure relative to the value at the same location if the tube diameter had not changed (dashed line). Thus, Poiseuille's law governs the actual flow through the tube while Bernoulli's law allows us to correct the pressure locally due to tube diameter variations.

Why is that so? The physics we discussed when deriving Bernoulli's law was correct. We neglected only the wall interaction, which we later found to be substantial enough that it cannot be neglected in practical cases. In a practical way, we can argue that the pressure gradient in a blood vessel (Eq. [36]) is small enough that its effect for short distances can be neglected. Thus, if a blood vessel changes its diameter along a distance of a few centimetres or millimetres, e.g., at a vasoconstriction, the pressure variation predicted by Bernoulli's law is still the dominant effect we will observe.

## Kirchhoff's Laws

Kirchhoff's laws describe how flow resistances have to be combined in cases in which a Newtonian fluid flows through tubes in series or parallel, e.g., when blood passes through the various sections of the cardiovascular system. Two laws are to be formulated,

one for **vessels in series** (e.g., the aorta and an artery leading to the liver) and one for **parallel vessels** (e.g., a bed of capillaries between an arteriole and a venule in the liver).

Robert Gustav Kirchhoff derived these laws in 1845, originally not for fluids but for flowing electric charges. In the physics literature, therefore, you find them primarily applied in electricity. However, in physiology they are more important in fluid flow.

## BLOOD VESSELS IN SERIES

Let's assume that a given amount of blood passes a vessel 1 with a given flow resistance $R_1$ and then passes a vessel 2 with a flow resistance $R_2$. We assume further that the blood vessel does not branch between vessel 1 and vessel 2.

The volume flow rate of each of the two vessels obeys Ohm's law as given in Eq. [31]. In other words, the respective drop in blood pressure along the vessel is equal to the product of the flow resistance in the vessel and the volume flow rate of blood through the vessel:

$$\Delta p_1 = R_1 \frac{\Delta V}{\Delta t}$$
$$\Delta p_2 = R_2 \frac{\Delta V}{\Delta t} \qquad [37]$$

Note that the volume flow rate is the same in both vessels, because the volume of blood is conserved for an incompressible fluid and does not change because no branching points exist between the two vessels in the combined system.

On top of studying each vessel separately, we can also describe the combined system with Eq. [31]:

$$\Delta p = R_{\text{equivalent}} \frac{\Delta V}{\Delta t} \qquad [38]$$

in which we introduce an equivalent flow resistance, $R_{\text{equivalent}}$, which must be a combination of the two individual flow resistances in Eq. [37]. The term $\Delta V/\Delta t$ in Eq. [38] is equal to the same terms in Eq. [37]. We can therefore combine Eqs. [37] and [38] to relate the equivalent flow resistance to the individual flow resistances by recognizing that $\Delta p = \Delta p_1 + \Delta p_2$, i.e., that the pressure drop along the first vessel and the pressure drop along the second vessel combine to give the total pressure drop along the two vessels in series. This leads to:

$$R_{\text{equivalent}} \frac{\Delta V}{\Delta t} = (R_1 + R_2) \frac{\Delta V}{\Delta t} \qquad [39]$$

i.e., for $n$ resistances in series we write:

$$R_{\text{equivalent}} = \sum_{i=1}^{n} R_i \qquad [40]$$

This is Kirchhoff's law for serial flow resistances.

*Kirchhoff's law for serial flow resistances states that flow resistances in series are added to obtain the equivalent flow resistance.*

## BLOOD VESSELS IN PARALLEL

In the second case we study a blood vessel that branches into two vessels, a vessel with flow resistance $R_1$ and a vessel with flow resistance $R_2$. Downstream, the two vessels recombine into a single vessel. No further branching occurs.

In this case, the pressure drop along the two separated vessels must be the same because there must be a well-defined pressure value in the vessel before branching and because there can be only one particular pressure value after the vessels merge. Thus, we write Eq. [31] for the two parallel vessels in the form:

$$\Delta p = R_1 \left( \frac{\Delta V}{\Delta t} \right)_1$$
$$\Delta p = R_2 \left( \frac{\Delta V}{\Delta t} \right)_2 \qquad [41]$$

Eq. [41] shows that the fraction of the blood passing through each of the two vessels depends on their respective flow resistances. We can alternatively study the two vessels as a combined system. For this we apply Eq. [31] to the combined system by assigning an equivalent flow resistance, $R_{\text{equivalent}}$:

$$\Delta p = R_{\text{equivalent}} \frac{\Delta V}{\Delta t} \qquad [42]$$

Eqs. [41] and [42] are combined to determine the dependence of the equivalent flow resistance on the two individual flow resistances. First we note that the total amount of blood flowing into the branching point per time, $\Delta V/\Delta t$, must be equal to the sum of the amounts of blood passing the two vessels during the same time interval, i.e.:

$$\frac{\Delta V}{\Delta t} = \left( \frac{\Delta V}{\Delta t} \right)_1 + \left( \frac{\Delta V}{\Delta t} \right)_2 \qquad [43]$$

Were this not so, either blood would have to accumulate in vessels 1 and 2, or blood would have to accumulate in the upstream vessel. Substituting Eqs. [41] and [42] in Eq. [43], we find:

$$\frac{\Delta V}{\Delta t} = \frac{\Delta p}{R_{\text{equivalent}}} = \left( \frac{\Delta V}{\Delta t} \right)_1 + \left( \frac{\Delta V}{\Delta t} \right)_2$$
$$= \frac{\Delta p}{R_1} + \frac{\Delta p}{R_2} \qquad [44]$$

From Eq. [44] we conclude that:

$$\frac{1}{R_{\text{equivalent}}} = \frac{1}{R_1} + \frac{1}{R_2} \qquad [45]$$

which can be generalized for $n$ flow resistances in parallel:

$$\frac{1}{R_{\text{equivalent}}} = \sum_{i=1}^{n} \frac{1}{R_i} \qquad [46]$$

This is **Kirchhoff's law for parallel flow resistances.**

*Kirchhoff's law for parallel flow resistances states that flow resistances in parallel are added inversely to obtain the equivalent flow resistance.*

## ● EXAMPLE 12.5

Fig. 12.19 shows a cylindrical blood vessel A of radius $r_1$, in which blood flows from point $P_1$ to point $P_2$ with the two points a distance $l_1$ apart. At point $P_2$ the blood vessel splits into three cylindrical vessels, one of which we label vessel B. Each of these parallel vessels has a radius $r_2 = \frac{1}{2} r_1$. The three vessels merge at a distance $l_2 = \frac{1}{2} l_1$ downstream from point $P_2$; this position we define as point $P_3$. (a) What fraction of the blood volume passing through vessel A is passing through vessel B? (b) What fraction of the drop in pressure between points $P_1$ and $P_3$ is occurring in vessel A?

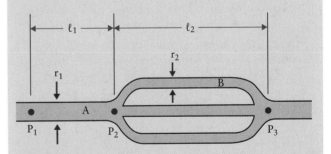

**FIGURE 12.19**

Example for Kirchhoff's laws. Shown is a single blood vessel A, which splits into three capillaries of type B. The capillaries reunite to form a single vessel at point $P_3$. Note the various geometric data shown in the figure. Blood is modelled as a Newtonian fluid in this example.

*Solution to part (a):* The volume flow rates at points $P_1$ and $P_3$ are equal. Using Eq. [32] for the flow resistance in a cylindrical vessel, we note further that the three parallel vessels have the same flow resistance because they have the same geometrical parameters. Using Eq. [31] we find, therefore, that the volume flow rate in each of the three parallel vessels must be the same. With this

● **EXAMPLE 12.5** (*continued*)

information we calculate the ratio of the volume flow rate in vessel A and in vessel B:

$$\frac{\left(\frac{\Delta V}{\Delta t}\right)_B}{\left(\frac{\Delta V}{\Delta t}\right)_A} = \frac{\frac{1}{3}\left(\frac{\Delta V}{\Delta t}\right)_A}{\left(\frac{\Delta V}{\Delta t}\right)_A} = \frac{1}{3} \qquad [47]$$

*Solution to part (b):* Using Eq. [31] for both the entire system in Fig. 12.19 and for vessel A, we write:

$$\Delta p_{P_1P_3} = R_{P_1P_3}\left(\frac{\Delta V}{\Delta t}\right)$$

$$\Delta p_A = R_A\left(\frac{\Delta V}{\Delta t}\right) \qquad [48]$$

These two formulas are combined:

$$\frac{\Delta p_A}{\Delta p_{P_1P_3}} = \frac{R_A}{R_{P_1P_3}} \qquad [49]$$

We obtain the ratio of the pressure drops on the left-hand side of Eq. [49] once the ratio of the equivalent flow resistances for the system in Fig. 12.19 has been determined. These equivalent flow resistances are calculated in three steps:

- we calculate $R_A$ and $R_B$,
- we combine the three parallel vessels and calculate their equivalent flow resistance, and
- the equivalent flow resistance for the three parallel vessels and the flow resistance for vessel A are combined to obtain the overall equivalent flow resistance.

*Step (i):* The flow resistances for sections A and B are calculated from Eq. [32]. We obtain:

$$R_A = \frac{8 \cdot l_1 \cdot \eta}{\pi \cdot r_1^4} \qquad [50]$$

and

$$R_B = \frac{8 \cdot l_2 \cdot \eta}{\pi \cdot r_2^4}$$

$$= \frac{8 \cdot \frac{1}{2} l_1 \cdot \eta}{\pi \left(\frac{1}{2} r_1\right)^4} = 8 \cdot R_A \qquad [51]$$

*Step (ii):* We combine the contributions of the three parallel vessels to an equivalent flow resistance for the part of Fig. 12.19 that lies between

points $P_2$ and $P_3$. For this we use Kirchhoff's law for parallel vessels:

$$\frac{1}{R_{P_2P_3}} = \frac{1}{R_B} + \frac{1}{R_B} + \frac{1}{R_B} = \frac{3}{R_B} \qquad [52]$$

*Step (iii):* In the last step we combine the flow resistances for the section between points $P_1$ and $P_2$ (vessel A with $R_A$) and the section between points $P_2$ and $P_3$. The equivalent flow resistance for the entire system in Fig. 12.19 is obtained from Kirchhoff's law for vessels in series:

$$R_{P_1P_3} = R_A + R_{P_2P_3} = R_A + \frac{R_B}{3}$$

$$= R_A + \frac{8 \cdot R_A}{3} = \frac{11 \cdot R_A}{3} \qquad [53]$$

in which we used Eq. [51] to replace $R_B$. By substituting Eq. [53] in Eq. [49], we find:

$$\frac{\Delta p_A}{\Delta p_{P_1P_3}} = \frac{R_A}{R_{P_1P_3}} = \frac{R_A}{\frac{11 \cdot R_A}{3}} = \frac{3}{11} \qquad [54]$$

Thus, only 27% of the drop in pressure occurs in vessel A.

# Newtonian Fluids in Physiology

## Flow Resistance in the Human Cardiovascular System

● **EXAMPLE 12.6**

In Fig. 12.3(b), we emphasized that 50% of the flow resistance in the systemic circulation is caused in the arterioles (small arteries), a higher fraction than in either the aorta or the capillaries. Using an average value for the viscosity of blood from Table 12.1 and data from Fig. 12.4, confirm that the total flow resistance is indeed greatest in the arterioles. Treat blood as a Newtonian fluid and blood vessels as cylinder-shaped. Calculate first the flow resistance for a single vessel; then calculate the flow resistance for all vessels of the same type by using Kirchhoff's laws.

*Solution:* We start with the aorta. The average length $\langle l \rangle$ of any vessel of a given type is determined from Fig. 12.4 by dividing the total cross-sectional area of the particular type of vessel by its total volume. For the aorta, this leads to:

$$\langle l \rangle = \frac{V}{A} = \frac{180 \text{ cm}^3}{5.3 \text{ cm}^2} = 34 \text{ cm} \qquad [55]$$

The radius of the tube, $r_{tube}$, is half of the inner diameter of the aorta, $r_{tube} = 1.1$ cm. The flow resistance then follows from Eq. [32]:

$$R_{aorta} = \frac{8 \cdot (0.34 \text{ m}) \left( 2.5 \times 10^{-3} \, \dfrac{\text{N} \cdot \text{s}}{\text{m}^2} \right)}{\pi \, (0.011 \text{ m})^4}$$

$$= 1.5 \times 10^5 \, \frac{\text{Pa} \cdot \text{s}}{\text{m}^3} \qquad [56]$$

Since there is only a single aorta in our body, the summation parameter $n$ is one ($n = 1$) in Kirchhoff's laws; i.e., Eq. [46] yields:

$$R_{total} = R_{aorta} \qquad [57]$$

The calculations of the corresponding values for the other blood vessel types proceed in the same fashion. For the capillaries, we have $n = 5 \times 10^9$; i.e., Eq. [46] yields:

$$\frac{1}{R_{total}} = \sum_i \frac{1}{R_{capillary}} = \frac{5 \times 10^9}{R_{capillary}}$$

$$\Rightarrow \quad R_{total} = \frac{R_{capillary}}{5 \times 10^9} \qquad [58]$$

The results for all vessel types are summarized in Table 12.2. We learn from Table 12.2 that two factors cause the arterioles to dominate the flow resistance in our body when compared to the smaller capillaries:

- the arterioles are significantly longer than the capillaries, and
- there are 20 times fewer arterioles than capillaries.

What consequence does this large flow resistance of the arterioles have for the systemic circulation? To answer, we study the pressure–current relation in Ohm's law. The current $\Delta V/\Delta t$ is constant throughout the systemic circulation, since otherwise blood would collect or disappear somewhere. Thus, a section with a large flow resistance $R$ must have a large pressure difference $\Delta p$: the blood pressure drops significantly in the arterioles. Therefore, shifting the flow resistance to the arterioles protects the capillaries, in which a significant pressure drop is undesirable due to the thinner and more fragile nature of these blood vessels.

## Snorkel Diving

### ● EXAMPLE 12.7

(a) How deep can a snorkel diver dive if the maximum gauge pressure on the thorax cannot exceed 11 kPa? Near that depth, which effects cause breathing problems when (b) the breathing tube to the surface is wide, and (c) the breathing tube is narrow?

*Solution to part (a)*: The role of the flow resistance of air in the respiratory system becomes evident when we study diving with a breathing tube. With a maximum gauge pressure of $\Delta p = 11$ kPa on the thorax, the maximum depth for snorkel diving is calculated from Pascal's law:

$$p_{max} - p_{atm} = \Delta p = \rho \cdot g \cdot d \qquad [59]$$

which yields:

$$d = \frac{\Delta p}{\rho \cdot g}$$

$$= \frac{1.1 \times 10^4 \, \text{Pa}}{\left( 1 \times 10^3 \, \dfrac{\text{kg}}{\text{m}^3} \right) \left( 9.8 \, \dfrac{\text{m}}{\text{s}^2} \right)} = 1.1 \text{ m} \qquad [60]$$

---

### TABLE 12.2

**Length, radius, individual flow resistance, and collective flow resistance for arterioles, aorta, and capillaries**

| Vessel type | Length (m) | Radius (m) | $R_{single}$ (Pa · s/m³) | $R_{total}$ (Pa · s/m³) |
|---|---|---|---|---|
| Arterioles | $2.5 \times 10^{-3}$ | $8.0 \times 10^{-6}$ | $3.9 \times 10^{15}$ | $2.4 \times 10^7$ |
| Aorta | $3.4 \times 10^{-1}$ | $1.1 \times 10^{-2}$ | $1.5 \times 10^5$ | $1.5 \times 10^5$ |
| Capillaries | $8.5 \times 10^{-4}$ | $3.5 \times 10^{-6}$ | $3.6 \times 10^{16}$ | $7.2 \times 10^6$ |

The arterioles contribute most to the flow resistance in the systemic circulation.

## ● EXAMPLE 12.7 (*continued*)

At a depth of 1.1 m, a pressure difference of 11 kPa must be generated in the lungs to open the thorax against the outside water pressure to inhale. An attempt to defy this physical limitation leads to anoxia (lack of oxygen supply to the body).

*Solution to parts (b) and (c):* At around 1 m depth, the diver struggles with either one of two problems. If the breathing tube is too wide, it creates too much dead space. Dead space in respiration refers to any space that is filled with air during inhalation but does not contribute to the exchange of oxygen with the blood. Any space between the outside air and the lungs excluding the alveoli is part of the dead space. The diver inhales hard, but only a small fraction of the inhaled air reaches the alveoli in the lungs; the rest is stuck in the trachea and its snorkel extension.

If the diver uses a narrower breathing tube to reduce the dead space then the flow resistance for the inhaled air increases dramatically, since $R \propto 1/r_{\text{tube}}^4$. Thus, pulling air through the breathing tube becomes an exhausting effort.

## Filtration in the Kidneys

## ● EXAMPLE 12.8

(a) Quantify the volume flow rate through a single pore in the basement membrane in the kidneys, using for the pressure difference across the membrane $\Delta p = 1.3$ kPa and a viscosity coefficient of $\eta = 1.4 \times 10^{-3}$ N · s/m$^2$ (this value lies between the values of blood serum and water). (b) How many pores are needed in the kidneys and how many pores are needed per nephron?

*Supplementary anatomical information:* The **kidneys** serve two purposes: to regulate the total water volume and the pH (acidity) of the blood, and to filter the end products of the metabolism, especially urea and uric acid, out of the blood. Both purposes are accomplished in the functional unit of the kidneys, called the **nephron**.

A kidney contains about 1.2 million nephrons. An overview of the nephron is shown in Fig. 12.20. The filtration process in the nephron is a two-step process. An arteriole branches into the **glomerulus**, which is embedded in **Bowman's capsule**. The glomerulus filters the blood by holding back only proteins and blood cells. About 180 L/day of filtrate reach the renal tube. There, more than 99% of the fluid is resorbed into the

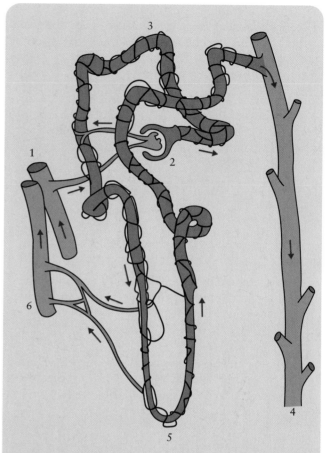

**FIGURE 12.20**

Overview of a nephron, showing the afferent arteriole (1), the glomerulus in Bowman's capsule (2), the renal tube (3), the urinary tract collection tube (4), the loop of Henle (5), and the efferent arteriole (6).

circulatory system. The remainder reaches the collecting tube and is eliminated from the body, leading to about 1.5 L/day excretion in the form of urine.

A detailed view of the glomerulus in Bowman's capsule is shown in Fig. 12.21, which is a sketch that shows from left to right two different magnifications of the glomerulus. In part (a), the supplying arteriole is visible at the top left. It leads to tangled loops of capillaries, resembling a skein of wool, that are embedded in a capsule and finally leave as a blood vessel at the top right. The renal tubule, which collects the filtrate, is shown at the bottom where it leaves Bowman's capsule, which therefore serves as the primary fluid collection container.

Fig. 12.21(b) shows a cross-section through the capillary inside Bowman's capsule. The capillary membrane (1) is porous, but enclosed by the **basement membrane** (2). The basement membrane is embraced by podocytes (3), which are cells with arm-like extensions, leaving slits open for fluid flow. The pores in the capillary membrane on the

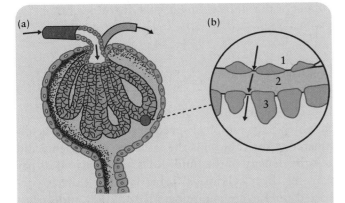

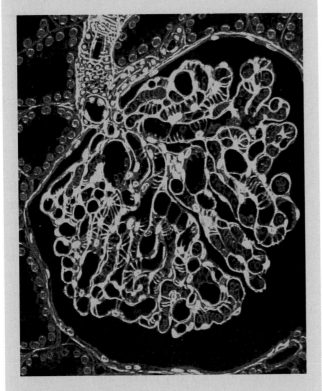

**FIGURE 12.21**

Detailed sketch of Bowman's capsule. (a) Blood supply to the capsule is shown at the top and the renal tube for filtrate removal at the bottom. (b) A cross-section of the wall inside Bowman's capsule is highlighted (green dot) with the capillary membrane (1), the basement membrane (2), and the podocytes (3). In this sketch blood is at the top and urine is at the bottom. (c) Computer graphic of Bowman's capsule (dark blue) with the glomerulus at centre (yellow). Part of the blood vessel is shown at the top left.

blood side are typically 20 nm in diameter. The basement membrane at the centre is 50 to 80 nm thick and contains pores of 12 nm diameter. Thus, the pores in the basement membrane determine the volume flow rate. Fig. 12.21(c) shows Bowman's capsule in a colour graphic.

The actual value for the pressure drop across the basement membrane varies between zero and 1.3 kPa to allow the body to regulate the flow by using variations in the blood plasma pressure.

*Solution:* We use $r_{tube} = 6$ nm for the radius of the pores in the basement membrane; the maximum pressure difference across the membrane of $\Delta p = 1.3$ kPa; a length of the pore of 50 nm, which is equivalent to the thickness of the basement membrane; and the viscosity coefficient as $\eta = 1.4 \times 10^{-3}$ N · s/m$^2$. With these values we find from Poiseuille's law the volume flow rate of a single pore:

$$\frac{\Delta V}{\Delta t} = \frac{\pi(6 \times 10^{-9}\,\text{m})^4(1.3 \times 10^3\,\text{Pa})}{8 \cdot \left(1.4 \times 10^{-3}\,\dfrac{\text{N} \cdot \text{s}}{\text{m}^2}\right)(5 \times 10^{-8}\,\text{m})}$$

$$= 9.5 \times 10^{-21}\,\frac{\text{m}^3}{\text{s}} \qquad [61]$$

To handle the daily filtration of 180 L, the two kidneys must have more than $N = 2 \times 10^{14}$ pores. This number is obtained from the result in Eq. [61]:

$$\left(\frac{\Delta V}{\Delta t}\right)_{\text{kidneys}} = \left(\frac{\Delta V}{\Delta t}\right)_{\text{pore}} \cdot N \qquad [62]$$

which leads to:

$$N = \frac{180\,\dfrac{\text{L}}{\text{day}}}{9.5 \times 10^{-21}\,\dfrac{\text{m}^3}{\text{s}}} = 2.2 \times 10^{14} \qquad [63]$$

The number of pores per nephron, the unit shown in Fig. 12.20, is obtained by dividing $N$ by the number of nephrons in our kidneys, which is about 2.4 million nephrons. Thus, we need roughly $9 \times 10^7$ pores per nephron, which is a number close to 100 million. We see that the physiological performance of the kidneys on a macroscopic scale is based on the physical properties of a tremendous number of microscopic functional units.

# Special Topics in Fluid Flow
## Beyond Laminar Flow: Turbulence and Convection

When local velocity gradients in the fluid become too big, turbulences occur. Turbulent flow is a superposition of laminar flow (discussed above) and vortex formation/vortex motion. The different flow patterns for laminar flow and turbulent flow around a solid cylinder are shown in Fig. 12.22. In the turbulent case, flow lines are not continuous, but terminate or start in vortices.

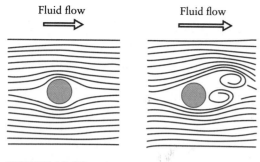

Fluid flow            Fluid flow

**FIGURE 12.22**

Two flow patterns: laminar flow (left) and turbulent flow (right) around a solid cylinder (blue dot) immersed in the fluid. Note the vortex formation for turbulent flow.

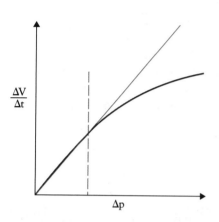

**FIGURE 12.23**

Transition of the volume flow rate as a function of pressure difference along a tube (red curve) from laminar to turbulent flow (dashed threshold line). Turbulent flow is characterized by minimum or negligible volume flow increments for increasing pressure differences.

**Turbulent flow** has a major effect on the volume flow rate. This is illustrated in Fig. 12.23, which shows the volume flow rate as a function of pressure difference along a given tube. At low pressure differences Ohm's law applies; i.e., the volume flow rate is proportional to the pressure difference. The vertical dashed line indicates the pressure difference at which the flow undergoes the transition from laminar to turbulent flow. At larger pressure differences Ohm's law no longer applies, and increasing the pressure difference to obtain a volume flow rate increase beyond the transition is ineffective. Thus, once the flow has become turbulent, no significant increase of the volume flow rate can be achieved.

A semi-empirical threshold number is introduced to determine whether flow is laminar or turbulent. It is called the **Reynolds number** $Re$, in honour of Osborne Reynolds, who proposed it in 1883. The present discussion is based on flow in a cylindrical

tube. For that tube geometry, the Reynolds number is given as:

$$Re = \frac{\rho \cdot \langle v \rangle \cdot d}{\eta} \qquad [64]$$

in which $\langle v \rangle$ is a typical speed of the fluid, $d$ is the diameter of the tube, $\eta$ is the viscosity coefficient, and $\rho$ is the density of the fluid. $Re$ is a dimensionless parameter. In a cylindrical tube, laminar flow is predicted for Reynolds numbers $Re \leq 2000$ and turbulent flow for $Re \geq 2000$.

The Reynolds formula is useful when we discuss systems in which turbulence control is required. For example, turbulence suppression is a design criterion for birds' wings besides providing lift and thrust to overcome air drag. Wings are primarily shaped such that air above the wing travels faster than that below. Due to Bernoulli's law, a lower air pressure results above the wing. The net effect is a lift force sufficient to compensate the effect of gravity on the bird. The faster the bird flies through the air the stronger the lift force, and flapping of the wings is no longer necessary. Energy conservation is, however, only one reason why large birds, such as most birds of prey, use a flap-and-glide flight pattern. Avoiding flapping or flapping slowly further addresses the Reynolds formula: air is a Newtonian fluid in which a transition from laminar to turbulent flow occurs at high relative speeds of air and wing surface, i.e., when large velocity gradients are involved. Ceasing wing motion minimizes the occurrence of turbulences. Smaller birds, particularly finches and woodpeckers, use another approach to minimize flow resistance related to slowing of their flight: they rise on one or two wing beats, then fold their wings to the body and dart through the air, eliminating turbulent air motion past their bodies at high speed. These birds can be identified by their undulating flight pattern because they need to re-establish lift through another few wing beats after several metres to avoid crashing to the ground.

Birds show a good sense for turbulences in many ways, even when they are not airborne. When frigid winds blow along the seashore in winter, you can see seagulls on the beach all facing in the same direction. As illustrated in Fig. 12.24, the birds align their streamlined bodies such that they offer the least resistance to the oncoming breeze. This leads to a laminar flow of air around their bodies, avoiding the ruffling of their feathers due to turbulences that would expose their body to the low temperatures and possibly cause hypothermia.

**FIGURE 12.24**

When cold winds blow across the shore, seagulls align their bodies with the wind to allow a laminar air flow. Minimizing turbulences is essential for these animals as the air vortices would ruffle some of their feathers and allow the body to lose heat.

● **EXAMPLE 12.9**

Determine the Reynolds number of the following three systems: (a) water flow in a creek, (b) air flow through the trachea, and (c) blood flow in the aorta.

*Solution to part (a):* In most creeks of 1.0 m width water flows at speeds of 1.0 to 10.0 m/s. The density of water is $1.0 \times 10^3$ kg/m$^3$ and its viscosity coefficient is $1.8 \times 10^{-3}$ N · s/m$^2$ (see Table 12.1). This leads to a Reynolds number of $1.0 \times 10^6 \leq Re \leq 1.0 \times 10^7$; i.e., the flow in a creek is always turbulent.

*Solution to part (b):* We assume 15 inhalations per minute of 0.5 L each. For the volume flow rate of air through the trachea, this yields:

$$\frac{\Delta V}{\Delta t} = 2 \cdot (15 \text{ min}^{-1})(0.5 \text{ L})$$

$$= 2.5 \times 10^{-4} \frac{\text{m}^3}{\text{s}} \qquad [65]$$

The additional factor of 2 in Eq. [65] is introduced since each inhalation is followed by an exhalation, doubling the volume flow through the trachea per breath. Using the diameter of the trachea as $d = 1$ cm, the average speed of air is determined from the equation of continuity:

$$v = \frac{1}{A} \frac{\Delta V}{\Delta t} = \frac{2.5 \times 10^{-4} \frac{\text{m}^3}{\text{s}}}{\pi (5 \times 10^{-3} \text{m})^2} = 3.2 \frac{\text{m}}{\text{s}} \qquad [66]$$

Using the density of air as $\rho = 1.2$ kg/m$^3$ and the viscosity coefficient as $\eta = 2 \times 10^{-5}$ N · s/m$^2$ (Table 12.1), we find $Re = 1900$, i.e., a value near the threshold to turbulent flow. The actual flow is turbulent because the inner trachea surface is not smooth. Turbulent flow is desired because the inhaled air must be moistened in the trachea; moistening occurs when dry air is brought in contact with the moist trachea wall. This contact is more efficient for turbulent flow. Fig. 12.23 then shows why air flow in the trachea has a Reynolds number close to the laminar-to-turbulent transition. Once flow is turbulent, little gain in the volume flow rate is achieved by increasing pressure gradients along the tube. Thus, operating far in the turbulent regime would unnecessarily increase the physical work required for breathing.

*Solution to part (c):* The average speed of blood in the aorta is 20 cm/s (see Example 12.1). Using $d = 2.2$ cm for the inner diameter of the aorta, $\eta = 2.5 \times 10^{-3}$ N · s/m$^2$ for the viscosity coefficient of blood, and $\rho = 1.06 \times 10^3$ kg/m$^3$ for the density of blood, we find that the Reynolds number is $Re = 1900$, i.e., again a value close to the transition laminar to turbulent. If you keep in mind that blood flow into the aorta is pulsatile with peak velocities in the 1–2 m/s range, turbulent flow seems to be favoured. However, turbulent flow is particularly undesirable in blood vessels since it greatly diminishes the volume flow rate for a given pressure gradient. Nature again

● **EXAMPLE 12.9 (continued)**

maximizes the efficiency of the aortic blood flow based on Fig. 12.23; it pushes the volume flow rate to the greatest possible value for laminar flow, then develops a way to compensate for the peak velocities at which blood flow would have to be turbulent: immediately beyond the heart the aorta arches 180°, which allows it to buffer the rushing blood with the Windkessel effect. We discuss this effect in Chapter 16, because the elastic response of the aortic wall plays a key role in it.

Pathological vasoconstriction, i.e., vessels becoming narrower due to illness, may cause turbulent blood flow. Based on the equation of continuity, the blood speed ⟨v⟩ increases in this case, because the heart still pumps the same amount of blood through the aorta. This leads to a potentially dangerous increase in the Reynolds number even though the diameter of the blood vessel, $d$, is reduced. To illustrate the net effect, we use the equation of continuity to determine the dependence of the blood speed on the vessel diameter:

$$|\mathbf{v}| \cdot A = |\mathbf{v}| \cdot \pi \left(\frac{d}{2}\right)^2 = \text{const} \quad \Rightarrow \quad |\mathbf{v}| \propto \frac{1}{d^2} \qquad [67]$$

Thus, even though the diameter of the blood vessel is reduced in the case of pathological vasoconstriction, the overall effect on the Reynolds number is an increase:

$$Re = \frac{\rho \cdot \langle \mathbf{v} \rangle \cdot d}{\eta} \propto \frac{1}{d} \qquad [68]$$

Let's focus specifically on the aorta. Peak blood velocities in the aorta can also increase due to a defective aortic valve. Fig. 12.25 shows the peak velocity of blood ejected from the heart as a function of time for a particular patient. The speed of blood is measured by Doppler ultrasound, a diagnostic tool we discuss in Chapter 17. This patient's peak blood flow velocity increased steadily during a three-year observation period, approaching a threshold at 5 m/s, which is considered clinically the maximum tolerable value. This value exceeds the value we used to calculate the Reynolds number for this system by a factor of 25, illustrating the added tolerance due to the elasticity of the blood vessel walls. Data such as that shown in Fig. 12.25 allow the medical team to plan a heart operation and prepare the patient for the subsequent treatment over a considerable time span.

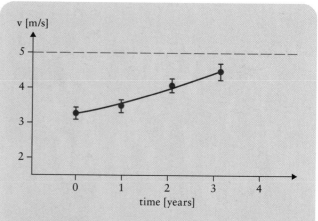

**FIGURE 12.25**

Peak velocity of blood ejected from the heart as a function of time for a particular patient, as measured by Doppler ultrasound. The patient's peak blood flow velocity increased steadily during a three-year observation period, approaching a threshold at 5 m/s. Once this threshold is reached, open-heart surgery is required to address a defective heart valve.

**FIGURE 12.26**

Instruments used to measure blood pressure. A stethoscope is used to listen to the sound of the flowing blood while the cuff, rubber bulb, and manometer allow us to measure the pressure exerted on the artery in the arm.

The **sphygmomanometer** is an instrument to measure the blood pressure, using the acoustic difference audible for blood streaming laminar or turbulent through a blood vessel. The setup of this instrument is shown in Fig. 12.26. A rubber bulb (front) is used

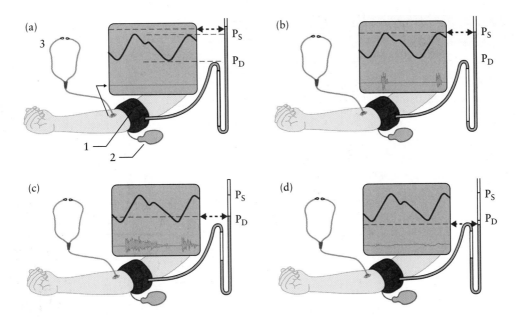

**FIGURE 12.27**

Four panels illustrating the blood pressure measurement with a sphygmomanometer. The recording of the blood flow is based on the health practitioner's listening to the artery with a stethoscope (3). The cuff (1) and the rubber bulb (2) are used to vary the pressure on the brachial artery. When the artery is partially open, turbulent flow of the blood causes a characteristic sound.

by the health practitioner to force air simultaneously into both a cuff (at right) wrapped tightly around the upper arm and a standard manometer.

Fig. 12.27 illustrates what the health practitioner hears with a stethoscope as a function of pressure. Each sketch shows the pressure relative to systolic ($P_S$) and diastolic ($P_D$) pressure at the right, the normal variation of the blood pressure (red curve), and the audible sound (orange curve). Initially (Fig. 12.27(a)), the pressure in the cuff is increased until the flow of blood through the brachial artery is stopped. At that point the practitioner hears nothing below the cuff. A valve on the bulb is then opened to lower the pressure in the cuff. When the pressure in the brachial artery falls just below the maximum pressure generated by the heart (which is the systolic pressure, where systole refers to the contraction of the heart muscle; see Fig. 12.27(b)), the artery opens momentarily on each beat of the heart. The velocity of the blood in the artery is high and the blood flow is turbulent during these events. This leads to a noisy blood flow easily recognizable by the health practitioner. The manometer now reads 120 mmHg for a standard man with a healthy heart.

When the pressure in the cuff is lowered further (Fig. 12.27(c)), intermittent sounds are heard until the pressure in the cuff falls below the minimum heart pressure (which is the diastolic pressure, where diastole refers to the expansion of the heart muscle).

Then a continuous background sound is heard, as illustrated in Fig. 12.27(d). The transition to the continuous sound occurs at about 80 mmHg for a standard man with a healthy heart.

Concept Question 12.7 relates the fluid flow properties to **convection**. Convection is the circulatory motion that occurs in a fluid that is held at nonuniform temperatures.

## Concept Question 12.7

Tuareg are a semi-nomadic Islamic people in the Saharan and Sahelian regions of northern Africa. Early European travellers' reports often referred to them as the "Blue Men of the Sahara Desert," referring to their traditional dark-dyed clothes. How would you combine the formulas for Reynolds number, the buoyant force, Charles's law, the velocity profile of a viscous fluid in a tube, and the definition of density to determine whether dark robes are suitable attire in the desert? Work with the following model: the Sun heats the outer surface of dark robes to temperatures about 6 degrees higher than on the inside. The air adjacent to a surface equilibrates to its temperature, let's say 40°C outside and 34°C inside the Tuareg's robe. Tuareg wear their robes loosely, allowing for an air cushion of a few centimetres between their body and the robe.

**Concept Question 12.7 (continued)**

ANSWER: Charles's law connects the temperature and the volume at constant pressure. If we consider a given amount of air that we treat as an ideal gas, we write:

$$V_{\text{outside}} = V_{\text{inside}} \frac{T_{\text{outside}}}{T_{\text{inside}}} \qquad [69]$$

With the definition of density as $\rho = m/V$, the density for a given amount of air on both sides of the robe is then determined:

$$\rho_{\text{inside}} = \frac{m}{V_{\text{inside}}}$$

$$\rho_{\text{outside}} = \frac{m}{V_{\text{outside}}} = \frac{m}{V_{\text{inside}}} \frac{T_{\text{inside}}}{T_{\text{outside}}} \qquad [70]$$

From this, the air density difference across the robe is determined:

$$\Delta\rho = \rho_{\text{inside}} - \rho_{\text{outside}}$$

$$= \frac{m}{V_{\text{inside}}}\left(1 - \frac{T_{\text{inside}}}{T_{\text{outside}}}\right) = \rho_{\text{inside}} \frac{\Delta T}{T_{\text{outside}}} \qquad [71]$$

with $\Delta T = T_{\text{outside}} - T_{\text{inside}}$. Using 1.2 kg/m³ for the cooler inside air, we find $\Delta\rho = 23$ g/m³. This situation is comparable to the situation for a hot-air balloon, except that the cooler, heavier air is inside the robe. Thus, net forces act on the air inside to move downward, and on the air outside to move upward (relative to cooler air a bit farther away from the robe), both due to buoyancy. The net force due to the density difference is:

$$F_{\text{net}} = g \cdot V \cdot \Delta\rho = g \cdot h \cdot A \cdot \Delta\rho \qquad [72]$$

in which $V$ is the volume of a given amount of air affected by buoyancy. This volume is written as a height and a horizontal area $A$, assuming that any buoyancy effect causes vertical air movement (which makes sense, since Tuaregs' robes are open at the bottom). Next we divide Eq. [72] by $A$, which expresses the net force per unit area acting on the studied amount of air. Then we divide by $h$ to obtain a gradient:

$$\frac{1}{h}\frac{F_{\text{net}}}{A} = g \cdot \Delta\rho \qquad [73]$$

The left-hand term in Eq. [73] is equivalent to the pressure gradient in Eq. [29] for the velocity profile of a flowing fluid. From this equation the average velocity with which the affected amount of air moves is determined. In the

case of the air inside the robe, a downward motion occurs that is related to the width of the air cushion between the body of the person and the robe; in the case of the outside air, the flow is upward and depends on the width of the hot-air layer. The resulting velocities are in the range of 5 m/s to 50 m/s, i.e., much faster than observed.

In the next step, the Reynolds number is determined for the flowing air. In both cases Reynolds numbers are found well in excess of the threshold value at 2000. Thus, the air flow is turbulent. This slows the air significantly, but

- increases heat removal from the surface of the clothes outside, effectively limiting the temperature increase due to the dark colour of the fabric, and
- creates a slight breeze passing over the person's body inside the robe, allowing the rather high air temperature to be perceived as tolerable.

Thus, convection is the result of a non-uniform temperature across a fluid. The temperature gradient causes a density gradient that in turn results in buoyancy. Buoyancy and gravity cause a circulatory motion in the fluid. Other natural examples of convection include

- convective heating in the liquid outer core of Earth (2900 km to 5100 km below the surface) in which solid parts of the lower mantle sink toward the solid, superheated core, melt, and float upward due to their smaller density, and
- brief but intense precipitation, such as downpours and thunderstorms. These are caused by the Sun warming Earth's surface on a sunny day, which in turn heats the adjacent layer of humid air. This warmer air has a lower density and starts to rise higher into the atmosphere. During its upward motion it expands adiabatically and cools below the water saturation point.

# Beyond Newtonian Fluids: The Viscosity of Blood

We have so far treated blood as a Newtonian fluid. However, its heterogeneous composition leads to novel properties that we cannot explain with the model developed for the Newtonian fluid. We illustrate this point for the viscosity coefficient of blood $\eta$, as listed in Table 12.1, and the flow resistance $R$, which we defined in Eq. [32]. As that equation showed, both parameters are closely related in the form $R \propto \eta$. Earlier in this chapter we defined the viscosity coefficient as a materials constant, which depends only on the temperature. As no dependence on other macroscopic parameters was identified, blood viscosity in the cardiovascular system of an endothermic species should be constant. The flow resistance $R$ in turn depends on geometric factors, such as the tube length and the tube radius, and the viscosity coefficient $\eta$. Thus, for blood flow in a particular blood vessel of an endotherm, the flow resistance should be constant as well. Physiological observations illustrate, however, that the viscosity of blood and its flow resistance in a given blood vessel depend strongly on two additional factors:

- *The* **hematocrit value,** which is the volume fraction of blood cells in blood. A higher hematocrit value leads to a higher viscosity. This is illustrated in Fig. 12.28, which shows the viscosity coefficient of blood (relative to the viscosity coefficient of water) as a function of the hematocrit value. With an average hematocrit value of 46 for males and 41 for females we note that the blood of males is more viscous.

- *The flow velocity of the blood:* The viscosity coefficient is inversely proportional to the flow velocity. This is illustrated in Fig. 12.29, which shows the volume flow rate of a Newtonian fluid (1) and the volume flow rate of blood (2) as a function of the pressure difference along a vessel.

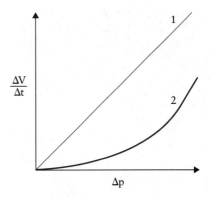

**FIGURE 12.29**

Pumping is required to force Newtonian and non-Newtonian fluids (e.g., water and blood) at various rates of flow through a straight tube. As the intended volume flow rate increases, the pressure the pump must produce increases as well. Note that for Newtonian fluids (1) the slope of the line relating flow rate and pressure is constant. However, for blood (2) the flow resistance is very high at low flow rates but approaches the value for Newtonian fluids at higher flow rates.

The viscosity coefficient affects the flow resistance; it is constant in the case of a Newtonian fluid (blue curve in Fig. 12.29) but varies as a function of pressure difference for blood (red curve).

As a consequence of Fig. 12.29, blood flow cannot be allowed to fall below a minimum speed as a dangerous feedback-loop effect may occur. We illustrate this feedback loop in the context of an anaphylactic shock. An **anaphylactic shock** is an allergic reaction of the body's immune system in response to a second contact with an antigen to which the body has become sensitized. An example is a severe peanut allergy. The initial reaction of the body is a histamine release that leads to a peripheral vasodilation, i.e., blood vessels widening. The increased cross-sectional area of the blood vessels causes the blood flow to slow down (as predicted by the equation of continuity). Due to the non-Newtonian behaviour of blood, the slower flow leads to an increase in the viscosity. This causes further slowing of the blood flow, which again results in a further increase in the viscosity. In the end, this feedback loop leads to the cessation of the volume flow rate, $\Delta V/\Delta t = 0$, a state called **stasis**.

But why does the viscosity change with the flow velocity? The answer lies in the fact that blood is heterogeneous. Normally, blood cells are well immersed in the blood plasma due to the fact that they are nucleus-free, contain a low-viscosity cytoplasm,

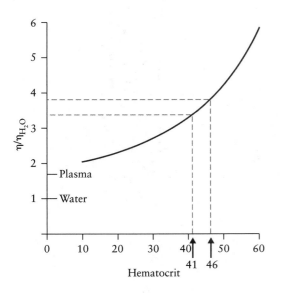

**FIGURE 12.28**

The viscosity coefficient for whole blood relative to the viscosity coefficient of water as a function of the hematocrit value, which is a parameter measuring the volume fraction of blood cells in whole blood. The average hematocrit value for males is 46 and for females 41. Thus, males have on average blood of a higher viscosity, as indicated by the dashed lines.

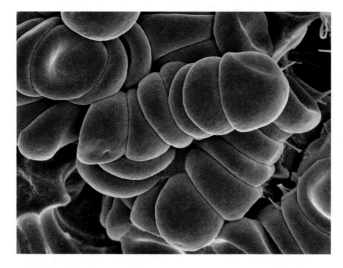

**FIGURE 12.30**

Nummulation of blood cells in blood that flows too slowly.

and have a highly flexible cell membrane. This allows blood to behave like a low-viscosity emulsion (mixture of two liquids). When blood flows slowly, however, aggregation of the red blood cells (erythrocytes) occurs in a process called **nummulation** (see Fig. 12.30). The red blood cells form a structure resembling a stack of coins. Nummulation creates a highly viscous suspension (mixture of solid in liquid).

# MULTIPLE CHOICE AND CONCEPTUAL QUESTIONS

## IDEAL DYNAMIC FLUID

**Q–12.1.** The volume flow rate and the mass flow rate in laminar flow are (A) the same, (B) proportional to each other, (C) inversely proportional to each other, (D) unrelated, (E) related in a non-linear fashion.

**Q–12.2.** The diameter of a tube increases from $d_1$ to $d_2 = 2 \cdot d_1$. As a result, the volume flow rate of laminar flow changes to (A) $\Delta V_2/\Delta t = \Delta V_1/\Delta t$, (B) $\Delta V_2/\Delta t = \frac{1}{2}\Delta V_1/\Delta t$, (C) $\Delta V_2/\Delta t = 2 \cdot \Delta V_1/\Delta t$, (D) $\Delta V_2/\Delta t = \frac{1}{4}\Delta V_1/\Delta t$, or (E) $\Delta V_2/\Delta t = 4 \cdot \Delta V_1/\Delta t$.

**Q–12.3.** Fig. 12.31 shows a cylindrical tube of changing diameter with an ideal dynamic fluid (blue) flowing toward the right with initial speed $v$. The vertical columns are connected to the main tube. Which of the five choices shows the proper elevations of the fluid in each of the three vertical columns?

**Q–12.4.** An artery has ballooned at one location outward (to a larger cross-section) due to an aneurysm. Which of the following statements is correct for blood flowing through this broadened section? Treat blood as an ideal dynamic fluid. (A) Blood will rush faster through the broadened section due to the equation of continuity. (B) The equation of continuity predicts an increase of the blood pressure in the broadened section. (C) Bernoulli's law predicts that the blood pressure in the broadened section is lower than in an adjacent section of the blood vessel, causing the blood vessel to temporarily collapse.

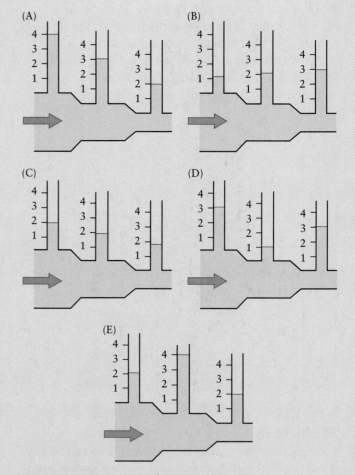

**FIGURE 12.31**

An ideal dynamic fluid (blue) flows through a cylindrical tube with initial speed $v$. Vertical columns are connected to the main tube to measure the fluid pressure.

(D) Bernoulli's law predicts that the blood pressure in the broadened section is higher than in an adjacent section of the blood vessel.

**Q–12.5.** The equation of continuity is an expression of (A) the conservation of mass, (B) the conservation of total energy, (C) the conservation of kinetic energy, (D) the conservation of velocity.

**Q–12.6.** Bernoulli's law contains a term $\frac{1}{2}\rho \cdot v^2$, which was derived from the kinetic energy of the ideal dynamic fluid. What units does this term carry? (A) J, (B) N, (C) m/s, (D) m/s$^2$, (E) Pa.

**Q–12.7.** Which law connects the speed of an ideal dynamic fluid to its pressure? (A) Pascal's law, (B) Newton's second law, (C) Bernoulli's law, (D) Laplace's law, (E) none of these.

**Q–12.8.** Bernoulli's law is an expression of (A) the conservation of mass, (B) the conservation of kinetic energy, (C) the conservation of total energy, (D) the conservation of velocity, (E) the conservation of momentum.

**Q–12.9.** The conservation of mass leads to the following law we use to describe laminar flow in a fluid: (A) Bernoulli's law, (B) Pascal's law, (C) equation of continuity, (D) Poiseuille's law, (E) Ohm's law.

**Q–12.10.** Do the following experiment as shown in Fig. 12.32: Push a pin through the centre of a thin sheet of cardboard. Locate the tip of the pin in the central hole of a thread spool from below. Hold the cardboard from below and start to blow through

the hole. The cardboard will not drop to the floor when you release it. Which law explains this effect? (A) Poiseuille's law, (B) Ohm's law, (C) equation of continuity, (D) Bernoulli's law, (E) Pascal's law.

**Q–12.11.** Do the following experiment: hold two sheets of paper parallel to each other at a distance of about 1 cm to 3 cm. Blow gently between the two sheets from their edges. The two sheets will be pulled together. Which law explains this observation? (A) Poiseuille's law, (B) Ohm's law, (C) equation of continuity, (D) Bernoulli's law, (E) Pascal's law.

**Q–12.12.** What additional information is needed to calculate the mass flow rate from the product of the cross-sectional area and the fluid speed in the equation of continuity? (A) none, (B) length of tube, (C) flow resistance, (D) density, (E) viscosity coefficient.

**Q–12.13.** An artery is partially clogged by a deposit on its inner wall, as shown in Fig. 12.33. Which of the following statements best describes the processes that occur when blood rushes through this constriction? Treat blood as a Newtonian fluid. (A) Blood will rush faster through the constriction due to the equation of continuity, causing additional wear and tear on the nearby blood vessel walls. (B) Bernoulli's law and the equation of continuity predict a variation of the blood pressure in the constricted zone, but the blood vessel walls prevent any adverse effect due to this pressure variation. (C) The blood pressure in the constriction zone is lower than in the adjacent blood vessel, causing the blood vessel to temporarily collapse at the constriction (vascular flutter). (D) The blood pressure in the constriction zone is higher than in the adjacent blood vessel, causing a ballooning effect of the blood vessel at the constriction (aneurysm).

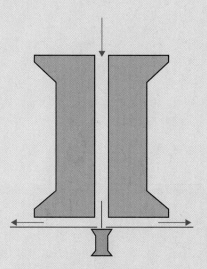

**FIGURE 12.32**

A pin is placed at the centre of a thin cardboard sheet. The pin's tip is then placed in the central hole of a thread spool. Hold the cardboard, then start blowing through the hole. Release the cardboard.

**FIGURE 12.33**

Cross-sectional view of a partially clogged artery.

**Q–12.14.** A blood vessel of radius $r$ splits into two smaller vessels, each with radius $r/4$. If the speed of the blood in the large vessel is $v_{large}$, what is the speed of the blood in each of the smaller vessels ($v_{small}$)? Treat blood as an ideal dynamic fluid. (A) $v_{small} = 8 \cdot v_{large}$, (B) $v_{small} = 4 \cdot v_{large}$, (C) $v_{small} = v_{large}$, (D) $v_{small} = v_{large}/4$, (E) $v_{small} = v_{large}/8$.

**Q–12.15.** North American prairie dogs live in underground burrows with several exits. They usually build a mound over one exit, which causes a draft past that hole. How does this arrangement allow for ventilation of the burrow with the air stagnant above all other exits?

**Q–12.16.** In chemistry laboratories, moderate vacuum conditions are obtained in an experimental setup when connecting the sealed apparatus to an aspirator. How does this instrument produce suction? *Note:* An aspirator is a device consisting of a T-shaped tube with tap water running through vertically and the side tube connected to the system you want to evacuate.

**Q–12.17.** Tornadoes and hurricanes can lift roofs off houses. A standard recommendation in affected areas is to keep windows open when a storm approaches. What happens to the roof, and why would open windows help?

## NEWTONIAN FLUIDS

**Q–12.18.** Use the viscosity coefficients from Table 12.1 for water at 20°C and for (whole) blood. With these values, a model for blood flow through the aorta is developed. We start with measuring the volume flow rate of water through an appropriately sized tube, using for the relevant parameters (such as pressure difference) physiological data for a standard man. Then we repeat the experiment with the same parameters and the same tube, but using whole blood. How will the volume flow rate change? (A) It is the same in both experiments. (B) It has increased due to Poiseuille's law. (C) It has increased due to Pascal's law. (D) It has decreased due to Poiseuille's law. (E) It has decreased due to Bernoulli's law.

**Q–12.19.** We study flow of a Newtonian fluid through two different tubes (index 1 and 2). The pressure differences between the two ends of the tubes, $\Delta p$, are the same for both tubes, $\Delta p_1 = \Delta p_2$. The tubes differ in radius and length: Length of tube 1 is $l_1 = 2$ m, length of tube 2 is $l_2 = 1$ m, radius of tube 1 is $r_1 = 2$ cm, and radius of tube 2 is $r_2 = 1$ cm. Which of the

following is the correct ratio of volume flow rates through the two tubes? (A) $\Delta V/\Delta t_1 : \Delta V/\Delta t_2 = 2 : 1$. (B) $\Delta V/\Delta t_1 : \Delta V/\Delta t_2 = 4 : 1$. (C) $\Delta V/\Delta t_1 : \Delta V/\Delta t_2 = 8 : 1$. (D) $\Delta V/\Delta t_1 : \Delta V/\Delta t_2 = 16 : 1$. (E) None of the above.

**Q–12.20.** Newtonian fluids include the following assumption that is excluded in ideal dynamic fluids: (A) incompressible fluid, (B) fluid molecules interact inelastically, (C) the flow is laminar, (D) flow tubes do not intersect, (E) flow lines do not vanish.

**Q–12.21.** Which of the following statements is wrong? (A) Poiseuille's law applies as derived only to laminar flow. (B) Poiseuille's law applies as derived only to ideal dynamic fluids. (C) Poiseuille's law applies as derived only to incompressible fluids. (D) Poiseuille's law and the equation of continuity can be used together for the same system. (E) Poiseuille's law applies as derived only to Newtonian fluids.

**Q–12.22.** Fig. 12.34 shows a cylindrical tube through which a Newtonian fluid flows. Which velocity profile $v(x)$ with $x$ the axis to the right best describes the actual velocity profile of the fluid?

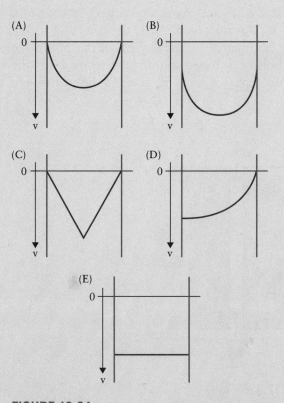

**FIGURE 12.34**

A Newtonian fluid passes through a cylindrical tube. Various velocity profiles $v(x)$ are proposed (red curves), with $x$ the axis to the right.

# ANALYTICAL PROBLEMS

## IDEAL DYNAMIC FLUIDS

**P–12.1.** What is the net upward force on an airplane wing of area $A = 20 \text{ m}^2$ if air streams at 300 m/s across its top and at 280 m/s past the bottom? Note that this airplane moves at subsonic speed with respect to the speed of sound (called Mach 1), about 330 m/s.

**P–12.2.** The instrument shown in Fig. 12.9 (Venturi meter) is used to measure the flow speed $v$ of a fluid in a tube of cross-sectional area $A$. This is done by integrating the instrument into the tube with the entry and exit cross-sectional areas identical to the primary tube. Between the entry and exit points, the fluid flows through a narrow constriction of cross-sectional area $a$. At the constriction the speed of the fluid is $v_{con}$. A manometer tube, connecting the wider and narrower portions of the main tube, shows a difference $\Delta h$ in the liquid levels in its two arms.

(a) Using Bernoulli's law and the equation of continuity, show that:

$$v = \sqrt{\frac{2 \cdot a^2 \cdot g \cdot \Delta h}{A^2 - a^2} \cdot \frac{\rho_{liquid}}{\rho_{fluid}}} \qquad [74]$$

(b) What is the volume flow rate $\Delta V/\Delta t$ if we use water for the fluid in the tube? The tube diameter is 0.8 m, the diameter of the constriction is 20 cm, and the pressure difference is 15 kPa.

**P–12.3.** A large water-containing tank is open to air. It has a small hole 16 m below the water surface through which water leaks at a rate of 2.5 L/min. Determine (a) the speed of the water that is ejected from the hole, and (b) the diameter of the hole.

**P–12.4.** An ideal dynamic fluid flows through a tapering tube. Upstream the tube has a cross-sectional area of 10 cm², the fluid pressure is 120 kPa, its density is $\rho = 1.65 \text{ g/cm}^3$, and the flow speed is 2.75 m/s. In the downstream section the cross-sectional area is 2.5 cm². Calculate in the downstream section (a) the fluid density, (b) the fluid flow speed, and (c) the fluid pressure.

**P–12.5.** Water is supplied to a building through a pipe of radius $R = 3.0$ cm. In the building, a faucet tap of radius $r = 1.0$ cm is located 2.0 m above the entering pipe. When the faucet is fully open, it allows us to fill a 25-L bucket in 0.5 minutes. (a) With what speed does the water leave the faucet? (b) What is the gauge pressure in the pipe entering the building? Assume that no other faucets are opened during the experiment.

**P–12.6.** Fig. 12.35 shows a tube A with radius $R$ that splits into two equal tubes B and C with radii $r = R/3$. (a) For an ideal dynamic fluid in this system of tubes, what is the ratio of the fluid speed in tubes A and B, $v_A/v_B$? (b) What is the pressure difference from the bifurcation point to the point of merger at the beginning of tube D? (c) If we substitute the ideal dynamic fluid for a Newtonian fluid with given viscosity coefficient, how do the results in parts (a) and (b) change? What additional parameter must be measured for tubes B and C? (d) Sketch the pressure in the fluid from left to right along tubes A, B, and D.

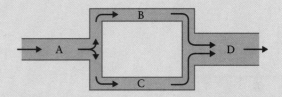

**FIGURE 12.35**

**P–12.7.** Fig. 12.36 shows a siphon. Flow in this device must be initiated with suction, but then proceeds on its own. (a) Show that water emerges from the open end at a speed of $v = (2 \cdot g \cdot h)^{1/2}$. (b) For what range of $y$-values will this device work?

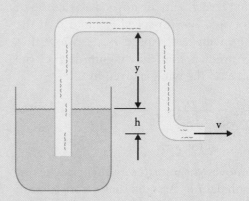

**FIGURE 12.36**

**P–12.8.** Fig. 12.37 shows a horizontal tube with a constriction and two open, vertical columns. The inner radius of the larger sections of the horizontal tube is 1.25 cm. Water passes through the tube at a rate of 0.18 L/s. If $h_1 = 10$ cm and $h_2 = 5$ cm, what is the inner radius at the constriction?

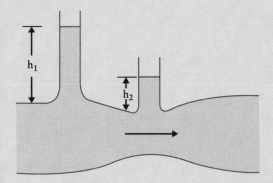

**FIGURE 12.37**

**P–12.9.** A beaker has a hole of radius $r = 1.75$ mm near its bottom from which water is ejected as shown in Fig. 12.38. Calculate the height $h$ of the water in the beaker if $h_1 = 1.0$ m and $h_2 = 0.6$ m.

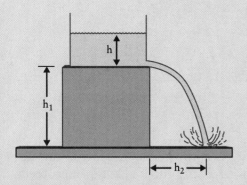

**FIGURE 12.38**

## EXAMPLES FROM MEDICINE AND BIOLOGY

**P–12.10.** During level flight, air flows over the top of a bird's wing of area $A$ with speed $v_{top}$ and past the underside of the wing with speed $v_{below}$. Show that Bernoulli's law predicts that the magnitude $F$ of the upward lift-force on the wing is given by:

$$F_{lift} = \frac{\rho \cdot A}{2} \left( v_{top}^2 - v_{below}^2 \right) \qquad [75]$$

with $\rho$ the density of the air.

**P–12.11.** Air moves through the human trachea at 3 m/s during inhalation. Assume that a constriction in the bronchus exists at which the speed doubles. Treating air as an ideal dynamic fluid, calculate the pressure in the constriction.

**P–12.12.** Confirm the data shown in Table 12.2 for the average length, radius, and individual and total flow resistance in (a) arterioles, (b) the aorta, and (c) capillaries. *Hint:* Use $\eta = 2.5 \times 10^{-3}$ N · s/m² as an average value for the blood viscosity coefficient from Table 12.1 at 37°C.

**P–12.13.** The hypodermic syringe in Fig. 12.39 contains water. The barrel of the syringe has a cross-sectional area $A_1 = 30$ mm². The pressure is 1.0 atm everywhere while no force is exerted on the plunger. When a force $F_{ext}$ of magnitude 2.0 N is exerted on the plunger, the water squirts from the needle. Determine the water's flow speed through the needle, $v_2$. Assume that the pressure in the needle remains at a value of $p_2 = 1.0$ atm and that the syringe is held horizontal. The final speed of the water in the barrel is negligible.

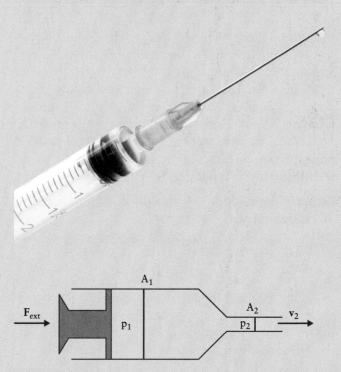

**FIGURE 12.39**

**P–12.14.** A hypodermic needle is 4.0 cm long and has an inner diameter of 0.25 mm. What excess pressure is required along the needle so that the flow rate of water through it is 1.0 g/s? Use the viscosity coefficient of water at 20°C from Table 12.1.

## NEWTONIAN FLUIDS

**P–12.15.** A horizontal tube of radius $r = 5.0$ mm and length $l = 50$ m carries oil ($\eta = 0.12$ N · s/m²). At the end of the tube the flow rate is 85 cm³/s and the pressure is $p = 1.0$ atm. What is the gauge pressure at the beginning of the tube?

**P–12.16.** A patient is to be injected with 0.5 L of an electrolyte solution in $\frac{1}{2}$ hour. Assuming that the solution is elevated by 1.0 m above the arm and the needle is 2.5 cm long, what inner radius should the needle have? Use water parameters for the solution, and assume that the pressure in the patient's vein is atmospheric pressure.

# SUMMARY

## DEFINITIONS

- Laminar flow: flow tubes (around flow lines) are not created in the flow; they do not intersect or vanish in the flow.
- Ideal dynamic fluid: a fluid that flows laminar. The fluid molecules interact only through elastic collisions with confining walls (frictionless motion).
- Newtonian fluid: a fluid that flows laminar. The fluid molecules interact inelastically with confining walls, causing a velocity gradient in the fluid.
- Viscosity is a property of resistance to flow in a fluid. It is quantified by the force needed to move a plate at constant velocity $\Delta v$ parallel to a plate at rest at distance $\Delta y$, both immersed in a fluid:

$$F_{ext} = \eta \cdot A \frac{|\Delta v|}{\Delta y}$$

$A$ is the cross-sectional area of the plates, $\eta$ is the viscosity coefficient, $|\Delta v|/\Delta y$ is a velocity gradient.

- Reynolds number for the transition from laminar to turbulent flow in a cylindrical tube ($Re < 2000$ is laminar, $Re > 2000$ is turbulent):

$$Re = \frac{\rho \cdot \langle v \rangle \cdot d}{\eta}$$

$\langle v \rangle$ is the average speed of the fluid, $d$ is the diameter of the tube, $\eta$ is the viscosity coefficient, and $\rho$ is the density of the fluid.

## UNITS

- Volume flow rate $\Delta V/\Delta t$: m$^3$/s
- Mass flow rate $\Delta m/\Delta t$: kg/s

- Viscosity coefficient $\eta$: N · s/m$^2$
- Flow resistance $R$: Pa · s/m$^3$

## LAWS

- Equation of continuity (fluid mass conservation) for laminar flow:

$$\frac{\Delta V}{\Delta t} = A \cdot |v| = const$$

where $\Delta V/\Delta t$ is the volume flow rate, $A$ is the cross-sectional area of the tube, and $|v|$ is the speed of the fluid.

- Bernoulli's law for an ideal dynamic fluid in a horizontal tube:

$$p + \frac{1}{2} \cdot \rho \cdot v^2 = const$$

where $p$ is the pressure in the fluid.

- Poiseuille's law for a Newtonian fluid in a cylindrical tube:

$$\frac{\Delta V}{\Delta t} = \frac{\pi}{8 \cdot \eta} r_{tube}^4 \frac{\Delta p}{l}$$

where $r_{tube}$ is the radius of the tube, and $\Delta p$ is the pressure difference along the length $l$ of the tube.

- Ohm's law for a Newtonian fluid:

$$\Delta p = R \frac{\Delta V}{\Delta t}$$

where $R$ is the flow resistance. The flow resistance in a cylindrical tube is:

$$R = \frac{8 \cdot l}{\pi \cdot r_{tube}^4} \eta$$

# CHAPTER 13

# THE WATER MOLECULE
## Static Electricity

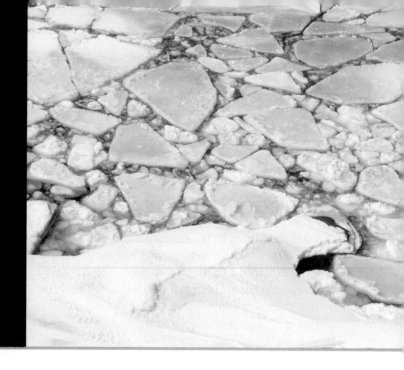

Biological systems are electrically active at the molecular level. Many of the phenomena we observe can be explained only when electric effects are included, from the unique role of water in aqueous solutions to the conduction of a nerve signal through an axon.

Electric charge and mass are two different properties of matter. Different from mass, charge is quantized and comes in two types: two equal electric charges repel each other, while two dissimilar charges attract each other. The force between point charges is a long-range contact-free force that varies in magnitude with the inverse square of their distance from each other (Coulomb's law).

The electric field is introduced to allow us to handle the many possible variations of charge arrangements. For stationary charge distributions it is derived from Coulomb's law. The electric field then represents at each point in space the net electric force per unit charge due to these stationary charges in the system.

The magnitude of the electric field due to a stationary point charge is inversely proportional to the square of the distance from the point charge; the magnitude of the electric field due to a dipole is inversely proportional to the cube of the distance to the dipole. Therefore, dipoles interact strongly at close proximity, whereas they show a significantly weaker electric interaction at longer distances. This short-range nature is evident in the tight hydration shells around ions in aqueous solutions.

The electric field has its simplest possible form for a parallel plate arrangement with equal but opposite surface charge densities on the two plates: the field is constant in magnitude and direction for all positions between the plates. This makes the charged parallel plate arrangement a preferred model for biological membrane systems.

The electric potential energy is introduced in analogy to the gravitational potential energy. It also resumes its simplest form for the parallel plate arrangement, for which the electric energy is linearly proportional to the distance of the charged particle to the oppositely charged plate.

For a system with a large number of stationary charges, the potential is introduced to simplify the calculation of electric energy in the same way that the electric field is introduced to simplify calculations of electric forces.

Water defines the conditions for life on Earth. It is the one chemical compound scientists seek on other planets to determine whether they may bear life. Water receives this extraordinary attention in the life sciences because it has a long list of unique physical properties.

- **Hydrogen-bond formation.** The water molecule is shown in Fig. 13.1. It consists of one oxygen atom and two hydrogen atoms, which are arranged at an angle of 104.5°. The bonds that hold the atoms in the molecule together are polar covalent bonds; that is, strong chemical bonds exist between hydrogen and oxygen, but the electrons that form these bonds are shifted toward the oxygen atom. As a result, the oxygen end of the molecule carries a partial negative charge $\delta_-$ and the hydrogen end carries a partial positive charge $\delta_+$. Opposite charges separated by a fixed distance define a dipole. Dipoles interact electrically with ions and other dipoles. The interaction is strongest at short range and more effective along the dipole axis than in other directions (directional anisotropy). In liquid water, the positive end of one dipole and the negative end of another dipole attract each other. In close proximity they form a hydrogen bond, which is an inter-molecular sharing of some of the excess electric charge carried by the oxygen atom.

- **Hydrogen bonds lead to cohesion.** Water molecules stick to each other as a result of hydrogen bonding. We observe this when water droplets form, such as on the branch shown in Fig. 13.2.

**FIGURE 13.2**

Water cohesion is seen in the formation of water droplets on leaves and branches.

When water is in its liquid form, its hydrogen bonds are fragile: they are only about 5% to 10% as strong as covalent bonds. Each hydrogen bond lasts only for about $1 \times 10^{-12}$ s, but so many of these bonds exist in a droplet of water at any given time that the net effect is profound. Thus, we have found a collective property: hydrogen bonds hold water together at a macroscopic scale. This effect is called **cohesion**.

Related to cohesion is the effect of surface tension, which is a measure of how much effort is needed to increase the surface area of a liquid. Water has a larger surface tension than most other liquids due to the cohesion between the water molecules. We note the large surface tension of water when we observe animals like water-striders standing on water without breaking the surface.

Large cohesion and surface tension allow water to be liquid at room temperature. Most other small molecules are in the gaseous state at room temperature; the closest is ammonia, which boils at −33°C. In an ammonia solution, all chemical processes are significantly slower because chemical reaction rates roughly double for every additional 10 K of temperature.

- **The high latent heat of vaporization of water favours evaporative cooling.** The latent heat of vaporization is the amount of energy required for the phase transition of one mol of a material from the liquid to the vapour state at its boiling point. Liquids with hydrogen bonds have a large latent heat of vaporization because the hydrogen bonds have to be broken during evaporation. Evaporation takes place at all temperatures when the vapour phase is under-saturated (compare

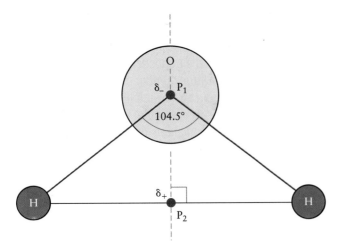

**FIGURE 13.1**

The water molecule consists of two hydrogen atoms and one oxygen atom. The hydrogen atoms are connected to the oxygen atom with covalent bonds. The electrons in these bonds are drawn closer to the oxygen atom, leading to a net negative charge $\delta_-$ near the oxygen end of the molecule at point $P_1$, and a net positive charge $\delta_+$ near its hydrogen end at point $P_2$.

Fig. 9.6 for the water vapour pressure as a function of temperature). Thus, a large amount of energy is required when water evaporates from a surface; this energy is taken from the internal energy of the substrate.

On a global scale, evaporative cooling helps moderate the climate: a significant fraction of the solar heat absorbed by equatorial oceans is stored in water vapour that forms during evaporation of surface water. This moisture then circulates toward the poles, where it releases the stored thermal energy when it condenses to form rain or snow. On the level of individual organisms, evaporative cooling allows perspiration to be an effective mechanism to prevent terrestrial animals from overheating. Water evaporation from leaves also keeps plant tissues from overheating in direct sunlight.

- **Ice floats on the surface of liquid water.** Water is one of the few materials that are less dense in solid form than in the liquid state. While most materials contract when they solidify, water expands to accommodate the hydrogen-bond structure. At temperatures above 4°C, water behaves like other liquids: it expands when heated and it contracts when cooled. Below 4°C, more and more hydrogen bonds remain stable, which requires a greater inter-molecular distance. At 0°C water then freezes as the thermal energy of the molecules is no longer sufficient to break hydrogen bonds. Ice is fully ordered with a wide-open molecular arrangement, leading to a 10% reduction in **ice density** compared to liquid water at 4°C. This effect is biologically important because if ice were to sink, ponds, lakes, and oceans would eventually freeze solid, making life as we know it impossible. To the contrary, floating ice thermally insulates the liquid water below—as shown in the image at the beginning of the chapter—allowing life to exist under the frozen surface.

- **Water is an effective solvent in chemistry.** Water forms in an exothermal reaction from the elements (which is the energy-supplying process in the production of ATP in the mitochondria) and is the by-product of many chemical reactions, including the main metabolic processes in our body (see Table 8.3). However, its chemical importance is based on its role as a solvent. A sodium chloride crystal would not dissolve if the water molecules could not form a hydration shell that stabilizes the ions in solution. A hydration shell consists of a large number of water molecules

that form a layer around a charged particle. This shell is energetically favoured because of an electric interaction between the charged particle and the water molecule.

Aqueous solutions are widespread: from seawater to the cytoplasm in cells, a great variety of dissolved ions are found. Water is a very versatile solvent. A compound does not need to be ionic to dissolve in water; sugar, for example, dissolves because it is a polar molecule (dipole structure). Even molecules as large as proteins dissolve in water as they often have ionic and/or polar regions. An economic application is shown in Fig. 13.3, which depicts salt farming in Southeast Asia.

All these phenomena point to the electric dipole structure of the water molecule in Fig. 13.1 as a common cause. In this chapter, we want to establish the fundamental laws that characterize electric systems. Choosing the interactions of a molecule as a focal point for this chapter also suggests that the discussion of electric phenomena will take quite a different path than the discussion of forces in mechanics. In mechanics, the fundamental force called

**FIGURE 13.3**

Salt farming in Southeast Asia.

gravity was simplified to a single application, called weight, because we are limiting our discussion to processes in the biosphere; it is always directed downward and its magnitude is proportional to the mass of the object. The discussion of the electric force won't be that short, because there is no single dominant charge that always plays the role of the mass of Earth.

It is therefore important that we avoid becoming overwhelmed by the multitude of electric phenomena. An introduction-level text must take a well-organized and selective approach to achieve this goal: we will start by defining the concept of charge and the law that describes the interaction of just two charges as the simplest possible case. But then we do not expand in what would be a futile effort to develop a complete overview of electricity. Rather, we pause after the introduction of the electric force and reflect on what we want to accomplish with the basic concept established. That discussion will lay out the plan for the remainder of this and the next two chapters: we find that the water dipole we referred to above and the charged membrane system we discuss in the next chapter for the nervous system are two versatile key models. Once we have studied these two models, most other electric systems can be discussed analogously. The electric activity of the heart in Chapter 15 serves as an example.

# Electric Charge and Force

## Beyond Mass: The Particle Property Electric Charge

A wide range of phenomena exist in which particles are not sufficiently characterized by their mass. Such phenomena include acidity regulation of the blood, salt dissolution in water, and salt counter-current filtration in the kidneys. In order to describe these phenomena, a second, mass-independent property of matter has to be introduced: the **electric charge**. The physical laws that govern the behaviour of objects carrying electric charge are distinct from the laws of mechanics because a new fundamental force is associated with electric charges: the electric force. This force is the second fundamental force we discuss in this textbook, following our earlier discussion of gravity and weight.

Electric charge is an intrinsic property of the particles that comprise matter, in the same fashion as mass is an intrinsic property of the same particles. Because particles carrying single charges are usually very small, the concept of a **point charge** is introduced.

*A point charge is a charged particle with negligible size.*

Mass and charge of a particle are independent from each other. In our discussion of mechanics we established that there is only one type of mass; objects may have more or less of it, but none can have a different type of mass, e.g., a negative mass. The idea of a negative mass had indeed been discussed for a while in the scientific community. It was postulated in 1697 as part of Georg Ernst Stahl's phlogiston theory to explain combustion. He claimed that combustion is the loss of particles with negative mass; he called these particles phlogiston. This theory was finally discredited in 1777 by Antoine Laurent de Lavoisier when he properly described combustion as a chemical reaction with oxygen.

For charges, on the other hand, two different types exist: two charges of the same type repel each other and two opposite charges attract each other. To distinguish these two kinds of charges we call one type of charge a **positive charge**, $q_+$, and the other type a **negative charge**, $q_-$. One could have called them blue and red charges instead, but invoking the notation of mathematical signs turned out to be convenient as opposite charges indeed offset each other in their physical effects: a given amount of positive charge is shielded by the same amount of negative charge in close proximity, which explains the apparent electric neutrality of matter.

To see point charges of either type display their physical properties at a macroscopic level, the electric charges in a system must be separated. This can be achieved in physical experiments, but also happens inadvertently in our daily life, e.g., when your shoe soles rub against plastic surfaces on a dry day. When you later touch another person or a conducting surface like a door knob, you feel a tingle as electric charges leave your skin. Hospital personnel therefore must wear special conducting shoes to avoid sparking when working with oxygen.

## The Magnitude of the Electric Force

We introduce the property charge quantitatively in terms of the force that occurs between separate point charges. The relation between electric force and charge was discovered by Charles Augustin de Coulomb in 1784 and is called Coulomb's law. He experimented with metal spheres carrying electric charges. He observed that:

*The magnitude of the electric force between two charged spheres is proportional to the absolute amount of charge on each sphere, and is proportional to $1/r^2$ where r is the distance between the spheres.*

His observations are summarized in a formula for the electric force $F_{el}$:

$$F_{el} \propto \frac{|q_1| \cdot |q_2|}{r^2} \qquad [1]$$

Note that $F_{el}$ is proportional to the absolute values of the two interacting charges $q_1$ and $q_2$. We will include the signs of the charges in the next section, when introducing the electric force as a vector. We also note from Eq. [1] that the force is reduced to $\frac{1}{4}$ when the distance $r$ between the spheres is doubled. The standard unit of charge is C (coulomb), named in honour of Coulomb's work.

To write the relation in Eq. [1] as an equation, a proportionality factor is used in the scientific literature. This factor is $1/(4 \cdot \pi \cdot \varepsilon_0)$, in which $\varepsilon_0$ is a fundamental physical constant called **permittivity of vacuum**: $\varepsilon_0 = 8.85 \times 10^{-12} \, C^2/(N \cdot m^2)$. How $\varepsilon_0$ is related to the idea of *reaching through vacuum* becomes clear later in this chapter when we discuss the electric field. The **electric force** is then written in the form:

$$F_{el} = \frac{1}{4 \cdot \pi \cdot \varepsilon_0} \frac{|q_1| \cdot |q_2|}{r^2} \qquad [2]$$

This is called **Coulomb's law**. Quantitatively, two equal point charges of 1 C each, placed at a distance of 1 m, attract each other with a force of $9 \times 10^9$ N. Compared to forces we saw in earlier chapters this force is very large; we will develop an intuitive sense for the strength of the electric force in the many examples we discuss below.

An important difference between mass and charge is the fact that the latter is **quantized**. What does this mean? The concept of quantization can be illustrated with our use of money. Goods you buy at a store cannot cost any amount of money; they can cost only a multiple of the smallest unit of currency, which in North America is 1 cent. Even when taxes are added to a bill, you will never be asked to pay 7.5 cents. Any payment will always be an amount that is an integer multiple of one cent. In nature, no such limitation exists for mass; any amount of mass can occur. However, with respect to charge, all processes are based on the transfer of an integer multiple of the smallest amount of charge, which we call the **elementary charge** $e = 1.6 \times 10^{-19}$ C.

Table 13.1 illustrates this for the mass and charge of the fundamental particles in atoms: the electron $(e^-)$, the proton $(p^+)$, and the neutron $(n^0)$. While the masses of elementary particles vary, their charges have the same value regardless of whether it is positive or negative. Charge quantization and the value of the elementary charge were first determined by Robert Andrews Millikan in 1909 with the experiment

**TABLE 13.1**

**Elementary particles in the atom**

| Particle | Mass (kg) | Charge (C) |
|---|---|---|
| Electron | $9.11 \times 10^{-31}$ | $-1.6 \times 10^{-19}$ |
| Proton | $1.673 \times 10^{-27}$ | $+1.6 \times 10^{-19}$ |
| Neutron | $1.675 \times 10^{-27}$ | 0 |

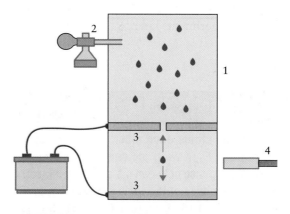

**FIGURE 13.4**

Robert Millikan's experiment. Oil mist, consisting of microscopic oil droplets, is sprayed into a chamber (1). Many of the oil droplets carry charges due to the friction of the oil when leaving the metallic nozzle of the vaporizer (2). The droplets sink downward due to their weight. It is possible to levitate individual oil droplets between two charged metallic plates (3) that form a horizontal parallel plate arrangement. A mechanical equilibrium can be observed with a microscope (4) and is due to the balance between the weight and the electric force acting upward, as indicated on the lower oil droplet by two arrows. From this experiment the electric charge on the oil droplet is determined. It has been shown that this charge is always a multiple of the elementary charge.

sketched in Fig. 13.4. His setup consisted of a chamber into which oil is sprayed from the metallic nozzle of an oil vaporizer. The oil mist consists of microscopic droplets that often carry an electric charge due to friction of the oil with the inner surface of the metallic nozzle during spraying. All oil droplets in the chamber sink slowly downward due to their weight. Some fall through a hole in a plate that separates the upper and lower parts of the chamber. In the lower part the oil droplets can be observed with a microscope. The separating plate with the hole and a second plate at the bottom of the chamber are electrically isolated and form a parallel plate arrangement when charged with a battery. As we see later in this chapter, parallel charged plates allow us to exert an electric force on a point charge that is located between them. In the case of Fig. 13.4, we choose the electric force such that it is directed upward, i.e., counteracting the weight. The electric force due to the two plates is adjusted such that a particular oil droplet, chosen with the microscope, levitates at a fixed height. This means that the electric force $F_{el}$ upward and the weight of the droplet **W** are balanced (application of Newton's first law). The charge of the droplet is determined from the amount of charges needed on the two plates in Fig. 13.4. This experiment has been done numerous times, and an oil drop with a charge other than an integer multiple of the elementary charge has never been found. We quantify Millikan's experiment later in this chapter in Example 13.9.

---

**Concept Question 13.1**

Two point charges attract each other with an electric force of magnitude $F_{el}$. If we triple one of the charges, and increase the distance between the points by a factor of 3, does the magnitude of the force between the particles become (A) $F_{el}/9$, (B) $F_{el}/3$, (C) 0 (zero), (D) $3 \cdot F_{el}$, or (E) $9 \cdot F_{el}$?

ANSWER: Choice (B). Eq. [2] is linear in the absolute amount of each charge but non-linear in their distance.

---

**● EXAMPLE 13.1**

(a) Find the magnitude of the electric force $F_{el}$ exerted on a point charge $+3 \cdot e$ by a point charge $-5 \cdot e$ that is located 7 nm away. (b) Compare the electric and gravitational forces between the electron and the nucleus (proton) in a hydrogen atom.

*Solution to part (a):* We use Coulomb's law. To find the magnitude of the force only the absolute values of both charges are entered:

$$F_{el} = \frac{|q_1| \cdot |q_2|}{4 \cdot \pi \cdot \varepsilon_0 \cdot r^2}$$

$$= \frac{\left(9 \times 10^9 \, \frac{N \cdot m^2}{C^2}\right)(4.8 \times 10^{-19} C)(8 \times 10^{-19} C)}{(7 \times 10^{-9} m)^2}$$

$$= 7.1 \times 10^{-11} N \qquad [3]$$

Numerically, the result in Example 13.1 seems to be a small force, particularly when you take the short distance between the two point charges into

account. However, the elementary charge is a small amount of charge.

*Solution to part (b):* It becomes evident that the electric force is very strong when we compare it to the gravitational force between the electron and the nucleus in a hydrogen atom. We have all the necessary data in Table 13.1 for this comparison except for the separation distance between the two particles. This distance is called the Bohr radius (Chapter 22), with $r_{Bohr} = 5.3 \times 10^{-11}$ m = 0.053 nm. Eq. [2] yields:

$$F_{electric} = \frac{1}{4 \cdot \pi \cdot \varepsilon_0} \frac{e^2}{r_{Bohr}^2} = 8 \times 10^{-8} N \quad [4]$$

while Eq. [3.4] yields:

$$F_{gravity} = G* \frac{m_e \cdot m_p}{r_{Bohr}^2} = 4 \times 10^{-47} N \quad [5]$$

i.e., the two forces are different by almost 40 orders of magnitude!

## The Direction of the Electric Force

As the discussion of Millikan's experiment suggests, the electric force, like any other force, is characterized by magnitude and direction. Including the direction based on vector notation, Coulomb's law expresses the force a point charge $q_1$ exerts on a point charge $q_2$:

$$\mathbf{F}_{12} = \frac{1}{4 \cdot \pi \cdot \varepsilon_0} \frac{q_1 \cdot q_2}{r^2} \mathbf{r}_{12}^0 \qquad [6]$$

in which $\mathbf{r}_{12}^0$ is a vector of unit length (denoted by the superscript 0) that points from point charge $q_1$ to point charge $q_2$. Note that Eq. [6] no longer requires the absolute amount of the two charges. The direction of the electric force is therefore determined by two factors:

• the relative positions of the two point charges, and

• the signs of the charges of the two interacting particles.

This is illustrated in Fig. 13.5(a) for two positive point charges, and in Fig. 13.5(b) when the two point charges carry opposite signs. Also included is the force $\mathbf{F}_{21}$, which is the reaction force to $\mathbf{F}_{12}$ and acts on point charge $q_1$.

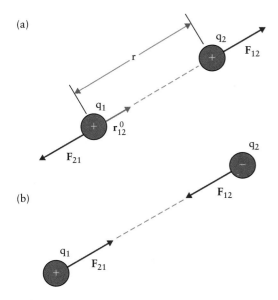

(a)

(b)

**FIGURE 13.5**

The direction of the electric force as a function of the relative positions of two point charges and the signs of their charges. (a) Two positive point charges. (b) Point charges that carry opposite signs.

## Concept Question 13.2

Fig. 13.6 shows eight possible cases for the horizontal arrangement of two point charges. The figure further shows the direction of the electric force vector acting in each case on the point charge represented by the large circle. To describe these arrangements with Coulomb's law the unit vector $r^0$ in Eq. [6] has to be identified. Do all eight unit vectors in Fig. 13.6 point in the same direction?

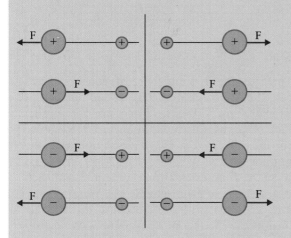

**FIGURE 13.6**

Eight cases showing the direction of the electric force on a point charge of interest (large circle) due to a second point charge (smaller circle) in its vicinity.

ANSWER: The unit vector in Eq. [6] is directed from the point charge that is the source of the force to the point charge on which the force acts. Thus, the unit vector points to the left for the four cases in the left column, and it points to the right for the four cases in the right column.

## Newton's Laws and Charged Objects

In the Newtonian approach to forces the electric force is treated like any other force we have discussed in the previous chapters of this textbook. In particular, if point charges are present in a system, free-body diagrams must also include the relevant electric forces. The net force acting on a point charge is calculated as the sum of all forces, including electric forces, that act on the object of interest. When $N$ electric forces act on an object of charge $Q$, the net electric force is written in vector notation:

$$\mathbf{F}_{el,net} = \sum_{i=1}^{N} \mathbf{F}_{el,i} = \frac{1}{4 \cdot \pi \cdot \varepsilon_0} \sum_{i=1}^{N} \frac{Q \cdot q_i}{r_i^2} \mathbf{r}_i^0 \qquad [7]$$

in which $r_i$ is the distance between the $i$-th point charge $q_i$ and point charge $Q$, and $\mathbf{r}_i^0$ is the unit vector that is directed from the $i$-th point charge to point charge $Q$.

## ● EXAMPLE 13.2

We consider three point charges that are positioned along an axis as illustrated in Fig. 13.7(a). Two of these point charges are positive—$q_1 = 20\ \mu C$, $q_2 = 5\ \mu C$—and are separated by a distance $L = 1.5$ m. At what distance $x_0$ from $q_2$ must a negative point charge $q_3$ be positioned such that the resulting force on it is zero?

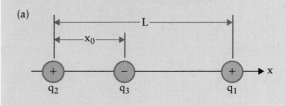

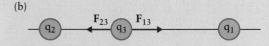

**FIGURE 13.7**

(a) Three point charges are positioned along the x-axis as shown. (b) Two forces act on point charge $q_3$, which is positioned between the other two point charges.

## ● EXAMPLE 13.2 (*continued*)

*Solution:* The sketch in Fig. 13.7(b) shows the same point charge arrangement as Fig. 13.7(a) but highlights the two forces acting on $q_3$. In that sketch $q_3$ is attracted toward each of the other two point charges since $q_3$ is negative while $q_1$ and $q_2$ are positive. As a consequence, the two forces shown in Fig. 13.7(b), $F_{13}$ and $F_{23}$, point in opposite directions. The circle for charge $q_3$ and the two forces acting on that point charge constitute the free-body diagram for this problem since the vertical components of both forces are zero. The absolute values of the horizontal components of the forces are equal to their magnitudes. Mechanical equilibrium is established when the horizontal component of the net force on $q_3$ is zero:

$$F_{el,net} = -\frac{1}{4 \cdot \pi \cdot \varepsilon_0} \frac{|q_1| \cdot |q_3|}{r_{13}^2}$$

$$+ \frac{1}{4 \cdot \pi \cdot \varepsilon_0} \frac{|q_2| \cdot |q_3|}{r_{23}^2} = 0 \qquad [8]$$

i.e., when $F_{23} = F_{13}$ due to Newton's first law. We substitute the given values for the charges and distances and cancel $q_3$ on both sides of the equation:

$$\frac{20 \times 10^{-6}\,C}{(L - x_0)^2} = \frac{5 \times 10^{-6}\,C}{x_0^2} \qquad [9]$$

Note that we need not define the origin of the axis along which the three point charges are located because only their distances enter Coulomb's law. Eq. [9] leads to a quadratic equation that is solved for the distance $x_0$ between $q_2$ and the central point charge:

$$5 \cdot (1.5 - x_0)^2 = 20 \cdot x_0^2 \qquad [10]$$

This yields:

$$0 = 15 x_0^2 + 15 x_0 - 11.25 \qquad [11]$$

Eq. [11] has two solutions:

$$x_0 = \frac{-15 \pm \sqrt{15^2 + 4 \cdot 15 \cdot 11.25}}{2 \cdot 15} \qquad [12]$$

i.e.,

$$x_{0,1} = -1.5\,m$$
$$x_{0,2} = +0.5\,m \qquad [13]$$

Since $q_3$ must lie between the other two point charges, the second solution in Eq. [13] is the proper answer. We can easily convince ourselves that this result makes sense. Coulomb's law contains the charge and the square of the distance. Thus, a doubling of the distance is compensated by a fourfold increase of the charge.

## ● EXAMPLE 13.3

Three point charges $q_1$, $q_2$, and $q_3$ are located at the corners of an equilateral triangle with side length $d$, as shown in Fig. 13.8. Assume $q_1 = q_2 = q_3 = 20\,\mu C$ and $d = 1.5$ m. What is the magnitude of the net force on point charge $q_1$?

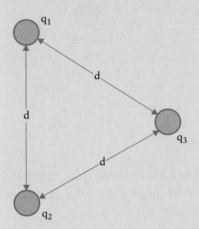

**FIGURE 13.8**

Three point charges $q_1$, $q_2$, and $q_3$ are located at the corners of an equilateral triangle with side length $d$.

*Solution:* We determine first the magnitude of force between any two of the point charges using Coulomb's law:

$$F_{el} = \frac{1}{4 \cdot \pi \cdot \varepsilon_0} \frac{|q_1| \cdot |q_2|}{r^2}$$

$$= \frac{\left(9 \times 10^9\,\dfrac{N \cdot m^2}{C^2}\right)(2 \times 10^{-5}\,C)^2}{(1.5\,m)^2}$$

$$= 1.6\,N \qquad [14]$$

The net force on point charge $q_1$ consists of two forces, one due to point charge $q_2$ and one due to point charge $q_3$. These two forces are not parallel to each other, as illustrated in Fig. 13.9. We solve the problem using Eq. [7]. We first note that the magnitudes of the two forces $\mathbf{F}_{13}$ and $\mathbf{F}_{23}$ are equal because the charges $q_2$ and $q_3$ are equal and each is at a distance $d$ from charge $q_1$. We also note in Fig. 13.9 that $\theta = 60°$, because the triangle formed by the three point charges is an equilateral triangle.

Next, we choose a coordinate system to write the two forces in component form. Our choice is shown in Fig. 13.9: the *x*-axis is directed toward the right and the *y*-axis is directed up. With this coordinate system we express the components of

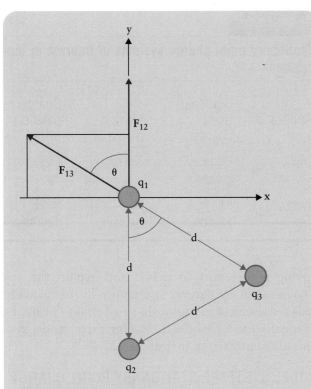

**FIGURE 13.9**

The same three point charges as shown in Fig. 13.8, forming an equilateral triangle. Two electric forces act on the point charge $q_1$ at the top, labelled $\mathbf{F}_{12}$ and $\mathbf{F}_{13}$ to indicate which point charge exerts the respective force. These two forces form an angle $\theta$; vector algebra is used to calculate the net force acting on point charge $q_1$.

the net force based on the components of the two forces $\mathbf{F}_{13}$ and $\mathbf{F}_{23}$. For the $x$-component, we find:

$$F_{\text{net},x} = -F_{13} \cdot \sin \theta = -(1.6 \text{ N}) \sin 60°$$

$$= -1.4 \text{ N} \qquad [15]$$

and for the $y$-component we get:

$$F_{\text{net},y} = F_{12} + F_{13} \cdot \cos \theta$$

$$= 1.6 \text{ N} + (1.6 \text{ N}) \cos 60°$$

$$= +2.4 \text{ N} \qquad [16]$$

The Pythagorean theorem is used to combine the two components:

$$F_{\text{el,net}} = \sqrt{F_{\text{net},x}^2 + F_{\text{net},y}^2} = 2.78 \text{ N} \qquad [17]$$

# How Do We Approach Electric Phenomena in Life Science Applications?

Faced with a huge number of possible charge arrangements, we need to organize our approach in two ways before we can proceed:

- We need to divide the force calculations based on Eq. [7] into three steps. This is done by distinguishing the different roles the various point charges play in an electric arrangement.

- We need to select a few representative model systems that allow us to establish the important physical concepts without getting lost in numerous applications.

To address the first point, we follow a method that Michael Faraday originally developed and that has proven very effective in all practical cases. The net force, as introduced in Eq. [7], requires a simultaneous inclusion of all point charges in a system, because the electric force is a contact-free force and non-negligible interactions take place across quite some distance. Faraday reasoned that it would be easier to study electric phenomena if we no longer had to consider all point charge interactions at once but could confine the discussion to a point charge of interest that interacts with what he called an electric field. The electric field then represents the effect of all point charges in the system at the position of the point charge of interest.

The success of Faraday's approach lies in the fact that it works for all electric systems. However, we choose to restrict the cases we study to diminish the risk of confusion during a first discussion of the electric field concept: we study only those systems in which the point charge sources of the electric field are stationary (i.e., do not move relative to each other). This then leads to a **stationary electric field,** and this approach is defined in the physical literature as **electrostatics.** This is a restrictive choice because in real life charges other than the charge of interest may move. We consider such cases later: in Chapters 14 and 15 we talk about changing electric fields at nerve membranes or in the heart, and in Chapter 20 we explore how moving charges and changing electric fields are related to magnetic fields and electromagnetic radiation. Our choice to confine the discussion in the current chapter to stationary electric fields has two important justifications: (i) it includes the most important systems in the life sciences, and (ii) it is conceptually easier to grasp and allows us therefore to lay a strong foundation for the discussion of more general cases later. Thus, our approach for the current chapter is as follows:

- **Step (i):** We divide the system into two groups of point charges: first, a single point charge that we consider the point charge of interest—conceptually this point charge should be a **mobile point charge** since otherwise no interesting electric processes could occur; second, an arrangement of point charges that constitute the **source point charges** for an electric field. We require (in this chapter) the source point charges to be stationary, and therefore usually refer to them as the **stationary point charges**.

- **Step (ii)**: For the stationary point charge arrangement, we determine its **stationary electric field**. The term *field* means mathematically that we assign a numerical value to each position in space within a system. In the case of an electric field, these values represent the strength of electric interaction that a mobile point charge of unit charge would encounter if placed at the respective position. The electric field is a vector field since its values are calculated with Coulomb's law, in which the force enters as a vector.

- **Step (iii)**: Dynamic properties of the point charge of interest are studied by inserting it into the system. Its motion is fully determined by the stationary electric field and Newton's second law, which then determines the magnitude and direction of the acceleration of the mobile point charge at every position.

Both steps (ii) and (iii) may require extensive mathematical calculations; however, once the stationary electric field is calculated for a particular arrangement of charges, this field can be used for a large number of dynamic calculations in step (iii) without a need to repeat step (ii). Were we not to introduce this procedure adopted from Faraday's reasoning, all such calculations would be a combination of steps (ii) and (iii); i.e., the calculations for every new starting position of a mobile point charge would include the entire field calculation.

For every new arrangement of stationary charges a new calculation of the stationary electric field is required. Thus, any means of limiting the number of arrangements we need to study reduces the overall effort. Specifically, we want to pick a small number of charge arrangements that are representative of as many practical cases as possible. These we consider our **model systems**. To arrive at their selection we can ask ourselves one of the following questions:

- Which models describe most electric systems that occur in nature?

- Which models describe most electric devices engineered for applications in life science laboratories and health care facilities?

- Which models allow us to study basic electricity with the least mathematical effort?

Interestingly, all three questions lead to the same three basic systems. This is not accidental—engi-

### TABLE 13.2

**Stationary point charge systems of interest in this textbook**

| Application in: | Stationary point charge | Electric dipole | Charged parallel plates |
|---|---|---|---|
| Physics | Electrons in a metal | Antenna | Capacitors |
| Biology | Ions in solution | Water molecule | Nerve membrane |

neering is an effort to mimic and exploit the approach taken by nature, and nature in turn usually finds the simplest solutions that also tend to be mathematically easiest to describe. Our three model systems are summarized in Table 13.2.

### MODEL SYSTEM I: STATIONARY POINT CHARGE

This is the most basic system. We already used it when we introduced Coulomb's law in Eq. [2]. Once we identify one of the two point charges in that equation as a mobile point charge, a single stationary point charge results as the system. Stationary point charges are frequently observed, e.g., each ion in an ionic salt can be treated as a point charge. We will use this approach in P–13.5 to study the electric properties of a void defect in a CsCl crystal, and in P–13.3 for interactions between elementary particles within an atomic nucleus.

For the point charge model, the force concept has been used in Examples 13.1, 13.2, and 13.3; electric fields will be calculated in the next section. The corresponding electric energy is then discussed for an ionic crystal in Example 13.12.

The simplest dynamic system for an arrangement of stationary point charges is an electron in a solid **metal**, because this system allows us to apply concepts we already developed in Chapter 7 for the ideal gas. Metal atoms (i.e., all elements left of a line from boron (B) to iodine (I) in the periodic table) consist of a tightly bound shell of inner electrons and one or a few loosely bound outer electrons, called **valence electrons**. When a large number of metal atoms are brought together, the atoms form an ordered lattice by releasing these outermost electrons into a cloud of **quasi-free electrons**. These electrons are mobile within the stationary lattice of metal ions. When no external force exists, the electron moves randomly like gas particles in a container, as discussed for the kinetic gas theory. Instead of collisions with other gas

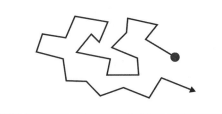

**FIGURE 13.10**

Model of an electron in a piece of metal. The electron moves freely, similar to a particle in a box filled with gas. However, the electrons scatter frequently off the densely packed immobile metal ions.

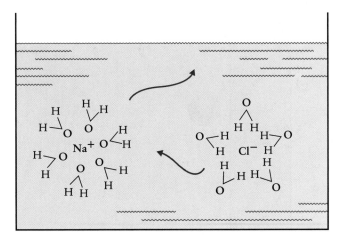

**FIGURE 13.11**

Sketch of a positive sodium ion and a negative chlorine ion in an aqueous solution. Water dipoles form a hydration shell around each ion while it moves through the solution, screening the ion's charge and thus reducing the interaction between ions.

particles, collisions with the metal ions occur as illustrated in Fig. 13.10. We use the electron in a metal system in Chapter 14 to introduce electric conduction.

## MODEL SYSTEM II: ELECTRIC DIPOLE

Even though one may argue that the electric dipole is just a special application of model system I with two stationary point charges, it is identified here as a separate model system due to its widespread applications.

For this model, the electric field will again be calculated in the next section and will be used to introduce the dipole moment as a parameter that identifies the strength of dipoles. Hydrogen bonds and the chemical concepts of electronegativity and ionic character of a chemical bond are linked to this discussion in Concept Questions 13.5 and 13.6 and Example 13.6. The potential is the corresponding energy concept, and is discussed in Example 13.14.

There are two important cases of mobile particles in the vicinity of stationary dipoles: an approaching point charge and an approaching dipole. The latter leads to dipole–dipole interactions that we refer to only qualitatively in this textbook due to the extensive nature of force calculations. In turn, the dipole–point charge interaction is addressed as a model for the interaction of ions in aqueous (water-based) solutions. Positively charged ions are called **cations** and negatively charged ions are **anions**. When a salt is dissolved in water, the water dipoles attack the salt crystal and attach themselves to the released cations and anions. The water molecule is of comparable size to most inorganic ions, which allows this interaction to be very effective. Choosing rock salt as an example, this process is written as $NaCl + n\,H_2O \longrightarrow Na_{aq}^+ + Cl_{aq}^-$. The index "aq" stands for aqueous. It indicates that each ion is embedded in a **hydration shell**. The hydration shell has a specific morphology for each of the salt ions: as illustrated in Fig. 13.11, the positive sides of

water molecules point toward the chlorine anion, and their negative sides point toward the sodium cation.

When the ion moves, the hydration shell is dragged along, as indicated for $Na^+$ and $Cl^-$ ions in the figure. Dragging the hydration shell slows the ion diffusion because the moving entity is much bigger. The hydration shell also causes a screening of the charge of the ion by smearing the charge over a much larger surface. As a result, the electric interactions of cations and anions in aqueous solutions are significantly reduced.

## MODEL SYSTEM III: CHARGED PARALLEL PLATE ARRANGEMENT

All systems with more than a few stationary charges require extensive mathematical analysis to determine the electric field. In the case of parallel plates with equal but opposite charges, however, a simple form of the electric field is found. This is one reason why the parallel plate arrangement is a preferred model. The other reason is its widespread applicability. It describes all biological membrane systems where charges are separated onto their opposite faces at a fixed distance determined by the lipid bilayer. This model allows us to discuss in particular charged membranes, such as nerve membranes in Chapter 14 and pacemaker cell membranes in the heart in Chapter 15. The electric field is discussed for this model again in the next section. The potential as the corresponding electric energy concept is then applied to electrophoresis.

Semipermeable membranes allow ions to pass, which establishes a major application of the interaction of a mobile point charge with the charged parallel plate systems, as illustrated in Fig. 13.12. The

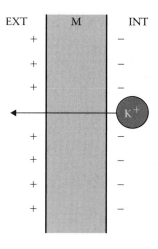

**FIGURE 13.12**

A potassium cation is ejected from the interior of a cell through the cell membrane (M), which carries surface charges.

figure shows a membrane with stationary charges—cations on the extracellular side (labelled EXT), and anions on the internal side (labelled INT)—with a potassium cation transported across the membrane. This process is quantified in Example 13.13. Point charges also move between charged parallel plates in other systems, such as in Millikan's experiment (see P–13.9), or in the atmosphere between a differently charged ground surface and cloud cover (see P–13.14).

# Electric Field

We now develop the concept of a static electric field. Keep in mind that Michael Faraday did not intend to find a simplifying mathematical trick when he developed this concept. This means that we should not focus on the mathematical aspect of writing a field. We have to focus, rather, on its conceptual value: disconnecting ourselves from Coulomb's law, which requires we study all individual interactions simultaneously by describing a field that summarizes the effect of an arrangement of charges at any position, in particular the position we are interested in. Note for this discussion that a position is a point in space. There is no requirement for a charged particle to actually be located at that position!

The best way to capture Faraday's method is based on rewriting Coulomb's law in the form:

$$\mathbf{F}_{el} = q_{mobile} \cdot \mathbf{E} \qquad [18]$$

with the unit of the electric field $\mathbf{E}$ as N/C.

*At every position within an arrangement of stationary charges the stationary electric field is the force vector that acts on a mobile point charge of unit charge if placed at that position.*

The great thing about the electric field is that it can be determined without the mobile point charge actually being present in the system. The electric field measures how capable the stationary charge arrangement is of interacting electrically; i.e., we predict an interaction that will occur if a point charge reaches that position in the future.

## The Electric Field of a Stationary Point Charge

We combine Eq. [18] with Eq. [6]:

$$\mathbf{F}_{el} = \frac{1}{4 \cdot \pi \cdot \varepsilon_0} \left( \frac{q_{stationary} \cdot \mathbf{r}^0_{stationary\ to\ mobile}}{r^2_{stationary\ to\ mobile}} \right) \cdot q_{mobile}$$

$$= q_{mobile} \cdot \mathbf{E} \qquad [19]$$

in which $r_{stationary\ to\ mobile}$ is the distance between the two point charges in the system. In the next step we remove the mobile charge. The distance, which we labelled $r_{stationary\ to\ mobile}$ in Eq. [19], then refers to the distance between the stationary point charge and the position at which the mobile point charge previously was. Dropping the index on the distance parameter $r$ means that it now represents the distance $r$ from the stationary point charge to any position in space:

$$\mathbf{E} = \frac{1}{4 \cdot \pi \cdot \varepsilon_0} \frac{q_{stationary}}{r^2} \mathbf{r}^0 \qquad [20]$$

Eq. [20] represents a **vector field**. This means that it assigns to each position in the vicinity of the stationary point charge a vector that represents both the magnitude and direction of a force acting on a mobile point charge at that position if it were brought there.

The magnitude of the electric field vector, $|\mathbf{E}|$, results from Eq. [20]:

$$|\mathbf{E}| = \frac{1}{4 \cdot \pi \cdot \varepsilon_0} \frac{|q_{stationary}|}{r^2} \qquad [21]$$

Eq. [21] defines the magnitude of the electric field due to a single stationary point charge: the field varies with distance from the stationary point charge as $1/r^2$. The magnitude of the electric field is sufficient for applications in which we study only one stationary point charge or when we study several stationary point charges located along a common axis. For more general cases, we need to use Eq. [20].

Eq. [20] shows that the electric field of a stationary point charge is a radial field; i.e., the electric field vector $\mathbf{E}$ points at every position in space along the connection line of that point and the stationary point charge. The electric field for a positive stationary

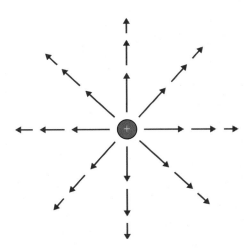

**FIGURE 13.13**

The electric field of a positive stationary point charge. The arrows represent the vectors of the electric field. The length of each vector indicates the magnitude of **E** at the respective position. The electric field of a point charge has a radial (in three dimensions therefore spherical) symmetry.

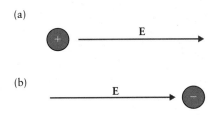

**FIGURE 13.14**

The electric field vector is always pointing (a) away from a positive charge or (b) toward a negative charge. If a positive mobile point charge is brought into the system, a force in the direction of the electric field will act on it.

point charge is illustrated in Fig. 13.13: each arrow in the figure represents the electric field vector at the point where the foot of the arrow is placed. Note the directional variation of the field and its variation in magnitude, which is indicated by the length of the arrows in the figure. In applications it will not be necessary to derive the direction of the electric field from Coulomb's law. We can use instead Fig. 13.14.

*The electric field vector for a single point charge is directed away from a positive point charge or toward a negative point charge.*

Thus, a positive mobile point charge brought into an electric field will feel a force in the direction of the field; a negative mobile point charge will feel a force in the direction opposite to the field.

If we consider a system with more than one stationary point charge, Eq. [20] has to be rewritten as a sum of all contributions due to each single stationary point charge in the system. Assuming $N$ stationary

point charges $q_i$, which can be located at as many different positions, we obtain in vector notation:

$$\mathbf{E}_{\text{net}} = \frac{1}{4 \cdot \pi \cdot \varepsilon_0} \sum_i q_i \frac{\mathbf{r}_i^0}{r_i^2} \qquad [22]$$

in which we consider all particles with index from $i = 1$ to $N$ to form the stationary configuration of charges. To apply Eq. [22], we use the same approach we discussed previously for vector sums: the equation consists of three component equations for the three Cartesian coordinates, each representing the respective component of the net electric field:

$$E_{x,\text{net}} = \sum_i E_x(q_i)$$
$$E_{y,\text{net}} = \sum_i E_y(q_i) \qquad [23]$$
$$E_{z,\text{net}} = \sum_i E_z(q_i)$$

To apply Eq. [23], the electric field due to each stationary point charge has to be written as three Cartesian components. In Example 13.4, we see how the components of the electric field are first determined for a single point charge. This is followed by a special example with $N = 2$ for the electric field of a dipole.

**Concept Question 13.3**

**What is the direction of the electric field at point $P$ in Fig. 13.15? (A) to the upper right, (B) to the lower right, (C) to the upper left, (D) to the lower left, (E) none of the above.**

ANSWER: Choice (B) based on Fig. 13.14.

**FIGURE 13.15**

A stationary point charge and a point $P$ in its vicinity. The purpose of the graph is to determine the direction of the electric field vector at point $P$.

**Concept Question 13.4**

**What is the direction of the electric field in the water molecule in Fig. 13.1?**

ANSWER: An electric field can be assigned to each of the two partial charges at points $P_1$ and $P_2$; they both point in the same direction and form a net electric field based on Fig. 13.14 with its direction from $P_2$ to $P_1$.

## ● EXAMPLE 13.4

Fig. 13.16 shows a positive stationary point charge at the origin. Calculate the electric field at point $P = (x_0, y_0)$. Note that the problem is set up in two dimensions to reduce the required mathematical effort.

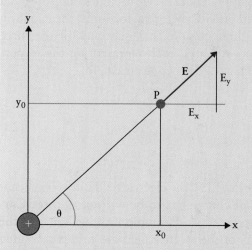

**FIGURE 13.16**

The electric field and electric field components in a Cartesian coordinate system at point $P = (x_0, y_0)$ with a positive point charge at the origin. Fig. 13.14 is used to determine the direction of the electric field.

*Solution:* We determine the two components of the electric field in two steps. First, the magnitude of the electric field $|\mathbf{E}|$ is calculated at point $P$. Then the geometric properties of the system in Fig. 13.16 are used to write its $x$- and $y$-components.

The magnitude of the electric field at point $P$ is calculated from Eq. [21]. If we label the charge of the stationary point charge $q$, we obtain:

$$|\mathbf{E}| = \frac{1}{4 \cdot \pi \cdot \varepsilon_0} \cdot \frac{|q|}{x_0^2 + y_0^2} \qquad [24]$$

in which the denominator in the second term on the right-hand side equals the square of the distance between the charge $q$ and the point $P$ according to the Pythagorean theorem.

The components $E_x$ and $E_y$ are derived from Eq. [24] and trigonometric considerations based on Fig. 13.16. We find for the $x$-component:

$$E_x = \frac{1}{4 \cdot \pi \cdot \varepsilon_0} \cdot \frac{|q|}{x_0^2 + y_0^2} \cos \theta \qquad [25]$$

and for the $y$-component:

$$E_y = \frac{1}{4 \cdot \pi \cdot \varepsilon_0} \cdot \frac{|q|}{x_0^2 + y_0^2} \sin \theta \qquad [26]$$

with

$$\sin \theta = \frac{y_0}{\sqrt{x_0^2 + y_0^2}} \qquad \cos \theta = \frac{x_0}{\sqrt{x_0^2 + y_0^2}} \qquad [27]$$

# The Electric Field of a Dipole

A stationary configuration of two point charges with (i) equal magnitude but (ii) opposite charges $q$ and (iii) a fixed separation distance $d$ is called an **electric dipole**. We discuss its electric field in Example 13.5.

## ● EXAMPLE 13.5

For the dipole shown in Fig. 13.17, find the electric field as a function of position along the dipole axis, i.e., the line through the two point charges. We define this direction as the $x$-axis.

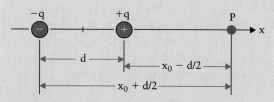

**FIGURE 13.17**

Dipole configuration: a dipole consists of two point charges separated by a fixed distance $d$. The point charges carry opposite charges of equal magnitude. The figure defines the axis of the dipole ($x$-axis) and identifies a point $P$ at a distance $x_0$ from the centre of the dipole. The electric field is calculated at point $P$. In the calculation, the distance $x_0$ is variable.

*Supplementary chemical information:* The restriction to study only the electric field along the axial direction of the dipole does not affect our ability to discuss the physical consequences of the role of the water molecule in aqueous solutions, particularly the formation and structure of the hydration shell. This is evident from Fig. 13.1. A net negative charge is present near the oxygen atom (at point $P_1$) and a net positive charge near the hydrogen atoms (at point $P_2$). Due to Coulomb's law, this dipole always approaches an anion with its positive end and a cation with its negative end. Thus, it is sufficient to know the electric field along the axial direction of the dipole because water molecules can freely rotate in liquid water.

*Solution:* Eq. [21] is sufficient to determine the components of the electric field at point $P$ because both point charges and the point $P$ in Fig. 13.17 are located along a common axis. The directional information is straightforward in this case as all vector components are aligned with this axis: the net electric field is therefore also directed along the $x$-axis. The remaining directional issue is then resolved with Fig. 13.14. Choosing the origin of the axis at the centre of the two dipole charges, we find for the two separate field components at $P$, which is located at position $x$:

$$E_{+q} = \frac{+q}{4 \cdot \pi \cdot \varepsilon_0 \cdot x^2_{+q}} = \frac{q}{4 \cdot \pi \cdot \varepsilon_0 \left( x - \dfrac{d}{2} \right)^2}$$

$$E_{-q} = \frac{-q}{4 \cdot \pi \cdot \varepsilon_0 \cdot x^2_{-q}} = \frac{-q}{4 \cdot \pi \cdot \varepsilon_0 \left( x + \dfrac{d}{2} \right)^2}$$

[28]

in which the first formula is the $x$-component of the electric field due to the positive charge, $+q$, and the second formula is its $x$-component due to the negative charge, $-q$. The net electric field is the sum of these two components:

$$E_{net} = \frac{q}{4 \cdot \pi \cdot \varepsilon_0} \left[ \frac{1}{\left( x - \dfrac{d}{2} \right)^2} - \frac{1}{\left( x + \dfrac{d}{2} \right)^2} \right] \quad [29]$$

Several algebraic operations are applied to simplify Eq. [29]. First, the two terms in the brackets are combined with a single denominator:

$$E_{net} = \frac{q}{4 \cdot \pi \cdot \varepsilon_0} \left[ \frac{\left( x + \dfrac{d}{2} \right)^2 - \left( x - \dfrac{d}{2} \right)^2}{\left( x - \dfrac{d}{2} \right)^2 \left( x + \dfrac{d}{2} \right)^2} \right]$$

[30]

The numerator and denominator in the brackets are further analyzed. For the numerator, we write:

$$\left( x + \frac{d}{2} \right)^2 - \left( x - \frac{d}{2} \right)^2$$

$$= x^2 + x \cdot d + \frac{d^2}{4} - x^2 + x \cdot d - \frac{d^2}{4}$$

$$= 2 \cdot x \cdot d \quad [31]$$

and for the denominator:

$$\left( x + \frac{d}{2} \right)^2 \left( x - \frac{d}{2} \right)^2$$

$$= \left[ \left( x + \frac{d}{2} \right) \left( x - \frac{d}{2} \right) \right]^2 = \left[ x^2 - \left( \frac{d}{2} \right)^2 \right]^2$$

$$= x^4 - \frac{x^2 \cdot d^2}{2} + \frac{d^4}{16} \quad [32]$$

Thus, the $x$-component of the electric field of a dipole at point $P$ is:

$$E_{net} = \frac{q \cdot x \cdot d}{2 \cdot \pi \cdot \varepsilon_0} \frac{1}{x^4 - \dfrac{x^2 d^2}{2} + \dfrac{d^4}{16}} \quad [33]$$

Eq. [33] is the proper answer to the question asked in Example 13.5. For most applications of dipoles, Eq. [33] can be simplified because we are interested only in the electric field at large distances from the dipole. In this case, we rewrite Eq. [33] for $x \gg d$, i.e., for the case in which the point $P$ is much farther from the dipole than length $d$. Mathematically this means that the leading $x^4$ term dominates the sum in the denominator on the right-hand side of Eq. [33]. Neglecting the other two terms yields a formula for the $x$-component of the electric field that is applicable far from the dipole:

$$\lim_{x \gg d} E_{net} = \frac{q}{2 \cdot \pi \cdot \varepsilon_0} \frac{d}{x^3} \quad [34]$$

*The electric field of a dipole drops proportional to $1/r^3$, i.e., more rapidly than the electric field of a single charge, for which the field is proportional to $1/r^2$.*

The $x$-dependence in Eq. [34] is not surprising, since a dipole looks like two very close point charges that compensate each other from a position far away. Had the problem text not limited the position of point $P$ to the axis of the dipole, electric field components would have had to be calculated at each point and would have had to be combined into a net effect, as outlined in Eq. [23].

Fig. 13.18 shows electric field lines for three cases to illustrate the variety of possible directional patterns of electric fields for just two charges. A plot of electric field lines illustrates the direction of the electric field: the electric field at any given point is directed tangentially to the field line at that position. The plot shows the magnitude of the electric field in only an indirect fashion; it is represented by the local density of field lines.

Fig. 13.18(a) illustrates the case of a dipole. The electric field lines point away from the positive charge and/or toward the negative charge as required by Fig. 13.14. The electric field of a dipole shows a significant directional variation; it approaches the radial symmetry of the electric field of a point charge only very close to either of the two point charges. The electric field lines along the dipole axis are straight lines, as discussed in Example 13.5.

Fig. 13.18(b) shows the electric field lines for two equal positive point charges. The electric field lines between these charges do not form closed curves as in Fig. 13.18(a). Fig. 13.18(c) indicates that electric fields become quite complex patterns rather easily. In the figure, the electric field lines are shown for a positive and a negative point charge where the positive charge is twice the magnitude of the negative charge. Far from the pair of point charges the positive charge

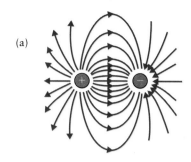

(a)

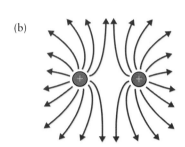

(b)

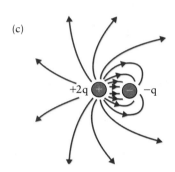

(c)

**FIGURE 13.18**

Plots of the electric field lines for three charged systems. An electric field line illustrates the direction of the electric field. At any given point the field points in the direction tangential to the field line. Note the variability of the directional patterns of electric fields. (a) The electric dipole. The electric field lines point away from the positive charge and toward the negative charge as required by Fig. 13.14. (b) The electric field lines for two equal positive point charges. (c) The electric field lines for two unequal point charges. This plot indicates that electric field lines can easily form quite complex patterns.

dominates the pattern, as is evident from following the electric field lines leaving the positive point charge.

## The Electric Dipole Moment

The product of charge and distance defines the **electric dipole moment** $\mu$ in Eq. [34]:

$$\mu = q \cdot d \qquad [35]$$

Electric dipole moments characterize the chemical and physical properties of molecules. Table 13.3 lists the electric dipole moment, the melting temperature,

**TABLE 13.3**

**The correlation of the dipole moment and the temperature interval between melting point and boiling point at 1 atm pressure for several small molecules**

| Molecule | Dipole moment (C · m) | Melting temperature (°C) | Boiling temperature (°C) |
|---|---|---|---|
| HF | $6.37 \times 10^{-30}$ | −84 | +20 |
| HCl | $3.57 \times 10^{-30}$ | −114 | −85 |
| $H_2O$ | $6.17 \times 10^{-30}$ | ±0 | +100 |
| $H_2S$ | $3.67 \times 10^{-30}$ | −86 | −61 |
| $NH_3$ | $4.80 \times 10^{-30}$ | −78 | −33 |
| $PH_3$ | $1.83 \times 10^{-30}$ | −134 | −88 |
| $AsH_3$ | $7.33 \times 10^{-31}$ | −117 | −62 |
| $CH_4$ | 0 | −182 | −161 |
| $SiH_4$ | 0 | −185 | −112 |

The data show that higher melting and boiling temperatures are associated with larger dipole moments.

and the boiling temperature for several hydrogen-containing molecules. Fig. 13.19 is a plot of the dipole moment of these molecules versus the range between melting temperature and boiling temperature at atmospheric pressure. The figure shows that water is distinct from the other molecules because its very large electric dipole moment yields melting and boiling points that are unusually high for such small molecules.

The electric dipole moment in Fig. 13.19 is one way to demonstrate quantitatively the direct relation between the electric properties of the water molecule and its applications as a key ingredient of life processes. Physically, this relation is established by the direct relation of the electric dipole moment to the strength of **hydrogen bonds**. A hydrogen bond between water molecules forms when a hydrogen atom of one water molecule approaches the oxygen atom in another water molecule. The hydrogen bond is therefore a dipole–dipole interaction that leads to the molecular arrangement illustrated in Fig. 13.20. In the figure, the large spheres represent oxygen atoms and the small spheres hydrogen atoms. Covalent bonds in each molecule are shown as dashed lines; hydrogen bonds are present where the spheres of hydrogen and oxygen atoms from neighbouring molecules touch. The covalent bonds of each water molecule correspond to the H—O lines in Fig. 13.1. Note

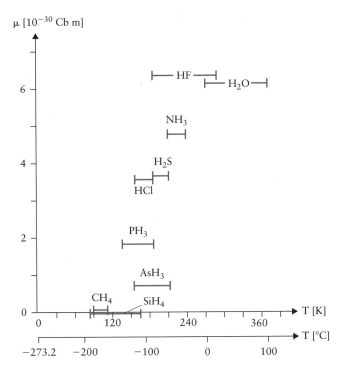

**FIGURE 13.19**

Graphic representation of the data of Table 13.3. The temperature axis is shown in units K and °C. For each molecule, the horizontal bar shown stretches from the melting point to the boiling point. Both phase transition temperatures increase with increasing dipole moment of the molecule.

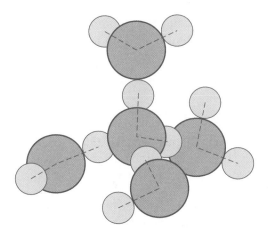

**FIGURE 13.20**

Typical arrangement of four neighbouring water molecules (each identified by dashed lines) in solid water (ice). The larger spheres represent oxygen atoms and the smaller spheres hydrogen atoms. Four hydrogen atoms are arranged tetrahedrally around each central oxygen atom. In liquid water, hydrogen bonds break frequently and the local order of molecules is less regular. The hydrogen bonds are about 5% to 10% as strong as chemical O—H bonds (dashed lines).

that every oxygen atom in Fig. 13.20 is symmetrically surrounded by four hydrogen atoms; i.e., it forms two hydrogen bonds. Recall that hydrogen bonds require only 5% to 10% of the energy needed to break

a covalent bond; however, this energy still exceeds the thermal energy available at sufficiently low temperatures. The structure shown in Fig. 13.20 therefore illustrates the local organization of water molecules in liquid water: it becomes the long-range order in solid ice.

**Concept Question 13.5**

**Do hydrogen bonds also occur elsewhere, e.g., in biomolecules? Try a literature or internet search.**

ANSWER: Yes. The DNA molecule consists of nucleotides, which in turn contain a nitrogenous base, a pentose sugar, and a phosphate group. The nitrogenous groups are cytosine, thymine, adenine, or guanine. Pairwise they connect with hydrogen bonds, as shown in Fig. 13.21. These bonds stabilize the DNA double-helix structure.

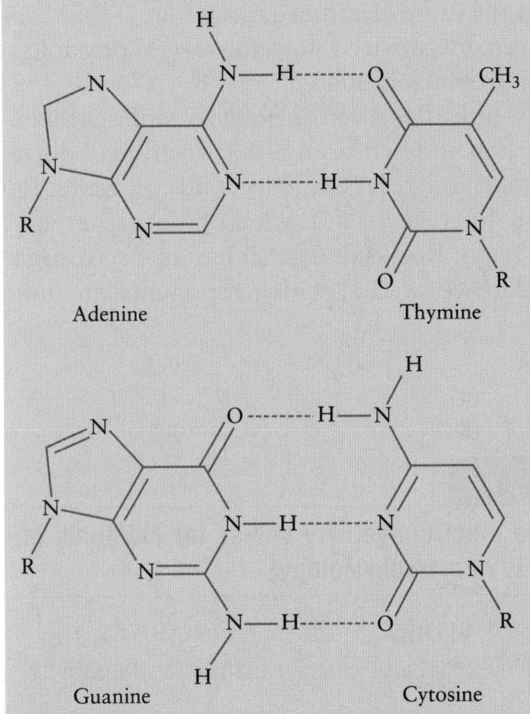

**FIGURE 13.21**

Hydrogen bonds also play a crucial role in the formation of DNA molecules. The nitrogenous bases of the nucleotides include either cytosine or thymine (pyrimidine compounds), or adenine or guanine (purine compounds). These groups bond in pairs to form the DNA double-helix structure.

When comparing the various molecules in Table 13.3 we note that the ability to form dipoles varies. In water oxygen succeeds in drawing electrons from hydrogen to form a strong dipole, while carbon in methane is much less efficient in this way. We quantify this observation with two new variables:

- **Electronegativity**, which is calculated from the energy of formation of the molecule. It is primarily used for systems with dominant covalent bonds.
- **Ionic character**, which is calculated from the dipole moment. It is used when the bond is considered partially ionic.

Electronegativity was introduced by Linus Pauling to quantify the propensity of an atom within a molecule to draw electric charges along a chemical bond toward itself and away from its partners (a property called electron affinity). To quantify the concept, Pauling used a comparison of the actual energy of a chemical bond to the energies of the respective bonds between the two atoms independently. The energy discrepancy is explained by the transfer of electric charge to the more electronegative atom. Table 13.4 shows electronegativity values for several physiologically important elements.

In methane, the electronegativity difference between carbon and hydrogen is 0.3. Such small differences favour non-polar covalent bonds. In water, the respective difference is 1.3, which points to a polar covalent bond. Rock salt (NaCl) has an electronegativity difference of 2.1, which represents an ionic bond.

## TABLE 13.4

### Selected electronegativity values for elements important to human physiology

| Element | Electro-negativity | Element | Electro-negativity |
|---------|--------------------|---------|--------------------|
| H | 2.2 | Li | 1.0 |
| B | 2.0 | C | 2.5 |
| N | 3.0 | O | 3.5 |
| F | 4.0 | Na | 0.9 |
| Mg | 1.2 | P | 2.1 |
| S | 2.5 | Cl | 3.0 |
| K | 0.8 | Ca | 1.0 |
| As | 2.0 | I | 2.5 |
| Ba | 0.9 | | |

## Concept Question 13.6

We study the acetylene molecule. This is a linear molecule with the chemical formula $HC \equiv CH$. Using the data in Table 13.4, which statement about the $C_2H_2$ molecule is correct? (A) Acetylene is not a dipole because the electronegativity values of carbon and hydrogen are close to each other. (B) Acetylene is not a dipole because the angle between the C—H bond and the $C \equiv C$ triple bond is 180°. (C) Acetylene is not a dipole because the charge distribution within the molecule is symmetric. (D) Whether a given molecule is a dipole or not can be determined only in an experiment.

ANSWER: Choices (A) and (C). (C) is also correct because even a molecule with large electronegativity differences can contain opposing dipoles that cancel each other, e.g., the linear $CO_2$ molecule.

## ● EXAMPLE 13.6

Calculate the ionic character for the water molecule. Determine the maximum dipole moment for the molecule by allowing each of the two hydrogen atoms to transfer one electron to the oxygen atom. The bond length O—H is 0.096 nm and the bond angle H—O—H is 104.5°.

*Supplementary chemical information:* Using the dipole moment from Table 13.3 and the distance between the positive and negative centres of a molecule allows us to define an **ionic character** Ic for the molecule:

$$Ic = 100 \frac{\mu_{actual}}{\mu_{max}} \qquad [36]$$

in which Ic is given as a percentage value. For example, for the HCl molecule the maximum dipole moment is based on the transfer of a single electron (elementary charge) from hydrogen to chlorine across the separation distance of the atoms in the molecule. The bond length is 0.127 nm. This leads to:

$$\mu_{max}(HCl) = (1.6 \times 10^{-19}\,C)(1.27 \times 10^{-10}\,m)$$
$$= 2.05 \times 10^{-29}\,C \cdot m \qquad [37]$$

Thus, with the measured dipole moment of HCl from Table 13.3, the ionic character of the HCl bond is:

$$Ic(HCl) = 100 \frac{3.57 \times 10^{-30}\,C \cdot m}{2.05 \times 10^{-29}\,C \cdot m}$$
$$= 17.4\% \qquad [38]$$

i.e., the HCl molecule is polar, but with a predominantly covalent bond character.

*Solution:* Fig. 13.1 illustrates the geometry of the water molecule and allows us to determine the maximum separation of the positive and the negative charges in the polarized molecule. This maximum separation would be reached when the single electron of each hydrogen atom is fully shifted to the oxygen atom. This corresponds to a double negative charge $(2 \cdot e)$ at point $P_1$ and a double positive charge at point $P_2$ due to the symmetry of the molecule. The distance between points $P_1$ and $P_2$ is obtained geometrically from the figure:

$$P_1 P_2 = r \cdot \cos\left(\frac{104.5°}{2}\right) = 0.059 \, \text{nm} \quad [39]$$

Next, we determine the maximum dipole moment of the water molecule using this distance:

$$\begin{aligned}
\mu_{max}(H_2O) &= (2 \cdot e)P_1 P_2 \\
&= (3.2 \times 10^{-19} \, \text{C})(0.059 \times 10^{-9} \, \text{m}) \\
&= 1.89 \times 10^{-29} \, \text{C} \cdot \text{m} \quad [40]
\end{aligned}$$

The ionic character of the water molecule then follows from the definition in Eq. [36], i.e., the ratio of the value given in Table 13.3 to the value determined in Eq. [40]:

$$\begin{aligned}
Ic(H_2O) &= 100 \, \frac{6.17 \times 10^{-30} \, \text{C} \cdot \text{m}}{1.89 \times 10^{-29} \, \text{C} \cdot \text{m}} \\
&= 32.6 \% \quad [41]
\end{aligned}$$

This value exceeds significantly the value for HCl.

## The Electric Field of Charged Parallel Plates

It is no longer practical to calculate the electric field from Eq. [22] when a significant number of stationary point charges are in the system. The sum in that equation must be rewritten using more advanced mathematical tools, leading to intermediate results that then require numerical methods to solve. These calculations are greatly simplified when two conditions are met: the stationary charges have a uniform density in the system, and the arrangement of these charges is symmetric. We are interested in only one such arrangement, a system with two parallel charged plates. This system is important for applications and leads to a mathematically simple electric field.

Our approach to systems with many charges is analogous to the approach taken when we studied extended objects or fluids: we no longer identified the system as a large number of particles but expressed the mass of the system as its volume and density. In a similar fashion, one can introduce two charge density terms:

- The volume charge density, or **charge density**, with $\rho = Q/V$ where $Q$ is the total charge, $Q = \sum_i q_i$, $V$ is the volume, and $\rho$ is the charge density. This parameter is needed for systems in which free point charges cannot move (insulator systems) and remain distributed in three dimensions. The unit of $\rho$ is $C/m^3$.

- The **surface charge density** $\sigma$ with

$$\sigma = \frac{Q}{A} = \frac{\sum_{i=1}^{N} q_i}{A} \quad [42]$$

in which $A$ is the surface area of the system, and $\sigma$ has unit $C/m^2$. This is a frequently used parameter because mobile point charges of equal sign drift apart as far as possible in a conducting system such as aqueous solutions. An example is the nerve membrane, where the charges that cause the signal transport are located on the inner and outer surfaces, leading to a uniform surface charge density of $700 \, \mu C/m^2$.

The resulting electric field between two infinitely large parallel plates, each with a uniform surface charge density $\sigma$, has the magnitude:

$$|\mathbf{E}_{\parallel}| = \frac{\sigma}{\varepsilon_0} \quad [43]$$

The direction of this field is uniform, with the vector $\mathbf{E}_{\parallel}$ pointing toward the negative plate along a line perpendicular to the plates.

*The electric field between charged parallel plates is independent of the position and is proportional to the area charge density of the plates.*

### ● EXAMPLE 13.7

What is the electric field between two parallel flat plates, where one plate is charged positively and one negatively with $\sigma = 700 \, \mu C/m^2$? This value is a typical surface charge density for nerve membranes.

*Solution:* Using Eq. [43], we find:

$$|\mathbf{E}_{\parallel}| = \frac{7 \times 10^{-4} \, \dfrac{C}{m^2}}{8.85 \times 10^{-12} \, \dfrac{C^2}{N \cdot m^2}} = 7.9 \times 10^7 \, \frac{N}{C} \quad [44]$$

Note that this value is not the proper value for the electric field across a nerve membrane. To calculate that value the membrane material has to be taken into account, as discussed in Chapter 14.

## ● EXAMPLE 13.8

A flat plate has a surface charge density value of $\sigma = +5 \ \mu C/m^2$. What is the electric field in close proximity to the surface of the plate?

*Solution:* The electric field of a single, flat plate is half the value of the parallel plate arrangement discussed in Eq. [43]—i.e., $|\mathbf{E}| = \varepsilon_0 \cdot \sigma/2$—and is directed perpendicular away from a positive plate. Thus:

$$|\mathbf{E}| = \frac{\sigma}{2 \cdot \varepsilon_0} = \frac{5.0 \times 10^{-6} \ \dfrac{C}{m^2}}{2 \cdot 8.85 \times 10^{-12} \ \dfrac{C^2}{N \cdot m^2}}$$

$$= 2.8 \times 10^5 \ \frac{N}{C} \qquad [45]$$

This is the correct value for the electric field at any point near the surface of the flat plate except close to the edges, where fringe effects require corrections.

Air breaks down electrically when an electric field of $3 \times 10^6$ N/C is reached, with air molecules ionizing and the gas becoming a conductor. These are the conditions that occur in the atmosphere during a lightning storm.

## ● EXAMPLE 13.9

In Robert Millikan's experiment as illustrated in Fig. 13.4, a constant electric field along the vertical axis is obtained with charged parallel plates, one located above and one below the observation chamber. The electric field is directed downward. An oil droplet of radius 1.4 $\mu$m and density 0.85 g/cm$^3$ levitates in the chamber when an electric field of $1.5 \times 10^5$ N/C is applied. Find the charge on the droplet as a multiple of the elementary charge $e$.

*Solution:* A levitating droplet is in mechanical equilibrium. Two forces that act on the droplet balance each other based on Newton's first law: the electric force upward and the weight downward:

$$m_{droplet} \cdot g = q_{droplet} \cdot |\mathbf{E}| \qquad [46]$$

We isolate the charge of the droplet:

$$q_{droplet} = \frac{m_{droplet} \cdot g}{|\mathbf{E}|} = \frac{4 \cdot \pi \cdot r_{droplet}^3 \cdot \rho \cdot g}{3 \cdot |\mathbf{E}|} \qquad [47]$$

in which the mass of the droplet has been replaced by its volume and density. We substitute the given values into Eq. [47]:

$$q_{droplet} = \frac{4 \cdot \pi (1.4 \times 10^{-6} m)^3 \left( 850 \ \dfrac{kg}{m^3} \right) \left( 9.8 \ \dfrac{m}{s^2} \right)}{3 \cdot 1.5 \times 10^5 \ \dfrac{N}{C}}$$

$$= 6.4 \times 10^{-19} C \qquad [48]$$

The oil droplet must carry a net negative charge, because the electric field $\mathbf{E}$ is directed down and the electric force $\mathbf{F}_{el}$ is directed up. In terms of the elementary charge, we find:

$$\frac{q_{droplet}}{e} = \frac{6.4 \times 10^{-19} C}{1.6 \times 10^{-19} C} = 4 \qquad [49]$$

i.e., the droplet carries four elementary charges. The benefit of a constant, position-independent electric field in this experiment is obvious.

# The Electric Energy

In Part II of this textbook we found it very useful to introduce the concept of energy. It simplified many calculations, particularly due to the conservation law, but also allowed us to move beyond the boundaries of mechanics, which are set by the force concept. Again, the force concept has dominated the discussion of electricity to this point. Thus, we may ask the question whether energy concepts can be as useful in electricity as they were in mechanics and thermal physics. After you read through the rest of this textbook you will agree that the answer is "yes," for the same reasons we discussed in Chapter 6 and due to two additional arguments:

- Note that we have been rather quiet so far on how we measure electric forces or fields practically. This is because we do not measure them directly. What we measure directly is an electric potential difference, a concept we derive below from energy concepts; electric fields or forces are then calculated only from the electric potential.

- Most electric phenomena of interest in the life sciences occur at the microscopic and atomic scale. We discuss the structure of atoms and their physical properties in Chapter 22. We will note then that energy concepts are much more suitable to describe these systems, while the application of the force concept becomes elusive.

Describing electricity with energy concepts is straightforward when we follow the approach we took in Chapter 6 in deriving the gravitational potential energy. At the time we relied on the fact that a gravitational force is assigned to each point in space (e.g., in your laboratory), which allowed us to develop the potential energy since it is defined as the form of energy stored in the relative position of objects. Replacing objects of a given mass with point charges that carry a particular amount of charge, and replacing gravity with the electric force, allows us to develop formulas for the electric potential energy in the same fashion.

The electric potential energy can be combined with kinetic and other forms of energy to determine the total or internal energy of a system. The possibility of converting electric energy into other forms of energy, the possibility of adding or removing it from a system in the form of work, and the conservation of the total energy of a system allow us to apply the many tools we developed earlier in thermal physics and mechanics. Thus, we have a greatly enhanced arsenal of physical tools available once the electric potential energy is defined.

## The Potential Energy for Charged Parallel Plates

In this section, we follow the approach taken in Chapter 6 for the gravitational potential energy to introduce the electric potential energy. We start with the definition of work $W$ for the case of a force $\mathbf{F}$ and a displacement $\Delta\mathbf{r}$:

$$W = f(\mathbf{F}, \Delta\mathbf{r}) \qquad [50]$$

In the electric case we consider a mobile point charge, which we move from an initial to a final equilibrium position within a system of stationary charges. An external force $\mathbf{F}_{ext}$ is needed to ensure the mechanical equilibrium. Once the work is determined, the electric potential energy $E_{el}$ is calculated from:

$$W = E_{el,final} - E_{el,initial} \qquad [51]$$

Eq. [50] is written as the product $W = \pm F_{ext} \cdot \Delta r$ if:

- the external force and the displacement are co-linear, and
- the external force is constant at every position along the displacement.

If one or both of these conditions do not apply, more complicated formulas have to be applied: if the external force is constant but not co-linear with the displacement vector, the dot product of the two vectors is used, $W = \mathbf{F}_{ext} \cdot \Delta\mathbf{r}$. If the force varies but is co-linear with the displacement vector, the work is based on graphic analysis of the area under the $F_{ext}(r)$ curve, as illustrated in Figs. 6.16 to 6.18. Since the product $F_{ext} \cdot \Delta r$ is easiest to evaluate, we start with the parallel plate arrangement, as it yielded an electric force that is constant at any position between the two plates.

We use Fig. 13.22 for the quantitative calculation. The plate at the top is charged positively and the plate at the bottom is charged negatively. This leads to a downward-directed electric field. We further

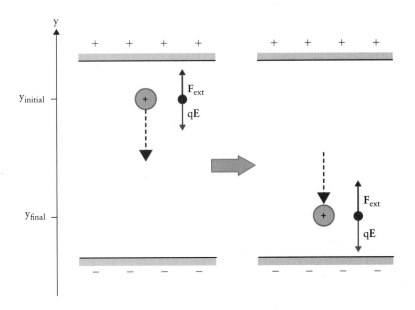

**FIGURE 13.22**

A parallel plate arrangement with an electric field **E** pointing downward. The forces acting on a positive mobile point charge are shown in a free-body diagram at its right side. The sketch at the left side shows the mobile point charge at its initial position $y_{initial}$ and the sketch at the right at its final position $y_{final}$. Note that the mobile point charge is in both cases in mechanical equilibrium.

assume that a positive mobile point charge moves from close to the positive plate to a position close to the negative plate, i.e., from position $y_{initial}$ to $y_{final}$. Moving a mobile point charge from one equilibrium position to another requires an external force $F_{ext}$ to prevent it from accelerating toward the negative plate. Consequently, in Fig. 13.22 the external force is positive and the displacement is negative. A negative work follows from anti-parallel external force and displacement; i.e., the mobile point charge in Fig. 13.22 releases work to the source of the external force:

$$W = F_{ext} \cdot \Delta y = q_{mobile} \cdot |\mathbf{E}| (y_{final} - y_{initial}) < 0 \quad [52]$$

Using Eq. [51], we determine the electric potential energy:

$$E_{el} = q_{mobile} \cdot |\mathbf{E}| \cdot y \quad [53]$$

in which we use Eq. [43] to specify the magnitude of the electric field:

$$E_{el} = q_{mobile} \frac{\sigma}{\varepsilon_0} y \quad [54]$$

*The electric energy of a mobile point charge in a parallel plate arrangement is a linear function of distance from the plate that carries a charge with opposite sign of the mobile charge.*

Note that Eq. [54] is mathematically similar to the formula derived for the gravitational potential energy, which is a linear function of height above ground ($E_{pot,grav} = m \cdot g \cdot h$). This simple form of Eq. [54] is the reason why parallel plate arrangements are an often-used model for studying electric phenomena. The analogy to the gravitational case goes even further. If we release an object held at a given height, it accelerates toward the ground due to the attractive gravitational pull. In the same fashion, if you remove the external force that holds the mobile point charge in Fig. 13.22, it will accelerate toward the plate with the opposite charge due to the attractive electric force.

## Concept Question 13.7

In the six processes shown in Fig. 13.23, a mobile point charge (green circle with positive or negative charge indicated in the circle) is moved from an initial to a final position (see arrow). In which cases is the work positive (energy is received by the mobile point charge

during the displacement)? (A) III and VI, (B) I and III, (C) II and IV, (D) I and IV, (E) II and V.

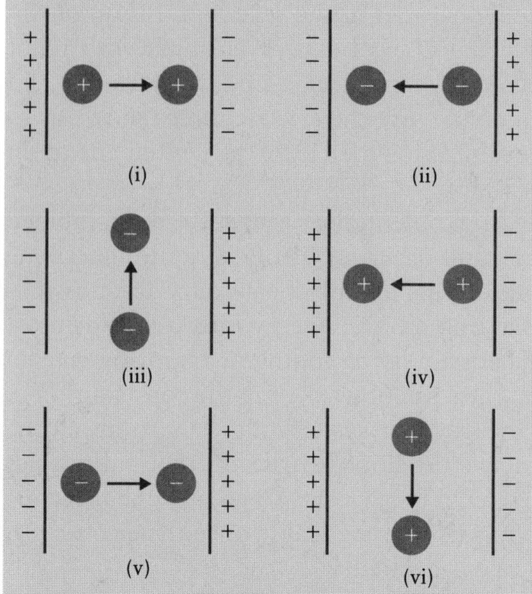

**FIGURE 13.23**

Six variations of a mobile point charge (shown as a small open circle with positive or negative charge indicated in the circle) that moves from an initial to a final position (see arrow) in a charged parallel plate arrangement.

ANSWER: Choice (C). II and IV are the cases in which the mobile point charge is moved toward the plate that carries the same charges.

## ● EXAMPLE 13.10

In Fig. 13.24 we are given a single, infinite, non-conducting sheet with a positive surface charge density $\sigma$. How much work is done by the external force as a positive mobile point charge $q_{mobile}$ is moved perpendicularly from the surface of the sheet at $z_{initial}$ to a final position at $z_{final}$?

*Solution:* The electric field of a single flat plate is given in the form $|\mathbf{E}| = \varepsilon_0 \cdot \sigma / 2$. The external force needed to create an equilibrium is directed opposite the Coulomb force, and is, therefore, anti-parallel to the displacement. Thus, the work is negative; i.e., work is done by the mobile point charge on the source of the external force. With the magnitude of the external force given by $F_{ext} = q \cdot |\mathbf{E}|$, we find:

$$W = -\frac{q_{test} \cdot \sigma}{2 \cdot \varepsilon_0} z_{final} < 0 \quad [55]$$

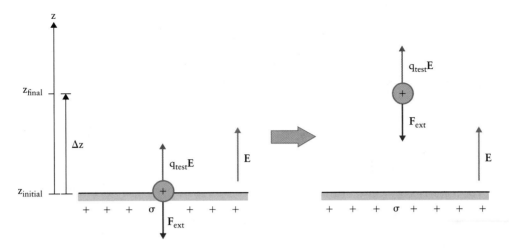

**FIGURE 13.24**

A positive mobile point charge moving from the surface of a single plate (position $z_{initial}$) with a positive surface charge density $\sigma$ (at left) to a final position $z_{final}$ (at right). The electric field of the plate points upward. The total displacement of the mobile point charge is $\Delta z$. It is in mechanical equilibrium in both positions.

# Electrophoresis

## ● EXAMPLE 13.11

A blood sample of a liver cirrhosis patient is analyzed by electrophoresis. During the protein separation, a $\gamma$-globulin molecule from this blood sample moves a distance of 7 cm toward the negative plate of the setup. The electric field between the parallel plates is $|E| = 2000$ N/C. How much work has been done on the $\gamma$-globulin molecule?

*Supplementary physiological information:* Electrophoresis is widely used to separate and identify charged components in solutions such as blood. Two types of experimental setup exist. In forensic science, DNA fragments are routinely separated across a gel after the original DNA molecule has been split by restriction enzymes. This setup is shown in Fig. 13.25: the sample is brought onto the gel close to the negative plate at right. Electrophoresis separates the charged molecule fragments on the basis of their rate of movement through the gel in a given electric field. Typically, larger fragments travel slower than smaller ones. The DNA sample is brought close to the negative plate because the fragments carry negative charges due to phosphate groups.

Fig. 13.26 shows a second setup that is more suitable for recovering the separated components. This approach is used for blood sample analysis of protein composition. The test sample travels downward through a cellulose matrix in a vertical arrangement, driven by the steady flow of a buffer solution from a reservoir at the top (1). Concur-

**FIGURE 13.25**

Electrophoresis setup used in forensic science. DNA fragments are separated across a gel after the original DNA molecule has been split by restriction enzymes. The sample is brought onto the gel close to the negative plate at right. Electrophoresis separates the charged molecule fragments on the basis of their rate of movement through the gel in a given electric field. Typically, larger fragments travel slower than smaller ones. The DNA sample is brought close to the negative plate because the fragments carry a negative charge due to their phosphate groups.

## ● EXAMPLE 13.11 (continued)

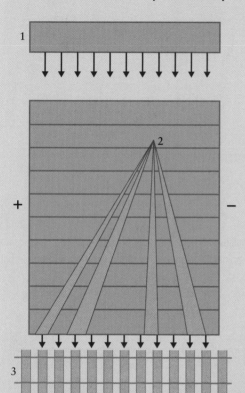

**FIGURE 13.26**

A second electrophoresis setup often used for blood sample separation. The proteins in the sample travel vertically downward in a cellulose matrix, driven by the steady flow of a buffer solution supplied from a reservoir at the top (1). The components of the blood sample drift toward left or right, driven by the electric field applied horizontally across the matrix. The negative plate, shown at the right, causes positive ions to drift to the right. Separation of equally charged ions occurs as the result of their molecular sizes. The various components of the sample can be collected in test tubes at the bottom (3) for further analysis.

rently, these components drift toward left or right, driven by the electric field applied horizontally across the matrix. In the figure, the negative plate is shown at the right, causing positive ions to drift to the right; the positive plate is shown at the left, causing negative ions to drift to the left. Separation of equally charged ions again occurs on the basis of molecular size. Thus, the test sample applied at point (2) separates as it is washed downward, and the various components can be collected in tubes at the bottom of the cellulose sheet (3).

Fig. 13.27 shows the result of electrophoretically separated blood samples for (a) a normal and (b–f) pathological cases. The components of blood identified are albumin (labelled A) and five different globulin proteins, labelled $\alpha_1$, $\alpha_2$, $\beta_1$, $\beta_2$, and $\gamma$. The relative concentration of these proteins

in the blood sample allows the physician to detect various diseases as indicated.

*Solution:* The electrophoresis setup is based on a charged parallel plate arrangement. Eq. [52] gives us the work done on a point charge between the two plates when it moves closer to one of the plates. The electric field between the plates in Fig. 13.27 points toward the negative plate at the right due to Fig. 13.14. The $\gamma$-globulin ion is positively charged because it drifts toward the negative plate. Therefore, the electric force on the protein ion is directed toward the right and the external force to hold it in mechanical equilibrium, $F_{\text{ext}}$, must be directed toward the left. The displacement of the protein ion occurs toward the right. If we define the positive $y$-axis toward the right, then $F_{\text{ext}} < 0$ and $\Delta y > 0$. Thus, the work calculated from $W = F_{\text{ext}} \cdot \Delta y$ is negative, $W < 0$.

For the numerical value of the work, we substitute the given values into Eq. [52]. An elementary charge is carried by the $\gamma$-globulin: $q_{\text{mobile}} = e = 1.6 \times 10^{-19}$ C. The magnitude of the field is $|\mathbf{E}| = 2.0 \times 10^3$ N/C and the displacement is $\Delta y = 7.0 \times 10^{-2}$ m:

$$W = -(1.6 \times 10^{-19}\,\text{C})\left(2 \times 10^3\,\frac{\text{N}}{\text{C}}\right)(0.07\,\text{m})$$

$$= -2.2 \times 10^{-17}\,\text{J} \qquad [56]$$

We want to discuss the sign in Eq. [56] a little further. Why is the work negative? Let's start with a positive ion between two charged plates in vacuum; i.e., we remove the cellulose matrix of the electrophoresis setup. In that setup the ion accelerates toward the negative plate. The ion and the charged plate represent an isolated system for which the conservation of energy applies. Thus, the potential energy of the ion decreases during the acceleration, but its kinetic energy increases by the same amount so that the internal energy (total energy) remains unchanged.

In the case of the electrophoresis experiment, the positive ion does not accelerate. It moves with a small constant speed toward the negative plate. This is due to the cellulose matrix, which acts as the origin of an external force. Thus, in the electrophoresis experiment, the system ion and charged plates is not an isolated system and the conservation of energy is written in the form $\Delta U = Q + W$; i.e., internal energy changes are due to exchange of work and heat with the environment. In electrophoresis, no heat exchange is observed and the point charge changes only its potential energy but not its kinetic energy. Thus, $\Delta E_{\text{el}} = W$: the negative work is due to the decrease in potential energy of the ion.

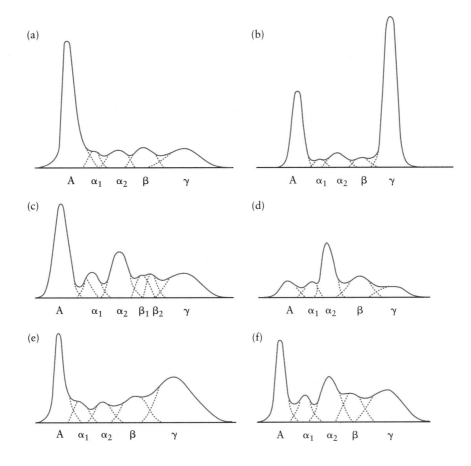

**FIGURE 13.27**

Typical results for blood samples that have been separated by electrophoresis using the setup in Fig. 13.26. The components of blood identified are albumin (labelled A) and five different globulin proteins, labelled $\alpha_1$, $\alpha_2$, $\beta_1$, $\beta_2$, and $\gamma$. The relative concentration of these proteins in the blood sample allows the physician to detect various diseases. (a) A comparison sample for a healthy patient. (b–f) Pathological cases: (b) plasma cell tumour, (c) acute inflammation, (d) severe nephrosis, (e) cirrhosis of the liver, (f) liver parenchyma damage (parenchyma refers to the essential and distinctive tissue of an organ).

## The Potential Energy for a Stationary Point Charge

We are interested in two other electric arrangements in the current chapter: a single point charge and a dipole. We saw earlier that the force varies in both cases with distance from the stationary charges; i.e., calculating work is slightly more complicated than in the case of charged parallel plates. We use the case of a single stationary point charge to illustrate a graphical approach.

Fig. 13.28 shows a positive mobile point charge (small circle) that is brought closer to a positive stationary point charge $Q$ (large circle) at position $r = 0$. The electric force acting on the mobile point charge is written as $q \cdot E$ at both the initial and final positions. To bring the mobile point charge closer to the stationary point charge, an external force is needed to transfer it through the displacement $\Delta r$. Bringing the mobile point charge closer requires work; i.e., the work is positive.

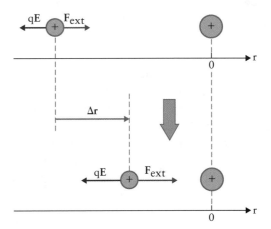

**FIGURE 13.28**

Sketch to illustrate the work associated with moving a positive mobile point charge (small circle) by a distance $\Delta x$ closer to a positive stationary point charge (large circle, positioned at $r = 0$). Both the initial position (top) and final position (bottom) of the mobile point charge are at negative positions along the axis. Note that the electric force $q \cdot E$ and the external force $F_{ext}$, which is required to establish a mechanical equilibrium, increase in magnitude as the mobile point charge moves closer to the stationary point charge.

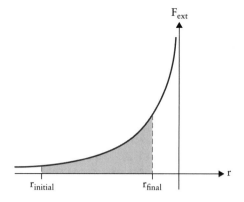

**FIGURE 13.29**

The electric potential energy for the system shown in Fig. 13.28 is obtained from the area under the curve for the electric force as a function of position. This leads to the mathematical form of Eq. [57].

Note that we set up Fig. 13.28 such that the mobile point charge moves directly toward the stationary point charge. This simplifies the discussion because the force and the displacement are parallel and we do not need to include vector notation to calculate the work. We draw a graph of the magnitude of the external force as a function of position in Fig. 13.29 and then determine the work as the area under the curve from $r_{\text{initial}}$ to $r_{\text{final}}$:

$$W = \frac{q_{\text{mobile}} \cdot Q}{4 \cdot \pi \cdot \varepsilon_0} \left( \frac{1}{|r_{\text{final}}|} - \frac{1}{|r_{\text{initial}}|} \right) \quad [57]$$

From Eq. [57] we derive the electric potential energy:

$$E_{\text{el}} = \frac{1}{4 \cdot \pi \cdot \varepsilon_0} \frac{q_{\text{mobile}} \cdot Q}{|r|} \quad [58]$$

Note that the result is independent of the sign of the position of the mobile point charge. This is indicated by the absolute bars of the variable $r$ in the denominators of Eqs. [57] and [58].

The existence of positive and negative charges distinguishes the electric potential energy from the gravitational potential energy. The gravitational force is always attractive; therefore, the external force vector establishing mechanical equilibrium always points away from Earth, as illustrated in Fig. 6.9. However, whether the electric force is attractive or repulsive depends on whether the two interacting charges are positive or negative. In Fig. 13.28 both charges are positive and the electric force is repulsive. The external force points toward $r = 0$, as shown in the figure. If the stationary point charge were in turn negative, then the electric force would be attractive and the

external force needed to establish a mechanical equilibrium would point away from the origin. Eq. [58] illustrates that the electric interaction between two particles with opposite charges always leads to a negative electric potential energy, which is an energy we have to overcome to separate the two point charges. This energy is particularly large if the initial separation of the two point charges is small.

## Concept Question 13.8

**Separating two opposite point charges requires work. Why is it, then, that sodium and chlorine ions of rock salt (NaCl) almost always occur separated in our body? Where does the energy to break up a digested rock salt crystal come from?**

ANSWER: Water, and particularly its electric dipole moment, provide the means of separating $Na^+$ and $Cl^-$ ions. If we break apart sodium and chlorine in a water-free environment, the separating $Na^+$ and $Cl^-$ ions turn neutral (via an electron exchange) at a distance of about 1 nanometre, as illustrated in Fig. 13.30. The figure compares, as a function of separation distance, the total energy of a pair of neutral Na and Cl atoms (dashed line) with the total energy of a $Na^+$ ion and a $Cl^-$ ion (red line).

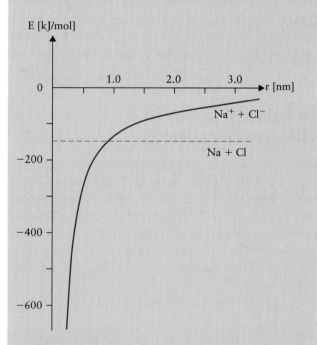

**FIGURE 13.30**

Comparison of the potential energy of a neutral sodium atom and a neutral chlorine atom (dashed line) with the potential energy of a positive sodium ion and a negative chlorine ion (red line) as a function of distance. Neutral atoms are favoured when the separation exceeds 1 nm.

At large distances, the energy difference results from the following thermodynamic relations:

$$
\begin{array}{llll}
\text{Na} & \rightarrow \text{Na}^+ + e^- & \Delta U = +498 \text{ kJ/mol} \\
\text{Cl} + e^- & \rightarrow \text{Cl}^- & \Delta U = -351 \text{ kJ/mol} \\
\hline
\text{Na} + \text{Cl} & \rightarrow \text{Na}^+ + \text{Cl}^- & \Delta U = +147 \text{ kJ/mol}
\end{array}
\qquad [59]
$$

Remember, a positive change in the internal energy means that the system requires energy from its environment. Thus, the transfer of one mol electrons from one mol sodium to one mol chlorine requires +147 kJ. However, Fig. 13.30 shows that when the atoms are at a distance of less than one nanometre from each other the ions in turn are energetically favoured due to the electric potential energy.

As a consequence, rock salt ions can be separated by distances greater than 1 nm only if this neutralizing electron exchange is prevented. A separation of ions across a typical 6-nm nerve membrane would be impossible. In order to do this, the energy of the separating ions must be lowered. In an aqueous solution, this is achieved by the formation of the hydration shell, as illustrated in Fig. 13.11. The hydration shell screens an ion, an effect that reduces the interaction with other ions. It also lowers the energy by redistributing the charge over a larger volume, which stabilizes the ion.

● **EXAMPLE 13.12**

Calculate the distance between the two ions in Fig. 13.30 at the point at which the two curves cross, i.e., the point where the potential energy of the neutral Na/Cl pair equals the electric potential energy of the $\text{Na}^+/\text{Cl}^-$ pair.

*Solution:* The electric energy of two point charges at infinite distance is 0 J, as follows from Eq. [58]. At any closer distance, the energy between a positive and a negative point charge is then negative. We want to find in particular the distance at which the electric energy is equal to the change of the internal energy in the neutralization process of a Na/Cl pair, $\Delta U = -147$ kJ/mol. This energy is converted into an energy $\varepsilon_{\text{Na/Cl}}$ for a single pair of neutral atoms by dividing $\Delta U$ by the Avogadro number. This yields a value of $\varepsilon_{\text{Na/Cl}} = -2.45 \times 10^{-19}$ J. We rewrite Eq. [58] to find the distance at which this energy equals the electric potential energy of the system:

$$
\begin{aligned}
r &= \frac{q_{\text{Na}^+} \cdot q_{\text{Cl}^-}}{4 \cdot \pi \cdot \varepsilon_0} \cdot \frac{1}{E_{\text{el}}} \\
&= \frac{(1.6 \times 10^{-19} \text{ C})(-1.6 \times 10^{-19} \text{ C})}{4 \cdot \pi \left( 8.85 \times 10^{-12} \dfrac{\text{C}^2}{\text{N} \cdot \text{m}^2} \right)(-2.45 \times 10^{-19} \text{ J})} \\
&= 9.4 \times 10^{-10} \text{ m}
\end{aligned}
\qquad [60]
$$

which is $r = 0.94$ nm. This calculation confirms a value close to 1 nm, which we read from Fig. 13.30 earlier.

For systems with $N$ stationary point charges, the electric energies of each pair interaction with the mobile point charge are added to obtain its total energy:

$$
E_{\text{el}} = \sum_{i=1}^{N} E_{\text{el},i}
\qquad [61]
$$

## The Electric Potential

When studying the electric force, we noted that the great variability of electric systems caused mathematical complexity. We dealt with this problem by using Faraday's method to split the electric force, defining the electric field. The same issues apply for the electric energy. Thus, an equivalent approach is taken to address energy-related issues: we find a field, called electric potential, that represents at every position in space the electric potential energy a mobile point charge of unit charge would have if brought to that point.

This means that we have two routes to the electric potential: we can proceed from the electric force to electric potential energy and then eliminate the mobile point charge, or we can proceed from the electric force to the electric field by eliminating the mobile point charge and then make the step from electric field to potential. Below we choose the first approach, since we just completed the discussion of the various forms of electric potential energy and want to use those results to establish the potential with the least mathematical effort.

We also note that we continue to limit the discussion to systems in which all charges but a single mobile point charge are stationary. Thus, the resulting potential will be a stationary field (time-independent field).

## Calculating the Electric Potential

We separate the electric energy into

- a mobile point charge, and
- a field due to all stationary point charges in the system. This field is called the **electric potential**, which should not be confused with the electric potential energy.

Different from the electric field, the potential is a **scalar field**. It is labelled $V$ and is defined by dividing the electric potential energy by the mobile point charge:

$$E_{el} = q_{mobile} \cdot V \qquad [62]$$

*The electric potential energy is the product of the electric potential and the charge of the mobile point charge. Both energy and potential are scalars; the potential is, therefore, a scalar field.*

A new unit is introduced for the potential, called **volt** $V = J/C$, named for Alessandro Count Volta. Two specific cases follow immediately from Eq. [62] and the energies we established in the previous section for the parallel plate arrangement and a stationary point charge. For the parallel plate arrangement, we obtain:

$$V_{\parallel} = \frac{E_{el}}{q_{test}} = |\mathbf{E}| \cdot y = \frac{\sigma}{\varepsilon_0} y \qquad [63]$$

in which $\sigma$ is the surface charge density on the plates. For a stationary point charge, we get:

$$V = \frac{E_{el}}{q_{test}} = \frac{1}{4 \cdot \pi \cdot \varepsilon_0} \frac{q}{|r|} \qquad [64]$$

Note that both equations seem to allow us to calculate absolute values for the potential. While this is correct, we have to remind ourselves that absolute potential values, like absolute values for a potential energy, are physically meaningless. It makes no difference whether you consider yourself to be at 0 V potential right now or whether you prefer to define your current potential as 1000 V. What matters are potential differences, like potential energy differences. There is no danger in touching an object that has the same potential as yourself; but do not touch objects that have significantly different potentials from the ground under your feet! In short, we always seek potential differences, $\Delta V$, when discussing real physical phenomena. Example 13.13 demonstrates this aspect of the concept of potential.

### ● EXAMPLE 13.13

A potential difference of 80 mV exists between the inner and outer surface of the membrane of a cell. The inner surface is negative relative to the outer surface. How much work is required to eject a positive potassium ion ($K^+$) from the interior of the cell?

*Solution:* Fig. 13.12 shows the environment of the diffusing potassium ion. Initially the ion is inside (as shown), where it is in close proximity to the negative surface charge on the membrane. Work is required to transfer the potassium ion through the membrane as the ion leaves a negative environment and approaches a positive environment. The work is calculated using Eq. [63], noting that a potassium ion carries a single positive elementary charge $q = e$:

$$W = q \cdot \Delta V = (1.6 \times 10^{-19}\,C)(80 \times 10^{-3}\,V)$$
$$= +1.28 \times 10^{-20}\,J \qquad [65]$$

The work is positive for a process into which work has to be invested.

### Concept Question 13.9

We consider the potential curve $V(x)$ in Fig. 13.31(b). Which of the four charged parallel plate arrangements in Fig. 13.31(a) is consistent with this potential curve?

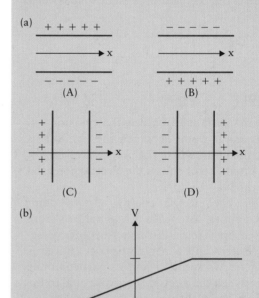

### FIGURE 13.31

(a) Four charged parallel plate arrangements. (b) A potential curve $V(x)$, i.e., a curve that shows the potential as a function of position along the x-axis.

ANSWER: Choice (D). Options (A) and (B) can be ruled out because the x-axis runs parallel to the electrically charged plates. In that direction the electric energy does not change, nor does the potential. Options (C) and (D) differ in that the x-axis points in one case toward the plate with positive charges, in the other toward the plate with negative charges. We can use the result from Example 13.13 to decide which case applies: the potassium ion is a positive mobile point charge. We found a positive work in Eq. [65], which means that the electric energy for the potassium ion increases as it moves in Fig. 13.12 toward the left. Dividing an increase in energy by the positive charge in Eq. [62] yields an increase in the potential. We can combine this result with Fig. 13.14 to state the relation of the direction of the electric field to the direction of increasing or decreasing potential.

*The potential increases when we follow a line that moves from an area with negative charges to an area with positive charges. The electric field points in the direction of decreasing potential.*

Next we address the energy and the potential of our third model system, a dipole. It is introduced as an example, based on two opposite point charges.

## ● EXAMPLE 13.14

Find the potential at point $P$, which is located at an arbitrary position relative to a dipole, as shown in Fig. 13.32(a). Assume that the point $P$ is far from the dipole.

*Solution:* For more than one stationary point charge, electric potentials have to be added in the same fashion as we discussed for the electric potential energy in Eq. [61]. In particular, the electric potential at point $P$ in Fig. 13.32(a), $V_P$, is:

$$V_P = V_{P,+q} + V_{P,-q}$$

$$= \frac{1}{4 \cdot \pi \cdot \varepsilon_0} \left( \frac{q}{r_+} + \frac{-q}{r_-} \right) \qquad [66]$$

with $P$ a distance $r_+$ from the positive point charge and a distance $r_-$ from the negative point charge of the dipole. Eq. [66] is rewritten with a common denominator for the term in the parentheses:

$$V_P = \frac{q}{4 \cdot \pi \cdot \varepsilon_0} \cdot \frac{r_- - r_+}{r_- \cdot r_+} \qquad [67]$$

If $P$ is close to the dipole, Eq. [67] cannot be simplified further and is therefore our final result.

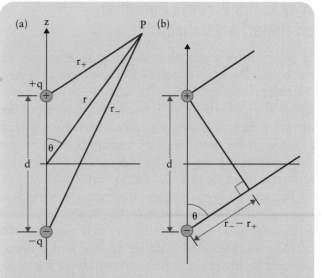

**FIGURE 13.32**
(a) A dipole oriented along the z-axis. The point $P$ is located at an arbitrary position relative to the dipole. (b) Geometric plot to determine the difference in the distances from each of the two point charges of the dipole in part (a) to a distant point $P$.

However, if $P$ lies far from the dipole with $r_+$, $r_- \gg d$, then both the numerator and denominator of the last term in Eq. [67] are rewritten using geometrical relations obtained from Fig. 13.32(b). In that figure, the two lines that extend from the dipole charges to point $P$ are treated as parallel. The difference in distance from the two charges to point $P$ is a side in the right-angle triangle shown in the figure. This triangle allows us to express the term $r_- - r_+$ as a function of the length $d$ and the angle $\theta$ between the dipole axis and the position vector to point $P$:

$$r_- - r_+ = d \cdot \cos \theta \qquad [68]$$

We further use $r_- \cong r_+ \cong r$ with $r$ the distance of the point $P$ from the centre of the dipole. This simplifies the denominator to:

$$r_- \cdot r_+ = r^2 \qquad [69]$$

Inserting Eqs. [68] and [69] in Eq. [67], we find:

$$\lim_{r \gg d} V_P = \frac{q}{4 \cdot \pi \cdot \varepsilon_0} \frac{d \cdot \cos \theta}{r^2}$$

$$= \frac{\mu}{4 \cdot \pi \cdot \varepsilon_0} \frac{\cos \theta}{r^2} \qquad [70]$$

in which $\mu$ is the electric dipole moment of the dipole in Fig. 13.32, as defined in Eq. [35]. Thus, the electric potential of a dipole diminishes more rapidly with distance than the electric potential of a point charge.

## Why Is the Electric Potential an Important Concept?

In your future work, should you expect to use the force or the energy concept? In the earlier chapters, the energy concept allowed us to move beyond a mechanical view of nature. Thus, in the context of the life sciences you expect arguments based on energy to occur more often, as this approach links to the thermodynamic description of systems. But is this also true when electric charges are involved?

The answer is that, again, the energy approach is more useful and therefore more often applied. From a life scientist's point of view, the first reason is the same as we developed in earlier chapters: in order to describe nature at the molecular level, force is a more elusive concept while energy connects to the thermal physics properties of the system. The link between electric and thermodynamic properties is established in the next chapter; its key physical law will be Nernst's equation. In the case of electricity, a second reason for the priority of energy over force has to be added: potentials can be measured while electric fields are experimentally inaccessible. The instrument allowing us to measure the potential is called a **voltmeter**. All we have to do is to position two metallic electrodes (wires) at two chosen points in a system and the voltmeter registers the **potential difference** between these two points.

## Equipotential Lines

The electric potential for more complex arrangements of charges is often illustrated using **equipotential lines** in a graphical sketch. Equipotential lines are lines that connect points of equal value of the electric potential. These lines are always perpendicular to electric field lines. Fig. 13.33 illustrates the equipotential lines for the three types of systems we discuss in the current chapter: Fig. 13.33(a) shows horizontal electric field lines (dashed arrows) and vertical equipotential lines (solid lines) for a uniformly charged parallel plate arrangement. Neither the electric field lines nor the equipotential lines indicate complicated position dependences in this case.

Fig. 13.33(b) shows radial electric field lines and concentric equipotential lines for a positive point charge. To illustrate the non-linear $r$ dependence, the equipotential lines are chosen with a constant difference $\Delta V$ between neighbouring lines.

Fig. 13.33(c) shows the more complex structure of electric field lines and equipotential lines for a dipole. Note that the electric field lines are straight only along the dipole axis, while a straight equipotential

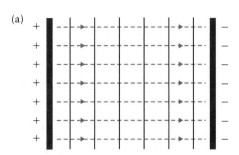

(a)

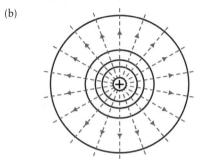

(b)

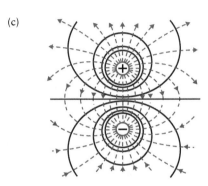

(c)

**FIGURE 13.33**

The electric potential for charge arrangements is often visualized by using equipotential lines in a sketch. Equipotential lines are lines that connect points of equal value of the electric potential. They are shown as solid lines in the figure. These lines are always perpendicular to electric field lines, shown as dashed lines. Illustrated are: (a) a uniformly charged parallel plate arrangement, (b) a positive stationary point charge, and (c) a dipole.

line exists perpendicular to the dipole axis at the centre of the dipole.

## Electroreceptors in Aquatic Vertebrates

Most species, including humans, cannot detect electric potentials in their environment. However, weak electric potentials are generated by all vertebrates with a nervous system. The action of nerves is discussed in Chapter 14. These are measured in modern medicine with methods such as electrocardiograms for the heart, electromyograms for muscle action, and electroencephalograms for brain activity. In Chapter 15 the ECG is chosen to illustrate how these methods work.

**FIGURE 13.34**
Electric eel.

The aquatic environment is best suited for the development and use of a sense for electric potentials because water conducts electricity better than air does. We find **electroreceptors** among many species of fish from lampreys to sharks, indicating that these receptors developed early in vertebrates' evolution. Fish species that can detect electric potentials are called **electroreceptive**.

A prominent type of electroreceptor is the ampullary organ, in particular the **ampullae of Lorenzini** clustered on the top and bottom of a **shark's** head. The ampullary organ consists of a short tube that runs subcutaneously parallel to the skin. The tube ends on one side in a pore at the body surface and on the other side in a slightly enlarged chamber, called the ampulla. The ampulla contains sensory cells with a single hair stretched into the ampulla's inner space. The tube, filled with a gelatinous substance, acts like a parallel plate arrangement, with the external plate affected by nearby electric potentials. The sensory cells respond to potential changes that result either from external potential variations with time, or from potential changes while the shark swims toward its prey.

Why did nature develop this additional sense in fish? Sharks, for example, already have an impressive set of sensory systems: good vision, olfaction, bone conduction–based hearing (for a description of this method see Chapter 1), and water vibration sensitivity with the lateral line system we discussed in Fig. 2.14. What is missing? These other senses respond to stimuli that are connected to non-essential vital activities of prey species. When predators are around, a reasonably camouflaged animal can lie

**FIGURE 13.35**
Electric ray.

patiently on the sea floor or even hide beneath a layer of sand. However, suppressing the involuntary action of the heart and respiratory muscles is impossible.

The ability to benefit from electric effects goes even further in some fish species. Species that can intentionally generate electric potentials are called **electrogenic**, and often are referred to as "electric fish." Electric potentials are generated for two objectives:

- Large potential differences are used to stun prey during hunting. The electric eel *Electrophorus* (see Fig. 13.34) can produce up to 500 V, and the electric ray species *Torpedo* (see Fig. 13.35) up to 50 V.

- Small potential differences are used for sex recognition and to navigate in murky water.

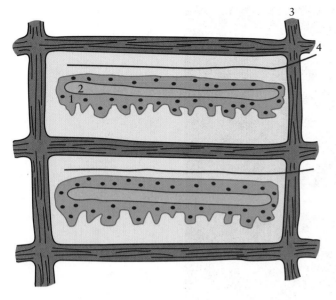

**FIGURE 13.36**

Disk-shaped electroplaques of fish such as the electric eel. Connective tissue (3) holds a stack of cells together that are flat (2) on the side with nerves (4), and highly folded on the opposite side (1). A resting potential difference of −84 mV applies across the plasma membrane. When the nerve depolarizes the membrane, the adjacent potential difference rises to +67 mV. At that moment a 151-mV potential difference occurs across the entire electroplaque because the opposite side of the cell remains polarized.

Electric potentials are generated by means of a series of disk-shaped **electroplaques**, which evolved from muscle cells or their motor end plate. Two electroplaques are shown in Fig. 13.36. Connective tissue (3) holds together cells that are flat on the innervated side (2, the side with nerves (4)) and highly folded on the opposite side (1). A −84-mV potential difference develops across the plasma membrane, as discussed in greater detail for nerve cells in the next chapter. When a cell membrane on the innervated side depolarizes, the potential difference rises to +67 mV. At that moment a 151-mV potential difference occurs across the entire electroplaque because the non-innervated side remains polarized. The electric eel's trunk contains 70 columns of up to 10 000 electroplaques on each side.

Electroreceptors and electroplaques can be discussed quantitatively only when several further physical concepts have been introduced, including the dielectric constant to describe the gelatinous substance in the ampullae of Lorenzini, and the electric current for the shock effect of an electroplaque discharge on nearby fish.

# Conservation of Energy

The electric energy is a form of energy that was not considered in Chapter 6. Therefore, we want to determine whether it has the same properties as the previously defined forms of energy. We are interested in seeing how key concepts of thermodynamics are applied to electric systems, particularly:

- that the internal energy of a system is governed by the first law of thermodynamics, and
- that the Gibbs free energy is equal for two systems in chemical equilibrium.

We consider the energy conservation here; the electrochemical equilibrium across a semipermeable membrane is discussed in Chapter 14. The conservation of energy is valid in all experiments that include electric effects; i.e., electricity does not contradict the previously introduced laws of thermodynamics. In a closed system of point charges that interact with their environment, the total work exchanged with the environment includes an electric work contribution in the form:

$$W = \Delta E_{el} = E_{el,final} - E_{el,initial} \qquad [71]$$

The inclusion of a new contribution to the total energy does not complicate the calculations, as the number of energy terms that are relevant for a given system is usually small. For example, in most physiological systems gravitational potential energy is negligible. The kinetic energy plays a role only when parts of the system may accelerate. For example, kinetic energy need not be included in the discussion of signal transport in nerves because essentially no acceleration of point charges along the nerve is involved, as we will establish in Chapter 14.

● **EXAMPLE 13.15**

In 1911, Ernest Rutherford conducted an ion scattering experiment that allowed him to postulate a planetary model for the atom (see also Chapter 22). In the experiment he studied fast alpha particles of charge $+2e$ and mass $6.6 \times 10^{-27}$ kg, which penetrated into a gold target as sketched in Fig. 13.37. If an alpha particle on a path leading to a head-on collision with a gold nucleus has a speed of $2.0 \times 10^7$ m/s while still far from the gold nucleus, how close does it get to the gold nucleus before turning back? Use for the charge of the gold nucleus $+79e$.

*Solution:* We use the conservation of energy. In this particular case, the kinetic energy and the electric potential energy are the only two energy forms that vary during the process. Thus, we write the conservation of energy in the form:

$$E_{kin,initial} + E_{el,initial} = E_{kin,final} + E_{el,final} \qquad [72]$$

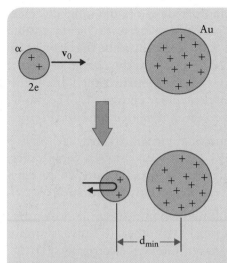

**FIGURE 13.37**

Microscopic sketch of Ernest Rutherford's experiment: a helium nucleus (alpha particle with two positive charges) approaches at high speed a gold nucleus at rest in the target.

in which the kinetic energy is related to the speed of the moving alpha particle as $E_{kin} = \frac{1}{2} \cdot m \cdot v^2$ and the electric potential energy is given by Eq. [58] since the interaction occurs between two point charges.

We choose the initial state, at a point where the alpha particle is still far away from the gold nucleus. In this context "far" essentially means farther than the radius of the gold atom. This very short distance is sufficient, as the negative electrons in the atomic shell of a neutral gold atom screen the positive charge centred in the nucleus. In the initial state the electric potential energy of the alpha particle is zero, as obtained from Eq. [58] for $d = \infty$. The speed of the particle is determined from the acceleration process available

in the laboratory. (Usually, the speed of the alpha particle would not be given as such but would be calculated from the energy transferred to the particle in the acceleration.)

The final state is given where the alpha particle reaches the closest proximity to the gold nucleus (distance $d_{min}$). The particle is now well within the innermost shell of atomic electrons and thus facing the unscreened charge of the Au nucleus. At that point, the kinetic energy of the particle becomes zero since the particle comes momentarily to rest before accelerating away from the nucleus. Its entire energy has been shifted into its electric potential energy. Substituting these two states into Eq. [72] yields:

$$\frac{1}{2} m \cdot v_{initial}^2 = \frac{1}{4 \cdot \pi \cdot \varepsilon_0} \frac{q_\alpha \cdot q_{Au}}{d_{min}} \quad [73]$$

which is equivalent to:

$$d_{min} = \frac{1}{4 \cdot \pi \cdot \varepsilon_0} \frac{2 \cdot q_\alpha \cdot q_{Au}}{m_\alpha \cdot v_{initial}^2} \quad [74]$$

With the data given in the example text, this yields:

$$d_{min} = \frac{2 \cdot \left( 9 \times 10^9 \frac{N \cdot m^2}{C^2} \right) \cdot 2e \cdot 79e}{(6.6 \times 10^{-27} \, kg) \left( 2 \times 10^7 \frac{m}{s} \right)^2}$$

$$= 2.8 \times 10^{-14} \, m \quad [75]$$

We compare this value to the radius of the gold nucleus, which is $r = 7 \times 10^{-15}$ m. Thus, the alpha particle approaches the gold nucleus to within a distance of twice the diameter of the nucleus! Still, the interaction is entirely electric; the nuclear force does not reach that far beyond the nucleus.

# MULTIPLE CHOICE AND CONCEPTUAL QUESTIONS

## PROPERTIES OF THE WATER MOLECULE

**Q–13.1.** Water consists of (A) positively charged atoms, (B) negatively charged atoms, (C) positively charged molecules, (D) negatively charge molecules, (E) none of the above.

**Q–13.2.** Which feature of water cannot be explained with its dipole character, and the related formation of hydrogen bonds? (A) high melting point, (B) high freezing point, (C) open crystal structure of ice (low density), (D) formation of hydration shells when

mixed with salts, (E) none of the four previous choices is a correct answer.

**Q–13.3.** Two sodium ions in an aqueous solution (A) repel each other, (B) do not interact at any separation distance, (C) attract each other, (D) seek each other to form metallic sodium precipitates, (E) do none of the above.

**Q–13.4.** The following is not a property of a hydrogen bond: (A) It connects a hydrogen atom to an oxygen atom in a different molecule. (B) It connects two hydrogen atoms between two different molecules. (C) It is a bond that is weaker than the covalent OH bond in a water molecule. (D) Its formation allows water to remain liquid at temperatures where most other small molecules are already in the gaseous state.

**Q–13.5.** The water molecule is an electric dipole. The following statement about the water molecule is therefore wrong: (A) The distance between the centres of positive and negative charge in the molecule is a stationary distance. (B) The amount of charge we assign to the positive end and the amount of charge we assign to the negative end of the molecule are equal but opposite. (C) The electric field points from the hydrogen atoms toward the oxygen atom. (D) If we choose the electric potential at infinite distance from the water molecule to be zero, $V = 0$, then the electric potential of the water dipole does not vanish anywhere within a distance of $5 \cdot d$ from the water molecule, where $d$ is the distance between the charged centres of the dipole.

**Q–13.6.** The force between a water dipole with electric dipole moment $\mu$ and charge separation distance $d$, and a negative ion of charge $q$ located along the dipole axis of the water molecule is calculated using the following formula (with $r$ the distance from the centre of the dipole to the negative charge):

(A)  $F = -\dfrac{1}{2 \cdot \pi \cdot \varepsilon_0} \dfrac{\mu \cdot q}{r^2}$

(B)  $F = -\dfrac{1}{2 \cdot \pi \cdot \varepsilon_0} \dfrac{\mu \cdot q}{r^3}$

(C)  $F = -\dfrac{1}{2 \cdot \pi \cdot \varepsilon_0} \dfrac{\mu \cdot q}{d^2}$    [76]

(D)  $F = -\dfrac{1}{2 \cdot \pi \cdot \varepsilon_0} \dfrac{\mu \cdot q}{d^3}$

(E)  $F = -\dfrac{1}{2 \cdot \pi \cdot \varepsilon_0} \dfrac{\mu \cdot q}{r \cdot d^2}$

## ELECTRIC FORCE AND COULOMB'S LAW

**Q–13.7.** Two point charges repel each other with an electric force of magnitude $f_0$. If we double both charges, the magnitude of the force between the point charges becomes (A) $f_0/4$, (B) $f_0/2$, (C) $f_0$ (i.e., it remains unchanged), (D) $2 \cdot f_0$, (E) $4 \cdot f_0$.

**Q–13.8.** Which statement about the electric dipole moment $\mu$ is correct? (A) A molecule is a strong dipole if the net charge separation occurs over a short distance within the molecule. (B) The unit of $\mu$ is C/m. (C) A dipole exerts a larger force on a point

charge than on another dipole at the same distance. (D) For strong dipole molecules, $\mu$ is typically a value on the order of $1 \times 10^{-30}$ C $\cdot$ m while the elementary charge is $1.6 \times 10^{-19}$ C. Thus, the charge separated in strong dipole molecules is many orders of magnitude less than an elementary charge. (E) The dipole moment can be zero even if neither $q$ nor $d$ is zero.

**Q–13.9.** Two dipoles at close proximity (A) always repel each other, (B) always attract each other, (C) never interact electrically, (D) attract or repel each other based on their relative orientation.

**Q–13.10.** A dipole and a point charge at close proximity (A) always repel each other, (B) always attract each other, (C) never interact electrically, (D) attract/repel each other based on the location of the point charge relative to the dipole axis.

**Q–13.11.** What do Newton's law of gravity and Coulomb's law have in common? (A) force dependence on mass, (B) force dependence on electric charge, (C) force dependence on distance, (D) the magnitude of the proportionality constant, (E) nothing.

## ELECTRIC FIELD

**Q–13.12.** We find an electric field of magnitude $E = 1.0 \times 10^7$ V/m across a particular nerve membrane of thickness 5 nm. What is the potential difference between the interior and exterior surface of the membrane? Choose the closest value. (A) 50 mV, (B) 500 mV, (C) 0.5 V, (D) 5.0 V, (E) 50 V.

**Q–13.13.** A mobile positive point charge is located between two parallel charged plates, with the upper plate carrying a positive surface charge density $+\sigma$ and the lower plate carrying a negative surface charge density $-\sigma$. How does the magnitude of the electric field at the position of the mobile point charge change if it moves to twice the distance from the negative plate (i.e., toward the positive plate)? (A) It remains unchanged, (B) it increases by a factor of 4, (C) it doubles, (D) it becomes half of the initial value, (E) it becomes one-quarter of the initial value.

**Q–13.14.** In electrophoresis, (A) ions are separated by diffusion, (B) atoms and molecules are separated in an electric field, (C) an electric field is applied to an ionic solution, (D) charged oil droplets are levitated in an observation chamber, (E) none of the above.

**Q–13.15.** The electric field of a dipole (A) is the same as for a point charge, (B) cannot be described with a formula, (C) decreases faster than for a point charge as we move away from it, (D) decreases slower than for a point charge as we move away from it.

**Q–13.16.** The HF molecule is a dipole with an electronegativity of 4.0 assigned to the fluorine atom and 2.2 to the hydrogen atom. In which direction does the electric field point between these two atoms in the molecule? (A) perpendicular to the line between the two atoms; (B) along the line between the two atoms, in the direction of the hydrogen atom; (C) along the line between the two atoms, in the direction of the fluorine atom; (D) at an angle of 104.5° relative to the line between the two atoms.

**Q–13.17.** In Millikan's experiment, (A) charged oil droplets are separated by diffusion, (B) neutral oil mist droplets are separated in an electric field, (C) an electric field is applied to an ionic solution, (D) charged oil droplets are levitated in an observation chamber, (E) none of the above.

**Q–13.18.** The electric field of a point charge (A) increases proportional to $r^2$ with distance, (B) decreases proportional to $r^2$ with distance, (C) increases linearly with distance, (D) decreases linearly with distance, (E) none of the above.

**Q–13.19.** In which direction does the electric field point at point $P$ for the two charges in Fig. 13.38? Assume that $q_+ = +1\ \mu C$ and $q_- = -1\ \mu C$. *Hint:* Draw the field due to each of the charges separately at $P$, then see for the resulting direction. (A) left, (B) right, (C) up, (D) down, (E) elsewhere.

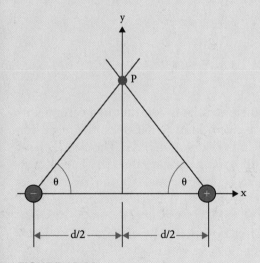

**FIGURE 13.38**
A system of two point charges for determining the electric field at point $P$.

**Q–13.20.** Can electric field lines ever cross? Explain your answer.

## WORK AND ELECTRIC POTENTIAL ENERGY

**Q–13.21.** In the four processes shown in Fig. 13.39 a mobile point charge (small green circle with positive or negative charge indicated) is moving in the

direction of the red arrow shown in the vicinity of an arrangement of stationary charges (either a stationary point charge, depicted as a large green circle with its charge indicated, or a pair of charged plates). In which case is the work negative (energy is released by the mobile point charge during the displacement)?

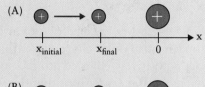

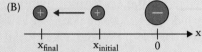

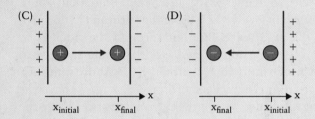

**FIGURE 13.39**
Four processes in which a mobile point charge (small green circle with positive or negative charge indicated) is moving in the direction of the red arrow shown in the vicinity of an arrangement of stationary charges (either a stationary point charge depicted as a large green circle with its charge indicated, or a pair of charged plates).

**Q–13.22.** Fig. 13.40 shows the potential energy for a mobile electron in a hydrogen atom (the nucleus is a positive stationary point charge at $r = 0$). Three total energies are considered, and are shown in the

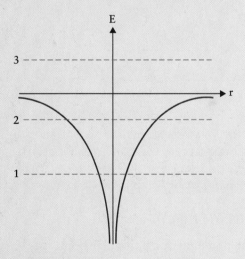

**FIGURE 13.40**
The potential energy for a mobile electron in a hydrogen atom (the nucleus is a positive stationary point charge at $r = 0$). Three total energies are indicated by horizontal dashed lines labelled 1, 2, and 3.

figure by horizontal dashed lines labelled 1, 2, and 3. Which statement is correct? (A) The electron with total energy at level 3 oscillates back and forth. (B) The electron with total energy at level 1 is the only electron that will never travel away from the nucleus. (C) The electron with total energy at level 2 is bound but can travel farther from the nucleus than the electron with total energy at level 1.

**Q–13.23.** Fig. 13.41 shows the electric potential energy of a proton (positive point charge) as a function of distance from a positively charged atomic nucleus, which is located at $r = 0$. Let's assume that the atomic nucleus is very heavy, e.g., the nucleus of a lead atom. We consider two values for the total energy of the proton: proton (1) with total energy $E_{total}(1)$ and proton (2) with total energy $E_{total}(2)$. Which statement about this system is wrong? (A) Neither proton (1) nor proton (2) will travel straight through the nucleus at $r = 0$. (B) Proton (2) will approach the nucleus to closer proximity than proton (1). (C) At the same distance from the nucleus, protons (1) and (2) have the same total energy. (D) At any given position along the $r$-axis, the electric potential energies for proton (1) and proton (2) are the same. (E) Proton (1) reaches the same electric potential energy as proton (2) when at infinite distance from the nucleus.

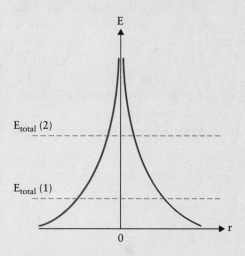

**FIGURE 13.41**

The electric potential energy of a proton (positive point charge) as a function of distance from a positive stationary nucleus at $r = 0$. We consider two values for the total energy of the proton: proton (1) with total energy $E_{total}(1)$ and proton (2) with total energy $E_{total}(2)$.

## POTENTIAL AND POTENTIAL DIFFERENCE

**Q–13.24.** If the potential at a particular point is 0 V, can you state that no point charges exist in the vicinity of that point?

**Q–13.25.** The absolute value of the potential difference between the interior and exterior surfaces of a particular membrane is 65 mV. What additional information will allow you to determine which surface of the membrane carries an excess of positive ions? (A) I need the thickness of the membrane. (B) I need to know which positive ions are involved (e.g., $K^+$, or $Na^+$, or $Ca^{2+}$). (C) I need to establish a Cartesian coordinate system. (D) I need to know the magnitude of the electric field across the membrane. (E) None of the above.

**Q–13.26.** The water molecule shown in Fig. 13.1 is an electric dipole. Given the orientation of the molecule in the figure, in which direction does the electric potential point within the molecule? (A) up, (B) down, (C) left, (D) right, (E) there is no direction because the electric potential does not contain directional information.

**Q–13.27.** The electric potential cannot be given in the following unit: (A) J/C (joule per coulomb), (B) V (volt), (C) N/C (newton per coulomb), (D) (N · m)/C (newton metre per coulomb), (E) More than one of these cannot be used.

**Q–13.28.** If the electric field has a constant magnitude and points in the positive $x$-direction, which of the following formulas is correct to describe the potential if $a$ is constant and $b$ and $c$ are positive non-zero constants (i.e., $b > 0$ and $c > 0$):

(A)  $V = a$
(B)  $V = a + b \cdot x$
(C)  $V = a - b \cdot x$          [77]
(D)  $V = a + b \cdot x + c \cdot x^2$
(E)  $V = a - b \cdot x - c \cdot x^2$

**Q–13.29.** If the potential is constant in a certain volume around a given point, what does this mean for the electric field in that volume? (A) The electric field is constant and has a negative value. (B) The electric field is inversely proportional to the distance to the nearest charges. (C) The electric field is zero. (D) The electric field depends linearly on the distance to the nearest charges. (E) The electric field is constant and has a positive value.

**Q–13.30.** Four point charges are positioned on a circular line. Their respective charges are $+1.5 \ \mu C$, $+0.5 \ \mu C$, $-0.5 \ \mu C$, and $-1.0 \ \mu C$. Assume that the potential at the centre of the circle due to the $+0.5$-$\mu C$ point charge is 45 kV. What is the potential at the centre of the circle due to all four point charges combined? (A) 180 kV, (B) 45 kV, (C) 0 V, (D) −45 kV.

**Q–13.31.** If a proton is released from rest in a uniform electric field, does the electric potential at its position increase, stay the same, or decrease?

# ANALYTICAL PROBLEMS

## ELECTRIC FORCE

**P–13.1.** We study three point charges at the corners of a triangle, as shown in Fig. 13.42. Their charges are $q_1 = 5.0 \times 10^{-9}$ C, $q_2 = -4.0 \times 10^{-9}$ C, and $q_3 = 2.5 \times 10^{-9}$ C. Two distances of separation are also given, $l_{12} = 4$ m and $l_{13} = 6$ m. Find the net electric force on $q_3$.

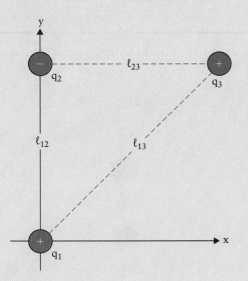

**FIGURE 13.42**

**P–13.2.** In Fig. 13.43(a) we study two particles A and B. They are separated by distance $a$. Particle A initially has a positive charge of $+Q$ and particle B is electrically neutral ($q = 0$). Thus, no electric force acts between them.

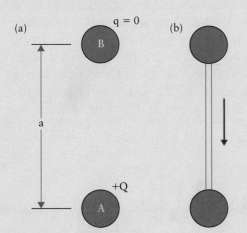

**FIGURE 13.43**

The particles are then connected, as shown in Fig. 13.43(b). This allows for an equal distribution of charges between the two particles. What is the electric force between the particles after the connection is removed?

**P–13.3.** The radius of atomic nuclei follows closely the formula

$$r = 1.2 \times 10^{-15} \cdot A^{1/3} \qquad [78]$$

in which $r$ has unit m, and $A$ is the atomic mass in unit g/mol. (a) Confirm that the density of nuclear matter is independent of the type of atom studied. This density is $2 \times 10^{17}$ kg/m$^3$! (b) Using Eq. [78] and $A(\text{Bi}) = 209.0$ g/mol, find the magnitude of the repulsive electrostatic force between two of the protons in a bismuth nucleus when they are separated by the diameter of the nucleus.

**P–13.4.** How much negative charge is in 1.0 mol of neutral helium gas? Each He atom has two electrons in its atomic shell.

**P–13.5.** A CsCl (cesium chloride) salt crystal is built from the unit cells shown in Fig. 13.44. Cl$^-$ ions form the corners of a cube and a Cs$^+$ ion is at the centre of the cube. The edge length of the cube, which is called the lattice constant, is 0.4 nm. (a) What is the magnitude of the net force exerted on the cesium ion by its eight nearest Cl$^-$ neighbours? (b) If the Cl$^-$ in the lower left corner is removed, what is the magnitude of the net force exerted on the cesium ion at the centre by the seven remaining nearest chlorine ions? In what direction does this force act on the cesium ion?

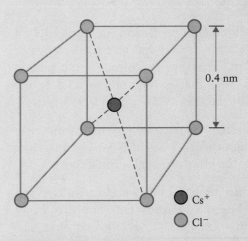

**FIGURE 13.44**

**P–13.6.** Determine the magnitude of the force between an electric dipole with a dipole moment of $3 \times 10^{-29}$ C · m and an electron. The electron is positioned $r = 20$ nm from the centre of the dipole, along the dipole axis. *Hint:* Assume that $r \gg d$ with $d$ the charge separation distance in the dipole.

## ELECTRIC FIELD

**P–13.7.** Fig. 13.45 shows three positive point charges, with two charges of magnitude $q$ at a distance $d$ along the negative $x$- and the positive $y$-axis, and one charge of magnitude $2 \cdot q$ at the origin. Calculate the electric field at point $P$ for $q = 1.0$ nC and a distance $d = 1.0$ m.

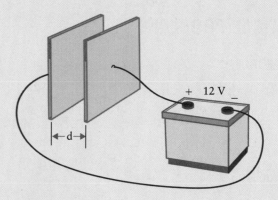

**FIGURE 13.46**

**P–13.13.** Three positive point charges are located at the corners of a rectangle, as illustrated in Fig. 13.47. Find the electric field at the fourth corner if $q_1 = 3$ nC, $q_2 = 6$ nC, and $q_3 = 5$ nC. The distances are $d_1 = 0.6$ m and $d_2 = 0.2$ m.

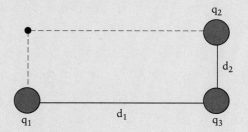

**FIGURE 13.47**

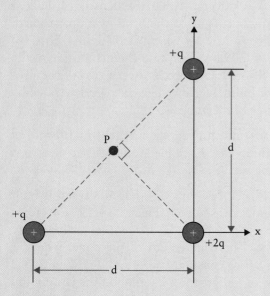

**FIGURE 13.45**

**P–13.8.** Calculate the electric field halfway between two point charges, one carrying $+10.0 \times 10^{-9}$ C and the other (a) $+5.0 \times 10^{-9}$ C at a distance of 20 cm; (b) $-5.0 \times 10^{-9}$ C at a distance of 20 cm.

**P–13.9.** In Millikan's experiment in Fig. 13.4, a droplet of radius $r = 1.9$ $\mu$m has an excess charge of two electrons. What are the magnitude and direction of the electric field that is required to levitate the droplet? Use for the density of oil $\rho = 0.925$ g/cm$^3$.

**P–13.10.** An electron is released into a uniform electric field of magnitude $1.5 \times 10^3$ N/C. Calculate the acceleration of the electron, neglecting gravity.

**P–13.11.** Humid air breaks down electrically when its molecules become ionized. This happens in an electric field $|E| = 3.0 \times 10^6$ N/C. In that field, calculate the magnitude of the electric force on an ion with a single positive charge.

**P–13.12.** A constant electric field is experimentally obtained with the setup shown in Fig. 13.46: a 12-V battery is connected to two parallel metal plates separated by a distance of $d = 0.25$ cm. Calculate the magnitude of the electric field between the plates.

## ELECTRIC POTENTIAL ENERGY AND ELECTRIC POTENTIAL

**P–13.14.** A large number of energetic cosmic-ray particles (more on these in Chapter 21) reach Earth's atmosphere continuously and knock electrons out of the molecules in the air. Once an electron is released, it responds to an electrostatic force that is due to an electric field $E$ produced in the atmosphere by other point charges. Near the surface of Earth this electric field has a magnitude of $|E| = 150$ N/C and is directed downward, as shown in Fig. 13.48. Calculate

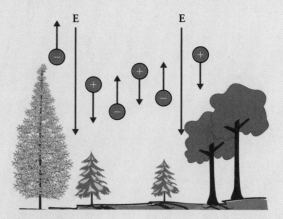

**FIGURE 13.48**

the change in electric potential energy of a released electron when it moves vertically upward through a distance $d = 650$ m.

**P–13.15.** (a) What is the electric potential $V$ at a distance $r = 2.1 \times 10^{-8}$ cm from a proton? (b) What is the electric potential energy in units J and eV of an electron at the given distance from the proton? (c) If the electron moves closer to the proton, does the electric potential energy increase or decrease?

**P–13.16.** (a) For the arrangement of charges in Fig. 13.45, calculate the electric potential at point $P$. Use $q = 1.0$ nC and $d = 1.0$ m, and assume that $V = 0$ V at infinite distance. (b) If a charge $-2 \cdot q$ is brought to point $P$, what is the electric energy of this charge? Assume again that the electric potential energy is zero at infinite distance.

**P–13.17.** We study the three point charges shown in Fig. 13.49. They are held at the corners of an equilateral triangle with $l = 0.2$ m. What is the electric potential energy of the system of three point charges? Use for the three charges: $q_1 = +2Q$, $q_2 = -3Q$, and $q_3 = +Q$ where $Q = 100$ nC. *Hint:* The solution is done in steps. Assume that you first bring one of the point charges from a very large (infinite) distance to its position. Then repeat this procedure for the second and third point charges.

**P–13.18.** An ion is accelerated through a potential difference of 60 $V$, causing a decrease in its electric potential energy of $1.92 \times 10^{-17}$ J. Calculate the charge the ion carries.

**P–13.19.** Fig. 13.50 shows three positive point charges at the corners of a rectangle. Find the electric

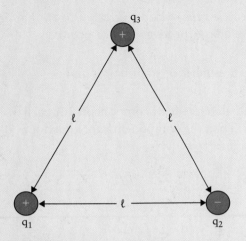

**FIGURE 13.49**

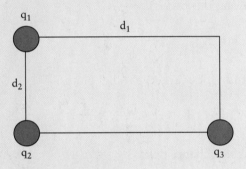

**FIGURE 13.50**

potential at the upper right corner if $q_1 = 8$ $\mu$C, $q_2 = 2$ $\mu$C, and $q_3 = 4$ $\mu$C. The distances are $d_1 = 6.0$ cm and $d_2 = 3.0$ cm. The potential is defined such that it is 0 $V$ at infinite distance from the point charge arrangement shown.

# SUMMARY

### DEFINITIONS

- Dipole moment: $\mu = q \cdot d$, in which $d$ is distance between charges $+q$ and $-q$ in a dipole.

### UNITS

- Charge $q$: C
- Electric force $\mathbf{F}_{el}$: N
- Electric field $\mathbf{E}$: N/C
- Electric potential energy $E_{el}$: J
- Potential $V$: V
- Dipole moment $\mu$: C · m

### LAWS

- Coulomb's law:

$$\mathbf{F} = \frac{1}{4 \cdot \pi \cdot \varepsilon_0} \frac{q_1 \cdot q_2}{r^2} \mathbf{r}^0$$

in which $\mathbf{r}^0$ is the unit vector that is directed to the charge on which the force acts, and $r$ is the distance between charges $q_1$ and $q_2$.

- Electric field:

(i) for a stationary point charge:

$$\mathbf{E} = \frac{q_{\text{stationary}}}{4 \cdot \pi \cdot \varepsilon_0} \frac{\mathbf{r}^0}{r^2}$$

The electric field vector is directed toward a negative charge or away from a positive charge.

(ii) for small number of stationary point charges:

first calculate the field components for each charge. Then the components are added for all charges:

$$E_{x,\text{net}} = \sum_i E_x(q_i)$$

$$E_{y,\text{net}} = \sum_i E_y(q_i)$$

$$E_{z,\text{net}} = \sum_i E_z(q_i)$$

(iii) magnitude far from a dipole in axial direction (along the $x$-axis):

$$\lim_{x \gg d} |\mathbf{E}_{\text{at } P}| = \frac{q}{2 \cdot \pi \cdot \varepsilon_0} \frac{d}{x^3}$$

(iv) magnitude for charged parallel plates:

$$|\mathbf{E}| = \frac{\sigma}{\varepsilon_0}$$

$\sigma$ is surface charge density $\sigma = q/A$.

• Electric energy for two point charges at distance $r$:

$$E_{\text{el}} = \frac{1}{4 \cdot \pi \cdot \varepsilon_0} \frac{q_1 \cdot q_2}{|r|}$$

• Electric potential:

(i) for a stationary point charge:

$$V = \frac{1}{4 \cdot \pi \cdot \varepsilon_0} \frac{q_{\text{stationary}}}{|r|}$$

(ii) for a dipole (at a position far from the dipole $r \gg d$):

$$V = \frac{\mu}{4 \cdot \pi \cdot \varepsilon_0} \frac{\cos \theta}{r^2}$$

$\mu$ is the dipole moment and $\theta$ is the angle between the dipole axis and the line from the centre of the dipole to point $P$.

(iii) for charged parallel plates:

$$V = |\mathbf{E}| \cdot y = \frac{\sigma}{\varepsilon_0} y$$

the $y$-axis is perpendicular to the parallel plates.

# CHAPTER 14

# NERVOUS SYSTEM
## The Flow of Charges

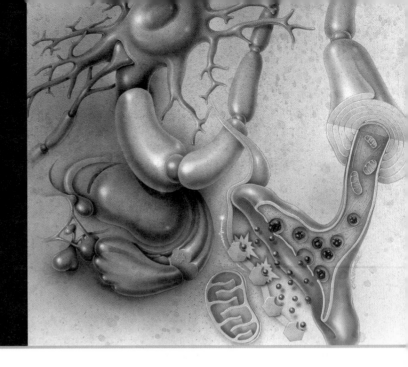

Electric currents flow when an electric potential difference is established along a conducting path. Point charges move such that they compensate the potential difference. If the moving particles are positive they travel in the direction of the electric field along the conductor. The current is proportional to the density of mobile point charges in the material, the number of elementary charges carried by each moving particle, the average velocity (drift velocity) of these particles, and the cross-sectional area of the conductor. The current per unit area is a materials-specific property and is called the current density.

Flowing point charges usually encounter resistance against their motion in a conductor. The resistance depends on the material, the length and cross-section of the conductor, and the proportionality factor between the electric current and the applied potential difference. Near the electrochemical equilibrium the relation between current and potential is linear and is called Ohm's law. The resistivity is the corresponding materials-specific property. Resistivities at room temperature vary from good conductors (e.g., copper) to good insulators (e.g., quartz glass) by more than 20 orders of magnitude.

The resting nerve is modelled as an electrically active non-equilibrium system. The nerve membrane is a capacitor with the phospholipid bilayer as the dielectric material between an outer positively charged surface and a parallel inner surface charged negatively. The Na/K pump generates a concentration gradient for $K^+$ and $Na^+$ with a membrane potential difference of $-70$ mV. Diffusion and electric drift across the membrane establish a leakage current.

In the physical sciences, electric effects are often discussed with engineering applications in mind, such as power plants, household appliances, or consumer electronics. Here, instead, we focus on the physiological relevance of electric effects. In particular, we want to further develop the fundamental electric concepts of the previous chapter to apply them to human nerves. An overview of the relevant anatomical and physiological properties of this system is presented first.

# Human Nerves

Nerves had been identified surprisingly early as important systems in our body. Galen, the physician to Emperor Marcus Aurelius in ancient Rome, had noted the existence of the spinal cord and its connection to muscle action. Luigi Galvani demonstrated in the late eighteenth century that electricity can trigger the muscles of frogs.

## Microscopic Nerve Anatomy

Nerves serve two purposes: (i) to communicate stimuli to the control centres of the nervous system (e.g., the brain) when they are registered by organs sensitive to the environment, and (ii) to communicate commands from these control centres to the organs in turn, either in response to a stimulus or without any external stimulus, e.g., when controlling the heart beat.

Both types of information transfer must occur within very short times. If you are driving your car and an obstacle suddenly appears on the road, your brain's command "Hit the brakes" reaches the muscles in your foot in less than 0.1 second. In this case, the command has to travel through two of the longest nerves in your body, the nerve from your brain to the lower back synapse and the nerve from there to the toes. These two nerves have a total length of up to 2 metres. Thus, an impulse speed in nerves in excess of 20 m/s is vital in our everyday lives. The evolutionary solution to the problem of communicating information at such high speeds is based on electric and electrochemical effects.

A nerve is a strand of up to 1000 nerve cells (**neurons**). These strands contain two types of nerves, **myelinated nerve cells** (about 30%) and **unmyelinated nerve cells** (about 70%). We will discuss the differences between these two types in detail later in this chapter.

Fig. 14.1 shows a microscopic sketch of a single myelinated nerve cell. Nerves have tentacle-like receptors, called **dendrites**. These respond to a wide range of stimuli, ranging from temperature change to motion parameters (e.g., acceleration in Pacinian corpuscles, as discussed in Example 3.12). The stimulus causes an electric response that travels along the nerve to the synapse. At the synapse, vesicles are triggered to release neurotransmitters, which pass through the synaptic cleft to a secondary receptor. This cleft is typically 10 to 20 nm wide if the secondary receptor is a dendrite (neural junction) and 50 to 100 nm wide if the secondary receptor is a muscle (myoneural junction).

The neuron and the synapse are connected by the **axon**. Axons of both myelinated and unmyelinated nerves are cylindrical tubes that contain a solution

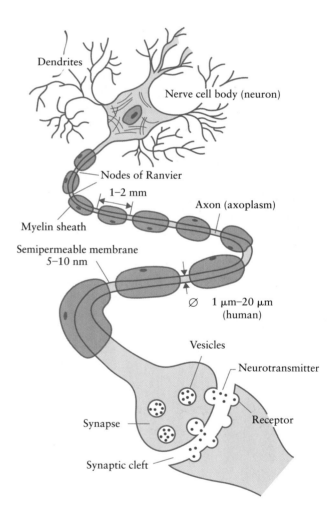

**FIGURE 14.1**

Sketch of a single myelinated nerve cell. The axon, containing the axoplasm, carries the nerve impulse from the dendrites to the synapse. The myelin sheath plays an important role in the mechanism of the nerve impulse propagation. Note that myelin sheaths are interrupted about every 1 to 2 mm by nodes of Ranvier.

TABLE 14.1

### Comparison of physiologically relevant data for myelinated and unmyelinated human nerve cells

| Human nerve cell type | Unmyelinated | Myelinated |
|---|---|---|
| Fraction of nerves | 70% | 30% |
| Cross-section of nerve cell | ≈1.5 $\mu$m | ≤20 $\mu$m* |
| Axon walls | Semipermeable membrane (5–10 nm thick) | Myelin sheath (2000 nm thick) |
| Impulse speed | 0.6–10 m/s | 10–100 m/s |
| Purpose | Slow information (e.g., temperature stimulation) | Motor information |

*Giant axon of squid with a diameter 500 $\mu$m = 0.5 mm.

called **axoplasm**. The axoplasm is separated from the **extracellular fluid** (also called **interstitium**) by a 5- to 10-nm-thick semipermeable membrane. As illustrated in Fig. 14.1, myelinated nerves are further encapsulated by a **myelin sheath** (also called **Schwann's cells** for their discoverer Theodor Schwann). Schwann's cells are 1 to 2 mm long and fully surround the axon. The myelin sheath is interrupted by short gaps, called **nodes of Ranvier** (named for Louis Ranvier).

Table 14.1 lists some of the properties of human nerve cells for myelinated and unmyelinated nerves. The table indicates that the presence of the myelin sheath makes a significant difference in the function of the nerves. Myelinated nerves are vital when high signal speeds are required, e.g., when attempting an emergency stop of a car. On the other hand, temperature information is processed by slower, unmyelinated nerves. You can establish this in a simple self-experiment. Consciously reach for a mug of coffee. You become aware that you touch the mug clearly before you can tell how warm it is.

## Electrochemical Processes in Nerves

To describe the electric mechanism of a nerve, a few additional microscopic observations are needed. We will find that two types of processes are essential for the understanding of nerves: non-equilibrium chemical processes and electric phenomena. On the other hand, neither fluid dynamics nor mechanics are required since signal conduction in nerves occurs without the nerve itself changing shape.

Fig. 14.2 shows the concentrations of key chemical components in both the axoplasm and the extracellular fluid. The data are given in unit mmol/L. Most important in both solutions are cations and anions, with NaCl (rock salt) the dominant compound outside the nerve and potassium salts (potassium bound by protein and phosphate ions, shown as miscellaneous anions in the figure) the major component inside. On either side of the membrane cations and anions are balanced, but the axoplasm carries the larger total salt concentration of 165 mmol/L.

We have to describe two states of nerves to fully understand their function: the resting nerve and the nerve when it carries an impulse. The resting nerve is not simply a nerve that is shut off; rather, this describes a dead nerve cell. Diffusion and ion drift in an electric field are continuous dynamic processes that establish a unique state for the resting nerve that we have to quantify before we can address nerve impulses. The adjective "resting" is still justified for two

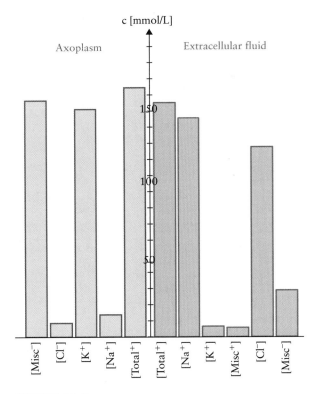

**FIGURE 14.2**

The concentration of various electrolyte components in the axoplasm (left) and in the extracellular fluid (right). The given values are based on mammalian spinal cord motor neurons.

reasons: the physical processes occurring in a resting nerve are minimal, and no time dependence of these processes can be observed macroscopically. Note that these conditions are consistent with a steady state as defined in Chapter 10. Thus, the **resting nerve** is a nerve in a steady state.

The potential change during the passage of an impulse through a nerve is illustrated in Fig. 14.3. This is the main data set we want to explain in the last part of the chapter. The electric potential is a measure of the strength of electric effects, and is often the first information available for a system because potential differences are relatively easy to measure. The existence of a non-zero electric potential difference across the nerve membrane indicates that cations and anions are separated across the nerve membrane. In Fig. 14.3 we follow the electric potential difference across the nerve membrane while a **nerve impulse** passes a particular point along the nerve as a function of time. The data in the figure can be described as a sequence of four steps:

(i) **Trigger:** An initial change in the potential difference across the membrane of 10 mV causes an impulse.

(ii) **Depolarization:** The nerve is polarized to a positive axoplasm potential within a millisecond.

(iii) **Repolarization:** The depolarization is followed immediately by a repolarization to a potential difference that is more negative than the resting potential difference.

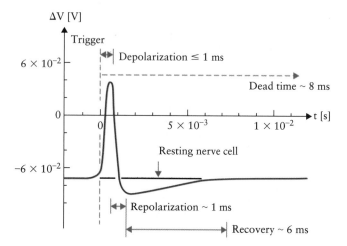

**FIGURE 14.3**

The changes in the electric potential across the membrane of a nerve cell when an impulse passes. Most of the changes occur within a millisecond, followed by a period of about 6 ms recovery time before the nerve can be stimulated again (i.e., a total of about 8 ms of dead time).

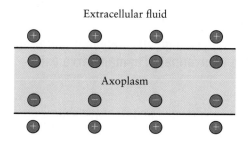

**FIGURE 14.4**

Simplified model of a nerve: the inner surface of the membrane (axoplasm side) carries negative charges; the outer surface of the membrane (extracellular fluid or interstitium side) carries positive charges.

(iv) **Recovery:** The nerve returns during a period of about 6 milliseconds to its resting potential difference. It can now carry another impulse.

Each impulse leads to the same time profile of the cross-membrane potential difference, i.e., the same shape and peak height of the impulse. Thus, information is communicated by the repetition frequency of impulses.

To understand these observations we need to develop a model of the nerve. We start with the unmyelinated nerve. A very simple model of such a nerve is shown in Fig. 14.4. The figure shows a cross-section, with the axoplasm inside a cylindrical tube and the extracellular fluid outside. The nerve membrane separates ions that we treat as electric point charges. The membrane is modelled as charged parallel plates, for which we studied some of the electrostatic properties in the previous chapter. There is an excess number of positive ions outside and an excess number of negative ions inside the nerve. This model is a good starting point to describe a nerve when no impulse is passing through, i.e., a resting nerve.

To fully quantify this model we need to introduce two additional physical concepts: the properties of a parallel plate capacitor with a dielectric placed between its plates, and electric leakage currents across the membrane. These topics are addressed first in this chapter, followed by a broader discussion of the electrochemical properties of nerves.

It is useful to note that we have already laid a good foundation for this discussion in Chapter 13. For example, Fig. 14.5 gives an overview of the potential difference (top panel) and the electric field across an axon (bottom panel). In the interior of the axon the potential is −70 mV relative to the potential outside; i.e., the potential changes by 70 mV between the inside and outside surfaces of the membrane, which are 6 nm apart. Inside the axoplasm and in the interstitium no uncompensated point charges occur.

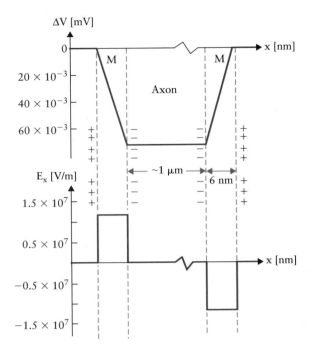

**FIGURE 14.5**

The potential (top panel) and the vector-component of the electric field (bottom panel) across a human nerve cell in the *x*-direction. The electric fields everywhere in the membrane point toward the inside of the axon. The potential decreases in the direction in which the electric field vector points.

---

● **EXAMPLE 14.1**

Confirm the value of the electric field across a human nerve membrane, as shown in Fig. 14.5.

*Solution:* The magnitude of the electric field across the membrane is calculated from the measured potential difference. We use the formula $\Delta V = |E| \cdot y$ for the variation of the potential across the gap of a parallel plate arrangement and set $y = 6$ nm for the full membrane width:

$$|E| = \frac{\Delta V}{y} = \frac{7 \times 10^{-2}\,\text{V}}{6 \times 10^{-9}\,\text{m}} = 1.17 \times 10^7 \frac{\text{V}}{\text{m}} \quad [1]$$

As a vector, the electric field points toward negative charge, i.e., $E_x = +|E|$ for the membrane on the left side in Fig. 14.5 and $E_x = -|E|$ for the membrane on the right side. The calculated value is used in the lower panel of Fig. 14.5 to sketch the electric field quantitatively. Note that the notion of positive or negative electric fields in Fig. 14.5 is of no practical meaning as the choice of the direction of the *x*-axis is arbitrary. The relevant conclusion from the figure is that the electric field points everywhere in the membrane toward the axoplasm, i.e., into the nerve.

# Capacitors

The potential and electric field curves of Fig. 14.5 are the direct consequence of the arrangement of the point charges at the interior and exterior membrane surfaces, with the surface charge density on the outside equal but opposite to the inside. This arrangement corresponds to two parallel conducting plates, which are separated by an insulator of thickness *b*, as illustrated in Fig. 14.6(a). This arrangement is called a **capacitor** when the two conducting plates are charged with an equal amount of charge of opposite signs, as sketched in Fig. 14.6(b). When two initially neutral plates are connected to the two terminals of a battery, positive charge builds up on the plate connected to the positive terminal and an equal amount of negative charge builds up on the plate connected to the negative terminal. Note that we have so far assumed that the insulator is a vacuum, but other insulators like the membrane in Fig. 14.5 are possible and have to be considered in this section.

Three quantities characterize a capacitor: the surface charge density $\sigma$, the capacitance C, and the dielectric constant $\kappa$. Of these, only the surface charge density has been introduced so far. Here we define the other two quantities. This allows us to quantify additional properties of the resting nerve, including the calculation of the surface charge density on the axon membrane.

To define capacitance we start with a parallel plate capacitor, as shown in Fig. 14.7. In contrast to previous arrangements, a specific common area A is

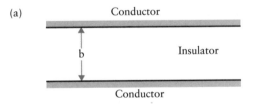

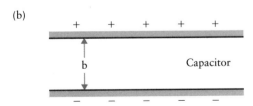

**FIGURE 14.6**

(a) The geometric configuration of a parallel plate capacitor with gap width *b*. Both plates must be electrically conducting, while the gap contains either a vacuum or an insulating material. (b) The electric configuration of a charged parallel plate capacitor.

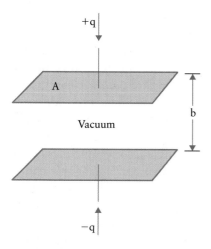

**FIGURE 14.7**

Three-dimensional sketch of a parallel plate capacitor illustrating its finite area *A*. Later in the section the vacuum identified inside the gap is replaced with electrically insulating materials.

defined for the plates. The upper plate is given a charge $+q$ and the lower plate a corresponding charge $-q$. The gap between the plates has a width $b$ and contains a vacuum.

For such a parallel plate capacitor we know that the potential between the plates is linear in the surface charge density and linear in the plate separation: $\Delta V = \sigma \cdot b/\varepsilon_0$. Using the definition of the surface charge density, $\sigma = q/A$, we conclude that the potential difference is proportional to the charge $q$, $\Delta V \propto q$. This proportionality is written as an equation by introducing the **capacitance** $C$ as the proportionality constant:

$$q = C \cdot \Delta V \qquad [2]$$

The unit of the capacitance is C/V = F. (F stands for **farad**, named in honour of Michael Faraday.)

*The potential difference across a parallel plate capacitor is proportional to the charge on the plates. The proportionality factor is the capacitance.*

Therefore, the capacitance of a capacitor is the ratio of the charge on each plate to the potential difference across the capacitor. The term *capacitance* is a fitting choice for $C$: a large capacitance means that a large amount of charge causes only a small potential difference; i.e., a system with a large capacitance can accommodate a lot of charge before a significant potential difference develops between its plates.

Starting with the potential as a function of position between charged parallel plates we derive an explicit expression for the capacitance. In Chapter 13, we found $V_\parallel = (\sigma/\varepsilon_0) \cdot y$, with $\sigma$ the surface charge

density and $y$ the position along the axis perpendicular to the parallel plates. The potential difference between the plates results when we define $\Delta V_\parallel = V_\parallel(y = b) - V_\parallel(y = 0)$:

$$\Delta V_\parallel = \frac{\sigma}{\varepsilon_0} b = \frac{q}{\varepsilon_0 \cdot A} b = \frac{q}{C} \quad \Rightarrow \quad C = \frac{\varepsilon_0 \cdot A}{b} \quad [3]$$

*The capacitance of a parallel plate capacitor depends only on geometric properties: it is proportional to the area of the plates and inversely proportional to the width of the gap between the plates.*

Eqs. [2] and [3] also explain the name of the constant $\varepsilon_0$, which is called the **permittivity of vacuum**. For a capacitor of fixed unit area ($A = 1$ m$^2$) and fixed unit plate gap width ($b = 1$ m), $\varepsilon_0$ is the proportionality factor of the charge brought onto the plates and the resulting potential difference between the plates. Thus, $\varepsilon_0$ is a measure of the ability of charge to reach through a vacuum to affect charge on the other side.

We can change the permittivity of the capacitor by replacing the vacuum with something else. The material that we place between the plates of a capacitor obviously may not cause the transfer of charge between the plates as this would short-circuit the device. Michael Faraday determined in 1837 that all electrically insulating materials qualify. We call an insulating material placed in a capacitor a **dielectric**. Faraday showed that inserting a dielectric into a capacitor can be taken into account with a correction factor to the formulas we have introduced so far: we change the permittivity of vacuum $\varepsilon_0$ to $\kappa \cdot \varepsilon_0$ in all formulas in which $\varepsilon_0$ appears. The dimensionless correction factor $\kappa$ is called the **dielectric constant**. It is a materials constant because it has a well-defined value for each material. Table 14.2 lists several values at room temperature. The product $\kappa \cdot \varepsilon_0$ represents, then, the **permittivity of the dielectric**.

We study a layer of water that is inserted in a parallel plate capacitor to illustrate Faraday's approach. Assuming that the capacitor has been charged and that the charging battery has then been disconnected, we know that the amount of charge on the plates is fixed. How the capacitance of the capacitor changes as the layer of water is inserted is derived from Eq. [3]:

$$C_{\text{vacuum}} = \frac{\varepsilon_0 \cdot A}{b}$$

$$\Rightarrow \quad C_{\text{water}} = \frac{\kappa \cdot \varepsilon_0 \cdot A}{b} = \kappa \cdot C_{\text{vacuum}} \quad [4]$$

## TABLE 14.2

### Dielectric constants for various materials at 25°C

| Material | Dielectric constant $\kappa$ |
|---|---|
| Vacuum | 1.0 |
| Air at 1.0 atm | 1.0005 |
| Polystyrene | 2.6 |
| Paper | 3.5 |
| Pyrex glass | 4.7 |
| Porcelain | 6.5 |
| Nerve membrane | 7.0 |
| Silicon | 12.0 |
| Ethanol | 25.0 |
| Water | 78.5 |

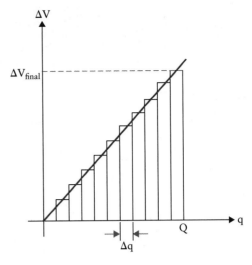

**FIGURE 14.8**

A sketch illustrating how the successive transfer of small amounts of charge from one plate to the other yields a charged parallel plate capacitor. The work required for this charging process is determined from the figure by determining the area under the curve.

i.e., the capacitance increases by a factor of 78.5 based on Table 14.2. The consequence of this change is derived from Eq. [2]:

$$q = C_{\text{vacuum}} \cdot \Delta V_{\text{initial}} \quad \Rightarrow \quad q = C_{\text{water}} \cdot \Delta V_{\text{final}} \qquad [5]$$

i.e., the potential difference across the capacitor drops by a factor of 78.5. Inserting a dielectric with a large dielectric constant means that the potential difference of a given parallel plate capacitor with a fixed charge is significantly decreased. Thus, materials with large dielectric constants effectively screen the effect of the charge on the plates.

Note that there is a second way in which the experiment to insert a dielectric can be performed. If the capacitor is not disconnected from its charging device, e.g., a battery with a given potential difference between its terminals, the potential difference in Eq. [5] remains fixed while the amount of charge on the plates must vary. In this case, the amount of charge on the parallel plates has to increase significantly when a layer of water is inserted. Note that this case also applies to the membranes of live nerves, because Na/K pumps maintain a −70-mV potential difference. The role of the Na/K pump (sodium–potassium pump) is discussed later in this chapter.

Charged capacitors store electric potential energy. This is illustrated in Fig. 14.8. To determine this potential energy quantitatively, we start with an uncharged capacitor. In the first step a small amount of charge, $\Delta q$, is transferred from one plate to the other.

In this step no work is done during the charge transfer because the capacitor still has a zero potential difference. However, as we continue to transfer the same amount of charge step by step, work is required. The formula for the work done when moving an amount of charge $\Delta q$ against an electric force is $W = \Delta q \cdot \Delta V$. The potential difference $\Delta V$ is due to the previously transferred charge, leading to the step function shown in Fig. 14.8. The total work is then the area under the curve in the figure. This area is described by a triangle for which we find:

$$W = \frac{1}{2} \cdot Q \cdot \Delta V_{\text{final}} \qquad [6]$$

$\Delta V_{\text{final}}$ is the final potential difference and $Q$ is the total amount of charge transferred. The result in Eq. [6] represents also the work stored in the capacitor, i.e., the electric potential energy of the device.

### Concept Question 14.1

**Fig. 14.9 shows four undissociated HCl molecules in an acid solution. The solution is placed in a parallel plate capacitor that is indicated by the charge on its opposite plates. The small HCl molecule is able to rotate freely in the solution. Which of the four orientations shown is the preferred orientation of the molecule?**

ANSWER: Choice (D). HCl is a dipole with a negative charge centre near the chlorine atom. The molecule rotates such that its negative end points toward the positive

## Concept Question 14.1 (continued)

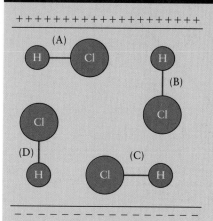

**FIGURE 14.9**

An HCl solution is inserted into a capacitor gap. We consider undissociated HCl molecules that can freely rotate in the solution. Four suggested orientations of the molecule are illustrated.

plate of the capacitor. This effect is called **polarization** of the dielectric and is generally observed for mobile dipole molecules.

## Concept Question 14.2

**Why is the dielectric constant of water in Table 14.2 so large?**

ANSWER: The large dielectric constant of water is due to its dipole moment, which we discussed in Chapter 13. Water molecules orient themselves in a parallel plate capacitor in the same fashion as discussed for HCl in the previous Concept Question: the positive end of the molecule is directed toward the negatively charged plate, and vice versa. The notable screening of charge in this case happens because the polarized molecules in the dielectric interact at close proximity more effectively with the electric charge on the capacitor plates than with the electric charge at the faraway opposite plate. The large dielectric constant of ethanol in Table 14.2 is a result of the same polarization effect due to the dipole moment of the OH group in the alcohol molecule.

## ● EXAMPLE 14.2

A parallel plate capacitor has an initial capacitance $C = 10$ pF (pF stands for picofarad). It has been charged with a 9.0-V battery. With the battery disconnected, a piece of Pyrex glass is placed between the plates. (a) What is the potential

energy of the device before the glass piece is inserted? (b) What is its potential energy afterward?

*Solution to part (a):* The electric potential energy is determined from Eq. [6]. The work term in the equation is equal to the change of the electric potential energy, $W = \Delta E_{el}$, and thus we find for the charging process:

$$\Delta E_{el} = \frac{1}{2} \cdot Q \cdot \Delta V_{final} \qquad [7]$$

To quantify the energy in Eq. [7], we use Eq. [2] to replace the unknown charge by the fixed capacitance and potential difference:

$$\Delta E_{el} = \frac{1}{2} \cdot Q \cdot \Delta V_{final} = \frac{1}{2} (C \cdot \Delta V_{final}) \Delta V_{final}$$
$$= \frac{1}{2} \cdot C (\Delta V_{final})^2 \qquad [8]$$

Next, we substitute the given values:

$$\Delta E_{el} = \frac{1}{2}(1.0 \times 10^{-11}\,F)(9.0\,V)^2$$
$$= 4.1 \times 10^{-10}\,J \qquad [9]$$

*Solution to part (b):* The next step is the disconnecting of the battery. This means that now the charge on the plates of the capacitor is fixed while its potential difference may vary. Eq. [8] is rewritten for this case:

$$\Delta E_{el} = \frac{1}{2} \cdot Q \cdot \Delta V = \frac{1}{2} \cdot Q\left(\frac{Q}{C}\right) = \frac{Q^2}{2 \cdot C} \qquad [10]$$

Using Faraday's approach, placing a Pyrex glass dielectric between the plates of the capacitor requires that we rewrite $\varepsilon_0$ as $\kappa \cdot \varepsilon_0$, with $\kappa$ the dielectric constant. In Eq. [10], the capacitance in the denominator is affected. Identifying the initial state of the capacitor when it is air-filled and the final state when the glass dielectric is placed between the plates, we find:

$$C_{initial} = \varepsilon_0 \frac{A}{b}$$

$$\Rightarrow \quad C_{final} = \kappa \cdot \varepsilon_0 \frac{A}{b} = \kappa \cdot C_{initial} \qquad [11]$$

Substituting Eq. [11] in Eq. [10] yields:

$$\Delta E_{el,final} = \frac{1}{\kappa} \cdot \Delta E_{el,initial}$$

$$= \frac{4.1 \times 10^{-10}\,J}{4.7} = 8.7 \times 10^{-11}\,J \qquad [12]$$

in which the dielectric constant for Pyrex glass is taken from Table 14.2. Note that the energy with the glass dielectric inserted is less than the energy without it. The energy difference was dissipated into the piece of glass.

## ● EXAMPLE 14.3

For a resting nerve, determine (a) the capacitance per unit area of membrane, and (b) the surface charge density on the nerve membrane in unit $C/m^2$.

*Solution to part (a):* We use the dielectric constant of a nerve membrane from Table 14.2. For the capacitance per unit area we find, in analogy to Eq. [4]:

$$\frac{C}{A} = \frac{\kappa \cdot \varepsilon_0}{b} = \frac{7.0 \left( 8.854 \times 10^{-12} \frac{C^2}{N \cdot m^2} \right)}{6 \times 10^{-9} \, m}$$

$$= 0.01 \frac{F}{m^2} \qquad [13]$$

in which $b$ is the membrane thickness of 6 nm. The unit $C^2/(N \cdot m^3)$ is equivalent to $F/m^2$ because $J/C = V$, $N \cdot m = J$, and $F = C/V$.

What does the result in Eq. [13] mean? We know from the discussion of Eq. [5] that a smaller capacitance allows a smaller amount of charge to sustain a fixed potential difference. We combine this observation with Eq. [3], which states that the capacitance is inversely proportional to $b$, $C \propto 1/b$. This has an important consequence for the comparison of myelinated and unmyelinated nerves later in the chapter: the membrane of myelinated nerves is 300 times thicker (axon membrane and myelin sheath together); myelinated nerves therefore have a significantly smaller capacitance than unmyelinated nerves. This means that myelinated nerves maintain the same $-70$-mV potential difference with significantly smaller surface charge densities.

*Solution to part (b):* Next, we determine the surface-charge density on the resting nerve membrane. We start with the magnitude of the electric field for charged parallel plates, $|E| = \sigma/\varepsilon_0$. With a dielectric and using the electric field across the membrane from Eq. [1] as $|E| = 1.17 \times 10^7$ V/m, we find:

$$\sigma = \kappa \cdot \varepsilon_0 |E| = 7.0 \left( 8.85 \times 10^{-12} \frac{C^2}{N \cdot m^2} \right)$$

$$\times \left( 1.17 \times 10^7 \frac{V}{m} \right) = 7 \times 10^{-4} \frac{C}{m^2} \quad [14]$$

Compare this calculation with Example 13.7; in particular, you should now understand why we got a wrong electric field value in that example even though we used the correct surface charge density for nerves.

We want to discuss this value a little bit further. $Na^+$, $K^+$, and $Cl^-$ ions at the nerve membrane are all singly charged; i.e., they carry a single

elementary charge of $e = \pm 1.6 \times 10^{-19}$ C. The number of ionized particles per unit area on the nerve membrane, $c_{ions}$, can therefore be determined from the surface charge density as:

$$c_{ions} = \frac{\sigma}{e} = \frac{7 \times 10^{-4} \frac{C}{m^2}}{1.6 \times 10^{-19} \frac{C}{ion}}$$

$$= 4.4 \times 10^{15} \frac{ions}{m^2} \qquad [15]$$

This surface concentration is small when compared with the density of atoms in the surface of a nerve membrane, which is about $10^{20}$ atoms/m²; only one in every 20 000 sites on the membrane is occupied by an ion.

## Concept Question 14.3

In a hospital or at an emergency scene patients are often revived with a defibrillator (see Fig. 14.10). How does this machine work? Use a literature or internet search.

ANSWER: While the amount of charge stored in a large capacitor is sufficient to kill a person, the flow of this charge through the heart can, under appropriate conditions, save the life of a heart attack victim. **Fibrillation** is a process in which the heart produces a rapid, out-of-control pattern of heart beats in response to which the heart muscles contract uncoordinatedly. A fast discharge of electric energy through such a heart is the only medical approach known to return the heart to its normal rhythm and thereby save the patient.

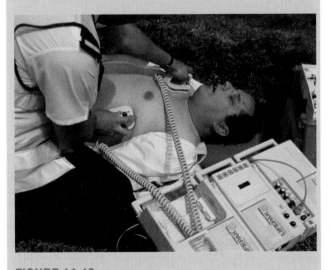

**FIGURE 14.10**

A portable defibrillator in use.

## Concept Question 14.3 (continued)

The device designed to allow a controlled discharge from a capacitor through a patient's body is called a defibrillator. It exists in stationary form in hospitals and in portable form carried by emergency medical units. The portable defibrillator consists of a large capacitor and a series of batteries capable of charging that capacitor to a large potential difference. When the defibrillator is discharged the charge flows through two electrodes (paddles) that are placed on both sides of the patient's chest.

The emergency paramedics have to wait between successive discharges due to the time delay for charging the capacitor (less than a minute). Typical defibrillators have a capacitance of about 70 $\mu$F and a potential difference of about 5 kV and thus release an electric potential energy of $\Delta E_{el} = \frac{1}{2} \cdot C \cdot (\Delta V)^2 = 875$ J. In an emergency discharge, about 200 J of this energy flows through the heart of the patient, carried by an impulse of about 2 ms duration.

The time that elapses between the occurrence of fibrillation and the application of the defibrillator is critical: if the response time is between 6 and 10 minutes, typically only 8% of the patients survive. With response times of about 3 minutes, the survival rate can be improved to about 20%. To shorten the response time, semi-automatic defibrillators have been developed that release an electroshock only after positively identifying fibrillation. Such instruments can in principle be operated by untrained personnel and have been installed in casinos (Las Vegas) and department stores and subway stations (Germany). As such instruments become more common, some basic training—e.g., with respect to the placement of the electrodes—is beneficial: training of personnel in Las Vegas achieved a survival rate of 80% of cases occurring in the casino!

# Moving Point Charges in a Resting Nerve

We take one more step toward a model for the resting nerve. The capacitor model developed in the previous section is not quite sufficient because it does not address a continuous flow of ions across the membrane. This leakage is added in Fig. 14.11(a). The various processes are modelled by their respective electric counterparts in Fig. 14.11(b). Shown is the parallel plate capacitor with capacitance $C$ and surface charge $Q$, establishing an electric potential difference $\Delta V$. In addition, a flow of charge across the membrane occurs, defined as a **leakage current** $I_m$ (the index m stands for membrane). To allow charge

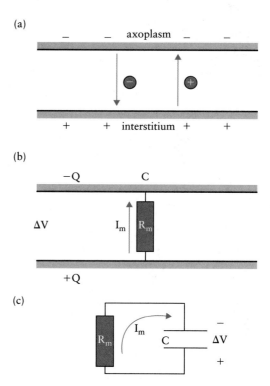

**FIGURE 14.11**

Model for the passive processes in a nerve membrane. (a) A real nerve is not a perfect capacitor, as ions continuously flow across the membrane, leading to a leakage current. (b) This phenomenon is modelled electrically by introducing a conducting connection across the membrane. This connection has a resistance $R_m$ leading to a leakage current of $I_m$, with the subscript m for membrane. (c) The electric model, as sketched in panel (b), is equivalent to an electric circuit, which we are able to analyze.

to flow, an electrically conducting connection between the plates of the capacitor must exist. This cannot be a simple conductor, however, as this would short-circuit the capacitor—which means that all charge would flow across the capacitor gap and neutralize (destroy) the nerve. Thus, along the electric connection between the capacitor plates must be a resistor $R_m$, as shown. Finally, in Fig. 14.11(c) these electric elements are arranged to form a circuit.

To understand the dynamic properties of point charges moving across the membrane in a resting nerve, we have to establish two new concepts in this section, as indicated in Fig. 14.11: (i) the electric current and (ii) the electric resistance.

## Electric Current

The flow of charge is called **electric current**. To introduce this concept, we return to our model of an electron in a metal that we introduced in Fig. 13.10. The metal in that figure consists of a lattice of stationary positive ions and very loosely bound electrons. These electrons are moving continuously on a microscopic-length scale similar to molecules in a stationary gas, but have to remain near their respective positive ions on a macroscopic scale.

An electric current is established when these electrons move collectively in a common direction. This requires an electric force acting on the electrons. Such a force causes an acceleration of each electron according to the equation of motion (Newton's second law), $F = m \cdot a$. Surprisingly, we will find that this leads only to a very small electron speed in metallic conductors; e.g., in household wires electrons typically move at 0.1 mm/s!

This small velocity will also allow us to use the model we develop for the electric current to describe the motion of ions in a solution when an electrochemical force is applied, e.g., in a battery where anions and cations drift toward opposite electrodes, or for ions moving across the membrane of a resting nerve, as illustrated in Fig. 14.11.

*An electric current I is defined as the amount of charge transferred through a cross-sectional area of a conductor per time unit.*

We write the electric current as:

$$I = \frac{\Delta Q}{\Delta t} \qquad [16]$$

in which $\Delta Q$ is the amount of charge transferred and $\Delta t$ is a time interval. The unit **ampere** (A) is introduced for the current, named in honour of André-Marie Ampère. Based on Eq. [16], it is related to the unit of charge as 1 A = 1 C/s. Note that A is the only electric unit identified as one of the fundamental standard (SI) units because it can easily be measured using the same instrument we referred to as a voltmeter, now rearranged as an ampere-meter. Since charge cannot be measured directly, it is preferable to define the current unit as fundamental rather than the unit of charge.

The actual speed of point charges in a conductor with an applied electric field is determined from Fig. 14.12. The figure shows a cylindrical conductor with a cross-sectional area $A$ along the $x$-axis. For simplicity we assume that positive point charges are mobile within the conductor, i.e., they move toward the right if an electric field is applied as shown. Note that this is a choice of convention. A consequence of the convention is that the electrons in metallic conductors actually move in the direction opposite to the current $I$.

The motion of point charges is indicated in Fig. 14.12 by an arrow labelled $\mathbf{v}_d = \Delta\mathbf{x}/\Delta t$, where $\mathbf{v}_d$ is the **drift velocity**. By introducing a single drift velocity we assume that point charges move through

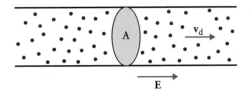

**FIGURE 14.12**

Simple, atomic scale model for a metallic conductor of cross-sectional area $A$ with an external electric field. In response to the field, positively charged particles move with the drift velocity $\mathbf{v}_d$.

the conductor with an average speed, although they are constantly accelerated by the electric field. This assumption will be justified after the magnitude of the drift velocity is found.

We now develop a formula for the current through area $A$ for Fig. 14.12. During the time interval $\Delta t$ all mobile point charges that are closer than a distance $|\mathbf{v}_d| \cdot \Delta t$ pass through $A$ because point charges can neither be created nor eliminated in the conductor. This defines the volume $V$, from which point charges pass through the area $A$:

$$V = A \cdot \Delta x = A \cdot v_d \cdot \Delta t \qquad [17]$$

We allow each point charge to carry an elementary charge $e$. The density of mobile point charges is labelled $n$ with unit $1/m^3$. The total amount of charge $\Delta Q$ passing through the area $A$ during $\Delta t$ is given by the product of the number of point charges and their individual charge:

$$\Delta Q = e \cdot n \cdot V = e \cdot n \cdot A \cdot v_d \cdot \Delta t \qquad [18]$$

In order to apply Eq. [16], we divide this equation by $\Delta t$ to obtain the current:

$$I = \frac{\Delta Q}{\Delta t} = n \cdot e \cdot v_d \cdot A \qquad [19]$$

We find that the current is proportional to the density of mobile point charges, the drift velocity, and the geometric cross-sectional area of the wire. The parameter $n$ is a materials constant and is large for good conductors. Note that the current $I$ is positive in Eq. [19], which corresponds to the case shown in Fig. 14.12.

Due to its dependence on the cross-sectional area $A$, the current $I$ is not a parameter characteristic for the conductor material; i.e., it is not a materials constant. If we want to classify materials according to their ability to carry electric charge, we define the **current density** $J$ with unit $A/m^2$. $J$ follows from Eq. [19] after division by the area $A$:

$$J = \frac{I}{A} = n \cdot e \cdot v_d \qquad [20]$$

*The current density is defined as the current per unit cross-sectional area of the conductor. It is a materials constant.*

Although $J$ does not depend on any geometrical factors, and thus is a fundamental property of a given material, many calculations and studies use current instead because the current is measured directly with an ampere-meter while the current density must be calculated using the definition in Eq. [20].

---

● **EXAMPLE 14.4**

A copper wire (cross-sectional area 1.0 mm²) carries a current of $I = 2.0$ A. Calculate (a) the density of mobile electrons in copper $n_{Cu}$, (b) the current density $J$, and (c) the drift velocity $v_d$.

*Solution to part (a):* The density of mobile electrons is estimated from basic chemical information about copper, in particular its molar mass $M_{Cu} = 63.5$ g/mol and its density $\rho_{Cu} = 8.95$ g/cm³. The density of mobile point charges is:

$$n_{Cu} = \frac{Z \cdot N_A}{V_{mol}} = \frac{Z \cdot N_A}{\dfrac{M_{Cu}}{\rho_{Cu}}} = \frac{Z \cdot N_A \cdot \rho_{Cu}}{M_{Cu}} \quad [21]$$

in which $V_{mol}$ is the volume of 1 mol of copper, $N_A$ is the Avogadro number, and $Z$ is the number of electrons released per atom. With $Z = 1$ for copper, we find:

$$n_{Cu} = \frac{(6.0 \times 10^{23}\,\text{mol}^{-1})\left(8.95 \times 10^3\,\dfrac{\text{kg}}{\text{m}^3}\right)}{0.0635\,\dfrac{\text{kg}}{\text{mol}}}$$

$$= 8.5 \times 10^{28}\,\text{m}^{-3} \quad [22]$$

*Solution to part (b):* Eq. [20] is used to determine the current density:

$$J = \frac{I}{A} = \frac{2.0\,\text{A}}{1.0 \times 10^{-6}\,\text{m}^2} = 2 \times 10^6\,\frac{\text{A}}{\text{m}^2} \quad [23]$$

*Solution to part (c):* The drift velocity follows from the last term in Eq. [20]:

$$v_d = \frac{J}{n \cdot e}$$

$$= \frac{2 \times 10^6\,\dfrac{\text{A}}{\text{m}^2}}{\left(8.5 \times 10^{28}\,\dfrac{1}{\text{m}^3}\right)(1.6 \times 10^{-19}\,\text{C})} \quad [24]$$

which leads to:

$$v_d = 1.5 \times 10^{-4}\,\frac{\text{m}}{\text{s}} = 0.15\,\frac{\text{mm}}{\text{s}} \quad [25]$$

---

**Concept Question 14.4**

A drift velocity of 0.15 mm/s for electrons in a metal wire is a surprisingly small value when we think, for example, of turning on a light switch and the light fixture operating immediately despite a distance of several metres between the switch and the light fixture. Explain the small value of the drift velocity by referring to Figs. 13.10 and 14.12.

ANSWER: The same density of mobile electrons is present throughout the metallic wire. Closing a light switch creates a continuous line of conducting electrons from the power plant, through the switch and the light fixture, and back to the power plant. The power plant causes an electric field in this loop, and all electrons simultaneously start to drift along the loop. The light fixture brightens up regardless of the speed of an individual electron in the wire: it operates due to the local motion of electrons in the fixture and not due to the flow of electrons from the switch to the light fixture.

The electric field generated by the power plant causes a significant acceleration of each electron. However, before the electron can pick up any significant speed it is scattered by one of the positive core ions in the metal, as illustrated in Fig. 13.10. Since the electron is much lighter than the core ion, the impact causes the electron to bounce backward. It has to slow down and then accelerate again in the direction of the field, only to be scattered again almost immediately by the same core ion or by one close by. In a way, the progress of the electron resembles that of an overly aggressive sports-car driver during rush hour in a big city!

## Resistivity and Resistance

The electric potential and current are not sufficient to characterize the flow of point charges. To see why, we compare it with the flow of fluids. For fluids we identified the pressure difference $\Delta p$ along a tube as the cause of flow in Chapter 12. The volume flow rate $\Delta V/\Delta t$ is then related to $\Delta p$ by the linear equation $\Delta p = R(\Delta V/\Delta t)$ in which $R$ is the flow resistance.

A resistance against the flow of point charges through a conductor is needed to relate current and potential difference in the same fashion. This can be confirmed experimentally. Eq. [19] does not contain the length of the conductor, yet when connecting a light bulb to a battery (which provides a potential difference) with variable lengths of wires, the bulb is brighter for the shorter wires. Comparing this situation to that for the flow of fluids, we note that the flow resistance in Eq. [12.32] introduces a length dependence. We expect the length dependence in the electric experiment to be caused by an electric flow resistance in the same fashion.

In this section we define three ways to express the flow resistance in electric systems: the resistivity $\rho$, the resistance $R$, and the conductivity $\gamma$. Resistivity and resistance are introduced as separate parameters to allow us to distinguish experimentally measurable and fundamental materials parameters, in the same fashion as we distinguished current and current density before.

## RESISTIVITY

We observe a current density when we apply an electric field across a piece of conducting material. If the electric field is not too large the current density increases linearly with the electric field, as illustrated in Fig. 14.13. The slope of this curve is constant and defines the **resistivity** $\rho$. Georg Simon Ohm wrote for the data in Fig. 14.13 the linear relation we call **Ohm's law**:

$$|\mathbf{E}| = \rho \cdot J \qquad [26]$$

*Resistivity is the proportionality factor between the magnitude of the electric field, which causes point charges to move, and the current density, which represents the charge flow rate.*

Both the electric field $\mathbf{E}$ and the current density $J$ are not directly measurable, and thus the resistivity $\rho$ is also not a quantity accessible to direct measurement.

Technically, Eq. [26] should be written as a vector equation, but we have not introduced the current density as a vector and thus limit the discussion to the scalar form of Eq. [26]. If we extend the experiment to much larger electric fields or to other classes

| **TABLE 14.3** | |
|---|---|
| **Resistivity values for various materials at $T = 20°C$** | |
| Material | Resistivity ($\Omega \cdot$ m) |
| *Insulators and semiconductors:* | |
| Yellow sulphur | $2.0 \times 10^{15}$ |
| Artificial lipid membrane | $1.0 \times 10^{13}$ |
| Quartz | $1.0 \times 10^{13}$ |
| Nerve membrane | $1.6 \times 10^{7}$ |
| Silicon | $2.5 \times 10^{3}$ |
| Axoplasm | $1.1 \times 10^{0}$ |
| Germanium | $5.0 \times 10^{-1}$ |
| *Metals:* | |
| Mercury | $1.0 \times 10^{-6}$ |
| Iron | $1.0 \times 10^{-7}$ |
| Gold | $2.4 \times 10^{-8}$ |
| Copper | $1.7 \times 10^{-8}$ |

of materials, such as semiconductors, we note that Ohm's law does not apply universally: the current density in those cases is not linearly proportional to the applied electric field. In this textbook we limit our discussion to cases in which the relation between electric field and current density is linear, i.e., follows Ohm's law. The material is then said to behave **ohmically**.

The unit of the resistivity follows from Eq. [26] as $(V/m)/(A/m^2) = V \cdot m/A$. For the ratio volt to ampere a new unit is introduced, called **ohm**, and is abbreviated by the Greek letter $\Omega$. Thus, the unit of the resistivity is $\Omega \cdot$ m. The resistivity is a materials constant with a very wide range of values, as illustrated in Table 14.3. At very low temperatures some materials become superconductors, i.e., perfect conductors in which the flow of point charges encounters no resistivity at all, $\rho = 0 \ \Omega \cdot$ m. On the other side, good insulators have extremely large resistivities against charge conduction. At room temperature, resistivities cover a range of 22 orders of magnitude.

Of particular interest is the value of the resistivity for the axoplasm and nerve membranes. The axoplasm is a fair conductor, with a resistivity of $1.1 \ \Omega \cdot$ m. For the nerve membrane, a value measured for thin, artificial lipid membranes was initially proposed: $\rho = 1 \times 10^{13} \ \Omega \cdot$ m. This is a very high value that would make the mechanism of impulse transport

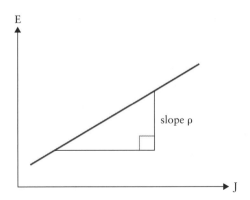

**FIGURE 14.13**

Illustration of Ohm's law: the magnitude of the electric field is proportional to the current density with the slope defining the resistivity $\rho$.

in nerves as we describe it later impossible. Luckily, the actual nerve membrane contains additional proteins that reduce the resistivity significantly to $\rho = 1.6 \times 10^7 \, \Omega \cdot m$. The nerve membrane is still an insulator, allowing us to use the capacitor model developed in Fig. 14.11.

## RESISTANCE

Resistance is used instead of resistivity when an actual conductor is described rather than an intrinsic property of a material. To define resistance, we revisit Eq. [26]. With measurability in mind, the electric field is replaced by the respective potential difference, and the current density is replaced by the current:

$$|\mathbf{E}| = \rho \cdot J \quad \Rightarrow \quad \frac{\Delta V}{l} = \rho \frac{I}{A} \qquad [27]$$

in which $l$ is the length of the conductor and in which we use the definition of the current density from Eq. [20]. Next, the various parameters in Eq. [27] are grouped such that a new constant, the **resistance R**, is introduced as the proportionality factor of electric potential difference and electric current:

$$\Delta V = \frac{\rho \cdot l}{A} I = R \cdot I \qquad [28]$$

with

$$R = \frac{\rho \cdot l}{A} \qquad [29]$$

The unit of resistance is V/A = $\Omega$. Eq. [28] is a second way to write **Ohm's law**.

*Resistance is the proportionality factor of the potential difference along a given conductor and the current it carries. It increases with increasing length and decreases with increasing cross-sectional area of the conductor.*

### Concept Question 14.5

**How does the resistivity of a piece of metal change if both its length and its diameter are reduced to one-half their original value? (A) It increases to four times the original value. (B) It doubles. (C) It remains unchanged. (D) It is halved. (E) It reduces to one-quarter of the original value.**

ANSWER: Choice (C). Recall that the resistivity is a materials constant. It does not change unless we switch materials.

### Concept Question 14.6

**How does the resistance of a piece of metal change if both its length and its diameter are reduced to one-half their original value? (A) It increases to four times the original value. (B) It doubles. (C) It remains unchanged. (D) It is halved. (E) It reduces to one-quarter of the original value.**

ANSWER: Choice (B). The resistance is defined in Eq. [29] as:

$$R = \rho \frac{l}{A} \propto \rho \frac{l}{d^2} \qquad [30]$$

in which the cross-sectional area of the conductor is proportional to the square of its diameter $d$. Halving $l$ and $d$ leads to twice the resistance.

## CONDUCTIVITY

The last quantity we introduce in this context is the **conductivity $\gamma$**. The conductivity is defined as the inverse value of the resistivity:

$$\gamma = \frac{1}{\rho} \qquad [31]$$

$\gamma$ has the unit $1/(\Omega \cdot m)$. It is used when we prefer to think in terms of a current passing through a resistor rather than in terms of hindrance to the motion of point charges.

### ● EXAMPLE 14.5

Considering again the copper wire we studied in Example 14.4, find (a) the electric field, (b) the potential difference along 10 m of wire, and (c) the resistance of the same 10 m of wire. Use (from Example 14.4) $A = 1.0 \, mm^2$, $J = 2 \times 10^6 \, A/m^2$, and $I = 2.0 \, A$. The resistivity of copper is given in Table 14.3.

*Solution to part (a):* the electric field is calculated from Eq. [26]:

$$|\mathbf{E}| = \rho \cdot J$$
$$= (1.7 \times 10^{-8} \, \Omega \cdot m)\left( 2 \times 10^6 \, \frac{A}{m^2} \right)$$
$$= 0.034 \, \frac{V}{m} \qquad [32]$$

Note that this value does not depend on the length or the diameter of the wire.

*Solution to part (b):* The potential difference $\Delta V$ along 10 m of wire is:

$$\Delta V = |\mathbf{E}| \cdot l = \left(0.034 \frac{\text{V}}{\text{m}}\right)(10\,\text{m}) = 0.34\,\text{V} \quad [33]$$

i.e., a rather small drop in potential for an appreciable length of wire.

*Solution to part (c):* The resistance can be obtained in two different ways. One possibility is to use Ohm's law in the form given in Eq. [28]:

$$R = \frac{\Delta V}{I} = \frac{0.34\,\text{V}}{2.0\,\text{A}} = 0.17\,\Omega \quad [34]$$

A second way is to use the definition of the resistance in Eq. [29]:

$$R = \frac{\rho \cdot l}{A} = \frac{(1.7 \times 10^{-8}\,\Omega \cdot \text{m})(10\,\text{m})}{1.0 \times 10^{-6}\,\text{m}^2}$$
$$= 0.17\,\Omega \quad [35]$$

## ● EXAMPLE 14.6

(a) Calculate the resistance along an axon 1 cm long with an inner radius of 0.5 $\mu$m (a value typical for an unmyelinated nerve). (b) Repeat the same calculation for an inner axon radius of 10 $\mu$m (a value near the upper limit of human myelinated nerves). Use the resistivity value for the axoplasm from Table 14.3.

*Solution to part (a):* For axoplasm we obtain from Table 14.3 a resistivity $\rho = 1.1\ \Omega \cdot$ m. The cylindrical axon has a cross-sectional area $A = \pi \cdot r^2$ with the radius given as $r = 5 \times 10^{-7}$ m. For a length of $l = 1.0 \times 10^{-2}$ m, we find for the resistance:

$$R = \frac{\rho \cdot l}{A} = \frac{(1.1\,\Omega \cdot \text{m})(1 \times 10^{-2}\,\text{m})}{\pi\,(5 \times 10^{-7}\,\text{m})^2}$$
$$= 1.4 \times 10^{10}\,\Omega = 14\,\text{G}\Omega \quad [36]$$

in which G$\Omega$ is the unit giga-ohm. This value is much larger than the result in Example 14.5 for two reasons:

- the resistivity of axoplasm is several orders of magnitude higher than that of typical metals, and
- the cross-sectional area $A$ of a nerve is orders of magnitude smaller than that of typical metal wires.

*Solution to part (b):* The only change in the second part of the problem is the modified radius, with $r = 1 \times 10^{-5}$ m leading to a resistance of:

$$R = \frac{\rho \cdot l}{A} = \frac{(1.1\,\Omega \cdot \text{m})(1 \times 10^{-2}\,\text{m})}{\pi\,(1 \times 10^{-5}\,\text{m})^2}$$
$$= 3.5 \times 10^7\,\Omega = 35\,\text{M}\Omega \quad [37]$$

in which M$\Omega$ is the unit mega-ohm. A bigger nerve leads to a smaller resistance of the axoplasm.

# Electrochemistry of Resting Nerves

At this point all basic physics concepts required to describe resting nerves have been introduced. Additional information we require from electrochemistry is presented in the current section; then, we will be prepared to discuss how both physics and electrochemistry concepts are combined to describe resting nerves and nerves carrying impulses.

## Nernst's Equation

We established in Chapter 8 that a closed or open system is in thermodynamic equilibrium when the Gibbs free energy ($G$) is equilibrated between system parts that are separated by membranes. This equilibrium condition remains true when the electric energy contributes to the enthalpy. Applying the concept of equilibrium across a semipermeable membrane for the specific system of a nerve—i.e., a thin biological membrane with an extracellular fluid outside and an axoplasm inside—we write:

$$(G^* + E_{\text{el}})_{\text{interstitium}} = (G^* + E_{\text{el}})_{\text{axoplasm}} \quad [38]$$

In this equation, $G^*$ is the part of the Gibbs free energy that is due to electrically neutral system parts (chemical energy) and $E_{\text{el}}$ is the part that is due to electric charge (electric energy). The reason we keep $G^*$ and $E_{\text{el}}$ separate is that this approach allows us to specifically track the role of the electric energy. Eq. [38] allows us to derive Nernst's equation, which governs all electrochemical phenomena at a membrane.

Walther Hermann Nernst used Eq. [38] for a system that contains electrolytes (i.e., ionic solutions) of different chemical species on the two sides of a semipermeable membrane. The interaction between electrically neutral solutions across a membrane has already been discussed in Chapter 10. We make the assumption that both solutions are ideal solutions, and that therefore their components do not interact. This means that the equilibrium condition in Eq. [38] applies to each chemical species separately and that we can replace the Gibbs free energy with the chemical potential defined in Chapter 9:

$$\mu_{i,\text{interstitium}} = \mu_{i,\text{axoplasm}} \qquad [39]$$

in which the index $i$ identifies a particular component in the system. Since the ideal solutions are electrolytes, Eq. [39] must be modified in analogy to Eq. [38]:

$$(\mu_i^* + Z_i \cdot e \cdot N_A \cdot V_i)_{\text{interstitium}}$$
$$= (\mu_i^* + Z_i \cdot e \cdot N_A \cdot V_i)_{\text{axoplasm}} \qquad [40]$$

with $\mu*$ the part of the chemical potential due to electrically neutral system parts. We continue to separate $\mu*$ and the electric contributions to the chemical potential to track the role of the electric energy. In Eq. [40], $Z_i$ is the charge state of the $i$-th ion species. With $e$ the elementary charge, $Z_i \cdot e$ is the charge of the $i$-th ion species. Since the chemical potential is a molar quantity, all other terms in Eq. [40] had to be written per mol. This requires that the charge per ion be multiplied by the Avogadro number: $Z_i \cdot e \cdot N_A$ is the charge per mol for the $i$-th ion species and $V_i$ is the potential that creates an electrochemical equilibrium for the $i$-th ion species. The product of charge and potential equals the electric potential energy.

We will see later in this chapter that only singly charged ions, $Na^+$, $K^+$, and $Cl^-$, play a role in the signal transport in nerves. For these ions $Z_i = 1$. We introduce further **Faraday's constant** $F$ as the charge per mol for singly charged ions: $F = e \cdot N_A$. This yields $F = 9.65 \times 10^4$ C/mol and allows us to simplify Eq. [40]:

$$(\mu_i^* + F \cdot V_i)_{\text{interstitium}} = (\mu_i^* + F \cdot V_i)_{\text{axoplasm}} \qquad [41]$$

Both the interstitium and the axoplasm are modelled as dilute solutions for which the concentration dependence of the chemical potential is given by Raoult's law:

$$\mu_{i,\text{solution}}^* = \mu_i^{0,*} + R \cdot T \cdot \ln(x_i) \qquad [42]$$

In this equation, the term $\mu_i^{0,*}$ represents the constant chemical potential of the vapour of the $i$-th component over the corresponding pure liquid. Thus, the chemical potential of the $i$-th species in a solution is equal to a constant term plus a term proportional to the molar fraction of this component in the solution. The standard chemical potential $\mu_i^{0,*}$ depends only on the temperature for a given chemical species. Since the nerve is in thermal equilibrium (i.e., the temperatures in the interstitium and in the axoplasm are the same), the standard chemical

potential $\mu_i^{0,*}$ is the same on both sides of the membrane. Substituting Eq. [42] in Eq. [41] yields:

$$\left( R \cdot T \cdot \ln\frac{c_i}{c_{\text{total}}} + F \cdot V_i \right)_{\text{interstitium}}$$
$$= \left( R \cdot T \cdot \ln\frac{c_i}{c_{\text{total}}} + F \cdot V_i \right)_{\text{axoplasm}} \qquad [43]$$

In Eq. [43], the molar fraction $x_i$ has been rewritten as $x_i = c_i/c_{\text{total}}$, where the total concentration for a dilute solution is essentially equal to the water concentration $c_{\text{total}} \cong c_{\text{water}}$. In the next step, the logarithmic terms are rewritten, using the mathematical identity $\ln(a/b) = \ln a - \ln b$ (see the Math Review "Powers and Logarithms" at the end of Chapter 1):

$$(R \cdot T \cdot \ln(c_i) - R \cdot T\ln(c_{\text{total}}) + F \cdot V_i)_{\text{interstitium}}$$
$$= (R \cdot T \cdot \ln(c_i) - R \cdot T \cdot \ln(c_{\text{total}}) + F \cdot V_i)_{\text{axoplasm}}$$
$$[44]$$

The second term on both sides is the same since the water concentration is constant on both sides of the membrane. Thus, this term can be removed from the equation. We further divide both sides of the equation by the Avogadro number to obtain:

$$(k \cdot T \cdot \ln(c_i) + e \cdot V_i)_{\text{interstitium}}$$
$$= (k \cdot T \cdot \ln(c_i) + e \cdot V_i)_{\text{axoplasm}} \qquad [45]$$

where $k$ is the Boltzmann constant ($R/N_A = k$). In the final step, this equation is rewritten by combining the concentration terms from both sides:

$$\ln\frac{c_{i,\text{interstitium}}}{c_{i,\text{axoplasm}}} = \frac{e}{k \cdot T}(V_{i,\text{axoplasm}} - V_{i,\text{interstitium}}) \qquad [46]$$

We eliminate the logarithm function to write the concentration ratio as the independent variable. With this last step **Nernst's equation** is obtained:

$$\frac{c_{i,\text{interstitium}}}{c_{i,\text{axoplasm}}} = \exp\left\{ -\frac{e}{k \cdot T}(V_{i,\text{interstitium}} - V_{i,\text{axoplasm}}) \right\}$$
$$[47]$$

*Nernst's equation defines the electrochemical equilibrium of a system separated by a semipermeable membrane. It states that the concentration ratio of the i-th component in solution on both sides of the membrane is proportional to an exponential term containing the difference of the electric potential between the two sides of the membrane.*

Of course, this formula applies only if an equilibrium across the membrane has been established for the $i$-th component of the solution. A necessary condition for this equilibrium is that the membrane is permeable for the respective component.

**How can Eq. [47] be rewritten using Faraday's constant?**

ANSWER: In the exponent, the Boltzmann constant is replaced by the gas constant, with $k = R/N_A$. This yields a factor $e \cdot N_A = F$ in the numerator:

$$\frac{c_{i,\text{interstitium}}}{c_{i,\text{axoplasm}}} = \exp\left\{-\frac{F}{R \cdot T}(V_{i,\text{interstitium}} - V_{i,\text{axoplasm}})\right\}$$

[48]

This formula is equivalent to Eq. [47] but contains only macroscopic parameters.

## Test of an Equilibrium Model for the Resting Nerve

We use Nernst's equation to determine whether nerves are in electrochemical equilibrium. As noted before, a resting nerve is not transporting an impulse; thus, its state is not changing with time. However, the nerve is an open system in which it is possible for energy and chemical components to be exchanged with the surrounding extracellular fluid. Radioactive tracer experiments have established that sodium and potassium ions penetrate the nerve membrane continuously. Therefore, the nerve is either in equilibrium or in a time-independent non-equilibrium state, i.e., a steady state. Our first task is to determine which of these two possibilities is actually the case. In the current section we test the possibility of describing resting nerves with an equilibrium model; we find that this model is not suitable. In the next section a non-equilibrium model will then be tested.

An equilibrium is expected if only passive processes occur in a system. We know from Fig. 14.2 that concentration differences exist across the nerve membrane for most ion species. If we focus for example on potassium, which has a much higher concentration in the axoplasm than in the extracellular fluid, then we expect the following processes to occur passively: potassium ions diffuse through the membrane into the extracellular fluid along the concentration gradient, following Fick's law of diffusion. Since potassium is present in the system as a cation, each potassium ion diffusing outward causes the axoplasm to become more negatively charged and the extracellular fluid to become more positively charged. Due to the competing electric and diffusive phenomena, we expect that the motion of potassium ions across the membrane is a self-terminating

process: each potassium ion that diffuses in the direction of the concentration gradient increases the electric potential difference in that direction, which makes it harder for the next potassium ion to diffuse as it must move from a negatively charged environment toward a positively charged environment.

These two competing passive processes occur in this form at the surface of **electrodes** in a **battery**. A simple type of battery arrangement is shown in Fig. 14.14. Shown are two **electrochemical half-cells**: at the left side a zinc metal strip immersed in an aqueous $ZnSO_4$ solution and at the right side, separated by a porous barrier (1), a copper strip immersed in an aqueous $CuSO_4$ solution. Thus, we follow the standard discussion in the electrochemical literature to evaluate our equilibrium model.

To study the phenomena occurring at the metal/solution interfaces, we focus first on the surface of the immersed zinc metal. The fundamental step that takes place at this surface is illustrated in Fig. 14.15; neutral zinc atoms dissolve into the solution as cations, leaving behind two electrons each:

$$Zn \rightleftharpoons Zn^{2+} + 2 \cdot e^-$$

[49]

This process is **self-terminating**, as every zinc atom that becomes an ion in the solution increases the negative charge of the metal, causing an increasing electric potential barrier for subsequent zinc atoms leaving the metal. It is important to note that the

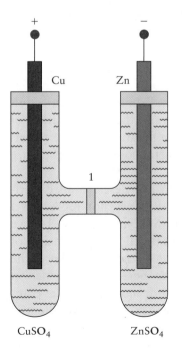

**FIGURE 14.14**

An electrochemical cell that consists of a $Zn/Zn^{2+}$ and a $Cu/Cu^{2+}$ half-cell. A porous barrier (1) separates the two half-cells.

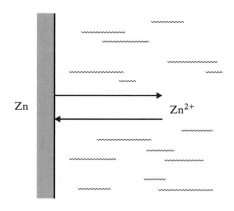

**FIGURE 14.15**

Conceptual sketch of the microscopic dynamic equilibrium at the Zn metal/solution interface.

term *self-terminating* is somewhat misleading because microscopically Zn atoms transfer as ions into the solution all the time. However, once the potential difference reaches a certain value, the electric potential difference causes an electric drift of ions toward the metal strip, as indicated by the double-arrow in Fig. 14.15 and in Eq. [49]. Zn ions, which reach the metal surface, pick up two electrons and condense onto the Zn strip as neutral atoms. The final state of the processes at the metal/solution interface is therefore called a **dynamic equilibrium**. When the dynamic equilibrium is reached, we can use Nernst's equation to quantify the concentration and potential differences across the interface:

$$\frac{c(\text{Zn})}{c(\text{Zn}^{2+})} = \exp\left\{-\frac{2 \cdot e(V_{\text{Zn}} - V_{\text{Zn}^{2+}})}{k \cdot T}\right\} \quad [50]$$

in which the factor 2 in the exponent on the right-hand side is due to the double charge of the Zn cations, $Z_{\text{Zn}} = 2$ in Eq. [40]. While the concentration in a pure metal does not vary, the concentration of the ions in solution, the temperature, and the potential difference across the metal/solution interface are variable in Eq. [50].

However, Eq. [50] does not describe an experimental setup since Eq. [49] does not represent a proper chemical reaction. Studying Fig. 14.14, we note that an electrochemical cell always consists of two half-cells, each based on a reaction similar to the one in Eq. [49]. While the potential difference in Eq. [50] is experimentally not measurable, the combination of two half-cells leads to an actual potential difference that we call the **electromotive force (emf)**, $\mathscr{E}$. Since we can choose which half-cells we combine, listed in the literature you find the standard electrode potentials, in which the term *standard* refers to $T = 25°C$ and a concentration of the solution of $c = 1.0$ mol/L. The reference potential, $V = 0$ V, is assigned to the **hydrogen gas half-cell**, which is shown in Fig. 14.16. This half-cell consists of an inert platinum foil immersed in a one-molar acid solution and is flooded with hydrogen gas at atmospheric pressure. A few examples of half-cell electrode potentials are listed in Table 14.4.

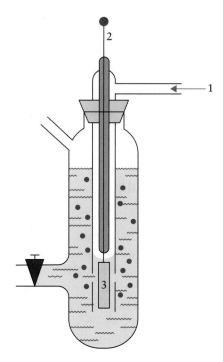

**FIGURE 14.16**

The standard hydrogen gas half-cell to which the potential of 0 V is assigned. An inert Pt metal strip (3) extends an isolated metal electrode (2) and is flooded with hydrogen gas at 1 atm (1) and surrounded by an acid solution. Blue dots indicate $H_2$ gas bubbles. Combining this half-cell with any other half-cell allows us to measure the electromotive force (emf) $\mathscr{E}$ of the second half-cell.

**TABLE 14.4**

| Electrode | Electrode process | $V$ (V) |
|---|---|---|
| Li⁺/Li | $Li^+ + e \rightleftharpoons Li$ | −3.045 |
| K⁺/K | $K^+ + e \rightleftharpoons K$ | −2.925 |
| Ca²⁺/Ca | $Ca^{2+} + 2e \rightleftharpoons Ca$ | −2.865 |
| Na⁺/Na | $Na^+ + e \rightleftharpoons Na$ | −2.715 |
| Zn²⁺/Zn | $Zn^{2+} + 2e \rightleftharpoons Zn$ | −0.763 |
| Pb²⁺/Pb | $Pb^{2+} + 2e \rightleftharpoons Pb$ | −0.125 |
| H⁺/H₂/Pt | $2H^+ + 2e \rightleftharpoons H_2$ | 0.0 |
| Cu²⁺/Cu | $Cu^{2+} + 2e \rightleftharpoons Cu$ | +0.337 |
| Ag⁺/Ag | $Ag^+ + e \rightleftharpoons Ag$ | +0.800 |

Selected standard electrode potentials for electrochemical half-cells with acid solutions at 25°C, calibrated against a standard hydrogen cell H⁺/H₂/Pt (as shown in Fig. 14.16)

## Concept Question 14.8

Fig. 14.17 shows two connected electrochemical half-cells. Let's assume that one electrode is made of potassium metal and is immersed in a 1.0 mol/L $K^+$ solution and the other electrode is made of silver and is immersed in a 1.0 mol/L $Ag^+$ solution. Considering the ions indicated in the figure (which we treat as positive point charges) and the electrons (which we treat as negative point charges), (a) which electrode has the higher electric potential, and (b) which electrode is the silver electrode?

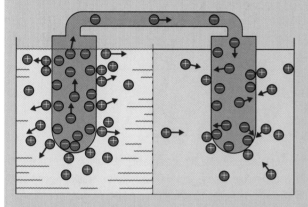

**FIGURE 14.17**

Two electrochemical half-cells are connected. Electrons are shown in the electrodes and their electric connection as small circles with − signs; metal ions are shown in the solutions surrounding the electrodes as circles with + signs.

ANSWER TO PART (a): The electrically conducting bridge at the top between the two electrodes illustrates that electrons move toward the right. Electrons move toward positive potentials; thus, the electrode at the right is at a higher potential.

ANSWER TO PART (b): Table 14.4 shows that the potential of a potassium cell is about −2.9 V and the potential of a silver cell is about +0.8 V. Thus, the higher potential is associated with the half-cell containing the silver electrode. Based on part (a) we conclude that the right electrode is the silver electrode.

## ● EXAMPLE 14.7

Calculate the electromotive force $\mathcal{E}$ of the electrochemical cell at $T = 25°C$, as in Fig. 14.14. The concentration of the $ZnSO_4$ solution is 1.0 mol/L and is 0.1 mol/L for the $CuSO_4$ solution.

*Solution:* The underlying chemical processes of the two half-cells are:

$$
\begin{array}{lll}
\text{(i)} & Zn & \rightleftharpoons Zn^{2+} + 2e^- \\
\text{(ii)} & Cu^{2+} + 2e^- & \rightleftharpoons Cu \\
\hline
& Zn + CuSO_4 \rightleftharpoons Cu + ZnSO_4 & [51]
\end{array}
$$

which together constitute a valid chemical reaction. Assuming first that both half-cells are standard cells, we calculate from Table 14.4 the electromotive force. Note that the reaction for the Zn cell is included backward in Eq. [51]:

$$
\begin{aligned}
\mathcal{E} &= V_{Cu^{2+}/Cu} - V_{Zn^{2+}/Zn} \\
&= +0.337\,V - (-0.763\,V) = +1.1\,V \quad [52]
\end{aligned}
$$

Next we correct for the non-standard concentration of the Cu solution with Nernst's equation applied along the electron connection at the top:

$$
\frac{c_{Cu^{2+},standard}}{c_{Cu^{2+},actual}} = \exp\left\{-\frac{2 \cdot e(V_{standard} - V_{actual})}{k \cdot T}\right\}
\quad [53]
$$

in which $V_{standard}$ stands for the standard potential from Table 14.4 and $V_{actual}$ is the actual potential for the given system. Eq. [53] yields:

$$
\begin{aligned}
V_{actual} - V_{standard} &= \frac{k \cdot T}{2 \cdot e} \ln\left(\frac{c_{Cu^{2+},standard}}{c_{Cu^{2+},actual}}\right) \\
&= \frac{\left(1.38 \times 10^{-23}\,\dfrac{J}{K}\right)(298\,K)}{2\left(-1.6 \times 10^{-19}\,C\right)} \ln 10 \\
&= -0.03\,V \quad [54]
\end{aligned}
$$

This leads to a correction to the value in Eq. [52], and thus the actual electromotive force is $\mathcal{E} = 1.1\,V - 0.03\,V = 1.07\,V$. The electromotive force of an electrochemical cell is primarily governed by the choice of half-cells. Variations in temperature or concentration of the solutions cause only minor corrections.

## The Non-Equilibrium Model for a Resting Nerve

A non-equilibrium model for the resting nerve is proposed in Fig. 14.18. We have to go through this complex figure step by step to understand all the details of the model. We will frequently use the following abbreviations: EXT for extracellular fluid (interstitium); INT for interior fluid (axoplasm); M for membrane; *Prot* for protein; and *Phos* for phosphate. Note that the concentration of a chemical species is higher on the side on which its chemical symbol is boldfaced.

The first of the five panels represents a passive (dead) nerve. The **potassium** and **sodium** concentrations

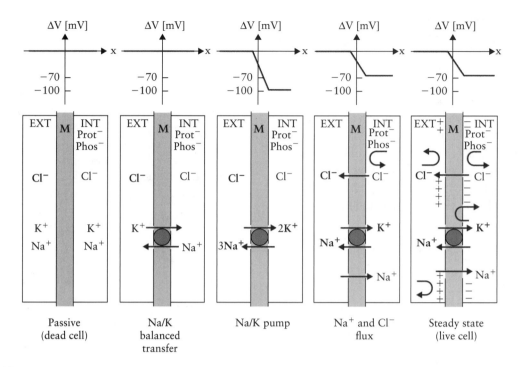

**FIGURE 14.18**

Non-equilibrium model of a nerve cell: a live cell is built up from a dead cell in equilibrium in several steps. The Na/K pump separates Na$^+$ and K$^+$ across the membrane. If the pump transferred sodium and potassium at an equal ratio, no electric potential would emerge (second panel). The actual biological Na/K pump transfers ions with a ratio Na$^+$:K$^+$ = 3:2, which yields an axoplasm potential of $-100$ mV (third panel) relative to the extracellular potential. As a result of the electric field Na$^+$ and Cl$^-$ drift across the membrane, lowering the axoplasm potential difference to the resting nerve value of $-70$ mV (fourth panel). The various transport processes lead to a steady state as further cross-membrane drift of ions is hindered by the surface charge densities on the membrane surfaces.

inside and outside the nerve cell are equal; the extracellular fluid has a slightly higher **chlorine** concentration because negative chlorine ions can permeate the nerve membrane, but negative phosphate and protein ions inside cannot. There is no potential difference across the membrane, as indicated at the top of the panels; nor are any ion transport processes active in the nerve membrane. The term "dead" applies in two ways: (i) this nerve cannot carry a nerve impulse, and (ii) the system nerve/extracellular fluid is in thermal and chemical equilibrium as the only remaining concentration gradient cannot be compensated because the membrane is impermeable to large negative protein and phosphate ions.

Starting from the dead cell, we build up a live cell in four steps. First, as shown in the second panel, a non-equilibrium process separates the positive potassium and sodium ions. The resting nerve needs an excess potassium concentration inside and an excess sodium concentration outside. To establish these concentrations, a transport of Na$^+$ and K$^+$ against their concentration gradients is required; therefore, a simple diffusion process cannot achieve the ion separation across the membrane. Instead, an active transport process is needed. This process is called the **Na/K pump (sodium–potassium pump)**. The energy for the

ion pump is provided by ATP molecules. A resting nerve cell consumes 30% of its ATP to maintain the Na/K ion imbalance across the membrane. The Na/K pump achieves the same result as the external flow of matter through an open system. The only difference is that the Na/K pump is integrated into the membrane and is therefore not external to the system.

If the same number of ions of each type pass through the membrane per time unit, as shown in the second panel of Fig. 14.18, the system remains electrically neutral. However, this is not the net result of the actual biological Na/K pump. The net effect of the active ion transport is illustrated in the third panel: for every three sodium ions transferred to the extracellular fluid, only two potassium ions are transferred to the axoplasm. This imbalance of charge transfer leads to a potential difference between the axoplasm and the extracellular fluid. Defining the potential of the extracellular fluid as 0 V, we observe the development of a $-100$-mV potential in the axoplasm. The potential in the axoplasm is negative because the number of positive charges is reduced as a result of the imbalanced pumping.

The $-100$-mV potential difference of the axoplasm subsequently has an effect on the chlorine ions that is similar to the effect of the emerging potential in a battery. Unlike the larger negative ions in the axoplasm (phosphate and protein ions), the chlorine ions are driven by the electric field to permeate the membrane, drifting against their concentration gradient toward the positive potential. Some amount of chlorine passes through the membrane, effectively lowering the potential difference to $-70$ mV, as shown in the fourth panel of Fig. 14.18. In the same fashion a minor electric drift occurs for the sodium ions toward the inside of the nerve.

At this stage a steady state of the system is reached. It is maintained by the Na/K pump and leads to a $-70$-mV potential difference between the axoplasm and the extracellular fluid. An imbalance of the potassium, sodium, and chlorine ion concentrations across the membrane is also established. The accumulated charge on the membrane surfaces (negative on the side of the axoplasm and positive on the side of the extracellular fluid) blocks a further net diffusive flow or net electric drift of all ion types across the membrane (indicated by curved arrows in the last panel of Fig. 14.18). However, there is a continuous flow of $Na^+$, $K^+$, and $Cl^-$ across the membrane, operating against the effect of the Na/K pump.

Which of the two models describes the live nerve cell better, the equilibrium model developed in analogy to Fig. 14.14, or the non-equilibrium model of Fig. 14.18? The method of presentation of both models seems to favour Fig. 14.18. But can we prove that this model is a better description than Fig. 14.14?

The proof is provided by Nernst's equation. The measured potential difference across the nerve membrane is $-70$ mV. At a core human body temperature of $37°C = 310$ K, a nerve in equilibrium would have the following concentration ratios based on Eq. [47]:

- for cations:

$$\frac{c_{cation,interstitium}}{c_{cation,axoplasm}} = \exp\left\{-\frac{(1.6 \times 10^{-19}\,C)(7 \times 10^{-2}\,V)}{\left(1.38 \times 10^{-23}\,\frac{J}{K}\right)(310\,K)}\right\}$$

[55]

which yields

$$\frac{c_{cation,axoplasm}}{c_{cation,interstitium}} = 13.7$$

[56]

- for anions:

$$\frac{c_{anion,interstitium}}{c_{anion,axoplasm}} = \exp\left\{-\frac{(-1.6 \times 10^{-19}\,C)(7 \times 10^{-2}\,V)}{\left(1.38 \times 10^{-23}\,\frac{J}{K}\right)(310\,K)}\right\}$$

[57]

which yields

$$\frac{c_{anion,axoplasm}}{c_{anion,interstitium}} = 0.073$$

[58]

Note that the ratios in Eqs. [56] and [58] are inverted. Now we compare these electrochemical equilibrium values with the actual concentration ratios. Using Fig. 14.2, we obtain:

$$\frac{c_{Na^+,axoplasm}}{c_{Na^+,interstitium}} = \frac{15\,mmol/L}{145\,mmol/L} = 0.103$$

$$\frac{c_{K^+,axoplasm}}{c_{K^+,interstitium}} = \frac{150\,mmol/L}{5\,mmol/L} = 30.0 \qquad [59]$$

$$\frac{c_{Cl^-,axoplasm}}{c_{Cl^-,interstitium}} = \frac{9\,mmol/L}{125\,mmol/L} = 0.072$$

This result applies to most mammalian nerve cells. The ratios for potassium and sodium deviate significantly from the respective equilibrium values, while the chlorine value is close to the equilibrium ratio. The deviations are due to the Na/K pump, which affects the two positive ion species, but not chlorine. Thus, the battery model cannot be used for the nerve and the more complex model shown in Fig. 14.18 is used for further study of a resting nerve.

### Concept Question 14.9

**When you observe fast electric processes at a nerve membrane, which ions do you suspect are involved?**

ANSWER: Chemical systems react to perturbations faster when they are already outside the thermodynamic equilibrium. We showed that an electrochemical equilibrium exists across a nerve membrane neither for potassium nor for sodium, but that the chlorine concentration is close to equilibrium. Thus, we suspect potassium and sodium to play a role in fast processes. We will confirm this later when discussing nerve signal propagation in the Hodgkin–Huxley model.

## The Signal Decay Time of a Resting Nerve

We are now in a position to analyze the electric model of a resting nerve in Fig. 14.11. Qualitatively, we expect that the membrane, acting as a resistor, allows the separated charge to recombine, thus neutralizing the capacitor. However, since the resistivity of the nerve membrane is quite high, the recombination might be a slow process that could then be neglected. The aim of this section is therefore to establish the time it takes to neutralize the nerve membrane electrically, which is called the **decay time** of the nerve. Note that Fig. 14.11 does not include the active effect of the Na/K pump, as we concentrate only on passive processes. We obtain the decay time by combining three equations that govern the motion of point charges through the membrane in Fig. 14.11:

- The amount of charge on the plates varies when an electric current flows according to Eq. [16]:

$$\frac{\Delta Q}{\Delta t} = -I_m \qquad [60]$$

in which $I_m$ is the current across the membrane. Note the minus sign on the right-hand side. A positive current $I_m$ means that the quantity of uncompensated charge $Q$ on both sides of the membrane in Fig. 14.11 diminishes; i.e., $\Delta Q/\Delta t$ is negative.

- A change in the number of point charges also leads to a change in the capacitor properties of the nerve membrane. We use Eq. [2] to relate the charge term to the capacitance and the potential:

$$\frac{\Delta Q}{\Delta t} = \frac{\Delta(C \cdot \Delta V)}{\Delta t} = C \cdot \frac{\Delta(\Delta V)}{\Delta t} \qquad [61]$$

in which the numerator in the last term on the right-hand side means that we study the change of a potential difference. The capacitance has been separated from that term because we know that it is constant (time independent).

- We assume that the actual flow of point charges across the membrane due to its resistance is governed by Ohm's law. We use it in the form introduced in Eq. [28]:

$$I_m = \frac{\Delta V}{R_m} \qquad [62]$$

in which $R_m$ is the resistance of the nerve membrane.

These three equations are combined to eliminate the charge and the current and provide us with an equation for the time change of the potential difference across the membrane. This is mathematically achieved in two steps. We first combine Eqs. [60] and [61] to eliminate the charge term $\Delta Q/\Delta t$:

$$-I_m = C \frac{\Delta(\Delta V)}{\Delta t} \qquad [63]$$

Next, we use Eq. [62] to eliminate the current:

$$\frac{\Delta(\Delta V)}{\Delta t} = -\frac{1}{R_m \cdot C} \Delta V \qquad [64]$$

This equation means that the time change of the potential difference is linearly proportional to the potential difference itself. We find this type of mathematical relation frequently in the sciences: the time change of a variable is proportional to its absolute value. Life sciences examples in which you will see this relation again are population growth studies (epidemiology) and applications of radioactive decay (radiology). Due to this widespread importance, we want to study Eq. [64] in detail as we continue our discussion of the time dependence of the nerve potential.

What does Eq. [64] imply? The rate of change of the potential difference is proportional to the potential difference at each instant of time. This linearity leads to an exponential function:

$$\Delta V(t) = \Delta V_{initial} \exp\left\{-\frac{t}{R_m \cdot C}\right\}$$
$$= \Delta V_{initial} \cdot e^{-t/\tau} \qquad [65]$$

$\Delta V_{initial}$ is the potential difference at the time $t = 0$, which is $\Delta V_{initial} = -70$ mV for a live nerve cell. The negative sign in the exponent means that $\Delta V$ decays with time. We introduce $\tau$ as a new parameter in Eq. [65]. The unit of $\tau$ is s, thus $\tau$ is a time constant. We find out what happens at time $\tau$ by substituting $t = \tau$ in Eq. [65]: $\Delta V(\tau) = \Delta V_{initial}/e$ with $e$ the Euler number. This means that the potential difference drops to $1/e \cong 37\%$ of its initial value after this time. After $2\tau$ the potential drops to about $14\%$, and after $3\tau$ to about $5\%$. Thus, $\tau$ is a measure of the time to observe a significant but not yet total decay; it is a **decay time constant**. The decay time constant follows from Eq. [65]:

$$\tau = R_m \cdot C \qquad [66]$$

This result for the decay time constant is not satisfactory. The membrane resistance is a quantity that depends on an arbitrary reference area (e.g., 1 m²). It is preferable to replace the resistance with the resistivity as this quantity contains only fundamental properties of the nerve membrane material. Therefore, we use Eqs. [4] and [29] to rewrite $\tau$:

$$\tau = R_m \cdot C = \frac{\rho_m \cdot b}{A} \frac{\kappa \cdot \varepsilon_0 \cdot A}{b} = \kappa \cdot \varepsilon_0 \cdot \rho_m \qquad [67]$$

Eq. [67] confirms that the decay time constant is a materials constant. We emphasize that this time constant in particular does not depend on the thickness of the membrane, $b$. From this we conclude that nature did not develop myelinated nerves—with the membrane thickness the main difference from unmyelinated nerves—to change the decay time constant. The reason why myelinated nerves work faster must lie elsewhere! Using Eq. [67], we quantify the time constant $\tau$ for a nerve:

$$\tau = 7\left(8.85 \times 10^{-12} \frac{C^2}{N \cdot m^2}\right)(1.6 \times 10^7 \Omega \cdot m)$$
$$= 1.0 \times 10^{-3}\,s = 1.0\,ms \qquad [68]$$

Thus, the potential difference across a nerve membrane may decay in the very short time of 1 millisecond! The Na/K pump prevents this, consuming energy (provided by ATP molecules) to maintain a steady state. We note again how thin a line nature has drawn between life and death: we saw in Chapter 10 that we are within a micrometre of suffocating with the given width of the membrane between alveoli and pulmonary blood capillaries; now we have found that we are always just a millisecond away from a catastrophic failure of our nervous system!

# Stimulated Nerve Impulses

We have fully characterized the resting nerve with the preceding discussion. We now move on to the response of the nerve to a stimulus. An impulse is triggered when an external stimulus causes the electric potential difference of a nerve to collapse momentarily at the stimulated point (usually a dendritic receptor). We will study two basic models for this response:

(I)  In **electrotonus spread** or **passive spread** the nerve membrane behaves ohmically; i.e., the resistivity of the membrane remains constant. This model is valid for smaller potential changes. We will find that electrotonus spread alone is not sufficient to explain impulse transport in unmyelinated nerves. However, the mechanism still plays an important role in the propagation of nerve impulses.

(II)  The **Hodgkin–Huxley model** is based on experimental evidence, originally obtained by Alan Lloyd Hodgkin and Andrew Fielding Huxley. Their observations of the nerve impulse transport in an unmyelinated nerve showed that a significant variation in the permeability of the membrane occurs during a potential change. This causes a non-ohmic, non-linear dependence of the membrane current $I_m$ on the potential difference $\Delta V$. We will see that the Hodgkin–Huxley model is sufficient to explain the nerve impulse transport in unmyelinated nerves.

## Electrotonus Spread

Let us assume a localized drop in the potential difference across an unmyelinated nerve membrane as shown in Fig. 14.19. To quantify the response to such a drop, we assume that the membrane resistivity does not change, i.e., that the membrane acts as a resistor obeying Ohm's law. The response of the nerve to a perturbation of the potential difference in this case is quantified in two ways: as a function of time and as a function of distance from the perturbation along the nerve.

### RESPONSE AS A FUNCTION OF TIME

We established in the previous sections that a resting nerve has a potential difference of $\Delta V_{rest} = -70$ mV and is thermodynamically in a steady state due to the continuous operation of the Na/K pump. In Chapter 10, we noted that steady states are stable near the equilibrium. This is the case here as well, since Ohm's law applies in the linear non-equilibrium regime. Thus, the system returns to the steady state in response to an external perturbation $\Delta V_{initial} = \Delta V_{perturbation} - \Delta V_{rest}$, with $\Delta V_{perturbation}$ the potential difference at the perturbation. This electrotonus response is quantitatively described in the same fashion as we derived Eq. [68] from Eq. [65], except that the potential difference does not drop to zero this time but returns to the steady-state value of $-70$ mV. Therefore, a perturbation diminishes as a function of time as:

$$\Delta V = \Delta V_{initial} \cdot e^{-t/\tau} \quad \text{with } \tau = \kappa \cdot \varepsilon_0 \cdot \rho_m = 1.0 \text{ ms} \qquad [69]$$

This change in the potential difference as a function of time is shown in Fig. 14.20(a). The perturbation reduces to $1/e \cong 37\%$ of its initial value after time $\tau$.

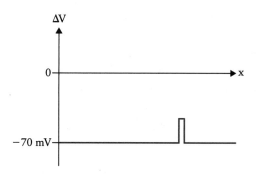

**FIGURE 14.19**

Sketch of a localized, minor perturbation in the electric potential difference across the nerve membrane, as a function of position along a nerve cell.

(a)

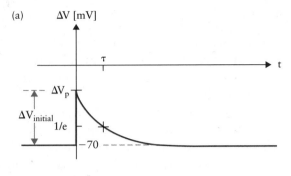

(b)

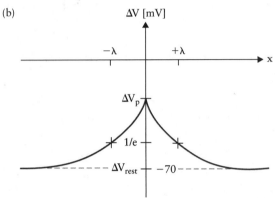

**FIGURE 14.20**

Electrotonus spread for the perturbation in Fig. 14.19 (a) as a function of time, and (b) as a function of distance from the perturbation along the nerve cell. A small perturbation in the electric potential of a nerve at time $t = 0$ disappears with a time constant $\tau$. A fixed perturbation leads to an exponentially decreasing potential profile along the nerve with a decay length $\lambda$. $\Delta V_{perturbation}$ is the potential difference of the perturbation, $\Delta V_{rest} = -70$ mV is the potential across the membrane of a resting nerve, and $\Delta V_{initial} = \Delta V_{perturbation} - \Delta V_{rest}$.

## RESPONSE AS A FUNCTION OF DISTANCE TO THE PERTURBATION

To evaluate the spatial spread of a localized perturbation, we assume that the perturbation itself is kept fixed, i.e., that the deviation $\Delta V_{initial}$ from the value of $-70$ mV at the place of the perturbation does not change with time. Consider, for example, the case qualitatively shown in Fig. 14.21. There is a potential of $-65$ mV on the inside (axoplasm) of the membrane relative to a potential of $-5$ mV on the outside of the membrane (extracellular fluid). This means that $\Delta V_{initial} = 10$ mV. Because this potential difference is maintained, mobile point charges in the vicinity of the perturbation respond. As indicated in Fig. 14.21, positive point charges move toward the more negative potential at the perturbation on the interstitium side, causing a current $I_{interstitium}$ toward the perturbation. At the same time, negative point charges move toward the more positive potential at the perturbation on the axoplasm side, causing a current $I_{axoplasm}$ along the nerve away from the perturba-

tion. The second current is in the direction away from the perturbation since we defined a current to be in the direction of moving positive point charges. The currents along the axoplasm or the extracellular fluid flow much more easily than a current across the membrane, as the resistivity of these fluids is about seven orders of magnitude lower than that of the membrane (see Table 14.3). As point charges move along the nerve membrane, the perturbation of the potential difference broadens spatially.

It is of interest to see which final profile of the potential difference results from this broadening. In particular, does the perturbation broaden as much as several tens of centimetres to a metre? If so, electrotonus spread would be sufficient to transport a signal (i.e., the perturbation of the potential difference) from the dendrite to the synapse of the nerve, and thus to the brain.

Instead of fully quantifying the case of electrotonus spread we study a semi-quantitative model, which is sufficient for understanding the important aspects. The model is based on Fig. 14.22, which illustrates in the top sketch the directions and the amount of point charges flowing near the membrane surface in the interstitium when a final, time-independent profile of the potential difference is reached, as shown in the lower part of the figure. An equivalent model with currents in the opposite directions can be sketched on the axoplasm side of the nerve membrane.

We focus in Fig. 14.22 on three arbitrarily chosen zones, each with a width of $\Delta x$. For the zone directly adjacent to the perturbation area, a large deviation of

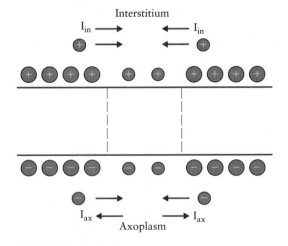

**FIGURE 14.21**

The motion of charged particles and the corresponding electric currents along a nerve cell in response to a potential perturbation between the dashed lines. $I_{in}$ is the current in the interstitium and $I_{ax}$ is the current in the axoplasm.

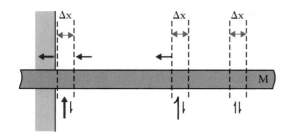

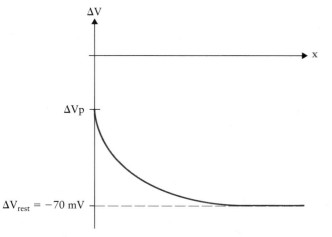

**FIGURE 14.22**

Illustration of how a time-independent potential profile due to electrotonus spread along a nerve cell could be maintained by a fixed perturbation (grey). Both charge flow across and along the nerve membrane are required.

the potential difference from the steady-state value of −70 mV causes the Na/K pump to produce a strong net flow of point charges across the membrane. This is indicated by a pair of vertical arrows, with the arrow directed upward much more prominent than the downward arrow. To maintain a potential difference of less than −70 mV across the membrane in this zone, a larger amount of charge must flow out of the $\Delta x$-zone along the nerve membrane (in Fig. 14.22 horizontally toward the left into the perturbation) compared to the amount of charge entering the $\Delta x$-zone along the nerve membrane from the right.

$\Delta x$-zones farther away from the perturbation, such as the one shown at the centre of Fig. 14.22, maintain a potential difference closer to −70 mV because fewer point charges can flow toward the perturbation zone. In a $\Delta x$-zone far away from the perturbation no net flow occurs through the membrane; i.e., charge exchange across the membrane is balanced, as indicated by a pair of equally strong vertical arrows.

The diminishing potential difference with distance from the perturbation is shown in Fig. 14.20(b) and is quantified by the formula:

$$\Delta V(x) = \Delta V_{x=0} \cdot e^{-x/\lambda} \qquad [70]$$

in which the $x$-axis is defined along the nerve and the perturbation is located at $x = 0$. The constant $\lambda$ has unit m and is called a **decay length**; it is given as:

$$\lambda = \sqrt{\frac{a \cdot b}{2} \frac{\rho_{membrane}}{\rho_{axoplasm}}} \qquad [71]$$

$\lambda$ depends on the axon radius, $a$, the membrane thickness, $b$, the resistivity of the membrane, $\rho_{membrane}$, and the resistivity of the axoplasm, $\rho_{axoplasm}$. $\lambda$ is called a decay length since a perturbation $\Delta V$ has dropped to $1/e \cong 37\%$ of its original value at that distance.

● **EXAMPLE 14.8**

Calculate the decay length for an unmyelinated nerve.

*Solution:* We use Eq. [71]. The resistivities in the equation are obtained from Table 14.3; the membrane thickness and axon diameter are given in Table 14.1. We use $b = 6$ nm and $a = 0.6$ $\mu$m, i.e., values for a large human unmyelinated nerve:

$$\lambda = \sqrt{\frac{(6 \times 10^{-7}\,\text{m})(6 \times 10^{-9}\,\text{m})(1 \times 10^7\,\Omega \cdot \text{m})}{2\,(1.1\,\Omega \cdot \text{m})}}$$

$$= 1.28 \times 10^{-4}\,\text{m} = 0.13\,\text{mm} \qquad [72]$$

This mechanism cannot carry a nerve impulse along an entire nerve of about 10 cm to 1 m length because the electrotonus spread has a decay length of less than a millimetre.

● **EXAMPLE 14.9**

In the literature, you find axoplasm resistivities reported from $\rho_{axoplasm} = 0.5\ \Omega \cdot$ m to $1.1\ \Omega \cdot$ m. We want to test what consequence this variability of the value has. (a) By how much does the time constant for electrotonus spread vary? (b) Assume a perturbation changing the potential difference across a nerve membrane from −70 mV to −60 mV. What is the potential difference across a nerve with axoplasm resistivity of $0.5\ \Omega \cdot$ m at the same distance from the perturbation at which the potential difference has fallen to 20% for a nerve with axoplasm resistivity of $1.1\ \Omega \cdot$ m?

*Solution to part (a):* There is no change, since the time constant $\tau$ does not depend on $\rho_{axoplasm}$.

*Solution to part (b):* Fig. 14.20(b) illustrates the case discussed in the second part of the problem. The resting nerve potential difference has the value of −70 mV. The change to −60 mV represents a perturbation of 10 mV. This perturbation

● **EXAMPLE 14.9** (*continued*)

of the potential difference decays toward the resting nerve value with distance from the perturbation as given in Eq. [70].

The example refers to a specific point $x_0$ along a nerve with axoplasm resistivity of $1.1\ \Omega \cdot$ m, $\Delta V(x_0) = 0.2\ \Delta V_{max} = 2$ mV. We first determine $x_0$ for the nerve with the higher axoplasm resistivity $\rho_{high} = 1.1\ \Omega \cdot$ m. Substituting $\lambda$, we rewrite Eqs. [70] and [71]:

$$\Delta V(x_0) = \Delta V_{max} \exp\left(-\frac{x_0}{\lambda}\right)$$

$$= \Delta V_{max} \exp\left\{-\frac{x_0}{\sqrt{\dfrac{a \cdot b}{2}\dfrac{\rho_{membrane}}{\rho_{high}}}}\right\} \quad [73]$$

This equation is solved for $x_0$:

$$\ln\frac{\Delta V(x_0)}{\Delta V_{max}} = \ln 0.2 = -1.609 = -\frac{x_0}{\lambda} \quad [74]$$

which yields:

$$x_0 = 1.609\sqrt{\frac{a \cdot b}{2}\frac{\rho_{membrane}}{\rho_{high}}} \quad [75]$$

In the second step, the potential difference remaining from a 10-mV perturbation is calculated at a distance $x_0$ from the perturbation for a nerve with the lower value of the axoplasm resistivity, $\rho_{low} = 0.5\ \Omega \cdot$ m. This is done by substituting the value for $x_0$ as found in Eq. [75] and the new resistivity $\rho_{low}$ into Eqs. [70] and [71]:

$$\Delta V(x_0) = \Delta V_{max} \exp\left(-\frac{x_0}{\lambda}\right)$$

$$= (10\,\text{mV}) \exp\left\{-\frac{1.609\sqrt{\dfrac{a \cdot b}{2}\dfrac{\rho_{membrane}}{\rho_{high}}}}{\sqrt{\dfrac{a \cdot b}{2}\dfrac{\rho_{membrane}}{\rho_{low}}}}\right\}$$

$$[76]$$

The argument of the exponential function now simplifies greatly, yielding:

$$\Delta V(x_0) = (10\,\text{mV}) \exp\left\{-1.609\sqrt{\frac{\rho_{low}}{\rho_{high}}}\right\}$$

$$= 3.4\,\text{mV} \quad [77]$$

Thus, the potential difference perturbation has not decayed to a value of 2 mV as before, but only to 3.4 mV at the same distance from the 10-mV perturbation.

# Hodgkin–Huxley Model

The discussion in the previous section demonstrated that the electrotonus spread is not sufficient to transport a nerve impulse. Since the electrotonus spread is based on Ohm's law, it is a model with a (charge) transport that has a linear relation between the driving force (the electric field) and the resulting flow (the current density). This model therefore belongs to the linear non-equilibrium regime, as defined in Chapter 10. In the current section, we discuss a more successful model for unmyelinated nerves, which is called the Hodgkin–Huxley model. In 1952, Hodgkin and Huxley proposed a model in which the charge transport does not obey Ohm's law; i.e., their model is a non-linear, non-equilibrium model. This once more confirms our observation in previous chapters that phenomena in the biological sciences often include non-linear, non-equilibrium processes.

The Hodgkin–Huxley model was introduced only about 50 years ago for two reasons:

- non-linear models require a more elaborate theoretical framework, and

- extensive and difficult experiments had to be done to put key elements of the model in place.

Hodgkin and Huxley's experiments are based on the setup sketched in Fig. 14.23: two electrodes are inserted into the axoplasm of a nerve and a third electrode runs along the nerve in the extracellular fluid. One of the electrodes inside and the electrode outside are used to measure the potential difference across

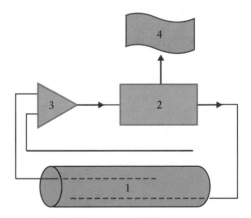

**FIGURE 14.23**

Experimental setup for the voltage-clamp experiment conducted by Hodgkin and Huxley. (1) Axon with two inserted electrodes. One electrode runs parallel to a second electrode outside the nerve cell. Both are connected to a potentiometer (3, an instrument that measures the potential difference between the electrodes). The potentiometer also serves as a controller because it is connected to a current generator (2), which allows the potential to be clamped (fixed) by supplying a current through the second intracellular electrode. The current output of the generator is recorded (4).

the nerve membrane. The way the experiment is then conducted is called a **voltage-clamp measurement**: the potential difference between the two electrodes is kept constant by the controller via a feedback connection to a current generator. Whenever a change in the potential difference occurs, it is compensated by a current from the current generator, which is sent through the third electrode. This way, we can measure the membrane current directly by recording the current output of the current generator.

It is not easy to insert two non-touching electrodes into an axon of a cross-section of 1.5 $\mu$m or less. It was only after the discovery of the giant axon of the squid (with diameters of up to 1 mm) in 1936 that experiments with single nerve cells became feasible. However, it is not possible to conduct these experiments on a live squid specimen. Therefore, the first issue was whether the nerve could be kept functional after the animal had been destroyed. After dissection, the axoplasm and the extracellular fluid had to be replaced by laboratory electrolytes. It turned out that the nerve continued to operate for a time period that was sufficient to conduct the experiments. The most important result of the early electrolyte experiments was that the crucial processes in nerve signal propagation occur across the membrane and not within the axoplasm. Several electrolytes were tested, identifying the ion species that are important for the nerve impulse transport process: sodium, potassium, and chlorine.

## ● EXAMPLE 14.10

(a) As a reference for the processes associated with sodium and potassium flow across a nerve membrane, calculate their respective electrochemical equilibrium potential difference. (b) What do these values mean physically?

*Solution to part (a):* We define electrochemical equilibrium potential differences for each ion species by using the concentration values from Fig. 14.2 and inserting these in Nernst's equation (Eq. [47]) at a temperature of 310 K.

- We find an equilibrium potential difference for sodium ions:

$$\Delta V_{Na^+,equilibrium} = \frac{k \cdot T}{e} \ln\left(\frac{c_{Na^+,interstitium}}{c_{Na^+,axoplasm}}\right)$$

$$= \frac{k \cdot T}{e} \ln\left(\frac{145 \frac{mmol}{L}}{15 \frac{mmol}{L}}\right) \quad [78]$$

which yields:

$$\Delta V_{Na^+,equilibrium} = +60\,mV \quad [79]$$

- The equilibrium potential difference for potassium ions is:

$$\Delta V_{K^+,equilibrium} = \frac{k \cdot T}{e} \ln\left(\frac{c_{K^+,interstitium}}{c_{K^+,axoplasm}}\right)$$

$$= \frac{k \cdot T}{e} \ln\left(\frac{5 \frac{mmol}{L}}{150 \frac{mmol}{L}}\right) \quad [80]$$

which yields:

$$\Delta V_{K^+,equilibrium} = -90\,mV \quad [81]$$

*Solution to part (b):* Nernst's equation expresses the electrochemical equilibrium. For a given concentration step across a membrane, this means that an electric current must occur unless the equilibrium potential difference is established. The results in Eqs. [79] and [81] also enable us to predict the direction of a current when it occurs. This is illustrated for the steady-state potential difference at −70 mV. Since neither of the equilibrium potential differences in Eqs. [79] and [81] are equal to −70 mV, a net current of both ion species across the membrane is observed in a resting nerve:

$$\Delta V_{actual} < \Delta V_{Na^+,equilibrium}$$

$$\Rightarrow \quad Na^+ \text{ flow to axoplasm}$$

$$\Delta V_{actual} > \Delta V_{K^+,equilibrium}$$

$$\Rightarrow \quad K^+ \text{ flow to interstitium} \quad [82]$$

From the five last equations, Eqs. [78] to [82], we conclude that the actual potential difference during an impulse should not exceed a potential difference of +60 mV and should not drop below a potential difference of −90 mV since beyond these values both ion species flow in the same direction across the nerve membrane. We note further that the flow of ions in Eq. [82] is exactly compensated by the Na/K pump for $\Delta V_{actual} =$ −70 mV, i.e., a resting nerve. For any other potential difference, different sodium and potassium currents follow; these are not compensated by the Na/K pump because the pump operates independently of the potential difference.

The specific result we focus on to illustrate the non-linear character of the Hodgkin–Huxley mechanism is shown in Fig. 14.24. The figure shows the response of the giant axon of a squid to an artificial nerve impulse at 20°C (room temperature). The dashed line with the corresponding axis at the right is the potential difference across the nerve membrane and is consistent with the curve in Fig. 14.3. Note that a minor initial change from −65 mV to a value of about −55 mV is sufficient to trigger an impulse. During the impulse the potential difference swings all the way to a positive value of +30 mV, and returns in less than 0.5 ms to negative values, falling first to a negative potential difference of about −75 mV before slowly recovering to the steady-state value. The solid and dash-dotted lines with the corresponding axis at the left show the conductivity of sodium and potassium relative to the sodium conductivity for the resting nerve, $\gamma_{Na}^0$. Recall that the conductivity and the resistivity are inversely proportional: $\gamma \propto 1/\rho$. Thus, an increase of the conductivity means a decrease in the resistivity, which yields an increased current and vice versa. The data show that the immediate response to the onset of an impulse is a strong but short-lived peak in the conductivity of sodium, followed by a slower but longer peak in the conductivity of potassium. Note that an ohmic response would be a fixed conductivity value for both sodium and potassium (horizontal lines).

To see how this non-ohmic response leads to a propagating nerve impulse, we use Figs. 14.25 and 14.26 to focus on the profile of an impulse as a function of position along the nerve. Fig. 14.25 shows the change in the potential difference, and Fig. 14.26 shows the corresponding change in the current along the axon surface on the axoplasm side.

We start with Fig. 14.25. This is again a detailed figure and we have to go through it step by step to understand what happens. The top graph in the figure shows the potential difference as a function of position for a nerve impulse travelling with a speed of about 1 m/s toward the right (positive $x$-direction). As noted in Table 14.1, this is an average speed for an unmyelinated human nerve. The spatial profile of the potential difference shown can be determined from the potential difference profile as a function of time in Fig. 14.3, and by taking into account that nerve impulses travel in only one direction along a given nerve cell. The origin of the $x$-axis is chosen such that the leading edge of the impulse has just reached it. The nerve impulse has a steep leading slope, with the potential difference rising to a maximum 0.5 mm behind the onset. At 1 mm behind the leading slope the potential difference drops sharply back below the initial, steady-state potential difference. For several more millimetres behind the leading slope, the potential difference is more negative than the resting value. In Fig. 14.25 we also highlight three points along this curve:

- **Resting nerve before the impulse arrives (circle at right).** A potential difference of −70 mV exists between the axoplasm and the extracellular fluid because the Na/K pumping and the passive diffusion of sodium and potassium are balanced, as discussed in Fig. 14.18. This potential difference is achieved by excess negative charges on the extracellular side of the membrane and excess positive charges on the axoplasm side.

- **The impulse front arrives, depolarization occurs (centre circle).** An initial, small drop in the potential difference triggers a sudden increase in the conductivity of sodium in the membrane (see solid line in Fig. 14.24), leading to a net sodium ion current inward. The sodium concentration in the axoplasm is sufficiently raised to reverse the charge distribution across the membrane, which temporarily establishes a negative surface charge

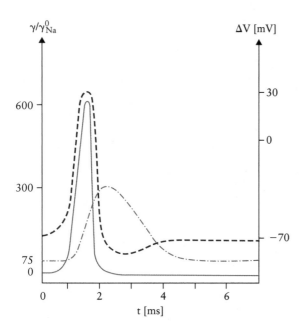

**FIGURE 14.24**

Response of a squid axon to an externally triggered impulse at 20°C (room temperature). The dashed line (with the corresponding potential axis at the right) is consistent with the same curve in Fig. 14.3, confirming that a nerve impulse is triggered by an initial 10-mV change in the potential difference. The solid curve (for sodium) and dash-dotted curve (for potassium) show their respective conductivity within the nerve membrane as a function of time. The conductivity is given as a value relative to the nerve membrane sodium conductivity for a resting nerve, $\gamma_{Na}^0$; the corresponding axis is shown at the left.

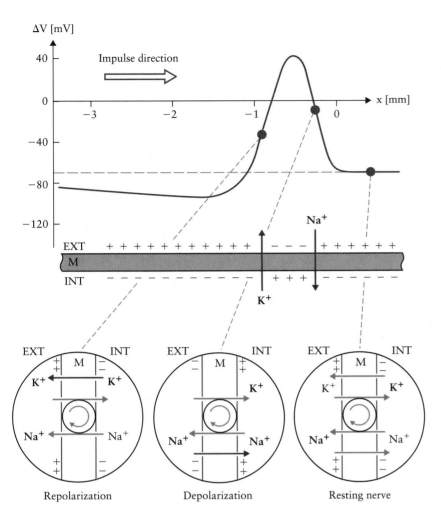

**FIGURE 14.25**
The potential difference across the nerve membrane as a function of the position along the nerve cell while a nerve impulse passes. The sketch below the curve shows the polarity of the corresponding charge on either side of the membrane. The three circular panels at the bottom illustrate the microscopic processes that dominate across the membrane at the respectively highlighted positions.

density on the extracellular side of the membrane and a corresponding positive surface charge density on the axoplasm side.

• **The tail end of the impulse passes, repolarization occurs.** When the membrane is fully depolarized the sodium conductivity falls off sharply and the potassium conductivity increases. As a result, the inward current of sodium ceases, but an outward current of potassium emerges. This quickly returns the charge distribution across the membrane to its original polarity, with excess positive charges on the extracellular side. The potential difference drops accordingly. After these fast processes are completed, a slower recovery of the steady state follows as the Na/K pump transports potassium and sodium back to their original side. This is associated with the slow approach of the potential difference from negative values as low as $-90$ mV to the steady-state value of $-70$ mV. While the potential difference has not recovered, the ability to trigger a new impulse is diminished, which reduces the risk of unintentional secondary impulses.

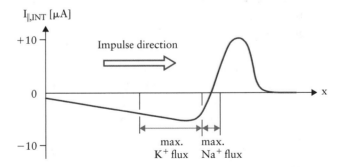

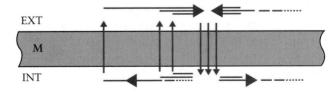

**FIGURE 14.26**

The electric current along the inner surface of a nerve membrane as a function of position along the nerve while an impulse passes. The sketch below the curve illustrates the formation of a current loop behind the crest of the impulse. A reduction in the amount of charge ahead of the impulse lowers the potential there, causing a Hodgkin–Huxley type of response. This leads to a forward motion of the impulse.

It becomes apparent how the impulse travels forward along the nerve when the current along the axon membrane is studied as a function of the position of the impulse at a given instant. This is shown in Fig. 14.26. Note carefully that the curve shows a different property of the system compared to Fig. 14.25 even though the two profiles appear superficially similar. The sketch of the membrane below the current density diagram in Fig. 14.26 once again illustrates the currents occurring across the membrane, which are also shown in Fig. 14.25: when the impulse front arrives, a strong sodium ion current occurs toward the axoplasm accompanied by a weaker potassium ion current across a broader zone toward the extracellular fluid farther upstream.

We focus first on the point at which the sodium current occurs across the membrane. The associated reduction of positive charge on the extracellular fluid side of the membrane causes other positive charge in the vicinity to move toward this point. In the same fashion, the sudden increase in positive charge on the axoplasm side of the membrane leads to an outflow of positive charge along the membrane in both directions. We studied a similar case in Fig. 14.21. The current parallel to the membrane in the axoplasm is shown in the top diagram of Fig. 14.26. The current is positive in the direction downstream and is negative in the direction upstream. These currents are very small, e.g., typically below 10 $\mu$A.

The current components in the downstream and upstream directions have different consequences. The current toward the left in Fig. 14.26—i.e., toward the side which the impulse front has already passed—is short-circuited by the countercurrent of potassium, leading to current loops trailing the impulse front. On the side where the parallel current flows ahead of the impulse front, it serves as the trigger for the impulse front to move forward by lowering the potential difference. As we noted before, a small drop in the potential difference is sufficient to cause the sodium conductivity to shoot up, pushing the nerve impulse front forward. Note that this current is the same we used in Fig. 14.22 to explain electrotonus spread. Thus, the signal propagates forward by electrotonus spread, triggering the adjacent segment downstream along the nerve.

## Impulse Transport Mechanism in a Myelinated Nerve

The Hodgkin–Huxley model explains most aspects of the impulse transport in unmyelinated nerves, which comprise about 70% of the nerve cells in the

human body. As Table 14.1 shows, the remaining 30% of myelinated nerves play an important part as they are responsible for transmission of motor information and response. They are designated for motor response because impulse transport in these nerve cells is much faster than in unmyelinated nerves.

We first want to establish the difference in impulse transport speeds of the two nerve types by studying Figs. 14.27 to 14.29. Fig. 14.27 is a linear plot of the signal transport speed of both nerve types as a function of axon radius for human nerves. The first panel covers radii up to 0.6 $\mu$m; the second panel then covers radii up to 10 $\mu$m, a range that includes the largest myelinated nerves in the human body. Both graphs clearly show that the impulse transport speed increases with axon radius, although the increase appears to be steeper for myelinated nerves. The figure also shows that a myelinated nerve transports impulses faster by a factor of almost 10 than an unmyelinated nerve of the same radius. The figure allows us to conclude that two factors play a role in nerve impulse speed: the size of the axon and the presence of a myelin sheath. The linear data representation in Fig. 14.27 is unsatisfactory, however, because it does not allow both curves to be usefully combined in a single plot.

Fig. 14.28 is a logarithmic plot of the same speed versus axon radius data. This graph allows us to see clearly that for both nerve types a strong dependence on the axon radius exists, a point that may get lost

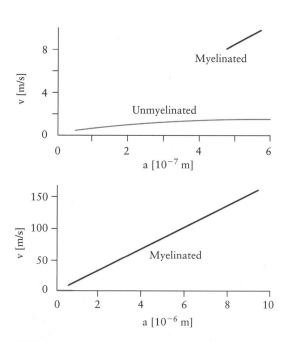

**FIGURE 14.27**

Linear plot of impulse transport speed versus axon radius for myelinated and unmyelinated nerves in the human body. Due to the large range of data, two separate plots are shown.

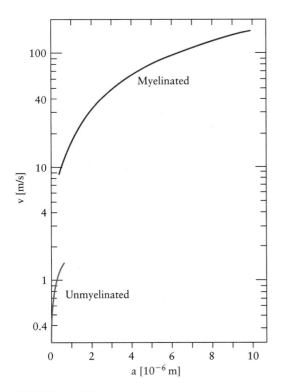

**FIGURE 14.28**

Logarithmic plot of the same data as plotted in Fig. 14.27. The curved slopes indicate that the speed *v* is not an exponential function of the axon radius *a*.

on the axon radius in comparison to the unmyelinated nerve. This aspect implies that a model must be found for the myelinated nerve that is distinct from the Hodgkin–Huxley model described in the previous section.

The best way to develop a model for the impulse transport in a myelinated nerve is to return to Fig. 14.1: the myelin sheath is too thick to allow ion diffusion or ion currents to pass through it. Therefore, the 1- to 2-mm-long myelinated sections are passive elements in which electrically only electrotonus spread is possible. However, the myelinated sections are interrupted by the nodes of Ranvier. At these nodes a membrane only 5 to 10 nm thick separates the axoplasm from the extracellular fluid, and the electric behaviour is the same as that of an unmyelinated nerve.

Based on these observations a mechanism has been established that combines electrotonus spread in the myelinated sections with Hodgkin–Huxley-type impulses in the nodes of Ranvier. This mechanism is called **saltatory conduction** because this mechanism is based on impulse stimulation jumping from one node of Ranvier to the next. To confirm this model, we establish first that electrotonus spread is sufficient to cause the next node to be triggered in response to an impulse at the previous node for a myelinated nerve. We cannot assume this to be the case without calculation: remember that in Eq. [72] we found for

in the linear representation of Fig. 14.27. However, Fig. 14.28 is not conclusive on the question as to whether the same mechanism explains both transport processes. They are both curved in a similar fashion, but qualitatively it seems that their curvatures do not match in the region of overlap.

Fig. 14.29, a double-logarithmic plot of the same data as in the previous two figures, addresses the question of whether the two types of nerve share the same mechanism. The answer is that, for both the myelinated and the unmyelinated nerve, the impulse transport speed and the axon radius obey a power law; however, the power-law exponents are different:

unmyelinated nerve: $v \propto a^{0.5} = \sqrt{a}$

myelinated nerve: $\quad v \propto a^{1.0} = a$    [83]

Thus, three main aspects of the impulse transport speed of a myelinated nerve must be explained:

- the dependence of the signal speed on the axon radius, i.e., the fact that the signal travels faster for larger nerves;
- the increase of speed by about an order of magnitude at the same axon radius as for an unmyelinated nerve due to the myelin sheath; and
- the different mechanism of signal transport as indicated by the different functional dependence

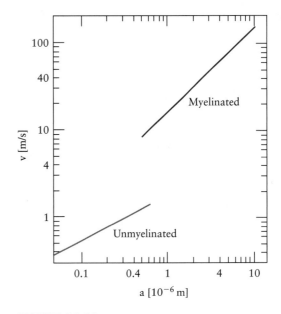

**FIGURE 14.29**

Double-logarithmic plot of the same data as plotted in Fig. 14.27. Different slopes for the two nerve types suggest that different mechanisms have to be found for the impulse transport in myelinated and unmyelinated nerves.

the unmyelinated nerve a decay length of only about 0.1 mm. If this value applied to myelinated nerves as well, the myelin sheath length of 1 to 2 mm might be too long for a Hodgkin–Huxley impulse in one node to trigger such an event in the next one.

The calculation starts from Eq. [70], which provides the decay length of a perturbation of the potential difference. For a typical myelinated nerve we use $a = 5$ μm and $b = 2$ μm. Combined with the resistivity data from Table 14.3, we find:

$$\lambda = \sqrt{\frac{a \cdot b \cdot \rho_{\text{membrane}}}{2 \cdot \rho_{\text{axoplasm}}}}$$

$$= \sqrt{\frac{(5 \times 10^{-6}\,\text{m})(2 \times 10^{-6}\,\text{m})(1 \times 10^{7}\,\Omega \cdot \text{m})}{2\,(1.1\,\Omega \cdot \text{m})}}$$

$$= 7 \times 10^{-3}\,\text{m} = 7\,\text{mm} \qquad [84]$$

This decay length is much longer than the corresponding value in the unmyelinated nerve in Eq. [72]. We compare the value for $\lambda$ more carefully with the distance $D$ between subsequent nodes of Ranvier. For a myelinated nerve with $a = 5$ μm, this distance is about $D = 1.4$ mm. Thus, the distance between two nodes of Ranvier is 20% of the decay length; not only will the next node of Ranvier be triggered, but several nodes farther downstream also should be stimulated in response to a Hodgkin–Huxley impulse at a given node. Exactly how many is calculated in Concept Question 14.10.

### Concept Question 14.10

How many nodes of Ranvier are triggered as a result of a Hodgkin–Huxley impulse at a given node upstream?

ANSWER: We note that the threshold for a node to be triggered is about 10% of the total change of the potential difference during a Hodgkin–Huxley impulse: the maximum potential difference variation is $\Delta V_{\text{HH}} = 100$ mV, as shown in Fig. 14.24. We saw above that a node of Ranvier is triggered when its potential difference changes to a value of $V_{\text{actual}} \geq -60$ mV, which is a variation of $\Delta V = 10$ mV. Based on Eq. [70], we find the following values for the fraction of the change of the potential difference due to electrotonus spread for the next 20 nodes of Ranvier:

$$\Delta V / \Delta V_{\text{HH}} = e^{-D/\lambda} = 0.80$$
$$\Delta V / \Delta V_{\text{HH}} = e^{-2D/\lambda} = 0.67$$
$$\Delta V / \Delta V_{\text{HH}} = e^{-5D/\lambda} = 0.37 \qquad [85]$$
$$\Delta V / \Delta V_{\text{HH}} = e^{-10D/\lambda} = 0.13$$
$$\Delta V / \Delta V_{\text{HH}} = e^{-20D/\lambda} = 0.02$$

Thus, at least the next 10 nodes of Ranvier are triggered as a result of an impulse at a given node. This is an effective design; with all the little things that can go wrong, it is better that we do not depend on each of the several hundred nodes of Ranvier along a nerve firing in sequence. *Procaine*, a common local anaesthetic, blocks the nodes of Ranvier in the vicinity of its application; clearly, this drug must act over more than a few centimetres to be effective.

## Model Calculations of Impulse Transport Speeds

We still need to quantify the speed of impulses for Hodgkin–Huxley-type conduction in unmyelinated nerves and for saltatory conduction in myelinated nerves. An analytical calculation of these speeds is not possible and therefore has to be done by computer simulations. It is instructive, however, to estimate a "ballpark figure" (common laboratory slang for a number that is correct to within an order of magnitude). This approach is used often in the sciences to judge whether a proposed model is feasible before undertaking lengthy model calculations. We want to develop a ballpark figure for the speed in both myelinated and unmyelinated nerves.

### UNMYELINATED NERVE

Speed is generally defined as distance divided by time. In the case of the unmyelinated nerve, the decay length in Eq. [70] establishes a characteristic length for how far a perturbation affects a nerve. The decay time in Eq. [69] introduces a characteristic time for how long a perturbation affects a nerve. Thus, we estimate the impulse speed by dividing these two numbers:

$$v \approx \frac{\lambda}{\tau} = \frac{\sqrt{\dfrac{a \cdot b \cdot \rho_{\text{membrane}}}{2 \cdot \rho_{\text{axoplasm}}}}}{\kappa \cdot \varepsilon_0 \cdot \rho_{\text{membrane}}}$$

$$= \frac{1}{\kappa \cdot \varepsilon_0} \sqrt{\frac{a \cdot b}{2 \cdot \rho_{\text{membrane}} \cdot \rho_{\text{axoplasm}}}} \qquad [86]$$

This formula is satisfactory because it reproduces the proper square-root dependence on the axon radius, $v \propto (a)^{1/2}$, as found experimentally in Fig. 14.29. Calculating the speed for a nerve of axon radius $a = 0.6$ μm results in a speed of $v = 0.22$ m/s. This value underestimates the proper value in Fig. 14.29

by a factor of 6 to 7. We are not surprised by this discrepancy, because $\lambda$ is defined for a drop of the potential difference to 37% but a drop to as much as 85 to 90% is sufficient to propagate the impulse.

## MYELINATED NERVE

For the myelinated nerve two alternative ways are available to estimate the speed because there are two characteristic lengths for this type of nerve: the distance between adjacent nodes of Ranvier, $D$, and the decay length of a perturbation of the potential difference, $\lambda$. We test both for a typical myelinated nerve with axon radius $a = 5\ \mu m$.

- If the impulse speed depends on the distance between neighbouring nodes of Ranvier, $D$, we find:

$$v \approx \frac{D}{\tau} = \frac{280 \cdot a}{\kappa \cdot \varepsilon_0 \cdot \rho_{membrane}} = 2.3\ \frac{m}{s} \qquad [87]$$

This formula satisfies the result of Fig. 14.29, which stated that $v \propto a$ for a myelinated nerve. However, the speed of 2.3 m/s is more than an order of magnitude too small.

- If the impulse speed of the impulse depends on the decay length, as it does for the unmyelinated nerve, the same formula as in Eq. [86] is used. What is different now, though, is the fact that the thickness of the myelin sheath, $b$, and the axon radius, $a$, are linearly proportional to each other for myelinated nerves, $b \propto a$. This means that the speed in Eq. [86] becomes a linear function of $a$, $v \propto a$. Substituting numerical values for a typical myelinated nerve with $a = 5\ \mu m$ and $b = 2\ \mu m$, we find $v = 11.4$ m/s. This value comes closer to the experimental values in Figs. 14.27 to 14.29, but underestimates it by a factor of 7 to 10. Recall that we found the same factor when we compared the result in Eq. [86] with the experimental impulse speed for the unmyelinated nerve: the deviation is again due to the decay length $\lambda$ underestimating the distance to which a Hodgkin–Huxley event affects the nerve downstream.

As a consequence, we see that nature gains a second advantage by not relying on the firing of each neighbouring node of Ranvier: besides the decreased risk of losing the signal, we also gain in speed by a factor of about 5.

What makes the signal transport in myelinated nerves faster than that in unmyelinated nerves of equal axon radius? It is in the end not a difference in mechanism, because we used the same formula (Eq. [86]) to estimate the signal speed; electrotonus spread determines in both cases how fast the signal travels along the nerve. The important difference between both types of nerves is the thickness $b$, i.e., the presence of the myelin sheath. Physically, the thicker myelin sheath reduces the capacitance of the nerve ($C \propto 1/b$; see Eq. [3]), which in turn means that fewer point charges are involved in establishing the resting potential difference in a myelinated nerve. The impulse propagates faster as less screening of the potential difference variations occurs.

In addition, we saw in Figs. 14.27 to 14.29 that myelinated nerves benefit from a larger axon radius. A larger axon radius is possible because the myelin sheath stabilizes the structure. The introduction of larger nerves adds another factor of 3 to 5 to the maximum speed at which a nerve impulse can travel.

# MULTIPLE CHOICE AND CONCEPTUAL QUESTIONS

## CAPACITORS AND DIELECTRIC MATERIALS

**Q–14.1.** How does the capacitance of a parallel plate capacitor change when its plates are moved to twice their initial distance and a slab of material with dielectric constant $\kappa = 2$ is placed between the plates to replace air? (A) It is increased to four times the original value. (B) It doubles. (C) It remains unchanged. (D) It is halved. (E) It is reduced to one-quarter of the original value.

**Q–14.2.** We treat an unknown biological membrane as a parallel plate capacitor with a dielectric material between its plates. If you know the capacitance per unit area in unit $F/m^2$, what additional parameter do you have to measure to determine the dielectric constant of the membrane material? (A) We need no other information. (B) We need to measure the area of the capacitor. (C) We need to measure the thickness of the membrane. (D) We need to measure the permittivity of a vacuum ($\varepsilon_0$). (E) We need to measure the resistance of the membrane.

**Q–14.3.** A capacitor provides an electric field that points from left to right. How will the water molecule shown in Fig. 13.1 rotate if it can rotate freely as in liquid water? (Assume its orientation as shown; i.e., left in the context of this question is left on the page.) (A) It will not rotate. (B) It will rotate such that the oxygen atom is left and the two hydrogen atoms are right. (C) It will rotate such that the oxygen atom is right and the two hydrogen atoms are left. (D) It will rotate such that the oxygen atom is up and the two hydrogen atoms are down. (E) It will rotate such that the oxygen atom is down and the two hydrogen atoms are up. (F) It will spin continuously, like a top.

**Q–14.4.** We consider the capacitor shown in Fig. 14.30. At which of the five positions (A–E) does the potential have its smallest value? *Hint:* Note that $+2 < +5$ and $-3 < -1$.

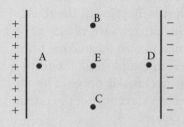

**FIGURE 14.30**

Parallel plate capacitor with five particular positions labelled A–E between the plates.

**Q–14.5.** Fig. 14.31 shows two capacitors that are rotated 90° relative to each other. In what direction does the electric field point at point $P$ at the centre of the arrangement? (A) up, (B) down, (C) left, (D) right, (E) in another direction.

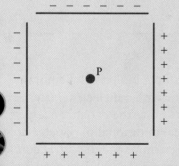

**FIGURE 14.31**

Two parallel plate capacitors oriented perpendicular to each other. The position at the centre of the arrangement is identified as point $P$.

**Q–14.6.** What does a large capacitance $C$ imply? (A) There are many point charges on the capacitor. (B) The capacitor is large. (C) The capacitor has a large leakage current. (D) The capacitor has a large area and a small plate separation. (E) None of the above.

**Q–14.7.** How does the capacitance of an air-filled parallel plate capacitor change when we place a material with dielectric constant $\kappa = 1.0$ between its plates? (Choose the closest value.) (A) It triples. (B) It doubles. (C) It remains unchanged. (D) It is halved. (E) It is reduced to one-third of the original value.

**Q–14.8.** We use a solid material with a large dielectric constant. We predict the following observation when a dielectric made of this material is removed from between the plates of a parallel plate capacitor: (A) If we keep the potential difference across the capacitor constant, the amount of charge on the plates increases. (B) If we keep the amount of charge on the capacitor plates constant, the potential difference between the plates decreases. (C) If we keep the amount of charge on the plates of the capacitor constant, the potential difference between the plates increases. (D) We cannot keep either the potential difference across the capacitor or the amount of charge on its plates constant. Thus, the first three answers are not valid.

**Q–14.9.** We compare myelinated and unmyelinated nerves. Remember that the latter have a much smaller membrane thickness. What consequence does this have for human nerves, which all have a resting potential difference of $-70$ mV? (A) The capacitance per unit membrane area of the myelinated nerve is larger than the capacitance per unit membrane area of the unmyelinated nerve. (B) The dielectric constant is much smaller for the myelinated nerves. (C) The potential difference across the myelinated membrane must be larger. (D) The amount of charge separated across the membrane per unit area is larger for the unmyelinated nerve. (E) The amount of charge separated across the membrane per unit area is larger for the myelinated nerve.

**Q–14.10.** You construct a parallel plate capacitor with a 1.0-mm-thick rutile dielectric layer ($\kappa_{rutile} = 100$). If the area of the capacitor plates is 1.0 cm$^2$, what is its capacitance? (Choose the closest value.) (A) 90 pF, (B) 180 pF, (C) 9 mF, (D) 100 mF.

**Q–14.11.** Why is it dangerous to touch the terminals of a capacitor with a high potential difference even after the charging source has been disconnected? What would you do to make the capacitor safer to handle?

**Q–14.12.** What design options do you have if you need a small-sized capacitor with a large capacitance?

**Q–14.13.** If the potential difference across a capacitor is doubled, by what factor does the stored electric energy change?

**Q–14.14.** What happens to the charge on the plates of a capacitor if the potential difference between the plates is doubled?

## CURRENT AND RESISTANCE

**Q–14.15.** Explain why all points in a conductor must have the same potential under stationary conditions.

**Q–14.16.** A potential difference of 1.0 V is maintained along a conductor with resistance of 10 Ω for a period of 20 seconds. What total charge passes through the conductor during that time interval? (Choose the closest value.) (A) 200 C, (B) 20 C, (C) 2.0 C, (D) 5.0 mC.

**Q–14.17.** (a) Why don't free electrons in a piece of metal fall to the bottom due to gravity? (b) Why don't free electrons in a piece of metal all drift to the surface as a result of mutual electric repulsion based on Coulomb's law?

**Q–14.18.** We study a current passing through a metallic wire. Leaving everything else unchanged, how does this current change when we reduce the magnitude of the electric field along the wire to 50% of its initial value? (A) The current remains unchanged. (B) The current becomes half of its initial value. (C) The current becomes one-quarter of its initial value. (D) The current becomes twice its initial value. (E) The current becomes four times its initial value.

**Q–14.19.** Which property causes point charges to move along a conductor? (A) The conductor's resistance, (B) the conductor's resistivity, (C) the electric current, (D) the electric potential, or (E) the electric charge of the electron.

**Q–14.20.** We assume that a negative mobile point charge is placed at point $E$ in Fig. 14.30. What happens to it when it is released? (A) It accelerates to the left. (B) It moves with constant speed to the left. (C) It accelerates to the right. (D) It moves with constant speed to the right. (E) Nothing; it remains at the same position.

**Q–14.21.** Which is the standard unit for resistance? (A) Ω, (B) Ω/m², (C) Ω · m², (D) Ω/m, (E) Ω · m.

**Q–14.22.** How does the resistance change if we exchange a conductor for a piece of metal with double the conductivity and double the cross-sectional area but leave its length unchanged? (A) It is increased to four times the original value. (B) It doubles. (C) It remains unchanged. (D) It is halved. (E) It is reduced to one-quarter of the original value.

**Q–14.23.** Which is the standard unit for resistivity? (A) V/A, (B) A/V, (C) none; it is a unitless materials constant, (D) same as for resistance, (E) none of the above.

**Q–14.24.** The term drift velocity refers to: (A) the current that passes the cross-sectional area of a conductor per second, (B) the velocity with which point charges buoy to the surface of a conductor in an external electric field, (C) the volume flow rate of charged particles in a conductor when it carries a current of 1.0 A, (D) the mass flow rate of charged particles in a conductor when it carries a current of 1.0 A, (E) none of the above.

**Q–14.25.** Which is the standard unit of the drift velocity? (A) V/Ω², (B) V/A, (C) Ω/m, (D) m/s, (E) V²/C.

**Q–14.26.** Which of the following parameters— (i) the cross-sectional area of the wire, (ii) the metal used for the wire, and (iii) the length of the wire—do not contribute to the conductivity of a metal wire? (A) only (i), (B) only (ii), (C) only (iii), (D) all three, (E) only (i) and (iii).

**Q–14.27.** The electric system in Fig. 14.32 is often used to model a nerve membrane. It consists of a series of identical resistors aligned in two parallel rows with identical capacitors bridging the two rows following each resistor. Which of the following assumptions in order (A) to (D) has to be revised for Fig. 14.32 to be a reasonable model for a nerve (rendering the subsequent assumptions invalid as well)? (A) The membrane can be divided into segments. (B) The segments can be chosen such that they have the same capacitance. (C) The resistances in each row are the same. (D) For each single segment, the resistances on both sides of the membrane are the same. (E) None of these assumptions needs to be revised.

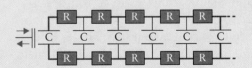

**FIGURE 14.32**

Electric axon model based on serial segments of capacitors and resistors.

# ANALYTICAL PROBLEMS

## CAPACITORS

**P–14.1.** We study some capacitor arrangements. (a) An air-filled parallel plate capacitor has a plate separation of $b = 1.5$ mm and an area $A = 4.0$ cm$^2$. Find its capacitance. (b) A capacitor with capacitance of $C = 4.5$ $\mu$F is connected to a 9-V battery. What is the amount of charge on each plate of the capacitor?

**P–14.2.** The plates of a parallel plate capacitor are 3 cm wide and 4 cm long. The plates are separated by a 1.5-mm-thick layer of paper. (a) Calculate the capacitance of the device using the dielectric constant of paper from Table 14.2. (b) Any dielectric material other than a vacuum has a maximum electric field that can be generated in the dielectric material before it physically or chemically breaks down and begins to conduct. This maximum electric field is called dielectric strength. The dielectric strength for paper is reached at a value of $15 \times 10^6$ V/m. Calculate the maximum charge that can be placed on the capacitor at this dielectric strength.

**P–14.3.** An air-filled parallel plate capacitor has a capacitance of 60 pF. (a) What is the separation of the plates if each plate has an area of 0.5 m$^2$? (b) If the region between the plates is filled with a material with $\kappa = 4.5$, what is the final capacitance?

**P–14.4.** An air-filled parallel plate capacitor has a plate area of 2.0 cm$^2$ and plate separation of 2.0 mm. How much charge does this device store when charged with a 6.0-V battery?

**P–14.5.** An air-filled parallel plate capacitor has a plate separation of 0.1 mm. What plate area is required to provide a capacitance of 2.0 pF?

**P–14.6.** An air-filled parallel plate capacitor has a plate area of 5.0 cm$^2$ and plate separation of 1.0 mm. It stores a charge of 0.4 nC. (a) What is the potential difference across its plates? (b) What is the magnitude of the electric field between its plates?

**P–14.7.** An air-filled parallel plate capacitor has a plate area of 2.0 cm$^2$ and plate separation of 5.0 mm. If a 12.0-V battery is connected to its plates, how much energy does the device store?

**P–14.8.** A water-filled parallel plate capacitor has a plate area of 2.0 cm$^2$ and plate separation of 2.0 mm. The potential difference between its plates is held at 6.0 V. Calculate (a) the magnitude of the electric field between its plates, (b) the charge stored on each plate, and (c) the charge stored on each plate after water is replaced by air.

**P–14.9.** A parallel plate capacitor carries a charge $Q$ on plates of area $A$. A dielectric material with dielectric constant $\kappa$ is located between its plates. We can show that the force each plate exerts on the other is given by:

$$F = \frac{Q^2}{2 \cdot \kappa \cdot \varepsilon_0 \cdot A} \qquad [88]$$

When a potential difference of 0.1 kV exists between the plates of an air-filled parallel plate capacitor of $C = 20$ $\mu$F capacitance, what force do the two plates exert on each other if they are separated by 2.0 mm?

**P–14.10.** Fig. 14.33 shows an electron at the origin that is released with initial speed $v_0 = 5.6 \times 10^6$ m/s at an angle $\theta_0 = 45°$ between the plates of a parallel plate capacitor of plate separation $D = 2.0$ mm. If the potential difference between the plates is $\Delta V = 100$ V, calculate the closest proximity of the electron to the bottom plate, $d$.

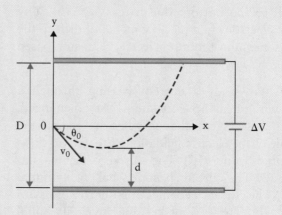

**FIGURE 14.33**

## CURRENT AND RESISTANCE

**P–14.11.** All commercial electric devices have identifying plates that specify their electrical characteristics. For example, a typical household device may be specified for a current of 6.0 A when connected to a 120-V source. What is the resistance of this device?

**P–14.12.** A person notices a mild shock if the current along a path through the thumb and index finger of one hand exceeds 80 $\mu$A. Compare the respective maximum allowable potential difference for the hand with (a) dry skin with a resistance of $R = 4.0 \times 10^5$ $\Omega$, and (b) wet skin with a resistance of $R = 2000$ $\Omega$.

**P–14.13.** A rectangular piece of copper is 2 cm long, 2 cm wide, and 10 cm deep. (a) What is the resistance of the copper piece as measured between the two square ends? (Use the resistivity of copper from Table 14.3.) (b) What is the resistance between two opposite rectangular faces?

**P–14.14.** A current of 6.0 A flows through a 20-Ω resistor for $t = 3$ minutes. What total amount of charge passes through any cross-section of the resistor in this time? (a) Express your result in unit C. (b) Express your result as the number of electrons passing through the cross-sectional area.

**P–14.15.** A conducting, cylindrical wire has a diameter of 1.0 mm, a length of 1.67 m, and a resistance of 50 mΩ. What is the resistivity of the material? Identify the material of which this conductor is made by using Table 14.3.

**P–14.16.** A mass of 3.25 g of gold is deposited on the negative electrode of an electrolytic cell in a period of 167 minutes. What current was flowing through the cell in that time period? Assume that the solution contained $Au^+$ ions.

**P–14.17.** You often see birds resting on power lines that carry currents of 50 A. The copper wire on which the bird stands has a radius of 1.1 cm. Assuming that the bird's feet are 4.0 cm apart, calculate the potential difference across its body.

## SPECIFIC LIFE SCIENCES APPLICATIONS

**P–14.18.** We develop a simplified model for Fig. 14.25, which shows at a given instant the potential along an axon while a nerve impulse travels through. This model is shown in Fig. 14.34. Assume that the axon radius is 8 $\mu$m. What is the current along the axon as a function of position? Use for the lengths the values $l_1 = 0.8$ mm and $l_2 = 0.4$ mm.

**P–14.19.** A current density of $0.8 \times 10^{-4}$ A/cm$^2$ stimulates a 6-nm-thick nerve membrane for 150 $\mu$s. How does the potential across the membrane change as a result of this current density?

**P–14.20.** For the myelinated nerve the axon radius is 10 $\mu$m, the resistivity of the membrane is $\rho_{membrane} = 1.0 \times 10^7$ Ω · m, the axoplasm resistivity is $\rho_{axoplasm} = 0.5$ Ω · m. Assume that the myelin sheath thickness $b$ is related to the axon radius $a$ as $a + b = 1.4 \cdot a$. (a) What is the electrotonus spread decay length $\lambda$ for this nerve? (b) Using $D = 280 \cdot a$ to quantify the distance $D$ between nodes of Ranvier for this nerve, how many nodes of Ranvier are triggered along the nerve as a result of a certain node being stimulated? Use a potential difference of $\Delta V = 100$ mV for the maximum potential change in the node that is initially stimulated, and allow other nodes of Ranvier to be triggered if electrotonus spread at their site causes at least a change from $-70$ mV to $-60$ mV.

**P–14.21.** Confirm both relations in Eq. [83] graphically by using Fig. 14.29.

**P–14.22.** Table 14.5 provides approximate values for the intracellular and extracellular concentrations in unit mmol/L for sodium, potassium, and chlorine ions in a frog muscle with a resting potential difference of $-98$ mV and for the squid axon with a resting potential difference of $-70$ mV. Calculate the equilibrium potential difference for each ion species in both cases at 20°C.

**TABLE 14.5**

**Intracellular and extracellular ion concentrations for muscle cells of frogs and nerve cells of squids, each in unit mmol/L**

| Ion species | Intracellular | Extracellular |
|---|---|---|
| *1. Frog muscle* | | |
| Na$^+$ | 9–13 | 120 |
| K$^+$ | 140 | 2.5 |
| Cl$^-$ | 3.5 | 120 |
| *2. Squid axon* | | |
| Na$^+$ | 50 | 440 |
| K$^+$ | 400 | 20 |
| Cl$^-$ | 40–100 | 560 |

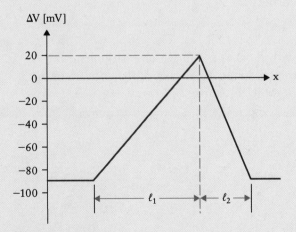

**FIGURE 14.34**

**P–14.23.** A simplified model for an erythrocyte is a spherical capacitor with a positively charged liquid interior of surface area $A$. The interior fluid is separated by a membrane of thickness $b$ from the surrounding, negatively charged plasma fluid. The potential difference across the membrane is 100 mV and the thickness of the membrane is about 100 nm with a dielectric constant of $\kappa = 5.0$. (a) Calculate the volume of the blood cell assuming that an average erythrocyte has a mass $1 \times 10^{-12}$ kg. From the volume determine the surface area of the erythrocyte. (b) Calculate the capacitance of the blood cell. For this calculation, model the membrane as a parallel plate capacitor with

the area found in part (a). (c) Calculate the charge on the surface of the membrane. How many elementary charges does this represent? Use 1.06 g/cm³ as the density of blood.

**P–14.24.** An X-ray tube used in cancer treatment operates at a potential difference of 4 MV, with a beam current of 25 mA striking the metal electrode. The energy deposited by this beam in the electrode has to be transferred to the cooling water flowing through the system. What mass flow rate in unit kg/s is needed if the temperature rise in the water cannot exceed $\Delta T = 50$ K?

# SUMMARY

## DEFINITIONS

- Capacitance: $C = q/V$
- Dielectric constant $\kappa$: $\kappa = 1$ vacuum; multiplied with permittivity of vacuum to obtain the permittivity of a material $\varepsilon_0 \Rightarrow \kappa \cdot \varepsilon_0$
- Current $I = \Delta q/\Delta t$
- Current density $J = I/A$ with $A$ the cross-sectional area of the conductor.

## UNITS

- Capacitance C: F = C/V (farad)
- Current $I$: A = C/s (ampere)
- Resistance $R$: $\Omega$ = V/A (ohm)
- Resistivity $\rho$: $\Omega \cdot$ m = V $\cdot$ m/A
- Dielectric constant $\kappa$: dimensionless materials constant

## LAWS

- Nernst's equation for a semi-permeable membrane (separating systems 1 and 2) and assuming only singly charged ions:

$$\frac{c_{i,1}}{c_{i,2}} = \exp\left\{-\frac{e}{k \cdot T}(V_{i,1} - V_{i,2})\right\}$$

with $e$ the elementary charge, $k$ the Boltzmann constant, $c_i$ the concentration of the $i$-th

component, and $\Delta V$ the potential difference across the membrane.

- Capacitance of charged parallel plates: $C = \varepsilon_0 \cdot A/b$ with $\varepsilon_0$ the permittivity of vacuum, $b$ the plate separation, and $A$ the plate area.
- Work stored in a parallel plate capacitor:

$$W = \frac{1}{2}Q \cdot \Delta V$$

with $Q$ the capacitor charge and $\Delta V$ the final potential difference.

- Ohm's law:
  - relation between electric field |E| and current density $J$:

  $$|\mathbf{E}| = \rho \cdot J$$

  with $\rho$ the resisitivity of the material carrying the current density.
  - relation between potential difference $\Delta V$ and current $I$:

  $$\Delta V = R \cdot I$$

  with $R = \rho \cdot l/A$ in which $l$ is the length, $A$ is the cross-sectional area of the conductor, and $R$ is the resistance.

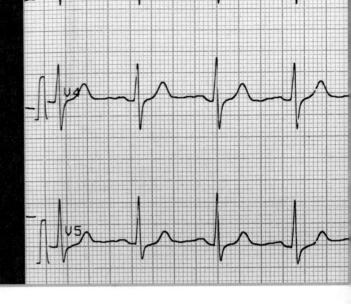

# CHAPTER 15

# ELECTRO-CARDIOGRAPHY
## Electric Phenomena of the Heart

The electrocardiogram (ECG) is a medical diagnosis and observation tool for time-resolved measurements of the electric activity of the cardiac muscle. The heart muscle of higher vertebrates is stimulated by the rhythmic action of pacemaker cells in the sino-atrial node (SA-node) of the autonomous nervous system of the heart.

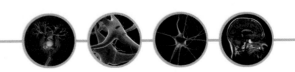

The complex human heart is a relatively recent evolutionary development we share only with mammals, birds, and some reptiles (see Fig. 12.5). Its physiological role has been understood since William Harvey discovered the circulatory flow of blood in the cardiovascular system in 1628. Almost 300 years later, in 1906, Willem Einthoven developed a method to observe the heart while it beats in the human chest. This method is called electrocardiography (ECG) and is based on the electric properties of the heart.

In this chapter, we first explore the nerve signals and muscle cell responses in the heart. Then we relate these to the corresponding electric potential variations on a patient's skin. The time-dependence of electric potential differences on the skin is illustrated for the most commonly used type of ECG as developed by Einthoven.

## Physiology of the Heart

### Anatomic Overview of the Heart

The human heart serves as the pump for two blood circulation systems, the systemic circulation and the pulmonary circulation. Blood flow in these circulations has been discussed in Chapter 12, with Fig. 12.1 providing an overview. To operate as an

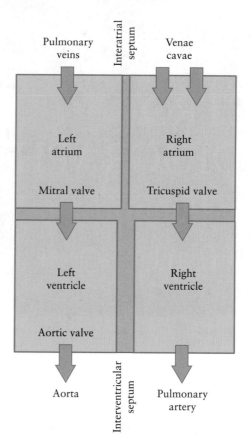

**FIGURE 15.2**

Sketch of blood flow patterns through the various anatomic components of the heart. Blood from the lungs passes through the left atrium and ventricle to the aorta, and blood from the venae cavae flows through the right atrium and ventricle to the pulmonary artery. The atria and ventricles are separated by valves; the left side and the right side of the heart are separated by the septum.

effective pump, the heart is divided into two halves, each consisting of a pair of chambers that are in turn separated by valves to ensure blood flow is one-directional. Its main anatomical components are shown in Fig. 15.1, including the right atrium (3), the right ventricle (4), the left atrium (5), the left ventricle (6), the aorta (7), and the two venae cavae (8). Fig. 15.2 illustrates how these components cooperate. On the left side, the pulmonary veins feed oxygenated blood, which arrives from the lungs, into the left **atrium**. The blood then passes through the mitral valve into the left **ventricle**. From there it leaves through the aortic valve into the aorta. In turn, the two venae cavae supply deoxygenated blood back to the right atrium. From there, it passes the tricuspid valve into the right ventricle. The right ventricle ejects blood into the pulmonary artery toward the lungs.

An interesting feature of the anatomy of the healthy human heart is the complete separation of both sides of the heart by the **septum**. This allows the

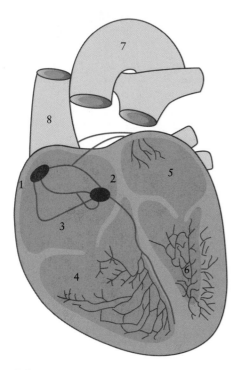

**FIGURE 15.1**

Anatomic sketch of the human heart. Shown are (1) the sino-atrial node (SA-node), (2) the atrio-ventricular node (AV-node), (3) the right atrium, (4) the right ventricle, (5) the left atrium, (6) the left ventricle, (7) the aorta with aortic bend, and (8) the two venae cavae.

heart to serve as a single pump for two circulatory systems simultaneously. Both halves of the heart have a similar set of heart muscles with a common electric trigger system to keep their operation synchronous. This indicates the uniqueness of the nervous system of the heart: the nerves are the only anatomical component passing through the septum, with nerve bundles extending from the right side, where the nervous centres are located, to the left side.

## Electric Systems of the Heart

Since the operation of the heart is unconditional, it is not controlled remotely by the brain but locally by a nerve centre above the right atrium and near the entry point of the superior vena cava ((1) in Fig. 15.1). This centre is called the **sinus node** or **sino-atrial node** (SA-node). It is a small amount of tissue that is embedded in the muscle with a diameter of 1 to 2 centimetres. Its rhythmic electric action is controlled by **pacemaker cells**. The electric properties of pacemaker cells are discussed in the next section.

The electric action caused by pacemaker cells is carried to the muscle cells of the heart through nerves at speeds of 0.5 m/s to 1.0 m/s in the same way we discussed in Chapter 14. The sketch in Fig. 15.3 highlights the hierarchy of the signal processing. The impulse from the SA-node travels along the internodal tracts to the **atrio-ventricular node** (AV-node),

which is a secondary nerve centre located at the bottom of the right atrium near the tricuspid valve. The internodal tract is illustrated in Fig. 15.1 by several nerve lines leading from the SA-node (1) to the AV-node (2).

The atrio-ventricular node operates similar to the SA-node, except at a slower rate of depolarization. As a result, a healthy SA-node triggers the AV-node every time before it triggers an impulse on its own. However, the AV-node still serves an important purpose in that it delays the nerve impulse by about 0.1 to 0.2 seconds in reaching the ventricular muscle cells, thus allowing the atria to empty into the ventricles before the blood is pushed out of the ventricles into the blood vessels.

Once the AV-node is triggered, the electric impulse leaves through the AV-bundle and splits into two major branches, one spreading along the right side of the heart (right-bundle branch) and the other, after passing through the interventricular septum, spreading along the left side of the heart (left-bundle branch). The impulses reach their final destination in the **Purkinje fibres** (named for the Czech physiologist Jan Purkyně, with the name usually shown in German spelling), which are the muscle cells of the heart that contract as a result of the stimulation. The mechanism of contraction is the same as we discussed in Fig. 3.3. The impulse speed from the AV-node to the Purkinje fibres, 1.0 m/s to 4.0 m/s, is slightly faster than from the SA-node to the AV-node.

We noted above that the heart serves two circulatory systems. With two atria and two ventricles, one could argue that the heart is actually a combination of two adjacent pumps. The fact that only one nervous system operates the heart dismisses the two-pump model. Indeed, the existence of only one nervous control system is vital as the synchronization of the contractions provides additional mechanical support for the pumping action in the larger systemic circulation, which can obviously benefit from a stronger pushing of the blood. This additional effect is achieved when the right atrium contracts slightly ahead of the left atrium (due to the location of the SA-node on the right side), but the left ventricle contracts between 10 ms and 30 ms ahead of the right ventricle, where the unit ms stands for milliseconds.

## Pacemaker Cells and Muscle Cell Response

To understand the properties of the heart, we must first establish the mechanism of the pacemaker cells. We know that these cells cannot be usual nerve cells: if they were, they could cause an impulse only if

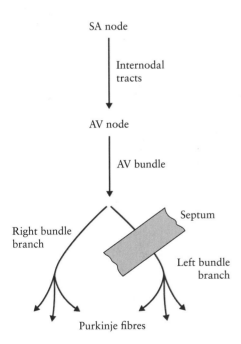

**FIGURE 15.3**

Paths of electric impulses from the SA-node. Note that the impulse is delayed in the AV-node. The impulse then passes the septum, spreading on both sides to the Purkinje fibres (heart muscles).

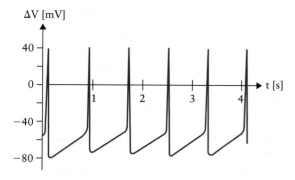

**FIGURE 15.4**

Rhythmic action of the SA-node. Pacemaker cells do not have a steady-state potential difference to which the nerve cell returns after stimulation. We associate this behaviour with an additional small calcium ion concentration in the interstitium.

triggered externally. Fig. 15.4 illustrates how the potential difference of the pacemaker cells in the SA-node develops as a function of time. In contrast to the electric profile of normal nerve cells in Fig. 14.3, no resting potential difference (steady-state level) exists for the pacemaker cells. Instead, the potential difference increases steadily from $-80$ mV to about $-55$ mV after the pacemaker cell has been triggered, i.e., undergoes a depolarization. This steady increase takes just under one second. When a potential difference of about $-55$ mV is reached, a new depolarization cycle is triggered. This different behaviour is achieved by adding a new ion species to those that are involved in cross-membrane exchange: **calcium ions** ($Ca^{2+}$) prevent the nerve cells from reaching their steady state, while $Na^+$ and $K^+$ play the same role in the pacemaker cells as they do in regular nerve cells.

The **rhythmic action** of the pacemaker cells in the SA-node triggers the response of the heart throughout its nervous system. Fig. 15.5 then shows the profile of the potential difference at various points throughout the system in comparison to the profile of the potential difference of the pacemaker cells in the SA-node, which is shown in the top panel. Every time the threshold near $-55$ mV is reached in the pacemaker cells, a depolarization is sent toward both the AV-node and the muscle cells of the two atrial chambers of the heart. The atrial muscle cells depolarize within 50 ms of the depolarization of the SA-node (Fig. 15.5(b)). This is indicated by a slight shift of the profile of the potential difference to the right. The shape of the depolarization profile of the atrial muscle cells adds another delay of about 50 ms following the initial overshoot to $+30$ mV. This shoulder-type feature of the profile of the potential difference is typical for heart muscle cells and is due to

$Ca^{2+}$ ions, as we will describe for the ventricular muscle cells below.

The impulse from the SA-node also reaches the AV-node and causes a depolarization, which is further delayed relative to the SA-node, as shown in Fig. 15.5(c). Fig. 15.5(d) illustrates the electric response of the Purkinje fibres (red curve) and their contraction (blue curve with a separate scale of relative contraction in percent at the right side of the figure). The delay varies from 100 ms to 150 ms for the cells close to the septum, which respond first, and those that are located on the outside wall of the heart. Note the characteristic shape of the depolarization and repolarization profile of the ventricular muscle cells, which prominently features a delay of up to 300 ms occurring near the 0-mV potential difference level, compared with a 1-ms period between depolarization and repolarization for regular nerve cells (as shown in Fig. 14.3).

This unusual profile of the potential difference is explained in more detail in Fig. 15.6. The top part of the figure shows again a single cycle of the potential difference of a heart muscle cell as a function of time, taken from Fig. 15.5(d). The middle part shows the

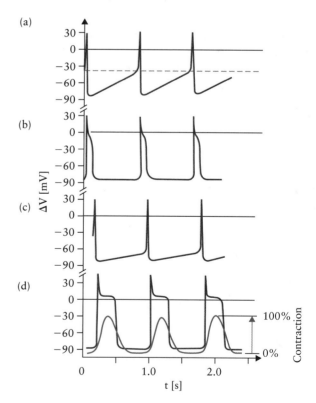

**FIGURE 15.5**

Comparison of the electric potential curves for nerve and muscle cells in the heart. (a) Pacemaker cells in the SA-node (see also Fig. 15.4), (b) atrial muscle cells, (c) AV-node cells, and (d) Purkinje fibre cells (red curve). Panel (d) shows also the muscle contraction profile of the fibre cells (blue curve with scale at the right).

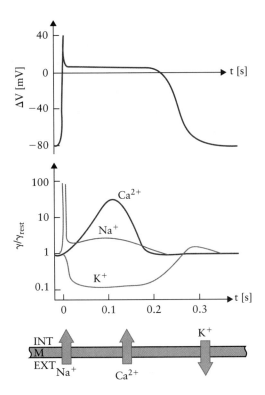

**FIGURE 15.6**

Profile of the potential difference (top), relative conductivity of the cell membrane (middle), and sketch of the dominant trans-membrane ion flux (bottom) for the Purkinje fibre cells. The figure illustrates how a small calcium ion concentration causes a significant delay in the repolarization of the cells.

**TABLE 15.1**

### Ion concentrations on the extracellular and intracellular sides of the membrane of a heart muscle cell

| Ion species | Intracellular concentration (mmol/L) | Extracellular concentration (mmol/L) |
|---|---|---|
| $Na^+$ | 12 | 145 |
| $Ca^{2+}$ | 0.0015 | 1.25 |
| $K^+$ | 150 | 4 |

The intracellular calcium value represents its maximum value during heart action; the corresponding value at rest is 0.1 $\mu$mol/L.

time profile of the relative conductivity (relative to a value of 1 for the resting muscle cell) for sodium, calcium, and potassium ions. Note that the relative conductivity is shown on a logarithmic scale. The sketch below the two plots identifies the dominant ion transport across the muscle cell membrane for each stage of the impulse.

The fast depolarization, initially taking place when the nerve impulse arrives, is due to a steep increase in the conductivity of sodium. This leads to the diffusion of sodium along its concentration gradient from the extracellular fluid into the cell (with the concentrations given in Table 15.1). This step is equivalent to the depolarization of a regular nerve cell, as discussed in Chapter 14.

The next step is unique to the muscle cells of the heart. The changed potential difference triggers an increased calcium transport across the membrane, leading to the plateau phase of the action potential difference near 0 mV for about 150 ms, i.e., more than a tenth of a second. The sodium transport across the membrane is significantly reduced at this potential difference, in the same fashion as we already saw for the nerve cells in Chapter 14. However, the calcium diffusion suppresses the membrane

conductivity of potassium, while transporting little charge across the membrane due to much smaller concentration levels of calcium inside and outside of the cell (see Table 15.1). Note that the very low intracellular calcium concentration increases by up to 50% during this period, to a maximum of 1.5 $\mu$mol/L. The calcium diffusion into the cell is notably slower than the diffusion of either sodium or potassium, thus leading to the long delay at this stage.

The continuous change in the calcium concentration eventually causes a reduction of the calcium diffusion rate, favouring a steep increase in the potassium conductivity. Once potassium flows across the membrane into the interstitium, the potential difference quickly drops in the repolarization stage to −80 mV. This last stage is analogous to the repolarization step for regular nerve cells, as discussed in Chapter 14. The electric effect due to the potassium flow is much larger than the effects during calcium diffusion because of the larger potassium concentrations involved, as shown in Table 15.1.

## The Electrocardiogram

The ECG is widely used in medicine to identify disturbances of the heart rhythm, the extent and location of myocardial damage, and the effects of drugs. It is routinely used to monitor patients during surgery.

### The ECG Signal

The long period of the depolarized state of the muscle cells in the heart that we found in Fig. 15.6 is important to the external electric detection of the heart action in electrocardiography. Before we can measure and interpret an electrocardiogram, we have to

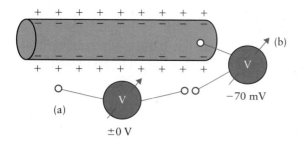

**FIGURE 15.7**

Comparison of a potential measurement (a) along a nerve membrane and (b) across the nerve membrane for a resting nerve cell.

understand how a measurable potential difference outside the cell membrane is formed, such as on a patient's skin.

In Chapter 14, our focus was on the potential difference across a nerve membrane, i.e., an experiment where one electrode is placed inside the axoplasm and the second one outside in the extracellular fluid. This corresponds to the experimental setup of Hodgkin and Huxley in Fig. 14.23. To measure this potential difference requires an intrusive technique—e.g., dissection, in the case of a squid. If such an experiment is done, as illustrated in Fig. 15.7(b), a potential difference of −70 mV is measured for a resting nerve cell. However, if the measurement is done non-intrusively, i.e., with both electrodes placed outside the nerve cell, no potential difference is observed, as indicated for a second voltmeter in Fig. 15.7(a).

The non-intrusive measurement in Fig. 15.7(a) can still lead to the observation of a non-zero potential difference when a nerve impulse passes through the section along which the two electrodes are placed. This is illustrated in Fig. 15.8, which shows in five steps the electric signal that is observed from a passing nerve impulse with two external electrodes placed alongside the nerve cell. In the first panel, the two electrodes are both located ahead of the nerve section currently carrying the nerve impulse (simplified as a grey area). Since the nerve is anatomically and electrically in the same stage at both electrode positions—i.e., the same potential difference applies—a zero potential difference is measured, shown as a red line on the oscilloscope sketched above the nerve.

In the second panel, the travelling nerve impulse has passed the first electrode, but has not reached the second electrode farther downstream. Thus, the electric effect at the two electrodes differs, with positive ions near the electrode where the nerve cell is still at rest and negative ions near the electrode where the nerve impulse has already arrived. A potential differ-

ence is measured between the two electrodes and is seen on the oscilloscope. Whether a positive or negative deviation from the reference line occurs depends on the polarity of the signal. The polarity of the potential difference for a passing nerve impulse in Fig. 15.8 is based on the definition of the electric field direction as a function of the electric charges, as shown in Fig. 13.14, and the connection between the direction of the field vector and the polarity of the potential difference, as illustrated in Fig. 14.5. From Fig. 14.5 we find that the potential difference is lower at the point where negative charges are present. The oscilloscope in the second panel of Fig. 15.8 therefore shows a positive value as it represents the poten-

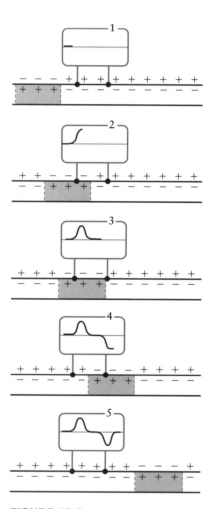

**FIGURE 15.8**

Development of a signal showing a change in the potential difference for a passing nerve impulse with two external electrodes. The location of the nerve impulse is shown as the grey section. The signal on the oscilloscope (above the nerve) is taken between the two electrode positions indicated by green wires. It is positive above and negative below the thin baseline (zero potential). No potential difference is detected in panels 1, 3, and 5, as the nerve depolarization (panel 2) and the nerve repolarization (panel 4) have respectively passed both electrodes.

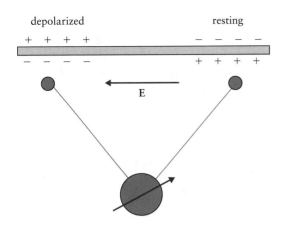

**FIGURE 15.9**

Illustration of the direction of the electric field between two electrodes when a depolarization has passed the first but not the second electrode.

tial at the leading electrode minus the potential at the trailing electrode.

In the third panel of Fig. 15.8 both electrodes are located along the depolarized section of the nerve, causing a zero potential difference. Looking at the fourth and the fifth panels illustrates that the measured potential difference has a peak with opposite polarity as the repolarization passes the electrodes in sequence.

Fig. 15.8 illustrates that the polarity of the signal matters, and that the depolarization and repolarization of a cell lead to signals of opposite polarity. Although a potential difference is a scalar quantity, the polarity and the orientation of the studied nerve tissue allow us to interpret the quantity we observe on the oscilloscope in Fig. 15.8 as the projection of a vector onto the line between the two electrodes. To simplify the later discussion of the ECG we define this vector as the **depolarization vector**.

*The depolarization vector is a vector pointing from depolarized tissue toward polarized tissue.*

It is important to distinguish the depolarization vector from electric field vectors. This is highlighted in Fig. 15.9, which shows a nerve (at the top) and the interstitium (bottom) in which the electric potential measurement takes place. For this nerve, the left part is depolarized (negative excess charges in the interstitium) and the right part is polarized or in the resting state, with positive excess charges in the interstitium. Based on Fig. 13.14, the electric field vector in the interstitium points from the resting/polarized section toward the depolarized section. We see that the depolarization vector and the electric field vector in the interstitium are anti-parallel.

The discussion of Fig. 15.8 illustrates that in general non-zero potential differences occur during nerve depolarization if measured with electrodes outside the nerve tissue itself. This establishes the possibility for non-intrusive measurements of nervous processes in the heart. We also note that the long delay of the repolarization in the muscle cells of the heart improves the measurability, as it guarantees that significant fractions of the tissue are depolarized for extended periods during the heart's cycle. However, Fig. 15.8 indicates that the potential difference measurement depends not only on time but also on the location of the two electrodes relative to each other and relative to the depolarized tissue.

What potential differences do we expect to measure on the patient's skin? Fig. 15.10 illustrates the equipotential lines for the human heart at a given instant in time, specifically during the R-peak of the ECG as defined below. The figure quantifies the absolute potential values in unit mV for each equipotential line shown when determined on the skin of the patient. If we now assume that two electrodes are attached to the skin of the patient, the potential difference measured for the R-peak corresponds to the difference of the potential values shown for the locations of the two electrodes. Comparing the equipotential lines of Fig. 15.10 with those of an electric dipole (solid lines in Fig. 15.11, which is equivalent to Fig. 13.33(c) but rotated by 90°) shows that the dipole is a useful model for approximating the skin surface potential for the heart action.

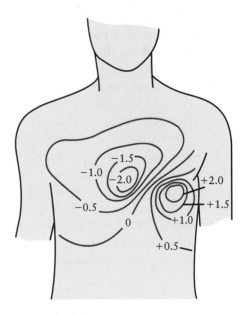

**FIGURE 15.10**

Equipotential lines for the human heart as measured on the skin surface during the R-peak of an ECG. The values given in the figure are in unit mV.

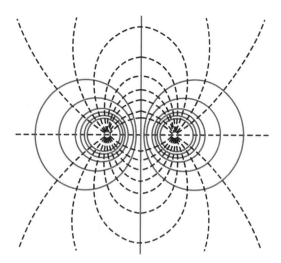

**FIGURE 15.11**

Electric field lines (dashed curves) and equipotential lines (green lines) for an electric dipole with the two charges indicated by open circles. This figure is the same as Fig. 13.33(c) but turned by 90°. Comparison with Fig. 15.10 allows us to approximate the electric field of the heart as a changing dipole field.

## The ECG Method of Einthoven

Fig. 15.10 shows that the measured potential difference depends on the location of the two electrodes attached to the patient's skin. Since equipotential line patterns at other stages of the heart's beating cycle are similar to those of Fig. 15.10, but are rotated due to the change of the direction of the depolarization vector as discussed below, it is important to establish a convention for the placing of the electrodes to ensure a consistent reading on the oscilloscope. The universally used convention is based on the work of Willem **Einthoven**, who developed the ECG in 1906. Einthoven noted that the potential of the heart action can be detected as far away as the limbs. These are therefore chosen as the locations for the electrodes since their positions relative to the heart are fixed.

Einthoven further decided to connect three electrodes to the patient, one each to the right arm, left arm, and left leg. This allowed him to measure three different signals between any pair of electrodes, which are called **leads**. Fig. 15.12(a) illustrates these leads in a conceptual sketch; Fig. 15.12(b) is a historical photograph illustrating Einthoven's original experimental arrangements. The triangle shown overlays a person in front view; i.e., the upper left corner is the lead on the right arm, the lower corner is the lead on the left leg.

The potential difference between electrodes 1 and 2 can be defined in two ways:

$$\text{(I)} \quad \Delta V = V_1 - V_2$$
$$\text{(II)} \quad \Delta V = V_2 - V_1 \qquad \text{[1]}$$

To distinguish between the two cases, we define the term **polarity** for an electrode such that the potential at positive polarity is added and the potential at negative polarity is subtracted. The electrodes cannot be chosen to have a fixed polarity for all three leads in Fig. 15.12 because each lead requires one electrode with positive polarity and one with negative polarity. The standard polarities for the three ECG leads are indicated by the respective + and − signs in Fig. 15.12. Highlighted as a thicker line in the figure is lead II, which is used in the modern application in Fig. 15.13(a) and for which the electrocardiogram for a full cycle of a healthy human heart is shown in Fig. 15.13(b).

We want to understand each of the features of the electrocardiogram in Fig. 15.13(b), and thus follow the electric processes of the heart step by step, as provided in Fig. 15.14. This figure consists of five panels, each illustrating the present direction of depolarization as an arrow overlaying a sketched heart (depolarization vector). Also depicted is a dashed line representing the reference line for lead II, onto which the depolarization vector is projected in this measurement. To the left of each panel is an oscilloscope,

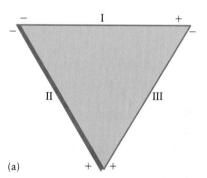

(a)

(b)

**FIGURE 15.12**

(a) Three leads as defined by Einthoven for the ECG measurement. Lead II is selected for further discussion in this chapter. (b) A person connected to an early electrocardiogram machine.

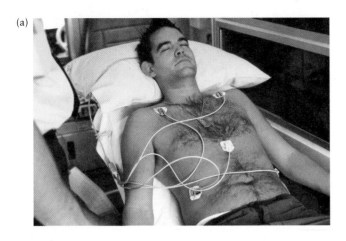

depolarized. The depolarization of the AV-node (lower dot in the sketch of the heart) occurs concurrently. Since the AV-node represents a small amount of tissue, no apparent progress of the depolarization occurs during this stage. This leads to a depolarization vector of zero length, and thus no projected length is present along the direction of lead II. As a consequence, the ECG signal is back to the zero potential line, which is called the PQ-interval. The **PQ-interval** coincides with the depolarization of the AV-node.

The same panel also shows the start of depolarization of the ventricles. The initial depolarization be-

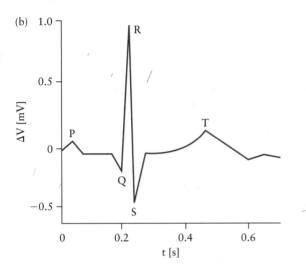

**FIGURE 15.13**

(a) A contemporary application of electrocardiography. (b) The repeating unit of an ECG signal using lead II from Fig. 15.12. Note the P-, Q-, R-, S-, and T-peaks, which are explained in detail in Fig. 15.14.

shown with the ECG signal as it develops at each stage. The figure starts at a time when the heart is fully polarized.

The first panel shows the stage when the SA-node has triggered an impulse and the resulting depolarization progresses to the two atrial chambers. The SA-node is the upper dot on the sketch of the heart. The depolarization vector points in this stage toward the apex of the heart. This direction is not perpendicular to the direction of lead II and, therefore, the projection of the depolarization vector onto the direction of lead II is needed to quantify the measured potential difference. Due to the polarity of lead II, as shown in Fig. 15.12, a positive potential difference is associated with this stage. The resulting positive peak in the ECG is called the **P-peak** and represents the atrial depolarization. This peak lasts for about 0.1 seconds.

The second panel contains two features. First, following the P-peak the two atrial chambers are fully

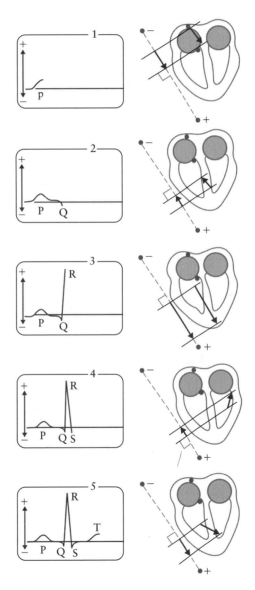

**FIGURE 15.14**

Development of an ECG profile in five steps. The oscilloscope image is shown at the left; the depolarization vector in the heart is shown in the sketches at the right. The dashed line represents lead II as defined by Einthoven. The two solid dots on each heart represent the SA- and AV-nodes, respectively.

gins on the left side of the septum and progresses initially toward the upper end of the heart. Projecting this direction onto lead II causes a negative potential difference (backward projection). This stage is called the **Q-peak,** which corresponds to the depolarization of the upper end of the ventricles.

Once the depolarization of the upper end of the ventricles is complete, the primary direction of the progressing depolarization is toward the apex of the heart. Projecting this depolarization vector in the third panel onto lead II shows that the sign of the measured potential difference switches to a positive value. The resulting peak is particularly strong as a large amount of tissue is present in this part of the ventricles. This peak is called the **R-peak** and represents the major depolarization of the ventricles. Note that the equipotential lines during the R-peak are shown in Fig. 15.10.

Not all parts of the heart are depolarized when the depolarization of the lower part of the ventricles is complete. A small part of the back left side of the heart (posterobasal region) depolarizes after the R-peak is complete, as shown in the fourth panel. Since the respective depolarization vector is associated with a projection onto lead II, which has again turned in direction, a second peak with negative potential difference is obtained. This peak is called the **S-peak** and represents the completion of the ventricle depolarization. The Q- and S-peaks are smaller than the R-peak because a smaller amount of tissue is affected by their respective depolarization.

The last panel shows the repolarization of the ventricles (note the $Ca^{2+}$ transport–related time delay discussed above). The repolarization starts at the apex of the heart and progresses upward. This constitutes the opposite direction to the R-peak. However, we also have a reversed process: a repolarization instead of a depolarization. Since we define the direction of the vector we project onto lead II as a depolarization vector, the inversion of its direction must be taken into account. Thus, the repolarization leads again to the measurement of a positive potential difference. The corresponding feature in the ECG is the **T-peak,** which represents the repolarization of the ventricles.

Now the repolarization of the heart is complete, and a new cycle can begin. Note that we did not identify a feature in the ECG that corresponds to the repolarization of the atrial chambers. This is due to the fact that the respective signal is overshadowed by the much stronger **QRS structure,** indicating that the repolarization of the atrial chambers occurs less than 0.2 seconds after the onset of the P-peak.

*P-peak: Atrial depolarization*

*PQ-interval: Depolarization of the AV-node*

*Q-peak: Depolarization of upper end of ventricles*

*R-peak: Major depolarization of the ventricles*

*S-peak: Completion of ventricle depolarization*

*T-peak: Repolarization of the ventricles*

# Medical Use of the ECG

The electric system of the heart is not a fixed entity. For example, the heart rate changes significantly during the heart's lifetime, as illustrated in Table 15.2. Further changes can be inherited or caused by disease. Fig. 15.15 shows typical examples of ECG diagrams for abnormal hearts. The QRS structure is widened in Fig. 15.15(a), indicating an enlarged heart. In Fig. 15.15(b) the usual relationship between the P-peak and the QRS structure is lost. This points toward a blockage of the electric conduction path between the SA-node and the AV-node. Finally, the diagram in Fig. 15.15(c) is characterized by the absence of the P-peak and an irregular spacing between QRS structures. This occurs for patients with a condition called fibrillation.

A **cardiac pacemaker** is an external device that is electrically attached to the heart (at the right ventricle) to provide a steady-state heart beat rate and thereby override the natural electric activity of the SA-node. Such a device is introduced when the natural activity of the SA-node is either weakened or irregular, e.g., due to old age or disease. The device itself consists of a capacitor that charges up to a certain potential and then automatically discharges.

**TABLE 15.2**

**Number of heart beats per minute for a resting healthy person as a function of age**

| Age | Cycles/min |
| --- | --- |
| Newborn | 130 |
| 2 years | 110 |
| 8 years | 90 |
| Adolescent /adult | 70 |
| Senior | 60 |

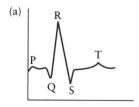

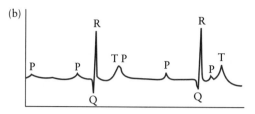

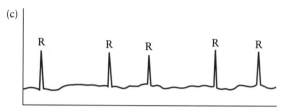

If the heart maintains its natural beating rate, the capacitor never charges fully and therefore does not discharge, because the impulse rate of the pacemaker (usually 60 beats/minute) is somewhat slower than the natural heart beat rate.

**FIGURE 15.15**

Three cases of ECG signals for an abnormal heart. (a) The QRS structure is broadened (b) the sequence between the P-peak and the QRS structure is lost, and (c) an absence of the P-peak and an irregular spacing of QRS structures.

# PART 4

# TAMASO MA JYOTIR

The next five chapters centre on the physical concept of waves. Waves introduce two new elements into our discussion of natural phenomena: the physical dualism between corpuscle and wave that we fully explore in the last part of this book, and the contrast between the sensitivity and reliability of our hearing and vision and our everyday lack of familiarity with the underlying principles that reveal the many ways in which these senses can be deceived.

Sound waves are introduced in two chapters, based on mechanical vibrations in a compressible medium. Thereafter, we explore light in two steps, first with a simplified geometric ray model that allows us to introduce reflection and refraction, and then as electromagnetic waves, needed to understand polarization and colours. In the latter approach magnetism is required as an additional physical concept, and we develop it in close analogy to electricity.

*Tamaso ma jyotir gamaya* means "lead me from darkness to light." It is part of an often-quoted Sanskrit verse, published originally in the philosophical texts of the Upanishads. The theme of **light** is ever-present in our lives, and is particularly celebrated in India with Diwali, the festival of lights. It also emphasizes our dependence on the acoustic and visual perception of the environment in which we live.

# CHAPTER 16

## ELASTIC TISSUE
### Elasticity and Vibrations

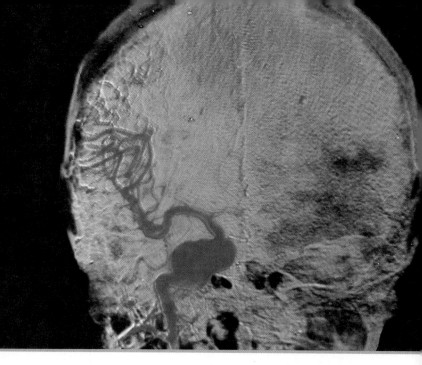

The rigid-object model we introduced in Chapters 4 and 5 is insufficient to describe many fundamental properties of extended objects, such as stretching, twisting, deformation, and rupture. In the current chapter, two more general models are provided: the elastic and the plastic object. An elastic object responds to a stress (a force acting on the surface of an extended object) with a strain (a change in size or shape of the object) that is linearly proportional to the stress. This linear relation is called Hooke's law. Examples include elongation in response to tensile stress, twisting as a result of shear stress, and compression due to hydraulic stress. Deformation of objects are called plastic when the stress exceeds the range of applicability of Hooke's law.

The most important property of elastic systems is their dynamic behaviour when released from a mechanical non-equilibrium state: the system undergoes sinusoidal vibrations about its equilibrium state in response to a restoring force that is linear in the displacement. The elastic potential energy is introduced as a new form of potential energy for such systems. It depends quadratically on the displacement from the equilibrium position.

We discuss three examples: the vibration of an object attached to a spring, which is a useful model for intramolecular vibrations; the pendulum, which is suitable to model bipedal walking; and a freely moving piston confining a gas. The latter system will allow us to discuss acoustic waves in the next chapter.

We continue in this chapter where we left off with the discussion of rigid objects in Chapter 5. In that chapter we found that the rigid object is a useful model when we want to describe rotations. It was an important extension of the previously introduced model of a point-like object because it allowed us to describe and quantify the basic processes of vertebrate locomotion.

Like any other physical model, the rigid-object model contains restrictions. The rigid object cannot change its shape or volume, vibrate, bend, or rupture. If any of these processes is important for life science applications, then we need to extend the rigid-object model once more. The objective of the current chapter is first to establish that these processes are relevant and then to introduce two new models that go beyond the rigid object: the elastic and the plastic object.

Mechanical processes in our body beyond rotation are easily established in a self-test. Push your right index finger into the skin of your lower left arm. You feel a localized force acting on your arm and you observe a deformation of the skin; the stronger you push, the further the skin is displaced. The skin reshapes into its original form when you withdraw your finger. The reversible deformation of the skin is an example of an elastic response to an external force. Plastic response occurs when the forces are larger. For example, bone fractures are the result of excessive forces acting on our skeleton.

The scientific relevance of these observations stems from the fact that corresponding microscopic processes exist in which the system responds elastically or plastically to external forces. We illustrate this with the intended operation of muscles (elastic response) and torn muscles (plastic response). In Fig. 3.2, we introduced the sarcomere as the unit that can actively contract when the myosin filaments slide toward the two terminal Z-discs along the actin filaments. The sarcomere can also be stretched passively by the action of an antagonistic muscle. Fig. 16.1 shows a simplified graph of the dependence of the contractile (active) force a sarcomere can exert after being stretched to a given length $l$. The length $l$ of the sarcomere is defined as the distance between two adjacent Z-discs. In the lower scale of the ordinate it is given as $l/l_{average}$, in which $l_{average}$ is the average (or resting) length of a muscle with $l_{average} = 2.1 \ \mu m$. The values are percentage values. The force in turn is displayed along the abscissa as a value relative to the maximum force the sarcomere can exert. The maximum force is available when a sarcomere is at its resting length.

The graph allows us to highlight some important features of the active muscle force: as the sarcomere length varies, the overlap of the myosin and actin filaments varies as well. As shown in the insets along the curve, the variation of overlap of actin and myosin filaments causes a loss of muscle force when operating far from the resting length. When the

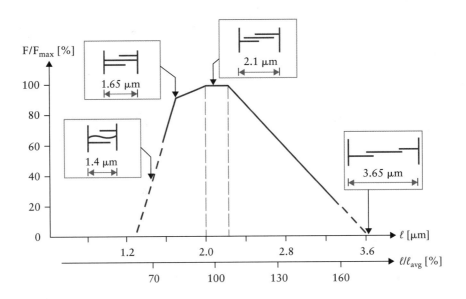

## FIGURE 16.1

The active muscle force is shown as a function of the sarcomere length. The force is given as a fraction of the maximum force a muscle can exert when it is at its average length $l_{average} = 2.1 \ \mu m$. The sarcomere length is given as an absolute value $l$ in unit $\mu m$ (top abscissa) and as a length relative to the resting length $l/l_{average}$ in % (bottom abscissa). For several specific sarcomere lengths the overlap of the myosin and actin filaments is illustrated in the inset boxes. These insets indicate the origin of loss of active muscle force when the muscle is stretched too far (too weak overlap between actin and myosin filaments) and when the muscle contracts too far (myosin filaments collide with Z-discs).

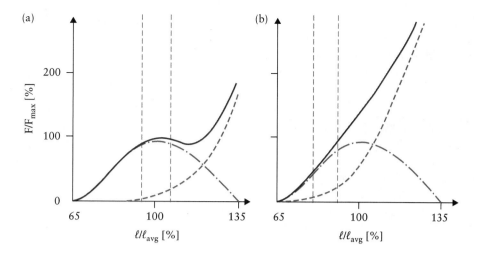

## FIGURE 16.2

Active (dash-dotted) and passive (dashed) components of the muscle force for (a) skeletal muscles, and (b) the heart muscle. The figures show the force, relative to the maximum force. It is plotted as a function of the muscle length, relative to the muscle length at the point where the muscle exerts a maximum active force. The red lines show the total force, which is the sum of the active force and the passive stretching force. The two vertical dashed lines indicate the normal operating regime of the muscle. The dash-dotted curve in part (a) is equivalent to the curve shown in Fig. 16.1. Note that the passive stretching force acts as a protection of the muscle, preventing an excessive stretching of the tissue.

sarcomere shortens to less than 1.65 $\mu$m in length, the myosin filaments touch the two adjacent Z-discs. This provides a physical limitation, as muscle contraction by more than 20 to 25% is not practically possible. When the sarcomere in turn is passively stretched to a length of 2.8 $\mu$m and more (i.e., when the muscle is stretched to 130% or more of its resting length), its ability to contract is significantly reduced as the overlap of the actin and myosin filaments is reduced. If there were no counteracting process, this would be dangerous for the muscle as its own ability to withstand the stretching through contraction is weakened.

The curves in Fig. 16.2(a) illustrate how the muscle is protected against overstretching. The dash-dotted curve shows again the active force the muscle can exert when stretched to various lengths (shown relative to the resting length). This curve corresponds to the curve in Fig. 16.1. Note that you find both Figs. 16.1 and 16.2 in the physiological literature; Fig. 16.2 is a plot of the actual forces, and Fig. 16.1 is used for conceptual discussions of muscle action. Comparing Figs. 16.1 and 16.2 we note the benefit of the simplified graph: the straight line segments in Fig. 16.1 are easier to quantify than the curved, dashed-dotted function in Fig. 16.2. Whether it is sufficient to use Fig. 16.1 or whether it is necessary to use Fig. 16.2 depends on the specific purpose or argument we want to make.

Fig. 16.2 shows a second curve applicable to the sarcomere. The dashed curve is the passive stretching force, i.e., the force by which the muscle tissue resists being stretched. This passive stretching force protects the muscle against being extended to a length from which it can no longer contract by its own action. The net force a muscle applies to oppose being stretched is shown in Fig. 16.2 as a red line. This net force is the sum of the active and passive forces. Muscles cannot be overstretched, because the passive force limits the stretching at large values of length $l$.

Fig. 16.2(b) illustrates that the same observations apply to muscles with other functions than skeletal muscles. For the heart muscle the passive force counteracting its stretching is even more dominant than in the case of a skeletal muscle. The total force acting on the tissue (red curve) is again a combination of the active force (dash-dotted curve) and the passive stretching force (dashed curve).

Figs. 16.1 and 16.2 illustrate two points. First, a muscle is not a rigid object, as it can contract or be stretched. Second, when a muscle is stretched beyond its average length, a force counteracts against further stretching. This force increases with increasing length of the muscle; i.e., it acts to restore the original length of the muscle. Thus, it is necessary to extend the rigid-object model to allow for deformations as a result of external forces. The ability of biological materials to be deformed and the response to the deformation are important to prevent damage to tissues. The response to a deformation is a force that aims at restoring the resting state of the tissue. We call this the **elastic behaviour** of tissue. However, external forces may exceed a threshold beyond which the restoring force can no longer prevent tissue damage. Once this threshold is passed, **permanent plastic deformations** occur that require medical attention.

**Concept Question 16.1**

In Chapters 2 to 5 we discussed mechanical concepts using the assumption that forces are position independent. (a) Can we use this assumption for the force shown in Fig. 16.1? (b) Can we use it for the forces shown in Fig. 16.2?

ANSWER TO PART (a): The force shown in Fig. 16.1 is only position-independent when the sarcomere length lies in the interval 2.0 μm to 2.2 μm.

ANSWER TO PART (b): The forces shown in Fig. 16.2 are position-dependent throughout the accessible range. Note that Fig. 16.1 is a simplification of the dash-dotted curve in Fig. 16.2(a). Thus, the answer to part (a) is correct only because of our choosing to simplify in that figure. In practice, forces in muscles cannot be treated as position independent, not even close to their resting length.

Elastic behaviour of tissues can lead to vibration, which is a form of motion we haven't discussed in earlier chapters. Note that vibration did not result in our earlier self-experiment involving pushing the skin on the lower arm. Two reasons prevent the skin from vibrating: it is too soft, and it is too well connected to the tissues below. However, the human body contains other systems that can vibrate: the vocal cords to create our voice, and the eardrum to couple sound into the middle and inner ear. Vibration is discussed later in this chapter.

# Elasticity

The quantitative description of elastic behaviour starts with a more specific look at the connection between an external force and the resulting deformation. We define **stress** as a force exerted per unit area of surface on an extended object. The stress leads to a **strain**, which is the relative change in the size of the object. We distinguish three types of deformation based on the type of strain: a change in the length of an object is called stretching, a change in an angle of the extended object is called twisting, and a change in the volume of an object is called a compression or an expansion. Each of these types of strain is caused by a different form of stress. Tensile stress leads to

stretching, shearing stress leads to twisting, and hydraulic stress causes expansion or compression.

## Tensile Stress and Stretching

**Stretching** of an extended object is illustrated in Fig. 16.3. Stretching in the vertical direction is achieved by two opposite forces, $\mathbf{F}_1$ and $\mathbf{F}_2$. The volume of the object, and therefore its density, are conserved in this process since the width and depth of the object are reduced simultaneously with the vertical stretching. This process is possible only for solids and liquids.

We quantify the terms *stress* and *strain* for Fig. 16.3. Strain is the relative change in length, expressed as $\Delta l / l$ with $\Delta l = l_{\text{final}} - l_{\text{initial}}$. Thus, strain is a dimensionless quantity. The stress leading to this stretching is called **tensile stress** and is given by $F/A$ with $F$ the magnitude of force $\mathbf{F}_1$. $A$ is the area of the object surface on which force $\mathbf{F}_1$ acts. $F/A$ has unit Pa, the same as the unit of pressure. The two forces in Fig. 16.3 are related by Newton's first law due to the condition of mechanical equilibrium: $\mathbf{F}_2 = -\mathbf{F}_1$. Note that this is not an application of Newton's third law, as both forces act on the same object!

We expect an elongation of an object with a tensile stress. The object stretches to a certain length at which the restoring force within the object balances the external forces, establishing a new mechanical equilibrium for the system. We call the response of the object **elastic** if the strain and stress are proportional to each

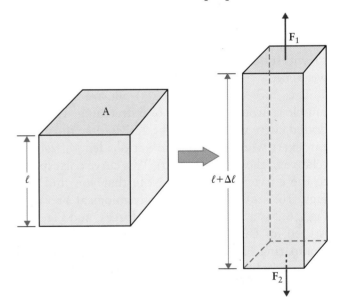

**FIGURE 16.3**

Sketch of a stretching deformation of an extended object, chosen to be initially a cube. Two equal but opposite forces pull on opposing surfaces of area *A*. The stress |**F**|/*A* leads to a strain in the form of a length increase from *l* to *l* + Δ*l*.

### Young's modulus for various materials

| Material | $Y$ (Pa) |
|---|---|
| Steel | $2 \times 10^{11}$ |
| Douglas fir wood | $1.3 \times 10^{10}$ |
| Compact bone (e.g., femur) | $1-2 \times 10^{10}$ |
| Teeth | $7 \times 10^9 - 1.5 \times 10^{10}$ |
| Cartilage | $1-4 \times 10^7$ |
| Tendon | $2 \times 10^7 - 1 \times 10^6$ |
| Rubber | $7 \times 10^6 - 2 \times 10^7$ |
| Blood vessels | $1.2-4.0 \times 10^5$ |

other, i.e., when the length change of the object increases linearly with the stress:

$$\frac{F}{A} = Y \cdot \frac{\Delta l}{l} \qquad [1]$$

The proportionality factor $Y$ is called **Young's modulus** (named for Thomas Young), with unit Pa. Since this formula is used frequently in the description of mechanical properties of solids and liquids, new variables are introduced: $\sigma$ for the stress, with $\sigma = F/A$; and $\varepsilon$ for the strain, with $\varepsilon = \Delta l/l$. With these variables, Eq. [1] is written as:

$$\sigma = Y \cdot \varepsilon \qquad [2]$$

A large value of Young's modulus, e.g., for steel, means that even a large force acting on a piece of material leads to only a small length increase. In turn, small values of Young's modulus, e.g., for a blood vessel, mean that even small forces cause a large length variation. We call materials with large Young's moduli **strong materials** and materials with small Young's moduli **soft materials**. Table 16.1 lists several values for Young's moduli, primarily comparing biological materials.

---

**Concept Question 16.2**

**What conditions apply to Young's modulus $Y$ when we say that the stress depends linearly on the strain in Eq. [2]?**

ANSWER: The answer is not simply that Eq. [2] is linear, because the strain occurs with an exponent 1 on the right-hand side of the equation; i.e., $\sigma = Y \cdot \varepsilon^n$ with $n = 1$. This is a necessary condition because $n \neq 1$ means that an *explicit* non-linearity exists. $n = 1$ is not sufficient,

---

however, because Eq. [2] does not rule out an *implicit* dependence of $Y$ on the strain, $Y(\varepsilon)$.

In turn, requiring that $Y$ be a constant is too severe a restriction. Indeed, $Y$ does depend on the temperature and is therefore only a materials constant. Thus, the proper way to ensure the linearity of Eq. [2] is to require $Y \neq f(\varepsilon, \sigma)$, i.e., that the Young modulus does not depend on the strain or stress.

Extensive stretching usually doesn't obey Eq. [2]. If we still use Eq. [2], then Young's modulus must become strain-dependent. Thus, an **elastic limit** for the strain is introduced that describes the strain threshold beyond which Eq. [2] is no longer applicable. For a larger strain the object encounters permanent plastic deformations. The elastic limit is discussed later in this section.

## Shearing Stress and Twisting

A different type of deformation results in Fig. 16.4: two equal but opposite forces, $\mathbf{F}_1$ and $\mathbf{F}_2$, are applied tangentially to two opposite faces of an extended

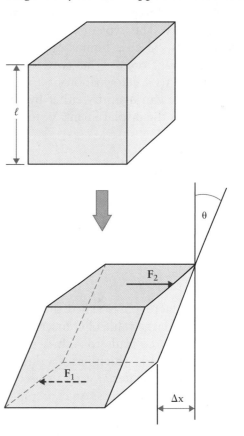

**FIGURE 16.4**

Sketch of a twisting deformation of an extended object, chosen to be initially a cube. Two tangential forces acting on opposing surfaces cause a change in the angle $\theta$. This change is expressed as a function of the lengths $\Delta x$ and $l$.

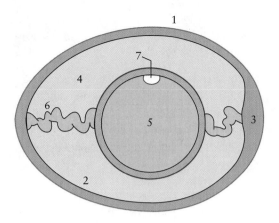

**FIGURE 16.5**

Twisting motion in a chicken egg. The yolk (5) and the germ disk (7) are attached to the inner shell membrane (2) with a pair of elastic cords (6). These allow the germ disk to remain at the top of the yolk at all times because the centre of mass of the combined yolk/germ disk lies off-centre away from the germ disk. This allows for a small net torque due to gravity when the germ disk is rotated sideways. Other components of the egg are: (1) shell, (3) air sac, and (4) egg white.

object; i.e., the force vectors lie parallel to the surfaces they act on, as shown in the figure. To maintain mechanical equilibrium, i.e., to avoid a torque acting on the object, additional forces must be applied to hold the object stationary. This type of deformation can occur only in solids, because liquids and gases cannot sustain tangential forces. The two forces shown in Fig. 16.4 lead to a deformation of a rectangular prism, which we can quantify either by the angle $\theta$ or by the ratio of the displacement $\Delta x$ to the width of the object $l$:

$$\tan \theta = \frac{\Delta x}{l} \qquad [3]$$

In analogy to the stretching case, a linear relation between stress and strain is observed for small values of $\Delta x$:

$$\frac{F}{A} = G \frac{\Delta x}{l} \qquad [4]$$

The proportionality factor $G$ is called the **shear modulus**, with unit Pa. A large value of $G$ means that even a large tangential force leads to only a small twisting. An example is steel, which has a value of $G = 8 \times 10^{10}$ Pa. In turn, a material with a small $G$ value is easily twisted by small forces. An example is cartilage with $G = 2.5 \times 10^7$ Pa.

An interesting application of the twisting motion is illustrated in Fig. 16.5 for the **chicken egg**. The egg yolk (5) is connected to the germ disk (7), from which the chicken develops. It is beneficial for the developing chicken to have the germ disk directed up-

ward at all times because the warmth of the body of the breeding hen flows into the egg from above. Rotation of the egg in the nest should not allow the germ disk to turn to the side or facing downward.

To stabilize the germ disk in the upward position, the yolk is connected to the inside of the egg shell (2) as shown. The spiral-shaped cords (6) have a very small shear modulus, allowing the yolk to turn easily about the longitudinal axis of the egg. The germ disk has a lower density than the yolk. Therefore, the centre of mass of the suspended yolk/germ disk unit, floating in the egg white (4), lies off-centre away from the germ disk. This provides a small net torque due to the gravitational force, enough to rotate the germ disk always to the top.

## Hydraulic Stress and Compression

A third type of deformation is possible for solids, liquids, and confined gases: a compression or expansion is obtained by applying a force of magnitude |F| perpendicular to the surface of an extended object from all sides, as illustrated in Fig. 16.6. In this case the stress not only carries the unit of pressure, Pa, but physically is a pressure. The strain is defined as the relative volume change, $\Delta V/V$.

An elastic deformation is given when the stress and strain are related linearly to each other:

$$p = -B \frac{\Delta V}{V} \qquad [5]$$

The negative sign is introduced in Eq. [5] to ensure that the coefficient $B$ is a positive number. It is needed since an increasing external pressure leads to a decreasing volume. The coefficient $B$ is a materials constant that we call **bulk modulus**. It has the unit Pa. A typical value for the bulk modulus of a solid material is $B = 1.6 \times 10^{11}$ Pa, which is the value for steel. Liquids have only slightly lower values; e.g., for water we find $B = 2.1 \times 10^9$ Pa. Gases in turn have

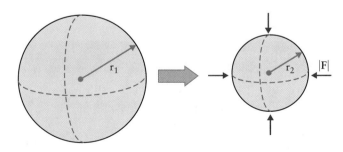

**FIGURE 16.6**

Sketch of a compression of a spherical extended object due to external forces of uniform magnitude |F|. The volume change is based on the radius change of the sphere.

significantly lower values as they are easily compressed. It is important to distinguish that the bulk modulus describes the change in volume of a material (with unit m³) while Young's modulus describes the change in length of a material (with unit m).

The bulk modulus is used to define the **compressibility** of a material. The compressibility is given by $1/B$; i.e., a material with a large bulk modulus has a small compressibility.

---

**Concept Question 16.3**

Using Eq. [5], which statement is wrong? (A) The relative volume change $\Delta V/V$ cannot depend linearly on pressure due to the negative sign on the right-hand side. (B) The compressibility is a materials constant. (C) The compressibility of a material is not linearly related to its bulk modulus. (D) The absolute volume change of an object, $\Delta V$, alone does not reveal anything about the elastic properties of the object. (E) Eq. [5] is not a linear relation if the compressibility depends on the absolute pressure.

ANSWER: Choice (A). In a linear relation the slope can be positive or negative.

---

## Plastic Deformations

The three elastic relations we introduced in Eqs. [1], [4], and [5] can be generalized in the form of Eq. [2]. An elastic deformation is reversible because the object resumes its original shape when the stress is removed.

We know from experience that Eq. [2] does not always hold. Only minor forces have to be applied to deform play dough permanently. This deformation is irreversible because the strain does not return to zero when the stress on the material is removed.

Stronger materials also respond to a large stress in an irreversible fashion, e.g., when a bone breaks. Fig. 16.7 shows the entire range of the stress–strain relation for a medium-strength steel. For low stress values a linear relation is observed (this elastic part of the curve is extended in a dashed line). As the stress is increased beyond the linear regime, microscopic structural alterations in the steel take place leading to a significant strain increase, often occurring in sudden bursts (3). In this regime a permanent **plastic deformation** of the material takes place. Eventually the material can no longer withstand the stress, passing through its **ultimate strength point** (4). Beyond this point the material approaches the rupture

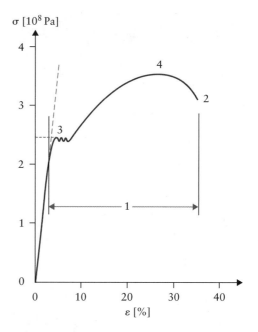

**FIGURE 16.7**

Stress–strain relation of medium-strength steel. The stress is linearly proportional to the strain for strain values up to about 3%. This linear regime is indicated by the dashed line. The plastic deformation regime (1) is more complex. Sudden bursts of strain increase indicate that structural changes occur within the material (3). The maximum strength is reached at a strain of about 28% (4). The ultimate strength is reached near a strain value of 40%, at which value the material ruptures (2).

point (2) quickly, without need for a further increase of the stress.

*A material is called elastic when it responds to external forces (stress) with a linear deformation (strain). Elastic deformations are reversible. A material is called plastic when it responds to a stress in a non-linear fashion. Plastic deformations are irreversible.*

---

**Concept Question 16.4**

Fig. 16.8 shows the stress–strain relation of compact bone. (a) Fig. 16.7 for steel shows only positive values for stress and strain. Does it make sense for Fig. 16.8 to show also negative values? (b) The red curve in Fig. 16.8 ends both at the lower left and at the upper right. Is there a physical meaning to this?

ANSWER TO PART (a): Yes. Positive and negative strain values mean physically different alterations, with positive strains representing stretching and negative strains a uniaxial compression. The corresponding stress intervals are called tensile stress (positive branch) and compressive stress (negative branch).

---

## Concept Question 16.4 (*continued*)

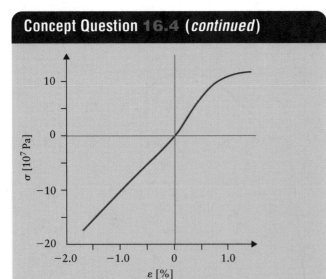

**FIGURE 16.8**

Stress–strain relation for compact bone. The graph includes both tensile stress, when the bone is stretched, and compressive stress, when the bone is compressed. The two branches of the curve differ slightly, but compact bone reaches its rupture point very quickly for either stress at strains of less than ±2%.

ANSWER TO PART (b): The curve ends in these points because the bone has then reached its ultimate strength points, in the same fashion as discussed for steel in Fig. 16.7. When the stress exceeds the corresponding values the bone gets crushed or splinters.

## ● EXAMPLE 16.1

We use again Fig. 16.8 for the stress–strain relation of compact bone. In an adult male the femur has a minimum diameter of about 3 cm. At what force along its axial direction will the femur break?

*Solution:* We read the maximum tensile and **compressive stress** from Fig. 16.8. Rupturing occurs where the curves end at each side. For bone this occurs at strains below 2%, which means that bones safely can be stretched only very little. The maximum compressive stress is $-1.7 \times 10^8$ Pa, and the maximum tensile stress is $1.2 \times 10^8$ Pa. The corresponding forces are obtained from the definition of the stress, $\sigma = F/A$, when rewritten as $F = \sigma \cdot A$. In this formula the cross-sectional area of the bone is identified as the area onto which the force acts. The area $A$ is calculated by assuming a cylindrical shape of the bone with a circular cross-section of radius $r$. With $r = 1.5$ cm, we find $A = r^2 \cdot \pi = 7.0 \times 10^{-4}$ m$^2$. The compressive force then follows as:

$$F_{\text{compressive}} = (1.7 \times 10^8 \text{ Pa})(7.0 \times 10^{-4} \text{ m}^2)$$
$$= 1.2 \times 10^5 \text{ N} \qquad [6]$$

Note that we used the absolute value of the maximum compressive stress because we seek the magnitude of the compression force. The tensile force is found in the same fashion:

$$F_{\text{tensile}} = (1.2 \times 10^8 \text{ Pa})(7.0 \times 10^{-4} \text{ m}^2)$$
$$= 8.4 \times 10^4 \text{ N} \qquad [7]$$

To obtain an idea of what these values mean, we convert the tensile force into a corresponding weight (using $F = m \cdot g$): the femur can withstand the pull of a mass of up to 8.5 tons (8600 kg). Although this is a large value the corresponding forces unfortunately do occur, even for only a fraction of a second—e.g., during a fall onto a hard surface.

Some systems don't display a linear stress–strain regime at all. The most prominent case is **blood vessel tissue**. Fig. 16.9 shows a light micrograph of a cross-section through a muscular artery. The thick wall is required to carry blood under pressure. It consists of three layers: the innermost *tunica intima* surrounds the lumen (white). It consists of a fine elastic sheet (dark purple, convoluted), which we call the *internal elastic lamina*. The centre layer, the thick *tunica media,* is mainly composed of smooth muscle fibres (purple) interspersed with a few connective collagen fibres (blue). The external *tunica adventitia* (blue) consists mainly of connective tissue.

Fig. 16.10 shows the stress–strain curve for the tissue material of large arteries. Blood vessel tissue contains two main structural materials, elastin and collagen. Their elastic properties are additive, leading

**FIGURE 16.9**

The three layers of a blood vessel wall shown in cross-section. The innermost layer is elastic thanks to a fine elastic sheet (dark purple, convoluted). Collagen strengthens the centre layer.

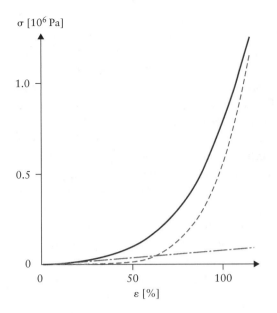

**FIGURE 16.10**

Stress–strain relation for blood vessel tissue. Note the absence of a linear regime. Blood vessels contain two components that play a role in its deformation properties: elastin, which has a small bulk modulus (dash-dotted curve), and collagen, with a bulk modulus that increases with strain (dashed curve). The two contributions combine to the red curve, which then represents the response of the actual blood vessel.

to a continuously curved dependence of the stress on the strain. Contractile smooth muscle cells are a third component of blood vessel walls, but do not contribute to their mechanical properties.

Elastin is a protein that determines the deformation of an artery at small stress values with its small bulk modulus. Collagen fibrils with a larger bulk modulus dominate when the strain increases beyond 25%. The collagen is slack while the artery is narrow, but stiffens notably when the artery widens.

We consider two physiological applications of this type of response to deforming forces in arteries: the Windkessel effect of the aorta and the development of aneurysms.

## WINDKESSEL EFFECT OF THE AORTA

The ability of a blood vessel to deform under stress is used in the aorta to buffer blood flow variations that result from the pulsatile operation of the heart. The Windkessel effect is illustrated in Fig. 16.11. Fig. 16.12(b) shows the aorta with its bend of almost 180° just beyond the heart. This bend must accommodate the largest fraction of the rush of blood ejected by the heart during each heart beat. When blood rushes into the aorta the blood pressure increases, as shown at the centre of Fig. 16.11. The pressure increases at stages 1 and 3 represent an in-

creased stress on the aorta wall. The aorta wall responds, as predicted by Fig. 16.10, with a widening. An enlarged aorta lumen accommodates the blood volume increase without an excessive blood pressure increase.

As blood now starts to flow from the bend its pressure drops. The resulting decrease in strain in the aorta wall contributes a forward push to the blood to overcome its flow resistance, as illustrated in stages 2 and 4 in Fig. 16.11. Note that blood cannot flow back to the heart at this point because the heart valve has closed.

The elasticity of blood vessel tissue reduces with age, causing the aorta to stiffen. This process is called **arteriosclerosis**. The age-related change in the

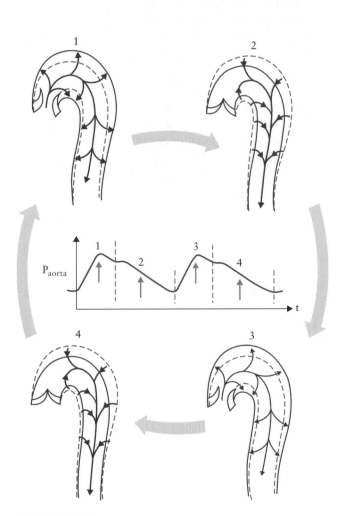

**FIGURE 16.11**

The Windkessel effect of the aorta. The aortic bend was already noted in Fig. 12.13. Shown here at the centre is a plot of the blood pressure in the aorta $p_{aorta}$ as a function of time for two heart beats. When blood is ejected from the heart (frames 1 and 3) the blood vessel tissue responds to the pressure increase (stress) by widening (strain). As the heart valve closes (at the left end of the aortic bend), we observe a lowered pressure (frames 2 and 4). This reduction of the stress leads to a contraction of the vessel (strain reduction), which pushes the blood downstream.

elasticity leads also to changes of the average blood pressure as indicated in Table 11.1.

## ANEURYSMS

The stress–strain curve shown in Fig. 16.10 applies to healthy blood vessel tissue. If a blood vessel is weakened, the tissue responds to the same blood pressure with a larger strain, as shown by the blue curve in Fig. 16.12(a).

We can predict the development of an aneurysm—i.e., the ballooning of the blood vessel at such a weakened spot in the cardiovascular system—by combining Fig. 16.12(a) with the fluid flow concepts of Chapter 12: the horizontal line in Fig. 16.12(a) indicates a given stress as exerted by a typical blood pressure on the blood vessel tissue. A healthy blood vessel opens as a result of this stress to its typical lumen value (red curve in Fig. 16.12(a)). At a weakened spot, a larger strain means that the blood vessel widens further locally (blue curve).

The equation of continuity then predicts that blood flow slows in the weakened section due to its large cross-section. This slowing causes a local increase in the blood pressure as described by Bernoulli's law. With the blood pressure rising locally, an increasing stress on the blood vessel occurs. We see from Fig. 16.12(a) that this leads yet again to a larger strain, i.e., a further widening of the vessel. This is called a positive feedback loop, which further enhances the size of the blood vessel and therefore has a negative effect on the affected patient.

Blood vessels can widen significantly due to this process. The widened section of the blood vessel is then called an **aneurysm**; typical examples for the aorta are shown in Fig. 16.12(b). Such aneurysms may eventually rupture, releasing blood into the adjacent tissue. Depending on where this happens the result may be fatal, e.g., in the brain. An aneurysm in the brain is shown in the figure at the beginning of this chapter. The figure is a false-colour arteriograph (angiograph) of the rear view of a human head. The aneurysm is the red, balloon-like swelling in the lower left part of the image. Arteriography is an X-ray examination technique. X-rays are discussed in Chapter 22.

Modern non-surgical treatment techniques include insertion of a curling platinum wire through a 0.7-mm-thick catheter into the expanded section to prevent further stress buildup in the aneurysm. The procedure is illustrated in Fig. 16.13. The wire is transported through a cannula along a blood vessel—e.g., from the thigh to the brain, as a surgical opening in the skull would be too dangerous for the patient.

(a)

(b)

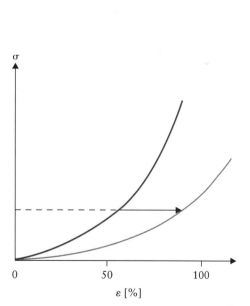

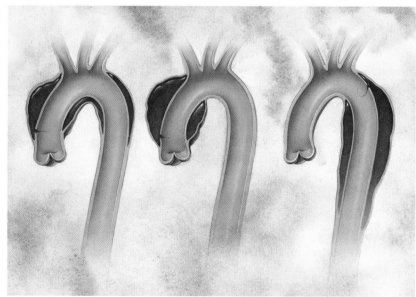

## FIGURE 16.12

(a) Stress–strain curves for healthy (red curve) and weakened blood vessel tissue (blue curve). The healthy tissue curve corresponds to the red curve shown in Fig. 16.10. The horizontal arrow indicates the excess strain for the weakened tissue in comparison to adjacent healthy tissue at a particular stress. (b) Typical aneurysms of the aorta. Usually an aortic aneurysm is a dissected aneurysm, i.e., a case in which the wall of the aorta partially ruptures and blood accumulates within the artery wall.

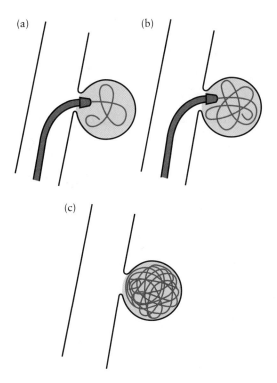

**FIGURE 16.13**

Non-surgical treatment of an aneurysm in the brain. A 0.7-mm-wide catheter is inserted through an artery in the thigh. A platinum wire is pushed through the catheter and fills the ballooned section of the blood vessel like a skein of wool.

## ● EXAMPLE 16.2

In 1934, Charles William Beebe of the New York Zoological Society made a record descent to a depth of 923 m into the ocean off Bermuda. For this descent, he and a second researcher used a steel sphere of 1.5 m diameter with a wall thickness of 5 cm (**bathysphere**). The weight of passengers and instruments was 4900 N. The bathysphere was suspended from a steel rope with a diameter of 3 cm ($\rho_{steel} = 7.5$ g/cm$^3$). What is the maximum depth to which the bathysphere could have been lowered before the rope ruptured? Use for the tensile stress at the ultimate strength point of steel $\sigma = 6.87 \times 10^8$ Pa, which is about 5 times the value of bone material.

*Solution:* We calculate first the total weight suspended from the steel rope. This includes the instruments, the passengers, and the bathysphere. The weight of the bathysphere is due to its steel wall of thickness $d$. With the surface of a sphere, $A = 4 \cdot \pi \cdot r^2$, the volume of the steel wall is $V = 4 \cdot \pi \cdot r^2 \cdot d$. This allows us to write for its weight:

$$W_{bathysphere} = (4 \cdot \pi \cdot r^2 \cdot d)\rho \cdot g$$

$$= 4 \cdot \pi (0.75\,\text{m})^2 (0.05\,\text{m})\left(9.8\,\frac{\text{m}}{\text{s}^2}\right)\left(7.5\,\frac{\text{g}}{\text{cm}^3}\right)$$

$$= 25\,980\,\text{N} \qquad [8]$$

Thus, the total weight of the fully equipped bathysphere was 30 880 N. Due to buoyancy, the steel rope did not need to support this entire weight. As we studied in Chapter 11, the weight is reduced by the weight of the displaced water:

$$F_{buoyant} = \frac{4}{3}\,\pi \cdot r^3 \cdot \rho_{H_2O} \cdot g$$

$$= \frac{4}{3}\,\pi(0.75\,\text{m})^3\left(9.8\,\frac{\text{m}}{\text{s}^2}\right)\left(1.0 \times 10^3 \frac{\text{kg}}{\text{m}^3}\right)$$

$$= 17\,320\,\text{N} \qquad [9]$$

Thus, only 30 880 N − 17 320 N = 13 560 N had to be supported by the rope. A rope of 3 cm diameter can carry a maximum weight of:

$$W_{max} = \sigma \cdot A = \sigma \cdot r^2 \cdot \pi$$

$$= (6.87 \times 10^8\,\text{Pa})(1.5 \times 10^{-2}\,\text{m})^2\,\pi$$

$$= 4.86 \times 10^5\,\text{N} \qquad [10]$$

This allows for an additional weight of the rope under water of $4.72 \times 10^5$ N. The length $l$ of a rope with this weight (again corrected for buoyancy) is calculated by using a cylindrical shape of the rope:

$$W_{rope} = \pi \cdot r^2 \cdot l\,(\rho_{steel} - \rho_{H_2O})g \qquad [11]$$

from which we obtain for the length $l$:

$$l = \frac{W_{rope}}{\pi \cdot r^2(\rho_{steel} - \rho_{H_2O})\,g} \qquad [12]$$

Substituting the values from above, this corresponds to:

$$l = \frac{4.72 \times 10^5\,\text{N}}{\pi(1.5 \times 10^{-2}\,\text{m})^2\left(6.5 \times 10^3 \frac{\text{kg}}{\text{m}^3}\right)\left(9.8\,\frac{\text{m}}{\text{s}^2}\right)}$$

$$= 10\,480\,\text{m} \qquad [13]$$

Beebe and his partner had to allow for a significant safety margin, thus they had to choose a shallower maximum depth. Nylon would have been a better choice for the rope material, because it has almost the same tensile stress at the ultimate strength point (85% of the value of steel) but a much lower weight.

## Hooke's Law

The stress–strain curves of most materials are similar to the curves shown in Figs. 16.7 and 16.8 in that there is a linear regime for small strain values where the stress $F/A$ and the strain are related in the form:

$$\frac{F}{A} \propto \frac{\Delta l}{l} \quad \text{or} \quad \frac{F}{A} \propto \frac{\Delta V}{V} \qquad [14]$$

The linear relation between stress and strain in this regime is called **Hooke's law.** It is named after Robert Hooke, who discovered this relation in the late 17th century.

*Hooke's law applies in the elastic regime of a material and states that the stress and the strain of the material are linearly proportional.*

Confining our discussion in this chapter to systems in the regime where Hooke's law is applicable, we study vibrations of the system as a new mechanical property resulting from this law. All three types of deformation introduced above lead to important vibrations:

- *The vibration of an ideal gas confined by a piston.* The vibration is the result of compressions and expansions under hydraulic stress.
- *The vibration of an object attached to a spring.* The vibration is the result of a stretching or compression of a spring under tensile stress.
- *Pendulum motion of an object attached to a massless string.* This case is discussed in analogy to the motion of an object attached to a spring.

In this section we first establish the specific form of Hooke's law for each of these cases. The resulting motion of the system is then discussed in the next section.

## Piston-Confined Gas Under Hydraulic Stress

Fig. 16.14 illustrates an ideal gas that is confined in a container with a mobile piston at its right end. Choosing a horizontal arrangement with the $x$-axis toward the right allows us to neglect gravitational effects on gas or piston. The piston is at its mechanical equilibrium position $x_{eq}$ when the pressure of the ideal gas inside is equal to the atmospheric pressure outside. The origin in Fig. 16.14 is chosen at the fixed left wall of the cylindrical container.

We displace the piston by a small distance $\Delta x$ to a new position at $x = x_{eq} - \Delta x$. To achieve this displacement, an external force of magnitude $|F_{ext}|$ is applied toward the left; i.e., the $x$-component of the external force is negative, $F_x = -F_{ext} < 0$. A new mechanical equilibrium, governed by Newton's first law, is established when we hold the piston at this position. The mechanical equilibrium then allows us to determine the specific form of Hooke's law for the piston-confined ideal gas. Defining the area of the piston as $A$, we find:

$$\sum_i F_{i,x} = -p_{atm} \cdot A - F_{ext} + p_{gas} \cdot A = 0 \quad [15]$$

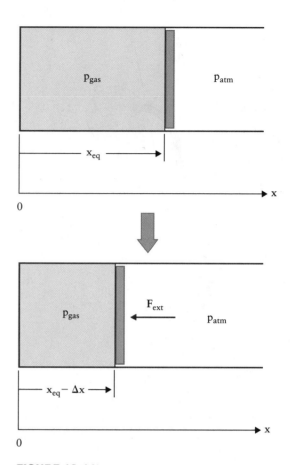

**FIGURE 16.14**

A mobile piston seals a gas in a horizontal container. The piston is in mechanical equilibrium at position $x_{eq}$ when the gas pressure $p_{gas}$ is equal to the external atmospheric pressure $p_{atm}$. An external force allows us to move the piston to a new position at $x_{eq} - \Delta x$. In this graph, the origin of the $x$-axis is chosen at the left end of the gas container.

Sorting the terms in Eq. [15] yields:

$$F_{ext} = A(p_{gas} - p_{atm}) \quad [16]$$

We assume isothermal conditions and use the ideal gas law to rewrite the pressure in this equation as $p = n \cdot R \cdot T/V$. We note that the gas pressure at the equilibrium position of the piston is equal to the atmospheric pressure, $p_{atm} = n \cdot R \cdot T/V_{eq}$. Thus:

$$F_{ext} = n \cdot R \cdot T \cdot A \left( \frac{1}{V_{gas}} - \frac{1}{V_{eq}} \right) \quad [17]$$

The volume terms in Eq. [17] are expressed as the product of the cross-sectional area of the cyclindrical piston, $A$, and the length of the container between the left wall and the piston:

$$F_{ext} = n \cdot R \cdot T \cdot A \left( \frac{1}{A(x_{eq} - \Delta x)} - \frac{1}{A \cdot x_{eq}} \right) \quad [18]$$

Cancelling the cross-sectional area $A$ in numerator and denominator simplifies this equation to:

$$F_{ext} = n \cdot R \cdot T \left( \frac{1}{x_{eq} - \Delta x} - \frac{1}{x_{eq}} \right) \quad [19]$$

The term in the parentheses can be simplified for small piston displacements, i.e., when we assume $\Delta x \ll x_{eq}$:

$$\lim_{\Delta x \ll x_{eq}} \left( \frac{1}{x_{eq} - \Delta x} - \frac{1}{x_{eq}} \right)$$

$$= \lim_{\Delta x \ll x_{eq}} \left( \frac{x_{eq} - (x_{eq} - \Delta x)}{x_{eq}(x_{eq} - \Delta x)} \right) = \frac{\Delta x}{x_{eq}^2} \quad [20]$$

Inserting Eq. [20] in Eq. [19] then leads to:

$$F_{ext} = \frac{n \cdot R \cdot T}{x_{eq}^2} \Delta x \quad [21]$$

Dividing both sides by $A$ yields a stress term $F/A$ on the left-hand side and converts one of the factors $x_{eq}$ in the denominator on the right-hand side into the equilibrium volume of the gas, $V_{eq} = A \cdot x_{eq}$. Further multiplying the right-hand side of Eq. [21] with a factor $A/A$ converts the other factor $x_{eq}$ in the denominator into $V_{eq}$ and converts the $\Delta x$ term in the numerator into a volume change, $-\Delta V$:

$$\frac{F_{ext}}{A} = - \frac{n \cdot R \cdot T}{V_{eq}} \frac{\Delta V}{V_{eq}} \quad [22]$$

The minus sign is included because an increasing external force causes a decreasing volume in Fig. 16.14. Comparing Eq. [22] with Eq. [5] yields for the bulk modulus of the ideal gas:

$$B_{ideal\ gas} = \frac{n \cdot R \cdot T}{V_{eq}} = p_{eq} \quad [23]$$

Thus, the bulk modulus for an ideal gas under isothermal conditions is equal to its equilibrium pressure. Note that Eq. [22] contains a linear proportionality between the stress and the volume strain despite the additional factor $V_{eq}$ in the denominator (compare with Concept Question 16.2).

*A small displacement of a piston sealing an ideal isothermal gas in a container is a valid case of Hooke's law.*

**Concept Question 16.5**

Assume that the external force $F_{ext}$ is suddenly removed in the lower panel of Fig. 16.14. Describe qualitatively what happens next.

ANSWER: The system discussed in Fig. 16.14 is in mechanical equilibrium since the external force is balanced by an equal but opposite force exerted by the gas on the piston. If we remove the external force by releasing the piston, a mechanical non-equilibrium situation is created, i.e., a case governed by Newton's second law. The unbalanced force acting on the piston is the force exerted by the gas on the piston. We call this force a **restoring force** since it points in the direction toward the equilibrium position of the piston.

The unbalanced restoring force accelerates the piston toward the right in Fig. 16.14. As the piston moves, it reaches the equilibrium position. At that instant no force acts on the piston; i.e., it no longer accelerates. However, the inertia of the piston due to Newton's first law prevents it from suddenly coming to rest. Thus, the piston moves farther to the right. Once the piston has moved beyond the equilibrium position the confined ideal gas has a pressure lower than the external atmospheric pressure. Therefore, a restoring force acts on the piston, pushing it back toward the equilibrium position; i.e., a force acts toward the left. This force slows the piston down to rest, which occurs at $x_{eq} + \Delta x$ if the piston is moving without friction in the cylindrical container. Thereafter, the piston continues to move back and forth. We discuss this motion in greater detail in the section on vibrations below.

## An Object Attached to a Spring

In Chapter 3 we studied single isolated objects and found that they display uniform motion along a straight line when left alone. We now attach such an object to a spring, as illustrated in Fig. 16.15. This establishes a continuous interaction with the object resulting in a different motion.

A spring is a device that causes an object to move toward its equilibrium position in response to a displacement, very similar to the motion we observe for the released piston in Fig. 16.14. Before quantifying the spring force further, we note that a horizontal arrangement is chosen in Fig. 16.15. An object could also be attached to a spring in a vertical arrangement. In that case, though, the gravitational force needs to be included in the discussion as an additional force. We avoid this in Fig. 16.15, as the gravitational force plays a negligible role at the microscopic-length scales to which we ultimately want to apply the spring force concept.

Before the object is released, it is held in mechanical equilibrium by an external force at the position shown in the figure. For a sufficiently small displacement

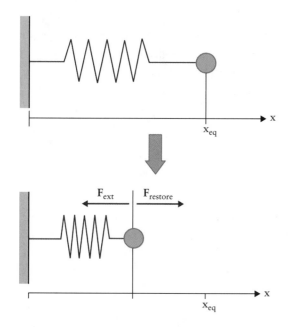

**FIGURE 16.15**

An object is attached to a spring, which in turn is attached horizontally to a rigid wall at the left. The equilibrium position of the object is at $x_{eq}$, where no external forces act on it. With an external force applied toward the left, the object is moved to a new equilibrium position in which the external force and the restoring force, exerted by the spring, are balanced.

$\Delta x = x - x_{eq}$, the external force is linearly proportional to the displacement:

$$F_{ext} = k(x - x_{eq}) \qquad [24]$$

This is Hooke's law for an object attached to a horizontal spring. The parameter $k$ is called the **spring constant** and has unit N/m. A large spring constant means a stiffer spring.

The mechanical equilibrium in Fig. 16.15 is due to a force exerted on the object by the spring. We call this force the **elastic spring force**:

$$F_{elast} = -k(x - x_{eq}) \qquad [25]$$

$F_{elast}$ is a restoring force as it causes the object to accelerate toward the equilibrium position once the external force is removed. The restoring character of the force is represented by the negative sign in Eq. [25]: for positions $x > x_{eq}$ the force $\mathbf{F}_{elast}$ is negative; i.e., the force pulls the object back to smaller values of $x$. For positions $x < x_{eq}$ the force $\mathbf{F}_{elast}$ is positive, pushing the object toward larger values of $x$.

The spring described by Eq. [25] is called an **ideal spring**, because real springs need not follow this law. In general, springs do not follow Hooke's law if the displacement is too large, i.e., too far from the equilibrium position. Most springs, however, are well described by Hooke's law near the equilibrium position, and this is the reason why applications of Eq. [25] are widespread—including the description of intra-molecular forces as discussed in the section on vibrations below.

*An object on an ideal spring that undergoes a small displacement from its equilibrium position is a valid case for Hooke's law.*

## Simple Pendulum

Fig. 16.16 illustrates a **simple pendulum**. An object of mass $m$ is attached to a taut, massless string of length $L$, which in turn is connected to a fixed pivot point at the ceiling. The equilibrium position of the object is reached when the string is vertical. After applying an external force, which is chosen to be tangential to the path of the object in Fig. 16.16, the object comes to rest at a new position shown in the figure. At this point, a mechanical equilibrium exists between three forces acting on the object: the tension in the string, the weight of the object, and the external force.

When the external force is removed, a mechanically unbalanced system results, as shown in Fig. 16.17. Two forces act on the object: the tension and the weight. These two forces are neither parallel nor perpendicular to each other. We choose the $x$- and $y$-axes as shown in Fig. 16.17 and then determine the $x$- and $y$-components of the weight, $W_x$ and $W_y$. We note that the forces in the $y$-direction are balanced while the $x$-component of the weight leads to an acceleration. $W_x$ represents a restoring force, because the acceleration of the object is toward its equilibrium

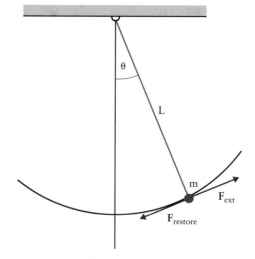

**FIGURE 16.16**

An object of mass $m$ is attached to a massless string of length $L$, which forms an angle $\theta$ with the vertical. We can model the system with two forces while the object is held in mechanical equilibrium: a restoring force $F_{restore}$ (which is a combination of the gravitational force and the tension in the string), and an external force $F_{ext}$.

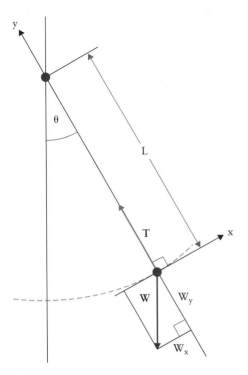

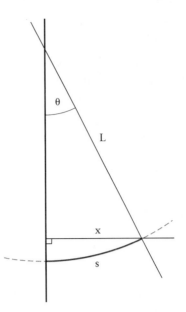

**FIGURE 16.17**

A simple pendulum that is not in mechanical equilibrium. The tension and the $y$-component of the weight compensate each other in the $y$-direction. The $x$-component of the weight leads to an acceleration toward the equilibrium position.

position. Based on Fig. 16.17, the restoring force is written as:

$$F_{restore} = W_x = -m \cdot g \cdot \sin \theta \qquad [26]$$

This restoring force is not linear in the angle $\theta$; i.e., Eq. [26] is not consistent with Hooke's law. Instead of dismissing the pendulum case, however, we study Eq. [26] with an additional assumption that $\theta$ is a small angle. In this case, the approximation $\sin \theta = \theta$ applies, as discussed in the Math Review at the end of this chapter. Eq. [26] in this limiting case reads:

$$F_{restore} = -m \cdot g \cdot \theta \qquad [27]$$

*A pendulum with small angle displacements is a valid case for Hooke's law.*

For many applications, Eq. [27] is rewritten such that the independent variable is not the angle $\theta$ but the distance of the object from the equilibrium position. This distance is defined in Fig. 16.18, which shows the circular path of the object on a massless string of length $L$. Highlighted is a displacement of length $s$ from the object's equilibrium position toward the right. If $\theta$ is small, the position of the object along the horizontal $x$-axis and the length of the path

**FIGURE 16.18**

Sketch defining the path segment $s$ and the horizontal displacement $x$ from the equilibrium position for an object on a massless string of length $L$ at an angle $\theta$ with the vertical.

segment, $s$, are essentially the same, $s = x$. Thus, the angle $\theta$ is replaced by the distance $x$ using:

$$\theta = \frac{s}{L} = \frac{x}{L} \qquad [28]$$

With this approximation, Eq. [27] becomes:

$$F_{restore} = -m \cdot g \cdot \theta = -\frac{m \cdot g}{L} x \qquad [29]$$

This equation is mathematically equivalent to Eq. [25]. Both forces therefore lead to the same motion, since we can replace the spring constant $k$ in Eq. [25] with the term:

$$k \implies \frac{m \cdot g}{L} \qquad [30]$$

Thus, a simple pendulum and an object attached to an ideal spring can be treated in an analogous fashion.

# Vibrations

We will use each of the three cases discussed in the previous section to describe the motion of a system with a restoring force:

- We start the discussion with a single object attached to a horizontal ideal spring. The spring in turn is attached to a rigid, immobile wall. This case is important as it can be applied to molecular vibrations.

- Thereafter, we develop the pendulum case in analogy to the spring case. Pendulum motion allows us to discuss some basic principles of bipedal walking.

- The case of a mobile piston sealing an ideal gas is pursued in the next chapter and leads to sound generation and detection.

## Object Attached to an Ideal Spring

Newton's second law of mechanics applies to an object that is attached to a spring and is allowed to perform horizontal motion with small displacements about its equilibrium position (e.g., the system shown in Fig. 16.15). Choosing the horizontal axis as the x-axis, the equilibrium position is written as $x_{eq}$ and Newton's second law reads:

$$\sum_i F_i = -k(x - x_{eq}) = m \cdot a \qquad [31]$$

Deriving the formula for the position of the object as a function of time from Eq. [31] is mathematically more complicated than solving previously discussed cases of Newton's second law. The reason is that Eq. [31] contains both the position x and the acceleration a. The acceleration is the change of velocity with time, and in turn the velocity is the change of position with time. Thus, we cannot simply isolate the position in Eq. [31] as the independent variable.

The energy concept allows for an alternative way to approach Eq. [31]. In a first step toward solving Eq. [31], we calculate the potential energy of the object on the spring. We call this energy the **elastic potential energy**, or just the **elastic energy**, to distinguish it from the gravitational potential energy we introduced in Chapter 6. Both are potential energies because they are energy forms dependent on the relative position of objects—here, the object relative to its equilibrium position.

Following the same reasoning as in Chapter 6, the potential energy is derived from the work required to displace the object. Let's assume that we move the object from its equilibrium position, for which we choose $x_{eq} = 0$, to a final position $x_{final}$, holding it at that point in a mechanical equilibrium with an external force $\mathbf{F}_{ext}$. From the discussion of Hooke's law for an object attached to a spring, we know that $\mathbf{F}_{ext} = -\mathbf{F}_{elast}$. We recall that the work is the area under the curve of the force as a function of position, as illustrated in Fig. 16.19 for the object on a spring. With the force linearly proportional to the displacement in

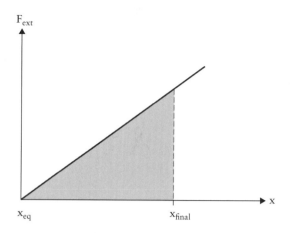

**FIGURE 16.19**

The external force as a function of displacement for an object attached to a spring. The work is given by the area under the curve. The elastic potential energy is related to this work because the external force is the force that establishes the mechanical equilibrium for the system.

Hooke's law—i.e., $F_{ext} = k \cdot x$—the area under the curve between positions $x = 0$ and $x = x_{final}$ is a triangle with area:

$$W = \frac{1}{2} F_{ext} \cdot x_{final} = \frac{1}{2}(k \cdot x_{final})x_{final}$$
$$= \frac{1}{2} k \cdot x_{final}^2 \qquad [32]$$

Thus, we define the elastic potential energy of an object attached to a spring:

$$E_{elast} = \frac{1}{2} k \cdot x^2 \qquad [33]$$

for $x_{eq} = 0$, i.e., when the equilibrium position of the spring is chosen as the origin, or:

$$E_{elast} = \frac{1}{2} k(x - x_{eq})^2 \qquad [34]$$

for $x_{eq} \neq 0$—i.e., when the origin is chosen arbitrarily.

*A system with a linear restoring force (Hooke's law) has an elastic potential energy that is proportional to the square of the displacement from the equilibrium position of the system.*

Fig. 16.20 compares the potential energies, shown as solid lines, (a) for gravity acting on an object and (b) for an object attached to a spring, i.e., an object on which an elastic force acts. The parabolic shape of the elastic potential energy in Fig. 16.20(b) results from Eq. [33] and defines a minimum in the elastic energy at the equilibrium position. No well-defined

(a)
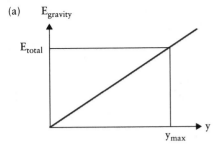

(b)
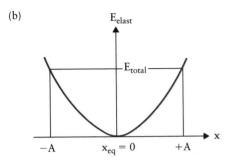

**FIGURE 16.20**

Comparison between the potential energy (a) due to gravity and (b) due to an elastic spring force. The potential energy is shown as the red curve. The horizontal lines indicate an arbitrarily chosen total energy for the system. The curve for the elastic spring force allows us to define the amplitude $\pm A$ for the motion of an object.

point of minimum potential energy exists in the case of gravity in Fig. 16.20(a) because the gravitational force is given as $\mathbf{F} = m \cdot \mathbf{g}$.

With the definition of the elastic potential energy in Eq. [33], the conservation of energy for an object on a horizontal spring is written as:

$$E_{total} = E_{kin} + E_{elast} = \frac{1}{2} m \cdot v^2 + \frac{1}{2} k \cdot x^2 \quad [35]$$

where we have chosen the $x$-axis such that $x_{eq} = 0$.

The interpretation of Eq. [35] is best done using Fig. 16.20. The two horizontal lines represent an arbitrarily chosen total energy. The difference between the total energy (black line) and the potential energy (red line) represents the kinetic energy. Obviously, positions for which the potential energy exceeds the total energy are not allowed. Thus, the gravitational system in Fig. 16.20(a) is not confined; it can move toward the left indefinitely. An object that travels in the graph toward the right (physically travelling upward) will turn around at the point where the kinetic energy becomes zero, but then never returns to this point. In contrast, the system in Fig. 16.20(b) is spatially confined; i.e., an object moves back and forth between the two points at which its kinetic energy is zero.

**Concept Question 16.6**

Fig. 16.21 shows the elastic potential energy of an object attached to a horizontal spring. The object slides on a table without friction. At which position does it reach its greatest total energy? **(A)** At the position labelled (i). **(B)** At both positions (i) and (iv). **(C)** At the position labelled (iii). **(D)** At the position labelled (ii). **(E)** None of the four answers (A) to (D) can be chosen.

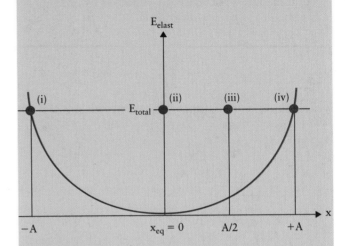

**FIGURE 16.21**

The elastic potential energy (red curve) of an object attached to a horizontal spring. The object slides on a table without friction.

ANSWER: Choice (E). Note that "none of the above" would not be correct either, because the total energy of the system—i.e., the sum of its elastic and kinetic energy—is conserved. Thus, it has the same total energy value at all four positions identified in Fig. 16.21.

**Concept Question 16.7**

At the position labelled (iii) in Fig. 16.21, the object is halfway between its greatest displacement and its equilibrium position. Why does it not store 50% of its total energy in each of the kinetic and elastic energies at this point?

ANSWER: The elastic energy in Eq. [33] is not linear in the displacement of the object because $E \propto x^2$. The red curve in Fig. 16.21 therefore cannot be a straight line as in the gravitational case in Fig. 16.20(a). When the displacement from the equilibrium position doubles, the elastic energy increases by a factor of 4.

### ● EXAMPLE 16.3

The elastic force and the elastic energy are sufficient to determine the spring constant if that parameter is not given. To illustrate this, we consider the spring in Fig. 16.22. The top panel shows the case when the spring is relaxed and the bottom panel when the spring is stretched by a distance $d = 0.15$ m. To pull the spring this distance, a total work of 20 J is needed (typical workout equipment). What force do you need to hold the stretched spring at that point?

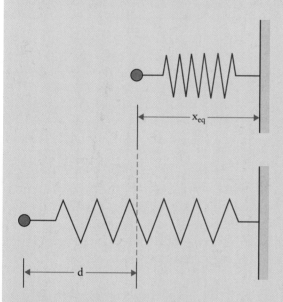

**FIGURE 16.22**
Sketches of a relaxed and a stretched horizontal spring. The spring in the bottom panel is elongated by distance $d$.

*Solution:* We use $x_{initial} = x_{eq} = 0$ and $x_{final} = d$. The work needed to pull the spring to the final position is given by:

$$W = \frac{1}{2}k(x_{final}^2 - x_{initial}^2) = \frac{k}{2}d^2 \quad [36]$$

which allows us to calculate the spring constant $k$:

$$k = \frac{2 \cdot W}{d^2} = \frac{2 \cdot 20 \text{ J}}{(0.15 \text{ m})^2} = 1780 \frac{N}{m} \quad [37]$$

The spring constant is then used in Hooke's law to determine the elastic force:

$$F_{elast} = -k(x - x_{eq}) = -k \cdot d$$

$$= -\left(1780 \frac{N}{m}\right)(0.15 \text{ m}) = -267 \text{ N} \quad [38]$$

Thus, an external force $F_{ext} = -F_{elast} = 267$ N is needed to hold the spring in its stretched position.

The **amplitude** of the motion of an object attached to a spring is defined with Fig. 16.20:

*The amplitude A is the maximum displacement of a vibrating object.*

When the object has moved to the amplitude its kinetic energy becomes zero, $E_{kin} = 0$, and $E_{total} = E_{elast}$:

$$E_{total} = \frac{1}{2}k \cdot A^2 \quad [39]$$

which yields for the amplitude:

$$A = \sqrt{\frac{2 \cdot E_{total}}{k}} \quad [40]$$

We can further determine the maximum speed of an object by studying the instant when $x = x_{eq} = 0$. At that point the elastic energy is zero, $E_{elast} = 0$, and the conservation of energy in Eq. [35] leads to:

$$E_{total} = E_{kin} = \frac{1}{2}m \cdot v_{max}^2 \quad [41]$$

which, for the maximum speed of the object, yields:

$$v_{max} = \sqrt{\frac{2 \cdot E_{total}}{m}} \quad [42]$$

A general relation between the amplitude and the maximum speed of an object attached to a spring is derived from Eqs. [40] and [42]:

$$E_{total} = \frac{1}{2}k \cdot A^2 = \frac{1}{2}m \cdot v_{max}^2 \quad [43]$$

which yields:

$$v_{max} = \sqrt{\frac{k}{m}} A \quad [44]$$

### ● EXAMPLE 16.4

An object of mass 1.0 kg is attached to a spring with spring constant $k = 1000$ N/m. If the object is displaced by 30 cm from its equilibrium position and is released, with what speed will it pass through the equilibrium position?

*Solution:* Using Eq. [40], we first calculate the total energy of the object on the spring:

$$E_{total} = \frac{1}{2}k \cdot A^2$$

$$= \frac{1}{2}\left(1000 \frac{N}{m}\right)(0.3 \text{ m})^2 = 45 \text{ J} \quad [45]$$

Using Eq. [42], we find the maximum speed of the object:

$$v_{\max} = \sqrt{\frac{2 \cdot E_{\text{total}}}{m}} = \sqrt{\frac{2 \cdot 45\ \text{J}}{1.0\ \text{kg}}} = 9.5\frac{\text{m}}{\text{s}} \quad [46]$$

You find the same result by substituting the given values in Eq. [44].

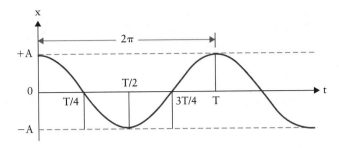

**FIGURE 16.23**

Position as a function of time, $x = f(t)$, for an object attached to a horizontal spring (harmonic oscillator).

This completes the discussion of the energy concept for the motion of an object attached to a spring. Now we continue to seek an algebraic formula that describes the position of the object as a function of time, $x = f(t)$. We start with Eq. [35], which contains the position and the velocity, with the velocity a change of the position with time. It is mathematically simpler than Eq. [31] since it does not contain the acceleration. However, Eq. [35] is still not simple to solve in the form $x = f(t)$ because it is a non-linear equation. Therefore, we don't discuss the required mathematical operations but just note the result, which is the equation for the position of the object on a spring as a function of time:

$$x(t) = A \cdot \cos\left(\sqrt{\frac{k}{m}} \cdot t\right) = A \cdot \cos(\omega \cdot t) \quad [47]$$

This formula describes a cyclic motion called **simple harmonic motion**. In simple harmonic motion, an object oscillates about a point of mechanical equilibrium. Eq. [47] is plotted in Fig. 16.23. In the last formula of Eq. [47] a new parameter is introduced, $\omega$ (lower-case Greek omega), which is called the **angular frequency** and has unit 1/s:

$$\omega = \sqrt{\frac{k}{m}} \quad [48]$$

Eq. [48] indicates that the angular frequency contains the physical parameters of the system, i.e., its mass and the spring constant. $\omega$ also governs the motion of the object as a function of time since it carries an inverse time unit. We illustrate this by following an object through a full cycle of its motion, i.e., between two instants in Fig. 16.23 where the argument of the cosine function has the same value—for example, $\cos(0)$ and $\cos(2 \cdot \pi)$. Any two such instants differ by $\omega \cdot t = 2 \cdot \pi$, which we define in Fig. 16.23 as the **period** $T$. Thus, $2 \cdot \pi = \omega \cdot T$, or:

$$\omega = \frac{2 \cdot \pi}{T} \quad [49]$$

Eq. [49] justifies the term "angular frequency" for the parameter $\omega$: $2 \cdot \pi$ is the angle for a full cycle (360°), and frequency refers to an inverse time. It is important to keep in mind that $\omega$ should not be used in unit of degree per second (°/s), but in unit of radians per second, rad/s (see the Math Review at the end of this chapter for the conversion between angles in degrees and radians). Further, $\omega$ cannot be referred to as "frequency," because we define frequency differently from Eq. [49]: the **frequency** $f$ is $f = 1/T$. The unit of frequency is Hertz, Hz, named after Heinrich Hertz, with $1\ \text{Hz} = 1\ \text{s}^{-1}$.

## ● EXAMPLE 16.5

We study a simplified model for the tympanic membrane in the human ear (eardrum): a circular membrane that can undergo a harmonic motion like a trampoline sheet. Assume a mass of 20 mg and a vibration frequency of 3.0 kHz. Calculate (a) the spring constant of the eardrum, and (b) the angular frequency and the period of the vibration.

*Solution to part (a):* We note that the frequency, not the angular frequency, is given in the example text. We combine Eqs. [48] and [49] to relate the frequency to the spring constant:

$$f = \frac{\omega}{2 \cdot \pi} = \frac{1}{2 \cdot \pi}\sqrt{\frac{k}{m}} \quad [50]$$

which yields:

$$k = 4 \cdot \pi^2 \cdot f^2 \cdot m \quad [51]$$

Substituting the given values, we find:

$$k = 4 \cdot \pi^2 (3000\ \text{Hz})^2\,(20 \times 10^{-5}\ \text{kg})$$

$$= 71\,000\,\frac{\text{N}}{\text{m}} \quad [52]$$

Comparing this result with other spring constants, we note that this value represents a very stiff membrane.

● **EXAMPLE 16.5** (*continued*)

*Solution to part (b):* The angular frequency $\omega$ is obtained from Eq. [49]:

$$\omega = 2 \cdot \pi \cdot f = 2 \cdot \pi (3000 \text{ Hz})$$

$$= 19\,000 \,\frac{\text{rad}}{\text{s}} \qquad [53]$$

Eq. [49] also relates the period and the frequency:

$$T = \frac{1}{f} = \frac{1}{3000 \text{ Hz}} = 3.3 \times 10^{-4} \text{ s}$$

$$= 0.33 \text{ ms} \qquad [54]$$

## Concept Question 16.8

**The amplitude of a system moving in simple harmonic motion is increased by a factor of 3. Determine the change in (a) the total energy, (b) the maximum speed, (c) the period, and (d) the angular frequency.**

ANSWER TO PART (a): The total energy increases by a factor $3^2 = 9$ due to Eq. [39].

ANSWER TO PART (b): The maximum speed is linear with the amplitude due to Eq. [44]. Thus, it increases by a factor of 3.

ANSWER TO PARTS (c) AND (d): The angular frequency depends only on the system parameters mass and spring constant in Eq. [48]; thus it does not change. The period and the frequency can be calculated from the angular frequency without using the amplitude; therefore these two parameters are also unaffected.

## Chemical Bonds in Molecules

The relative motion of atoms in a molecule is an important application of simple harmonic motion. This is illustrated for the HCl molecule and a NaCl bond in a rock salt crystal. HCl is a binary molecule in which the chlorine atom is about 35 times heavier than the hydrogen atom. This allows us to simplify the model for the HCl molecule as shown in Fig. 16.24, where the chlorine atom is considered to be immobile—like the wall to which the spring is attached on the right side in Fig. 16.22. The hydrogen atom is modelled as an object attached to the Cl atom by an ideal spring. In comparison, the description of a chemical bond with atoms of similar masses, e.g., NaCl, requires a formalism allowing both atoms to vibrate simultaneously relative to their common centre of mass.

**FIGURE 16.24**

Simplified model of the HCl molecule. The chlorine atom is considered immobile. The spring allows the hydrogen atom to undergo simple harmonic oscillations.

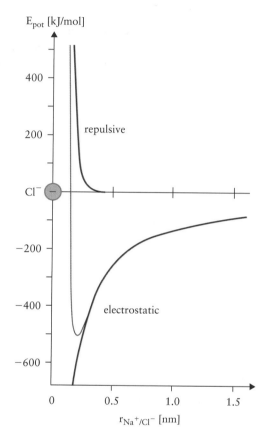

**FIGURE 16.25**

Potential energy as a function of distance between $Na^+$ and $Cl^-$ ions in rock salt (NaCl). The electrostatic attraction between the ions (red curve at negative energies) is overcompensated by a repulsive term (red curve at positive energies) at closer proximity. The combined potential energy curve for the Na—Cl bond is shown as an asymmetric blue curve.

We test whether the model proposed in Fig. 16.24 is adequate to describe real chemical bonds. For this we analyze the interaction between two neighbouring atoms or ions. Their interaction has two contributions, as illustrated in Fig. 16.25 for NaCl:

● an attractive component shown at negative energies. In the case of an electrostatic interaction, the attractive component is the electrostatic potential energy:

$$E_{\text{attract}} = -\frac{1}{4 \cdot \pi \cdot \varepsilon_0} \frac{e^2}{r} \qquad [55]$$

which we derived from Coulomb's law in Chapter 13. $\varepsilon_0$ is the permittivity of vacuum and $e$ is the elementary charge. If this attraction were the only interaction in the Na—Cl system, the sodium atom would crash into the chlorine atom as if it were swallowed up by a black hole.

- This doesn't happen, because the attraction is shielded when the two ions penetrate each other and negative electrons and positive nuclei come respectively close to each other, adding a repulsive term shown in Fig. 16.25 as a red curve at positive energy values. Max Born determined a semi-empirical formula for the repulsive contribution:

$$E_{\text{repulsive}} = b \cdot e^{-a \cdot r} \qquad [56]$$

in which $a$ and $b$ are constants that have to be determined experimentally for each chemical bond. The exponential function in Eq. [56] is steeper than the $1/r$ dependence in Eq. [55]. Therefore, the repulsive term dominates at shorter distances between the two ions and the attractive term dominates at longer distances.

Both contributions were combined by Heitler and London in 1927, describing the complete potential function as shown as the blue line in Fig. 16.25 for an NaCl bond, and as shown as the red line in Fig. 16.26 for an HCl molecule. In the case of HCl, a minimum energy is reached when the H atom is separated by a distance $r_0$ of about 0.13 nm from the Cl atom.

The combination of the potential energies in Eqs. [55] and [56] doesn't result in the potential curve for an object on an ideal spring. This is highlighted in Fig. 16.26, where the blue line is the curve for an object attached to an ideal spring while the actual po-

tential energy curve for the HCl molecule is shown as the red line. Recall that the spring model in Fig. 16.24 predicts a potential energy of the form $E_{\text{elast}} = \frac{1}{2}k(x - x_{\text{eq}})^2$. The disagreement between the two potential energy curves is particularly large at high total energies.

Do we therefore dismiss the harmonic oscillator as a model for a molecular bond? Not necessarily: at typical temperatures, such as room temperature or temperatures that molecules reach during most chemical reactions in solutions, almost all of the HCl molecules have a total energy corresponding to the ground state, which is indicated in Fig. 16.26 by the horizontal line labelled $n = 0$. Note that the energy of this ground state is higher than the minimum of the potential energy curve for quantum–mechanical reasons (Heisenberg's uncertainty relation; see Chapter 22). Only a negligible fraction of the HCl molecules have an energy corresponding to one of the excited states of the molecule (labelled $n = 1, 2, \ldots$). The reason for this small fraction of molecules being at an energy other than the ground state is discussed in Chapter 22. There we first find that the molecules cannot have any other total energy than the ones indicated by the horizontal lines in Fig. 16.26. Thus, for a molecule to reach an excited state from the ground state, a significantly higher amount of energy is needed than is available as a result of the ambient thermal energy, which is on the order of $k \cdot T \approx 4 \times 10^{-21}$ J at room temperature ($k$ is the Boltzmann constant).

Remember that the hydrogen atom in Fig. 16.26 cannot travel beyond the two points at which its potential energy is equal to its total energy. The range accessible to the atom coincides with the range in which the potential energy of the harmonic oscillator (dashed blue line) and the actual potential energy curve (red line) match quite well.

*The simple harmonic oscillator is a good model for chemical molecules in their ground state.*

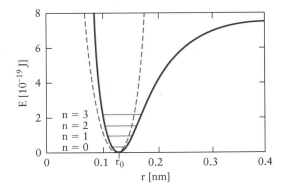

**FIGURE 16.26**

Intra-molecular potential curve (red line) and harmonic oscillator model (dashed blue curve) as a function of the separation distance between the atoms in an HCl molecule. Horizontal lines represent the allowed total energy levels of the molecule.

## ● EXAMPLE 16.6

We quantify key properties of HCl molecules using the simple harmonic oscillator model. The mass of a hydrogen atom is $m = 1.67 \times 10^{-27}$ kg and the spring constant of the molecule is $k = 484$ N/m, which is a value obtained from spectroscopic data listed in Table 16.2. Calculate (a) the angular frequency, (b) the frequency, and (c) the period for the vibration of the hydrogen atom in the HCl molecule.

● **EXAMPLE 16.6** (*continued*)

**TABLE 16.2**

**Spring constants for various chemical bonds**

| Bond | Molecule | $k$ (N/m) |
|------|----------|-----------|
| H—Cl | HCl | 484 |
| H—O | $H_2O$ | 780 |
| H—C | $CH_3R$ | 470–500 |
| C—C | | 450–560 |
| C=C | | 950–990 |
| C≡C | | 1560–1700 |
| N—N | | 350–550 |
| C—O | | 500–580 |
| C=O | | 1180–1340 |

R stands for *rest*, i.e., an organic extension of the functional group.

*Solution to part (a):* We use Eq. [48] to determine the angular frequency:

$$\omega = \sqrt{\frac{k}{m}} = 5.38 \times 10^{14} \frac{rad}{s} \quad [57]$$

*Solution to part (b):* Substituting the value for the angular frequency from Eq. [57] in Eq. [49], we find for the frequency:

$$f = \frac{\omega}{2 \cdot \pi} = 8.6 \times 10^{13} \, Hz \quad [58]$$

*Solution to part (c):* Frequency and period are inversely related:

$$T = \frac{1}{f} = 1.2 \times 10^{-14} \, s \quad [59]$$

The hydrogen atom in the HCl molecule vibrates with an extremely short period.

The short period of vibration of molecules is very important for their chemical properties. The hydrogen atom moves away from the chlorine atom once during each vibration cycle. If another molecule is close to the HCl molecule, this represents the opportunity for the hydrogen atom to engage in a chemical reaction with a neighbouring molecule. Therefore, $f$ is the frequency with which the hydrogen atom tries to escape from the molecule by moving toward the outer limit of the potential energy barrier in

**TABLE 16.3**

**Vibration frequencies for various chemical bonds in organic molecules**

| Bond | $f$ (Hz) |
|------|----------|
| H—O | $1.05 \times 10^{14}$–$1.11 \times 10^{14}$ |
| H—N | $9.9 \times 10^{13}$–$1.05 \times 10^{14}$ |
| H—C | $8.64 \times 10^{13}$–$9.09 \times 10^{13}$ |
| C=C | $4.8 \times 10^{13}$–$5.04 \times 10^{13}$ |
| C≡C | $6.6 \times 10^{13}$–$6.78 \times 10^{13}$ |
| C=O | $4.98 \times 10^{13}$–$5.61 \times 10^{13}$ |

Fig. 16.26. While no neighbouring molecule is present, a dissociation of the HCl molecule does not take place (which would require the hydrogen atom to move all the way beyond the right end of Fig. 16.26). However, when a neighbouring molecule is close enough for a strong interaction, an escape attempt may result in a regrouping of atoms, i.e., in the successful completion of a chemical reaction. Since the period of closest proximity between molecules in a reaction volume is short, a high frequency of attempts is vital to obtain an appreciable rate at which chemical reactions take place. Due to the relevance of the vibrational frequency for chemical kinetics, some $f$ values are summarized in Table 16.3.

● **EXAMPLE 16.7**

Read the total energy of the HCl molecule in the ground state from Fig. 16.26 and calculate the amplitude and the maximum speed of the hydrogen atom in the molecule.

*Solution:* The total energy of the molecule in the ground state is $E_{total} = 2.87 \times 10^{-20}$ J. With this value we use Eq. [40] to obtain the amplitude of the vibrating hydrogen atom:

$$A = \sqrt{\frac{2 \cdot E_{total}}{k}} = 1.09 \times 10^{-11} \, m \quad [60]$$

The amplitude is 0.011 nm, or about 10% of the distance to the chlorine atom. From Eq. [44] we obtain the maximum speed of the vibrating hydrogen atom (see data in Example 16.6):

$$v_{max} = \sqrt{\frac{k}{m}} A = 5860 \frac{m}{s} \quad [61]$$

# Simple and Physical Pendulum

We noted in Eq. [30] that the restoring force formulas of a simple pendulum (an object on a taut massless string) and for an object attached to an ideal spring are equivalent as long as we replace the spring constant $k$ by the factor $m \cdot g/L$, in which $m$ is the mass of the object and $L$ is the length of the massless string. Applying the same approach to the energy and motion parameters of both systems allows us to quantify pendulum motion without further calculations. The potential energy of a pendulum system is derived from Eq. [33]:

$$E_{pot} = \frac{1}{2} \frac{m \cdot g}{L} x^2 \qquad [62]$$

which yields:

$$-2 \cdot L \cdot h + h^2 + x^2 = 0 \qquad [64]$$

For small displacements of the object from the equilibrium position we know that $h \ll L$ and therefore $h^2 \ll h \cdot L$. Using this approximation in Eq. [64], we find:

$$0 = -2 \cdot L \cdot h + h^2 + x^2 \cong -2 \cdot L \cdot h + x^2 \qquad [65]$$

which yields:

$$h = \frac{x^2}{2 \cdot L} \qquad [66]$$

Substituting $h$ from Eq. [66] in $E_{pot} = m \cdot g \cdot h$ confirms the validity of Eq. [62].

---

**Concept Question 16.9**

**Validate Eq. [62] by starting with Fig. 16.17, for which we know that the potential energy of the object is equal to $E_{pot} = m \cdot g \cdot h$, where $h$ is the height of the object above the equilibrium position.**

ANSWER: Fig. 16.27 shows how the various geometric parameters are related for the simple pendulum. We use the Pythagorean theorem for the triangle in Fig. 16.27 to derive Eq. [62] from $E_{pot} = m \cdot g \cdot h$. From the figure, we find:

$$(L - h)^2 + x^2 = L^2 \qquad [63]$$

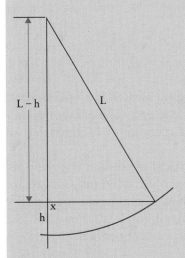

**FIGURE 16.27**
Sketch relating the geometric parameters of an object attached to a taut massless string that is displaced toward the right. The equilibrium position lies vertically below the pivot point.

Other relations for the simple pendulum are obtained by substituting the term $m \cdot g/L$ for the parameter $k$ in spring-system equations:

- The amplitude of the simple pendulum is:

$$A = \sqrt{\frac{2 \cdot E_{total} \cdot L}{m \cdot g}} \qquad [67]$$

- The maximum speed of the object on the massless string is:

$$v_{max} = \sqrt{\frac{g}{L}} A \qquad [68]$$

- The angular frequency of the pendulum motion is:

$$\omega = \sqrt{\frac{g}{L}} \qquad [69]$$

- The period of the pendulum motion is:

$$T = 2 \cdot \pi \sqrt{\frac{L}{g}} \qquad [70]$$

Note that the period $T$ does not depend on the mass $m$ of the object.

We complete our discussion with Table 16.4, which provides a summary of the relevant formulas for an object on a horizontal spring (spring system) and an object on a vertical massless string (pendulum system).

**TABLE 16.4**

**Comparison between the various parameters of motion for an object (mass *m*) on a horizontal spring or an object attached to a vertical massless string of length *L***

| Property | Symbol | Spring system | Pendulum |
|---|---|---|---|
| Force constant | | Spring constant $k$ | $m \cdot g/L$ |
| Angular frequency | $\omega$ | $(k/m)^{1/2}$ | $(g/L)^{1/2}$ |
| Frequency | $f$ | $1/T = \omega/(2 \cdot \pi)$ | $1/T = \omega/(2 \cdot \pi)$ |
| Period | $T$ | $2 \cdot \pi \, (m/k)^{1/2}$ | $2 \cdot \pi \, (L/g)^{1/2}$ |
| Kinetic energy | $E_{kin}$ | $\frac{1}{2} \cdot m \cdot v^2$ | $\frac{1}{2} \cdot m \cdot v^2$ |
| Potential energy | $E_{pot}$ | $\frac{1}{2} \cdot k \cdot x^2$ | $m \cdot g \cdot h$ |

$h$ is the height above the lowest position.

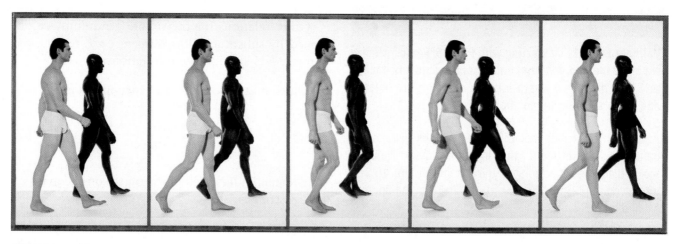

**FIGURE 16.28**

Five panels show two standard men walking. The time elapsed from the first to the last panel corresponds to half a period. Following the front leg, the sequence highlights the harmonic pendulum motion of the legs.

A pendulum motion of special interest in biomechanics is the natural motion of a standard man's leg during walking, as illustrated with five consecutive snapshots in Fig. 16.28. In the figure the right leg describes half a period corresponding to the forward motion while the left leg describes the other half of a full period.

The simple pendulum is not a suitable model for quantifying the walking process as the mass of the leg is not centred in the foot but distributed along the entire leg (with a larger fraction in the thigh). We therefore extend the model of the simple pendulum to a **physical pendulum**. A physical pendulum is defined as an extended rigid object with a rotation axis that is not located at the centre of mass. The easiest physical pendulum consists of a uniform rod of length $L$, pivoted at one end. The pendulum motion of such a physical pendulum is illustrated in Fig. 16.29.

The motion of a physical pendulum is closely related to the motion of a simple pendulum, as both are derived from Hooke's law. The different mass distribution of the physical pendulum leads, however, to a different formula for the natural period:

$$T = 2 \cdot \pi \sqrt{\frac{2 \cdot L}{3 \cdot g}} \qquad [71]$$

Note that the period is again independent of the mass of the rigid object.

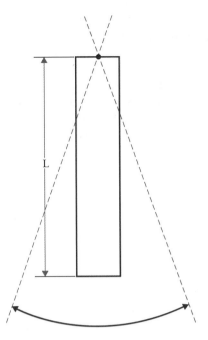

**FIGURE 16.29**

A physical pendulum of length $L$ with uniform mass distribution and the pivot point (blue dot) at its upper end.

● **EXAMPLE 16.8**

A comfortable walking pace for a standard man requires the least effort because the legs move with the natural period. We model the leg as a uniform rod, pivoted at the hip joint, and use a length $L = 95$ cm for the leg. What is the period of the standard man's leg during walking?

*Solution*: We substitute the given values in Eq. [71]:

$$T = 2 \cdot \pi \sqrt{\frac{2 \cdot L}{3 \cdot g}}$$

$$= 2 \cdot \pi \sqrt{\frac{2 \cdot 0.95 \text{ m}}{3 \cdot 9.8 \frac{\text{m}}{\text{s}^2}}} = 1.6 \text{ s} \quad [72]$$

● **EXAMPLE 16.9**

One of the best known dinosaurs is *Tyrannosaurus rex*, which lived during the Cretaceous period ending about 65 million years ago. This large carnivore walked on two legs like we do, although it was anatomically different in that it balanced the weight of the upper body with a massive tail (compare with the human and chimpanzee hip joints in Chapter 5). We can derive the following data from the fossil record and petrified footsteps: the average length of *T. rex*'s leg from the hip joint to the sole was $L = 310$ cm and its stride length,

which is the distance between two footprints of the same foot, was $l = 400$ cm. Estimate the natural walking speed of the dinosaur.

*Solution*: We can solve this problem by using Eq. [71] if we assume a uniform mass distribution along the dinosaur's leg:

$$T = 2 \cdot \pi \sqrt{\frac{2 \cdot L}{3 \cdot g}} = 2 \cdot \pi \sqrt{\frac{2 \cdot 3.1 \text{ m}}{3 \cdot 9.8 \frac{\text{m}}{\text{s}^2}}} = 2.9 \text{ s} \quad [73]$$

This leads to a walking speed for *T. rex* of:

$$v = \frac{l}{T} = \frac{4.0 \text{ m}}{2.9 \text{ s}} = 1.38 \frac{\text{m}}{\text{s}} \cong 5.0 \frac{\text{km}}{\text{h}} \quad [74]$$

Note that both the human leg and the leg of *T. rex* are not uniform. This leads to corrections that are more significant for the dinosaur, with its more massive upper leg. The actual value is $v = 3.6$ km/h for the standard man with a stride length of 1.6 m. For *T. rex*, $v = 8$ km/h and a period of 1.8 s are more appropriate values.

Note that this does not imply that *T. rex* was slow. Comparison between walking and running is not straightforward: additional parameters play a role in the ability to run that do not matter when walking. As an example of such a parameter, Fig. 16.30 shows the correlation between the

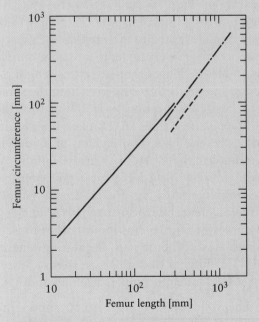

**FIGURE 16.30**

Double-logarithmic plot of the correlation between femur length and circumference for select mammals and dinosaurs; the solid line represents living mammals that hop and/or run fast, the dash-dotted line represents ornithomimids (dinosaur subgroup), and the dashed line represents humans and related hominid species. The straight lines indicate that a power law relation exists for each group.

● **EXAMPLE 16.9 (continued)**

femur length and the femur circumference. The solid line represents various living mammals that hop and/or run fast; the dash-dotted line represents dinosaurs of the subgroup ornithomimids, including the various *Tyrannosaurus* species; and the dashed line represents humans and hominid species. The straight lines (representing power law relations for each group) illustrate that the

robustness of the dinosaur legs matches that of the various fast-running mammals, while we humans have rather slender legs. Robustness of the femur in particular is important when running, as this bone has to accommodate major forces. The conclusion from Fig. 16.30 is that the ornithomimids were designed for fast motion, while the human leg anatomy is based on other principles.

# MULTIPLE CHOICE AND CONCEPTUAL QUESTIONS

## ELASTICITY

**Q–16.1.** The dash-dotted curve in Fig. 16.2(a) is the active stretching force for a human muscle. This curve shows the force (as a fraction of the maximum force in %) a muscle can exert at a given length. For example: the maximum force can be exerted when the muscle is at its resting length, but only about 50% of that force can be exerted when the muscle has contracted to 80% of its resting length. The dashed curve in Fig. 16.2(a) shows the passive stretching force for a human muscle. This curve indicates the external force required to stretch the muscle at the given length. For example, to stretch a muscle when it is about 5% longer than its resting length requires about double the force as stretching the same muscle just beyond its resting length. Which of the following statements is true? (A) Hooke's law is suitable to describe the passive stretching of a muscle near its resting length. (B) Hooke's law is suitable to describe the active muscle force for a given muscle near its resting length. (C) Fig. 16.2(a) does not allow us to verify statements like those made in (A) and (B). (D) Both curves in Fig. 16.2(a) indicate that muscle tissue has no elastic regime near the resting length. (E) Fig. 16.2(a) implies that a muscle released after stretching should undergo simple harmonic motion.

**Q–16.2.** The solid curve in Fig. 16.10 shows the stress–strain relation for blood vessel tissue. Up to which stress value does the strain in the blood vessel respond linearly to the exerted stress? Choose the closest value. (A) The stress–strain relation is not linear for any stress. (B) $\varepsilon = 100\%$. (C) $\varepsilon = 50\%$. (D) $\sigma = 0.5 \times 10^6$ Pa. (E) $\sigma = 1.0 \times 10^6$ Pa.

**Q–16.3.** The elastic behaviour of the blood vessel in Fig. 16.10 is the result of two contributing com-

ponents in the tissue: elastin (dash-dotted curve) and collagen, with a bulk modulus increasing with strain (dashed curve). Based on Fig. 16.10, which of the following statements is wrong? (A) The elastic properties of elastin can be described by Hooke's law. (B) Collagen shows a non-linear stress–strain behaviour. (C) Up to strains of about 60%, elastin will dominate the elastic response of the system. (D) The actual blood vessel wall shows non-linear stress–strain behaviour due to its collagen component. (E) All four statements are correct.

**Q–16.4.** Fig. 16.31 shows the stress–strain curve for compact bone from Fig. 16.8. It further includes four points (i) to (iv) along this curve. In which interval is the response of the compact bone not fully elastic? (A) From the origin to point (iii). (B) From the origin

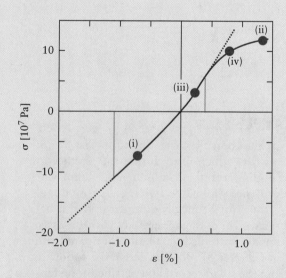

**FIGURE 16.31**

Same stress–strain curve for compact bone as Fig. 16.8. The figure also includes four points (i) to (iv).

to point (iv). (C) From the origin to point (i). (D) From point (i) to point (iii). (E) Its response is fully elastic in all four intervals.

**Q–16.5.** What do we imply when we say that a force acting on an object is an elastic force? (A) We imply that we hold the object in a mechanical non-equilibrium position. (B) We imply that the object moves fast in the vicinity of the equilibrium position. (C) We imply that the elastic energy exceeds 10 J. (D) We imply that the total energy of the object is conserved. (E) We imply that the strain is proportional to the stress for the system we study.

## SIMPLE HARMONIC MOTION

**Q–16.6.** We consider an object that is attached to a horizontal spring and moves frictionless on a flat surface. The object is displaced by a given distance such that the spring is stretched relative to its equilibrium length. Then the external force is removed (i.e., the object is released). Immediately after its release, which statement is *correct* regarding the object? (A) The object is in mechanical equilibrium. (B) The object moves with its maximum speed. (C) The object moves away from the equilibrium position. (D) The object remains at rest. (E) The object decreases its elastic potential energy.

**Q–16.7.** We define the positive $x$-direction as the direction in which an object stretches a spring ($k = 100$ N/m) during a simple harmonic motion. At the instant the object moves through its equilibrium position after having been released at the amplitude point, $x = +A = +0.1$ m, what is the elastic force acting on the object? (A) $F_{elast} = -100$ N. (B) $F_{elast} = -10$ N. (C) $F_{elast} = 0$ N. (D) $F_{elast} = +10$ N. (E) $F_{elast} = +100$ N.

**Q–16.8.** An object is attached to a horizontal spring and moves along the $x$-axis. It is initially displaced to the positive amplitude point, $x = +A$. At that point its elastic potential energy is $E_1$. Then the object is released. At what point along its path will the total energy of the system be smaller than $E_1$? (A) At no point. (B) At all points other than the point $x = -A$. (C) At all points with $x < 0$. (D) At all points where the kinetic energy exceeds $\frac{1}{2}E_1$. (E) At all points where the object's speed is positive, $v > 0$.

**Q–16.9.** An object is attached to a horizontal spring. It is initially displaced by a distance $\Delta x$ from the equilibrium position and then released from rest. The object passes the equilibrium position with speed $v$. From this speed we can calculate the initial displacement $\Delta x$ by using this formula:

(A)  $\Delta x = \sqrt{k \cdot v}$

(B)  $\Delta x = \sqrt{m \cdot v}$

(C)  $\Delta x = \sqrt{\dfrac{m}{k}}\, v$      [75]

(D)  $\Delta x = \sqrt{\dfrac{k}{m}}\, v$

(E)  $\Delta x = \sqrt{m \cdot k \cdot v}$

**Q–16.10.** An object is attached to a horizontal spring, which is oriented along the $x$-axis. The object is initially located at the equilibrium position of the spring and is at rest. Then we hit the object such that it moves along the $x$-axis, stretching the spring. At what point of its motion along the $x$-axis does the object reach its highest kinetic energy? (A) at the equilibrium position, (B) at the positive amplitude position, (C) at midway between the amplitude and equilibrium positions, (D) at the negative amplitude position, (E) the kinetic energy is the same at all positions.

**Q–16.11.** An object is attached to a horizontal spring, which is oriented along the $x$-axis. The object is initially located at the equilibrium position of the spring and is at rest. Then we hit the object such that it moves along the $x$-axis, stretching the spring. At what point of its motion along the $x$-axis does the object reach its lowest kinetic energy? (A) at the equilibrium position, (B) at the positive amplitude position, (C) at midway between the amplitude and equilibrium positions, (D) at the initial position, (E) the kinetic energy is the same at all positions.

**Q–16.12.** How many mechanical equilibrium positions has an object that is attached to a spring? (A) zero, (B) one, (C) two, (D) a finite number larger than two, (E) an infinite number.

**Q–16.13.** We study an object that is attached to a spring and performs a harmonic oscillation on a frictionless horizontal surface. Which parameter set *does not* allow us to calculate the angular frequency of the motion? (A) mass of object and spring constant, (B) frequency of the motion, (C) period of the motion, (D) mass of the object and amplitude of the motion.

**Q–16.14.** Why is the force acting on an object attached to a spring called a restoring force? (A) It restores the system to the state in which it was just prior to the release of the object. (B) It acts in the direction of the equilibrium position. (C) It causes a repetitive motion. (D) The force always acts in the negative $x$-direction. (E) The system restores the initial state of elastic potential energy (a special type of energy conservation).

Q–16.15. An object is attached to a horizontal spring and moves along the $x$-axis. It is initially displaced to the positive amplitude point, $x = +A$. At that point its elastic potential energy is $E_1$. Next the object is moved to the opposite amplitude point at $x = -A$. Now its elastic potential energy is $E_2$. The following relation holds for $E_1$ and $E_2$: (A) $E_2 = E_1$. (B) $E_2 = -E_1$. (C) $E_2 = 2 \cdot E_1$. (D) $E_2 = -2 \cdot E_1$. (E) None of the above.

Q–16.16. An object is attached to a horizontal spring. It is initially displaced by a distance $\Delta x$ from the equilibrium position and then released from rest. When the object passes the equilibrium position, its speed will be:

$$\text{(A)} \quad v = \frac{\Delta x}{\sqrt{k}}$$

$$\text{(B)} \quad v = \frac{\Delta x}{\sqrt{m}}$$

$$\text{(C)} \quad v = \frac{\Delta x}{\sqrt{\dfrac{m}{k}}} \qquad [76]$$

$$\text{(D)} \quad v = \frac{\Delta x}{\sqrt{\dfrac{k}{m}}}$$

$$\text{(E)} \quad v = \frac{\Delta x}{\sqrt{m \cdot k}}$$

Q–16.17. We replace an object on a spring with one that has four times the mass. How does the frequency of the system change? (A) by a factor of 0.25, (B) by a factor of 0.5, (C) it remains unchanged, (D) by a factor of 2, (E) by a factor of 4.

Q–16.18. An object is attached to a horizontal spring and undergoes simple harmonic motion with an amplitude $A$. Does the total energy of the system change if the mass of the object is doubled but the amplitude remains unchanged? In particular, are the potential and/or kinetic energies at a given point along the object's motion affected?

Q–16.19. Does the acceleration of a simple harmonic oscillator remain constant during its motion? Is it ever zero?

Q–16.20. What is the total distance travelled by an object attached to a spring during a full period of its simple harmonic motion? Use $A$ for its amplitude.

Q–16.21. Determine whether the following vectors can point in the same direction during a simple harmonic motion: (a) displacement and velocity, (b) velocity and acceleration, and (c) displacement and acceleration.

## SIMPLE PENDULUM

Q–16.22. A grandfather clock is modelled as a heavy object suspended from a massless stick. The object undergoes simple pendulum motion. If such a clock runs slow, how would you adjust the length of the massless stick?

# ANALYTICAL PROBLEMS

## ELASTICITY

P–16.1. For the graph in Fig. 16.1, express the force (in % of the maximum force) as a mathematical function of the sarcomere length $l$ (in $\mu$m) for the linear segments in the interval (a) 2.2 $\mu$m $\le l \le$ 3.2 $\mu$m, (b) 2.0 $\mu$m $\le l \le$ 2.2 $\mu$m, and (c) 1.4 $\mu$m $\le l \le$ 1.65 $\mu$m.

P–16.2. Assume a leg contains a 50-cm-long bone with an average cross-sectional area of 3 cm². By how much does the bone shorten when the entire body weight of the person (use 700 N) is supported by the leg? Use for Young's modulus of the bone $Y = 1.8 \times 10^{10}$ Pa.

P–16.3. We determine an upper limit of the maximum height of building construction on Earth. This limit is due to the maximum stress in the building material prior to rupture. For steel of density $\rho = 7.9$ g/cm³ the maximum stress is $\sigma = 2.0 \times 10^8$ Pa. Note that the pressure in the steel at the ground level may not exceed the maximum stress.

P–16.4. If the ultimate strength for a particular steel is reached at $5.0 \times 10^8$ Pa, determine the minimum diameter of a wire made of this steel that can support a standard man (see Table 3.3).

**P–16.5.** The four tires of a car are inflated to a gauge pressure of $2.0 \times 10^5$ Pa. Each tire is in contact with the ground with an area $A = 240$ cm$^2$. Determine the weight of the car.

## PENDULUM

**P–16.6.** We suspend a uniform rod of length $L$ and let it swing as a physical pendulum. (a) What is the period of the pendulum if the length $L = 2.0$ m? (b) If we want a simple pendulum with an object at the end of a massless string of length $l$ to have the same period as the pendulum in part (a), what must the length $l$ be?

**P–16.7.** Assume that you have no metre stick but a precise clock. You can then measure the height of buildings by attaching an object to the end of a massless string, with the string pivoted at the top of the structure and the object at the bottom. (a) If the object swings 10 times back and forth in 110 s, what is the height of the structure? (b) If you change the object on the massless string to one with double the mass, how does the answer given in part (a) change?

## OBJECT ATTACHED TO A SPRING

**P–16.8.** An object has a mass $m = 0.7$ kg. It is attached to a spring that has spring constant of $k = 80$ N/m. At time $t = 0$ the object is pulled to a distance of 10 cm from its equilibrium position (which you may choose conveniently at $x = 0$). The surface on which the object moves is frictionless. (a) What force does the spring exert on the object just before it is released? (b) What are the angular frequency, the frequency, and the period of the oscillation? (c) What is the amplitude of the oscillation? (d) What is the maximum speed of the object?

**P–16.9.** (a) What is the total energy of the system in P–16.8? (b) What is the elastic potential energy of this system when the object is halfway between the equilibrium position and its turning point?

**P–16.10.** An object undergoes a simple harmonic motion. During that motion the object needs 0.4 s to reach one point of zero velocity from the previous such point. If the distance between those points is 50 cm, calculate (a) the period, (b) the frequency, and (c) the amplitude of the motion.

**P–16.11.** An object has a mass of 250 g. It undergoes a simple harmonic motion. The amplitude of that motion is 10 cm and the period is 0.5 s. (a) What is the spring constant (assuming that the spring obeys Hooke's law)? (b) What is the maximum magnitude of the force that acts on the object?

**P–16.12.** An object is attached to an ideal spring. It undergoes a simple harmonic motion with a total energy of $E = 1.0$ J. The amplitude of the motion is 15.0 cm and the maximum speed of the object is 1.2 m/s. Find (a) the spring constant, (b) the mass of the object, and (c) the frequency of the oscillation.

**P–16.13.** An object of mass $m$ starts from rest and slides a distance $d = 10$ cm down a frictionless inclined plane of angle $\theta = 50°$ with the horizontal, as shown in Fig. 16.32. It then attaches to the end of a relaxed spring with spring constant $k = 100$ N/m. By what length does the object compress the spring by the time it comes (momentarily) to rest?

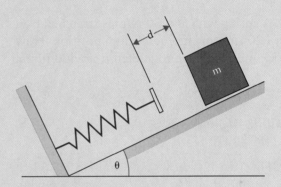

**FIGURE 16.32**

**P–16.14.** An object of mass $m = 250$ g is placed on a vertical spring with $k = 5.0$ kN/m. It is pushed down, compressing the spring by 10 cm. When the object is released, it leaves the spring and continues to travel upward. What maximum height above the release point does the object reach? Neglect air resistance.

**P–16.15.** In Fig. 16.32, the object of mass $m = 2.0$ kg is brought into contact with the spring. The object and spring are at rest with the spring compressed by 10 cm. If $\theta = 30°$, what is the spring constant?

**P–16.16.** In Fig. 16.33, a spring with $k = 160$ N/m rests vertically on the bottom of a beaker filled with water. A block of wood of mass $m = 500$ kg and density $\rho = 0.65$ g/cm$^3$ is attached to the spring. The system reaches a new static equilibrium, shown in the figure at right, after the spring is elongated by a length $\Delta L$. Calculate $\Delta L$. (Consult Chapter 11 for physics concepts needed to solve this problem.)

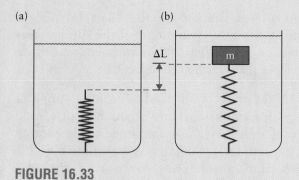

**FIGURE 16.33**

**P–16.17.** An object of mass $m = 0.3$ kg is attached to a horizontal spring. Its position varies with time as:

$$x = (0.25 \text{ m})\cos(0.4 \cdot \pi \cdot t) \qquad [77]$$

Find (a) the amplitude of its motion, (b) the spring constant, (c) the position at $t = 0.3$ s, and (d) the speed of the object at $t = 0.3$ s.

**P–16.18.** A spring with $k = 30$ N/m is stretched by a distance of 20 cm from its equilibrium position. How much work must be done to stretch it an additional 10 cm?

## APPLICATIONS IN CHEMISTRY AND THE LIFE SCIENCES

**P–16.19.** Fig. 16.34(a) shows a fly and Fig. 16.34(b) shows a simplified model for the insect's moving wings during flight. The wing is pivoted about the outer chitin capsule (on red arrowhead). The end of the wing lies $l_1 = 0.5$ mm inside the insect's body and moves up and down by 0.3 mm. We use an effective spring constant of $k = 0.74$ N/m for the elastic tissue in the insect's body surrounding the end of the wing, and an effective mass of 0.3 mg for the wing. The wing motion is described as a vibration of the end of the wing attached to a spring (elastic tissue). (a) With what frequency do the wings of the insect flap during flight? (b) What is the maximum speed of the inner end of the wing? (c) What is the maximum speed of the outer tip of the wing if the wing is treated as a rigid object? Use $l_2 = 1.4$ cm.

**P–16.20.** The vibration frequencies of atoms in solids at room temperature are about $10^{13}$ Hz, similar to the values shown in Table 16.3. Using a simplified model for a solid in which the atoms are connected by ideal springs, we want to study how a single atom in a piece of copper vibrates with this frequency relative to surrounding atoms that are at rest.

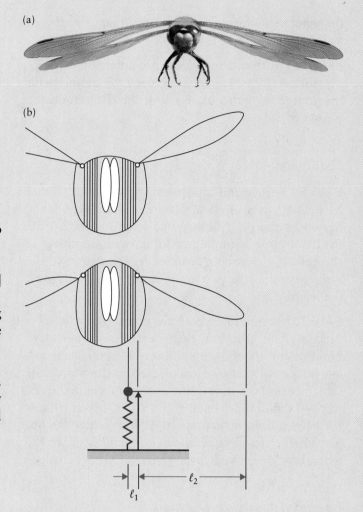

**FIGURE 16.34**

(a) Calculate the (effective) spring constant, using $M_{\text{Cu}} = 63.55$ g/mol. (b) What is the ratio of the (effective) spring constant of a gold atom in a piece of gold and the copper atom in part (a)?

**P–16.21.** A pogo stick (see Fig. 16.35(a)) is a toy that stores energy in a spring with typical spring constant $k = 25\ 000$ N/m. Fig. 16.35(b) shows a child at three different instants when playing with a pogo stick. At position $d_1 = -10$ cm (panel (A)), the spring compression is at a maximum and the child is momentarily at rest. At position $d = 0$ (panel (B)), the spring is relaxed and the child is moving upward. At position $d_2$ (panel (C)), the child reaches the highest point of the jump and is momentarily at rest. Assume that the combined mass of the child and the pogo stick is 25 kg. (a) Calculate the total energy of the system if we choose the gravitational potential energy to be zero at $d = 0$. (b) Calculate $d_2$. (c) Calculate the speed of the child at $d = 0$. (d) Calculate the acceleration of the child at $d_1$. (e) *For those interested*: should any of these results be a matter of concern to the parents?

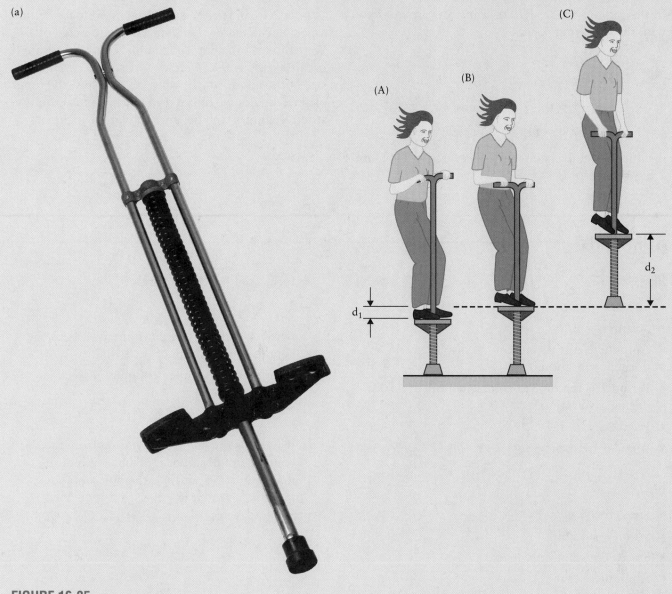

(a)

**FIGURE 16.35**

# MATH REVIEW

## DEGREES AND RADIANS

In the physical sciences, we often use the approximation $\sin \theta = \theta$. This approximation holds generally for small angles $\theta$. However, to be more quantitative, we need to first review the definition of an angle. An angle is measured as the ratio of the length of the arc it subtends in a circle to the radius of that circle. For example, in Fig. 16.18 the angle $\theta$ is given by $\theta = s/L$. This angle carries the unit **radians** (rad). In physical applications angles must always be used in radians; other units of angles, such as degree (°) or revolutions (rev) have to be converted to radians to obtain proper quantitative results. It is worthwhile to study your pocket calculator to figure out how it deals with the unit radians. Most calculators allow you to switch between a degree mode and a radians mode. In the degree mode (DEG) it provides you with the following results:

$$\sin(0°) = 0.0 \qquad \cos(0°) = 1.0$$

$$\sin(90°) = 1.0 \qquad \cos(90°) = 0.0$$

$$\sin(180°) = 0.0 \qquad \cos(180°) = -1.0$$

$$\sin(270°) = -1.0 \qquad \cos(270°) = 0.0$$

In the radians mode (RAD), it instead provides you with the following results:

$$\sin(0) = 0.0 \qquad \cos(0) = 1.0$$
$$\sin(\pi/2) = 1.0 \qquad \cos(\pi/2) = 0.0$$
$$\sin(\pi) = 0.0 \qquad \cos(\pi) = -1.0$$
$$\sin(3\pi/2) = -1.0 \qquad \cos(3\pi/2) = 0.0$$

in which the conversion is given as $\pi$ rad = 180°, and 1 rad = 57.3°.

Now we can test the approximation $\sin\theta = \theta$ with a pocket calculator. Let's start with an angle of 10°. We can confirm that 10° qualifies as a small angle because $10° = 0.1745$ rad and $\sin 10° = 0.1736$; i.e., both values vary by only 0.5%. Thus, the range of small angles we referred to in the text isn't too restrictive; angles well beyond 10° can be included.

# SUMMARY

## DEFINITIONS

- Stress: $\sigma = F/A$
- Strain: $\varepsilon = \Delta l/l$
- Amplitude $A$ is the maximum displacement during a vibration.
- Period $T$ is the time to complete a full cycle during a vibration.
- Frequency: $f = 1/T$
- Angular frequency: $\omega = 2 \cdot \pi \cdot f = 2 \cdot \pi/T$

## UNITS

- Stress $\sigma$: $N/m^2 = Pa$
- Strain $\varepsilon$: no units
- Spring constant $k$: N/m
- Amplitude $A$: m
- Period $T$: s
- Frequency $f$: 1/s = Hz
- Angular frequency $\omega$: rad/s

## LAWS

- Elastic deformation (Hooke's law)
  - for tensile stress (stretching):

  $$\sigma = Y \cdot \varepsilon$$

  where $Y$ is Young's modulus.
  - for hydraulic stress (volume compression):

  $$p = -B \frac{\Delta V}{V}$$

  where $B$ is bulk modulus.

- form used for elastic spring:

$$F_{elast} = -k(x - x_{eq})$$

where $k$ is the spring constant, and $x_{eq}$ is the equilibrium position of the spring.

- form used for simple pendulum:

$$F_{restore} = -m \cdot g \cdot \theta = -\frac{m \cdot g}{L} x$$

where $\theta$ is the angle of deviation from the equilibrium position, $L$ is the length of the massless string, and $x$ is the horizontal displacement from the vertical position.

- Elastic energy for an object attached to a spring
  - for $x_{eq} = 0$:

  $$E_{elast} = \frac{1}{2} k \cdot x^2$$

  - for $x_{eq} \neq 0$:

  $$E_{elast} = \frac{1}{2} k \, (x - x_{eq})^2$$

- Simple harmonic oscillation:

$$x(t) = A \cdot \cos(\omega \cdot t)$$

where $\omega$ is angular frequency, which is given for an object attached to a spring:

$$\omega = \sqrt{\frac{k}{m}}$$

where $k$ is the spring constant.

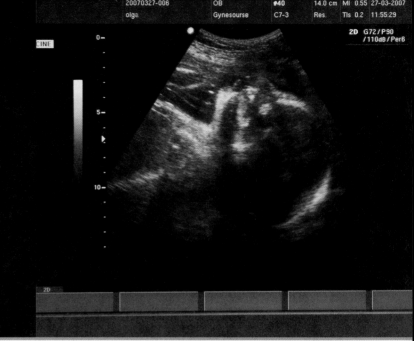

# CHAPTER 17

# THE EAR AND COMMUNICATION
## Longitudinal Waves

A mechanical deformation caused in a medium is not confined to its source but travels as a perturbation at a given speed away from the source. This perturbation is called a wave; acoustic waves (sound) and light waves are the two physiologically most important examples. Sound and light also represent the main fundamental categories of waves: transverse waves are waves for which the propagation direction is perpendicular to the direction in which the deformation oscillates (e.g., a wave along a rope that is connected to a wall when moving one end up and down). Longitudinal waves are waves for which the propagation direction is collinear with the direction in which the deformation oscillates (e.g., air elements in a sound wave vibrate back and forth in the direction in which the sound travels). Light is discussed in Chapters 18 to 20; here, we establish first the basic concepts for acoustic waves.

The perturbation in a gas that carries sound is an oscillating variation of the density and pressure of small gas elements. The displacement and motion of the gas element represent the total energy contained in the wave. This energy travels with the speed of sound. The product of energy and speed defines the sound intensity. The intensity of a point sound source attenuates with the inverse square of the distance from the source. It further diminishes exponentially when energy is absorbed by the medium (Beer's law).

In confined media, such as closed or half-closed tubes, the wave is described by a sinusoidal function if it is caused by an elastic vibration obeying Hooke's law; such waves are called harmonic waves. When harmonic waves reflect off the closed end of the tube and are superimposed on themselves, standing waves emerge if a half-wavelength is a multiple of the length of the tube. Such standing waves are called harmonics. Harmonics result from an external excitation that couples into the confined system resonantly. An example is the vibration of the vocal cords causing the human voice. The inverse process causes the vibrations of the eardrum when sound enters the outer ear.

Beats result when two waves of similar frequency overlap. The Doppler effect describes the recorded sound frequency when the source and/or the receiver are in motion relative to the sound-carrying medium.

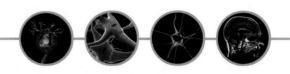

**Psychophysics** is the term invented by Gustav Fechner in the late 19th century to describe the physics and physiology of the human senses. This term combines the scientific physical approach with the more interpretive concepts of psychology. We will find in this and the next chapters that stimulus detection and signal processing of our senses is quite complex and that the naïve assumption of objectivity is often not applicable. Whether we hear a symphony, see a painting, taste a sweet dessert, or smell the freshness of a crisp winter morning, we have to understand that the beauty of these things does not exist anywhere but in our mind. It is the interpretation our brain attaches to the tremendous flow of stimuli arriving from the environment that we perceive as reality, while the physical and chemical reality is a much more profane maze of electromagnetic frequencies, acoustic waves, and chemical reactions in our mucous membranes.

Of the human senses, we have already discussed two simpler ones: the sense of equilibrium and the sense of touch. Our two most powerful senses are vision and hearing. Both are discussed in detail in this textbook, hearing in the present chapter and vision in Chapters 18 to 20. Comparing these two senses, we note a number of similarities. Both are sufficiently developed to analyze a wide range of different external stimuli (light in vision and sound in hearing). These stimuli originate in the environment and reach the eye or the ear across appreciable distances, which usually allows for sufficient time to react.

To lay the foundation for the physical properties of the stimuli and the physiological principles of their detection, the concept of waves is introduced in the present chapter. We will note key differences between the respective wave models for light and sound that justify discussing them in separate chapters: sound is carried by air, while light needs no medium. We have discussed in detail the properties of gases and are therefore well prepared to expand on these concepts to develop a model for sound propagation. On the other hand, to understand the wave nature of light, magnetism still has to be introduced.

## The Acoustic Environment

An almost infinite number of different sound sources exist. Humans can distinguish about 400 000 different sounds. On one end are the various forms of noise, ranging from the crackling of wood in a fireplace to a jet engine, and on the other end are the harmonic sounds of musical instruments and the characteristic patterns of the human voice. All of these sources create different sound patterns, resulting in a highly complex sound environment for our ear. Yet we can distinguish all of these sounds; we are as confident in picking out a familiar voice as we are in recognizing a person's face. To be able to distinguish so many sounds several different parameters must exist to characterize sound. Fig. 17.1 provides an example of the many concepts we need to define and relate to the physics of sound. It shows an amplitude

**FIGURE 17.1**

Time dependence of the sound amplitude (top) and the frequency band width (bottom) for the spoken word *acoustic*. The physical pattern varies primarily with individual letters.

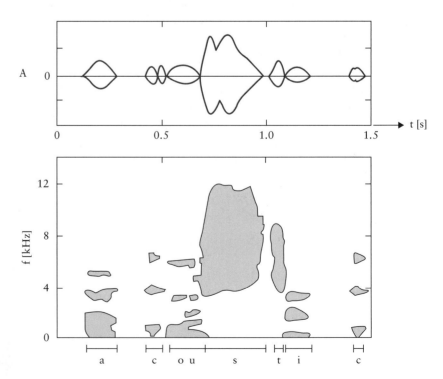

profile and frequency spectrum for the human voice. The top part of the figure shows the time dependence of the sound amplitude for the spoken word *acoustic* (as recorded with a microphone). The corresponding frequency bands for each sound are illustrated in the lower graph. This word has seven different sounds, as distinguished at the bottom of the figure, each displaying different amplitudes, frequency bands, and time lengths. To appreciate the formation of voice and to develop a model of how our ear can detect voices, the concepts of frequency and amplitude have to be established for sound waves and their relation to pitch, timbre, and loudness have to be developed.

Once we understand acoustic waves in open space, we need to study the additional phenomena that emerge when sound waves occur in spatial confinement. We use closed tubes and tubes open at one end as model systems. This allows us to develop concepts of resonant sound amplification applicable to the outer ear canal and the vocal tract. The outer ear acts as a half-open tube in which arriving sound waves cause the eardrum to vibrate. These vibrations are mechanically amplified in the middle ear and then propagate as a wave through the fluids in the inner ear (cochlea). There, the wave is analyzed for its frequency bands.

We conclude the chapter with three special features: stereoscopic hearing, which is the detection of the direction of the sound source; acoustic illusions that result from beats; and the Doppler effect, which describes the role of moving sound sources and/or receivers.

# Waves in an Unconfined Medium

Since the particles in any homogeneous medium (e.g., solids, liquids, and gases) interact with each other, local vibrations of atoms or molecules around their equilibrium position affect other particles in the close vicinity. These interactions lead to a propagating wave.

## Physical Properties of Waves: Speed, Wavelength, and Frequency

The easiest way to illustrate the connection between a local vibration and the resulting wave is to attach a rope to a wall and swing its free end up and down. The formation of a wave along the rope is shown in Fig. 17.2. Assume that the rope is initially stretched horizontally. At time $t = 0$, you start to move your hand up and down so that it oscillates vertically with amplitude $A$. At time $t = T/4$, your hand has com-

pleted a quarter period and has reached position $+A$. Since the rope is continuous, its parts adjacent to your hand must have been pulled up as well, as illustrated in the second frame of Fig. 17.2. Later, at time $t = T/2$, your hand has returned to its original position. However, since the rope has been following your hand, it is not stretched as it was initially but contains a bulge, as shown in the third frame of Fig. 17.2. In the next two frames your hand completes another half period by moving to the position $-A$ and back. Again, the adjacent part of the rope follows and a downward bulge results. The initial, upward-directed bulge did not disappear, but has moved farther to the right. Thus, at time $t = T$, the

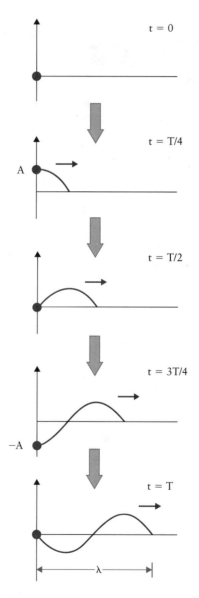

**FIGURE 17.2**

Various stages of the motion of a rope when the free end at the origin oscillates up and down with period $T$. Once a full period of the vibration is completed (bottom panel), the rope is displaced to a distance $\lambda$, called the wavelength.

local oscillation of your hand has been transformed into a full sinusoidal shape of the rope, reaching to a point at distance $\lambda$ from your hand. The rope now describes a wave with $\lambda$ the **wavelength**, which we combine with the **period** $T$ to calculate the speed at which the perturbation caused by your hand propagates along the rope:

$$v_{\text{wave}} = \frac{\lambda}{T} = \lambda \cdot f \qquad [1]$$

in which $f$ is the **frequency**, which is related to the period as $f = 1/T$.

*The speed of a wave is equal to the product of its wavelength and frequency.*

## Concept Question 17.1

**In air at room temperature, the wavelength of a sound increases as a result of the following change in parameters: (A) a frequency increase, (B) a frequency decrease, (C) a speed of sound increase, or (D) a speed of sound decrease.**

ANSWER: (B). Eq. [1] shows that wavelength and frequency are inversely proportional to each other for a given speed of sound. The speed of sound does not vary with wavelength or frequency; it is a parameter that exclusively depends on the properties of the sound-carrying medium.

## ● EXAMPLE 17.1

(a) The musical note $C_4$ (Middle C) on a piano is caused by a string vibrating with a frequency of 261.6 Hz. The vibrating string interacts with the adjacent air, causing a sound wave to propagate away from the piano with a wavelength of 1.31 m. What is the speed of sound in air? (b) An FM station broadcasts at $f = 100$ MHz with radio waves of wavelength $\lambda = 3$ m. Find the speed of the radio wave.

*Solution to part (a):* The speed of waves is given by Eq. [1]:

$$v_{\text{wave}} = \lambda \cdot f = (1.31 \text{ m}) \cdot (261.6 \text{ Hz})$$

$$= 342.7 \, \frac{\text{m}}{\text{s}} \qquad [2]$$

The speed of a sound wave at room temperature is about 340 m/s.

*Solution to part (b):* We again use Eq. [1]:

$$v_{\text{wave}} = \lambda \cdot f = (3 \text{ m}) \cdot (100 \text{ MHz})$$

$$= 3 \times 10^8 \, \frac{\text{m}}{\text{s}} \qquad [3]$$

The speed of a radio wave is significantly higher than the speed of sound.

## ● EXAMPLE 17.2

Bats use ultrasound echolocation to detect small insects in flight. For this to work, the wavelength used by bats must be smaller than or equal to the size of their prey. Bats therefore use frequencies of about 80 kHz. Dolphins and porpoises also use ultrasound echolocation for hunting. (a) If a dolphin's prey were as small as the insects eaten by bats, what frequency would dolphins have to use? (b) Dolphins actually use frequencies up to 225 kHz. How much bigger is their smallest prey when compared to the insects that bats hunt? *Hint:* Use $c_{\text{air}} = 340$ m/s for the speed of sound in air and use $c_{\text{sea}} = 1530$ m/s for the speed of sound in seawater.

*Solution to part (a):* We use Eq. [1], written once for the medium air and once for the medium seawater. In both cases, the wavelength is specified by the smallest length required for each predator, $\lambda = L_{\text{insect}}$ for the bat and $\lambda = L_{\text{squid}}$ for the dolphin (assuming that squid is the smallest prey a dolphin hunts):

$$\text{bat in air:} \qquad c_{\text{air}} = L_{\text{insect}} \cdot f_{\text{bat}}$$
$$\text{dolphin in sea:} \quad c_{\text{water}} = L_{\text{squid}} \cdot f_{\text{dolphin}} \qquad [4]$$

In part (a) we assume that $L_{\text{insect}} = L_{\text{squid}}$. This leads to the frequency needed by a dolphin to detect a squid the size of an insect:

$$f_{\text{dolphin}} = \frac{c_{\text{water}}}{c_{\text{air}}} f_{\text{bat}}$$

$$= \frac{1530 \text{ m/s}}{340 \text{ m/s}} \cdot (80 \times 10^3 \text{ Hz})$$

$$= 360 \text{ kHz} \qquad [5]$$

*Solution to part (b):* The result in Eq. [5] shows that dolphins cannot hunt prey as small as the insects that are hunted by bats. To answer part (b), we allow for the size of a squid and the size of an insect to differ, using the two formulas in Eq. [4] to calculate the ratio $L_{\text{squid}}/L_{\text{insect}}$:

$$\frac{L_{\text{squid}}}{L_{\text{insect}}} = \frac{c_{\text{water}}}{c_{\text{air}}} \frac{f_{\text{bat}}}{f_{\text{dolphin}}}$$

$$= \frac{1530\,\text{m/s}}{340\,\text{m/s}} \cdot \frac{80 \times 10^3\,\text{Hz}}{225 \times 10^3\,\text{Hz}} = 1.6 \quad [6]$$

Thus, among those hunting in three-dimensional space dolphins are probably the most versatile. Given the typical size of an insect hunted by bats, with a size just over 4 mm, the much larger dolphin can detect objects as small as 7 mm in size under water. The smallest adult squid are 2 to 3 cm long. In addition, the dolphin can detect objects of that size over a much longer distance because sound absorption in water is much less than in air.

## Longitudinal and Transverse Waves

It is worthwhile to analyze the results of Example 17.1 in more detail. The wave propagation speed in part (a) is consistent with the range of speeds we calculated for air molecules at room temperature using the kinetic gas theory in Chapter 7. Thus, we propose that air is the **medium** that carries sound waves. We will see that the vibration of a sound source creates a periodic variation in the density of the adjacent air, and this density perturbation travels through the medium, superimposed on the random motion of the gas particles. The speed of individual air molecules limits the propagation speed of sound, as they need to collide with gas molecules in neighbouring gas elements.

Accepting this reasoning requires us to identify a different medium for the propagation of radio waves as studied in part (b) of Example 17.1. We recognize the speed found in that case to be the speed of light. Thus, we expect that radio waves and light are similar. Indeed, we know that both types of waves do not need a medium as both are transmitted through the vacuum of outer space (the field of radioastronomy analyzes radio signals from astronomical objects).

Waves are not just distinguished by different wavelengths, frequencies, and wave propagation speeds. We illustrate another major difference by looking once more at Fig. 17.2. Note that the vibration that causes the wave is based on an up–down motion of the left end of the rope. The propagating wave in turn moves toward the right, i.e., in a direction perpendi-

cular to the vibration. We call such a wave a **transverse wave.** Important examples of this type of wave are radio and light waves, which we discuss in Chapter 20.

Other wave forms, in particular the sound waves that interest us in this chapter, differ from the transverse wave type. This is illustrated with the five sketches in Fig. 17.3, showing a gas in which an acoustic wave is generated. In the first frame at time $t = 0$ the gas shown to the right of the piston has a uniform density. The equilibrium position of the piston is indicated by a vertical dashed line. The gas density is indicated graphically as the density of vertical lines in the gas. At time $t = 0$ the piston is set into motion toward the right, as indicated by an arrow. At $t > 0$ the piston will undergo a harmonic oscillation, as introduced in the previous chapter. In the current context our focus is on the air in front of the piston.

The four lower frames in Fig. 17.3 are equivalent to frames (b) to (e) in Fig. 17.2 for the formation of

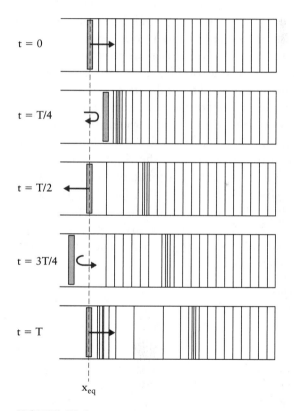

**FIGURE 17.3**

Five snapshots illustrating the development of an acoustic wave in a gas-filled container due to the vibrational motion of a piston about its equilibrium position $x_{\text{eq}}$. The piston reaches the amplitude point toward the right at time $T/4$ and the amplitude point toward the left at time $3 \cdot T/4$. When the piston moves toward the right the air pocket adjacent to the piston is compressed (indicated by an increased density of vertical lines). When the piston moves toward the left the air pocket adjacent to the piston is expanded (indicated by a decreased density of vertical lines).

a wave on a rope. When the piston reaches its amplitude toward the right at $t = T/4$, a locally compressed pocket of air is created in front of the piston (indicated by a high density of vertical lines). The gas molecules in this area of increased density have also been given an additional velocity component toward the right. When the piston then moves back to its equilibrium position (reached at time $t = T/2$), the gas molecules in front of the piston are pulled back toward the left, causing an area of decreased air density (indicated by a low density of vertical lines).

By moving beyond the equilibrium position to the amplitude point at the left (reached at time $t = 3 \cdot T/4$), the piston increases the volume of the gas pocket directly in front of it at the right. Thus, the volume with decreased air density is further enlarged. In the meantime, the initially created zone of increased air density has travelled toward the right and remains present in the system (illustrated as a zone of denser vertical lines). Note that it is the density variations that travel, not the individual molecules in the gas. The absolute density of the gas is very high and thus individual gas molecules encounter frequent collisions that essentially keep them near their original position.

In the last frame of Fig. 17.3 we see that the piston, turning toward the right after $t = 3 \cdot T/4$, compresses the air in front of it once more while completing a full period of motion. Thus, at the final time $t = T$, a second zone of increased air density is generated that subsequently travels toward the right following the initial high-density zone at a constant distance.

What distinguishes the case in Fig. 17.3 from the case in Fig. 17.2 is the fact that the direction of the vibration of the piston and the direction of the propagating sound wave are collinear. Such waves are called **longitudinal waves.**

*The direction of the exciting oscillation and the direction of the propagating wave are collinear for longitudinal waves and perpendicular for transverse waves.*

Important differences exist between longitudinal and transverse waves. We will discuss one such difference in detail in Chapter 20 when introducing the linear polarization of light. Acoustic waves do not have this feature, because longitudinal waves cannot be polarized.

### Concept Question 17.2

**Identify examples of (a) transverse waves and (b) longitudinal waves. Use a literature or internet search for this question.**

---

ANSWER TO PART (a): Electromagnetic waves including visible light, ultraviolet and infrared light, microwaves, and radio waves. **Seismic waves** caused by an earthquake contain both a longitudinal and a transverse component. They travel with different speeds in Earth's crust and are recorded in sequence by a seismograph. The relative delay allows earth scientists to determine the epicentre of the earthquake.

ANSWER TO PART (b): Sound waves, including audible sound and ultrasound for medical applications. Note that we did not list surface waves of water because the medium (small water elements) in this case moves in a circular fashion.

## Longitudinal Waves in a Gas

We want to take a step toward a quantitative description of wave propagation in a gas. This step is based on Fig. 17.4, in which we study the speed and the pressure variations of a gas element. The notation $p(x)$ means $p = f(x)$, i.e., the pressure is a function of position along the $x$-axis, and $v(x)$ means $v = f^*(x)$, i.e., the gas element's speed is also a function of position. We use the asterisk to note that the two functions $f(x)$ and $f^*(x)$ are initially not assumed to be the same. A small gas element of length $\Delta x$ is highlighted in grey in Fig. 17.4. It lies between two dashed vertical lines. To simplify its motion, we assume that the gas is contained in a cylindrical tube that is aligned with the $x$-axis. The gas to the left of the element causes a local pressure $p(x)$ at position $x$ and the gas to the right causes a local pressure $p(x + \Delta x)$ at position $x + \Delta x$. The small gas element is not in mechanical equilibrium if we assume that somewhere to the left a piston vibrates, as in Fig. 17.3. This means that the two local pressure values differ and therefore

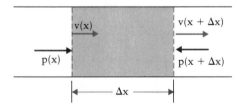

**FIGURE 17.4**

A small gas element is shown in a cylindrical tube with a one-dimensional sound wave generated by a vibrating piston, which is somewhere to the left of the grey gas element. The vertical dashed lines define its length $\Delta x$. We distinguish the gas pressure and the speed of the gas at both interfaces confining the gas element.

cause an acceleration of the small gas element. Newton's second law relates the pressure change along the $x$-axis to the change of gas element speed with time, i.e., its acceleration.

Also, the speeds of the two interfaces that separate the gas element from the gas outside in Fig. 17.4 vary as well, with values $v(x)$ and $v(x + \Delta x)$. This difference leads to a change in the volume of the small gas element. A volume change causes a change in pressure based on the ideal gas law. Thus, the change in speed along the $x$-axis causes a change in pressure.

When these two arguments are combined a **wave equation** follows, i.e., an equation that relates the time and position dependence of the parameters of a wave to each other. The specific dependence of the displacement, the pressure variations, and the density variations on position and time (called the **wave function**) obviously cannot be specified based on Fig. 17.4 alone, as the choice of a particular vibration that causes the wave will lead to different wave forms. Thus, additional information is needed to specify the wave function. We study the most important case, in which the vibration of the piston is a simple harmonic oscillation, in the next section.

*Pressure differences in a gas cause the acceleration of small gas elements. Their velocity differences in turn cause pressure differences. Both effects combine to create a wave function that relates the time and position dependences of gas pressure variations or small gas element displacements.*

A few general properties of waves apply regardless of the specific form of vibration causing the wave. Here, we discuss two of these issues for a wave that may result from an experiment like the one shown in Fig. 17.4: the dependence of position and time for pressure variations, and the speed of sound.

- *Inter-dependence of position and time in a wave.* We define the **displacement** of a small gas element in Fig. 17.4 as $\xi$, with $\xi = x - x_{eq}$. For a sound wave the displacement varies from point to point in space and also in time. Thus, the most general mathematical form for the displacement is $\xi = f(x, t)$. This means that the displacement is a function that contains two independent variables, time and position. However, writing $\xi = f(x, t)$ is too general because the variables $x$ and $t$ are not independent from each other. To see this, we study an arbitrary wave that travels along the $x$-axis at two different times $t_1$ and $t_2$. You can do this by dropping a pebble in a pond and observe the evolving pattern of water surface waves moving away from the impact point.

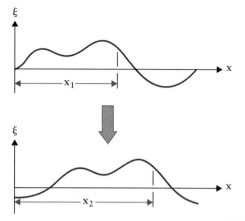

**FIGURE 17.5**

A displacement of a gas element from its equilibrium position, $\xi = x - x_{eq}$, due to a perturbation moving through the medium. The figure shows the wave twice, at time $t_1$ (top) and at time $t_2$ (bottom). During the time interval $\Delta t = t_2 - t_1$ the wave travels a distance $\Delta x = x_2 - x_1$ toward the right. The speed of the wave is $c = \Delta x / \Delta t$.

At the earlier time $t_1$ the wave function has a particular profile as a function of the position, for example, the profile shown in the top sketch of Fig. 17.5. Studying the wave at a later time $t_2$ we find the case illustrated in the lower sketch of Fig. 17.5. The wave function differs at the later time only in that the wave pattern has moved along the $x$-axis. This is highlighted in Fig. 17.5 by identifying the position of a specific feature of the wave, which is initially at position $x_1$ and later at position $x_2$. The wave function is in both cases identical if the appropriate combination of position shift and elapsed time between an initial and final snapshot is taken into account:

$$x_1 - c \cdot t_1 = x_2 - c \cdot t_2 \qquad [7]$$

i.e., the position shift from $x_1$ to $x_2$ is linearly related to the elapsed time, from $t_1$ to $t_2$, with a prefactor $c$ for the time. This prefactor must have the unit of speed, m/s, for Eq. [7] to be physically correct. Since both sides of Eq. [7] have the same mathematical form, we conclude that the displacement of the gas element depends on position and time in the form:

$$\xi = f(x - c \cdot t) \qquad [8]$$

which states that the displacement depends on a single independent variable, which is $x - c \cdot t$. This variable is called the **phase of the wave**, and the constant $c$ is the speed of sound.

- *Speed of sound.* We can quantify the speed of sound from Eq. [7]:

$$c = \frac{x_2 - x_1}{t_2 - t_1} \qquad [9]$$

$c$ is specifically called the **phase velocity** of the wave. This quantity should not be mixed up with the speed of a particular gas particle or the root-mean-square speed introduced in Chapter 7.

Sound propagation is not limited to gaseous media. Fig. 17.4 illustrates that the occurrence of a travelling sound wave in a gas is due to the compressibility of the gas. In Chapter 16 we determined that real solids and liquids are also compressible. Thus, wave phenomena occur in these two states of matter as well. Compressibility in solids is directional, as we discussed at the beginning of Chapter 16. Liquids and gases are fluids in which compression must occur from all directions. Their compressibility is governed by the bulk modulus $B$. The speed of sound then follows from the bulk modulus and the density of the medium:

$$c_{\text{fluid}} = \sqrt{\frac{B}{\rho}} \qquad [10]$$

*Wave equations describe the wave as a function of position and time. In a sound wave position and time dependences are linked through the speed of sound, which depends on the elastic properties and the density of the medium.*

The speed of sound in a gas can be derived from Eq. [10]. Note that we calculated the bulk modulus for an isothermal ideal gas in Eq. [16.23]. We cannot substitute that result in Eq. [10] because Eq. [16.23] is derived with the assumption of a constant temperature ($T = \text{const}$). For a gas expansion to occur isothermally, it must be done slowly. This does not apply to the fast vibrations of air in a travelling sound wave. The sound vibrations of air have to be described by an adiabatic compression since the time during which the compression occurs is too short to allow a heat exchange with the adjacent air. Using an adiabatic process to calculate the bulk modulus of an ideal gas leads to **Laplace's equation** for the speed of sound:

$$c_{\text{sound in gas}} = \sqrt{\frac{\kappa \cdot p}{\rho}} \qquad [11]$$

in which $\kappa = C_p/C_V$ is the adiabatic coefficient, with $C_p$ the molar heat capacity of the gas at constant pressure and $C_V$ at constant volume. Table 17.1 summarizes values for the speed of sound in various solids, liquids, and gases.

## TABLE 17.1

### Speed of sound in various materials

| Material | Speed of sound (m/s) | Temperature (K) |
|---|---|---|
| *Gases:* | | |
| Air | 331 | 273 |
| Air | 343 | 293 |
| Air | 386 | 373 |
| *Liquids:* | | |
| Water | 1400 | 273 |
| Water | 1490 | 298 |
| Seawater (3.5% salt) | 1530 | 298 |
| *Solids and soft matter:* | | |
| Steel | 5940 | |
| Granite | 6000 | |
| Human body tissue | 1540 | 310 |
| Vulcanized rubber | 55 | |

## Concept Question 17.3

**The speed of sound in a gas is limited by the speed of the gas particles in the gas. Why then can a solid carry sound even though its atoms or molecules remain at the same location within the lattice?**

ANSWER: Gas molecules are not chemically or physically bound to each other and interact only through collisions. Thus, a physical change of the parameters for a given gas particle can reach other gas particles only when the initial particle has travelled into their vicinity and undergone a collision. In a solid, all particles are chemically or physically bound to each other. When a physical parameter in one neighbourhood changes, neighbouring atoms or molecules are affected very fast due to the strong interactions along these bonds. Thus, the speed of sound in a solid is usually much higher than in a gas.

## ● EXAMPLE 17.3

The adiabatic coefficient $\kappa$ for air under normal conditions is $\kappa = 1.4$. If we use for the density of air at 0°C the value $\rho = 1.293$ kg/m³, confirm the speed of sound at 0°C and for air pressure 1 atm, as shown in Table 17.1.

*Solution:* Substituting the given values in Eq. [11], we find:

$$c_{air} = \sqrt{\kappa \cdot \frac{p}{\rho}} = \sqrt{1.4 \cdot \frac{1.013 \times 10^5 \,\text{Pa}}{1.293 \,\frac{\text{kg}}{\text{m}^3}}}$$

$$= 331.3 \,\frac{\text{m}}{\text{s}} \qquad [12]$$

As Table 17.1 shows, the speed of sound in gases and liquids depends strongly on the temperature. We quantify this for gases by using the ideal gas law. We know from Charles's law that the ideal gas expands linearly when the temperature is increased. Charles's law is rewritten with the reference volume $V_0$ at 0°C: $V = V_0 (1 + \alpha \cdot T)$. In this formula, $\alpha$ is the **linear expansion coefficient** for an ideal gas with $\alpha = 1/273.15 \,\text{K}^{-1}$. This means that the gas expands by a fraction of 1/273.15 per degree of temperature increase. With this volume formula, the definition of the gas density, $\rho = m/V$, is written in the form:

$$\rho = \frac{\rho_0}{1 + \alpha \cdot T} \qquad [13]$$

in which $\rho_0$ is the reference density at 0°C temperature. Eq. [13] is substituted into Eq. [11] to determine the temperature dependence of the speed of sound at constant gas pressure:

$$c = c_0 \sqrt{1 + \alpha \cdot T} \qquad [14]$$

in which $c_0$ is the reference speed at 0°C temperature.

## Concept Question 17.4

Are Eq. [13] and Eq. [7.44] consistent with each other? Eq. [7.44] stated that the density of an ideal gas can be written in the form: $\rho = M \cdot p/(R \cdot T)$.

ANSWER: The difference between both equations is that the temperature in Eq. [13] is given in degrees Celsius, while it is given in unit Kelvin in Eq. [7.44]. To test consistency, we convert the Celsius temperature in Eq. [13] into the unit Kelvin with $T(\text{K}) = T(°\text{C}) + 273.15 \,\text{K}$. Multiplying by the coefficient $\alpha$ yields $\alpha \cdot T(\text{K}) = \alpha \cdot T(°\text{C}) + 1$. Substituting this term in Eq. [12] then leads to:

$$\rho = \frac{\rho_0}{\alpha \cdot T} \qquad [15]$$

Eqs. [7.44] and [15] are equivalent if:

$$\frac{\rho_0}{\alpha} = \frac{M}{R} p \qquad [16]$$

which shows that $\rho_0$ and the coefficient $\alpha$ are materials-dependent (due to the dependence on $M$) and have a different pressure dependence. Both of these conclusions are consistent with what we expect: the density at 0°C is proportional to $p$ and the coefficient $\alpha$ is independent of pressure.

## ● EXAMPLE 17.4

Using the data for air at 0°C from Table 17.1, find at $p = 1$ atm and $T = 20°\text{C}$ (room temperature) (a) the density, and (b) the speed of sound of air. *Hint:* Use an ideal-gas approximation for the linear expansion coefficient for air.

*Solution to part (a):* We calculate the density of air at room temperature from Eq. [13] first, using a temperature change of 20 K:

$$\rho = \frac{1.293 \,\frac{\text{kg}}{\text{m}^3}}{1 + \left(\frac{1}{273.15 \,\text{K}}\right)(20 \,\text{K})} = 1.205 \,\frac{\text{kg}}{\text{m}^3} \qquad [17]$$

*Solution to part (b):* Eq. [14] allows us to calculate the speed of sound at 20°C:

$$c = \left(331.3 \,\frac{\text{m}}{\text{s}}\right) \sqrt{1 + \frac{20 \,\text{K}}{273.15 \,\text{K}}}$$

$$= 343.2 \,\frac{\text{m}}{\text{s}} \qquad [18]$$

## Harmonic Waves

In our discussion of vibrations we identified a unique role for the harmonic vibrations because they are the result of a mechanical system that obeys Hooke's law with a linear restoring force.

*The waves caused by harmonic vibrations are called harmonic waves. This name was chosen since sinusoidal functions describe these waves.*

With harmonic vibrations causing the wave, the general wave function in Eq. [8] takes a specific form for the displacement of the gas element $\xi$:

$$\xi = A \cdot \sin\left(2 \cdot \pi \cdot f\left(t - \frac{x}{c}\right)\right)$$

$$= A \cdot \sin\left(2 \cdot \pi\left(f \cdot t - \frac{x}{\lambda}\right)\right) \qquad [19]$$

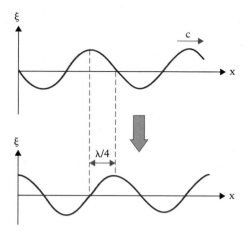

**FIGURE 17.6**

Two harmonic waves. The top curve shows the harmonic wave at time $t = 0$ and the bottom curve shows it a quarter of a period later ($t = T/4$). During this time the wave has travelled toward the right by a quarter of a wavelength, $\lambda/4$ (dashed interval).

in which $A$ is the amplitude, $f$ the frequency, $\lambda$ the wavelength, and $c$ the speed of sound. The negative sign in the argument of the sine function is due to Eq. [8]. Eq. [19] applies for a wave travelling in the $x$-direction (plane wave). Other interesting wave forms include spherical waves travelling outward from a point source. For spherical waves the position parameter in the wave equation is the radius $r$, replacing $x$ in Eq. [19].

The harmonic wave function is illustrated in Fig. 17.6 at two different times. The top curve shows the harmonic wave function at time $t = 0$ and the bottom curve shows it at time $t = T/4$ when the wave has travelled a quarter of a wavelength; i.e., the wave function has shifted by $\lambda/4$.

The harmonic wave function is often written in a slightly different form in the literature, using the **angular frequency** $\omega = 2 \cdot \pi \cdot f$ and the **wave number** $\kappa = 2 \cdot \pi/\lambda$. With these two parameters, Eq. [19] reads:

$$\xi = A \cdot \sin(\omega \cdot t - \kappa \cdot x) \qquad [20]$$

Fig. 17.4 indicates that the pressure in the gas element varies in the same fashion as the displacement of the gas element. This remains true for harmonic waves, leading to another way in which this wave function can be written:

$$\Delta p = \Delta p_{max} \cdot \cos(\omega \cdot t - \kappa \cdot x) \qquad [21]$$

in which the cosine function is used to indicate that displacement and pressure maximums do not occur at the same time and position. The maximum pressure variation, $\Delta p_{max}$, is linearly related to the maximum displacement (amplitude $A$) in Eq. [20]:

$$\Delta p_{max} = (c \cdot \rho \cdot \omega)A \qquad [22]$$

in which $c$ is the speed of sound and $\rho$ is the density of the medium. It is always useful to check the units for new equations, particularly when we do not derive them in the text. In Eq. [22], the units on the right-hand side are: m/s for the speed of sound, $kg/m^3$ for the density of the medium, rad/s for the angular frequency, and m for the amplitude. Neglecting the non-physical unit rad, these units combine to $kg/(m \cdot s^2) = N/m^2 = Pa$, i.e., the unit of pressure. This unit is consistent with the term on the left-hand side of Eq. [22].

● **EXAMPLE 17.5**

The equation of a wave travelling along the $x$-axis is given as:

$$\xi = (2.0 \text{ cm}) \sin\{(1.0 \text{ s}^{-1})t - (1.5 \text{ cm}^{-1})x\} \qquad [23]$$

in which $\xi$ is the displacement, given in unit cm. Determine: (a) the amplitude, (b) the wavelength, (c) the angular frequency, (d) the period, (e) the frequency, and (f) the travelling speed of the wave. (g) Draw two sketches for the wave: $\xi$ versus $x$ at time $t = 0$, and $\xi$ versus $t$ at the position $x = 0$.

*Solution to part (a):* We compare the specific case in Eq. [23] with the harmonic wave equation in Eq. [19]. The amplitude is the prefactor of the *sine* function, i.e., $A = 2.0$ cm. The units of $A$ and $\xi$ must be the same since the sine term cannot carry a physical unit.

*Solution to part (b):* The wave number is read from Eq. [23] as $\kappa = 1.5 \text{ cm}^{-1}$. With the definition of the wave number, $\kappa = 2 \cdot \pi/\lambda$, we find the wavelength:

$$\lambda = \frac{2 \cdot \pi}{\kappa} = \frac{2 \cdot \pi}{1.5 \text{ cm}^{-1}} = 4.2 \text{ cm} \qquad [24]$$

*Solution to part (c):* The angular frequency is read directly from Eq. [23] as $\omega = 1.0$ rad/s.

*Solution to part (d):* The period follows from $\omega$:

$$T = \frac{2 \cdot \pi}{\omega} = \frac{2 \cdot \pi}{1.0 \dfrac{\text{rad}}{\text{s}}} = 6.3 \text{ s} \qquad [25]$$

*Solution to part (e)*: The frequency is inversely proportional to the period:

$$f = \frac{1}{T} = \frac{1}{6.3\,\text{s}} = 0.16\,\text{Hz} \qquad [26]$$

*Solution to part (f)*: The travelling speed of the wave follows from Eq. [1]:

$$v_{\text{wave}} = \lambda \cdot f = (0.042\,\text{m}) \cdot (0.16\,\text{Hz})$$
$$= 6.7 \times 10^{-3}\,\frac{\text{m}}{\text{s}} = 0.67\,\frac{\text{cm}}{\text{s}} \qquad [27]$$

Because of the negative sign in the argument of the sine function in Eq. [23], the wave travels with 0.67 cm/s in the positive *x*-direction.

*Solution to part (g)*: The two sketches are shown in Fig. 17.7. Note that the following trigonometric identity holds: $\sin(-1.5 \cdot x) = -\sin(1.5 \cdot x)$.

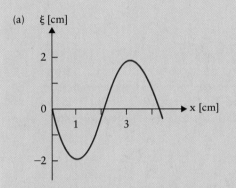

(a)  ξ [cm]

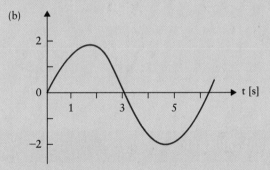

(b)

**FIGURE 17.7**

Displacement function for a given wave. (a) The displacement as a function of position along the *x*-axis at time *t* = 0; (b) the displacement as a function of time at the origin *x* = 0.

● **EXAMPLE 17.6**

The maximum pressure variation that is acceptable for the human ear is about 30 Pa. What is the amplitude of a gas element in this case at 20°C when the sound source emits a frequency of 3.0 kHz, which is a frequency in the range where the ear is most sensitive?

*Solution*: We use the air density we calculated in Example 17.4. From Eq. [22], we find:

$$A = \frac{\Delta p_{\text{max}}}{c \cdot \rho \cdot \omega}$$

$$= \frac{30\,\text{Pa}}{\left(343.2\,\dfrac{\text{m}}{\text{s}}\right)\left(1.205\,\dfrac{\text{kg}}{\text{m}^3}\right)2 \cdot \pi(3000\,\text{Hz})}$$

$$= 3.85 \times 10^{-6}\,\text{m} \qquad [28]$$

i.e., the maximum amplitude tolerated is 3.85 μm. Note that both the pressure variations and the amplitude are comparably small values. The maximum pressure variation used in this example corresponds to less than 0.03% of the normal air pressure (1 atm) and the amplitude of 3.85 μm is a distance we cannot see with the naked eye (the size range of large bacteria is 1 to 2 μm).

## Sound Intensity

**Intensity** is a measure of the amount of energy transported by a wave per time interval Δ*t* through a plane of unit area that is placed perpendicular to the wave's propagation direction. To evaluate the intensity of a sound wave, we first have to establish the total energy carried in a wave. The total energy is the sum of the kinetic and potential energies of the local vibration of its small gas elements:

$$E_{\text{total}} = \frac{1}{2}\,m \cdot v^2 + \frac{1}{2}\,k \cdot \xi^2 \qquad [29]$$

in which *v* is the speed at which the gas element moves when displaced by ξ. We quantify the total energy in analogy to the calculation we used in Chapter 16 to determine the total energy of a vibrating system. We found that the total energy can be expressed as the elastic potential energy at the point of maximum displacement (amplitude) or, alternatively, as the kinetic energy at the maximum speed, i.e., when the object passes through its equilibrium position. The same applies to a vibrating gas element. We use the instant when the gas element passes through its equilibrium position and express the total energy as the kinetic energy at that instant. From Chapter 16 we know that $v_{\text{max}} = \omega \cdot A$ and therefore can write the kinetic energy as:

$$E_{\text{kin,max}} = \frac{1}{2}\,m \cdot \omega^2 \cdot A^2 \qquad [30]$$

where $m$ is the mass of the vibrating gas element. We want to circumvent the need to identify this mass, because the gas element size is arbitrary. We therefore replace $m$ with the density of the gas, $\rho$, multiplied by the volume of the gas element, $V$:

$$E_{\text{total}} = \frac{1}{2}\rho \cdot V \cdot A^2 \cdot \omega^2 \qquad [31]$$

By dividing both sides in Eq. [31] by the arbitrary volume of the gas element, we introduce the **energy density** $\varepsilon_{\text{total}}$ with unit $J/m^3$:

$$\frac{E_{\text{total}}}{V} = \varepsilon_{\text{total}} = \frac{1}{2}\rho \cdot A^2 \cdot \omega^2 \qquad [32]$$

Introducing the energy density relieves us therefore of the problem to specify what we mean by a small gas element: the right-hand side of Eq. [32] no longer contains arbitrary parameters like $V$.

*The energy density of a sound wave is proportional to the square of the amplitude, $\varepsilon_{\text{total}} \propto A^2$.*

The energy density travels with speed $c$ in a medium carrying sound. Thus, the **intensity** $I$ is given as:

$$I = c \cdot \varepsilon_{\text{total}} = \frac{1}{2}c \cdot \rho \cdot A^2 \cdot \omega^2 \qquad [33]$$

with the unit for the intensity $J/(m^2 \cdot s)$.

*The intensity of a wave is the amount of energy passing through a plane of unit area perpendicular to the propagation direction of the wave. It is proportional to the square of the amplitude.*

Eq. [22] allows us to relate the intensity to the pressure variation: the intensity of the sound wave is proportional to the square of the maximum pressure variation; i.e., $I \propto (\Delta p_{\text{max}})^2$. This result is useful when we quantify the sound intensity as judged by the human ear. This relation also allows us to convert sound intensities to sound pressure variations, which is important since both quantities are used in the literature.

The most commonly used unit system for sound pressure and intensity variations is based on a logarithmic scale, because both parameters vary widely—e.g., between a whisper and a running jet engine by about seven orders of magnitude (a factor of $10^7$). The pressure variation in a sound wave is defined as **sound pressure level (SPL)**:

$$\text{SPL} = 20 \cdot \log_{10}\frac{p}{p_0} \qquad [34]$$

with $p_0$ a constant chosen as $p_0 = 2 \times 10^{-5}$ Pa. In Eq. [34] the notation $\log_{10}$ indicates the logarithm with the base 10 (not the natural logarithm with the

base $e$). The reference pressure $p_0$ is chosen near the faintest detectable sound for the human ear. The unit of SPL is called **decibel (dB)**. The prefactor 20 is chosen arbitrarily, except that a factor of 2 is included to accommodate the difference to the **intensity level (IL)**. The relation $I \propto \Delta p^2$ leads to $2 \cdot \log_{10}(p/p_0) = \log_{10}(I/I_0)$. Thus:

$$\text{IL} = 10 \cdot \log_{10}\frac{I}{I_0} \qquad [35]$$

with reference intensity $I_0 = 1 \times 10^{-12}$ J/(m$^2$ · s). We do not provide a table of IL values because such values could be misleading. The human ear judges sounds of equal IL values as quite different depending on the frequency of the sound (you do not hear a loud dog's whistle at all). Thus, later we introduce a different parameter to measure loudness.

## ● EXAMPLE 17.7

A sound has an intensity $5.0 \times 10^{-7}$ J/(m$^2$ · s). What is the intensity level IL of this sound?

*Solution:* The intensity level IL is defined in Eq. [35]. Substituting the given intensity value yields:

$$\text{IL} = 10 \cdot \log_{10}\left( \frac{5.0 \times 10^{-7} \, \frac{\text{J}}{\text{m}^2 \cdot \text{s}}}{1.0 \times 10^{-12} \, \frac{\text{J}}{\text{m}^2 \cdot \text{s}}} \right)$$

$$= 57 \, \text{dB} \qquad [36]$$

## Concept Question 17.5

**How does the sound intensity change with distance from a point sound source?**

*Solution:* Fig. 17.8 shows a point sound source. Two concentric spherical surfaces with areas $A_1$ and $A_2$ are drawn with the point-like source at the centre. We know that the same amount of energy must flow through each of these surfaces per time unit to satisfy energy conservation, $\Delta E/\Delta t = $ const. Sound would have to pile up or disappear between the two spheres were this not the case. Thus, for Fig. 17.8 we specifically write:

$$\left( \frac{\Delta E}{\Delta t} \right)_{A_1} = \left( \frac{\Delta E}{\Delta t} \right)_{A_2} \qquad [37]$$

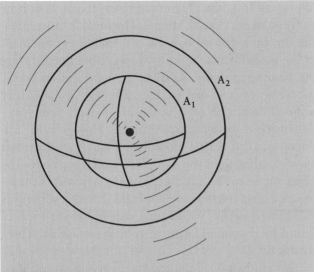

**FIGURE 17.8**

A point sound source (blue dot) shown at the centre of two concentric spherical surfaces with areas $A_1$ and $A_2$. The sound intensity per unit area, travelling through the two surfaces, diminishes as their areas increase.

In Eq. [37], we want to replace the time change of the total energy with the intensity. Starting from the first formula in Eq. [33], we write:

$$I = c \cdot \varepsilon_{total} = c \frac{\Delta E}{V} = \frac{\Delta r}{\Delta t} \frac{\Delta E}{A \cdot \Delta r} = \frac{\Delta E/\Delta t}{A} \quad [38]$$

in which the speed of sound is expressed as the change of the radial position with time, $c = \Delta r/\Delta t$, and in which the volume containing the sound energy is calculated as the area multiplied with the width, $V = A \cdot \Delta r$. This volume is the volume of a spherical shell of thickness $\Delta r$. Thus, the intensity is the rate of change of the total energy per unit area. Substituting this in Eq. [37] yields:

$$I_1 \cdot A_1 = I_2 \cdot A_2 \quad [39]$$

which provides us with the intensity ratio:

$$\frac{I_2}{I_1} = \frac{A_1}{A_2} = \frac{4 \cdot \pi \cdot r_1^2}{4 \cdot \pi \cdot r_2^2} \quad [40]$$

After cancelling the term $4 \cdot \pi$ on the right-hand side of Eq. [40], we find $I \propto 1/r^2$; i.e., the intensity diminishes in proportion to the square of the distance from the sound source.

This reduction of sound intensity in Concept Question 17.5 is a purely geometric effect. The sound travelling through a medium can further diminish due to energy loss to the medium when the vibration of the gas elements is not perfectly harmonic. The maximum sound pressure level produced by an animal is 188 dB, for the low-frequency moans of the blue whale. These sounds can be heard by other whales for hundreds of kilometres.

## Sound Absorption

The sound intensity diminishes when sound energy is absorbed by the medium. This absorption is caused by vibrations that are not perfectly adiabatic. Thermal energy loss occurs, which slightly heats up the medium.

For a quantitative description, let us choose a one-dimensional wave, e.g., a wave travelling in a tube. This eliminates the geometric sound intensity loss we discussed in Concept Question 17.5 and allows us therefore to isolate the absorption effect called **Beer's law.** Beer's law states that the loss of intensity per unit length of distance travelled, $\Delta I/\Delta x$, is proportional to the absolute intensity of the sound wave, $I$:

$$\lim_{\Delta x \to 0} \frac{\Delta I}{\Delta x} = -\beta \cdot I \quad [41]$$

The limit $\Delta x \to 0$ is needed in Eq. [41] to be mathematically exact since the intensity $I$ on the right-hand side of the equation varies continuously; i.e., $I = f(x)$.

*Beer's law states that the slope of the intensity variation with position (gradient) is proportional to the intensity at the respective position.*

The constant $\beta$ is the **absorption coefficient** and has unit $m^{-1}$. It is a materials constant but also depends on the frequency and type of wave (visible light and X-rays are also absorbed). When a gradient is linearly proportional to the absolute value of the parameter, as in Eq. [41], an exponential function describes the explicit position dependence of the parameter:

$$I = I_0 \cdot e^{-\beta \cdot x} \quad [42]$$

where $I_0$ is the intensity emitted by the source at $x = 0$.

We want to investigate the implications of Eq. [42] a little bit further. For this we rewrite the equation by introducing the length $x_{absorption} = 1/\beta$, which is called the **absorption length.** This yields:

$$\frac{I}{I_0} = \exp\left\{ -\frac{x}{x_{absorption}} \right\} \quad [43]$$

At the origin, which is the location of the sound source, the intensity is $I = I_0$. When we move from the source to a distance equal to the absorption length—i.e., to $x = x_{absorption}$—then Eq. [43] yields $I/I_0 = 1/e = 0.37$. Moving further to a distance twice the absorption length, $x = 2 \cdot x_{absorption}$, we find $I/I_0 = 1/e^2 = 0.14$, and finally at a distance of three times the absorption length, $x = 3 \cdot x_{absorption}$, we obtain $I/I_0 = 1/e^3 = 0.05$. Thus, the sound intensity

(a)

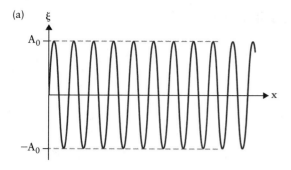

(b)

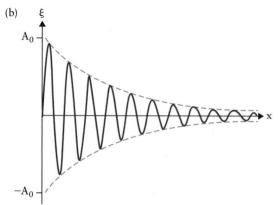

## FIGURE 17.9

Two harmonic waves with initial amplitude $A_0$. (a) The sound-carrying medium is (ideally) non-absorbing, and (b) the sound-carrying medium absorbs sound energy with an absorption coefficient $\alpha > 0$.

drops to about one-third of the initial intensity at the absorption length, and drops to 5% at three times the absorption length. Therefore, the absorption length is a good measure of the distance at which the sound intensity is significantly reduced due to absorption.

We saw in the previous section that the intensity is proportional to the square of the amplitude of the vibration of the small gas element, $I \propto A^2$. Thus, we can extend Eq. [20] for an absorbing medium in the form:

$$\xi = A_0 \cdot e^{-\alpha \cdot x} \cdot \sin(\omega \cdot t - \kappa \cdot x) \qquad [44]$$

in which $\alpha$ is the decay coefficient of the sound amplitude, with an initial sound amplitude of $A_0$. Fig. 17.9 presents a comparison between a one-dimensional sound wave in an idealized, absorption-free medium obeying Eq. [20] in part (a), and a one-dimensional wave in an absorbing medium obeying Eq. [44] in part (b). The dashed line is called the **envelope** and corresponds to the first two factors in Eq. [44], $A_0 \cdot e^{-\alpha \cdot x}$.

## Waves in a Confined Medium

The previous two sections allow us to understand how sound travels from a sound source through air. However, the concepts introduced are not sufficient for us

to understand how the human voice operates, or how the human ear detects sound. The most important issue not included up to now is a spatial confinement of the sound wave. Sound waves are confined during the hearing process, as illustrated by the anatomic overview of the ear in Fig. 17.10. The auditory canal (1) resembles a cylindrical tube, allowing one-dimensional waves to travel inside. However, the auditory canal is a half-closed tube and sound cannot travel farther than the eardrum, which separates the outer ear from the middle ear. The current section focusses on waves that are confined in either closed or half-closed tubes. We assume that the absorption of sound by the medium in the tube is negligible. Thus, we use Eq. [20] and not Eq. [44] for this discussion.

The study of a longitudinal wave in a confined space begins with a simple model system: a cylindrical tube filled with an ideal gas and closed at both ends. We use **closed tubes** to introduce the most important features of confined waves, such as standing waves, harmonics, and the concept of resonance.

## Standing Waves

The biggest difference between waves in open space and waves in a confined medium is the presence of reflected waves. The easiest case is the closed tube, where waves reflect at both ends and travel back and forth inside the tube. We treat a wave and the corresponding reflected wave as two separate waves. This is necessary because each of these waves is described by a different wave function. Thus, the first issue to tackle in a discussion that leads toward wave phenomena in a closed tube is the superposition of two waves. This discussion is actually simplified when we

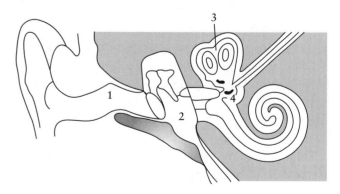

## FIGURE 17.10

Overview of the human ear. We can distinguish three main sections of the ear: the outer ear with the auditory canal (1) ending at the eardrum; the middle ear with the three ossicles, hammer, anvil, and stirrup (from left, 2); and the inner ear with the vestibular organ. The vestibular organ includes the semicircular canals (3) and the maculae (4), both discussed in Chapters 2 and 3.

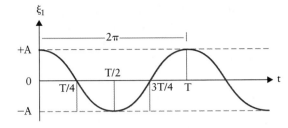

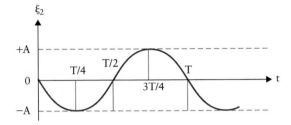

**FIGURE 17.11**

Two sinusoidal waves at $x = 0$ that differ by a phase shift of $\Delta\phi = \pi/2$.

choose a wave and its reflection because several wave parameters are identical for both waves: the wavelength or wave number and the angular frequency do not change at the time of reflection.

To see what happens with more than one wave present, consider two waves travelling in a tube in the same direction with the same wavelength and angular frequency. To study how these waves interact, their respective wave functions have to be written in a more complete form than that given in Eq. [20]:

$$\xi_1 = A \cdot \sin(\omega \cdot t - \kappa \cdot x + \phi_1)$$
$$\xi_2 = A \cdot \sin(\omega \cdot t - \kappa \cdot x + \phi_2) \qquad [45]$$

Why does the inclusion of the terms $\phi_1$ and $\phi_2$ in the argument make the wave function more general? To see this, assume that we study the waves at the particular position $x = 0$. Fig. 17.11 shows the waves with $\phi_1 = 0$ (top) and $\phi_2 = \pi/2$ (bottom). We see that the term $\phi$ in Eq. [45] is a phase shift, because the two waves are different only in that the lower wave is shifted to the left by a time difference of $\Delta t = T/4$. We refer to this observation in Eq. [45] by introducing $\Delta\phi = \phi_2 - \phi_1$, which we call a **phase angle difference** between both waves.

As long as the amplitudes are not too large, the principle of **additive superposition** of waves is valid. This simply means that the superposition of the two waves is the sum of their respective displacements at each point along the tube. This leads to two cases of particular interest for the waves in Eq. [45]:

- when the two waves are shifted relative to each other by half a wavelength—i.e., when the phase angle difference is $\phi_2 - \phi_1 = (2 \cdot n + 1)\pi$ with $n$ an integer number—**destructive superposition** oc-

curs and the resulting wave has a vanishing amplitude, $A_{\text{sup}} = 0$. This is illustrated in Fig. 17.12(a), where the two initial waves are indicated by a dashed and a dash-dotted line. The superpositioned wave is coincident with the $x$-axis (no wave).

- when the two waves are shifted by a multiple of a full wavelength, which corresponds to $\phi_2 - \phi_1 = (2 \cdot n) \cdot \pi$. This case is called **constructive superposition** and is shown in Fig. 17.12(b). Again, the dashed and dash-dotted curves are the original waves, drawn beside each other only to allow them both to be seen. The superposition of both waves yields a wave with double the amplitude (solid red curve).

Harmonic waves travelling back and forth in a closed tube are a special application of the superposition principle since the reflection at the end of the tube automatically guarantees that both waves have the same amplitude (assuming no sound absorption), angular frequency, and wave number because the initial and the reflected wave are caused by the same vibration. In this case, the two waves are written as:

$$\xi_1 = A \cdot \sin(\omega \cdot t - \kappa \cdot x)$$
$$\xi_2 = -A \cdot \sin(\omega \cdot t + \kappa \cdot x) \qquad [46]$$

(a) $\xi$

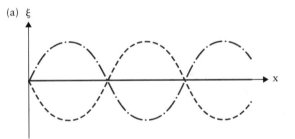

(b) $\xi$

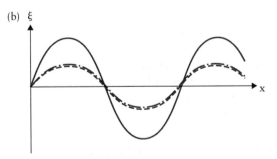

**FIGURE 17.12**

(a) Destructive superposition of two harmonic waves with same angular frequency, wave number, and amplitude. This occurs for a half-wavelength phase shift between the two waves. The two original waves are shown as dashed and dash-dotted curves. The resulting wave coincides with the $x$-axis. (b) Constructive superposition of two harmonic waves with same angular frequency, wave number, and amplitude. This occurs for a phase shift equal to a multiple of a full wavelength between the two waves. The two original waves are shown as dashed and dash-dotted curves. The resulting wave is shown as a solid red curve with double the amplitude.

(a)

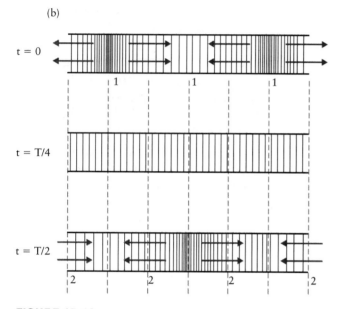

(b)

**FIGURE 17.13**

Standing wave in a closed, air-filled tube. (a) A mobile piston varies the length of the tube. A standing wave occurs when the distance between the piston and the end of the tube is a multiple of a half-wavelength of the sound wave. (b) The air density profile in the tube at three different times. Note that a standing wave does not travel toward the left or the right. Amplitude nodes (1) and pressure or density nodes (2) remain stationary.

Note that the reflected wave carries an additional negative sign. This results because the wave has a phase shift of $\Delta\phi = \pi$ when reflected off a wall. Fig. 17.13 illustrates how this arrangement can lead to a **standing wave**. Fig. 17.13(a) shows a sound source at the right end of an enclosed tube filled with a gas. The sound waves moving back and forth coincide such that the amplitude of the local vibration of a small gas element becomes time-independent. A standing wave is generated if the distance between the sound source and the wall of the tube at the left end is a multiple of half a wavelength.

We can also derive this result mathematically from Eq. [46]. Additive superposition of the two waves leads to:

$$\xi_{\text{superposition}} = A(\sin(\omega \cdot t - \kappa \cdot x)$$
$$- \sin(\omega \cdot t + \kappa \cdot x)) \quad [47]$$

We use a trigonometric relation from the Math Review section "Trigonometry" at the end of this chapter, $\sin(\alpha - \beta) - \sin(\alpha + \beta) = -2 \cdot \cos\alpha \cdot \sin\beta$, to simplify this equation:

$$\xi_{\text{superposition}} = -\{2 \cdot A \cdot \cos(\omega \cdot t)\}\sin(\kappa \cdot x) \quad [48]$$

This is a wave with a fixed wavelength of $\lambda = 2 \cdot \pi/\kappa$, and an amplitude that varies with time as given in the curly braces in the equation. The maximum amplitude is $2 \cdot A$.

We want to interpret Eq. [48] with a microscopic picture. Fig. 17.13(b) shows a section of the tube and the respective motion of the gas elements. In a standing wave, certain points have a zero amplitude all the time. These points are labelled 2 in the three snapshots of the gas in the tube, i.e., at times $t = 0$, $t = T/4$, and $t = T/2$. They are called **pressure nodes**. Between two pressure nodes the gas pressure and density oscillate between an increased value, indicated by a higher density of lines, and a decreased value, indicated by a lesser density of lines.

The points labelled 1 in Fig. 17.13(b) are **velocity nodes** since the gas element at those points does not move (motion of gas is indicated by arrows). Velocity nodes are alternatively called amplitude nodes since they identify gas elements with $A = 0$. Such a node must be located at the end of the tube in Fig. 17.13(a), since the gas cannot move into the wall. Thus, no pressure node occurs at the end of the tube. This is important in the ear because pressure variations cause the eardrum to vibrate and thereby transmit sound to the middle ear.

*A standing wave forms in a closed tube when the wavelength of the sound and the distance to the end wall in the tube allow for a velocity node at that wall.*

**Concept Question 17.6**

**What is the meaning of "standing" in the term standing wave? (A) The amplitude is time-independent. (B) The frequency is time-independent. (C) The location of density nodes is time-independent. (D) The wavelength is time-independent.**

ANSWER: Choice (C). All four statements are correct, but only answer (C) specifically characterizes standing waves. The amplitude is time-independent for non-attenuating waves; the frequency is time-independent for a wave of given energy density (see Chapter 20); and the wavelength is time-independent in a uniform medium.

## ● EXAMPLE 17.8

Consider again the wave travelling along the $x$-axis as described in Eq. [23]. Assume that this wave reflects off a rigid surface. (a) What is the equation for the reflected wave? (b) What is the equation of a resulting standing wave? (c) Sketch the standing wave at $t = 0$ and $t = T/2$, with $T$ being the period.

*Solution to part (a):* The reflected wave has exactly the same properties as the incoming wave, except that (i) it travels in the opposite direction, and (ii) it is phase-shifted by half a wavelength (i.e., a phase shift of $\pi$ radians). This is achieved in Eq. [23] by (i) switching the sign of the position-dependent term and by (ii) switching the sign of the amplitude term in the same fashion as in Eq. [46]:

$$\xi_{\text{reflect}} = -(2.0\,\text{cm})\sin\{(1.0\,\text{s}^{-1})t + (1.5\,\text{cm}^{-1})x\}$$

[49]

*Solution to part (b):* The standing wave is the superposition of the wave in Eq. [23] and the wave in Eq. [49]. We need not repeat the mathematical steps leading to the resulting standing wave because the calculation has already been done from Eq. [46] to Eq. [48]. Inserting the specific values from Eq. [23] or from Eq. [49], we find:

$$\xi_{\text{superposition}} = -\{(4.0\,\text{cm})\cos(1.0\,\text{s}^{-1})t\}$$
$$\times \sin(1.5\,\text{cm}^{-1})x \quad [50]$$

*Solution to part (c):* The two sketches are shown in Fig. 17.14, with the solid curve for $t = 0$ and the dashed curve for $t = T/2$.

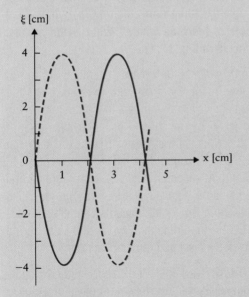

**FIGURE 17.14**

Sketch of a standing wave. The solid curve represents it at time $t = 0$; the dashed curve represents the same wave at time $t = T/2$, i.e., half a period later.

## Harmonics

In free space, waves may occur with any combination of wavelengths and angular frequencies consistent with the speed of sound in the medium. In a confined space, only certain waves, the standing waves, can be sustained. Their selection rule is based on the size and type of the confining space: for longitudinal waves in a closed tube a multiple of half-wavelengths must fit into the space of the tube. However, any integer number of half-wavelengths is acceptable, and thus several standing waves with different wavelengths can form in the same closed tube.

Fig. 17.15 shows the three longitudinal waves with the longest wavelengths between the ends of the tube. The standing wave in part (a) is called the **first harmonic**, which has the lowest frequency that the tube can support. The standing waves in parts (b) and (c) are the second and third harmonics, respectively. Note that the harmonic of $n$-th order has two amplitude nodes at the fixed ends of the tube, and $n - 1$ amplitude nodes between the ends at equal distances. The term *harmonic* is derived from the use of the term in music. It is applied in the current context despite the fact that we are not studying a string on a guitar because a string on a musical instrument must be set into transverse motion.

Table 17.2 lists the wavelengths and frequencies for the various longitudinal harmonics for a one-dimensional closed tube. The frequencies and wavelengths are related to each other by the speed of

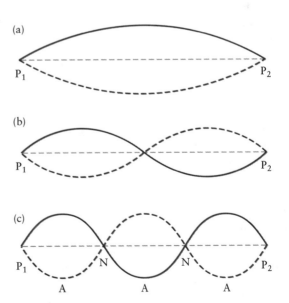

**FIGURE 17.15**

(a) The first, (b) second, and (c) third harmonics for a standing longitudinal wave in a closed tube between $P_1$ and $P_2$. N identifies amplitude nodes and A anti-nodes. The vertical deviation from the horizontal line is a measure of the longitudinal displacement of the gas element.

## TABLE 17.2

**Wavelengths and frequencies for various harmonics of air in a tube closed at both ends**

| Mode | Wavelength | Frequency |
|---|---|---|
| 1st harmonic | $\lambda_1 = 2 \cdot L$ | $f_1 = c/(2 \cdot L)$ |
| 2nd harmonic | $\lambda_2 = L$ | $f_2 = c/L = 2 \cdot f_1$ |
| 3rd harmonic | $\lambda_3 = 2 \cdot L/3$ | $f_3 = 3 \cdot c/(2 \cdot L) = 3 \cdot f_1$ |
| ⋮ | ⋮ | ⋮ |
| $n$-th harmonic | $\lambda_n = 2 \cdot L/n$ | $f_n = n \cdot c/(2 \cdot L) = n \cdot f_1$ |

$n$ is an integer number.

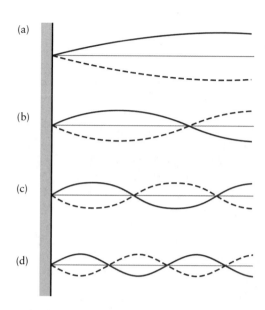

**FIGURE 17.16**

(a) The first harmonic and (b–d) the corresponding higher harmonics in a tube open at one end. Note that an amplitude anti-node (a pressure node) forms at the open end (right end of red curves). The vertical deviation from the horizontal line in the figure indicates the longitudinal displacement of a gas element in the tube.

sound, $c = \lambda_n \cdot f_n$. As the table illustrates, higher harmonics have shorter wavelengths and higher frequencies but the same wave speed.

For applications, we have to supplement the discussion of closed tubes with a second system in which a confined gas can sustain a longitudinal wave: a **half-open tube**. The half-open tube is, e.g., a model for the outer ear in Fig. 17.10. The waves sustained in a half-open tube differ from the harmonic waves of the closed tube because the air can move back and forth at the open end of the tube. Indeed, a half-open tube has an amplitude anti-node at its open end; i.e., a standing wave forms such that a pressure node instead of an amplitude node lies in the open end. This is illustrated in Fig. 17.16, where the open end of the tube lies at the right end of the plot. Fig. 17.16(a) shows the first harmonic, and Fig. 17.16(b–d) illustrates the three next-lowest harmonics. For the half-closed tube the frequencies of the allowed harmonics are given by:

$$f = \frac{n \cdot c}{4 \cdot L} \quad \text{with } n = 1, 3, 5, 7, \ldots \quad [51]$$

i.e., only odd-numbered harmonics are possible.

*Closed and half-closed tubes can sustain standing waves, which we call harmonics.*

Higher harmonics play an essential role in the human voice. Human voices are characterized by the number and relative amplitude (or intensity) of higher harmonics generated. The first harmonic in a human voice is defined as the **pitch** and the higher harmonics define the **timbre**. When these data are plotted, e.g., in the lower part of Fig. 17.1, the resulting graph is called a spectrum. In a **spectrum**, a dependent variable, such as the intensity, is shown as a function of frequency.

## Concept Question 17.7

Fig. 17.17(a) shows a blue whale and Fig. 17.17(b) shows the intensity spectrum of its moan. (a) What model would you use to describe the technique of sound generation by the blue whale: an air column closed at both ends, or a half-open air column? (b) What is the first harmonic of the blue whale? What is the highest harmonic shown in Fig. 17.17?

*Biological information:* Blue whales generate two types of sound. The low-frequency moans shown in Fig. 17.17 and the high-frequency click sounds are in the range between 21 kHz and 31 kHz. The moans occur in the range of 12.5 Hz to 200 Hz, with the greatest intensities between 20 Hz and 32 Hz. The sound duration lies usually between 15 seconds and 40 seconds; however, with more careful measurements more detailed features can be identified than are revealed in Fig. 17.17, including amplitude modulations at 0.26-second repetition cycles and, later during the sound, with 0.13-second repetition cycles.

ANSWER TO PART (a): Table 17.2 and Fig. 17.15 show that the frequencies of the various harmonics of a closed tube are all equally spaced:

$$\Delta f = f_{n+1} - f_n = \frac{c}{2 \cdot L} = \text{const} \quad [52]$$

(a)

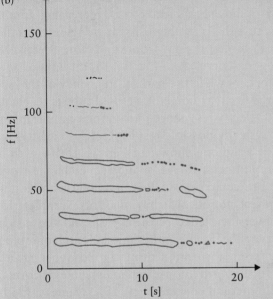

(b)

**FIGURE 17.17**

(a) Blue whale. (b) Spectrum of the sound intensity emitted by a blue whale. Bands represent frequency ranges of high sound intensity. These low-frequency moans last for 15 to 40 seconds.

which applies for all values of $n \geq 1$. This frequency spacing is equal to the absolute frequency of the first harmonic:

$$\text{closed:} \quad f_1 = \Delta f \qquad [53]$$

On the other hand, Eq. [51] and Fig. 17.16 show that the frequencies of the various harmonics of a half-closed tube, while also spaced as given in Eq. [52], are twice as wide-spaced as the value of the first harmonic:

$$\text{half-closed:} \quad 2 \cdot f_1 = \Delta f \qquad [54]$$

The frequencies shown in Fig. 17.17 are 17 Hz, 34 Hz, 51 Hz, 68 Hz, 85 Hz, 102 Hz, and 119 Hz. Thus, from comparison with Eqs. [53] and [54], we conclude that a closed-tube model describes the moans of the blue whale best, because the lowest frequency measured is equal to

the frequency spacing between the harmonics shown in Fig. 17.17.

ANSWER TO PART (b): The first harmonic is the lowest frequency emitted. In the case of the moan of the blue whale shown in Fig. 17.17, this frequency is 17 Hz. Every higher-frequency band shown indicates the next higher harmonic according to Table 17.2. Thus, the highest harmonic shown at 119 Hz is the seventh harmonic.

## Resonance

In the first two parts of this section we deviated from our earlier approach and derived the concepts of sound in a confined space from the wave model and not from the vibrations that cause the wave. For the description of resonances, now it is useful to return to our original approach and link the vibration of an object to the sound phenomenon.

If you consider the human voice, or, more simply, a musical instrument such as a flute, you notice that neither generates a sound unless a mechanical excitation is applied. In the case of the human voice, you sense the effort involved in speaking. In both cases, the voice or the flute, the external excitation is usually not a vibration with a frequency perfectly matching the frequency of a standing wave in the adjacent air column. This is obvious for the flute when you quickly blow into the mouthpiece. In this case, you obviously do not provide a harmonic vibration at all. But even if you tried to vibrate the piston in Fig. 17.13, it is unlikely that you would do so with the right frequency for a standing wave. Still, the flute responds to the blowing with a sound, representing the first and several higher harmonics characteristic of the length of the flute's barrel. In the same fashion, the human voice has a characteristic frequency pattern, as shown in Fig. 17.1.

To understand the response of a flute or of the vocal tract, we need to study two phenomena:

- the sound amplitude in a closed or half-closed tube in response to an external excitation, and

- the reason why a sudden excitation as much as a harmonic excitation causes harmonic waves.

### RESONANCE FORMATION

We start with Fig. 17.13 and assume that an external force is used to move the piston harmonically back and forth with a maximum force of magnitude $F_{max}$ and an angular frequency $\omega_{ext}$:

$$|\mathbf{F}_{ext}| = F_{max} \cdot \cos(\omega_{ext} \cdot t) \qquad [55]$$

Note that we need not consider the vector character of the force, as the entire experiment is done one-dimensionally along the *x*-axis. We will find that such an externally caused vibration can lead to high sound intensities under certain conditions.

We use Eq. [55] to extend Newton's second law for a vibrating object, as written in Eq. [16.31], to describe the piston displacement in response to the external force:

$$-k \cdot x + F_{max} \cdot \cos(\omega_{ext} \cdot t) = m \cdot a \qquad [56]$$

The second term on the left-hand side is a newly introduced force acting on the piston. Solving Eq. [56] is not particularly easy; instead, we choose an approach based on an experiment: an object is attached to a horizontal spring. A taut string is also attached to the object, which allows us to exert the force given in Eq. [55] by moving the string continuously back and forth. Depending on the frequency with which we move the string, the object's response will be somewhere between little and very strong. We express the response to the motion of the string as the amplitude of the vibration of the object.

The observed amplitude is illustrated in Fig. 17.18. If you move the string very slowly back and forth, the object follows the motion with exactly the same amplitude as the external motion. We define this amplitude as $A_0$. The plot shows values near $A/A_0 = 1$ for angular frequencies near $\omega_{ext} = 0$, where $\omega_{ext}$ describes the angular frequency of the motion of the externally driven string. In this case, the motion of the object is not altered by the spring to which it is attached.

As we increase the frequency with which we move the string back and forth, we get closer and closer to the natural angular frequency of the object on the spring, which is its angular frequency without an external force:

$$\omega_{natural} = \sqrt{\frac{k}{m}} \qquad [57]$$

Equally, if we consider the case of a piston moving back and forth at the end of an air column, moving the piston faster means that we are getting closer to the angular frequency of the first harmonic of the standing wave forming in the closed gas tube, $\omega_{standing}$. As Fig. 17.18 shows, this leads to an increasing amplitude because the external push transfers energy to the vibrating object (or piston) more and more effectively.

Following curve (a) in Fig. 17.18, an infinite amplitude occurs when the natural frequency of the object or the first harmonic of a closed tube is reached. This is called a **resonance**. An infinite amplitude is not a physically possible result. Real systems follow curves like the one shown in Fig. 17.18(b), with a finite amplitude at the resonance. The change from curve (a) to curve (b) is called **damping**. Damping is the result of non-ideal behaviour, for example friction between the edge of the piston and the inside wall of the tube. In an energy-based picture, damping represents the absorption of mechanical energy and its conversion into non-mechanical energy forms, primarily thermal energy. Curve (b) assumes a moderate damping, which results in a finite amplitude oscillation at the resonance. The shock absorbers in your car, for example, have a significantly stronger damping—you do not want increased vertical amplitude for the car's cabin when you are driving over potholes!

The resonance is reached when the external angular frequency equals the natural angular frequency or the angular frequency of the first harmonic of the system. Fig. 17.18 shows that the confined system responds to an external excitation with an enhanced amplitude in the vicinity of the resonance, and therefore with an enhanced sound intensity, since we saw earlier that the intensity is proportional to the square of the amplitude.

If we increase the frequency of the external vibration beyond the resonance frequency, we observe a decrease in the amplitude of the object. When the external frequency is much larger than the natural frequency of the object, the amplitude of the object ceases and the object does not respond at all to the external force; this is due to the inertia of the system. In order to follow the motion of the string, the object

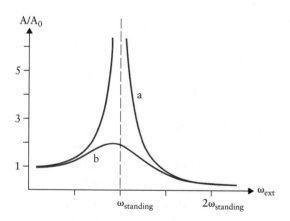

**FIGURE 17.18**

The amplitude in a resonant system, shown as a value relative to the amplitude $A_0$ for small external angular frequencies, $\omega_{ext}$. The system follows the sinusoidal variation of the external force when $\omega_{ext} \ll \omega_{standing}$, with $\omega_{standing}$ the natural angular frequency of the system. When $\omega_{ext}$ reaches $\omega_{standing}$, an amplification of the amplitude occurs, which is called a resonant amplification. Curve a applies when damping is negligible, and curve b when moderate damping occurs.

must constantly accelerate back or forth. Every object requires some time for that: the heavier the object, the slower the response to a force. You can redirect a tennis ball in an instant; redirecting a shot-put thrown to you takes longer. With the change of direction of the external force occurring faster and faster, eventually the inertia of the object no longer allows enough time for the object to follow.

The curve labelled (a) in Fig. 17.18 is described quantitatively in the form:

$$A = \frac{F_{max}}{m(\omega_{standing}^2 - \omega_{ext}^2)} \quad [58]$$

in which $F_{max}$ is the magnitude of the maximum force exerted on the system of mass $m$, $\omega_{ext}$ is the angular frequency of the external force, and $\omega_{standing}$ is the angular frequency of the first harmonic of the system. The difference of quadratic terms in the denominator causes the steep increase close to the resonance. This formula is useful for systems with negligible damping.

*A system is in resonance when an external harmonic excitation causes it to respond with a maximum amplitude. This occurs at the first harmonic of a closed or half-closed tube.*

### ● EXAMPLE 17.9

Calculate the size of a room in which a person singing in one of the major opera categories listed in Table 17.3 obtains a maximum intensity amplification of the sound.

### TABLE 17.3

**Frequency range of opera voices**

| Opera voice | Frequency range (Hz) |
| --- | --- |
| Bass | 66–350 |
| Tenor | 100–520 |
| Alto | 130–700 |
| Soprano | 200–1050 |

*Solution:* From Eq. [58], we know that the condition for maximum resonance is:

$$\omega_{ext} = \omega_{standing} \quad [59]$$

This holds independent of the degree of damping, as illustrated in Fig. 17.18. Thus, the frequencies in Table 17.3 must be equal to the first harmonic

### TABLE 17.4

**Frequency range and spatial dimensions for Example 17.9**

| Opera voice | Frequency range (Hz) | Dimension $L$ (m) |
| --- | --- | --- |
| Bass | 66–350 | 0.5–2.6 |
| Tenor | 100–520 | 0.33–1.7 |
| Alto | 130–700 | 0.25–1.3 |
| Soprano | 200–1050 | 0.16–0.85 |

of an air column in a closed tube, in which the length of the tube equals the dimensions of the room. We use the formula for $n = 1$ in Table 17.2 to calculate the room dimension $L$, using the speed of sound at room temperature from Table 17.1:

$$L = \frac{c}{2 \cdot f} = \frac{343 \frac{m}{s}}{2 \cdot f} \quad [60]$$

The resulting length intervals are summarized in Table 17.4. Table 17.4 shows that the singer with the higher-frequency voice sets the air in a smaller room into resonance. For a real opera singer on stage, such resonances are undesirable. Indeed, opera houses are much larger than the dimensions we calculated in Table 17.4, and therefore none of these effects in fact occur. However, such resonance-enhanced sounds might be perceived as satisfactory by a person singing aloud. Loosely spoken, women get the best "singing in the shower" effect in their own home, while men sound better in the showers at the gym.

### NON-HARMONIC EXCITATION

The second phenomenon we want to study in this section is the observation that a non-harmonic external excitation, such as a brief blow into a flute, can excite a standing wave in a tube. To illustrate this effect we consider a piano, even though generating a sound with this instrument leads to a transverse standing wave on a string in the instrument. The concepts are, however, the same for a flute—it is just easier to do the following experiment on a piano, as originally proposed by Hermann von Helmholtz.

We consider the piano keys shown in Fig. 17.19, which represent the second to tenth harmonics of a string when $C_3$ is the first harmonic (note that $C_4$ is

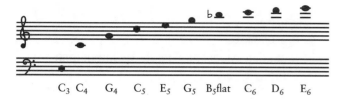

**FIGURE 17.19**

The first harmonic of the $C_3$ key on a piano and its second to tenth harmonics. The higher the harmonic, the weaker the resonance when conducting Helmholtz's experiment described in the text.

the C-key in the middle of a piano). In the first step of the experiment, you soundlessly press a key for one of the higher harmonics—i.e., push it down very slowly. This lifts the damper off the string inside the piano. Now, you hit the $C_3$ key quickly and forcefully. You hear a resonance at the pitch of the higher harmonic that corresponds to the key you are holding down. If the key you are holding down is not one of the higher harmonics of the $C_3$ key, you hear no resonance. Confirm that the resonance does indeed correspond to the key you are holding down by hitting this key afterward.

The reason why a short, non-harmonic hit can excite many different frequencies in a free medium, or many harmonics of a standing wave in a closed or half-open tube, was first given by Jean Baptiste Fourier. He took a non-sinusoidal function such as the triangular function shown in Fig. 17.20(a). Note that this is a periodic function; we will consider non-periodic functions a little bit later. Since the function in Fig. 17.20(a) is periodic with period $T$, there is a lowest angular frequency $\omega = 2 \cdot \pi/T$, which is consistent with the periodicity of the function. Starting with the lowest angular frequency, Fourier constructed a function of time, $f(t)$, which represents a superposition of all higher harmonics:

$$f(t) = A_0 + A_1 \cdot \cos \omega \cdot t + A_2 \cdot \cos 2\omega \cdot t + \cdots$$
$$+ B_1 \cdot \sin \omega \cdot t + B_2 \cdot \sin 2\omega \cdot t + \cdots \quad [61]$$

which can be written in condensed form (see Math Review on "Summations" at the end of Chapter 3):

$$f(t) = A_0 + \sum_{n=1}^{\infty} A_n \cdot \cos n \cdot \omega \cdot t$$
$$+ \sum_{n=1}^{\infty} B_n \cdot \sin n \cdot \omega \cdot t \quad [62]$$

in which $A_n$ and $B_n$ are constant coefficients. Fig. 17.20(b) shows a plot of the values of these coefficients, which cause Eq. [62] to match the triangular function of Fig. 17.20(a) for the specific case of

$f = 10$ Hz. To do so, all $B$- and even $A$-coefficients are zero and the odd $A$-coefficients follow the relation $A_n \propto 1/n^2$.

If the function $f(t)$ is not periodic, a more general approach is needed as no discrete spectrum can be found, such as the one given in Fig. 17.20(b), with integer multiples of the fundamental frequency $\omega$. It is, however, possible to determine continuous spectra for non-periodic functions, as illustrated in Fig. 17.21. In that figure, two box-shaped functions are shown in the left column, describing a constant excitation that lasts for a time $t = \tau$. Such a function corresponds to hitting a string in a piano or blowing air into a flute. The corresponding amplitudes are shown in the right column as a function of frequency. These are obtained from a mathematical procedure that is closely related to Eq. [62] and is called **Fourier analysis.** Comparing the spectra at the right for the two cases in Fig. 17.21, we note that a shorter hit (bottom) is capable of exciting more frequencies than a longer hit (top). For this reason, we need a short hit of the $C_3$ key in Helmholtz's experiment to excite the resonances at higher frequencies.

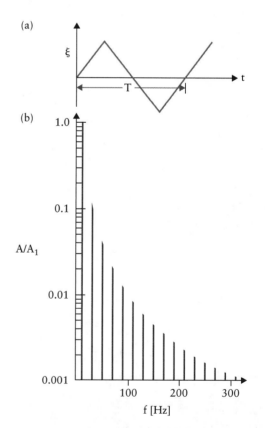

**FIGURE 17.20**

The Fourier series (based on Eq. [62]) for the periodic triangular function shown in part (a). The curve represents the displacement as a function of time with the period $T$. The relative amplitudes in part (b) form a discrete spectrum (i.e., only specific frequencies contribute, as shown). The particular case is based on a frequency of $1/T = 10$ Hz for the function in part (a).

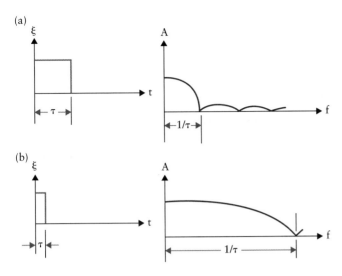

**FIGURE 17.21**

If a function is not periodic, like the two box-shaped functions shown at the left in parts (a) and (b), Fourier analysis provides amplitude spectra based on the assumption of a superposition of an infinite number of harmonic waves. The spectra, shown at right, are therefore continuous, not discrete. Comparison between parts (a) and (b) shows how the respective amplitude spectra are related for a longer (a) and a shorter (b) box-shaped function, representing a longer or shorter hit of a string in a piano or blow into a flute.

# The Acoustic Systems of the Human Body

We now apply the concepts introduced above to the formation of sounds in the human voice tract and to the hearing of the human ear.

## Voice

Fig. 17.22 shows a medical illustration of the upper respiratory tract including the human vocal tract. It includes the pharynx above the larynx. The pharynx splits into the nasal cavity and the mouth. This system of cavities extends to the lungs at the bottom through the trachea. The larynx contains the vocal folds, which are elastic bands set in vibrational motion by the air flowing from the lungs when they are almost closed.

The high-frequency vibration of the vocal folds is a result of the equation of continuity and Bernoulli's law, both discussed in Chapter 12: the air arriving from the lungs must accelerate to a higher speed when passing through the narrow vocal fold to satisfy the equation of continuity. The higher air speed leads to a reduction in air pressure in the vocal fold relative to the pressure in the trachea, due to Bernoulli's law. The reduced pressure leads to a tem-

porary closing of the vocal folds. In the next instant the air flow from the lungs forces the vocal folds open again. The repetitive closing and opening of the vocal folds leads to a vibration analogous to the forced vibration of a piston in a half-closed gas system. These vibrations lead to resonances in the vocal tract.

The variation in the speed of the air flowing from the lungs contributes to the variations in loudness of the voice. But why does every voice sound different? The basic difference between male and female voices is associated with the design of the larynx and the first harmonic it generates: males have a range of 100 to 170 Hz, and females have a range of 220 to 330 Hz.

A more detailed analysis is necessary to establish speech characteristics. We can modify the resonances in the vocal tract by varying the relative positions of three components of the system: (a) the tongue,

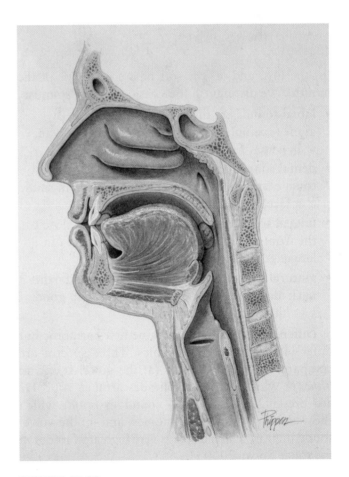

**FIGURE 17.22**

Medical illustration of the vocal tract, which consists of the larynx below the pharynx, the nasal cavity, and the mouth. Air is supplied from the lungs (not shown) through the trachea. The vocal tract is a half-closed gas system. The vocal folds close the vocal tract. They allow us to generate a forced vibration that in turn causes a resonance in the vocal tract.

(a)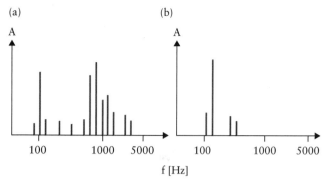

(b)

(c)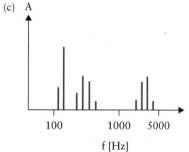

**FIGURE 17.23**

Spectra for three vowels: (a) the vowel sound in *hunt*, (b) the vowel sound in *hood*, and (c) the vowel sound in *heat*.

(b) the lips, and (c) the soft palate (the roof of the mouth). We distinguish four basic forms of sounds:

- **labial sounds** are made by the lips and teeth alone (examples: *p* in part, *b* in brain, *v* in van, *w* in water, *f* in five, *m* in mouth),
- **dental sounds** are formed by the teeth and the tongue (examples: *d* in done, *t* in table, *s* in sand, *c* in face, *n* in never),
- **lingual sounds** result when the tongue is close to the front end of the soft palate (examples: *l* in language, *sh* in ship), and
- **guttural sounds** form when the tongue is farther back along the soft palate (examples: *g* in good, *k* in kite, *c* in carrot).

Different vowels have the same first harmonic but differ in their higher harmonics. Three spectra are compared in Fig. 17.23 for (a) the vowel sound in *hunt*, in which higher amplitudes around 1000 Hz are present, (b) the vowel sound in *hood*, which shows a lack of higher harmonics, and (c) the vowel sound in *heat*, which displays very high amplitudes in the range above 2000 Hz.

## The Outer Ear

The human ear is an extremely sensitive sound detection system. It can analyze sound intensities ranging over 12 orders of magnitude and is able to distinguish frequencies between 16 Hz and 20 kHz.

To achieve this performance, all three components of the ear shown in Fig. 17.10—the outer ear, the middle ear, and the inner ear—are essential. The outer ear is a half-closed tube with a first harmonic that generates a resonant amplification across most of the range of audible frequencies. The mechanical mechanism in the middle ear circumvents a major loss in intensity that would occur if the external medium air were directly coupled to the inner ear's fluid. The inner ear provides frequency analysis that is then encoded in electric signals sent to the brain.

### ● EXAMPLE 17.10

What is the first harmonic of the human auditory canal?

*Supplementary anatomical information:* The outer ear consists of the auditory canal and ends at the eardrum. The auditory canal is about 2.5 cm long.

*Solution:* We use Eq. [51] for a half-closed tube to calculate the first harmonic. We find for $n = 1$:

$$f_1 = \frac{c}{4 \cdot L} = \frac{343 \frac{\text{m}}{\text{s}}}{4 \cdot 2.5 \times 10^{-2} \text{ m}} = 3.4 \text{ kHz} \quad [63]$$

This value is close to the frequency at which the ear reaches its greatest sensitivity.

Due to the width of the peak of the resonance curves in Fig. 17.18 (the range where $A/A_0 > 1$), an appreciable range of frequencies around the first harmonic is amplified. This range and the amplification factor depend on the damping of the resonance curve. The outer ear amplifies the arriving sound by about a factor of two; i.e., the curve in Fig. 17.18(b) is a good representation of the resonance behaviour of the auditory canal. We benefit from the resonant amplification of the outer ear in the frequency interval from about 2 kHz to 7 kHz.

### Concept Question 17.8

**Prior to the development of modern hearing aids, people with age-related hearing loss used funnel or conical ear trumpets, long tubes they held to their outer ear. These devices improved hearing because of two effects: the sound intensity reaching the eardrum was increased as the result of the large opening of the ear trumpet, and the frequency range of resonant sound amplification in**

## The Middle Ear

The middle ear transports the sound signal from the eardrum to the oval window. The anatomical setup is shown in Fig. 1.3. The vibrations of the oval window (5) cause waves in the **perilymph** (6). Perilymph is a fluid similar to highly filtered blood plasma, comparable to the extracellular fluid. Like other body fluids, perilymph is an electrolyte with a concentration of 14 mmol/L $Na^+$, but it has only a low concentration of proteins.

The middle ear is physiologically necessary because the sound travels toward a medium of significantly altered density (air to perilymph). It consists of the hammer (2), which is attached to the eardrum (1); the anvil (3); and the stirrup (4), which is attached to the oval window of the cochlea (7).

To understand the purpose of the middle ear, assume for a moment that it did not exist. In this case the eardrum and the oval window would be the same membrane and the sound would have to be coupled across this membrane from air to perilymph. The interface between both media (the hypothetical combined membrane) is shown schematically in Fig. 17.24 as a blue line. An incoming wave (1) is partially reflected (2) and partially transmitted (3). To quantify the efficiency of sound transmission across the membrane, we compare the reflected to the transmitted wave intensity. For the ear, we find that the transmitted intensity would be significantly less than the incoming intensity if the eardrum and the oval window were merged into a single interface. This,

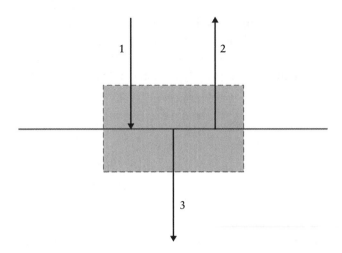

**FIGURE 17.24**

Conceptual sketch of a wave passing through an interface (blue line). At the interface section (grey box) three wave components have to be considered: (1) an incoming wave, (2) a reflected wave, and (3) a transmitted wave. The transfer of sound intensity is particularly ineffective when the densities of the media on both sides of the interface differ significantly.

then, justifies the complex middle ear as a necessary sound amplification component.

To quantify the model in Fig. 17.24, we study a small section of the interface (grey box). On the incoming side, a superposition of the incoming and reflected waves occurs. Two conditions must apply in the grey section:

- to satisfy the continuity of physical properties across the interface, both the amplitude and the maximum speed of the vibrations on the two sides of the membrane must be equal. We use the condition for the maximum speed of vibration here: with $v_{incoming}$ the speed for the incoming wave and $v_{reflected}$ the speed for the reflected wave, their sum must match $v_{transmitted}$, which is the maximum speed of the transmitted wave:

$$v_{incoming} + v_{reflected} = v_{transmitted} \qquad [64]$$

- Further, the energy passing through the interface must be conserved. The transported energy is given as an intensity in Eq. [33]. In that equation, we rewrite the angular frequency in the form $v_{max} = \omega \cdot A$:

$$\frac{1}{2} \rho_1 \cdot c_1 \cdot v_{incoming}^2$$

$$= \frac{1}{2} \rho_1 \cdot c_1 \cdot v_{reflected}^2 + \frac{1}{2} \rho_2 \cdot c_2 \cdot v_{transmitted}^2 \qquad [65]$$

in which index 1 represents the medium in which the incoming wave travels and index 2 the medium with the transmitted wave.

We are ultimately interested in the ratio of the transmitted intensity to the incoming intensity, i.e., $I_{transmitted}/I_{incoming}$. We obtain this ratio from Eq. [65] if we can rewrite $v_{reflected}$ as a term containing only $v_{incoming}$ and $v_{transmitted}$. We use Eq. [64] to eliminate $v_{reflected}$ in Eq. [65]:

$$\rho_1 \cdot c_1 \cdot v_{incoming}^2$$
$$= \rho_1 \cdot c_1 (v_{transmitted} - v_{incoming})^2 + \rho_2 \cdot c_2 \cdot v_{transmitted}^2$$
$$= \rho_1 \cdot c_1 \cdot v_{transmitted}^2 - 2 \cdot \rho_1 \cdot c_1 \cdot v_{transmitted} \cdot v_{incoming}$$
$$+ \underline{\rho_1 \cdot c_1 \cdot v_{incoming}^2} + \rho_2 \cdot c_2 \cdot v_{transmitted}^2 \qquad [66]$$

Note that the underlined term on the right-hand side cancels with the underlined term on the left-hand side. We divide this equation by $v_{transmitted}$ to obtain:

$$2 \cdot \rho_1 \cdot c_1 \cdot v_{incoming} = (\rho_1 \cdot c_1 + \rho_2 \cdot c_2) v_{transmitted} \qquad [67]$$

This yields a linear relation between the transmitted and the incoming speeds:

$$v_{transmitted} = \frac{2 \cdot \rho_1 \cdot c_1}{\rho_1 \cdot c_1 + \rho_2 \cdot c_2} v_{incoming} \qquad [68]$$

Substituting Eq. [68] and the definition of the intensity of a wave from Eq. [33], $I = \frac{1}{2} \cdot c \cdot \rho \cdot v^2$, into the ratio of incoming and transmitted intensity, we find:

$$\frac{I_{transmitted}}{I_{incoming}} = \frac{\frac{1}{2} c_2 \cdot \rho_2 \cdot v_{transmitted}^2}{\frac{1}{2} c_1 \cdot \rho_1 \cdot v_{incoming}^2}$$
$$= \frac{c_2 \cdot \rho_2}{c_1 \cdot \rho_1} \left( \frac{2 \cdot \rho_1 \cdot c_1}{\rho_1 \cdot c_1 + \rho_2 \cdot c_2} \right)^2$$
$$= \frac{4 \cdot \rho_1 \cdot \rho_2 \cdot c_1 \cdot c_2}{(\rho_1 \cdot c_1 + \rho_2 \cdot c_2)^2} \qquad [69]$$

This formula can be simplified when media 1 and 2 differ significantly in their density and/or their respective speed of sound. Let us for example assume that $\rho_2 \cdot c_2 \gg \rho_1 \cdot c_1$. In this case, Eq. [69] becomes:

$$\frac{I_{transmitted}}{I_{incoming}} = 4 \frac{\rho_1 \cdot c_1}{\rho_2 \cdot c_2} \qquad [70]$$

First, we test the condition $\rho_2 \cdot c_2 \gg \rho_1 \cdot c_1$ for our hypothetical membrane between outer and inner ear. We approximate the properties of perilymph by those of water. Taking the ambient temperature to be 20°C, we find:

$$\text{system 1:} \quad \rho_{air} = 1.205 \frac{kg}{m^3} \quad c_{air} = 343.2 \frac{m}{s}$$
$$[71]$$
$$\text{system 2:} \quad \rho_{H_2O} = 1000 \frac{kg}{m^3} \quad c_{H_2O} = 1485 \frac{m}{s}$$

thus, $\rho_2 \cdot c_2 \gg \rho_1 \cdot c_1$ is satisfied. Eq. [70] allows us then to calculate the ratio of sound intensities between air and perilymph:

$$\frac{I_{perilymph}}{I_{air}} = 4 \frac{\left(1.205 \frac{kg}{m^3}\right) \left(343.2 \frac{m}{s}\right)}{\left(1000 \frac{kg}{m^3}\right) \left(1485 \frac{m}{s}\right)}$$
$$= 1.1 \times 10^{-3} \qquad [72]$$

We conclude that sound transfer between media of significantly different densities is very ineffective. In particular, this means that nature could not construct our ear with a single membrane between outer and inner ear, as a sound intensity transfer of only about 0.1% would leave us essentially deaf.

So, how does the middle ear circumvent this problem? It transports the vibration of the eardrum as a mechanical vibration to the oval window. This eliminates the intensity loss discussed above. Beyond that, the middle ear provides a moderate amplification of the vibration due to the specific design of the interacting mechanical components. This amplification has two components, a force amplification and a pressure amplification. We calculate each component separately and then combine them to arrive at the overall sound amplification of the middle ear.

## FORCE AMPLIFICATION IN THE MIDDLE EAR

Fig. 17.25 shows a comparison of the anatomy of the middle ear of (a) humans and (b) reptiles. The figure illustrates the more recent evolution of the complex arrangement in the mammalian ear. Focussing first on the human ear in Fig. 17.25(a), we note that sound transmission from the eardrum (4) to the oval window (5) is accomplished by **three ossicles.** The ligaments in Fig. 17.25(a) identify their mechanical mobility. The *ligamentum mallei superius* (1) and the *ligamentum incudis superius* (2) hold the hammer and the anvil in position. The *ligamentum mallei laterale* (3) is responsible for allowing a rotation of the hammer. We identify this last ligament as the fulcrum. Fig. 17.26 is a sketch of the hammer as a mechanical lever-arm system. The eardrum can exert a force $\mathbf{F}_1$ and the anvil can exert a force $\mathbf{F}_2$ on the lever arm at distances $r_1$ and $r_2$ from the fulcrum, respectively. The hammer is in mechanical equilibrium when a torque equilibrium is established, as defined in Chapter 5:

$$\sum_i \tau_i = r_1 \cdot F_1 - r_2 \cdot F_2 = 0 \qquad [73]$$

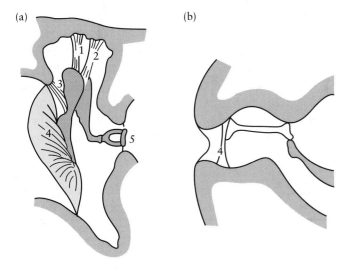

**FIGURE 17.25**

(a) Human middle ear anatomy, highlighting the ligaments that stabilize the three ossicles between the eardrum (4) and the oval window (5). *Ligamentum mallei superius* (1) and *Ligamentum incudis superius* (2) hold the hammer and the anvil in position. *Ligamentum mallei laterale* (3) acts as a fulcrum for the rotation of the hammer. (b) Middle ear anatomy of reptiles. Note that only one bone bridges the middle ear section.

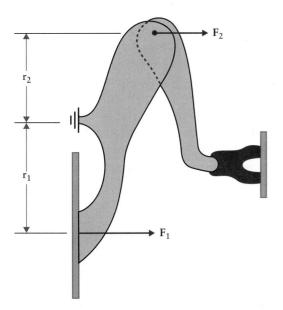

**FIGURE 17.26**

Mechanical arrangement of the three ossicles in the middle ear. The hammer is a lever-arm system with a fulcrum at $r_1 = 1.5 \cdot r_2$. In mechanical equilibrium, the torques due to the forces exerted by the eardrum ($F_1$) and the anvil ($F_2$) must be equal. The stirrup (dark red) connects the anvil to the oval window (green).

which yields:

$$F_2 = \frac{r_1}{r_2} F_1 \qquad [74]$$

With the fulcrum located above the halfway point of the lever arm, i.e., $r_1 = 1.5 \cdot r_2$, we find that the force

acting on the oval window is about 1.5 times the force exerted by the eardrum.

In turn, reptiles have only a single bone connecting the eardrum (4) to the inner ear, as illustrated in Fig. 17.25(b). In some large dinosaur species these bones were quite heavy, which allowed them at most to hear very low frequencies. The less-developed ear of the dinosaur has been inherited by modern birds. As a consequence, most bird species do not hear above 4 to 5 kHz, while some marine mammals can hear up to 200 kHz.

## PRESSURE AMPLIFICATION IN THE MIDDLE EAR

A pressure amplification is the result of the difference in area of eardrum and oval window. The pressure on the eardrum equals the force acting on the eardrum divided by its area. Equally, the pressure at the oval window equals the force on the oval window divided by its area. Anatomically, we find an area for the eardrum of 65 mm² (of which, however, as little as 45 mm² might be mechanically active), and an area of 3.2 mm² for the oval window. Thus, the pressure amplification accounts for a factor of 15 to 20.

Combining force and pressure amplifications, we get:

$$\Delta p_{\text{oval}} = \frac{F_{\text{oval}}}{A_{\text{oval}}} = \frac{1.5 \cdot F_{\text{eardrum}}}{A_{\text{oval}}}$$

$$= 1.5 \frac{A_{\text{eardrum}} \cdot \Delta p_{\text{air}}}{A_{\text{oval}}} \qquad [75]$$

which yields:

$$\frac{\Delta p_{\text{oval}}}{\Delta p_{\text{air}}} = 1.5 \frac{65 \, \text{mm}^2}{3.2 \, \text{mm}^2} = 30 \qquad [76]$$

The middle ear provides an amplification of the pressure difference arriving at the eardrum by a factor of 30, instead of diminishing the signal to less than 1% as expected for a single membrane separating outer and inner ear! Note that the factor of 30 is derived neglecting a damping loss across the middle ear. This damping loss means that the total energy transferred from the auditory canal to the inner ear is reduced; however, focussing the energy transfer onto the small area of the oval window means that the intensity, which is energy transfer per unit area, is still enhanced.

## The Inner Ear

The acoustic components of the inner ear are located in the **cochlea**, shown in Fig. 17.10 in its characteristic curled shape for mammals. This shape is the ori-

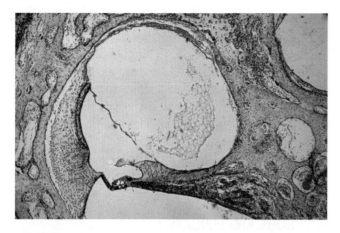

**FIGURE 17.27**

Light micrograph of a cross-section of the cochlea. Three liquid-filled channels are shown: the vestibular chamber (top centre) and the tympanic chamber (bottom), both containing perilymph; the cochlear duct (centre left), containing endolymph. The tympanic chamber on one side and the vestibular chamber and the cochlear duct on the other side are separated by the basilar membrane. The vestibular chamber and the cochlear duct are separated by Reissner's membrane. The organ of Corti is supported by the basilar membrane in the cochlear duct. It consists of hair cells and the tectorial membrane.

gin of its name, which means *snail* in Latin. The cochlear cross-section is shown in Fig. 17.27, highlighting its three separate channels. The **vestibular chamber** (top cavity) starts at the oval window and runs along the cochlea to its far end, called the apex or helicotrema. There the vestibular chamber is open to the **tympanic chamber** (bottom cavity), which runs back to the round window at the end of the inner ear. Both chambers are filled with perilymph and are separated by the **basilar membrane.** The third channel, called the **cochlear duct** (at the centre left), contains the organ of Corti (named for Alfonso de Corti). The cochlear duct is separated from the other two channels by the basilar membrane and by Reissner's membrane (named for Ernst Reißner) and is filled with endolymph, a liquid solution similar to the perilymph but that contains 145 mmol/L K$^+$. This difference in ionic concentrations leads to an electric potential of the endolymph relative to the perilymph of +80 mV. In the present discussion we neglect the related electric phenomena.

Dendrites emerge from the organ of Corti and run through the basilar membrane toward the brain. The **organ of Corti** is shown separately in Fig. 17.28. The basilar membrane (horizontal section at the bottom) carries an array of support cells in which three external (at left) and one internal auditory hair cells are embedded. The auditory hair cells can be seen as they each carry about 80 hair-like extensions, called stereovilli (just below the plate-like structure that

extends from the right). The stereovilli extend into the cochlear duct, which forms a narrow gap between the basilar membrane and the tectorial membrane above the auditory hair cells.

These components allow for sound detection and sound frequency analysis in the following fashion. The inner ear represents a closed tube (both confining windows are elastic membranes). However, an excitation at the oval window cannot form resonances along this tube because that would limit the frequencies we hear to a set of harmonics, as discussed in the previous section. Instead, the excitation at the oval window leads to a one-dimensional travelling wave, similar to the single bulge you form on a rope stretched between your hand and the wall if you briefly swing your hand up and down. Such a **travelling wave** is sketched in Fig. 17.29. The figure illustrates the amplitude of a wave in the perilymph as a function of position along the vestibular chamber; however, the figure is not correct in that the travelling wave is a longitudinal and not a transverse wave as the graphics may imply. The two arrows indicate the initial excitation at the oval window and the later mechanical response at the round window below. For each sound frequency, a specific point exists, between the oval window and the apex, where the travelling wave amplifies in the perilymph and causes the basilar membrane to vibrate. This process is controlled by the stiffness of the basilar membrane, which reduces by a factor of $10^4$ along its entire length. This is caused by a thickness variation of the basilar membrane. It starts with a thickness of 0.04 mm at the oval window and ends with a thickness of 0.5 mm at the apex.

**FIGURE 17.28**

Detail of the organ of Corti. The basilar membrane (at bottom) supports a layer of supportive cells in which three external and one internal auditory hair cells are embedded. The auditory hair cells have hair-like extensions (stereovilli) that extend into a gap between the basilar membrane and the tectorial membrane, which extends from the upper right.

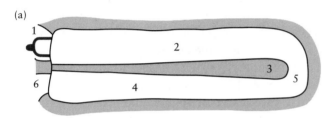

## FIGURE 17.29

A travelling wave in the vestibular chamber, caused by a vibration of the stirrup at the oval window (upper arrow). The basilar membrane vibrates at a point determined by the frequency of the travelling wave. This vibration causes the wave to be transferred to the perilymph in the tympanic chamber, in which it travels toward the round window (lower arrow).

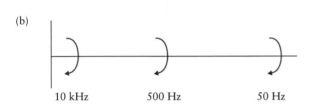

## FIGURE 17.30

Schematic sketch of the path taken in the inner ear by a wave of specific frequency. (a) Overview of the cochlea with the stirrup and the oval window (1), the vestibular chamber (2), the basilar membrane (3) with its varying thickness, the tympanic chamber (4), the apex (5), and the round window (6). (b) Waves of higher frequencies travel a shorter distance along the cochlea.

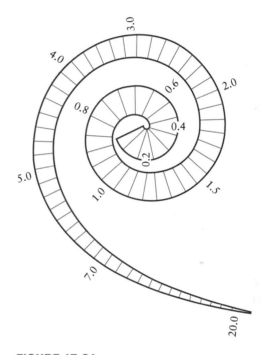

## FIGURE 17.31

Plot of the location of the resonant vibration of the basilar membrane as a function of the travelling wave frequency in unit kHz. Frequencies near 20 kHz are detected near the oval window (pointed end at the bottom right), while frequencies at 200 Hz (0.2 kHz) and below travel close to the apex (shown as the wide end).

Two figures are provided to illustrate the position dependence of the point at which a certain frequency causes the basilar membrane to vibrate: Fig. 17.30(a) shows a conceptual sketch in which the cochlea is shown as if stretched out. The oval window is excited by the stirrup (1). The wave then travels along the perilymph (2). The frequency properties are shown in Fig. 17.30(b). For higher frequencies, e.g., 10 kHz, the wave causes the basilar membrane (3) to vibrate close to the oval window. This causes the wave to transfer to the tympanic chamber (4), where it travels back to the round window (6). At an intermediate frequency, e.g., 500 Hz, the wave travels to an intermediate point along the basilar membrane, and at low frequencies, e.g., 50 Hz, the wave travels all the way to the apex.

Fig. 17.31 illustrates the connection between frequency and distance from the oval window (in the figure at the pointed end at the bottom), with numbers representing the respective frequencies in unit kHz.

How does the resonance of the basilar membrane cause a signal to the brain? The vibration of the basilar membrane causes the tectorial membrane in the organ of Corti to vibrate in synchrony. The mechanism by which this leads to an excitation of the dendrites in the organ of Corti is illustrated in

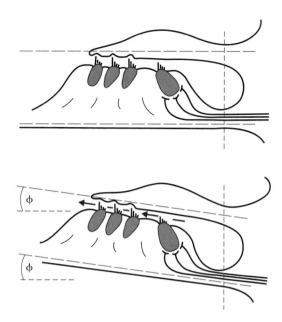

**FIGURE 17.32**

Mechanism of dendrite excitation in the organ of Corti. The basilar membrane and the tectorial membrane vibrate in synchrony in response to a travelling wave. The upper sketch shows the equilibrium position and the lower sketch shows the position at the instant when both membranes are moved upward by an angle $\phi$. The stereovilli of the auditory hair cells are bent sideways in this process due to the narrowness of the gap between the two membranes. A signal is sent to the brain only from the internal auditory hair cell.

Fig. 17.32, which shows the two membranes in their equilibrium position in the upper sketch, and when moved upward by an angle $\phi$ in the lower sketch. The narrowness of the gap between both membranes causes the stereovilli to bend sideways during the vibration. Only the internal auditory hair cell is connected to dendrites; thus the stereovilli of the internal auditory cell must be bent for a signal to be sent to the brain.

What is reported to the brain? Two components of the vibrational motion of the basilar membrane are encoded in the sequence of the nerve impulses:

- **Tonotopic Mapping (Frequency-to-Place Mapping).** The response of a particular dendrite identifies the position along the cochlea where the resonance in the basilar membrane has occurred. If the travelling wave contains different frequencies, they are separately and concurrently detected by different dendrites along the cochlea, pretty much in the same fashion that a Fourier analysis is developed mathematically. This mechanism was already proposed by Georg Ohm and Hermann von Helmholtz in the 19th century.

- **Temporal Coding of Frequencies.** The frequency at which the dendrites in the organ of Corti send their signals to the brain is synchronized with the actual frequency of the sound wave.

The human ear is extremely sensitive to sounds ranging from between 15 and 20 Hz to about 20 kHz (dogs hear up to 40 kHz, while elephants communicate subsonically as these frequencies carry much farther in air). However, the sensitivity of human hearing varies across this frequency interval, primarily as the result of the resonance properties we discussed earlier for the outer ear. This is illustrated quantitatively in Fig. 17.33. The figure shows the frequency range from about 10 Hz to 16 kHz and sound pressure levels from 0 dB to 140 dB (for the definition of the sound pressure level scale, see Eq. [34]). Each curve in the plot represents the pressure levels as a function of frequency that a person judges to be equally loud. The thicker line at the bottom corresponds to the **normal acoustic reflex threshold**, and the thicker line at the top corresponds to the **pain threshold**. The range of normal conversation is shown as a grey area near the centre of the plot.

A maximum sensitivity near 3 kHz, in agreement with Example 17.10, is clearly demonstrated. As frequencies are lower or higher, the sensitivity diminishes until it ceases at the lower- or higher-frequency limit of the ear. The variations in perceived **loudness** as a function of frequency render the physical scales

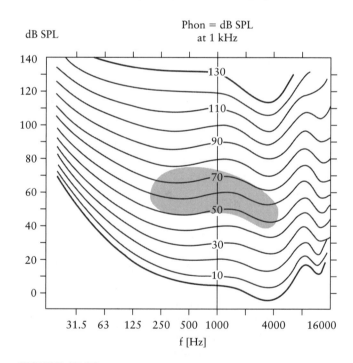

**FIGURE 17.33**

The hearing range of the human ear, shown as a function of the frequency of the sound ($f$, abscissa) and as a function of the sound pressure level (SPL, ordinate). Each line in the plot represents sounds that are judged to be equally loud. The lowest curve is the acoustic reflex threshold and the highest curve is the pain threshold. The grey area corresponds to the normal range of conversations. The loudness in unit phon is equal to the intensity level (IL) or sound pressure level (SPL) in unit dB at 1 kHz.

## TABLE 17.5

### Sound perception in unit phon

| Loudness (phon) | Example |
|---|---|
| 4 | Threshold of normal hearing |
| 20 | Rustle of leaves |
| 40 | Whispering, talking in a low voice |
| 60 | Normal conversation |
| 80 | City traffic noise |
| 100 | Industrial plant |
| 110 | Comfortableness limit |
| 120 | Thunder |
| 130 | Pain threshold |
| 140 | Jet engine |

of intensity level (IL, see Eq. [35]) and sound pressure level (SPL, see Eq. [34]) less useful, because we all disagree with the idea that a 100-dB sound at 40 Hz is equally as loud as a 100-dB sound at 3000 Hz. For this reason, a new parameter for loudness is introduced based on Fig. 17.33 and is recorded in unit **phon**. The convention is to set the decibel scale and the phon scale equal at a sound frequency of 1 kHz: 100 dB = 100 phon at 1 kHz. Loudness values deviate from SPL or IL values at all other frequencies. Table 17.5 provides several examples for sounds, with loudness reported in unit phon.

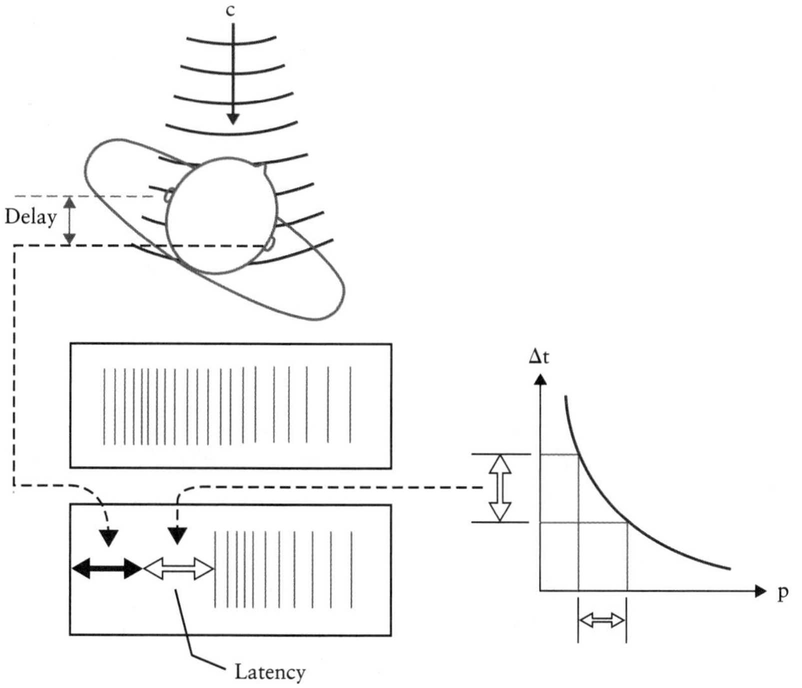

# Special Properties of the Auditory System

## Stereoscopic Hearing

The human head has two ears. As we all know from listening to music, this allows us to detect the direction from which a sound reaches us. We can distinguish deviations as small as 4° between two sound sources. This is based on two signal-delay phenomena at the farther ear, as illustrated in Fig. 17.34:

- The sound travels on the order of $10^{-5}$ s longer, and

- the sound pressure level is slightly lower due to the reduction of intensity with distance. A lower pressure level is associated with a longer **latency time**, which is the time between the arrival of a sound wave at the ear and the instant the dendrites in the organ of Corti send the first signal to the brain.

## The Role of the Brain: Beats

Our brain does not necessarily interpret signals received from the ears in an objective fashion, i.e., the way a computer records the output of a physical instrument. Acoustic illusions can be caused by a range of effects. For the healthy ear, for example, the preferential absorption of higher frequencies in the medium air causes us to believe that a lower-frequency sound comes from a farther distance. This

**FIGURE 17.34**

Mechanism of stereoscopic hearing. Two delay mechanisms contribute to the ability to detect the direction of a sound source: a delay due to the longer distance from the sound source to the farther ear, and a latency delay due to the slightly lower sound pressure level of the sound at the farther ear (indicated by the inverse proportionality between the delay time $\Delta t$ and the sound pressure $p$ in the plot at the right). The two boxes below the sketched person show the time dependence of the nerve impulses sent to the brain for the closer ear (upper box) and the farther ear (lower box).

effect is used in movies to create anxiety when the sound pitch is raised as a climactic event approaches. Acoustic illusions are more frequent for patients with impaired hearing. All diseases of the middle ear, such as otitis media or otosclerosis, can cause phantom sound perception as the brain attempts to correct for sensory data missing from the ear. This effect is called **tinnitus**, with the heard sounds a subjective ringing, buzzing, or hissing. Here we discuss in more detail two phenomena that are frequently observed: the formation of beats and the Doppler effect.

Our ear is able to distinguish several sounds arriving at the ear at the same time. The ear can even tune in to a specific pattern of a first harmonic and the corresponding higher harmonics, enabling us to listen to a specific person in spite of high background noise at a party. However, when two first harmonics are too close (below a difference of $\Delta f = 15$ Hz), they are no longer interpreted as two separate sounds. The origin of this effect is illustrated by studying the superposition of two such waves. We assume for simplicity that the two waves are studied at position $x = 0$ and have equal amplitudes:

$$\xi_{\text{superposition}} = A \cdot \sin(\omega_1 \cdot t) + A \cdot \sin(\omega_2 \cdot t) \quad [77]$$

We rewrite this equation using a trigonometric identity for the sum of two sine terms (see the Math Review at the end of this chapter):

$$\xi_{\text{superposition}} = 2 \cdot A \cdot \sin\left(\frac{\omega_1 + \omega_2}{2} t\right)$$
$$\times \cos\left(\frac{\omega_1 - \omega_2}{2} t\right) \quad [78]$$

The function in Eq. [78] is shown in Fig. 17.35. The two separate wave functions in Eq. [77] are shown as the two upper curves. The superposition is shown below. The higher frequency in the sine term in Eq. [78] is very similar to the two frequencies of the original waves. The lower frequency in the cosine term leads to the frequency that causes the envelope in Fig. 17.35. If the envelope frequency is equal to or less than 7.5 Hz, it is called a **beat frequency** because the brain does not interpret the pattern in Fig. 17.35 as two distinct sounds, but as one sound with the average frequency and with a time-dependent amplitude, which we obtain from Eq. [78]:

$$A_{\text{superposition}}(t) = 2 \cdot A \cdot \cos\left(\frac{\omega_1 - \omega_2}{2} t\right) \quad [79]$$

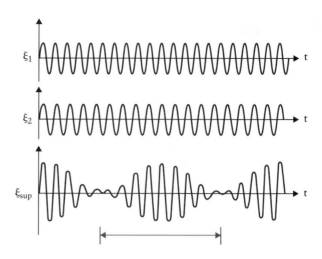

**FIGURE 17.35**

Superposition of two waves (top two curves) with the same amplitude but slightly different frequencies. The result of the superposition is shown in the bottom curve. The ear can either interpret this function as two separate waves or, if the frequency difference is less than 15 Hz, as a single wave with a time-dependent amplitude (beat). The interval indicated below the graph with two arrow heads indicates the beat period.

● **EXAMPLE 17.11**

Two sounds are originally generated with equal amplitudes, and frequencies $f_1 = 1000$ Hz and $f_2 = 1010$ Hz. What does a person hear?

*Solution:* Eq. [78] leads to a superposition frequency for the pitch we hear:

$$f_{\text{superposition}} = \frac{1}{2}(f_1 + f_2) = 1005 \text{ Hz} \quad [80]$$

Played separately, the sounds with $f_1$, $f_2$, and $f_{\text{superposition}}$ could barely be distinguished. However, when the sounds with $f_1$ and $f_2$ are received at the same time, the sound amplitude varies with a beat frequency of:

$$f_{\text{beat}} = \frac{1}{2}(f_1 - f_2) = 5 \text{ Hz} \quad [81]$$

This is heard as an up- and down-swelling of the sound. You can easily verify the phenomenon with a piano. All neighbouring keys from $A_0$ up to about $C_4$ have a frequency difference of 15 Hz or less. Hit any two of these keys together and listen to the sound.

**Concept Question 17.9**

Fig. 17.36 shows two thresholds for the hearing of frequency differences. Below both curves, our hearing is deceived. Relate the two thresholds to your everyday experience.

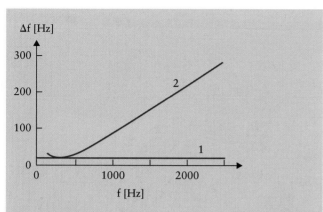

**FIGURE 17.36**

Two threshold curves matter to the auditory perception of two waves of different frequencies: if the frequency difference is less than 15 Hz (curve 1), we hear a beat; if the frequency difference lies between curve 1 and curve 2, we perceive the sound as uncomfortably harsh.

ANSWER: Shown as curve 1 is the frequency difference $\Delta f = 15$ Hz, below which we hear beats, as discussed in the text above. The figure illustrates that this threshold is independent of the frequency of the sound.

The figure shows a second curve labelled 2. This curve indicates the threshold of frequency difference $\Delta f$, below which we perceive two sounds as uncomfortably harsh. The cause for this phenomenon is, again, the beat given in Eq. [78]. However, above a difference of 15 Hz our ear is no longer able to resolve the timing of the beat frequency $f_1 - f_2$. Note that the threshold curve 2 is essentially proportional to the original sound frequency.

## Doppler Effect and Doppler Ultrasound

An altered sound frequency is detected when the sound source or the receiver (e.g., the human ear) moves relative to the medium. Two cases are distinguished: (I) the sound source at rest and the receiver moving with speed $v_{receiver}$, and (II) the sound source moving with speed $v_{source}$ while the receiver is at rest. We know the latter case well from hearing the sound of police sirens as we pull over to allow them to approach or move away from us on a roadway. Both cases are called the Doppler effect, named for Christian Doppler.

### THE RECEIVER MOVES, THE SOUND SOURCE IS AT REST

The first case is illustrated in Fig. 17.37. The source emits waves that travel outward. Between every two red lines indicating the waves lies a full wavelength of the sound; the red lines are separated by equal dis-

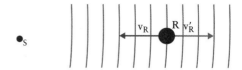

**FIGURE 17.37**

Sketch of the motion of a receiver moving with speed $v_{receiver}$ toward a sound source or moving with speed $v'_{receiver}$ away from the sound source, with the source at rest, $v_{source} = 0$. The red lines indicate the waves emitted by the source; the distance between the red lines corresponds to the wavelength.

tances as long as the frequency of the source does not change. When the receiver moves toward the source, it receives more waves per time unit than if the receiver were at rest. Correspondingly, when the receiver moves away from the sound source a smaller number of waves is received per time unit.

We quantify this effect for a source of frequency $f_0$. We consider a time interval $\Delta t$ in which a receiver at rest receives $f_0 \cdot \Delta t$ wavelength cycles. During the same time interval the receiver moves by a distance $v_{receiver} \cdot \Delta t$. This distance corresponds to $v_{receiver} \cdot \Delta t / \lambda$ wavelength cycles. The total number of wavelength cycles received is the sum of both contributions. The frequency is obtained after dividing by $\Delta t$:

$$f_{receiver} = f_0 \pm \frac{v_{receiver}}{\lambda} = f_0 \left( 1 \pm \frac{v_{receiver}}{c} \right) \quad [82]$$

The $\pm$ sign in Eq. [82] has been introduced to allow the formula to describe both possible cases: the receiver moving toward $(+)$ or away from $(-)$ the source.

### THE SOUND SOURCE MOVES, THE RECEIVER IS AT REST

The second case is illustrated in Fig. 17.38. The source emits waves of wavelength $\lambda$. The concurrent motion of the source leads to an apparent wavelength $\lambda_{source}$. Using for the speed of the source $v_{source}$, we calculate an audible wavelength of $\lambda_{source} = \lambda_0 \pm v_{source}/f_0$ if the source moves straight toward or straight away from the receiver. We obtain the audible frequency from $c = \lambda_{source} \cdot f_{source}$:

$$f_{source} = \frac{c}{\lambda_{source}} = \frac{c}{\lambda_0 \pm \dfrac{v_{source}}{f_0}} = f_0 \frac{c}{c \pm v_{source}} \quad [83]$$

which leads to:

$$f_{source} = f_0 \frac{1}{1 \pm \dfrac{v_{source}}{c}} \quad [84]$$

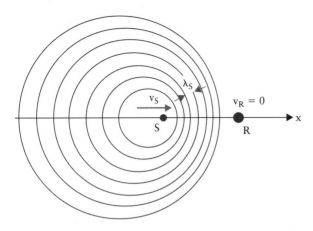

**FIGURE 17.38**

Sketch of the motion of a sound source moving with speed $v_{source}$ toward a receiver at rest, $v_{receiver} = 0$. The large circles represent spherical sound waves emitted from a point-like sound source. The motion of the source along the x-axis leads to a change in the wavelength $\lambda_{source}$ of the emitted sound as detected by the receiver.

**Concept Question 17.10**

The ± sign in Eq. [83] has been introduced to allow the formula to describe the source moving both toward and away from the receiver. Which sign corresponds to which case?

ANSWER: The (+) sign applies when the source moves away from the receiver and the (−) sign applies when the source moves toward it. A negative sign in the denominator of Eq. [84] leads to a higher frequency. This is consistent with your observations of emergency vehicles with sirens passing you: while the vehicle approaches you its apparent frequency is higher than when it moves away from you.

## DOPPLER ULTRASOUND DIAGNOSIS

A combination of both effects leads to an interesting application in the field of medicine: **Doppler ultrasound.** Ultrasound is sound at frequencies beyond the limit of human hearing, usually between 20 kHz and 10 GHz. A typical clinical ultrasound setup is shown in Fig. 17.39. It is widely used as a diagnostic tool in medicine, where it is best known for studying the unborn child.

The ultrasound technique is also used to detect the speed of moving components in the human body, such as blood cells. An application of this technique is given in Fig. 12.25. The principle of the measurement

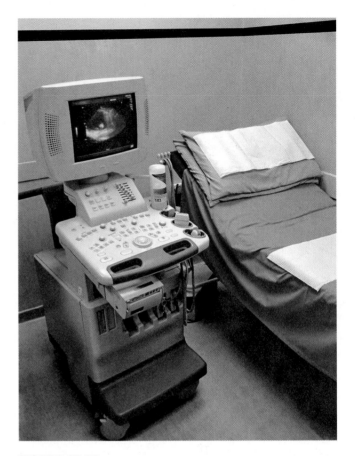

**FIGURE 17.39**

Typical ultrasound equipment in a hospital setting.

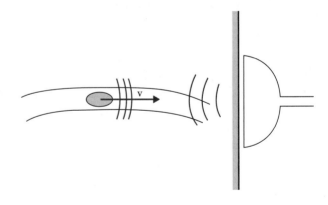

**FIGURE 17.40**

Sketch of the Doppler ultrasound method. A transducer at right, in contact with the skin, sends an ultrasound signal that is reflected by an object moving with speed v, e.g., an erythrocyte.

is illustrated in Fig. 17.40. A standard transducer (shown at right) is brought into air-free contact with the skin. A typical transducer frequency in this technique lies between 2 and 8 MHz. At the same time, the transducer serves as a receiver. The rate of switching between the two functions is 1 kHz. Three steps are included in the Doppler ultrasound technique:

(*Step I*) The sound wave emitted by the resting transducer is received by the moving blood cell (receiver). The blood cell moves with speed $v$, e.g., toward the transducer in Fig. 17.40, but possibly at an angle for which further corrections are needed that we do not discuss here.

(*Step II*) At the same instant it receives the ultrasound, the erythrocyte becomes a passive source by reflecting the sound wave (echo).

(*Step III*) The transducer then receives the sound wave emitted from a moving source.

To describe the overall effect of all three steps, the two cases of the Doppler effect discussed above must be combined. For the first and third steps, we write:

$$\text{(Step I)} \quad f_{\text{erythrocyte}} = f_0\left(1 + \frac{v}{c}\right)$$

$$\text{(Step III)} \quad f_{\text{transducer}} = f_{\text{erythrocyte}}\left(\frac{1}{1 - v/c}\right) \quad [85]$$

The + sign is chosen in step (I) because the receiver moves toward the sound source in Fig. 17.40, and the − sign is chosen in step (III) because, as a source, the erythrocyte moves toward the transducer. The velocity parameter $v$ has no subscript because it is the velocity of the erythrocyte in both cases. Eq. [85] leads to:

$$f_{\text{transducer}} = f_0\left(\frac{1 + v/c}{1 - v/c}\right) \quad [86]$$

Note that Eq. [86] also confirms that the measured frequency would remain $f_0$ if both receiver and source moved with the same velocity in the same direction. In this case, the signs in both step (I) and step (III) would be the same and the expression in parentheses in Eq. [86] would become one.

The difference between the frequencies emitted and received by the transducer is called the **Doppler shift** $\Delta f$. Eq. [86] can be simplified in the limiting case where the speed of the blood cell is much slower than the speed of sound in the tissue, $v \ll c$. Since this is always the case, the Doppler shift is linearly dependent on the speed of the blood cell:

$$\Delta f = f_{\text{transducer}} - f_0 = f_0\left(\frac{1 + v/c}{1 - v/c} - 1\right)$$

$$= f_0\left(\frac{1 + v/c - (1 - v/c)}{1 - v/c}\right) \quad [87]$$

which leads to:

$$\lim_{v \ll c} \Delta f = 2 \cdot f_0 \frac{v}{c} \quad [88]$$

## Concept Question 17.11

**How does a Doppler ultrasound measurement change for a blood vessel with a stenosis, i.e., with a constriction?**

SOLUTION: We first describe the result of a Doppler ultrasound measurement for a healthy blood vessel. The average speed of the erythrocytes in the aorta is calculated in Example 12.1 as $v = 0.22$ m/s, while the speed of sound in body tissue is 1540 m/s. Thus, the assumption $v \ll c$ is satisfied and Eq. [88] applies. Assuming a transducer frequency of 5 MHz, an average Doppler shift of about 1 to 2 kHz is expected:

$$\Delta f = \frac{2 \cdot f_0 \cdot v}{c}$$

$$= \frac{2(5 \times 10^6 \text{ s}^{-1})\left(0.22 \dfrac{\text{m}}{\text{s}}\right)}{1540 \dfrac{\text{m}}{\text{s}}}$$

$$= 1430 \text{ Hz} \quad [89]$$

Since the blood pressure varies, variations in the speed of the erythrocytes during the pumping cycle of the heart are expected. This is illustrated in Fig. 17.41(a), in which the Doppler shift is plotted as a function of time, and in Fig. 17.41(b), which shows a typical profile on a screen.

For a stenosis, a different blood speed pattern is expected. An example is shown in Fig. 17.42, which is a colour angiogram of the heart with an obstruction in the circumflex coronary artery, one of the arteries that supply the heart with blood. The stenosed section appears as the narrowed section immediately above the inverted U-shaped artery in the centre.

Such a constriction in a blood vessel causes the flow speed to increase and even to reverse due to turbulence. A range of different erythrocyte speeds exists in each blood vessel section near a stenosis; thus a broadening of the speed-versus-time curves of a Doppler ultrasound measurement is observed.

(a)

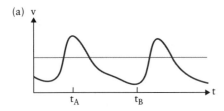

(b)

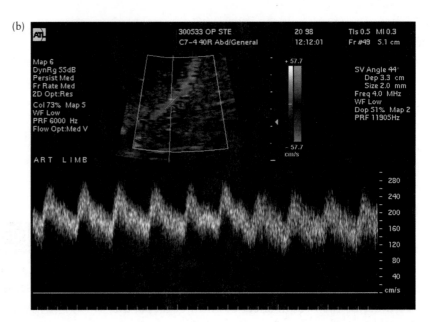

## FIGURE 17.41

(a) Typical Doppler shift pattern for erythrocytes in an artery. The Doppler shift is converted to a speed of blood, using Eq. [88]. The periodic speed variation between times $t_A$ and $t_B$ is due to the rhythmic action of the heart. (b) The same data as recorded with a clinical ultrasound setup.

## FIGURE 17.42

Coloured angiogram of the heart with a blood vessel obstruction (stenosis). The stenosed section occurs in the circumflex coronary artery: find the narrowed section immediately above the inverted U-shaped artery in the centre.

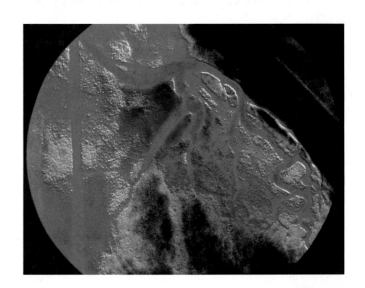

# MULTIPLE CHOICE AND CONCEPTUAL QUESTIONS

## SOUND WAVE PARAMETERS

**Q–17.1.** The frequency of a sound wave has the following unit: (A) s, (B) 1/s, (C) m/s, (D) $s^2$, (E) $1/s^2$.

**Q–17.2.** We compare two sound waves in air at room temperature. Wave II has twice the frequency of wave I. The following relation holds between their speeds of sound: (A) $c_I = c_{II}$, (B) $c_I > c_{II}$, (C) $c_I < c_{II}$, (D) Such a conclusion cannot be drawn with the given information.

**Q–17.3.** We compare again two sound waves in air at room temperature. Wave II has twice the frequency of wave I. The following relation holds between their wavelengths: (A) $\lambda_I = \lambda_{II}$, (B) $\lambda_I > \lambda_{II}$, (C) $\lambda_I < \lambda_{II}$, (D) Such a conclusion cannot be drawn with the given information.

**Q–17.4.** Waves are typically characterized by frequency, angular frequency, period, wavelength, and amplitude. Which of these parameters are related to each other in a linear fashion? (A) period and frequency; (B) period and angular frequency; (C) frequency and angular frequency; (D) wavelength and period; (E) amplitude and frequency. *Note:* More than one answer may apply.

**Q–17.5.** We frequently modelled tendons as massless strings. Why is this not a useful model when describing waves on strings?

**Q–17.6.** The distance between a crest of a sinusoidal water wave and the next trough is 2 m. If the frequency of the water wave is 2 Hz, what is its speed? (A) 8 m/s, (B) 4 m/s, (C) 2 m/s, (D) 1 m/s, (E) Not enough information is given to determine the wave speed.

**Q–17.7.** A sound source I generates sound with twice the frequency of sound source II. Compared to the speed of sound of source I the speed of sound of source II is (A) twice as fast, (B) half as fast, (C) four times as fast, (D) one-fourth as fast, (E) the same.

## SOUND INTENSITY

**Q–17.8.** If you perceive a point-like source of sound as too loud, you should move away from the source. This is because of the following relation between the sound intensity and the distance from the source: (A) Intensity is independent of distance. (B) Intensity increases linearly with distance. (C) Intensity increases non-linearly with distance. (D) Intensity decreases linearly with distance. (E) Intensity decreases non-linearly with distance.

**Q–17.9.** The intensity level of a sound is reported in unit decibel (dB). How does IL change if we increase a sound intensity by a factor of 10? (A) It remains unchanged. (B) It increases by 1 dB to 2 dB. (C) It increases by 2 dB to 20 dB. (D) It increases by 20 dB to 200 dB. (E) It decreases.

**Q–17.10.** Doubling the rate at which a sound source emits energy at a single frequency leads to the following increase of the sound intensity level: (A) 0.5 dB, (B) 2.0 dB, (C) 3.0 dB, (D) 20 dB, (E) none of the above.

## SOUND ABSORPTION AND REFLECTION

**Q–17.11.** When sound is absorbed in a medium, its intensity level IL decreases with distance travelled through the medium $x$ as: (A) IL $\propto e^{-\beta \cdot x}$, (B) IL $\propto -x$, (C) IL $\propto \beta$, (D) IL $\propto \ln(-x)$, (E) none of the above. *Note:* $\beta$ is a constant.

**Q–17.12.** A sound travels from medium I into medium II. Consider the following four conditions: (I) For the speed of sound $c_I = c_{II}$ applies. (II) For the density of the medium $\rho_I = \rho_{II}$ applies. (III) For the wavelengths in the two media $\lambda_I = \lambda_{II}$ applies. (IV) For the frequencies in the two media $f_I = f_{II}$ applies. No reflection of sound intensity at the interface between media I and II occurs if the following conditions are fulfilled: (A) only (I), (B) only (II), (C) both (I) and (II), (D) both (I) and (III), (E) both (II) and (IV).

**Q–17.13.** As a wave and its reflected wave move through each other in a tube that is aligned with the $x$-axis, there is an instant when the gas in the tube shows no displacement from equilibrium, $\xi = 0$ for all positions $x$. At that instant, where is the energy carried by the wave?

**Q–17.14.** Why is it not possible for two divers to communicate by talking under water?

## HARMONICS

**Q–17.15.** A tube is initially filled with air (use $c_{air} = 340$ m/s), then with water ($c_{water} = 1500$ m/s). How does the frequency of the first harmonic change for the tube? (A) no change, (B) it increases, (C) it decreases.

**Q–17.16.** Which of the following does a sound wave transmitted to the inner ear form in the perilymph? (A) a standing wave, (B) the first and second harmonic, (C) a travelling wave, (D) no wave at all.

## BEATS AND DOPPLER EFFECT

**Q–17.17.** Ultrasound cannot be heard by humans because: (A) its intensity is too low, (B) its frequency is too low, (C) its amplitude is too high, (D) its pressure variations are too high, (E) its frequency is too high.

**Q–17.18.** Fig. 17.43 shows a bat using echolocation to detect its prey. The animal uses the reflected frequency to analyze the state of motion of the insect. This is possible because of: (A) the formation of beats, (B) the formation of standing waves, (C) the Doppler effect, (D) the adiabatic processes during sound propagation, (E) the formation of a second harmonic.

**Q–17.19.** A moth flies along a path perpendicular to the flight path of a bat. While the moth is within a narrow range of angles in front of the bat, the bat detects a reflected frequency that is (A) less than its emitted frequency, (B) the same as its emitted frequency, (C) more than its emitted frequency, (D) no longer in the range it can hear, (E) in a range that attracts dogs like a dog whistle.

**FIGURE 17.43**

A bat catching prey in the dark.

Q–17.20. Doppler ultrasound is used in medicine to detect the following physiological feature: (A) bone fractures, (B) blood flow velocity, (C) blood pressure, (D) nervous breakdowns, or (E) respiration rate under stress.

Q–17.21. You are moving toward a stationary wall while emitting a sound. Is there a Doppler shift in the echo you hear? If so, is it the case of a moving source or the case of a moving receiver?

Q–17.22. When two tuning forks sound at the same time, a beat frequency of 5 Hz is observed. If one tuning fork has a frequency of 245 Hz, what is the frequency of the other one? (A) 240 Hz, (B) 242.5 Hz, (C) the same, (D) 247.5 Hz, (E) 250 Hz, (F) none of the above, or more than one answer is correct.

# ANALYTICAL PROBLEMS

## SOUND WAVE PARAMETERS

P–17.1. A wave with frequency 5.0 Hz and amplitude 40 mm moves in the positive $x$-direction with speed 6.5 m/s. What are (a) the wavelength, (b) the period, and (c) the angular frequency? (d) Write a formula for the wave.

P–17.2. The best way to measure the compressibility of liquids or solids is to measure the speed of sound in the material. If such a measurement for water yields $c$ = 1.4 km/s (which is about four times the value in air!), what is the compressibility of water?

P–17.3. The range of frequencies heard by the healthy human ear stretches from about 16 Hz to 20 kHz. What are the corresponding wavelengths of sound waves at these frequencies?

P–17.4. Bats can detect small insects that are about equal in size to the wavelength of the sound the bat makes with its echolocation system. A bat emits a chirp at a frequency of 60 kHz. Using the speed of sound in air as 340 m/s, what is the smallest insect this bat can detect?

P–17.5. Fig. 17.44 shows a 25-Hz wave travelling in the $x$-direction. Calculate (a) its amplitude, (b) its wavelength, (c) its period, and (d) its wave speed. Use $L_1$ = 18 cm and $L_2$ = 10 cm.

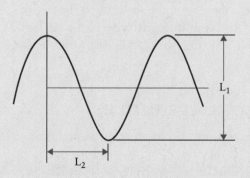

**FIGURE 17.44**

P–17.6. An FM radio station broadcasts at 88 MHz. Determine for the radio waves (a) their period, and (b) their wavelength.

**P–17.7.** A piano emits sounds in the range of 28 Hz to 4200 Hz. Find the range of wavelengths at room temperature for this instrument.

**P–17.8.** A sound wave has a frequency of 700 Hz and a wavelength of 0.5 m. What is the temperature of the air in which this sound wave travels?

**P–17.9.** A person hears an echo 3.0 seconds after emitting a sound. In air of 22°C, how far away is the sound-reflecting wall?

**P–17.10.** A supersonic jet travels at 3.0 Mach, i.e., at three times the speed of sound. It cruises at 20 000 m above ground. We choose $t = 0$ when the plane passes directly overhead of an observer, as shown in Fig. 17.45(a). (a) At what time $t$ will the observer hear the plane? (b) What distance $\Delta x$ has the plane travelled by that time?

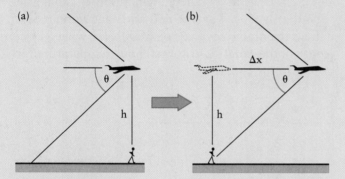

(a)            (b)

**FIGURE 17.45**

**P–17.11.** The only supersonic jet ever used for commercial air travel was the Concorde. It travelled at 1.5 Mach. What was its angle $\theta$, as defined in Fig. 17.45(b), between the direction of propagation of its shock wave and the direction of flight?

## SOUND INTENSITY

**P–17.12.** The sound intensity of $1.0 \times 10^{-12}$ J/(m² · s) is the threshold of hearing for humans. What is the amplitude of the motion of the air molecules? Use $c = 340$ m/s and 1.2 kg/m³ as the density of air.

**P–17.13.** (a) A microphone has an area of 5 cm². It receives during a 4.0-s time period a sound energy of $2.0 \times 10^{-11}$ J. What is the intensity of the sound? (b) Using the sound intensity from part (a), what is the variation in pressure in the sound wave, $\Delta p$? Use $T = 293$ K and $\rho_{air} = 1.2$ kg/m³.

**P–17.14.** A jet airplane has an intensity 100 J/(m² · s) when heard at a distance of 30 m. (a) What is the maximum sound intensity heard by a person on the ground when the airplane cruises 10 000 m above the ground? (b) What is the intensity level IL heard?

**P–17.15.** A certain sound has an intensity that is four times the intensity of a reference sound at the same frequency. (a) What is the difference in the intensity level of the two sounds? (b) If the reference sound causes a sound perception of 60 phon, what is the sound perception value of the more intense sound?

**P–17.16.** An underwater microphone is used to record sounds emitted by porpoises. The minimum intensity level the instrument can record is 10 dB. Assuming a porpoise emits sound at a rate of 0.05 J/s, what is the maximum distance at which the animal will still be recorded? Neglect sound absorption in water, and treat the porpoise as a point sound source.

**P–17.17.** Two sound waves have intensities of $I_1 = 100$ J/(m² · s) and $I_2 = 200$ J/(m² · s). By how many decibels do the two sounds differ in intensity level?

**P–17.18.** A standard man shouting loudly produces a 70-dB sound at 5 m distance. At what rate does the person emit sound energy? Express the result in J/s.

## BEATS AND DOPPLER EFFECT

**P–17.19.** Ultrasound echolocation is used by bats to enable them to fly and hunt in the dark. The ultrasound used by bats has frequencies in the range from 60 kHz to 100 kHz. We consider a bat that uses an ultrasound frequency of 90 kHz and flies with a speed of 10 m/s. What is the frequency of the echo the bat hears reflected off an insect that moves toward the bat with a speed of 3 m/s?

**P–17.20.** Table 17.6 presents the frequencies of the eight C and D keys on a well-tuned piano. For which

## TABLE 17.6

**Frequencies of various piano keys**

| Octave $n$ | $f$ (Hz) for $C_n$ | $f$ (Hz) for $D_n$ |
|---|---|---|
| 0 | 16.35 | 18.35 |
| 1 | 32.70 | 36.71 |
| 2 | 65.41 | 73.42 |
| 3 | 130.8 | 146.8 |
| 4 | 261.6 | 293.7 |
| 5 | 523.3 | 587.3 |
| 6 | 1046 | 1175 |
| 7 | 2093 | 2349 |
| 8 | 4186 | 4699 |

cases do you expect to hear a beat, and what is the beat frequency when you hit neighbouring C and D keys together?

## HUMAN EAR

**P–17.21.** A hypothesis says the upper limit in frequency a human ear can hear can be determined by the diameter of the eardrum, which should have approximately the same diameter as the wavelength at the upper limit. If we use this hypothesis, what would be the radius of the eardrum for a person able to hear frequencies up to 18.5 kHz?

**P–17.22.** Neglecting the additional delay due to the difference in sound pressure levels, we want to verify the statement made in the text that stereoscopic hearing is based on a delay in the time the sound travels to the farther ear. Using Fig. 17.46 for a sound source far from the person, we define $d$ as the distance between both ears and $\theta$ as the angle between the direction of the sound source and the direction perpendicular to the line connecting both ears.

(a) Find a formula for the time delay $\Delta t$ of the sound from the source at a very large distance as a function of $d$ and $\theta$. (b) Calculate the delay for the same sound source at $\theta = 45°$ for $d = 16$ cm.

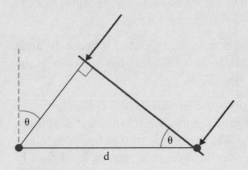

**FIGURE 17.46**

**P–17.23.** If we model the human auditory canal as a tube that is closed at one end and that resonates at a fundamental frequency of 3000 Hz, what is the length of the canal? Use normal body temperature for the air in the canal.

# MATH REVIEW

## TRIGONOMETRY

The following theorems for the sine function apply:

$$\sin(\alpha + \beta) = \sin \alpha \cdot \cos \beta + \cos \alpha \cdot \sin \beta$$
$$\sin(\alpha - \beta) = \sin \alpha \cdot \cos \beta - \cos \alpha \cdot \sin \beta$$

For the cosine function, we find:

$$\cos(\alpha + \beta) = \cos \alpha \cdot \cos \beta - \sin \alpha \cdot \sin \beta$$
$$\cos(\alpha - \beta) = \cos \alpha \cdot \cos \beta + \sin \alpha \cdot \sin \beta$$

And for the tangent function we use:

$$\tan(\alpha + \beta) = \frac{\tan \alpha + \tan \beta}{1 - \tan \alpha \cdot \tan \beta}$$

$$\tan(\alpha - \beta) = \frac{\tan \alpha - \tan \beta}{1 + \tan \alpha \cdot \tan \beta}$$

Further, we note for the sum or difference of two sine functions:

$$\sin \alpha + \sin \beta = 2 \sin\left(\frac{\alpha + \beta}{2}\right)\cos\left(\frac{\alpha - \beta}{2}\right)$$

$$\sin \alpha - \sin \beta = 2 \cos\left(\frac{\alpha + \beta}{2}\right)\sin\left(\frac{\alpha - \beta}{2}\right)$$

and for the sum or difference of two cosine functions:

$$\cos \alpha + \cos \beta = 2 \cos\left(\frac{\alpha + \beta}{2}\right)\cos\left(\frac{\alpha - \beta}{2}\right)$$

$$\cos \alpha - \cos \beta = 2 \sin\left(\frac{\alpha + \beta}{2}\right)\sin\left(\frac{\alpha - \beta}{2}\right)$$

# SUMMARY

## DEFINITIONS

- One-dimensional harmonic wave function:

$$\xi = A \cdot \sin(\omega \cdot t - \kappa \cdot x)$$

where $\kappa$ is the wave number, with $\kappa = 2 \cdot \pi/\lambda$, and $\lambda$ is the wavelength.

- Speed of wave: $c = \lambda \cdot f$, with $f$ the frequency.
- Energy density $\varepsilon$ of a sound wave:

$$\varepsilon_{\text{total}} = \frac{1}{2}\rho \cdot A^2 \cdot \omega^2$$

where $A$ is the amplitude, $\rho$ is the density, and $\omega$ is the angular frequency.

- Intensity $I$ of a sound wave, defined as the energy passing an area $A$ per time unit $\Delta t$:

$$I = c \cdot \varepsilon_{\text{total}} = \frac{1}{2} c \cdot \rho \cdot A^2 \cdot \omega^2$$

where $c$ is the speed of sound.

- Sound pressure level SPL (in unit dB):

$$\text{SPL} = 20 \cdot \log_{10} \frac{p}{p_0} \quad \text{with } p_0 = 2 \times 10^{-5}\,\text{Pa}$$

- Intensity level IL (in unit dB):

$$\text{IL} = 10 \cdot \log_{10} \frac{I}{I_0} \quad \text{with } I_0 = 1 \times 10^{-12}\,\frac{\text{J}}{\text{m}^2 \cdot \text{s}}$$

- Sound absorption:
  - for intensity (Beer's law):

$$I = I_0 \cdot e^{-\beta \cdot x} = I_0 \cdot e^{-x/x_{\text{absorption}}}$$

where $I_0$ is the source intensity at $x = 0$, $\beta$ is the absorption coefficient, and $x_{\text{absorption}}$ is the absorption length.

  - for the displacement $\xi$:

$$\xi = A_0 \cdot e^{-\alpha x} \cdot \sin(\omega \cdot t - \kappa \cdot x)$$

where $\alpha$ is the decay coefficient for the sound amplitude.

## UNITS

- Wave number $\kappa$: $\text{m}^{-1}$
- Wavelength $\lambda$: m
- Frequency $f$: Hz
- Energy density $\varepsilon$: $\text{J/m}^3$
- Intensity of a sound wave $I$: $\text{J/(m}^2 \cdot \text{s)}$
- Sound pressure level SPL and intensity level IL: dB
- Sound absorption coefficient $\beta$: 1/m
- Sound absorption length $x_{\text{absorption}}$: m
- Sound amplitude decay coefficient $\alpha$: 1/m

## LAWS

- Speed of waves
  - in fluids:

$$c = \sqrt{\frac{B}{\rho}}$$

with $B$ the bulk modulus and $\rho$ the density of the medium.

  - in air, assuming adiabatic pressure variations (Laplace's equation):

$$c = \sqrt{\kappa \frac{p}{\rho}}$$

with $\kappa$ the adiabatic coefficient, $p$ the pressure, and $\rho$ the density of the medium.

- Standing waves for a reflected wave:

$$\xi_{\text{superposition}} = -\{2 \cdot A \cdot \cos(\omega \cdot t)\}\sin(\kappa \cdot x)$$

where $\xi_{\text{superposition}}$ is the displacement in the wave that results from the superposition.

- Harmonics
  - for a closed tube for $n$-th harmonic:
    - wavelength: $\lambda_n = 2 \cdot L/n$
    - frequency: $f_n = n \cdot c/(2 \cdot L) = n \cdot f_1$
  - for a half-open tube:

$$f_n = \frac{n \cdot c}{4 \cdot L} \quad \text{with } n = 1, 3, 5, 7, \dots$$

- Amplitude for resonant coupling of a system with negligible damping:

$$A = \frac{F_{\text{max}}}{m(\omega_{\text{standing}}^2 - \omega_{\text{ext}}^2)}$$

where $F_{\text{max}}$ is the maximum of the periodic external force applied to the system, $\omega_{\text{ext}}$ is the angular frequency of the external force, and $\omega_{\text{standing}}$ is the angular frequency of the first harmonic (standing wave).

- Beats: Displacement function for the superposition of two waves with the same amplitude $A$:

$$\xi_{\text{superposition}} = 2 \cdot A \cdot \sin\left(\frac{\omega_1 + \omega_2}{2} t\right)$$
$$\times \cos\left(\frac{\omega_1 - \omega_2}{2} t\right)$$

which defines the superposition amplitude:

$$A_{\text{superposition}}(t) = 2 \cdot A \cdot \cos\left(\frac{\omega_1 - \omega_2}{2} t\right)$$

- Doppler effect
  - for moving receiver:

$$f_{\text{receiver}} = f_0\left(1 \pm \frac{v_{\text{receiver}}}{c}\right)$$

  - for moving sound source:

$$f_{\text{source}} = f_0\left(\frac{1}{1 \pm \dfrac{v_{\text{source}}}{c}}\right)$$

  - for receiver and source moving relative to the medium:

$$f_{\text{combined}} = f_0\left(\frac{1 \pm v_{\text{receiver}}/c}{1 \pm v_{\text{source}}/c}\right)$$

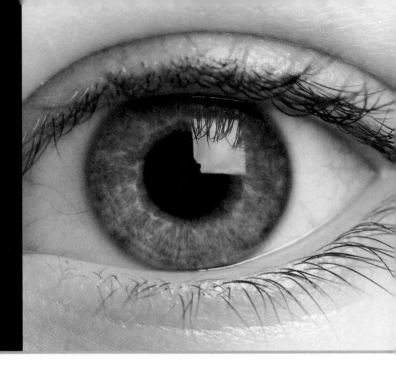

# CHAPTER 18

# THE EYE
## Ray Model of Light (Geometric Optics)

The physics of light is described in the field of optics. It is divided into three major branches: geometric optics is concerned with phenomena that can be modelled with light rays, wave optics characterizes light as an electromagnetic wave, and photon optics describes light as corpuscles. The ray model is easiest to apply, and therefore introduced first, followed by wave optics in Chapter 20 and the photon model in Chapter 22. In the ray model, light is assumed to travel along straight lines until it reaches an interface between two different media. At such an interface it will be reflected and/or pass the interface (refraction).

Reflection is studied with mirrors. The angles of light rays that hit a mirror are defined with the normal direction of the mirror surface. The angles of an incoming light ray and the corresponding reflected light ray are equal. For a spherical mirror, sharp images of objects in front of the mirror form when the mirror has a focal point. The mirror equation then relates the inverse focal length to the sum of the inverse object and image distances. The image is magnified if the object is closer to the mirror than its radius of curvature.

When a light ray passes through an interface it travels closer to the normal direction of the interface in the medium with the higher index of refraction (usually the denser medium). If the interface is spherical, an object in front of the interface forms a sharp image if the interface has a focal point. Lenses are combinations of two spherical interfaces. The thin-lens formula and the equation for the magnification of a lens are identical to the respective equations for the spherical mirror. The inverse focal length of a lens is defined as the refractive power of the lens, measured in diopters.

The path of light through the human eye and the formation of images on the retina can be described with the ray model. The cornea is modelled as a transparent, single spherical interface. Cornea and lens contribute to the refractive power of the eye. Eye defects, such as myopia (nearsightedness) and hyperopia (farsightedness), are corrected with prescription lenses that are customized based on the optical properties of the eye, and that are manufactured by using the lens maker's equation.

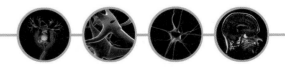

One of the three necessary conditions for life is the recognition of external stimuli and the ability to respond. Arguably one of the most astonishing achievements of the evolutionary process in satisfying this condition is vision. The human eye's complexity in design and versatility in function is unmatched by engineered imitations. The anatomy of the human eye, shown as a cross-sectional side view in Fig. 18.1, identifies at least eight individual components required for us to see: light reaches the eye at the cornea (3), then passes through the anterior chamber (2). Its intensity is adjusted by the iris (4) and the light rays are focussed by the lens (1). To accomplish the focussing, the lens must be adjusted, which is achieved by the ciliary muscles (6). Before forming an image on the retina (7), the light passes through the vitreous body (5). The retina then converts the image into electrical signals, which are sent to the brain through the optic nerve (9). The interplay of these components allows us to clearly see structures on an object as far away as the Moon, or to read small letters in a book at just 20 centimetres in front of the eye.

The eye's complex design and its perfect adaptation to the purpose of vision had been presented during Darwin's times as strong proof of supernatural creation. Yet, we know of the many improvements light-sensitive organs have undergone during evolution. Fig. 18.2 shows an example for several invertebrates. Starting with simple pigmented cells, which serve as photoreceptors and allow for the distinction of bright and dark, successive steps of cup formation and closure of the cups with a transparent cornea led to the camera-style eye of the octopus. These developments took place independent of the development of the human eye, which becomes evident when

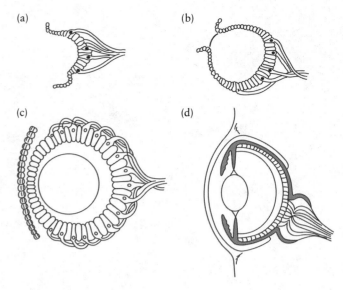

**FIGURE 18.2**

Increasing complexity of the eyes of invertebrates. (a) The simplest form of a light detector is found for *Limpet ocellus:* a shallow depression in the epidermis that contains pigmented cells acting as photoreceptors. These cells are embedded in a patch of regular epithelium cells and are connected with nerve fibres to the animal's nerve centre. (b) The abalone eye has an additional spherical lens, embedded in an eye-cup for protection. (c) The eye of a typical land snail. The primitive lens is enclosed in a cavity and the pigmented layer is now called the retina. The nerve has evolved in complexity and is called the optic nerve. (d) The eye of an octopus. The pupil responds to external stimuli, such as changing light conditions, and allows the octopus to see distinct images, e.g., to distinguish visually mate from enemy. Octopi are nearsighted, as are many animals living in the sea (see Example 18.7 and the section on eye defects and diseases).

comparing the approach toward focussing: humans use the ciliary muscles to change the shape of a pliable lens, while the octopus moves its lens back and forth.

But does the complex human eye indeed work as precisely as an instrument? What does it measure, and how does it measure? Even though we return with these questions to the psychophysical boundary between the exact physical sciences and the subjective psychological perception we discussed in the context of hearing, it is necessary to investigate the physics of our vision to understand its limitations.

An interesting hint concerning the imperfections of human vision is provided by the many optical illusions we easily fall victim to. The most stunning examples involve colour vision, and are discussed in Chapter 20. We will learn there that optical illusions are never just imaginings, but are most often linked to an attempt to correct an adverse physical effect. A well-known example is shown in Fig. 18.3. Close your left eye and look at the cross with your right

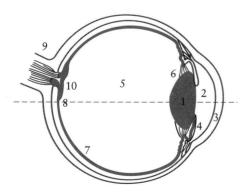

**FIGURE 18.1**

Cross-sectional sketch of a human eye: (1) lens, (2) anterior chamber, (3) cornea, (4) iris, (5) vitreous body, (6) ciliary muscle, (7) retina, (8) fovea centralis, and (9) optic nerve. (10) locates the blind spot, which is due to the optic nerve passing through the retina to the brain.

eye. Now bring the textbook slowly toward you. You will notice that the black spot disappears when the distance from your eye to the book is about 30 cm! Continue to bring the textbook closer to your eye. When you come closer than 20 cm the spot reappears. This self-experiment clearly illustrates that part of the image we see is the result of intelligent image extrapolation rather than fact.

Let's briefly explain the effect of Fig. 18.3. The position of the blind spot in our field of vision is shown in Fig. 18.4. The plot applies to the left eye. Each concentric circle represents an angle increment of 10°, with the outermost circle corresponding to 90°. Plots like Fig. 18.4 are called **polar plots**. The black line encloses the field of vision for black/white vision; the other lines enclose the field of vision for various colours. The solid dot at about 15° on the temporal

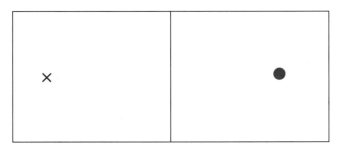

**FIGURE 18.3**

Self-test to illustrate the existence of the blind spot in our field of vision. With the left eye closed, look at the cross with your right eye. Move the textbook toward you from about a metre (arm's length). When the page is about 20 cm to 30 cm from your eye the blue dot disappears.

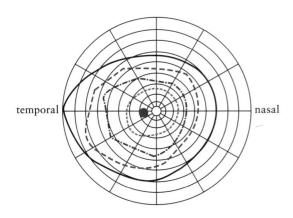

**FIGURE 18.4**

A polar plot illustrating the field of vision for the left eye. The field of vision depends on the viewed colour: the largest field applies to black/white vision (black line), the blue line is for blue colour vision, the red line is for red vision, and the green line is for green vision. The concentric circles correspond to angle increments of 10°, with the centre as the direction in which the person looks and the outermost circle at 90° to that direction.

side is the **blind spot** that we noticed in the experiment from Fig. 18.3.

You can easily verify Fig. 18.4: close your right eye, and with your left eye look straight ahead. Stretch your left arm, bending it slightly behind your shoulder line. Rapidly flutter the fingers on your left hand as you move the arm slowly forward in an arc. You should see your finger movement at the periphery of your field of vision when your arm reaches an angle of about 80° to 90° with the direction of vision. Now repeat the same experiment with the right arm, but still using the left eye. This time you have to bring it much farther forward before you notice the finger movement, to about 60° with the direction of vision. The asymmetry of the field of vision is because of your nose. The combined field of vision of both eyes compensates for this asymmetry.

Leaving the issue of colours raised by Fig. 18.4 for Chapter 20, here we want to understand the physiological origin of the blind spot, particularly because it is inconveniently located near the middle of our field of vision. For this, we look at the anatomy of the human eye in Fig. 18.1. The spot on the retina that light reaches when travelling straight through the centre is called the fovea centralis (8) and is the most light-sensitive area in the eye. This point is located at the centre in Fig. 18.4. The blind spot (10 in Fig. 18.1) is the point at which the optic nerve is bundled and leaves the eye. This leads to an area with no vision because the optic nerve has to interrupt the retina to pass through it to the brain.

As in other cases of optical illusions, our brain corrects for otherwise confusing signals from the eye. In this case, the brain does not allow us to have a missing spot near the middle of our field of view. Instead, it modifies the received image by filling in the blind spot based on a best guess before allowing the image to reach our consciousness. Usually this works without problems as we move our head and eyes constantly. However, in the case of Fig. 18.3, the uniform white area around the spot is too tempting not to correct for the blind spot by adding a uniform white!

## What Is Optics?

Three different models have been developed to describe the physics of light: the ray model, the wave model, and the corpuscle model. The initial development of the field came in the 17th century when René Descartes, Christiaan Huygens, and Sir Isaac Newton tried to interpret their experiments with visible light. Already the ancient Greeks had thought that light consisted of corpuscles, an idea further developed by

Newton. Newton believed that light consists of a stream of small particles that interact with matter like mechanical objects. At the same time, Huygens promoted a **wave model** for light, treating light as a propagating wave similar to surface waves on water. He encountered problems with that model when comparing it to sound waves, mainly because he couldn't identify a medium that carried the light waves. On balance, however, the wave model appeared to his contemporaries as more consistent with an increasing body of experimental observations, and Huygens's theory was widely accepted from about 1800 to 1905—in particular after James Clerk Maxwell derived the properties of visible light from electromagnetic wave equations in 1865.

The **corpuscle theory** was revived in the early 1900s when Albert Einstein used a corpuscle model (in which light particles are called **photons**) to explain the photoelectric effect, which describes the ability of light to knock electrons out of solid matter. Our modern view of light is that it has a dual, wave-and-corpuscle character. It may be described best by one model or the other depending on the specific experiment. At the same time, we have to be aware that neither model grasps all aspects of light by itself!

In this chapter, we start our discussion of optics with a simpler model, called the **ray model**. This greatly simplified model is applicable as long as the objects involved in an optical study are not smaller than the wavelength of light, which lies in the vicinity of 500 nm. The physical laws that we derive with the ray model are summarized by the term **geometric optics**, because we can construct its features with geometric methods.

*In the ray model, the assumption is made that light moves along straight lines while travelling within a homogeneous medium. It may change its direction when reflected by and/or passing through an interface into another medium.*

The concepts of geometric optics are established in the current chapter. These include reflection off a mirror and refraction when light passes through a transparent interface. Geometric optics fails to describe many other light-related phenomena, e.g., the existence of colours. Therefore, we replace the ray model with the wave model in Chapter 20. The wave model of light requires several steps as it differs from the wave concepts we developed for sound in Chapter 17. In turn, we consider the corpuscle theory of light only in Chapter 22, when we discuss light absorption and light emission by atoms and molecules.

# Reflection
## Flat Mirror

Fig. 18.5 shows a light ray that is reflected off a planar mirror. The direction of the travelling light ray is shown by arrows. We will frequently use the following two features:

- The incoming and reflected rays are in the same plane as the vector directed perpendicular to the mirror surface. This vector is called the **normal vector**, in which the word "normal" is synonymous with "perpendicular" (in the same fashion as we used the term when we defined the normal force in mechanics).

- The angle between the incoming ray and the normal vector, $\alpha_{incoming}$, is equal to the angle between the reflected ray and the normal vector, $\alpha_{outgoing}$.

These two conditions constitute the **law of reflection**. It is quantitatively written in the form:

$$\alpha_{incoming} = \alpha_{outgoing} \qquad [1]$$

The angle $\alpha_{outgoing}$ is called the **specular angle**.

*The law of reflection states that the angle of an incoming light ray with the normal direction of the mirror is equal to the angle of the reflected light ray with the normal direction of the mirror.*

We use Fig. 18.6 to illustrate how the law of reflection leads to the formation of an image, as we are

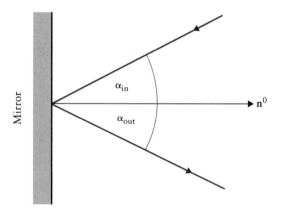

**FIGURE 18.5**

A light ray reflects off a flat mirror: $\mathbf{n}^0$ indicates the direction perpendicular to the mirror surface (i.e., the normal vector); $\alpha_{incoming}$ is the angle of the incoming light ray with the normal; and $\alpha_{outgoing}$ is the angle of the outgoing, reflected light ray with the normal. The two angles are related by the law of reflection.

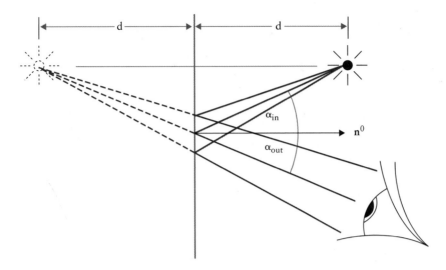

## FIGURE 18.6

When a person observes a point-like light source located a distance $d$ in front of a flat mirror, a virtual image of the light source is seen at the same distance $d$ behind the mirror surface. The image of the light source is constructed using the law of reflection, as indicated for the light ray at the centre. Solid lines indicate the actual paths of light rays; dashed lines represent extrapolations of the light rays behind the mirror (vertical blue line).

used to seeing it in a flat mirror. We start with a point-like light source (solid dot at top right). The light source emits light rays that travel along straight lines in all directions. When such a straight line reaches the mirror surface (shown for three rays in the figure) the law of reflection is applied, as illustrated for the centre ray in Fig. 18.6. After reflection, the rays continue to travel along straight lines, until they reach the eye of the observer. Observers can interpret the light rays reaching the eye in two ways. Either they are aware of the presence of the mirror and draw the rays as shown in front of the mirror, or they are not aware of the mirror and extrapolate the rays straight to the dashed point behind the mirror at the left in the figure. At the point where these lines cross, the image of the point-like light source forms. The position of the light source (object) and its image are both at a distance $d$ from the mirror. This is a direct consequence of the law of reflection.

We call an image a **real image** when light rays actually reach the image. In Fig. 18.6, light cannot physically reach the image since a mirror contains a metallic layer that prevents light from passing through. In this case, the image is called a **virtual image**.

In Fig. 18.7, we generalize our choice of object, replacing the point-like light source of Fig. 18.6 with an extended object of height $h$ (reaching from point $P_2$ to point $P_1$). The object is still at distance $d$ from the mirror. Using the law of reflection for light rays coming separately from points $P_2$ and $P_1$, i.e., $\alpha_1 = \alpha_1'$ and $\alpha_2 = \alpha_2'$, we find that the image in Fig. 18.7 is

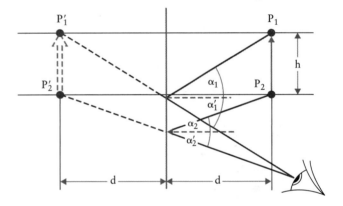

## FIGURE 18.7

Formation of the image of an extended object in a flat mirror. Light rays from both the top and the bottom ends of the object are used to construct a virtual image (green dashed arrow).

a virtual image, forming at distance $d$ behind the mirror. For comparison with later cases, note also that the image is upright; i.e., the corresponding image points $P_2'$ and $P_1'$ are at positions $y = 0$ and $y = h$ with a vertical $y$-axis, respectively.

## Concept Question 18.1

**Fig. 18.8 shows a setup with three flat mirrors. An approaching light ray is reflected by at least two mirrors before it leaves the setup. Which of the four choices shown is the correct path the light ray travels?**

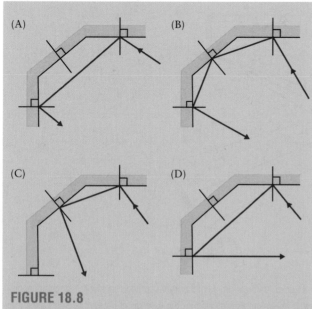

**FIGURE 18.8**

An arrangement of three flat mirrors. A light ray approaches a mirror such that it reflects off at least one more mirror before leaving the arrangement.

ANSWER: Choice (A). The other choices each violate the law of reflection.

## Concept Question 18.2

**Flat mirrors allow us only to see the object the same way it looks when viewing it directly. Why, then, do we use flat mirrors at all?**

ANSWER: One object exists that we cannot view directly: ourselves, in particular our own face. People have been obsessed with their reflections since the dawn of humankind. The first human-made mirrors came from Turkey and were polished volcanic glass. The ancient Egyptians switched to bronze metal surfaces, and the ancient Greeks had schools in which sand polishing of reflective surfaces was taught. The modern design of a thin metal film (mercury–tin alloy) on the back of a glass plate emerged in the 14th century in Venice, Italy.

Flat mirrors do, of course, have one other application: they expose the vampires among us!

## Spherical Mirror

The applications of mirrors expand greatly if we do not require them to be flat. Of the many possible mirror shapes, you will find only two in actual instruments: the parabolic mirror in astronomical facilities, and the spherical mirror in all other applications. We limit our discussion to spherical mirrors, i.e., mirrors

for which the reflecting surface is shaped as a partial sphere. Spherical mirrors can be arranged in two ways:

- Light rays approach from the side of the centre of curvature (point *C*) of the mirror, as shown in Fig. 18.9. In this case the mirror is called a **concave mirror**.
- Light rays approach from the opposite side of the mirror. In this case the mirror is called a **convex mirror**.

For convenience, we mostly use concave mirrors for the discussions in this chapter. This is done with no loss of generality, because every relation we introduce applies to convex mirrors in an analogous fashion.

The centre of curvature in Fig. 18.9 further allows us to introduce the **optical axis**: an incoming light ray defines the optical axis if it passes through the centre of curvature (point *C*). To establish the key physical properties of a spherical mirror, we follow several parallel light rays in Fig. 18.9 as they reflect off its surface. We notice that the reflected rays do not intersect at a common point. We will find such an intersection point very useful in developing the concepts of geometric optics and therefore dismiss the setup of Fig. 18.9 as not sufficient. To correct for this problem we need to introduce a further restriction on the mirrors we use. This additional restriction follows from comparing Fig. 18.9 and Fig. 18.10(a). In both cases we assume that the light source is at a very large distance from the mirror (an infinite distance) and, therefore, that the light rays from the light source (object) approach the mirror parallel to each other. The two figures vary

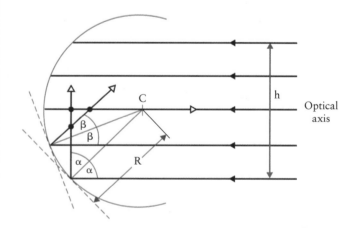

**FIGURE 18.9**

Concave spherical mirror. Replacing a flat mirror with a spherical mirror does not yield a useful image if light rays reach the mirror far from the optical axis (*h*/2) compared to the radius of curvature of the mirror *R*. The figure illustrates that the light from an object at infinite distance (parallel incoming light rays) does not form a focal point, in contrast to the setup in Fig. 18.10.

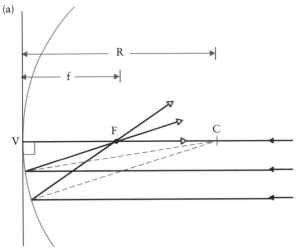

(a)

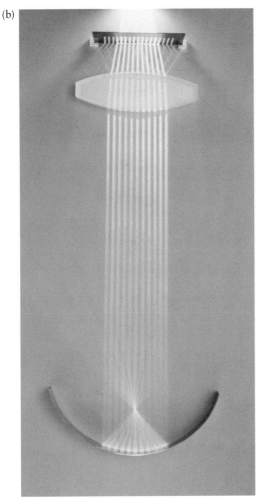

(b)

**FIGURE 18.10**

(a) Spherical mirrors can be used to form images if the incoming light rays travel close to the optical axis, i.e., at a distance that is small compared to the radius of curvature of the mirror. Light from an object at infinite distance (parallel light) allows us to define the focal point at the position on the optical axis where all reflected light rays cross. V is the point at which the optical axis intersects the mirror surface. F is the focal point with f the focal length. C is the centre of curvature, with R the radius of the spherical surface. (b) The crossing of the reflected light rays at the focal point is illustrated with an experimental setup. The mirror is the circular piece at the bottom.

only in the spread of the light rays that are allowed to reach the mirror: in Fig. 18.10(a) the separation of the incoming light rays from the optical axis is small compared to the **radius of curvature R** of the mirror. As a result, the reflected light rays in Fig. 18.10(a) intersect at a common point F, as illustrated by the experimental setup in Fig. 18.10(b). The point at which the reflected rays cross is called the **focal point**; the **focal length** f is then the distance from the mirror surface to the focal point.

If in practice we observe the outcome shown in Fig. 18.9—i.e., a case with no focal point—we refer to it as **spherical aberration**. To avoid such cases we use **apertures**, which confine the spread of the incoming light. Another way to state this restriction is to say that a focal point must exist, i.e., that incoming parallel light rays must intersect at a single point F after reflection.

Where is the focal point located for a given mirror? Firstly, the focal point lies on the optical axis. Secondly, the focal point of a spherical mirror is at half the distance between the centre of curvature and the point V at which the optical axis intersects with the mirror:

$$f = \frac{R}{2} \qquad [2]$$

Eq. [2] is proven with Fig. 18.11, which allows for a geometrical derivation of the relation between f and R. The two horizontal lines in the figure are the optical axis and an incoming light ray that is reflected at point P, then passes through point F. The law of reflection states that $\alpha_1 = \alpha_2$. Further, we know that $\alpha_3 = \alpha_1$ because the line PC intersects two parallel lines to form these two angles. Thus, the triangle PFC is isosceles; i.e., the lines PF and FC are equally long.

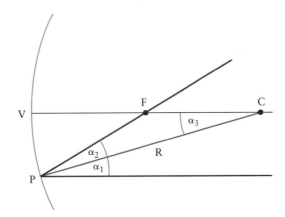

**FIGURE 18.11**

Geometric construction of the relation between the focal length (length VF) and the radius of curvature (length VC) for a spherical mirror with C its centre of curvature.

If we now bring the incoming light ray closer and closer to the optical axis, all three angles $\alpha$ approach $0°$ and $VF = FC = R/2$. Since $VF$ is the focal length $f$, we have confirmed Eq. [2]. The need to look at very small angles $\alpha$ reinforces once more the point made for Figs. 18.9 and 18.10 that a focal point exists only when we limit our considerations to light rays that move very close to the optical axis.

Comparing Figs. 18.5 and 18.10, we note that concave mirrors can form images at distances that differ from the object distance. In the particular case of Fig. 18.10, a point-size light source at infinite distance has generated an image at the focal point. To develop the properties of a concave mirror further, we consider in Fig. 18.12 an object at finite distance $p$ from the mirror. To find the image in this and other cases geometrically, three different light rays must be followed, one along the optical axis from the lower end of the object (which is always placed on the optical axis) and two from the upper end of the object. The optical axis is used for convenience to reduce the amount of graphic construction needed. We need two rays from the upper end of the object as the position of the corresponding upper end of the image does not lie on the optical axis. The upper end of the image is then defined as the point at which the two light rays from the upper end of the object intersect after reflection.

We choose two light rays such that one reaches the mirror parallel to the optical axis and the other reaches it after passing through the focal point $F$. Using these two light rays, we can construct their path after reflection using the observations we made in Fig. 18.10: the light ray moving parallel to the optical axis passes through the focal point after reflection and vice versa—the light ray passing through the focal point becomes a ray that moves parallel to the optical axis.

Using these principles, we find that the image in Fig. 18.12 is inverted (upside down) and real. Defining the distance between the image and the mirror as **image distance** $q$, we are now able to develop a general relation between object distance $p$, image distance $q$, and focal length $f$. This formula is called the mirror equation and originally was derived by Newton.

We call $h_O$ the height of the object and $h_I$ the height of the image. The derivation is based on the geometrical similarity of two pairs of triangles in Fig. 18.12, $\triangle_1$, $\triangle_2$ and $\triangle_3$, $\triangle_4$, respectively, leading to:

$$\triangle_1 \text{ and } \triangle_2 \quad f : (p - f) = h_I : h_O$$
$$\triangle_3 \text{ and } \triangle_4 \quad f : (q - f) = h_O : h_I \quad [3]$$

Eq. [3] contains two relations for $h_I/h_O$:

$$\frac{h_I}{h_O} = \frac{f}{p - f} = \frac{q - f}{f} \quad [4]$$

The last formula in Eq. [4] leads to:

$$f^2 = (p - f)(q - f) = f^2 - (p + q)f + p \cdot q \quad [5]$$

in which the $f^2$ term is dropped on both sides:

$$p \cdot q = (p + q)f \quad [6]$$

Eq. [6] is further rewritten with $1/f$ as the dependent variable:

$$\frac{1}{f} = \frac{p + q}{p \cdot q} \quad [7]$$

which leads to the **mirror equation**:

$$\frac{1}{f} = \frac{1}{p} + \frac{1}{q} \quad [8]$$

*The mirror equation relates the focal length of a mirror with the object and image distances.*

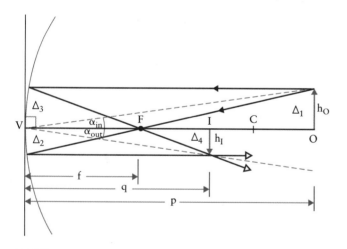

### FIGURE 18.12

Formation of an image $I$ for an object $O$ at finite distance $p$ from a concave mirror. Three light rays are used to construct the image, one along the optical axis (line $CFV$) since the bottom end of the object is placed on the optical axis. The second and third rays come from the top of the object of size $h_0$, with one ray travelling parallel to the optical axis and one ray passing through the focal point $F$. The image has a size $h_I$, is inverted, and is located at the image distance $q$. The various triangles labelled in the figure are used for geometric constructions because of their similarity, e.g., $\triangle_1$ and $\triangle_2$.

An interesting feature of the spherical mirror that is not a feature of the flat mirror is the possibility of obtaining a magnified image. This is not the case in Fig. 18.12, since $h_I < h_O$. However, if the object in Fig. 18.12 is removed and instead placed where the figure shows the image, then object and image switch places as all light rays can travel along the same paths in the opposite direction. In this case a magnified image has formed.

Eq. [4] allows us to quantify the magnification $M$, which is defined as the ratio of the size of the image to the size of the object:

$$M = \frac{h_I}{h_O} = -\frac{f}{p - f} \qquad [9]$$

The negative sign is due to the fact that the image in Fig. 18.12 is inverted. The magnification can alternatively be expressed in terms of the object distance $p$ and the image distance $q$, again using Fig. 18.12. Due to the law of reflection, the two angles $\alpha_{\text{incoming}}$ and $\alpha_{\text{outgoing}}$, which are formed by the dashed line in the figure, are equal. From geometry we find:

$$\tan \alpha_{\text{incoming}} = \frac{h_O}{p}$$
$$\qquad [10]$$
$$\tan \alpha_{\text{outgoing}} = -\frac{h_I}{q}$$

which leads to:

$$M = \frac{h_I}{h_O} = -\frac{q}{p} \qquad [11]$$

Eq. [9] allows us to establish the cases for which the magnification is larger than one; i.e., when the image is larger than the object: $M > 1$ follows for $p - f < f$, which is equivalent to $p < 2 \cdot f = R$. Thus, the image is larger than the object if the object is placed closer to the mirror than the centre of curvature.

*A spherical mirror produces a magnified image when the object distance is smaller than the image distance. This requires the object distance to be smaller than twice the focal length.*

If the object is closer to the mirror than the focal point, a magnified but virtual image is formed that is no longer inverted. This case is illustrated in Fig. 18.13. Again, to construct the image, two rays are followed from the upper end of the object, one that travels parallel to the optical axis and then reflects through the focal point, and one that travels in the direction away from the focal point and becomes parallel to the optical axis after reflection. These two light rays do not intersect anywhere on the right (real) side of the mirror, but they do intersect on the left (virtual) side of the mirror. This is therefore the point where the image forms.

To use the mirror equation consistently in all such cases, Table 18.1 summarizes the sign conventions for mirrors. In the table, as throughout the chapter,

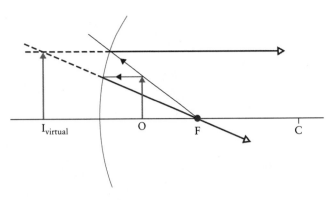

**FIGURE 18.13**

Formation of an upright virtual image for an object that is closer to the mirror than to the focal point. $C$ is the centre of curvature of the mirror.

**TABLE 18.1**

### Sign conventions for mirrors

| | |
|---|---|
| $p$ is positive | Object is in front of the mirror (real object) |
| $p$ is negative | Object is behind the mirror (virtual object) |
| $q$ is positive | Image is in front of the mirror (real image) |
| $q$ is negative | Image is behind the mirror (virtual image) |
| $f$ and $R$ are positive | Centre of curvature is in front of the mirror (concave mirror) |
| $f$ and $R$ are negative | Centre of curvature is behind the mirror (convex mirror) |
| $M$ is positive | Image is upright |
| $M$ is negative | Image is inverted |

These conventions are used when the mirror equation and mirror magnification formulas are applied.

$p$ is the object distance, $q$ is the image distance, $f$ is the focal length, $R$ is the radius of curvature of the mirror, and $M$ is the magnification as defined in Eq. [11].

You can qualitatively verify several of the possible combinations of parameters in Table 18.1 by doing the following experiment at home: Take a well-polished table spoon and a small object such as the tip of a pencil. Hold the spoon at arm's length and move the pencil closer and closer to the spoon while observing the changes to its image: the magnification, whether the image is inverted or upright, and whether it is real or virtual. By using either the back or front side of the spoon as a mirror you can switch between concave and convex mirrors. The spoon's use as a concave mirror is illustrated in Fig. 18.14(a).

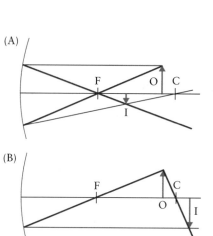

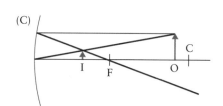

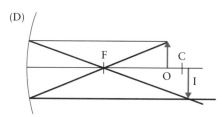

## FIGURE 18.14

(a) A spoon is used as a concave mirror. (b) The centre of curvature $C$, focal point $F$, and object $O$ are shown for a concave mirror. Four attempts to construct the image are included.

### Concept Question 18.3

**Fig. 18.14(b) shows the centre of curvature $C$, the focal point $F$, and an object $O$ for a concave mirror. Which of the four proposed image constructions is correct?**

ANSWER: Choice (D). In (A), the light ray from $O$ through $F$ to the mirror violates the law of reflection; in (B), the light ray from $O$ through $C$ does not reflect off the mirror; and in (C) the light ray from $O$ to $I$ contributes to the image before it has been reflected off the mirror.

### ● EXAMPLE 18.1

A dentist uses a mirror to examine a tooth. The tooth is 1.0 cm in front of the mirror, and the image is formed 10.0 cm *behind* the mirror. Determine (a) the radius of curvature of the mirror, and (b) the magnification of the image.

*Solution to part (a):* The focal length of the mirror is found from the mirror equation with

$p = +1.0$ cm and $q = -10.0$ cm. The image length is negative due to the sign conventions of Table 18.1. Thus:

$$\frac{1}{f} = \frac{1}{p} + \frac{1}{q} = \frac{1}{0.01 \text{ m}} - \frac{1}{0.1 \text{ m}} \quad [12]$$

which yields:

$$f = +1.11 \text{ cm} \quad [13]$$

Thus, the radius of curvature of the mirror is $R = 2 \cdot f = 2.22$ cm.

*Solution to part (b):* We obtain the magnification from Eq. [11]:

$$M = -\frac{q}{p} = -\frac{-10.0 \text{ cm}}{1.0 \text{ cm}} = +10.0 \quad [14]$$

The image is upright because the magnification is positive. This is convenient, since this is the way the dentist prefers to look at the image.

## Fermat's Principle

Although the law of reflection is simple and in agreement with experimental observations, it does not reveal any fundamental property of nature. This is because it is a descriptive law, only connecting two angles but not relating them to any other physical quantity. It also does not allow us to predict any other property of light rays, e.g., what happens when light passes an interface between two media (e.g., an air–glass interface), as discussed in the next section.

For this reason, a more fundamental formulation for the law of reflection was sought. Pierre de Fermat postulated the **Fermat principle of least time**: the actual path of light rays between two points (in the same or different media) is such that it takes less time for the light to traverse this path than it would to traverse any other path. This principle provides a fundamental characterization of light and allows us to derive the law of reflection. It is also intriguingly different from an analogous principle in classical mechanics, which states that any physical object free of external forces travels along the path between two points that is the shortest in length.

## Refraction

### Flat Interface

Light can pass through transparent media; e.g., visible light passes through window glass. Except in a vacuum, the intensity of light attenuates as it passes through any medium, leading to the definition of the **optical depth** of a medium. As an example, you have no problem seeing an object at the bottom of a beaker filled with water, but you cannot see the bottom surface of a deep lake. Also, you can see the ground through Earth's atmosphere from outer space (e.g., from the International Space Station), but you cannot see the surface of Jupiter during a fly-by mission. Still, for short distances, the gases in Jupiter's atmosphere (helium and hydrogen) are transparent to visible light. In the remainder of this chapter we refer to transparent materials with the assumption that their thickness is chosen such that light travels through the material without a noticeable loss in intensity.

When light is incident upon an interface between two transparent media under a not-too-steep angle, we observe that a fraction of the light is reflected and a fraction of the light passes through the interface into the second medium. This is illustrated in Fig. 18.15, with a sketch of a light ray approaching a glass surface from a vacuum in part (a) and with an experimental

setup in part (b). The reflected ray obeys the law of reflection: $\alpha_{\text{incoming}} = \alpha_{\text{outgoing}}$. The angle between the direction of the normal vector of the glass surface (along the thin vertical line) and the light ray that has passed through the interface, labelled $\beta$ in Fig. 18.15(a), depends on the material forming the interface with the vacuum. The relation of this angle to the incoming ray's angle is **Snell's law** (named for Willebrord Snell):

$$\frac{\sin \alpha_{\text{incoming}}}{\sin \beta} = n \qquad [15]$$

with $n$ the **index of refraction**, which is a dimensionless materials constant. Table 18.2 lists indices of refraction for a range of materials. Note that gases have values very close to the value of the vacuum. This is convenient from a practical point of view: we need not distinguish whether we do the experiment in air or in a vacuum. We discuss the reason for the

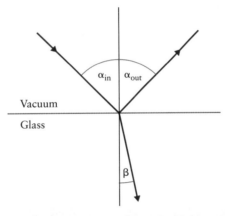

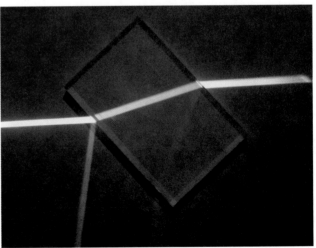

**FIGURE 18.15**

(a) A light ray arriving through a vacuum reflects off a transparent glass surface. Part of the light passes through the interface and forms a refracted light ray in the glass. The angles $\alpha_{\text{incoming}}$ and $\beta$ are related by Snell's law. (b) Photograph of an experimental setup illustrating Snell's law.

## TABLE 18.2

### Index of refraction for various materials

| Material | Index of refraction |
|---|---|
| *Solids at* 20°C | |
| Diamond (C) | 2.42 |
| Sapphire ($Al_2O_3$) | 1.77 |
| Fluorite ($CaF_2$) | 1.43 |
| Fused quartz ($SiO_2$) | 1.46 |
| Crown glass | 1.52 |
| Flint glass | 1.61 |
| Ice ($H_2O$, at 0°C) | 1.31 |
| Sodium chloride (NaCl) | 1.54 |
| *Liquids at* 20°C | |
| Benzene ($C_6H_6$) | 1.50 |
| Carbon tetrachloride ($CCl_4$) | 1.46 |
| Ethanol ($C_2H_5OH$) | 1.36 |
| Glycerine | 1.47 |
| Water ($H_2O$) | 1.33 |
| Sugar solution (30%) | 1.38 |
| Sugar solution (80%) | 1.49 |
| *Gases at* 20°C *and* 1 atm | |
| Air | 1.00027 |
| Carbon dioxide ($CO_2$, at 0°C) | 1.00045 |
| Vacuum | 1.0 |

The data are measured with light rays of vacuum wavelength 589 nm.

wavelength restriction noted below Table 18.2 in Chapter 20, when we study the effect of dispersion. We can omit this issue from the further discussion in the present chapter.

As Fig. 18.15 indicates, refraction causes light to travel closer to the normal direction in denser materials. Since the path of a light ray is reversible, light can of course also be sent across an interface approaching from the denser medium. Fig. 18.15(b) shows that in this case the light is refracted away from the normal direction. This allows us to choose an angle $\beta^*$ such that the angle on the vacuum side becomes 90°. This is called the threshold angle for **total reflection**, since light approaching the interface

from the denser side at angles larger than $\beta^*$ cannot leave into the less-dense medium. The threshold angle for total reflection is calculated from Eq. [15].

## Concept Question 18.4

**Total reflection is used in fibre-optics to guide light over longer distances without intensity loss. Is it also the underlying design feature of polar bear fur? Polar bears have transparent, hollow hair that appears white because of small air pockets embedded in the hair.**

ANSWER: Waveguides are cables of transparent material that have a core with a high index of refraction and a mantle with a lower index. When light is coupled into the waveguide at a small angle with its axis, it travels without loss because total reflection keeps it from passing the interface to the low-index mantle.

The structure of polar bear hair is opposite: the hollow core is air-filled with $n = 1$, while the mantle contains fibres with $n > 1$. A light ray entering the hollow hair does not undergo total reflection when it passes into the outer fibre layer. It has been suggested that the hollow hair may guide light to the bear's skin like a pipe guides water to a fountain. This idea has not been confirmed, even though it has repeatedly been stated in the media.

Note that Snell's law is not in the simplest possible mathematical form, which would be $n = \alpha_{incoming}/\beta$. The actual law is, of course, the result of experimental observations when varying the angle $\alpha_{incoming}$ for a given interface. But we want to know why nature chooses the relation as given in Eq. [15]. The underlying effect is a variation of the speed of light. The speed of light in a vacuum is $c = 3 \times 10^8$ m/s. However, when light rays pass through a medium the light interacts with the medium, and that slows it down. With the assumption that light is slower in a dense medium, Fermat's principle applied across an interface from a vacuum to a denser medium, in which the speed of light is $v_{light} < c$, yields:

$$\frac{\sin \alpha}{\sin \beta} = \frac{c}{v_{light}}$$  [16]

The subscript *incoming* of the angle $\alpha$ has been dropped, because the reversibility of the light ray means that we do not need to specify whether $\alpha$ is associated with an incoming or outgoing beam.

Eq. [16] shows that the ratio of the two sine terms is constant, since $c$ and $v_{light}$ are both constant across a given interface. Due to Eq. [15], the index of refraction represents the factor by which the speed of light is lowered in a medium in comparison to a vacuum. This index is never smaller than 1, as light cannot be faster in any medium than in a vacuum. It can be slowed down considerably—e.g. in diamond, by more than a factor of 2!

If we replace the vacuum in Fig. 18.15(a) with a second medium with another index of refraction $n_2 > 1$, Snell's law is generalized as the **law of refraction**:

$$n_1 \cdot \sin \alpha_1 = n_2 \cdot \sin \alpha_2 \qquad [17]$$

*A light ray passing through an interface is refracted. The law of refraction relates the angles of the light ray with the normal on both sides of the interface to the two indices of refraction. Snell's law is a special case where one medium is a vacuum (or air).*

## Concept Question 18.5

**The conceptual difference between Fermat's principle and Newton's first law of mechanics is particularly obvious when refraction effects are involved. Modern Inuit still hunt fish with spears. Where does the Inuit aim upon spotting a fish?**

ANSWER: The Inuit throws the spear toward a point closer to the boat than where the fish appears. This idea becomes evident if you use Fig. 18.15(a) but replace glass with water. The fish is below the water surface. Light from the fish travels with a small angle to the water surface normal because it is slower in water than in air. The refracted path of the light ray is the result of Fermat's principle; however, the spear travels along a straight line according to Newton's laws. Assuming, for example, that the Inuit is at the top end of the light ray shown in Fig. 18.15(a) and the fish is at the lower arrowhead, the spear has to be thrown at a significantly steeper angle.

For an intriguing illustration of Fermat's principle in refraction, assume that rows of soldiers march past a foreign dignitary leaving a plane on a rainy day. Because the soldiers started with a small misalignment with the direction of the tarmac, they come off the asphalt and march into the mud, where their progress is much slower. Like light waves, the direction of the unit marching in the mud turns away from the airstrip.

## ● EXAMPLE 18.2

As shown in Fig. 18.16, a light ray travels through a transparent medium with index of refraction $n_1$ and then passes through a thick transparent slab with parallel surfaces and index of refraction $n_2$. Show that the light ray emerging from the slab is parallel to the incident ray.

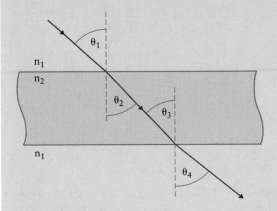

**FIGURE 18.16**

A light ray passes through a sheet of transparent material with index of refraction $n_2$. The sheet forms two parallel interfaces with an external medium of index of refraction $n_1$. The four angles shown in the figure are used to determine the angle $\theta_4$, at which the light ray leaves the sheet. Compare also with Fig. 18.15(b).

*Solution:* We apply the law of refraction twice, once at the upper interface and once at the lower interface. Since both interfaces are parallel and the light ray travels along a straight line inside the slab, we know from geometry that $\theta_2 = \theta_3$. The law of refraction at the upper interface reads:

$$n_2 \cdot \sin \theta_2 = n_1 \cdot \sin \theta_1 \qquad [18]$$

At the lower interface, it reads:

$$n_2 \cdot \sin \theta_3 = n_1 \cdot \sin \theta_4 \qquad [19]$$

Combining Eqs. [18] and [19] and using $\theta_2 = \theta_3$, we get:

$$n_1 \cdot \sin \theta_1 = n_1 \cdot \sin \theta_4 \qquad [20]$$

which yields:

$$\theta_1 = \theta_4 \qquad [21]$$

## ● EXAMPLE 18.3

A light ray travelling through air is incident on a flat slab of transparent solid material. The incident beam makes an angle of 40° with the normal, and the refracted beam makes an angle of 26° with

● **EXAMPLE 18.3** (*continued*)

the normal. Find the index of refraction of the transparent material.

*Solution:* We use the law of refraction to solve for the unknown index of refraction of the transparent material with the given data and the index of refraction of air as $n = 1$ (see Table 18.2):

$$n_{slab} = n_{air} \frac{\sin \alpha_{air}}{\sin \alpha_{slab}} = 1.00 \frac{\sin 40°}{\sin 26°} = 1.47 \quad [22]$$

If we want to identify the material based on the result in Eq. [22], we might suggest fused quartz with $n = 1.46$ from Table 18.2, since glycerine is a liquid.

● **EXAMPLE 18.4**

A light ray travelling through air is incident on a flat slab of crown glass at an angle of 30° to the normal, as illustrated in Fig. 18.17. Find the angle of refraction. (*Note:* Crown glass is an exceptionally hard and clear type of glass that has low refraction and low dispersion.)

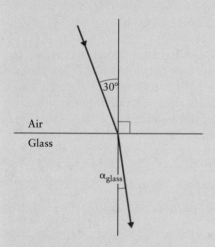

**FIGURE 18.17**

A light ray is refracted at an air–glass interface.

*Solution:* The index of refraction for crown glass is found in Table 18.2. Using the law of refraction, we get:

$$\sin \alpha_{glass} = \frac{n_{air}}{n_{glass}} \sin \alpha_{air}$$

$$= \frac{1.00}{1.52} \sin 30° = 0.329 \quad [23]$$

which leads to:

$$\alpha_{glass} = 19.2° \quad [24]$$

● **EXAMPLE 18.5**

Find the speed of light in ice at 0°C.

*Solution:* We use Snell's law and Eq. [16]:

$$\frac{c}{v_{ice}} = n_{ice} \quad [25]$$

Thus:

$$v_{ice} = \frac{c}{n_{ice}} = \frac{3 \times 10^8 \frac{m}{s}}{1.31} = 2.29 \times 10^8 \frac{m}{s} \quad [26]$$

This is slightly more than 75% of the speed of light in a vacuum.

## Single Spherical Interface

As in the case of reflection, the more interesting applications of refraction result for spherical interfaces. Spherical interfaces of transparent materials include all types of lenses, e.g., in optical instruments and corrective eye glasses.

Before studying lenses, which have two spherical interfaces, we first establish the basic relations for a single, spherical interface between two different transparent media. We start with Fig. 18.18, showing a spherical slab of material with radius $R$. The indices of refraction are $n_2$ at the right side and $n_1$ at the left side. We choose $n_1 < n_2$. When introducing a point light source $O$ at a distance $p$ from the interface, we automatically define the optical axis as the line passing through $O$ and $C$, the centre of curvature of the spherical slab.

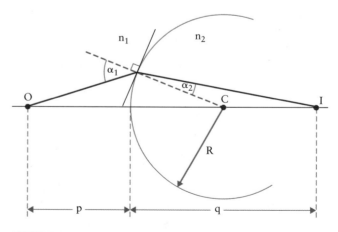

**FIGURE 18.18**

Refraction of the light from a point source $O$ at distance $p$ from a spherical interface separating two media of indices of refraction $n_1$ and $n_2$. $C$ is the centre of curvature of the interface; its radius is $R$. An image $I$ is formed at distance $q$ from the interface.

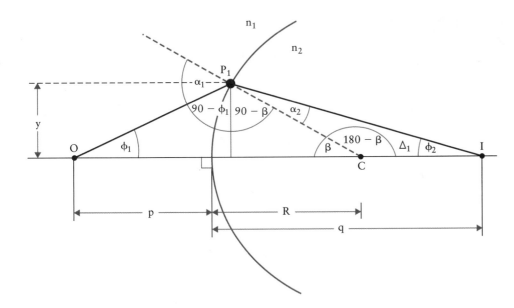

**FIGURE 18.19**

This figure is identical to Fig. 18.18, but contains several additional angles to allow us to derive Eq. [27], which is the relation connecting the various distances and the two indices of refraction.

Following the path of light rays from $O$ that are incident on the interface, we observe that they pass through a common point on the optical axis as long as the incident angle $\alpha_1$ is not too large. This point defines the image $I$. We obtain the distance $q$ between this point and the interface by using the law of refraction for the spherical interface:

$$\frac{n_1}{p} + \frac{n_2}{q} = \frac{n_2 - n_1}{R} \qquad [27]$$

This equation relates the image and object distances with the two indices of refraction and the radius of curvature of the interface. It is derived in the following Concept Question. If you are not interested in its derivation, you may continue to read below.

## Concept Question 18.6

**Derive Eq. [27]. More specifically, use Fig. 18.19, in which Fig. 18.18 is redrawn with several additional geometric features defined.**

ANSWER: Applying geometry to Fig. 18.19, we find at point $P_1$:

$$\alpha_1 + (90° - \phi_1) + (90° - \beta) = 180° \quad [28]$$

which yields:

$$\alpha_1 - \phi_1 = \beta \qquad [29]$$

We further find for triangle $\triangle_1$:

$$\alpha_2 + \phi_2 + (180° - \beta) = 180° \qquad [30]$$

which yields:

$$\alpha_2 + \phi_2 = \beta \qquad [31]$$

Several relations can be introduced because we assume that angles $\alpha_1$, $\alpha_2$, $\beta$, $\phi_1$, and $\phi_2$ are small angles in Fig. 18.19. Recall that we found that the sines and tangents of these angles are equal to the angle in radians; e.g., $\sin \phi_1 = \tan \phi_1 = \phi_1$. First, we find:

$$\tan \phi_1 = \phi_1 = \frac{y}{p}$$

$$\tan \phi_2 = \phi_2 = \frac{y}{q} \qquad [32]$$

$$\tan \beta = \beta = \frac{y}{R}$$

Further, the law of refraction applies for small angles in the form:

$$\frac{n_2}{n_1} = \frac{\sin \alpha_1}{\sin \alpha_2} = \frac{\alpha_1}{\alpha_2} \qquad [33]$$

With the preliminary steps in Eqs. [28] to [33] established, we now combine the two geometric relations of Eqs. [29] and [31]:

$$\alpha_1 - \phi_1 = \alpha_2 + \phi_2 = \beta \qquad [34]$$

and then replace the angles $\phi_1$ and $\phi_2$ using the trigonometric relations in Eq. [32]:

$$\alpha_1 - \frac{y}{p} = \alpha_2 + \frac{y}{q} = \frac{y}{R} \qquad [35]$$

In the next step, $\alpha_2$ in Eq. [35] is replaced using Eq. [33]:

$$\alpha_1 - \frac{y}{p} = \frac{n_1}{n_2}\alpha_1 + \frac{y}{q} = \frac{y}{R} \qquad [36]$$

## Concept Question 18.6 (continued)

This equation is now used twice:

- The equation between the first and last terms in Eq. [36] allows us to isolate $\alpha_1$ as the dependent variable:

$$\alpha_1 = \frac{y}{R} + \frac{y}{p} \qquad [37]$$

- The equation between the first and second terms in Eq. [36] allows us to substitute the result in Eq. [37] for $\alpha_1$:

$$\frac{n_1}{n_2}\left(\frac{y}{R} + \frac{y}{p}\right) + \frac{y}{q} = \frac{y}{R} \qquad [38]$$

This is further rewritten in the form:

$$\frac{n_1}{R} + \frac{n_1}{p} + \frac{n_2}{q} = \frac{n_2}{R} \qquad [39]$$

which is rearranged in the form of Eq. [27].

Based on Eq. [27], the refractive effect of the interface is determined by the term $\Delta n/R$ on the right-hand side. This term is called the **refractive power** of a single interface and has unit **diopter** (dpt), which corresponds in SI units to dpt = m$^{-1}$. We will use this term when light rays pass single spherical interfaces in an optical setup, e.g., when light passes through the cornea into the human eye.

*The refractive power of a single interface is equal to the difference in indices of refraction across the interface divided by its radius of curvature.*

When using Eq. [27], a new set of sign conventions for $p$, $q$, and $R$ is required, analogous to those for mirrors in Table 18.1. The sign conventions for refracting surfaces are given in Table 18.3.

Eq. [27] can also be applied to a flat refracting surface, which is important for judging the depth of an object in another medium. We extrapolate Eq. [27] for $R \to \infty$. We find for the relation between object and image distance:

$$\frac{n_1}{p} + \frac{n_2}{q} = 0 \qquad [40]$$

which leads to:

$$q = -\frac{n_2}{n_1}p \qquad [41]$$

Following the sign conventions in Table 18.3, the image and the object are on the same side of the

## TABLE 18.3

### Sign conventions for single refracting surfaces

| | |
|---|---|
| $p$ is positive | Object is in front of the surface (real object) |
| $p$ is negative | Object is behind the surface (virtual object) |
| $q$ is positive | Image is behind the surface (real image) |
| $q$ is negative | Image is in front of the surface (virtual image) |
| $R$ is positive | Centre of curvature is behind the surface |
| $R$ is negative | Centre of curvature is in front of the surface |

refracting surface as shown in Fig. 18.20. Their respective distance to the interface depends on the difference of the two indices of refraction with the case $n_1 > n_2$ illustrated in (a) and the case $n_1 < n_2$ illustrated in (b).

Besides Eq. [27], we introduce a formula that allows us to calculate the magnification for the image size $h_I$ of an object of height $h_O$:

$$M = \frac{h_I}{h_O} = -\frac{n_1 \cdot q}{n_2 \cdot p} \qquad [42]$$

We do not derive this formula in this textbook. However, you can do a simple experiment at home to illustrate that Eq. [42] indeed allows for a magnification of objects seen across a single spherical interface. Cut off the bottom and top lid of a food can.

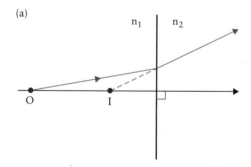

(a)

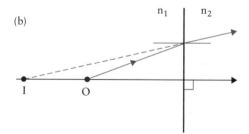

(b)

### FIGURE 18.20

Formation of image *I* for a point source *O* for a flat refracting surface. (a) $n_1 > n_2$; (b) $n_1 < n_2$. Actual light rays are shown as solid lines. The dashed lines allow us to construct the image.

Then cover one end of the can with transparent plastic wrap. Fill your kitchen sink with water and drop a penny in the water. Push the can below the water surface with the plastic wrap down. The water pressure forces the plastic wrap upward, which creates a spherically shaped interface. If you now observe the penny through the can, you will see it magnified.

## ● EXAMPLE 18.6

A small fish is swimming at a depth $d$ below the surface of a fishbowl, as shown in Fig. 18.21. What is the apparent depth of the fish as viewed directly from above?

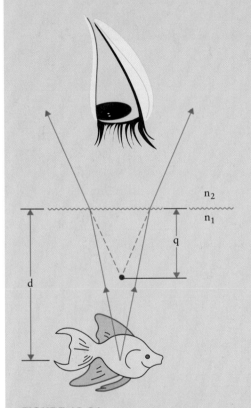

**FIGURE 18.21**

A fish is observed from a position vertically overhead.

*Solution:* In this problem, the refracting interface is flat and the object is in the denser medium, which is the medium with the higher index of refraction. This case corresponds to Fig. 18.20(a). We apply Eq. [42] with $n_2 = 1$ (for air) and $n_1 = 1.33$ (for water) to find the image distance:

$$q = -\frac{n_2}{n_1}p = -\frac{1}{1.33}d = -0.75d \quad [43]$$

Thus, the apparent depth of the fish is three-quarters of its actual depth.

## Concept Question 18.7

The index of refraction changes abruptly at a given interface in Figs. 18.20 and 18.21. (a) Can you imagine a case where it changes gradually within a medium instead? Describe the consequences for light rays travelling through the system. (b) Under what circumstances does no change in the direction of a light ray occur at the interface of two transparent media?

ANSWER TO PART (a): The index of refraction is a materials constant. A gradual change in a material requires a non-uniform system. Alternatively, a uniform system with a non-uniform temperature distribution can also display a gradual change of the index of refraction because it is temperature-dependent (as are most materials constants). A well-known phenomenon of this type is the **mirage** you observe as the apparent wetness of the asphalt on the road ahead when driving a car in the hot summer Sun (see Fig. 18.22). What you actually see is an image of the sky as the heat radiating from the asphalt increases the temperature of the air immediately above the road surface, which causes a reduction in the index of refraction. Fermat's principle then implies that light from the sky above the horizon ahead of your car requires a shorter time to travel to your eye if it travels first toward the asphalt, then along the road surface, and finally up into the cooler air just before it reaches your eyes.

ANSWER TO PART (b): The law of refraction allows light rays to travel straight through an interface under two conditions:

• the light ray is incident along the normal direction of the interface, $\alpha_{\text{incoming}} = 0°$, or

• the indices of refraction for the two adjacent media are the same, $n_{\text{incoming}} = n_{\text{outgoing}}$. This is exploited by some jellyfish for camouflage under water, but it means that invisibility in air cannot be achieved. Even if an object is perfectly transparent, its surface can be observed wherever it is not directed along the line of view. The various values in Table 18.2 allow us to suggest that jellyfish benefit from the index of refraction of water ($n = 1.33$), because many solid materials have similar indices. In air ($n = 1$), only other gases and a vacuum have a matching value. In the H. G. Wells novel *The Invisible Man*, a man has discovered a method to turn every part of his body transparent. This alone is not sufficient to become invisible; the man would further have to modify the materials in his body such that they have an index of refraction close to one.

**FIGURE 18.22**
Formation of a mirage when looking at a hot road surface.

## Lenses: Thin-Lens Formula and Magnification

Lenses are transparent objects with either two partially spherical refracting surfaces, or a combination of a flat and a spherical refracting surface. Light passes through both surfaces before an image is formed. Lenses come in many shapes, as illustrated in Fig. 18.23. They are characterized by two physical parameters:

- lenses are grouped as either **converging lenses** (Fig. 18.23(a)) or **diverging lenses** (Fig. 18.23(b)), based on their effect on incoming light rays, and

- lenses are distinguished as **thick lenses** or **thin lenses,** based on their thickness in relation to other lengths, such as the object and image distances. A thin lens is modelled by a single refracting plane that combines the contributions of both surfaces.

In this textbook, we limit our discussion to thin lenses and more often choose converging lenses for examples. The discussion of diverging lenses is entirely analogous, though, and therefore a duplication of the presentation is omitted without loss of generality. We do need to consider diverging lenses when discussing eye defects later in the chapter. The discussion of thick lenses would lead to mathematically complicated formulas, but does not contribute additional insight. Also, applications of lenses in the life sciences are based almost exclusively on thin lenses.

(a)

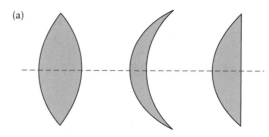

(b)

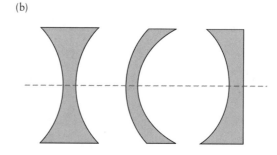

**FIGURE 18.23**
Various types of commonly used lenses. (a) Converging lenses, which are thicker at the optical axis than toward the edges. (b) Diverging lenses, which are thinner at the optical axis. The dashed lines are the respective optical axes.

We first reintroduce the concept of a focal point for a thin lens. Fig. 18.24 shows several parallel incoming light rays as in Fig. 18.10(a), where we defined the focal point for a mirror. Incoming parallel light rays correspond to a light source (object) at infinite distance. The focal point is the point (if it exists) at which all these light rays intersect, i.e., where they form a point image of the light source.

This approach is sufficient to define a focal point $F$ for a thin lens if the light rays travel not too far from the optical axis, as chosen in Fig. 18.24.

Fig. 18.24 illustrates the thin lens simplification: a dashed line is drawn perpendicular to the optical axis at the centre of the lens, allowing us to limit the ray refraction to a single step in geometric image constructions. We use three light rays to determine

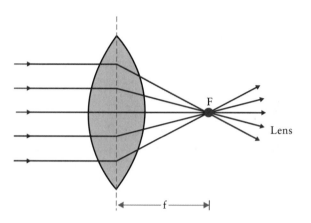

**FIGURE 18.24**

Definition of the focal point for a converging lens. As in the case of the mirror, parallel incoming light rays are used, such as light rays from an object at infinite distance. $F$ is the focal point and $f$ the focal length. The lens is a thin lens, which is indicated by the dashed vertical line at which the refraction is drawn in a single step.

the position and size of images, as we did in the case of mirrors:

- a light ray travelling along the optical axis,
- a ray incident on the lens along a path parallel to the optical axis, and
- a ray incident on the lens after passing through its focal point.

We show how this approach allows us to construct an image for an object at finite distance from the lens in Fig. 18.25. The object $O$ of height $h_O$ is placed at distance $p$ to the left of a thin converging lens. The image is constructed by placing one end of the object on the optical axis. Two light rays are followed from the upper end of the object. The ray parallel to the optical axis is refracted through the focal point on the right side of the lens, i.e., the side of the lens opposite the object, passing through the optical axis at that point with an angle $\theta$. A second ray, emerging from the upper end of the object, passes through the focal point at an angle $\phi$ on the left side, which is the same side of the lens on which the object is located. This ray becomes a light ray travelling parallel to the optical axis beyond the lens. Both light rays that emerge from the upper end of the object intersect at a distance $q$ from the lens, defining the upper point of the image $I$. This point determines the height of the image, $h_I$.

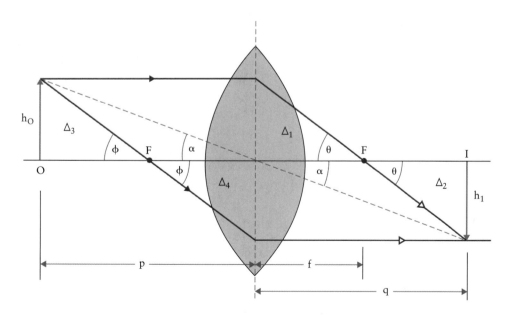

**FIGURE 18.25**

Construction of the image $I$ at distance $q$ for an object $O$ at distance $p$ from a converging lens. The lens is a thin lens with the refraction drawn at the dashed vertical line. $F$ indicates the focal point. Note that only three rays are needed to find the image size $h_I$: (I) a light ray along the optical axis from the bottom end of the object, (II) a light ray travelling from the top of the object parallel to the optical axis, then refracting through the focal point, and (III) a light ray travelling through the focal point and proceeding parallel to the optical axis after refraction.

We first derive the magnification of a thin lens from Fig. 18.25. To allow for a simple geometric derivation, a light ray is drawn from the top of the object to the top of the image (dashed line), crossing the optical axis at the centre of the lens and defining an angle $\alpha$ on both sides. We find $\tan \alpha = h_O/p$ for the triangle on the left side of the lens and $\tan \alpha = -h_I/q$ for the triangle on the right side. Thus, with the definition of the magnification as $h_I/h_O$, we find:

$$M = \frac{h_I}{h_O} = \frac{-q \cdot \tan \alpha}{p \cdot \tan \alpha} = -\frac{q}{p} \qquad [44]$$

which is the magnification of the lens, and, conveniently, is the same formula that we obtained for the magnification of a concave mirror in Eq. [11].

Further using Fig. 18.25, we develop a relation between the various distances relevant for the refraction of a lens, i.e., $p$, $q$, and $f$. To do this, we start with the two triangles labelled $\triangle_1$ and $\triangle_2$ in the figure. $\triangle_1$ and $\triangle_2$ are similar, since both contain the angle $\theta$. From the geometric relations for these two triangles, we find:

$$\triangle_1: \quad \tan \theta = \frac{h_O}{f}$$
$$\triangle_2: \quad \tan \theta = \frac{-h_I}{q - f} \qquad [45]$$

which leads to:

$$\frac{h_I}{h_O} = -\frac{q - f}{f} \qquad [46]$$

Using Eqs. [44] and [46], we find:

$$-\frac{q}{p} = -\frac{q - f}{f} \qquad [47]$$

which is rewritten as:

$$\frac{q}{p} = \frac{q}{f} - 1 \qquad [48]$$

and finally leads to:

$$\frac{1}{p} + \frac{1}{q} = \frac{1}{f} \qquad [49]$$

Eq. [49] is called the **thin-lens formula**. Note that it is the same formula we found for the spherical mirror in Eq. [8].

*The formulas for the magnification and for the relation between focal, object, and image lengths are the same for spherical mirrors and thin lenses.*

All formulas derived in this section for converging lenses apply to diverging lenses as well. A set of sign conventions must be followed, as summarized in Table 18.4.

## TABLE 18.4

### Sign conventions for thin lenses

| | |
|---|---|
| $p$ is positive | Object is in front of the lens |
| $p$ is negative | Object is behind the lens |
| $q$ is positive | Image is behind the lens |
| $q$ is negative | Image is in front of the lens |
| $R_1$ and $R_2$ are positive | Centre of curvature for each surface is behind the lens |
| $R_1$ and $R_2$ are negative | Centre of curvature for each surface is in front of the lens |
| $f$ is positive | Converging lens |
| $f$ is negative | Diverging lens |

These conventions are used when the thin-lens formula and the lens magnification formula are applied. $R_1$ is the radius of curvature of the front surface of the lens and $R_2$ is the radius of curvature of its back surface. These are used when the lens maker's equation is applied.

## Lenses: Lens Maker's Equation

We can approach the quantitative treatment of a lens in a second fashion, starting with the results above for a single spherical interface. Fig. 18.26 is introduced to quantify the optical properties of two consecutive refracting surfaces. The first interface separates material 1 with index of refraction $n_1$ and material 2 with index of refraction $n_2$. The two materials are chosen such that this interface alone does not allow the formation of an image on the right side. This means specifically that the change in the index of refraction at the first interface is not sufficient to cause diverging light rays from the object $O$ at distance $p$ in front of the interface to converge after passing the interface. A second interface, from material 2 to material 3 with index of refraction $n_3$, is needed so that an image $I$ at distance $q$ is formed. Note that the distance $q$ is defined with reference to the same point along the optical axis as the distances $p$, $p'$, and $-q'$. This is a good approximation for the case of a thin lens, where the thickness of material 2 is negligible when compared with $p$, $q$, $R_1$, and $R_2$.

A formula describing the relations among the relevant parameters in Fig. 18.26 is developed. For this, we apply Eq. [27] at the first interface:

$$\text{(I)} \quad \frac{n_1}{p} + \frac{n_2}{q'} = \frac{n_2 - n_1}{R_1} \qquad [50]$$

where $q'$ is the image distance, which is negative as shown in Fig. 18.26. $R_1$ is the radius of curvature of

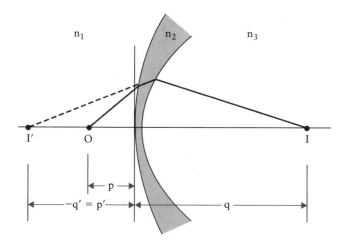

**FIGURE 18.26**

Formation of an image *I* for a point-like light source *O* located on the optical axis. Light passes two refracting surfaces, travelling through three media with indices of refraction $n_1$, $n_2$, and $n_3$. Note that the two interfaces are located very close to each other to allow us to develop relations applicable to thin lenses.

the first interface, i.e., the interface that light from the object hits first. Eq. [27] further applies at the second interface:

$$\text{(II)} \quad \frac{n_2}{p'} + \frac{n_3}{q} = \frac{n_3 - n_2}{R_2} \quad [51]$$

Note that the image distance of the first interface has become the object distance for the second interface, $p' = -q'$:

$$\text{(II)} \quad -\frac{n_2}{q'} + \frac{n_3}{q} = \frac{n_3 - n_2}{R_2} \quad [52]$$

The intermediate term $n_2/q'$ is eliminated by combining Eqs. [50] and [52]:

$$\frac{n_1}{p} + \frac{n_3}{q} = \frac{n_2 - n_1}{R_1} + \frac{n_3 - n_2}{R_2} \quad [53]$$

The left-hand sides of Eqs. [53] and [27] are the same, containing the parameters of the medium left and right of the studied interfaces. Thus, several interfaces do not change the left-hand side of the equation. Additional interfaces have an effect on the right-hand side, as we see when comparing Eqs. [27] and [53]: a term of the form $\Delta n/R$ is added for each interface. We defined the term $\Delta n/R$ earlier as the refractive power of an interface.

● **EXAMPLE 18.7**

Can you see clearly under water without diving goggles? For the discussion, combine cornea and lens of the human eye to be a single symmetric lens with $n = 1.5$. Take $n = 1.3$ for the vitreous body.

*Solution*: Eq. [53] connects the object distance, the image distance, and the radii of curvature for two consecutive refractive interfaces. The setup is shown in Fig. 18.26, illustrating that the light travels from a medium with refractive index $n_1$, through a medium of refractive index $n_2$, and finally into a medium of refractive index $n_3$.

In the current example we want to compare a tourist, first looking at other people at the beach and then looking at an approaching shark under water. When looking at the beach, medium 1 is air, medium 2 is the lens of the eye, and medium 3 is the vitreous body behind the lens, with $n_1 = 1.0$, $n_2 = 1.5$, and $n_3 = 1.3$. With these values, Eq. [53] yields for a symmetric lens—i.e., when $-R_1 = R_2 = R$:

$$\frac{1}{p} + \frac{1.3}{q} = \frac{2 \cdot 1.5 - 1.0 - 1.3}{R} = \frac{0.7}{R} \quad [54]$$

If people at the beach are practically at infinite distance, $p = \infty$, they generate a focussed image on the tourist's retina (using $q = 2.8$ cm for a typical distance between lens and retina) if the effective radius of curvature of the lens is $R = 1.5$ cm. This is a value well within the range of accommodations of the human eye, which can reach a maximum effective accommodation of $R = 1.0$ cm.

Once underneath the water surface, the index of refraction of the medium containing the object—now the shark—changes to $n_1 = 1.33$. This changes Eq. [54] to:

$$\frac{1.33}{p} + \frac{1.3}{q} = \frac{2 \cdot 1.5 - 1.33 - 1.3}{R}$$

$$= \frac{0.37}{R} \quad [55]$$

A shark at infinite distance ($p = \infty$) leads to an image distance of $q = 3.5$ cm for the maximum effective accommodation of the eye with $R = 1.0$ cm. Thus, the shark's image is significantly blurred on the retina, which lies only 2.8 cm behind the lens.

The situation does not improve when the object comes closer. If we choose, for example, $p = 25$ cm, we find $q = 4.1$ cm at the maximum effective accommodation of the eye. Thus, the image of a near object under water is even more blurred. All these optical effects, of course, will escape the tourist's attention.

Eq. [53] simplifies when media 1 and 3 are identical. This is also the most common case as it applies specifically to artificial lenses, where media 1 and 3 are usually air ($n_1 = n_3 = 1$) and medium 2 is a transparent material with $n_2 = n$. In this case, Eq. [53] becomes the **lens maker's equation** for thin lenses:

$$\frac{1}{p} + \frac{1}{q} = (n - 1)\left(\frac{1}{R_1} - \frac{1}{R_2}\right) \qquad [56]$$

Again, note that $p$ and $q$ are measured to the same point along the optical axis; i.e., the transparent material 2 is of negligible thickness.

● **EXAMPLE 18.8**

The lens in Fig. 18.27 has an index of refraction of 1.5. The radius of the front surface is $R_1 = 10$ cm and for the back surface $R_2 = -15$ cm. Find the focal length $f$ of the lens.

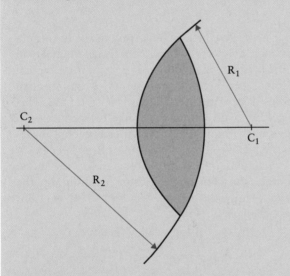

**FIGURE 18.27**
A lens with two different radii of curvature, $R_1$ and $R_2$.

*Solution:* Note that the positive and negative signs in the example text are chosen from Table 18.4: the centre of curvature for $R_1$ is on the side of the lens opposite the object, and the centre of curvature for $R_2$ is on the same side as the object.

We combine the lens maker's equation (Eq. [56]) with the thin-lens formula (Eq. [49]):

$$\frac{1}{f} = (n - 1)\left(\frac{1}{R_1} - \frac{1}{R_2}\right) \qquad [57]$$

which yields:

$$\frac{1}{f} = (1.5 - 1)\left(\frac{1}{10 \text{ cm}} - \frac{1}{-15 \text{ cm}}\right) \qquad [58]$$

with the result:

$$f = 12 \text{ cm} \qquad [59]$$

## Lenses: Refractive Power

Note that the left-hand side of Eq. [49] connects the object and image distances of a lens in the same fashion as the left-hand side of Eq. [27]; the right-hand side is therefore a measure of the ability of the lens to refract the light. Using this observation, the **refractive power of a lens** $\Re$ is defined:

$$\Re = \frac{1}{f} \qquad [60]$$

Eq. [60] combines the effect of two refractive interfaces; for single interfaces the refractive power had been defined earlier as $\Delta n/R$, with $R$ the radius of curvature of a spherical interface. Eq. [60] is consistent with that definition; i.e., the combined refractive power of two spherical interfaces, which is the sum of two $\Delta n/R$ terms, is equal to the inverse focal length of the lens formed by the two interfaces.

*The refractive power of a thin lens $\Re$, in unit diopters (dpt), is equal to its inverse focal length.*

● **EXAMPLE 18.9**

A converging lens with $f = 10$ cm (i.e., a lens of refractive power $\Re = +10$ dpt) forms images of objects at (a) 30 cm, (b) 10 cm, and (c) 5 cm from the lens. In each case, find the image distance and describe the image.

*Solution to part (a):* Substituting the given values in the thin-lens formula, we find:

$$\frac{1}{10 \text{ cm}} = \frac{1}{30 \text{ cm}} + \frac{1}{q} \qquad [61]$$

which corresponds to $q = +15$ cm. Further substitution in the magnification formula yields:

$$M = -\frac{q}{p} = -\frac{15 \text{ cm}}{30 \text{ cm}} = -0.5 \qquad [62]$$

A positive $q$ value means that a real image is formed on the side of the lens opposite the object. The image is half the height of the object and is inverted due to the negative sign of $M$. This case is shown in Fig. 18.28(a).

*Solution to part (b):* Replacing $p = 30$ cm with $p = 10$ cm in Eq. [61] leads to $q = \infty$. Note that this case is equivalent but with reverse light rays to Fig. 18.24, where an object at the focal length has an image at infinite distance.

*Solution to part (c):* In the third case, the object lies inside the focal length. Replacing $p = 30$ cm with $p = 5$ cm in Eq. [61] leads to:

$$\frac{1}{10 \text{ cm}} = \frac{1}{5 \text{ cm}} + \frac{1}{q} \qquad [63]$$

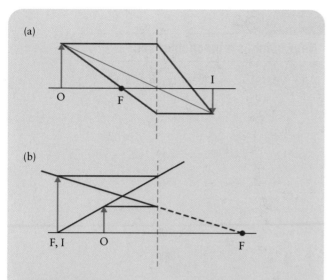

**FIGURE 18.28**

(a) Sketch of an image *I* formed for an object *O* located farther away than the focal length. For convenience, the thin lens is not drawn but represented by a dashed vertical line. The three rays shown allow us to construct the image. (b) Sketch of an image *I* formed for an object *O* located closer than the focal length. Again, three rays are used to construct the image.

which yields $q = -10$ cm. Further substituting the new values in Eq. [44] leads to:

$$M = -\frac{q}{p} = \frac{10 \text{ cm}}{5 \text{ cm}} = +2.0 \qquad [64]$$

This result is illustrated in Fig. 18.28(b). The negative image distance represents a virtual image, i.e., an image on the same side of the lens as the object. A positive magnification $M > 1$ means that the image is enlarged and upright.

**Concept Question 18.8**

In Fig. 18.28(a), you see an object *O* and its image *I* that forms for a converging lens we represent by a vertical dashed line. Which of the following quantities is a negative number in this case? (A) object distance *p*, (B) image distance *q*, (C) focal length *f*, (D) refractive power of the lens $\Re$, or (E) magnification *M*?

ANSWER: Choice (E). Confirm this result with Table 18.4 and Eq. [44].

# Applications in Optometry and Ophthalmology

Two main applications of the ray model of optics exist in the life sciences: vision and microscopy. We discuss both in this textbook, beginning with the

healthy eye in this section. We then proceed to the most common eye defects and their corrections. The discussion of light microscopes, which allow us to see objects too small to observe with the naked eye, follows in the next chapter.

## The Eye

Fig. 18.1 is a sketch of the side view cross-section of a human eyeball. The optically active parts of the eye are the cornea and the lens. The **cornea** contains a convex external interface (*facies externa*) and a concave internal interface (*facies interna*). It has a small radius of curvature of about 8 mm and bridges the biggest difference in indices of refraction, from $n = 1.0$ for air to $n = 1.33$, which is close to the value for water. Thus, the cornea provides the biggest fraction of the refractive power of the eye, with:

$$\Re_{cornea} = \frac{\Delta n}{R} = \frac{1.33 - 1.0}{0.008 \text{ m}} = 41 \text{ dpt} \qquad [65]$$

Due to the variability of the curvature of the cornea, a value of $\Re_{cornea} = 40$ dpt is generally adopted in the literature.

The **lens** is suspended by fibres (suspensory ligament of the lens, or *zonula ciliaris*) that are stretched or loosened by **ciliary muscles**. The **iris** defines the opening of the lens, allowing light to pass through only the visible area of the lens, which is called the **pupil**. The iris can vary the diameter of the pupil to adjust the total light intensity reaching the **retina**. We do not emphasize light-intensity-related issues in the current context since the related topic of sound intensity is extensively discussed in Chapter 17.

The lens is a transparent, pliable, biconvex body with an index of refraction of $n = 1.41$. The elastic variation of the lens is illustrated in Fig. 18.29, which allows for a change of refractive power between $\Re = 18$ dpt and $\Re = 32$ dpt. When the ciliary muscle is relaxed (lower part of Fig. 18.29) the suspension fibres of the lens are stretched and the lens is elongated. This leads to a flatter surface with increased radius of curvature and reduced refractive power $\Re$. When the relaxed eye looks at an object at infinite distance (approximated by $p \geq 60$ m), its focal length is calculated from the two contributions to the refractive power of the eye:

$$\Re_{relaxed \, eye} = \Re_{cornea} + \Re_{lens} = (40 \text{ dpt}) + (18 \text{ dpt})$$
$$= 58 \text{ dpt} \qquad [66]$$

which results in $f = 1.7$ cm.

While focussing up close, as illustrated in the upper part of Fig. 18.29, the ciliary muscle is contracted,

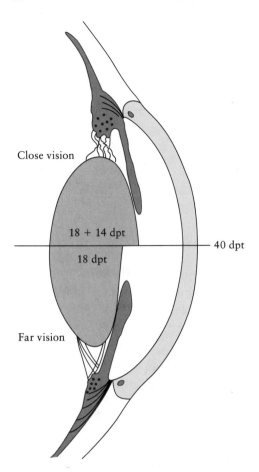

**FIGURE 18.29**

Anatomy of the lens, ciliary muscles, and ligaments of the human eye; note the changes of these three components between close vision (top half of figure) and far vision (bottom half of figure). The cornea has a fixed refractive power of 40 dpt, to which the lens adds a refractive power between 18 dpt and 32 dpt.

relaxing the suspension fibres and allowing the lens to contract in response to its elasticity. The surfaces of the contracted lens have smaller radii of curvature, and thus a larger refractive power:

$$\Re_{\text{focussed eye}} = \Re_{\text{cornea}} + \Re_{\text{lens}} = (40 \text{ dpt}) + (32 \text{ dpt})$$

$$= 72 \text{ dpt} \qquad [67]$$

which results in a focal length of less than 1.4 cm. The process of changing the refractive power of the lens due to ciliary muscle action is called **accommodation**.

The ability to view objects close up deteriorates with age due to the sclerosing effects of the lens. Physiologically, this is quantified by defining the **near point**. The near point is the shortest object distance $p$ for which the human eye produces a sharp image on

**TABLE 18.5**

### Near point as a function of age

| Age (years) | Near point (cm) |
|:-----------:|:---------------:|
| 10 | 7 |
| 20 | 9 |
| 30 | 12 |
| 40 | 22 |
| 50 | 40 |
| 60 | 100 |
| 70 | 400 |
| >75 | ∞ |

For the standard man a near point of $s_0 = 25$ cm is used.

the retina. Table 18.5 illustrates the change of the near point distance with age.

## Eye Defects and Diseases

Six commonly occurring eye defects are listed below. Two are discussed in greater detail as examples of how prescription eyeglasses are used to correct vision deficiencies.

### ASTIGMATISM

For an eye with astigmatism, a point light source (object) leads to an elongated image on the retina, as sketched in Fig. 18.30. This is usually caused by a difference between the horizontal and vertical radii of curvature of the cornea. Astigmatism is often inborn and inherited. Some cases occur as the result of cornea injury. Glasses with asymmetric lenses correct this deficiency.

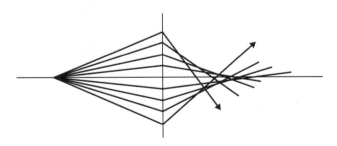

**FIGURE 18.30**

Sketch to illustrate the effect of astigmatism on the focussing of light that arrives at the eye from a point light source.

## Concept Question 18.9

**Art historians have claimed that Domenikos Theotokopoulos, famous under the name El Greco, must have been highly astigmatic since he painted people and their faces unnaturally elongated. Does this argument make sense?**

ANSWER: No. Assume that El Greco (1541–1614) intended to paint his models as he saw them. In this case he would only have been satisfied with his work once the painted image looked exactly like the model. Thus, he would have painted the image without distortions no matter whether he suffered from astigmatism. If he suffered from astigmatism, he might have seen the model as elongated, but his painting would have looked right to him only when it showed the same elongation. The same elongation requires that the actual image (as we see it) be perfect in proportion.

El Greco was a Crete-born painter, living in Toledo, Spain (thus his name). The elongated distortions of humans and human faces in his paintings were intentional because he was associated with the school of Mannerism, a style developed by Raphael's students in Rome after 1520 reflecting a highly cultivated religious spirituality.

## CATARACTS

With cataracts, the lens becomes cloudy and eventually opaque. This condition is usually inborn or caused by traumatic injury, diabetes, old age, or as a side effect of diseases. It requires surgical removal and exchange of the lens.

## GLAUCOMA

Glaucoma is a collective term for various eye diseases associated with an increase in the fluid gauge pressure in the eye from a normal value of 2 kPa to values between 7 kPa and 11 kPa (acute case). Glaucoma is often treatable with drugs.

## GRAVES' DISEASE

The eyeball is pushed forward as a side effect of thyroiditis, which is a thyroid inflammation.

## HYPEROPIA (FARSIGHTEDNESS)

Hyperopia is an eye defect associated with an insufficient elasticity of the lens, leading to an incomplete reshaping when the suspension fibres of the lens are relaxed. As a result, the maximum refractive power of the lens of $\Re = 32$ dpt is not reached and the eye cannot form an image of nearby objects on the retina.

Hyperopia is illustrated in Fig. 18.31. Part (a) shows the optical properties of a hyperopic eye when observing an object at great distance. The ciliary muscle is relaxed, the suspension fibres and the lens are stretched, and an image is formed properly on the retina. Thus, the person is called farsighted. Part (b) illustrates the problem of the patient when focussing on a nearby object, i.e., when the ciliary muscle contracts and the lens should relax toward its most spherical shape. If the object is closer than the near point, the image is formed behind the retina. If this near point is too far from the eye the patient has a problem, for example, when reading. This is a typical effect of old age, but may also occur when the eyeball is too short. The correction is done with prescription glasses, as illustrated in Fig. 18.31(c). The corrective lens is a convex

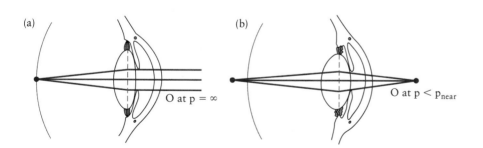

O at p = ∞

O at p < $p_{near}$

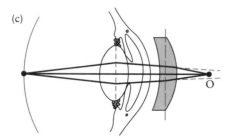

O

**FIGURE 18.31**

Hyperopia or farsightedness. (a) Far vision, (b) close vision, (c) correction with prescription glasses.

lens with a positive refractive power $\Re$ to add to the too-small refractive power of the eye. As indicated in the figure, the glasses cause an apparent shift of the object to greater distance, a distance at which the defective eye is able to see it clearly.

● **EXAMPLE 18.10**

The near point of a particular person is at 50 cm. What focal length must a corrective lens have to enable the eye to clearly see an object 25 cm away?

*Solution:* We use the thin-lens formula with an object distance of $p = 25$ cm. The lens we want to prescribe must form an image on the same side of the lens as the object, but at a distance of 50 cm. Then the eye of the person looks at that image and sees it clearly. Due to the sign in Table 18.4, we write $q = -50$ cm:

$$\frac{1}{f} = \frac{1}{p} + \frac{1}{q} = \frac{1}{0.25 \text{ m}} + \frac{1}{-0.5 \text{ m}} \quad [68]$$

This leads to a focal length of:

$$f = 0.5 \text{ m} \quad [69]$$

$\Re = 1/f = +2.0$ dpt is the refractive power of the prescribed glasses.

## MYOPIA (NEARSIGHTEDNESS)

Myopia is an eye defect due to an insufficient stretching of the lens when a person tries to obtain a lower refractive power of $\Re = 18$ dpt. Myopia is illustrated in Fig. 18.32. Part (a) shows the eye trying to observe an object at great distance. The lens is not sufficiently elongated, and thus the image is formed in front of the retina. The same person can see an object at the near point of the standard man (at 25 cm distance) without any problem as the elasticity of the lens is sufficient to reshape the lens to form an image on the retina (illustrated in 18.32(b)). Fig. 18.32(c) shows how myopia is corrected with prescription glasses: parallel light rays reaching the eye from an object at great distance are refracted away from the optical axis such that they form an image $I'$ at a point closer to the eye. This image is observed with the myopic eye, forming the final image on the retina.

Typical causes of myopia are elongated eyeballs or weakened ligaments and muscles, e.g., due to diabetes mellitus. The prescription glasses are concave to lower the too-high refractive power $\Re$ of the eye.

● **EXAMPLE 18.11**

A certain person cannot see objects clearly when they are beyond a distance of 50 cm. What focal length should the prescribed lens have to correct this problem?

*Solution:* We choose the object distance as infinite, $p = \infty$, since we want to enable the eye to see anything beyond 50 cm, including objects very far away. The image of the prescription lens must be on the same side of the lens as the object, and cannot be further than 50 cm; that means $q = -50$ cm (the negative sign results from the sign conventions in Table 18.4). If the lens accom-

### FIGURE 18.32

Myopia or nearsightedness. (a) Far vision, (b) close vision, (c) correction with prescription glasses.

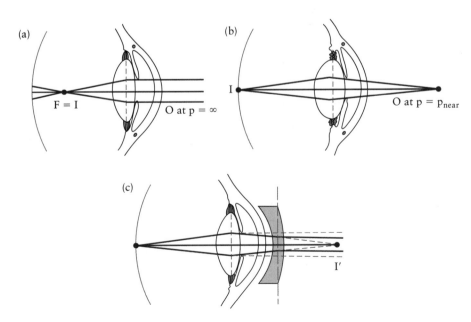

plishes this, then the eye can look at the intermediate image and see it properly. The thin-lens formula reads:

$$\frac{1}{f} = \frac{1}{p} + \frac{1}{q} = \frac{1}{\infty} + \frac{1}{-0.5 \text{ m}} \qquad [70]$$

which yields for the focal length:

$$f = -0.5 \text{ m} \qquad [71]$$

A negative focal length means that a concave lens must be prescribed (based on the sign conventions in Table 18.4). The lens has a refractive power $\Re = -2.0$ dpt.

## ● EXAMPLE 18.12

An artificial lens is implanted in a patient's eye to replace a diseased lens. The distance between the artificial lens and the retina is 2.8 cm. In the absence of the lens, the image of a very distant object (formed by the refraction of the cornea) is formed 2.53 cm behind the retina. The lens is designed to put the image of the distant object on the retina. What is the refractive power $\Re$ of the implanted lens? *Hint:* Consider the image formed by the cornea as a virtual object.

*Solution:* Following the hint, we consider the image formed by the eye without the implanted lens as a virtual object for the implanted lens. To later use the thin-lens formula to determine the focal length of the implanted lens, we need to determine the object distance for the implanted lens from the image distance of the cornea without a lens. The image distance is $q = (2.53 \text{ cm} + 2.8 \text{ cm}) = 5.33 \text{ cm}$, as shown in Fig. 18.33(a). The

two lengths are added since the original image is formed behind the retina, i.e., farther away from the location of the missing lens.

When the new lens is implanted, the image distance calculated above becomes the object distance for the implanted lens. The object distance is $p = -5.33$ cm, where the negative sign indicates that this is a virtual object, i.e., an object that appears behind the lens. The implanted lens must now form a final image on the retina as indicated in Fig. 18.33(b), i.e., at a distance $q = +2.8$ cm behind the lens. The thin-lens formula yields:

$$\frac{1}{f} = \frac{1}{p} + \frac{1}{q} = \frac{1}{-5.33 \text{ cm}} + \frac{1}{2.8 \text{ cm}} \qquad [72]$$

which allows us to calculate:

$$f = +5.9 \text{ cm} \qquad [73]$$

Using Eq. [60], we find the refractive power of the implanted lens to be $\Re = +17.0$ dpt. Note that this is a much larger value than a typical refractive power for a prescription lens, but close to the value of the natural lens in Fig. 18.29.

## Concept Question 18.10

**Can you think of a mammal that would benefit from myopic eyes?**

ANSWER: Any mammal for which vision under water is more critical than vision in air would benefit from myopic eyes, as these allow better vision for objects at greater distances under water due to the loss of refractive power at the cornea. Polar bears (see Fig. 18.34) indeed have myopic vision, since they hunt primarily in the water.

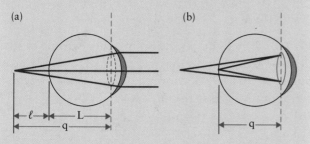

(a)        (b)

**FIGURE 18.33**

(a) Eye with a surgically removed lens (dashed lines indicate the missing lens). The cornea (light-red crescent) is the only focussing component of this eye, but does not have a sufficient refractive power to focus light from a source at infinite distance. Thus, the image forms behind the retina. The person would see only a very blurred image. (b) The artificial lens implanted into the eye must correct the position of the image such that the image is formed on the retina.

**FIGURE 18.34**
Polar bear.

# MULTIPLE CHOICE AND CONCEPTUAL QUESTIONS

## FLAT MIRRORS

**Q–18.1.** A candle produces an image of 0.2 m in height with the wick pointing downward when observed in a flat mirror. What statement is true about the candle in the observer's hand? (A) The candle is 2 cm high and is held upside down. (B) The candle is 2 cm high and is held upright. (C) The candle is 20 cm high and is held upside down. (D) The candle is 20 cm high and is held upright. (E) None of the above.

**Q–18.2.** An object is placed 35 cm in front of a flat mirror. Where does the image form? (A) 1 m in front of the mirror; (B) 0.35 m in front of the mirror; (C) at the focal length behind the mirror; (D) 0.35 m behind the mirror; (E) none of the above.

**Q–18.3.** When you look at yourself in a flat mirror, you see yourself with left and right sides switched, but not upside down. Why? *Hint:* Remember that you are a three-dimensional body. Study the image of the following three vectors: (I) head to foot, (II) left to right hand, and (III) nose to back of head. The remainder of the puzzle is perception of the brain!

**Q–18.4.** Can a virtual image be photographed?

**Q–18.5.** Tape a picture of a person on a flat mirror. Approach the mirror to within 20 to 25 cm. Can you focus on the picture and your image at the same time?

## SPHERICAL MIRRORS

**Q–18.6.** A spherical mirror has a radius of 25 cm. What is the focal length $f$ of the mirror? (A) $f = 0.125$ m, (B) $f = 0.25$ m, (C) $f = 0.5$ m, (D) $f = 1$ m, (E) $f = 5$ m.

**Q–18.7.** A spherical mirror has a focal length of 20 cm. What is the radius of curvature $r$ of the mirror? (A) $r = 0.04$ m, (B) $r = 0.1$ m, (C) $r = 0.4$ m, (D) $r = 1$ m, (E) $r = 4$ m.

**Q–18.8.** An object at distance $p = +0.3$ m in front of a spherical mirror forms a virtual image at a distance of 15 cm from the mirror. What is the focal length of the mirror? (A) $f = -30$ cm, (B) $f = -10$ cm, (C) $f = +10$ cm, (D) $f = +30$ cm, (E) none of the above.

**Q–18.9.** An object is placed at $p = +20$ cm in front of a spherical mirror. The image is magnified by a factor of 2 and is inverted. What is the image distance? (A) $q = +0.4$ m, (B) $q = +0.1$ m, (C) $q = -0.1$ m, (D) $q = -0.4$ m, (E) none of the above.

**Q–18.10.** In this line, the word DECEITFUL is capitalized and printed in a sans serif font. Take a transparent rod (e.g., a water-filled test tube in your chemistry or biology lab) and read this word through the rod. Why are the first five letters unchanged, while the last four letters are upside down when using the plastic rod?

## REFRACTION

**Q–18.11.** Why does the fish in Fig. 18.21 appear closer to the observer than it actually is? (A) Because we look at the fish in the direction perpendicular to the water surface. (B) Because the fish is in water and the observer is in air. (C) Because the index of refraction of the water is smaller than the index of refraction of the air. (D) Because the fish floats toward the surface. (E) Because the water surface is flat, not spherically shaped.

**Q–18.12.** Light is incident on a flat horizontal interface from a vacuum to an unknown type of glass. The light travels at 45° with the normal of the glass surface in the vacuum and at 35° in the glass. What is the refractive index $n$ of the glass? Choose the closest value. (A) $n = 0.8$, (B) $n = 1.0$, (C) $n = 1.2$, (D) $n = 1.5$, (E) $n = 2.0$.

**Q–18.13.** Light is incident at an angle of 45° with the vertical on a flat horizontal interface from a vacuum to an unknown type of glass. What is the speed of light in that glass if it travels in the glass with an angle of 27° with the vertical? Choose the closest answer. (A) $v = 4 \times 10^8$ m/s, (B) $v = 3 \times 10^8$ m/s, (C) $v = 2 \times 10^6$ km/s, (D) $v = 2 \times 10^5$ km/s, (E) $v = 2 \times 10^4$ km/s.

**Q–18.14.** A light ray travelling through air is incident on a flat slab of crown glass ($n = 1.52$) at an angle of 30° to the normal. What is the angle of refraction? Choose the closest value. (A) $\alpha_{glass} = 50°$, (B) $\alpha_{glass} = 40°$, (C) $\alpha_{glass} = 30°$, (D) $\alpha_{glass} = 20°$, (E) $\alpha_{glass} = 10°$.

**Q–18.15.** Sunlight refracts while passing through the atmosphere due to a small difference between the indices of refraction for air and vacuum. We define dawn optically as the instant when the top of the Sun just appears above the horizon, and we define dawn geometrically when a straight line drawn from the observer to the top of the Sun just clears the horizon. Which definition of dawn occurs earlier in the morning?

**Q–18.16.** Put a straw in a glass of water. Why does the straw look bent, as in Fig. 18.35?

**FIGURE 18.35**
A straw in a glass of water.

## LENSES

**Q–18.17.** Which of the four bodies in Fig. 18.36, each showing a thin lens made of flint glass ($n = 1.61$), has the smallest refractive power? *Note:* Choose (E) if two bodies tie for the smallest value.

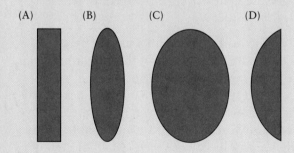

(A)     (B)     (C)     (D)

**FIGURE 18.36**
Four designs of a thin lens made of flint glass.

**Q–18.18.** In Fig. 18.28(b), you see an object (O, at left) and its image (I, farther at the left), the latter forming as the result of a converging lens represented by the vertical dashed line. Which of the following statements is false? (A) The magnification is larger than one. (B) The image forms in front of the lens.

(C) The image is upright. (D) The image distance $q$ is a positive length, $q > 0$. (E) The object is closer to the lens than the focal length.

**Q–18.19.** A converging lens with focal length $f = 20$ cm is used to view an object 50 cm from the lens. How far from the lens does the object appear? Choose the closest value. (A) 120 cm, (B) 90 cm, (C) 30 cm, (D) 20 cm, (E) 5 cm.

**Q–18.20.** For a thin lens, we find the image distance $q = +10$ cm for an object placed at $p = +20$ cm. What is the refractive power of the lens in diopters? (A) $\mathfrak{R} = 2$ dpt, (B) $\mathfrak{R} = 5$ dpt, (C) $\mathfrak{R} = 10$ dpt, (D) $\mathfrak{R} = 15$ dpt, (E) none of the above.

**Q–18.21.** A lens forms an observable magnified image (an image that is larger than the object) if (A) the image is on the same side of the lens as the object; (B) the object is placed at the focal point of the lens; (C) the object is placed closer than twice the focal length in front of the lens; (D) the image distance is smaller than the object distance; (E) none of the above.

**Q–18.22.** A diverging lens with focal length $f = 30$ cm is used to view an object 90 cm from the lens. How far from the lens does the object appear? Choose the closest value. (A) 120 cm, (B) 90 cm, (C) 30 cm, (D) 22.5 cm, (E) 18.5 cm.

**Q–18.23.** Two coaxial converging lenses, with focal lengths $f_1$ and $f_2$, are positioned a distance $f_1 + f_2$ apart, as shown in Fig. 18.37. This arrangement is called a **beam expander**, because it is often used for widening laser beams. If $h_1$ is the size of the incident beam, the size of the emerging beam is

(A) $h_2 = \dfrac{f_2}{f_1}h_1$        (B) $h_2 = \dfrac{f_1}{f_2}h_1$

(C) $h_2 = (f_2 + f_1)h_1$    (D) $h_2 = (f_2 - f_1)h_1$

(E) $h_2 = (f_2 \cdot f_1)h_1$              [74]

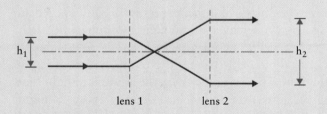

**FIGURE 18.37**
Two coaxial converging lenses, with focal lengths $f_1$ and $f_2$, that are positioned a distance $f_1 + f_2$ apart. $h_1$ is the size of the incident light beam and $h_2$ is the size of the emerging beam.

**Q–18.24.** What is the closest distance between an object and a screen such that an image is formed on the screen using a diverging lens with focal length $-f$? (A) $f/2$, (B) $f$, (C) $2 \cdot f$, (D) $4 \cdot f$, (E) no image will form.

**Q–18.25.** A person's face is 30 cm in front of a concave mirror. What is the focal length of the mirror if it creates an upright image that is 1.5 times as large as the actual face? Choose the closest value. (A) 12 cm, (B) 20 cm, (C) 70 cm, (D) 90 cm.

## APPLICATIONS IN MEDICINE AND BIOLOGY

**Q–18.26.** (a) Some gardeners advise against watering flowers in full sunshine to avoid burns to leaves due to the focussing effect of water droplets. Is this advice reasonable? *Hint:* Treat the water droplet as a sphere placed on the leaf, as shown in Fig. 18.38, and use the thin-lens formula. (b) *If you are interested:* Do you know why it is still not a good idea to water flowers in full sunlight?

**FIGURE 18.38**
A drop of water on a flower.

**Q–18.27.** Many nocturnal or crepuscular mammals have eye-shine, like the lesser bush baby shown in Fig. 18.39: when a bright light is shone into their eyes, a reflection comes back. The reflection is due to a crystalline layer behind the retina, called **tapetum lucidum**. This layer increases the amount of light that passes across the retina, and thereby assists in night vision. What optical system is a good model for the *tapetum lucidum* based on Fig. 18.39? (A) a single, thin lens, (B) a flat mirror, (C) a flat refractive interface, (D) a spherical mirror, (E) a double-lens system as in a microscope.

**FIGURE 18.39**
A lesser bush baby looking at a photographer's camera at night.

**Q–18.28.** Stereoscopic vision is very important to us. A person may lose vision in one eye due to an accident. How can that person judge with just one eye the distance to a nearby object? Choose the statement that best describes how it is done. (A) The lens has a fixed refractive power; the size of the eyeball is variable. Thus, sensing the pressure in the brain behind the eye when a focussed image is obtained on the retina provides a measure of the object distance. (B) The size of the eyeball is fixed, but the lens is pliable to vary the refractive power. The extent of contraction of the ciliary muscles is used to judge the distance. (C) The eyes must produce a thick water coat on the cornea (as when the person cries). The eyelid then senses the thickness of the water layer when a focussed image is obtained on the retina. That value is a measure of the object distance. (D) If we open and close the eye very fast, the rods in the retina measure the time it takes for the light to reach the retina. The longer the light travels through the eye, the farther away the object is.

**Q–18.29.** The near point of a particular person is at 50 cm. This is due to a defect of the person's eye; an image forms behind the retina for objects closer than 50 cm, as indicated in Fig. 18.31(b). To correct this problem, what refractive power must a corrective lens have (shown in Fig. 18.31(c)) to enable the eye to clearly see an object at 25 cm? (A) $\Re = -2.0$ dpt, (B) $\Re = -1.0$ dpt, (C) $\Re = 0.0$ dpt, (D) $\Re = +1.0$ dpt, (E) $\Re = +2.0$ dpt.

**Q–18.30.** Optometrists use the **Snellen test** to evaluate their patients' vision. The Snellen test consists of letters of different sizes that a person with healthy eyes can read at particular distances. The patient is placed 6.1 m (20 feet) from the chart and asked to read the letters. If the patient's eyes are healthy, he/she will read the same line without errors that the healthy reference group was able to read at that distance. We therefore call this 20/20 vision. A juvenile may have 20/10 vision, which means that he/she can read a line that a healthy adult can read only at a distance of 3.05 m (10 feet). Vision-impaired patients may score as low as 20/200, which corresponds to the single, largest letter at the top of the Snellen test. A person with healthy eyes can read that letter as far away as 61 m (200 feet), which coincides with the distance at which the eye is accommodated for vision of objects at infinite distance. Many optometrists have offices in a mall with high rent. To keep the cost down, the examination room may have a length of only 4 metres, with the patient sitting at the examination instruments near the centre of the room. Suggest an appropriate setup for the Snellen test in this room.

## ANALYTICAL PROBLEMS

### MIRRORS

**P–18.1.** When you look at your face in a small bathroom mirror from a distance of 40 cm, the upright image is twice as tall as your face. What is the focal length of the mirror?

**P–18.2.** A concave spherical mirror has a radius of curvature of 20 cm. Locate the images for object distances as given below. In each case, state whether the image is real or virtual and upright or inverted, and find the magnification. (a) $p = 10$ cm; (b) $p = 20$ cm; (c) $p = 40$ cm.

**P–18.3.** Construct the images for the three objects shown in Fig. 18.40.

(a)

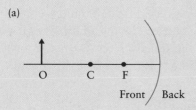

(b)

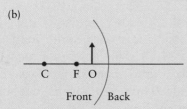

(c)

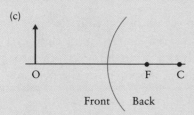

**FIGURE 18.40**

### REFRACTION

**P–18.4.** A light ray enters a layer of water at an angle of 36° with the vertical. What is the angle between the refracted light ray and the vertical?

**P–18.5.** A light ray strikes a flat, $L = 2.0$-cm-thick block of glass ($n = 1.5$) in Fig. 18.41 at an angle of $\theta = 30°$ with the normal. (a) Find the angles of incidence and refraction at each surface. (b) Calculate the lateral shift of the light ray, $d$.

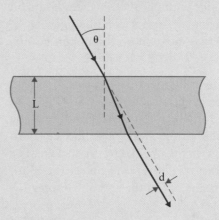

**FIGURE 18.41**

**P–18.6.** In Fig. 18.42, an ultrasonic beam enters an organ (grey) at $\theta = 50°$, then reflects off a tumour (green) in the surrounding organ and leaves the organ with a lateral shift $L = 12$ cm. If the speed of the wave is 10% less in the organ than in the medium above, determine the depth of the tumour below the organ's surface.

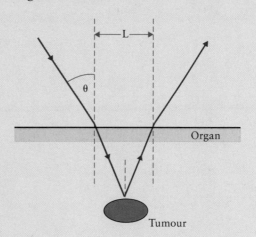

**FIGURE 18.42**

**P–18.7.** A light ray travels through air and then strikes the surface of mineral oil at an angle of 23.1° with the normal to the surface. What is the angle of refraction if the light ray travels at $2.17 \times 10^8$ m/s through the oil?

**P–18.8.** A light source at the bottom of a 4.0-m-deep water pool sends a light ray up at an angle so that the ray strikes the surface 2.0 m from the point straight above the light source. What is the emerging ray's angle with the normal in air?

**P–18.9.** The laws for refraction and reflection are the same for light and sound. If a sound wave in air approaches a water surface at an angle of 12° with the normal of the water surface, what is the angle with the normal of the refracted wave in water? Use for the speed of sound in air 340 m/s and 1510 m/s in water.

**P–18.10.** A slab of ice with parallel surfaces floats on water. What is the angle of refraction of a light ray in water if the light ray is incident on the upper ice surface with an angle of 30° to the normal?

**P–18.11.** A light ray is incident from air onto a glass surface with index of refraction $n = 1.56$. Find the angle of incidence for which the corresponding angle of refraction is one-half the angle of incidence. Both angles are defined with the normal to the surface. For mathematical operations with sine terms see the Math Review on "Trigonometry" at the end of Chapter 17.

## LENSES

**P–18.12.** Construct the images for the three lenses shown in Fig. 18.43. Note that the third case is a diverging lens.

(a)

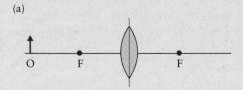

(b)

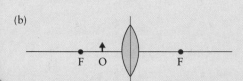

(c)

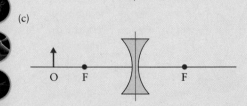

**FIGURE 18.43**

**P–18.13.** A converging lens has a focal length $f = 20.0$ cm. Locate the images for the object distances given below. For each case state whether the image is real or virtual and upright or inverted, and find the magnification. (a) 40 cm; (b) 20 cm; (c) 10 cm.

**P–18.14.** Where must an object be placed to have no magnification ($|M| = 1.0$) for a converging lens of focal length $f = 12.0$ cm?

**P–18.15.** Fig. 18.44 shows an object at the left, a lens at the centre (vertical dashed line), and a concave mirror at the right. The respective focal lengths and the distance between lens and mirror are indicated at the bottom of the figure. Construct the image that forms after light from the object has passed through the lens and has reflected off the mirror.

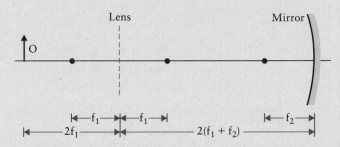

**FIGURE 18.44**

**P–18.16.** An object is placed in front of a converging lens with $f = 2.44$ cm. The lens forms an image of the object 12.9 cm from the object. How far is the lens from the object if the image is (a) real, or (b) virtual?

## EXAMPLES FROM OPTOMETRY AND OPHTHALMOLOGY

**P–18.17.** A contact lens is made of plastic with an index of refraction of $n = 1.58$. The lens has a focal length of $f = +25.0$ cm, and its inner surface has a radius of curvature of $+18.0$ mm. What is the radius of curvature of the outer surface?

**P–18.18.** A person can see an object in focus only if the object is no farther than 30 cm from the right eye and 50 cm from the left eye. Write a prescription for the refractive powers $\Re$ (in diopters) for the person's corrective lenses.

**P–18.19.** The near point of an eye is 100 cm. A corrective lens is to be used to allow this eye to focus clearly on objects 25 cm in front of it. (a) What should be the focal length of the lens? (b) What is the refractive power $\Re$ of the lens?

**P–18.20.** A person who can see clearly when objects are between 30 cm and 1.5 m from the eye is to be fitted with bifocals. (a) The upper portion of the corrective lenses is designed such that the person can see distant objects clearly. What refractive power $\Re$ does that part of the lenses have? (b) The lower portion of the lenses has to enable the person to see objects comfortably at 25 cm. What refractive power $\Re$ does that part of the lenses have?

**P–18.21.** The near point of a patient's eye is 75.0 cm. (a) What should be the refractive power $\Re$ of a corrective lens prescribed to enable the patient to clearly see an object at 25.0 cm? (b) When using the new corrective glasses, the patient can see an object clearly at 26.0 cm but not at 25.0 cm. By how many diopters did the lens grinder miss the prescription?

# SUMMARY

### DEFINITIONS

- Focal length of a spherical mirror: $f = R/2$; $R$ is the radius of curvature of the mirror.

- Magnification of a spherical mirror or thin lens:

$$M = \frac{h_I}{h_O}$$

with $h_I$ the height of the image and $h_O$ the height of the object.

- Index of refraction $n$ (Snell's law; the incoming ray must travel through a vacuum or air):

$$\frac{\sin \alpha_{incoming}}{\sin \beta} = n$$

with $\alpha_{incoming}$ and $\beta$ the respective angles of the light ray with the normal.

- Refractive power
  - for a single interface: $\Re = \Delta n/R$
  - for a thin lens: $\Re = 1/f$

### UNITS

- Refractive power $\Re$: dpt (diopters) $= \text{m}^{-1}$

### LAWS

- Reflection, flat mirror:

$$\alpha_{incoming} = \alpha_{outgoing}$$

where angles are measured to the normal of the mirror surface.

- Law of refraction at the interface between media 1 and 2:

$$n_1 \cdot \sin \alpha_1 = n_2 \cdot \sin \alpha_2$$

where angles are measured to the normal of the interface.

- Mirror equation and thin-lens formula:

$$\frac{1}{f} = \frac{1}{p} + \frac{1}{q}$$

where $p$ is the object distance and $q$ is the image distance.

- Magnification of spherical mirror or thin lens:

$$M = -\frac{q}{p} = \frac{f}{f - p} = \frac{f - q}{f}$$

- Law of refraction for a spherical interface between media 1 and 2:

$$\frac{n_1}{p} + \frac{n_2}{q} = \frac{n_2 - n_1}{R}$$

- Magnification of a spherical interface between media 1 and 2:

$$M = \frac{h_I}{h_O} = -\frac{n_1 \cdot q}{n_2 \cdot p}$$

# CHAPTER 19

# THE MICROBIAL WORLD
## Microscopy

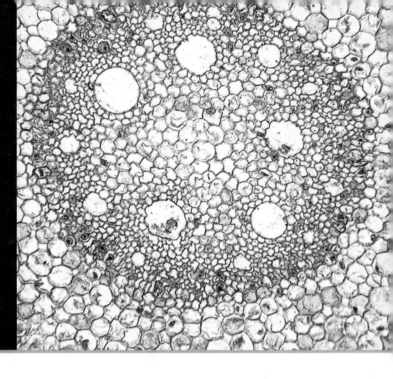

The geometric optics concepts introduced in the previous chapter are applied to the magnifying glass and the compound microscope. To properly quantify the magnification of a microscope, the observer's eye has to be included as part of the optical setup. This leads to the definition of the angular magnification. Variable combinations of eyepieces and objective lenses are studied for their total angular magnification, which is the product of the angular magnification of the eyepiece and the magnification of the objective lens.

No other technological development influenced the early history of biology and medicine as much as the development of the microscope. The first light microscopes were introduced in the late 1600s. Modern instruments, such as the one shown in Fig. 19.1, allow us to see small cells such as human erythrocytes and bacteria. Later in the chapter we discuss electron microscopes, which improve the size resolution to 1 nm. The first electron microscope was developed by Ernst August Ruska in 1932. A contemporary instrument allows us to see viruses, proteins, and even amino acids. We need more powerful instruments, such as the scanning tunnelling microscope, to see single atoms.

For biologists or medical researchers, microscopes like the one shown in Fig. 19.1 are an essential tool used on a daily basis. It is likely you will develop a great level of familiarity with this instrument. It is dangerous, though, to confuse familiarity with a good understanding of technical specifications and limitations: microscopes can easily deceive you, as many examples of faulty discoveries, particularly during the 19th century, illustrate. While modern instruments are designed to minimize the occurrence of artefacts that caused such mistakes, it is the user's knowledge of the physical properties of the instrument that can prevent unwarranted embarrassment. We build a solid foundation of the properties of the light microscope in this chapter, using the optics concepts developed in the previous chapter. Some issues, such as diffraction effects, spectral resolution, and Abbe's theory of the resolving power of a microscope, are not included as their discussion requires more advanced concepts from wave optics. For these, the reader should consult advanced texts on optics.

# From Lenses to Microscopes

In the previous chapter, we saw that a single lens allows us to obtain magnified images. The formula describing the magnification of a single lens was introduced:

$$M = -\frac{q}{p} = \frac{f}{f-p} = \frac{f-q}{f} \qquad [1]$$

with $p$ the object distance, $q$ the image distance, and $f$ the focal length. To obtain a magnified image ($M > 1$), the object must be closer to the lens than the image, which is possible when $p - f < f$ or $p < 2 \cdot f$: an object placed closer than twice the focal length

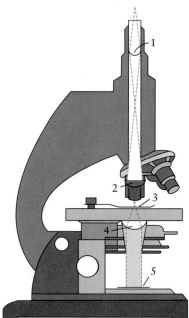

**FIGURE 19.1**

(a) Photograph of a modern light microscope. (b) In a light microscope, visible light from a light source (5) is focussed on a sample (3) by a condenser lens (4). This light is used to form an image that is magnified by an objective lens (2) and an eyepiece (1).

generates a magnified image. Note that the magnification in Eq. [1] is only a function of $f$, $p$, and $q$—it does not depend on the position of the observer! Thus, the magnification is a property of the physical lens but does not tell us what an observer actually sees.

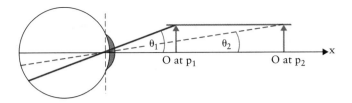

**FIGURE 19.2**

When the observer's eye becomes part of the optical system, we define an angular magnification based on the angle under which an object appears to the observer. The figure shows a geometrical sketch to illustrate that the apparent size of an object $O$ varies with its distance from the observer's eye.

A microscope, in turn, is not just a device, but also a process that allows the observer to obtain a particular outcome: to see an object larger than it is. Thus, the step from lens to microscope requires us to include the observer to quantify the apparent size of an object. This is illustrated in Fig. 19.2. The position of the observer defines the angle $\theta$ between two light rays reaching the eye from opposite ends of the object. The figure compares the size of the image on the retina for two identical objects, one at object distance $p_1$ and the other one at object distance $p_2$. The figure defines the **angular magnification** $m$:

$$m = \frac{\theta}{\theta_0} \quad [2]$$

in which $\theta_0$ is the angle subtended by the object when it is placed at $p = 25$ cm, which we define as the **standard near point** $s_0$ of a healthy adult eye.

*The angular magnification is the ratio of the angle subtended by a given object and the angle subtended by the same object when placed at the standard near point $s_0$.*

Based on this definition, an object you hold at a distance of 25 cm from your eye has an angular magnification of $m = 1$. Any object farther away appears smaller ($m < 1$), while any object closer appears bigger ($m > 1$).

The justification for defining the angular magnification as a new parameter is that this is the quantity in which we are ultimately interested. However, it also illustrates the limitations of our ability to see things larger than they are with the naked eye. Even the juvenile eye cannot focus on an object closer than about 7 cm before the eye. We can easily illustrate this with a self-test: touch your nose with the ball of your right thumb and try to see the palm of your hand in focus.

Using a small object of size $h_O$ in Fig. 19.3, e.g., a human hair, we determine the maximum angular

magnification that a juvenile eye can achieve relative to the eye of the standard man. We start with the definition in Eq. [2]. For a small object, the two angles are small, allowing us to use the approximation $\tan \theta = \theta$. The trigonometric terms are analyzed from Fig. 19.3 as $\tan \theta = h_O/p$ and $\tan \theta_0 = h_O/p_0$. We use $p_0 = s_0$; i.e., the reference object distance is the standard near point:

$$m = \frac{\theta}{\theta_0} = \frac{\tan \theta}{\tan \theta_0} = \frac{p_0}{p} = \frac{s_0}{p} = \frac{25 \text{ cm}}{7 \text{ cm}} = 3.6 \quad [3]$$

We are, of course, not satisfied with this result, particularly not for research in the life sciences. An entire world exists at microscopic-length scales we cannot see, as illustrated in Fig. 19.4. The lower limit of objects we can see without optical instruments is

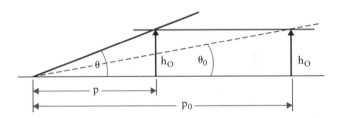

**FIGURE 19.3**

Sketch illustrating the angular magnification of the human eye.

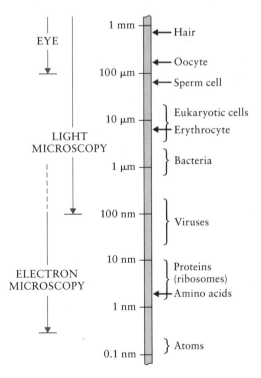

**FIGURE 19.4**

Size range of typical objects of biological interest. The vertical range indicators at the left-hand side illustrate what is visible with the eye, a light microscope, and an electron microscope.

about 100 $\mu$m (e.g., a human oocyte). Below, first we discuss a simple magnifying glass (with angular magnification of $m = 5$–$10$), and then we discuss the light microscope. These allow us to see objects as small as 200 nm, a value determined by the wavelengths of visible light.

---

**Concept Question 19.1**

Fig. 19.2 shows an observer's eye representing the optical system. The figure is used to define the angular magnification. What fact about the figure did we use for that definition? (A) That the object at $p_1$ is larger than the object at $p_2$. (B) That angles $\theta_1$ and $\theta_2$ are the same. (C) That the object moves back and forth between positions $p_1$ and $p_2$. (D) That we use the same object at $p_1$ and $p_2$. (E) None of the above.

ANSWER: Choice (D). The same object is required to make a relative statement at two distances; however, there is no need to move an actual object back and forth because Fig. 19.2 can be viewed as a Gedanken experiment, i.e., an experiment that we do only on paper.

---

**Concept Question 19.2**

Fig. 19.4 shows that a standard man can see objects as small as 100 $\mu$m. When the same person uses a microscope with an angular magnification of $m = 1000$, the person can observe objects as small as (choose closest value): (A) 100 $\mu$m (e.g., an oocyte), (B) 50 $\mu$m (e.g., a sperm cell), (C) 1 $\mu$m (e.g., an average bacterium), (D) 100 nm (e.g., a large virus), (E) 10 nm (e.g., large biomolecules, such as DNA).

ANSWER: Choice (D). We extend Fig. 19.3 as shown in Fig. 19.5, which includes additional geometric details. Using Fig. 19.5 means that we interpret the use of the

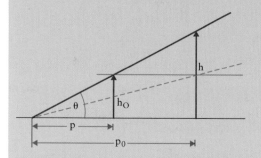

**FIGURE 19.5**
Sketch extending Fig. 19.3 with additional geometric details.

microscope as if it allows us to move the object much closer to the eye. How close the object would have to be is calculated from Eq. [3]:

$$p = \frac{p_0}{m} = \frac{25 \text{ cm}}{1000} = 2.5 \times 10^{-4} \text{ m} \qquad [4]$$

This distance is obviously not practical, and indicates why a microscope is needed. However, based on Fig. 19.5 we can further rewrite the ratio $p_0/p$ based on the similarity of the two triangles shown:

$$\frac{h_0}{p} = \frac{h}{p_0} \qquad [5]$$

We substitute $p$ from Eq. [4] in Eq. [5]:

$$h_0 = \frac{h}{m} = \frac{100 \ \mu\text{m}}{1000} = 100 \text{ nm} \qquad [6]$$

## The Magnifying Glass

As shown earlier, a lens produces an image larger than the object size if the object is placed closer than twice the focal length. Using Eq. [1], we see that the object has to be placed very close to the focal point to obtain a large magnification $M$. Thus, we arrange the lens such that $p \approx f$. Next we include the observer; i.e., we determine the angular magnification $m$ for this arrangement. We illustrate this approach assuming that the observer looks at the object as if it is at infinite distance (with a relaxed eye).

In Fig. 19.6 an object $O$ of size $h_O$ is placed at the focal point $F$ of a lens, because this causes light rays emerging from the object to travel parallel behind the lens. This simulates the case where the object is at infinite distance from the observer's eye. More specifically, the lens forms an intermediate image at infinite distance, which in turn is the object for the observer's eye. Thus, the observer looks at the intermediate

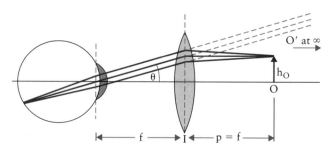

**FIGURE 19.6**
A magnifying glass is used to observe an object $O$ with relaxed eyes. The lens simulates an object $O'$ at infinite distance.

image with relaxed eyes. The angular magnification is determined from Fig. 19.6: $\theta$ is the angle under which the object appears for the observer. We further need the distance of the lens from the eye. This distance is the focal length of the magnifying glass, $f$, because a light ray from the top of the object that travels parallel to the optical axis crosses the optical axis at a distance $f$ behind the lens. We use the small-angle approximation $\theta = \tan \theta$ and find $\theta = h_O/f$. We substitute this angle in the definition of the angular magnification. For the angle $\theta_0$ we use the standard man looking at the object with the naked eye:

$$m = \frac{\theta}{\theta_0} = \frac{h_O/f}{h_O/s_0} = \frac{s_0}{f} \qquad [7]$$

The shorter the focal length $f$ of the magnifying lens the larger the angular magnification.

An observer with eyes focussed can do better than Eq. [7]. In this case, the object is placed closer to the lens, $p < f$, and the intermediate image is at a finite distance. The most the observer can do, though, is to bring the intermediate image to his/her near point at $s_0$. A full calculation yields $m = 1 + s_0/f$ for this case, which is called the **maximum angular magnification**. Example 19.1 illustrates that using focussed eyes with a magnifying lens does not provide a notable improvement, and is therefore neglected in the further discussions.

## ● EXAMPLE 19.1

(a) What is the angular magnification when an observer with relaxed eyes uses a lens with focal length $f = 5$ cm to observe an object? (b) By what factor does an observer with a focussed eye increase the angular magnification at most?

*Solution to part (a):* We use Eq. [7] for the angular magnification:

$$m = \frac{25 \text{ cm}}{5 \text{ cm}} = 5.0 \qquad [8]$$

*Solution to part (b):* As expected, the magnifying glass works better for the relaxed eye:

$$m_{max} = 1 + \frac{25 \text{ cm}}{5 \text{ cm}} = 6.0 \qquad [9]$$

However, this is only a factor of 6/5 = 1.2, or 20%, better than the observation with relaxed eyes. Instead of focussing the eye all day with a magnifying glass, biologists are better served using more powerful microscope arrangements, as discussed in the next two sections.

# Microscopes
## Optical Compound Microscope

To achieve angular magnifications larger than a value of about $m = 10$, a single magnifying lens is no longer sufficient, and compound microscopes are used that have two or more lenses. An instrument with two lenses is sketched in Fig. 19.7. It combines an **objective lens**, which has a very short focal length of $f_O < 1$ cm, and an **ocular lens (eyepiece)**, which has a focal length $f_E$ of a few centimetres. The two lenses are separated by a distance $L$ with $L \gg f_O, f_E$. The instrument allows the observer to look with the eyepiece at the image of the objective lens; i.e., $I_O = O_E$. The small object that is to be viewed is positioned just outside the focal length of the objective lens. This generates a real, enlarged image $I_O$ far from the lens. This image lies within the focal distance of the eyepiece. Therefore, treating the image of the objective lens as the object for the eyepiece leads to a virtual image $I_E$. The eye then looks at the image $I_E$. Note that several lines in Fig. 19.7 are drawn to illustrate the construction of the two images, $I_O$ and $I_E$. As for single lenses in the previous chapter, the construction is based on three light rays, one defined by the optical axis. The other two emerge from the top of the object: one ray is incident on the lens parallel to the optical axis, and one ray is incident through its focal point.

We determine the **total angular magnification** for this arrangement from two contributions: the magnification of the objective lens, $M_O$, and the angular magnification of the eyepiece, $m_E$:

$$m_{total} = M_O \cdot m_E \qquad [10]$$

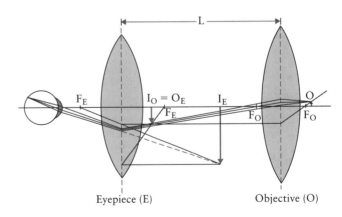

**FIGURE 19.7**

A typical compound microscope with objective lens and eyepiece at a distance $L$ that coincides with the length of the tube of the microscope. The final image $I_E$ is constructed with the same three light rays we used previously for single lenses and mirrors.

Note that we use the magnification for the objective lens because the size of the image $I_O$ does not depend on the position of the observer. In turn, the angular magnification of the eyepiece is used since we want to know the total angular magnification seen by the observer. For $m_E$, the value for the relaxed eye is used in the literature. We find from Eqs. [1] and [7]:

$$(I) \quad M_O = -\frac{q_O}{p_O} \cong -\frac{L}{f_O}$$

$$(II) \quad m_E = \frac{s_0}{f_E} \quad [11]$$

with $s_0 = 25$ cm for the near point of the standard man. The length of the microscope tube in formula (I) is introduced as a simplification, because neither the image nor the object distance of the objective lens is easily quantified for Fig. 19.7. We find the first formula in Eq. [11] by inserting the approximation $q_O - f_O \cong L$ in Eq. [1]. $M_O$ is negative, since the image of the objective lens is inverted. The total angular magnification of the two-lens arrangement is then:

$$m_{total} = M_O \cdot m_E \cong -\frac{L}{f_O} \cdot \frac{s_0}{f_E} \quad [12]$$

Both relations in Eq. [12] can be used to calculate the total angular magnification of a compound microscope with two lenses. As illustrated in Examples 19.2 and 19.3, the second, approximate formula is much faster to apply.

## Concept Question 19.3

The total angular magnification quoted for a compound microscope does not depend on the following parameter: (A) the distance from the objective lens to the eyepiece, (B) the focal length of the objective lens, (C) the focal length of the eyepiece, (D) the near point of the observer.

ANSWER: Choice (D). Note that $s_0$ is the near point of the standard man, not of any particular person using the microscope.

## EXAMPLE 19.2

A microscope has two interchangeable objective lenses. One has a focal length $f_O = 20$ mm, and the other has a focal length $f_O = 2$ mm. Also available are two eyepieces with focal lengths $f_E = 2.5$ cm and $f_E = 5$ cm. If the length of the microscope is 18 cm, what range of total angular magnifications is available?

*Solution:* We substitute $f_O = 2.0$ cm or $f_O = 0.2$ cm, $L = 18.0$ cm, and $f_E = 2.5$ cm or $f_E = 5.0$ cm in the approximate form of Eq. [12], using $s_0 = 25$ cm. This yields four angular magnifications, $m_{total} = -54, -99, -540,$ and $-990$; i.e., the microscope offers total angular magnifications between 50 and 1000.

## EXAMPLE 19.3

The length of a microscope tube is 15.0 cm. The focal length of the objective lens is 1.0 cm and the focal length of the eyepiece is 2.5 cm. What is the total angular magnification of the microscope if the observer's eye is relaxed? (a) Calculate the exact result using Eq. [12], and (b) calculate the approximate result using Eq. [12].

*Solution to part (a):* To apply the exact formula in Eq. [12], we need to determine the angular magnification of the eyepiece, $m_E$, and the magnification of the objective lens, $M_O$. The parameter $m_E$ is obtained from Eq. [7] using the focal length of the eyepiece, $f_E$:

$$m_E = \frac{s_0}{f_E} = \frac{25.0 \text{ cm}}{2.5 \text{ cm}} = 10 \quad [13]$$

The magnification of the objective lens is defined by the object and image distances of the lens, $M_O = -q_O/p_O$. Both of these terms have to be calculated separately. We begin with the image distance of the objective lens. For the compound microscope, $q_O$ is related to the object distance of the eyepiece via $q_O = L - p_E$, in which $L$ is the distance between the two lenses in the microscope. $p_E$ is determined from the thin-lens formula for the eyepiece (note that $q_E = \infty$ because the observer looks at the image with a relaxed eye):

$$\frac{1}{p_E} = \frac{1}{f_E} - \frac{1}{q_E} = \frac{1}{2.5 \text{ cm}} - \frac{1}{\infty} \quad [14]$$

which yields:

$$p_E = 2.5 \text{ cm} \quad [15]$$

and

$$q_O = L - p_E = 12.5 \text{ cm} \quad [16]$$

The object distance $p_O$ is then found from the thin-lens formula applied to the objective lens:

$$\frac{1}{p_O} = \frac{1}{f_O} - \frac{1}{q_O} = \frac{1}{1.0 \text{ cm}} - \frac{1}{12.5 \text{ cm}} \quad [17]$$

which yields:

$$p_O = 1.09 \text{ cm} \quad [18]$$

We know now all the data needed to determine the magnification of the objective lens. Note that we do not calculate the angular magnification of the objective lens, as the observer is not involved in the process of its image formation. We find with Eq. [1]:

$$M_O = -\frac{q_O}{p_O} = -\frac{12.5 \text{ cm}}{1.09 \text{ cm}} = -11.5 \quad [19]$$

Thus, the total angular magnification of the microscope is:

$$m_{total} = M_O \cdot m_E = -11.5 \cdot 10.0 = -115 \quad [20]$$

*Solution to part (b):* The problem becomes a simple substitution problem when applying Eq. [12] in its approximate form:

$$m_{total} = -\frac{L}{f_O}\frac{s_0}{f_E}$$

$$= -\frac{(0.15 \text{ m})(0.25 \text{ m})}{(0.01 \text{ m})(0.025 \text{ m})} = -150 \quad [21]$$

The difference between the results in Eqs. [20] and [21] illustrates the extent to which the second approach yields an approximate result. For most applications, the result in Eq. [21] is sufficient.

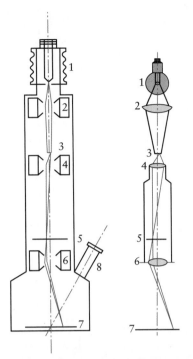

# Electron Microscope

The light microscope becomes useless when the object size is on the order of the wavelength of visible light; i.e., $h_O \le 200$ nm. To observe even smaller objects, a microscope would be needed that uses light of smaller wavelength than visible light, e.g., X-rays. This is not a practical solution. A significant improvement is, however, achieved when using **electron beams**. We show in Chapter 22 that electrons can be treated as waves under certain conditions. The electron microscope is a setup that exploits the wave properties of electrons. Louis Victor de Broglie calculated the wavelength of electrons based on their kinetic energy; for electrons of energy 300 eV he found 0.07 nm, and even shorter when the energy of the electrons is further increased.

With equivalent ray manipulation components available, the electron microscope and the light microscope are compared in Fig. 19.8(a). In the electron microscope, like the instrument shown in Fig. 19.8(b), an electron beam is generated in the electron source (1), then electrically extracted from the source and focussed onto the objective plane. After passing through the object (3), which must be very thin, the electron beam forms an initial image that is then focussed onto a fluorescent screen (7) to produce

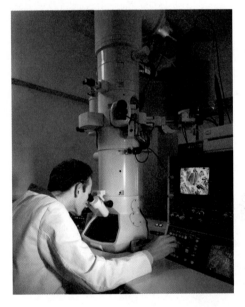

**FIGURE 19.8**

(a) Comparison of an electron microscope (left) and a light microscope (right). The numbers indicate corresponding components in both systems: (1) the radiation source, (2) a condenser lens to focus the beam on the object for maximum illumination, (3) the object, (4) the objective lens, (5) the intermediate image, labelled $I_0$ in Fig. 19.7, (6) the eyepiece, and (7) the recording film or fluorescent screen. The electron microscope has an additional magnifying glass (8) for observation of the screen. (b) Photograph of a modern electron microscope.

the final image. The observer uses a standard light microscope (8) to look at the fluorescent screen. This is possible because the electrons striking the ZnS or ZnSe coating of the screen cause visible light emission in the same way that light is emitted from a TV screen.

# MULTIPLE CHOICE AND CONCEPTUAL QUESTIONS

## MAGNIFYING GLASSES

**Q–19.1.** A person with a near point of 35 cm tries to see a text with small print better by bringing the page closer to the eye. The person will achieve what angular magnification? (A) none; (B) $m = 1$ (no gain); (C) $m < 1$ (the person does worse than the standard man); (D) $m > 1$ but $m < 2$—a moderate angular magnification is achieved; (E) $m \gg 1$ (for this person, this is the way to go to see small objects).

**Q–19.2.** The optic nerve and the brain invert the image formed on the retina. Why then do we not see everything upside down?

**Q–19.3.** Assume you use a converging lens as a magnifying glass. Initially, you hold the lens far from a page with small print. Then you move the lens closer and closer to the text until the lens lies on the page, as shown in Fig. 19.9. What do you observe? (A) The text is always upright, no matter how far the lens is held. (B) The text is initially inverted, then blurs and becomes upright. (C) The text is initially upright, then blurs and becomes inverted. (D) When the magnifying glass is held far enough from the page the text will run from right to left.

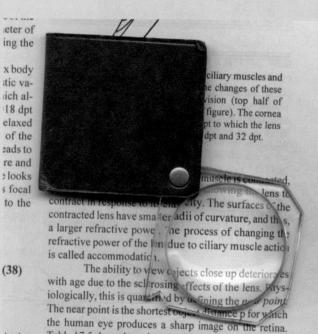

**FIGURE 19.9**

A magnifying lens lying on an open book page.

## COMPOUND MICROSCOPES

**Q–19.4.** Which of the following statements about the angular magnification is correct? (A) The angular magnification can be calculated for an optical device without taking the observer's eye into account. (B) A larger angular magnification can be obtained when the observer uses the optical device with a relaxed eye. (C) The eye of a juvenile usually has the same angular magnification as the eye of a standard man. (D) The angular magnification of a compound microscope depends on the near point of the particular person using the microscope. (E) Two different values for the angular magnification result when we distinguish between an observer with a relaxed eye and one with a focussed eye.

**Q–19.5.** Which of the following total angular magnifications $m_{total}$ can be selected with a compound microscope with an eyepiece of angular magnification $m_E = 20$ and three switchable objective lenses with magnifications $M_O$ of 10, 30, and 50? (A) $m_{total} = 100$, (B) $m_{total} = 300$, (C) $m_{total} = 500$, (D) $m_{total} = 700$, (E) none of the four total angular magnifications above can be selected with this microscope.

**Q–19.6.** What happens if the object in Fig. 19.7 shrinks to one-twentieth of its current size? (A) The image the observer sees becomes larger. (B) The image the observer sees becomes smaller. (C) The observer can see only a part of the object magnified. (D) The microscope cannot produce an image of the object. (E) No light-ray construction is possible, as shown for the larger object in Fig. 19.7.

**Q–19.7.** Most commercial microscopes have an additional lens, called the condenser lens, which is located between the light source and the object (see (4) in Fig. 19.1(b)). What does this lens do? (A) Enhance the overall angular magnification. (B) Invert the image so that we don't see everything upside down. (C) Substitute for the eyepiece when the eyepiece becomes defective due to poor upkeep of the instrument. (D) Focus light from a light source on the object. (E) Illuminate the image for faster photographic exposure.

**Q–19.8.** We study again the condenser lens discussed in Q–19.7. What focal length would you choose for this lens? (A) It doesn't matter as long as the lens is transparent. (B) For a microscope of length 20 cm, we would choose a focal length of about 20 cm to focus the light from the light source into the eye. (C) A focal length would be best that focusses the light of the light source at the intermediate image, i.e., the image that we observe through the eyepiece. (D) We would use a short focal length to focus the light from the light source on the object.

**Q–19.9.** You are unhappy with the overall magnification you achieve with your homemade microscope. Which alteration will improve the results? (A) Shorten the distance between the objective lens and the eyepiece. (B) Exchange the objective lens for a lens with a larger focal length. (C) Exchange the eyepiece for a lens with a larger focal length. (D) Loosen up and look through the microscope with a relaxed eye. (E) None of the above.

**Q–19.10.** Two thin lenses, one with focal length $f$ and the other with focal length $-f$, are placed very close to each other along the optical axis. Their combined effect is the same as if a thin lens of the following focal length replaces them: (A) $f_{combined} = 0$; (B) $f_{combined} = f/2$; (C) $f_{combined} = 2 \cdot f$; (D) $f_{combined} = -2 \cdot f$; (E) $f_{combined}$ is infinite.

**Q–19.11.** We study two thin lenses, where lens 1 with $f_1 = 15$ cm is placed a distance of $L = 35$ cm to the left of lens 2 with $f_2 = 10$ cm. An object is then placed 50 cm to the left of lens 1. What is the magnification of the final image taken with respect to the object? *Note:* The magnification you determine is not an angular magnification. (A) $M = 0.6$, (B) $M = 1.0$ (no magnification), (C) $M = 1.2$, (D) $M = 2.4$, (E) $M = 3.6$.

**Q–19.12.** An optical compound microscope has an objective lens with $f_O = 0.8$ cm and an eyepiece with $f_E = 4.0$ cm. If the microscope is 15 cm long, what is the total angular magnification? Choose the closest answer. (A) 3.5, (B) 6.5, (C) 50, (D) 120, (E) 500.

# ANALYTICAL PROBLEMS

## MAGNIFYING GLASSES

**P–19.1.** A magnifying glass is used to examine the structural details of a human hair. The hair is held 3.5 cm in front of the magnifying glass, and the image is 25.0 cm from the lens. (a) What is the focal length of the magnifying glass? (b) What angular magnification is achieved?

## OPTICAL COMPOUND MICROSCOPE

**P–19.2.** Two converging lenses that have focal lengths of $f_1 = 10.0$ cm and $f_2 = 20.0$ cm are placed $L = 50$ cm apart. The final image is shown in Fig. 19.10. (a) How far to the left of the first lens is the object placed if $l = 31$ cm? (b) What is the combined magnification (not the total angular magnification in this case!) of the two lenses using the same data as in part (a)?

**P–19.3.** A microscope has an objective lens with $f = 16.22$ mm and an eyepiece with $f = 9.5$ mm. With the length of the microscope's barrel set at 29.0 cm, the diameter of an erythrocyte's image subtends an angle of 1.43 mrad with the eye. If the final image distance is 29.0 cm from the eyepiece, what is the actual diameter of the erythrocyte? *Hint:* Start with the size of the final image. Then use the thin-lens formula for each lens to find their combined magnification. Use this magnification to calculate the object size in the final step.

**P–19.4.** Fig. 19.11 shows two converging lenses placed $L_1 = 20$ cm apart. Their focal lengths are $f_1 = 10.0$ cm and $f_2 = 20.0$ cm. (a) Where is the final image

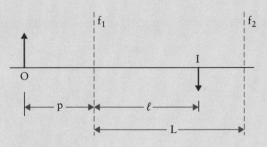

**FIGURE 19.10**

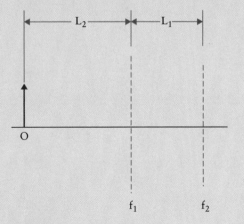

**FIGURE 19.11**

located for an object that is $L_2 = 30$ cm in front of the first lens? (b) What is the total magnification of the lens system? *Note:* Do not calculate a total angular magnification in this case, since we are not dealing with a microscope.

**P–19.5.** An object is located 20 cm to the left of a converging lens of focal length 25 cm. A diverging lens with focal length 10 cm is located 25 cm to the right of the converging lens. Find the position of the final image.

## SUMMARY

### DEFINITIONS

- Standard near point: $s_0 = 25$ cm.
- Angular magnification: $m = \theta/\theta_0$, with $\theta$ the angle subtended by the object and $\theta_0$ the angle subtended by the same object placed at the standard near point.

### LAWS

- Angular magnification $m$ of a lens
  - for a relaxed eye:

$$m = \frac{s_0}{f}$$

- for an eye focussed at the near point:

$$m = 1 + \frac{s_0}{f}$$

- Total angular magnification of a compound microscope:

$$m_{\text{total}} = M_O \cdot m_E \cong -\frac{L}{f_O} \cdot \frac{s_0}{f_E}$$

in which index O stands for objective lens and index E stands for eyepiece. $L$ is the distance between both lenses.

# CHAPTER 20

# COLOUR VISION
## Magnetism and the Electromagnetic Spectrum

Colours are a physiological measure of the various wavelengths in the visible part of the electromagnetic spectrum. This spectrum consists of all waves that travel in a vacuum with the speed of light carried by their own electric and magnetic fields.

The magnetic force is observed when moving electric charges interact. It is proportional to the two currents for a set of parallel conductors. The force is also inversely proportional to the distance between the conductors. The magnetic field is obtained from the magnetic force by redefining one of the currents as a test current; thus, a single conductor carrying an electric current possesses a magnetic field. The magnetic field resumes its simplest possible form (constant direction and magnitude) inside a solenoid.

When charges oscillate along an antenna, alternating magnetic fields (when the charges move) and electric fields (when the charges are separated, as in a dipole) cause electromagnetic waves that allow energy to propagate radially away from the antenna. Electromagnetic waves are transverse waves, as the propagation direction is perpendicular to both electric and magnetic fields. The electric field vector cannot oscillate across an interface, allowing light to be polarized after refraction. The visible part of the electromagnetic spectrum constitutes the major fraction of the light reaching the surface of Earth from the Sun (irradiance). It is explained with the blackbody model of radiation and the absorption occurring in Earth's atmosphere.

Two paintings of the Japanese Bridge by Claude Monet (1840–1926): (top) *Le bassin aux nymphéas*, 1900 (Museum of Fine Arts, Boston, USA); (bottom) *Le pont japonais*, 1923 (Musée Marmottan, Paris, France).

We have learned a great deal about the manipulation of light in the two previous chapters. We saw how it travels to the observer, either as a straight light ray or re-directed with reflecting mirrors or refracting surfaces and lenses. The simple concepts of ray optics allowed us also to follow light through the eye of the observer, from entering the cornea to forming an image on the retina. At no point in the whole discussion did we need to refer to colour, nor did we find anything that would allow us access to defining colours. Yet, colours matter to us as much as focussed vision.

A famous example of a human struggling with problems of colour vision is the French impressionist **Claude Monet** (1840–1926). He reported the first signs of cataracts in 1908, suffering thereafter from a steady deterioration of his eyesight. Two operations in 1923 had only partial success. During the later period of his life he chose a narrow number of motifs; from 1906 on he repeatedly painted water lilies and the Japanese bridge across the pond in his garden in Giverny, near Paris, France. Two paintings of the Japanese bridge are shown at the beginning of the chapter, one from 1900 and one from 1923. It is interesting to correlate changes in these paintings with his progressive vision impairment, which he described in detail in his diary.

The following are two excerpts from Monet's diary. He wrote in 1918: "I can no longer perceive colours with the same intensity, I do not paint light with the old accuracy. Red appears muddy, pink appears insipid. The intermediate tones escape me. Initially I tried to pretend all this doesn't happen to me. How often did I try to . . . recapture the freshness that has disappeared from my palette! It's a wasted effort. What I paint is more and more dark, like an old picture. When I compare my paintings now with my former work, I am seized by a frantic rage. I have slashed all my canvases with a knife." By about that time his eyesight had deteriorated to the point where the cataracts had discoloured his lenses in a yellow-brownish tint. Several dominantly yellowish paintings date from that period, like the second piece on the previous page.

Cataract surgery was done in early 1923 on his right eye only. However, his cataract glasses were of poor quality. Now he observed, "I see blue, but I no longer see red or yellow. This bothers me very much since I know that these colours exist. I know that there is red and yellow, a special green and a particular shade of violet on my palette, but I do not see them anymore as I saw them before. I only recall the colour impressions they gave me." Paintings dating from that period are predominantly blue.

Colour has not yet entered our discussion for two reasons:

- The concept of colour can be developed only with the wave model of light. The ray model of Chapter 18 allowed us to describe how light travels between different points in space. In the current chapter we will use the wave model to separate the various colour components of white light and discuss the properties of these components.

- We need wave optics also to explain the generation and detection of light; however, we have avoided these issues so far because they also require the corpuscle model of light and the atomic model of matter. Emission and absorption of light have to be postponed further until these fundamental concepts are introduced in Chapter 22.

We need to devote an entire chapter to the issue of colour because proceeding beyond the concepts of Chapters 18 and 19 in developing the field of optics meets with several challenges: First, the wave model of light is based on two fundamental physical disciplines, electricity and magnetism. Of these, we have discussed only electricity, in Chapters 13 and 14. Thus, an introduction to magnetism and the combination of electric and magnetic phenomena as electromagnetic waves has to precede our discussion of the wave properties of light. Second, in no other area of biophysics must we distinguish between the objective laws of physics and our subjective perception as carefully as in the case of interpreting the colour images formed on the retina. This is due to the experimentally inseparable physicochemical processes of image formation and light detection and the psychological process of interpretation by the brain. This point is illustrated with three self-tests:

- Fig. 20.1 shows a brownish pudding on a dish,
- Fig. 20.2 shows a thunderbolt striking from a cloud, and
- Fig. 20.3 shows a white fish in one of two adjacent fishbowls.

If you carefully follow the instructions below, you will become aware how each of these three simple images can irritate the interplay of physical vision and psychological "seeing" of a picture. We begin with the pudding. As kids most of us liked pudding, not just for its taste but also for the funny way in which it wobbles on a plate. Obviously, the ability to wobble should be limited to the real thing; a pudding in a picture cannot do that. Or can it? The following test works best in dimmed light. Hold the textbook at arm's length while

**FIGURE 20.1**

A brown pudding on a dish in front of a blue-green background. In dimmed light, hold the textbook at arm's length and move it left and right in a slow but steady motion. You should see the pudding wobble!

**FIGURE 20.3**

A red fish in one of two adjacent fishbowls. Hold the picture at usual reading distance from your eyes and focus on the fish in the bowl at the left. You need to do this for a while; a minute is recommended for the best effect. Then suddenly focus on the black dot in the empty fishbowl. For a split second you will see first a white fish and then bluish-green water around the fish.

**FIGURE 20.2**

A thunderbolt striking from a cloud. In dimmed light, hold the picture at usual reading distance and focus for a while on the blue sky left of the lightning bolt. Then let your eyes jump fast (a couple of jumps per second) back and forth to focus on the blue sky right or left of the lightning bolt. You should see the lightning bolt flash for each jump.

observing Fig. 20.1. Slowly move the book left and right (somewhere between 5 cm and 20 cm) about once every half-second to a second. You should now see the pudding wobble!

Of course, the pudding in the picture did not really wobble. This is an optical illusion based on the difference in colours, with the pudding a reddish-brown and the background a bluish-green. It works because vision physiology for different colours is not the same; in particular, our vision of red differs significantly from our vision of blue and green in that the eye needs much longer to switch to the next colour impression after it has seen red. This is usually not a handicap because the brain processes the signals for red differently than for the other colours. The pudding allows us to exploit this timing phenomenon.

That red vision is different from blue and green vision is further illustrated with Fig. 20.2, which shows a lightning bolt. Again, we need dimmed light. Hold the textbook at the usual reading distance and focus for a while on the blue sky left of the lightning bolt. Now let your eyes quickly jump back and forth, looking at the blue sky right and left of the lightning bolt. Do this with a few jumps per second. You should see the lightning bolt flash each time as if it were real.

What happens? Again, the eye quickly adjusts to seeing blue wherever blue occurs in your field of vision. However, it takes the retina a little longer to notice that red no longer occurs where there was red just an instant before. Thus, for a split second the retina sends a signal for red and blue to the brain where the image of the lightning bolt was formed just a moment ago. The brain adds the blue and red, which makes almost white—thus the flash. It's a flash because our colour vision is highly developed; optical illusions of this type work for only a very short instant until the eye and the brain have sorted out what image to communicate to your consciousness.

In an attempt to dismiss such irritating observations, one may blame the dimming of the light. But sure enough, such illusions also work in bright daylight. To convince you, let us look at Fig. 20.3, which shows a fish and two fishbowls. One fishbowl holds a fish, and one fishbowl is empty—right? Maybe not. Hold the textbook at the usual reading distance and focus on the eye of the fish in the bowl at the left. You need to stare for a while; a minute is recommended for the best effect. After a minute, suddenly look at the black dot in the empty fishbowl. Sure enough, there is a red fish: you see it for a split second. Even more amazingly, the bowl around the fish turns from white to bluish-green, as if suggesting real water.

When you observe a red area for a while the red-sensitive cones saturate, i.e., they become insensitive to red light. Switching vision then to a white area causes only the blue and green receptors to respond and to send a signal to the brain while the red receptor cannot respond to the red part of white light. This causes the previously red area in the left bowl to appear bluish-green in the right bowl. The brain corrects for this optical error of the eyes by adding a red impression to the image. It does this across the entire area of view, causing a red fish as the result of the addition of red to white.

Should we worry, therefore, which of all the things we think we see are in reality made up by our brain? Experience tells us no. After all, vision has been developed in a long evolutionary process to exploit the light that reaches us from our environment to give us an edge in the struggle for survival. Thus, we can safely assume that the glitches in the vision system are minimal. Indeed, the illusion in Fig. 20.3 works only because the picture contains a second, identical fishbowl and a black dot to define where to focus. In real life our eyes often move autonomously to prevent such an effect from fooling us.

Still, the three illusions in Figs. 20.1 to 20.3 should motivate us to investigate the issue of colour. After all, only once we have developed the concept of colour can we truly claim that we understand what we see.

# Anatomical Components of Colour Vision

We begin with the micro-anatomy of the **retina** to identify the detection systems of light. As shown in Fig. 20.4, light arriving at the retina passes through three layers of tissue to reach about 120 million **retinal rods** and 3–6 million **retinal cones**. These light receptors are embedded in the neuroepithelium just inside of Bruch's membrane, which is the barrier between the eye and the brain. The fact that we already identify two different types of light detectors means that there must be several parameters that characterize the incoming light.

The rods are sensitive only to the brightness of the light; thus, they produce a black and white picture. The cones in turn are colour-sensitive. In 1807, Thomas Young postulated that the retina must

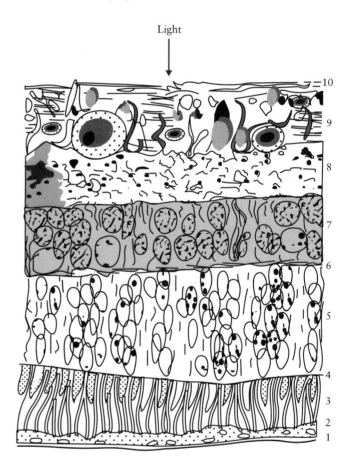

**FIGURE 20.4**

Cross-section of the retina. (1) Bruch's membrane, which is the boundary layer to the brain. The first neuron consists of (2) the retinal pigmented epithelium, (3) the neuroepithelium with the light-sensitive rods and cones, (4) the *membrana limitans externa*, (5) the external granular layer, and (6) the external reticular layer. The second neuron consists of (7) the internal granular layer and (8) the internal reticular layer. The third neuron consists of (9) the optic nerve's ganglion cells and (10) the *membrana limitans interna*, which forms the interface to the vitreous body.

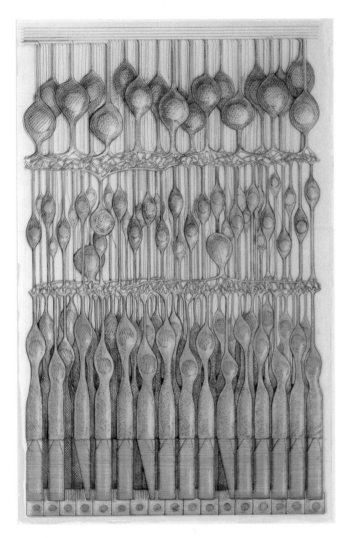

**FIGURE 20.5**

Hierarchy of retinal nerves. The retina is at the top and the brain is at the bottom.

a significant data reduction takes place before the signal leaves the eye. Three hierarchically ordered layers of neurons participate in this process.

But what is colour? Do colours exist as a real physical quantity, or does our brain make them up, assigning colours to objects to highlight them like we do when applying false-colour enhancement in computer graphics? The latter is not necessarily unrealistic; after all, people with a red–green defect can drive on roads with traffic lights with the same confidence as people who have no colour-vision impediment. However, we can easily prove that colours are a real physical phenomenon. Consider foreign flags, which for most of us consist of an arbitrary arrangement of colours. For example, the Italian flag has three vertical bars that are green, white, and red; the French flag is blue, white, and red; and the Nigerian flag is green, white, and green. If our brain assigned such colours based on independent knowledge, it would not know what to do with an isolated flag.

Thus, we started the current chapter with a description of what colours are and how light carries a particular colour. The aim of this part of the chapter is to enable us to understand the experiment shown in Fig. 20.6. White light arriving from the Sun is guided through a transparent slab of glass, which is cut in the shape of a **prism**. The light leaving the prism consists of many colours (rainbow effect), and the rays for the various colours no longer travel parallel to each other. Developing the physical explanation of the phenomenon seen in Fig. 20.6 requires a slightly longer discussion because we need to develop the wave model for light—which, in turn, requires concepts from electricity and magnetism. Thus, in

contain at least three independent colour receptors to enable us to see colours the way we do. While some debate still exists about the exact details of the mechanism, Young's receptors have indeed been identified as the retinal cones; the chemical properties of these cones vary to allow for sensitivity in three different colour intervals.

Have a second look at Fig. 20.4. It is certainly surprising that the cones and the rods are embedded so deep in the retina. This leads to two questions: why are they not located at the surface of the retinal layer, and why does the retinal layer consist of so many different layers as indicated in the figure? The answer to the first question is simply that it is a twist of nature we can live with, as no detrimental consequences result. The answer to the second question is based on the complex signal-switching pattern between the cones and the rods at one end and the visual centre of the brain at the other. Fig. 20.5 illustrates that

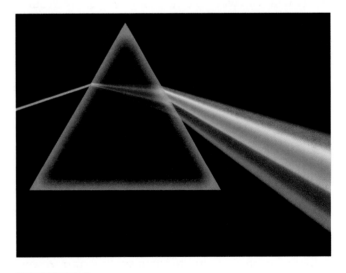

**FIGURE 20.6**

When white light passes through a prism it is split into the colours of the rainbow.

the early part of this chapter we introduce the fundamental properties of magnetism. To avoid turning this chapter into a chapter on magnetism, we consider only the components of magnetism necessary for the discussion of light waves. Other important aspects of magnetism are postponed to the next chapter, where they become important in understanding the motion of individual charged particles.

Once we have established the wave model of light, we will return to the colour vision of humans. At that point this will seem less straightforward than it does now, because the wave model does not tell us whether an object is red or green. All it will establish are two parameters, the frequency and the wavelength of light. Thus, the light from an object can be characterized, for example, by a wavelength of $\lambda = 700$ nm or by a frequency of $f = 4.3 \times 10^{14}$ Hz, and the response of the cones in the retina depends solely on these values. Interestingly, in the end it is indeed only the brain that assigns colour perception to the objects we see, except it does so not arbitrarily or based on experience, but based on the measurement of wavelengths in the eye.

# Toward the Wave Model of Light: Magnetism

The first time we encountered waves in this textbook was in the context of the motion of a piston vibrating around its equilibrium position (Chapter 17). This vibration led to motion of gas elements adjacent to the piston. The interactions within the gas caused the initial perturbation to propagate through the medium as a wave. Note that the medium itself does not travel with the wave but just vibrates locally around its equilibrium position, as we illustrated in Fig. 17.2 with a rope connected to a wall. The wave concept connects the parameters of frequency, wavelength, and velocity with which the wave travels through the medium.

Recall that we excluded light waves explicitly in Chapter 17 due to fundamental differences from sound waves. The most striking difference is that light does not need a medium such as air; we see light from distant stars in spite of the vast empty space separating them from Earth. To apply the wave model to light we have to find new physical properties that allow energy to propagate through space without a carrying medium. We will find the electric field to be part of this mechanism (we introduced electric fields in Chapter 13). But electric fields cannot propagate on their own; they need to be coupled with magnetic fields. To show this and to show how this coupling leads to a propagating wave, we first have to introduce magnetism.

The discussion of magnetism is divided into two parts in this textbook. In the current chapter we introduce its fundamental properties, mostly following an analogy to the introduction of electricity in Chapter 13. Magnetism is based on electric currents, for which we initially consider the currents in a wire and later, as a generalization, changing electric fields. Combining electric and magnetic fields allows us to establish the properties of electromagnetic waves, which include visible light.

We return for a further discussion of magnetism in Chapter 21, when we abstract from a current to the motion of single charged particles. This enables us to understand such phenomena as the intensive radiation belts around Earth and their relevance to human space exploration, but also explains applied analytical techniques such as mass spectrometry.

What may appear unusual about our approach to magnetism is the fact that the most prominent everyday occurrence of magnetism—i.e., magnetic materials such as refrigerator magnets—does not form the starting point of the discussion. This has a conceptual and a practical explanation:

- Magnetism is closely related to electricity since the magnetic force is caused by electric currents. This is not obvious when looking at a permanent magnet since the electric current in this case is a peculiar feature of atomic properties and their collective interactions.

- Magnetic materials play a very limited role in living organisms. Some bacteria synthesize linear strings of up to 20 magnetite particles ($Fe_3O_4$, which is also the iron-richest ore found on Earth) in their cells. Magnetite responds to the Earth's magnetic field essentially like the needle of a compass, allowing bacteria in the Northern Hemisphere to identify the direction toward North. The benefit to the bacteria is that they are able to identify directions independent of their immediate environment, allowing them to avoid moving in circles as humans do when lost in the desert. Magnetic materials are also used by some species in the animal kingdom for orientation purposes. Magnetite particles are found in bees, pigeons (in the dura, the outer covering of the brain), and fish (e.g., the yellowfin tuna). Illustrating their purpose in these cases is complicated, as these animals process a range of sensory information. Recent results suggest that migrating birds operate with three types of compasses to adjust to the significant deviation of the magnetic and geographic North Poles on Earth. The Savannah sparrow uses a magnetic compass, a compass associated with the position of stars at night, and a visual compass using cues from the sky at sunset.

## Magnetic Force

In Chapter 13 we introduced the electric force based on Coulomb's experiment with charged spheres. To do so, we first established that a charge exists and that it is a property of particles independent of mass. Trying in the same fashion to find magnetic monopoles to introduce the magnetic force was unsuccessful. Thus, the **magnetic force** must be the result of properties we have already introduced.

In 1819, Hans Christian Oersted and André-Marie Ampère established the magnetic force as the interaction between two electric currents. Fig. 20.7 shows two metallic wires of length $l$ at a distance $d$. Varying the distance, the lengths, and the electric currents $I_1$ and $I_2$ in both conductors, Ampère found that the magnitude of the magnetic force is proportional to the two currents and the length, and inversely proportional to the distance between the conductors:

$$|\mathbf{F}_{mag}| \propto \frac{I_1 \cdot I_2}{d} \, l \qquad [1]$$

which can be rewritten as a force per unit length of the conductor:

$$\frac{|\mathbf{F}_{mag}|}{l} \propto \frac{I_1 \cdot I_2}{d} \qquad [2]$$

Note that the two forces shown in Fig. 20.7, $\mathbf{F}_{1\,on\,2}$ and $\mathbf{F}_{2\,on\,1}$, are an action–reaction pair as defined by Newton's third law.

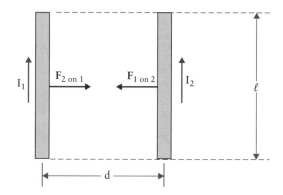

### FIGURE 20.7

Two parallel conductors of length *l* and distance *d* carry currents $I_1$ and $I_2$. As a result a magnetic force is observed, $\mathbf{F}_{2\,on\,1}$ acting on conductor 1 and $\mathbf{F}_{1\,on\,2}$ acting on conductor 2. The two forces shown are an action–reaction pair as defined by Newton's third law.

*The magnitude of the magnetic force between two currents is proportional to each current and inversely proportional to the distance between the conductors.*

### Concept Question 20.1

**The magnitude of the magnetic force between two parallel, current-carrying wires is not linear in (A) the current in the wire we choose to label wire 1, (B) the current in the wire we choose to label wire 2, (C) the distance between the wires, (D) the length along which the wires interact with each other, or (E) none of the above; the force depends linearly on all four parameters.**

ANSWER: Choice (C). Using Eq. [1] we note that the magnitude of the magnetic force is inversely proportional to the distance between the wires. The farther apart the wires, the smaller their interaction force.

Because the electric force is a contact-free force we rewrote Coulomb's law by eliminating the mobile test charge from a system of fixed charges, thereby introducing the electric field due to the stationary charges. As we see from Fig. 20.7, the magnetic force is also a contact-free force. Therefore, we want to take the same approach and assign a magnetic field to a single current. That this is a reasonable approach is evident when considering how Oersted actually discovered the magnetic force between two currents in the first place: he accidentally noted that a compass needle responded when he sent an electric current through a wire nearby.

The definition of the magnitude of the **magnetic field**, labelled **B**, follows from Eq. [1] with one of the currents identified as a test current and removed from the system:

$$|\mathbf{B}| = \frac{\mu_0}{2 \cdot \pi} \frac{I}{d} \qquad [3]$$

*The magnitude of the magnetic field of a conductor is proportional to its current and inversely proportional to the distance from the conductor.*

Several comments help in working with Eqs. [1] to [3]:

• The magnitude of the magnetic field of a straight conductor is shown in Fig. 20.8. It has a cylindrical symmetry; i.e., the absolute value of the field is the same in all directions at a fixed distance from the conductor. The field drops off inversely proportional to the distance from the conductor, as discussed in Concept Question 20.1.

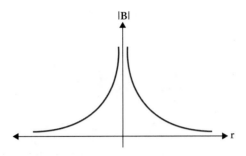

**FIGURE 20.8**

Sketch of the magnitude of the magnetic field |**B**| as a function of distance *r* from a straight wire carrying an electric current.

- The magnetic field is related to the force per unit length between the conductors in Eq. [2]. Therefore, the length of the conductor is not a parameter in the definition of the magnetic field.

- We wrote Eq. [3] as an equation, which required the introduction of a proportionality constant, $\mu_0/(2 \cdot \pi)$. This constant is introduced in an analogous fashion as the permittivity of a vacuum in Chapter 13: the factor $2 \cdot \pi$ takes the cylindrical symmetry of the magnetic field around a straight wire into account. $\mu_0$ is called the **permeability of a vacuum**, with $\mu_0 = 1.26 \times 10^{-6}$ N/A$^2$.

- The unit of the permeability of a vacuum, and the unit of the magnetic field are derived from Eqs. [1] to [3]: For $\mu_0$ we relate the force in Eq. [1] with unit N, the current with unit A, and the length and distance with units m each. The unit of the magnetic field |**B**| follows from Eq. [3]:

$$\frac{N}{A^2} \cdot \frac{A}{m} = \frac{N}{A \cdot m} = \frac{N}{C \frac{m}{s}} = T \qquad [4]$$

A new unit is introduced: **tesla** (T), to honour Nikola Tesla. Several non-standard units are still in use in the literature, including the unit gauss (G, named after Carl Friedrich Gauss), with the conversion $1 \text{ G} = 1 \times 10^{-4}$ T, and the unit oersted (Oe) for $|\mathbf{B}|/\mu_0$, for which 1.0 Oe = 79.59 A/m. Typical values include Earth's magnetic field at the surface, with the magnitude $|\mathbf{B}| = 5 \times 10^{-5}$ T, a standard bar magnet with $|\mathbf{B}| \approx 1 \times 10^{-2}$ T, and the largest superconducting magnets with fields of up to 20 T. Magnetic resonance imaging (MRI) magnets are currently approved in North America for diagnostic applications up to $|\mathbf{B}| = 3.0$ T.

- The direction of the magnetic field has to be evaluated separately. We note from Fig. 20.7 that the magnetic force is directed perpendicular to the

direction in which the current flows through the wires. Since the force is a vector, we have to be able to write the right-hand side of Eq. [1] also as a vector. If the right-hand side of Eq. [1] were to contain only one quantity with vector character, that vector must point in the same direction as the force for mathematical reasons. However, this is not the case. This suggests a vector product notation for Eq. [1].

The best way to see this is to consider Eq. [3]. The magnetic field of a long, straight wire is illustrated in Fig. 20.9: the magnetic field is perpendicular to the direction of the conductor carrying the current and is also perpendicular to the radial direction pointing away from the conductor. The circular lines in the figure connect positions of equal magnitude of the magnetic field. The direction of the magnetic field vector is at every point tangential to the field lines, as illustrated at one point in the figure. The direction of the magnetic field can be determined with a (modified) right-hand rule: when the thumb points in the direction of the current (direction of flow of positive charges in the conductor), the remaining fingers with of the right hand curl in the same fashion as the magnetic field.

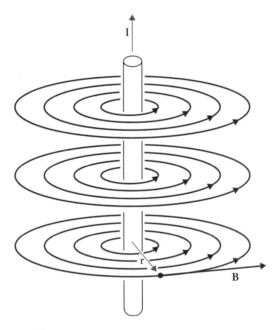

**FIGURE 20.9**

The magnetic field is perpendicular to the direction of the wire at any point in space near a current-carrying conductor. The field is also perpendicular to the radius vector pointing away from the conductor to a point in space. Instead of drawing each magnetic-field vector separately, the figure illustrates the direction of the magnetic field with red lines connecting all points in a plane perpendicular to the conductor that has a magnitude equal to that of the magnetic field.

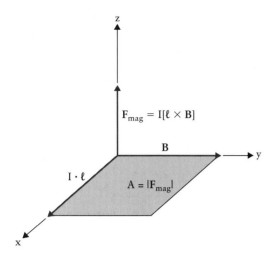

**FIGURE 20.10**

The right-hand rule illustrated for the vector product in Eq. [5], which expresses the magnetic force on a current-carrying wire as a function of the orientation of the wire and the magnetic field.

Eq. [1] contains three vectors that are perpendicular to each other: the force, the direction of the flow of the current in the test wire, and the magnetic field of the original wire. This is the second time we have encountered the need for the vector product notation to fully describe a physical phenomenon; the first occurred when we discussed torque (see the Math Review "Vector Product" at the end of Chapter 5). In analogous fashion, we write:

$$\mathbf{F}_{mag} = I \cdot \left[ \boldsymbol{\ell} \times \mathbf{B} \right] \qquad [5]$$

Then we use the **right-hand rule** to determine the relative directions of the three vectors in Eq. [5] as illustrated in Fig. 20.10: stretch the thumb, index finger, and middle finger of your right hand such that they form pair-wise right angles with each other. The thumb represents the first vector of the vector product in Eq. [5], $I \cdot \boldsymbol{\ell}$; the index finger points in the direction of the second vector, **B**. The middle finger then represents the direction of the resulting vector in Eq. [5], $\mathbf{F}_{mag}$. The shaded area in the figure represents the product in Eq. [5]; i.e., this area is equal to the magnitude $|\mathbf{F}_{mag}|$.

The components of the force vector in Eq. [5] can be calculated from the components of the wire orientation (length) vector and the magnetic field, as outlined in the Math Review at the end of Chapter 5. For the applications in this book, the magnitude of the force is determined from Eq. [1], or the magnitude of the magnetic field is determined from Eq. [3]. In a second step, the direction of the resulting vector quantity is then determined from Fig. 20.9 or 20.10.

## Concept Question 20.2

**Based on the right-hand rule in Fig. 20.10, how do you determine the direction of the magnetic field in Fig. 20.9?**

ANSWER: Spread open your right hand according to Fig. 20.10, with the thumb in the *x*-direction. Then curl the other two fingers while the thumb points in the direction of the wire in which the current flows (the direction of the current density, or $I \cdot \boldsymbol{\ell}$). Your curled fingers now indicate the direction of the magnetic field lines.

## Concept Question 20.3

**Fig. 20.11 shows two long, straight conductors, one running along the *y*-axis and the other along the *x*-axis. Each conductor carries a current as indicated. The axes divide the plane into four quadrants, numbered I to IV in the figure. In which quadrant does the contribution to the magnetic field from both conductors point in the positive *z*-direction (confirm that this direction points out of the plane of the page)? (A) I, (B) II, (C) III, (D) IV. (E) It happens in more than one quadrant.**

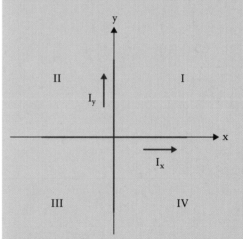

**FIGURE 20.11**

Two long, straight conductors (red), one running along the *y*-axis and the other along the *x*-axis.

ANSWER: (B). Use the right-hand rule as discussed in Concept Question 20.2 to confirm this result.

## ● EXAMPLE 20.1

A straight wire is placed between the poles of a permanent horseshoe magnet. The magnet produces a uniform magnetic field of 2.0 T. The wire

## ● EXAMPLE 20.1 (*continued*)

runs through the gap between the poles of the magnet, perpendicular to the direction of the magnetic field. The length of the wire is 0.3 m in the gap of the magnet. When the wire is connected to a battery, it carries a current. What current must flow to obtain a force of 1.0 N?

*Solution:* The horseshoe magnet provides the magnetic field acting on the wire. We combine Eqs. [1] and [3] for the force acting on the wire:

$$|\mathbf{F}_{\text{on wire}}| = |\mathbf{B}| \cdot I \cdot l \qquad [6]$$

This leads to:

$$I = \frac{F}{l \cdot B} = \frac{1.0 \text{ N}}{(0.3 \text{ m})(2.0 \text{ T})} = 1.67 \text{ A} \qquad [7]$$

Note that the wire runs perpendicular to the direction of the magnetic field in this example. If the wire and the magnetic field have any other relative orientation, Eq. [6] must be corrected. If $\theta$ is the angle between the direction of the magnetic field and the direction normal to the cross-sectional area through which the current passes, then an additional $\sin \theta$ term is introduced due to the magnitude of a vector product:

$$|\mathbf{F}_{\text{on wire}}| = |\mathbf{B}| \cdot I \cdot l \cdot \sin \theta \qquad [8]$$

In the current example, $\theta = 90°$ or $\sin \theta = 1$; i.e., Eq. [8] becomes Eq. [6].

## ● EXAMPLE 20.2

Two long wires cross at the origin, as illustrated in Fig. 20.12. One wire runs along the *x*-axis and carries a current of $I_1 = 2$ A. The other wire runs along the *y*-axis and carries $I_2 = 3$ A. What are the magnitude and direction of the magnetic field at point *P*, which is located 4 cm from the *x*-axis and 6 cm from the *y*-axis?

*Solution:* If several currents are present in a system their magnetic fields are added at each point in space. Thus, we use Eq. [3] to calculate the magnitude of the magnetic field at point *P* for each of the two wires. For wire 1, we find:

$$|\mathbf{B}_1| = \frac{\mu_0 \cdot I_1}{2 \cdot \pi \cdot d_1} = \frac{\left(1.26 \times 10^{-6} \dfrac{\text{N}}{\text{A}^2}\right)(2 \text{ A})}{2 \cdot \pi (0.04 \text{ m})}$$
$$= 1.0 \times 10^{-5} \text{ T} \qquad [9]$$

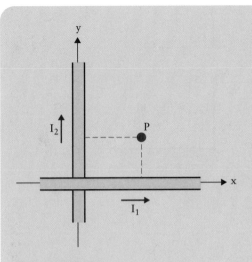

**FIGURE 20.12**

Two straight conducting wires are positioned perpendicular to each other, each carrying a current as indicated. The magnetic field at point *P* is calculated in the text.

and for wire 2:

$$|\mathbf{B}_2| = \frac{\mu_0 \cdot I_2}{2 \cdot \pi \cdot d_2} = \frac{\left(1.26 \times 10^{-6} \dfrac{\text{N}}{\text{A}^2}\right)(3 \text{ A})}{2 \cdot \pi (0.06 \text{ m})}$$
$$= 1.0 \times 10^{-5} \text{ T} \qquad [10]$$

The respective directions of the two contributions to the magnetic field at point *P* are determined with the right-hand rule: for the current along the *x*-axis the magnetic field at *P* is directed out of the plane of the paper, and for the current running along the *y*-axis it is directed into the plane of the paper. Thus, the two contributions have to be subtracted from each other. The net magnetic field at point *P* vanishes, i.e., $\mathbf{B}_{\text{net}} = 0$ T.

When we developed the concept of the electric field in Chapter 13 we noted that one benefit of the approach is to allow us to calculate the electric field for systems with large numbers of charges prior to studying the properties of the mobile charge in the field. While the calculation of the field may be a difficult mathematical task, once a formula for the field has been obtained it can be used in many contexts. This has proven particularly valuable for the parallel plate arrangement in Chapters 13 and 14: it allowed us to describe many experimental capacitor arrangements (including the nerve membrane) with a very simple formula for the electric field.

We proceed with the magnetic field concept again in analogy to the electric case. Instead of a straight wire, many other arrangements of one or several wires of practical interest have been studied. One particular arrangement was found that has a magnetic field with a simpler formula than Eq. [2]. As in the electric case, we study this arrangement in more detail as it provides us with a convenient model system for applications of magnetism.

The arrangement is called a **solenoid**, which is a single conductor that is wound as shown in Fig. 20.13. The radius of the cross-sectional area of the cylindrical shape of the solenoid is constant, as is the number of windings $N$ per length $l$ of the solenoid. When a current is sent through the wire, a magnetic field develops outside of the wire in the same fashion we discussed before for the straight wire in Fig. 20.9. Both the magnitude and the direction of the magnetic field within a solenoid take particularly simple forms. The magnitude is given by:

$$|\mathbf{B}_{\text{solenoid}}| = \mu_0 \frac{N}{l} I \qquad [11]$$

i.e., the magnitude of the magnetic field in a solenoid has a constant value everywhere. The direction of the magnetic field is shown by the thin lines in Fig. 20.14: the direction of the field does not vary and runs parallel to the axis of the solenoid.

Eq. [11] describes indeed a much simpler case than Eq. [3] since in Eq. [3] the magnitude of the magnetic field varies with distance from the wire; i.e., the magnetic field in Eq. [3] is not position-independent. Also, the magnetic field in the vicinity of a straight wire changes its direction from point to point as illustrated in Fig. 20.9, while the magnetic field in a solenoid is always directed along its axis.

Due to these simple properties, solenoids are widely used as electromagnets (i.e., devices that act as magnets when an electric current passes through). The lenses used in state-of-the-art electron micro-

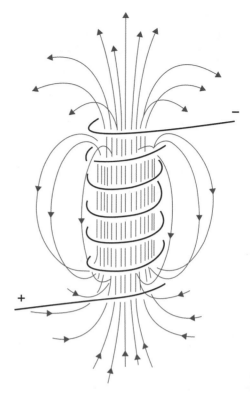

**FIGURE 20.14**

Sketch illustrating the magnetic field of a solenoid. Inside the coil exists a magnetic field that is position-independent both in direction and magnitude. The direction of the magnetic field inside the solenoid is parallel to the axis of the solenoid.

scopes like the one shown in Fig. 19.8 are magnetic devices based on solenoids.

## Electromagnetic Waves

When magnetism was discovered, it was initially considered an entirely separate natural phenomenon. However, in many experiments it became clear that magnetic and electric effects are very similar. Magnetism causes electric effects and vice versa. In 1865, James Clerk Maxwell combined the electric theory and the theory of magnetism in four equations that relate electric and magnetic fields. When he applied these formulas to a region without charges (e.g., to outer space), differences due to electric and magnetic fields vanished. Thus, Maxwell concluded that magnetism and electricity are essentially the same and it is only a matter of perspective whether we interpret a phenomenon as electric or magnetic. We call fields electric that are due to resting charges, and we call fields magnetic that are due to moving charges.

**Maxwell's equations** further allow us to describe how a combination of electric or magnetic fields leads to a travelling wave, called an **electromagnetic**

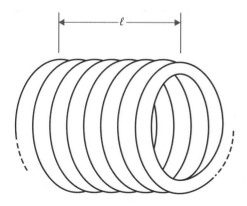

**FIGURE 20.13**

A solenoid is a coiled conductor with a fixed radius of the coils and a constant number $N$ of coils per length $l$.

**wave.** His equations reveal the speed at which these electromagnetic waves move, i.e., the speed of light. The equations also confirm that electromagnetic waves are not carried by the medium. Therefore, the origin and the propagation mechanism of electromagnetic waves are physically very different from those of sound waves. Maxwell's equations are mathematically rather complex. Instead of deriving them, a qualitative approach using experimental observations is chosen to illustrate how electromagnetic waves are generated. Our discussion of sound waves illustrated two principles we want to apply again:

- waves are generated by vibrations, and
- sound waves are harmonic waves that result from harmonic vibrations in a source.

Based on Ampère's and Oersted's observations, we want to use the harmonic vibration of electric charges instead of a mechanical vibration. The device in which we set charges in vibrational motion is called an antenna.

We use a straight conductor as a model for an **antenna**. Fig. 20.15 illustrates the harmonic motion

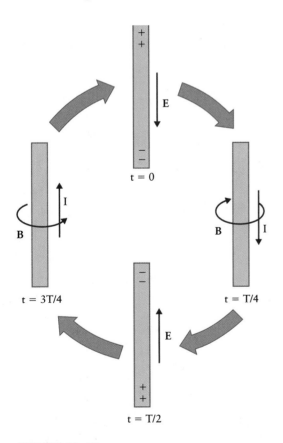

**FIGURE 20.15**

Four frames at fixed time intervals $\Delta t = T/4$ illustrating the concept of an antenna. Positive and negative charges are separated along the antenna in a periodic fashion. When the charges move along the conductor, a magnetic field forms.

of charges. At time $t = 0$ the antenna is charged like a dipole, with the positive charges at the upper end and the same number of negative charges at the lower end. Associated with the separated charges is an electric field. At time $t = T/4$ we allow the charges to neutralize (the antenna is a conductor), which requires the motion of charges along the wire, which yields a current. Associated with the current is a magnetic field, as illustrated in Fig. 20.9. The current continues to flow until, at $t = T/2$, the charges are again separated; however, this time the negative charges are at the top and the positive charges are at the bottom. Therefore, the electric field now points in the reverse direction. At the next time frame, at $t = 3 \cdot T/4$, the charges are once more neutralized. The current now flows upward, causing a magnetic field opposite to the one observed at time $t = T/4$. A harmonic oscillation of charges in the antenna follows if we force the charges to move as shown in Fig. 20.15 in a periodic fashion, with period T.

The magnetic field near the antenna itself changes periodically with time. In 1831, Michael Faraday illustrated the effect of such a changing magnetic field. His experiment is shown in Fig. 20.16: a bar magnet is moved through the loop of a conductor that is connected to an ampere-meter (galvanometer). The galvanometer shows a flowing current while the magnetic field changes. We conclude that the changing magnetic field must cause an electric field at the position of the wire, since in Chapter 14 we identified electric fields as the only way to set charges in motion in a wire. This effect is called **induction**. The direction of the current in the loop is such that the magnetic field of the current is directed against the external magnetic field.

In Ampère's and Faraday's experiments we allowed the magnetic field to develop in the free space outside a conductor, but we restricted the electric field to the conducting wire since we wanted an observable current. What happens in the vicinity of a changing magnetic field where no conductor loop is present? Maxwell postulated that the changing magnetic field causes a changing electric field in free space instead of a current. The vector direction of this electric field is perpendicular to the vector direction of the magnetic field. This addition to the list of electric and magnetic interactions by Maxwell is illustrated in Fig. 20.17: A changing magnetic field $\Delta B_1/\Delta t$ causes a changing electric field $\Delta E/\Delta t$, which in turn causes a changing magnetic field $\Delta B_2/\Delta t$ that is opposed to the original magnetic field.

Now we return to the harmonic vibration of charges in the antenna of Fig. 20.15. The changing magnetic field shown in the figure causes a changing

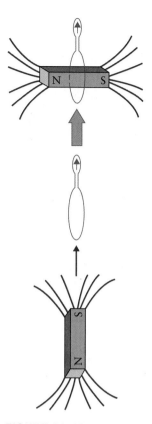

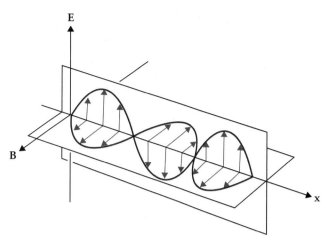

**FIGURE 20.18**

Maxwell's theory allows changing magnetic and electric fields to sustain each other as they travel outward from the vibrating charges of an antenna. The resulting electromagnetic waves are characterized by magnetic and electric field vectors that are perpendicular to each other and to the direction of wave propagation. The speed of the wave is identical to the speed of light.

**FIGURE 20.16**

Michael Faraday's experiment: a bar magnet is moved into a single loop of a conductor that is connected to a galvanometer (measuring the electric current in the loop). In this experiment the magnetic field encircled by the wire changes as the magnet is moved. While the magnetic field changes, a current is detected.

electric field, which in turn causes a changing magnetic field as illustrated in Fig. 20.17. These interacting electric and magnetic fields travel outward from the antenna like water surface waves travel outward when you poke the water surface. In the current case no medium is needed as the electric and magnetic fields sustain each other. This is illustrated in Fig. 20.18, where the perpendicular magnetic and electric fields are indicated by arrows. The perturbation travels in the direction perpendicular to both the electric and magnetic fields (**transverse wave**) with the speed Maxwell found to be $c = (\varepsilon_0 \cdot \mu_0)^{-1/2}$, in which $\varepsilon_0$ is the permittivity of a vacuum from Coulomb's law and $\mu_0$ is the permeability of a vacuum from Eq. [3]. $c$ is the **speed of light** in a vacuum.

*Visible light is an electromagnetic wave that propagates in a vacuum with the speed of light.*

Electromagnetic waves carry energy. Their intensity—i.e., the amount of energy passing through a unit area per second—is proportional to the maximum electric field $\mathbf{E}_{max}$ and the maximum magnetic field $\mathbf{B}_{max}$, as shown in Fig. 20.18:

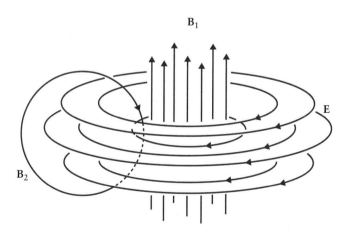

**FIGURE 20.17**

Maxwell discovered that a changing magnetic field $\Delta\mathbf{B}_1/\Delta t$ not only can cause a current in a conductor, but also can cause a changing electric field $\Delta\mathbf{E}/\Delta t$ outside a conducting medium. The changing magnetic and electric fields cause each other, as illustrated with the secondary magnetic field $\Delta\mathbf{B}_2/\Delta t$.

$$\frac{1}{A}\frac{\Delta E_{electromagnetic}}{\Delta t} \propto |\mathbf{E}_{max}| \cdot |\mathbf{B}_{max}| \propto |\mathbf{E}_{max}|^2 \qquad [12]$$

in which the last relation holds because the maximum magnetic and electric fields in the wave are proportional to each other.

# Polarization of Light

The first wave property of light we discuss is due to its transverse character. We define the **polarization** of light based on the orientation of its electric field vector in Fig. 20.18: if the orientation of the vector **E** of a light ray is time-independent (e.g., always along the y-axis), then we call the light **linearly polarized light**. Usually, visible light is not polarized since it emerges from a very large number of independent atomic transitions, as discussed in detail in Chapter 22. Each atomic transition contributes a random orientation of the electric field vector.

*The electric field vector of linearly polarized light points in a fixed direction relative to the propagation direction of the electromagnetic wave.*

Even though light does not require a medium to carry it, when it travels through matter interactions between matter and light occur. We noted this in the previous chapter, when we found that light slows down while passing through a transparent material. Based on the discussion of the interaction between water molecules and an external electric field, we can understand the nature of the interaction between light and matter: the electric field of the light ray interacts with the electric fields within the molecules of the material. In turn, this interaction allows us to control the properties of a light ray. Two types of materials in particular interfere with the polarization of light in an interesting fashion.

## LIGHT POLARIZING CRYSTALS

Some materials allow only a fraction of the incident light to pass through, which is the light with a particular electric field component. Light with an electric field component perpendicular to that orientation is blocked. This property is common among many crystals that are not too symmetric. A frequently used material is $CaCO_3$, which forms transparent crystals that are highly symmetric about only one axis. These materials are used for **polarizers** and **analyzers,** as illustrated in the top sketch of Fig. 20.19: randomly oriented light enters the polarizer

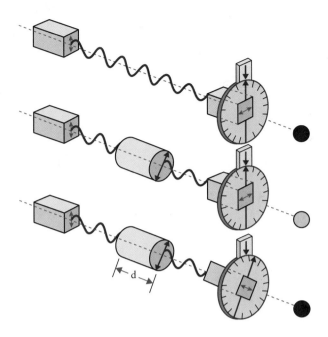

**FIGURE 20.19**

Optical polarizer (left) and analyzer (right) to measure the optical activity of a sample. Both are transparent crystals that only allow light with one component of the electric field vector to pass through. The analyzer is initially set to a position at 90° such that the observation screen is dark. If the sample (centre) turns the polarization plane of the light, as indicated in the middle panel, the screen is illuminated. The angle of rotation is determined by rotating the analyzer until the screen is dark again (bottom panel).

from the left. Only light with the electric field pointing in the up–down direction is allowed to pass through on account of the orientation of the crystal in the polarizer. The light then passes through a second crystal of the same type, but turned 90° relative to the first crystal. As a result, the incident light is fully blocked and the screen behind the second crystal is dark (indicated by a black dot). A mechanical rotary dial is connected to the second crystal to allow fine-tuning for the complete shielding of the polarized light.

The light passing through the polarizer has a well-defined electric vector, which we label $\mathbf{E}_{polarizer}$. If the analyzer is rotated by an angle $\theta$ relative to the polarizer, the electric field vector of the light passing through the analyzer, $\mathbf{E}_{analyzer}$, is turned by an angle $\theta$ relative to $\mathbf{E}_{polarizer}$ and has a magnitude of

$$|\mathbf{E}_{analyzer}| = |\mathbf{E}_{polarizer}| \cdot \cos\theta \qquad [13]$$

which means that only the field component parallel to the analyzer axis passes through the analyzer. We stated in Eq. [12] that the intensity of light is proportional to the square of its maximum electric field vector. Thus, the intensity of light passing through an analyzer that is turned by an angle $\theta$ relative to the polarizer is diminished from the intensity passing through the polarizer as:

$$I_{\text{analyzer}} = I_{\text{polarizer}} \cdot \cos^2 \theta \qquad [14]$$

This is called **Malus's law**.

## POLARIZATION BY REFLECTION

Under most conditions, light reflection leads to a partial polarization. No polarization occurs only when the light is incident along the normal of the reflecting surface. Fig. 20.20 illustrates what happens at all other angles of incidence. An unpolarized light ray approaches an interface. It forms an angle $\theta_p$ with the normal of the interface. We describe the ray by two electric field vectors, one that is parallel to the interface (blue dots) and one that is perpendicular to the first component (blue arrows). This light is unpolarized, as it may contain any combination of components along the two electric field directions. The refracted and reflected beams are partially polarized for all angles $0° < \theta_p < 90°$. However, complete polarization of the reflected beam, as shown in the figure, occurs when the reflected and refracted beams together form an angle of 90°. This is due to the fact that the reflected beam cannot carry the same component indicated by a double arrow for the refracted beam, since this electric field component would point in the direction of the travelling beam. This is impossible because electromagnetic waves are transverse waves, i.e., the propagation direction is perpendicular to the electric field vector.

The angle $\theta_p$ is then called the polarizing angle or **Brewster's angle**, named in honour of Sir David Brewster. Fig. 20.20 indicates that Brewster's angle

depends on the index of refraction of the two materials that meet at the interface. We calculate Brewster's angle with the law of refraction we introduced in Chapter 18. From Fig. 20.20, we see that:

$$\theta_p + 90° + \theta_2 = 180° \qquad [15]$$

which yields:

$$\theta_2 = 90° - \theta_p \qquad [16]$$

Choosing the medium in which the wave travels toward the interface as air with $n_1 = 1$, and dropping the subscript 2 for the index of refraction of material 2, we find from Snell's law:

$$n = \frac{\sin \theta_p}{\sin \theta_2} \qquad [17]$$

which yields:

$$n = \frac{\sin \theta_p}{\sin(90° - \theta_p)} = \frac{\sin \theta_p}{\cos \theta_p} = \tan \theta_p \qquad [18]$$

This is called **Brewster's law**.

**Concept Question 20.5**

**What is Brewster's angle for crown glass with $n = 1.52$?**

ANSWER: We substitute $n$ in Eq. [18]:

$$\theta_p = \tan^{-1} n = \tan^{-1}(1.52) = 56.6° \qquad [19]$$

## OPTICALLY ACTIVE MATERIALS

In 1815, Jean Baptiste Biot discovered that some organic molecules actively turn the polarization direction of light. These materials are called optically active materials. As an example, the glucose molecule shown in Fig. 20.21 is **optically active**. A detectable level of glucose in the urine is an indication for diabetes mellitus. Thus, a simple (contact-free) analysis technique for the glucose concentration in urine is clinically desirable. The second and third sketches in Fig. 20.19 illustrate how glucose is detected in a urine sample with polarized light. After the polarizer and analyzer are placed such that the light is completely blocked (top sketch in the figure), the urine sample of given length $d$ is inserted between the two crystals. If no optically active component is in the sample, the screen behind the analyzer remains dark. However, if an optically active component is contained in the sample light will reach the screen. By turning the rotary dial of the analyzer (bottom sketch in Fig. 20.19), an angle is found at which the light is fully

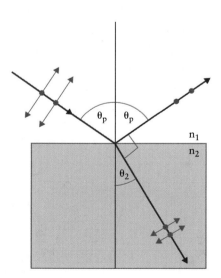

**FIGURE 20.20**

Light becomes polarized when it reflects off a planar surface such that the reflected and refracted beams form a 90° angle.

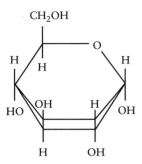

**FIGURE 20.21**

Glucose molecule. This molecule is optically active. Its presence in a urine sample is an indication for diabetes mellitus.

blocked again. The angle through which the analyzer had to be turned, $\alpha$, is read from the instrument.

The information obtained about the sample can be analyzed qualitatively by determining whether the light has been turned toward the right or toward the left, which corresponds to a clockwise or a counter-clockwise turn of the analyzer, respectively. This may not be sufficient if the sample contains one of several possible optically active components, or when the absolute concentration of the optically active compo-nent is sought. To quantify a light polarization mea-surement to obtain the concentration of the optically active component in the sample, $c$, we need to know the **specific rotation** $\alpha_{\text{specific}}$, which is a characteristic property of the molecule (like the melting point). Ob-taining the specific rotation from a tabulation of such values, we quantify the concentration by:

$$c = \frac{\alpha}{d \cdot \alpha_{\text{specific}}} \qquad [20]$$

Note that $\alpha_{\text{specific}}$ depends on the temperature and the wavelength of the light. Standard values are re-ported, therefore, for room temperature and for a particular wavelength obtained from a sodium lamp ($\lambda = 589$ nm).

How can irregularly moving molecules in a solu-tion turn the polarization of the light in this fashion? At the molecular level, the answer is the same as for the polarizer and analyzer crystals: the intra-molecu-lar electric fields interact with the electric field of the light ray passing through the molecule. But this would lead only to a back-and-forth wobbling of the direction of the electric field vector of the light ray, as the ray passes through a very large number of ran-domly oriented molecules before leaving the sample. This is indeed the case, and therefore most chemical solutions do not turn the polarization of light in a de-tectable fashion.

Exceptions are solutions in which only one type of enantiomer is present. **Enantiomers** are optically active structural isomers, i.e., chemical compounds with the same chemical formula that exist in more than one structural variation. Enantiomers have identical physical properties, except for the direction of rotation of the plane of polarized light. They also have identical chemical properties except for their in-teractions with other optically active reagents. This exception is important since such reactions occur very frequently in biological systems. For example, only one enantiomer of chloromycetin acts antibioti-cally, and (−)-carvone causes the well-known odour of spearmint oil while (+)-carvone is the essence of caraway.

An organic molecule is an enantiomer, or has one or more enantiomer groups, if it contains a carbon atom with four different ligands, C—WXYZ, as il-lustrated in Fig. 20.22. Note that the tetrahedral structure shown to the left of the dashed line and the tetrahedral structure shown to the right of the dashed line are mirror symmetric to each other (e.g., with the dashed line as a mirror). Neither molecule can be su-perimposed on the other molecule by rotations. A so-lution containing 50% of molecules of the left type and 50% of the right type is optically inactive. How-ever, a solution that contains only one type of the molecules shown in Fig. 20.22 is optically active, be-cause any small turn of the polarization of light in one molecule cannot be compensated by the light ray's passing through a second molecule with its intra-molecular electric field turning light the oppo-site way.

Living systems often rely on only one of two enan-tiomers. Two examples are illustrated in Fig. 20.23: part (a) shows lactic acid, of which (+)-lactic acid can be extracted from human muscle tissue; and part (b) shows a by-product of the fermentation of starch to ethanol, of which only (−)-2-methyl-1-butanol is naturally synthesized. The notation in the bracket preceding the chemical name is defined as follows: a molecule that turns the polarization of light to the right (i.e., the analyzer in the setup in Fig. 20.19 is turned clockwise) is labelled (+).

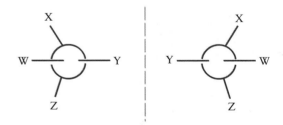

**FIGURE 20.22**

Optically active organic isomers (enantiomers) require four different ligand groups attached to a carbon atom. The dashed line indicates the mirror sym-metry of the isomers.

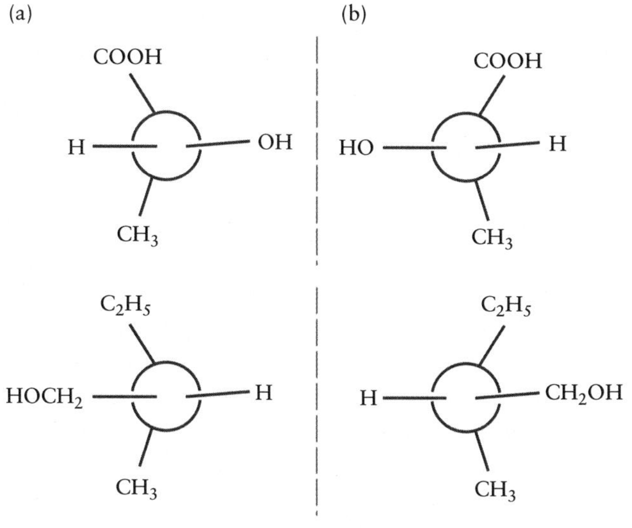

**FIGURE 20.23**

Two examples of optically active molecules: (a) lactic acid and (b) 2-methyl-1-butanol.

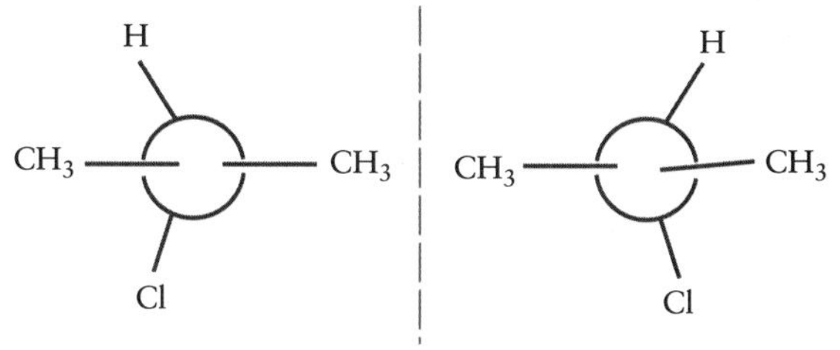

**FIGURE 20.24**

Isopropyl chloride is an example of an organic molecule that is not optically active.

Not all organic molecules are optically active. An example of an optically inactive molecule is shown in Fig. 20.24. Note that the isopropyl molecules on both sides of the mirror plane can be transferred into each other by rotation.

Polarized light is applied in modern medicine for diagnosing skin ailments. Light that is reflected from the skin is a combination of two components:

- light reflected from the skin surface according to the law of reflection. This component is called **glare**; and

- light that initially penetrated the skin surface but is backscattered from deeper layers.

A technique allowing for the separation of these two components enables us to independently study the skin surface and the tissue below the skin surface, e.g., pigmentation, infiltrates, and other intra-cutaneous components. This separation is possible when using polarized incident light and a polarizer to study the skin; the glare does not affect the polarization of the light, while the backscattered component

no longer sustains the polarization. Thus, depending on the rotation of the polarizer used by the health practitioner, either the skin surface or intra-cutaneous structures are highlighted. Note that in this context, contrary to our intuition, only 4% to 7% of the incident light is indeed reflected off the surface, while 93% to 96% penetrates the outermost layer. This reminds us of *The Invisible Man*, a novel written by H. G. Wells in 1897. We are not invisible, but it would be fair to characterize the outermost layer of our skin as almost transparent!

Many biochemical processes in our body operate with only one enantiomer of an optically active compound, the other enantiomer being inactive or even toxic. How is it possible that nature developed enantiomer-specific processes in the first place? For this, we need a natural process that distinguishes enantiomers. This process must involve naturally available polarized light. Sunlight is not polarized when it reaches Earth's atmosphere. A fraction of this light is **scattered** by small ice particles in the upper atmosphere. If the scattered light reaches a detector from a direction perpendicular to the initial light ray, it is found to be polarized. Replacing the detector with a biochemical process allowed nature to exploit optically active compounds.

# Physics and Physiology of Colour

## Dispersion

Are there further effects on a propagating electromagnetic wave due to the medium? Since the speed of light is affected, we know that at least one of the quantities wavelength $\lambda$ and frequency $f$ must vary as light passes through an interface because

$$v_{light} = \lambda \cdot f \qquad [21]$$

Fig. 20.25 determines which of the parameters on the right-hand side varies from medium to medium. Shown in the figure are two media with different indices of refraction $n_1$ (top) and $n_2$ (bottom). We assume that $n_2 > n_1$. Light of wavelength $\lambda_1$ and frequency $f_1$ approaches the interface from the top. From Chapter 18 we know that light travels slower in medium 2, $v_{light,2} < v_{light,1}$.

Let's assume that two observers, at positions A and B, count the number of wave maxima passing through their respective dashed observation planes. If observer A were to count a smaller number of wave maxima than observer B, then eventually there would be no wave maxima left in the range between the two observers and the whole experiment would somehow

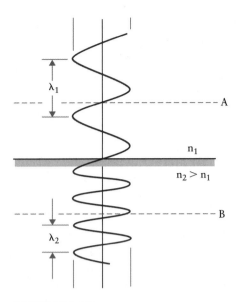

**FIGURE 20.25**

Light wave passing through an interface. The wavelength varies; the frequency remains unaltered.

collapse. If, in turn, observer A were to count a larger number of wave maxima than observer B, then wave maxima would pile up between the two dashed lines. Since neither case makes sense, we conclude that the same number of wave maxima must pass observers at A and B during any time interval; i.e.,

$$f_1 = f_2 \implies \lambda_2 < \lambda_1 \quad [22]$$

Thus, the speed of light and the wavelength of light change when light passes through an interface (as illustrated for the wavelength in Fig. 20.25), but the frequency of the light remains fixed. From this we conclude that the frequency of light is the most fundamental of the three quantities frequency, wavelength, and speed of light in a medium, as nature conserves it for light travelling through different media.

Finding the frequency more fundamental than the wavelength or the speed of light in a particular medium is consistent with the corpuscle theory of light, which we use in Chapter 22 when discussing the atom. Light corpuscles are called **photons**. If a corpuscle travels as indicated in Fig. 20.25, we expect its energy to remain unchanged. Thus, the corpuscle energy should not be linked to the wavelength or its speed. Indeed, we note that the energy of a photon is given by:

$$E_{\text{photon}} = h \cdot f \quad \text{with } h = 6.6 \times 10^{-34} \text{J} \cdot \text{s} \quad [23]$$

where $h$ is the **Planck constant**, named in honour of Max Planck.

A further conclusion is that the **index of refraction** $n$ must depend on the wavelength of light, $\lambda$. This

follows from the fact that both $n$ and $\lambda$ change from one medium to another while the frequency $f$ remains constant.

*The dependence of the index of refraction on the wavelength, $n = f(\lambda)$, is called **dispersion**.*

Typical dispersion curves for three different types of glass are shown in Fig. 20.26. Dispersion also explains the observation illustrated in Fig. 20.6 that white light incident on a prism is split into several different light rays of different colours. White light is composed of light rays of different wavelengths, and since the index of refraction of the glass depends on the wavelength, some light rays are refracted more strongly and others less. Specifically, the light component that looks red to us is refracted less than the light component that looks blue to us.

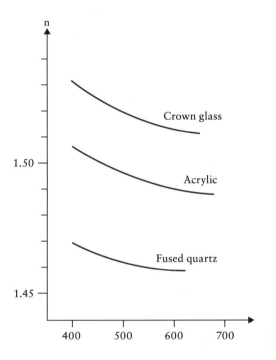

**FIGURE 20.26**

Dispersion relation $n(\lambda)$ in the visible part of the electromagnetic spectrum for three types of glass: crown glass, acrylic, and fused quartz.

### Concept Question 20.6

**The angle of refraction depends on the wavelength of the incident light. Shouldn't the angle of reflection also depend on the wavelength?**

ANSWER: No. Dispersion is the result of electric interaction between the light ray and the medium through which it travels. The reflected beam interacts to only a very limited extent with the material surface.

Dispersion affects any transparent material, including the lenses in our eyes. This leads to several colour-related illusions. An example is the perception that the red and blue bars of the French flag differ in width. For a red and a blue field at the same distance, the lens must be bent more to focus the red light as it is refracted less by a given lens. The focussing of the eye is associated with adjustments of the lens caused by action of the ciliary muscle. The brain notices the degree of work the ciliary muscle is doing and interprets this information as a measure of distance to the observed object. Thus, while you focus on the red area of the flag your brain thinks *near* and while you focus on the blue area of the flag your brain thinks *farther away*. A lot of motion occurs in your eyes while looking at an object such as the French flag in order to get the picture right. The apparent difference in width of the two bars is an illusion that is caused by the brain as it tries to correct for the obviously inconsistent depth information; you know that the three bars of the flag are at the same distance since they are woven together.

Why then do we not have the same problem with the Italian flag? The dispersion effect is greatest for colours at opposite ends of the visible spectrum, such as red and blue. The Italian flag has a red and a green bar; thus, the same effect applies but is less noticeable. Note that the flag of Haiti has a blue and a red bar, like the French flag. Why does the problem discussed for the French flag not occur with this flag? For a while, French legislators had a law that required flag manufacturers to compensate for the dispersion effect by using uneven widths for the three bars; no such law ever existed in Haiti. Historically, the Haitian flag is the result of the removal of the white bar in the French flag when this former colony separated from France. Physically removing the white bar eliminates a neutral visual separation between the two colour bars. Our eyes are in constant motion and can adjust for optical illusions more easily when the two affected areas are adjacent to each other. This is why another good example of the dispersion effect is stained-glass church windows, in which coloured panels are separated by lead strips.

## Colour as a Physical Concept

The fact that electromagnetic waves have different wavelengths and frequencies is not sufficient to explain why we see colours. To understand colour vision, we must discuss two additional phenomena. The first is the range of visible wavelengths of the electromagnetic spectrum. This also explains why we see white light emerging from the Sun and why white

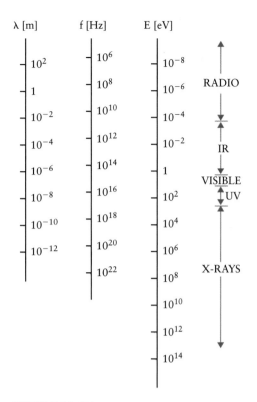

**FIGURE 20.27**

Electromagnetic spectrum showing the relation between frequency $f$, wavelength $\lambda$, and photon energy $E = h \cdot f$. IR is infrared and UV is ultraviolet.

light is a mixture of all colours of the rainbow. These issues can be addressed with physical concepts and are discussed in this section.

The other necessary ingredient for understanding colour vision is the mechanism by which our eye and our brain convert wavelengths into colour impressions. This second issue requires us to study the interplay of physics and physiology, which we reserve for the last section of this chapter.

The complete **spectrum** of electromagnetic waves is shown in Fig. 20.27. It reaches from radiowaves with wavelengths in the centimetre and metre range, to microwave and infrared radiation in the micrometre-to-centimetre wavelength range, to visible and ultraviolet light with wavelengths in the nanometre range, and finally to X-rays at the shortest wavelengths. The fraction of this spectrum that is visible is very small, reaching from about 370 nm (violet) to about 760 nm (red). This visible part of the electromagnetic spectrum is highlighted in Fig. 20.28, which correlates the names of various colours to the respective wavelengths, frequencies, and energies of the light. Note that the reason we can give an energy scale in Figs. 20.27 and 20.28 is due to the corpuscle theory of light, which defines the energy of light photons of frequency $f$ as $E = h \cdot f$ with $h$ the Planck constant. That $E$ is indeed an energy is evident when you let sunlight

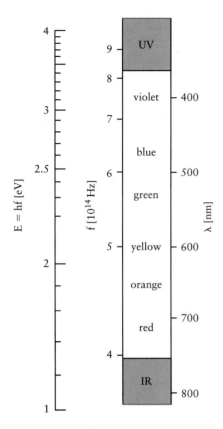

**FIGURE 20.28**

Visible part of the electromagnetic spectrum. The colours indicated correspond to the respective wavelengths.

shine on your skin. The warmth you feel is the energy of the photons deposited in your skin, retained as the result of light absorption.

Do we have to conclude from Figs. 20.27 and 20.28 that our vision is rather ill-adapted to the real world around us because it cannot detect most of the electromagnetic spectrum? No, because only a small fraction of the entire electromagnetic spectrum reaches our eye. To understand why, we need to introduce the concept of **blackbody radiation**.

A blackbody is defined as an object that perfectly absorbs all the light that reaches it; i.e., it does not reflect any of that light. As a blackbody absorbs the incoming light, the light's energy is converted into thermal energy, raising the temperature of the blackbody. If light shines on the blackbody continuously, it is not in thermal equilibrium but becomes hotter and hotter. When a body becomes hotter, however, we know that it starts to emit light. Examples include the metal filament in an incandescent light bulb. By balancing light absorption, this light emission establishes a thermal equilibrium for a blackbody immersed in a fixed light radiation field.

Fig. 20.29 illustrates the intensity of light of various wavelengths emitted from a blackbody at three

different temperatures. Both the overall intensity (area under the curve) and the wavelength of the maximum intensity vary with temperature. The peak in Fig. 20.29 shifts to shorter wavelengths with increasing temperature. This observation is called **Wien's displacement law** and is quantified in the form:

$$\lambda_{max} \cdot T = 0.29 \times 10^{-2}\,\text{m} \cdot \text{K} \qquad [24]$$

Let us assume the Sun is a blackbody. Due to its high temperature it radiates light with a spectrum like that shown in Fig. 20.29. The actual spectrum (total intensity and wavelength of radiation peak) depends on the Sun's surface temperature. While the interior of the Sun reaches temperatures of $1 \times 10^7$ K, the electromagnetic spectrum is determined by the surface temperature of the Sun, which is 5800 K. Light from greater depths does not leave the Sun because the Sun's surface layer is not transparent to that light. Using Fig. 20.29, we predict a maximum intensity of the radiation reaching Earth from the Sun in the visible wavelength range. As a consequence, many processes on Earth are tuned in to this maximum, including photosynthesis and our vision.

Fig. 20.29 also shows that the total intensity of light emission from a blackbody depends strongly on the temperature of the blackbody. The total intensity is the area underneath the curve, and can be calculated analytically using the correct formula for the

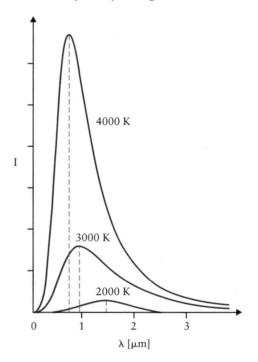

**FIGURE 20.29**

Emission intensity *I* of a blackbody at three different temperatures. The vertical dashed lines indicate the wavelengths of the respective maximum intensities.

curves in the figure. The intensity curves in Figure 20.29 follow from a quantum-mechanical calculation done initially by Max Planck. In 1879, Josef Stefan wrote **Stefan's law for the blackbody:**

$$\frac{\Delta Q/\Delta t}{A} = -\frac{2 \cdot \pi^5 \cdot k^4}{15 \cdot c^2 \cdot h^3} T^4 = -\sigma \cdot T^4 \quad [25]$$

in which $\Delta Q/\Delta t$ is total rate of emission of heat in unit J/s and $A$ is the surface area of the blackbody. The term $(\Delta Q/\Delta t)/A$ is the rate of energy loss per unit area, i.e., a term we calculated for Earth based on heat conduction in Chapter 10. The right-hand side contains the Boltzmann constant $k$ because it is part of the thermal energy of a system in the form $k \cdot T$; the speed of light $c$ because it converts energy density to intensity as discussed in Chapter 17; and the Planck constant $h$ because of the discrete nature of transitions in the blackbody that cause the radiation. We discuss this latter aspect in more detail once we introduce the atomic model in Chapter 22. The constants on the right-hand side of Eq. [25] are combined in a single constant, called $\sigma$, the **Stefan–Boltzmann constant**, with value $\sigma = 5.67 \times 10^{-8}$ J/(m$^2 \cdot$ s $\cdot$ K$^4$). Note that Eq. [25] contains a negative sign on the right-hand side following our convention that energy lost by the object of interest is negative.

Insofar as Stefan's law applies only to a true blackbody, it is a model equation. However, it can be applied to actual objects if the right-hand side is corrected with an object-specific constant, called $\varepsilon$, the **emissivity**. In most cases it is sufficient to know the material of the object to find a tabulated value for $\varepsilon$, with $\varepsilon = 1$ for a true blackbody and $0 < \varepsilon \leq 1$ for any other object. Once we include the emissivity, **Stefan's law for arbitrary objects** is written as:

$$\frac{\Delta Q/\Delta t}{A} = -\varepsilon \cdot \sigma \cdot T^4 \quad [26]$$

Energy loss by radiation is also significant for objects near room temperature, as shown in Table 10.2 for the energy loss from the human body.

### Concept Question 20.7

**On a clear cold night in Northern Europe, the Northern United States, or Canada, why does frost tend to form on the tops of objects but not on their sides?**

ANSWER: Objects lose some fraction of their energy through radiation. During a clear night little radiation comes from above (outer space), while objects exchange radiative heat sideways with other objects in their environment. This effect is not observed farther south because the air temperature at night remains warm enough to compensate the energy loss by radiation with energy gain due to heat conduction.

### ● EXAMPLE 20.3

A person with a skin temperature of 37°C is in a room at 20°C. How much heat does the person's body lose per hour if the human body has a surface area of 1.5 m$^2$ and is modelled as a blackbody with emissivity $\varepsilon = 0.9$?

*Solution:* Modelling the human body as a blackbody means that the human body is in a radiative equilibrium when placed in an environment of the same temperature. As a consequence, the emissivity $\varepsilon$ for radiative loss and radiative gain must be the same; otherwise, the body's temperature would eventually differ from the 37°C temperature of the environment.

Placing the human body in an environment with a different temperature means that no radiative equilibrium is established and the warmer object loses energy to the colder object. In the given case, we determine the radiative energy loss and radiative energy gain from the surroundings using Eq. [26]:

$$\left(\frac{\Delta Q}{\Delta t}\right)_{loss} = -\sigma \cdot \varepsilon \cdot A \cdot T^4_{body}$$
$$\left(\frac{\Delta Q}{\Delta t}\right)_{gain} = +\sigma \cdot \varepsilon \cdot A \cdot T^4_{environment} \quad [27]$$

which leads to a net heat balance of:

$$\Delta Q_{net} = \sigma \cdot \varepsilon \cdot \Delta t \cdot A(-T^4_{body} + T^4_{environment}) \quad [28]$$

Inserting the numerical values in Eq. [28] leads to:

$$\Delta Q = \left(5.67 \times 10^{-8} \frac{J}{m^2 \cdot s \cdot K^4}\right) 0.9(3600\,s)$$
$$\times (1.5\,m^2)(293^4 K^4 - 310^4 K^4)$$
$$= -5.1 \times 10^5\,J \quad [29]$$

Note that the heat loss discussed in this example is due to radiation at electromagnetic wavelengths, and thus is not dependent on a medium to carry the heat. However, heat cannot pass through opaque interfaces radiatively. This is the reason for the **greenhouse effect**. In a greenhouse, incoming energy from the Sun passes through the glass surfaces in the visible range. The radiation of the plants in the greenhouse occurs at much longer wavelengths (infrared) since the temperature of the plants is much lower than the surface temperature of the Sun. At infrared wavelengths glass is opaque; i.e., the radiation cannot escape from the greenhouse, thus increasing the temperature in the greenhouse beyond the temperature outside.

## Ultraviolet Light in Our Environment

Fig. 20.29 is still not sufficient to explain why our vision is limited to a narrow range of wavelengths, because it is not determined by the emission of the Sun (heat radiated by the Sun) but by the irradiance at the surface of Earth.

> **Irradiance** is the amount of energy incident per unit surface of an object, with unit $J/(m^2 \cdot s)$. Irradiance of the Sun is energy incident on Earth exclusively due to the Sun's radiation.

Fig. 20.29 indicates that the most intensive emission of radiation from a blackbody at the surface temperature of the Sun indeed occurs near the visible wavelength range. How much of this energy reaches us? We need to test two possible reasons why the figure may not represent the irradiance reaching our eyes:

- fundamentally, we have to confirm that modelling the Sun as a blackbody is appropriate, and

- practically, we have to test whether any of the Sun's radiation is lost, most likely in Earth's atmosphere.

The short-dashed and long-dashed lines in Fig. 20.30 test the blackbody assumption for the Sun. The long-dashed curve represents the actual intensity data as received outside Earth's atmosphere, and the short-dashed line is the calculated radiation from a blackbody at 5800 K. The two curves coincide very well, indicating the assumption that the Sun is a blackbody is appropriate for wavelengths above 300 nm.

Fig. 20.30 shows a third intensity curve as a function of wavelength: the red curve is the intensity measured at sea level. Oxygen, ozone, water, and carbon dioxide molecules in the atmosphere attenuate the Sun's irradiance across the entire spectrum. While absorption clearly alters the intensity profile, the red curve in Fig. 20.30 still confirms that the most intense light present at sea level lies in the visible range, from 400 nm to 700 nm.

However, Fig. 20.30 does not tell the complete story of radiation received from the Sun. Particularly

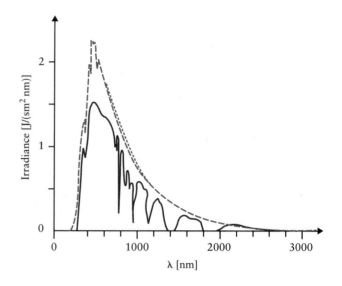

**FIGURE 20.30**

Comparison of the solar irradiance on Earth with the radiation of a blackbody at 5800 K (short-dashed curve). The agreement in the wavelength interval shown is very good above the atmosphere (long-dashed curve). At sea level (red curve), attenuation occurs due to absorption of radiation by various molecular components of the atmosphere.

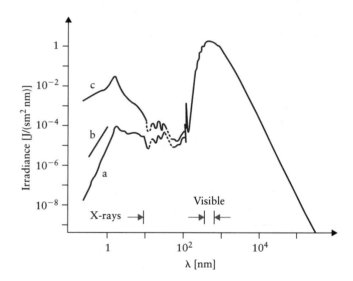

**FIGURE 20.31**

Irradiance of electromagnetic radiation above Earth's atmosphere as a function of wavelength. In the double-logarithmic plot the irradiance is given in unit $J/(m^2 \cdot s)$ and further per nanometre interval of the electromagnetic spectrum. It is predominantly caused by the Sun, with the largest peak due to the blackbody radiation of the Sun emitted at 5800 K. The short-wavelengths radiation depends on the Sun's activity levels: (a) quiet Sun, (b) active Sun, and (c) during Sun flares.

during the active periods of the Sun and when solar flares occur, energetic radiation reaches Earth. This radiation contains both electromagnetic waves and particles. Fig. 20.31 shows the electromagnetic spectrum of the Sun for wavelengths from the infrared region ($\lambda = 10^4 - 10^5$ nm) to wavelengths of less than 1 nm. We compare this spectrum with the spectrum in Fig. 20.30. Note that the data are represented in Fig. 20.31 in a double-logarithmic plot, while Fig. 20.30 is a linear plot. The double-logarithmic plot emphasizes smaller intensities. The ordinate in both figures is the irradiance, in unit J/(m² · s), as a function of wavelength; i.e., each value corresponds to the irradiance in a wavelength interval of a width of 1 nm, which contributes an additional unit nm⁻¹ to the unit as shown.

In Figs. 20.30 and 20.31, the peak of irradiance lies in the visible range of the electromagnetic spectrum, which is consistent with a blackbody model for the Sun. However, Fig. 20.31 shows additional radiation at wavelengths that are clearly not explained by the blackbody model. Attention is drawn to the radiation intensity stretching across the entire ultraviolet range below 400 nm.

Before we discuss the significance of radiation in the range from 1 nm to 400 nm (ultraviolet light), we need again to establish which fraction of that radiation passes through the atmosphere. This leads to a division of the ultraviolet part of the electromagnetic spectrum into several bands, as outlined in Table 20.1.

XUV, FUV, and UVC effectively destroy cellular DNA, usually by separating adjacent bases across the double-helix structure. Thymine bases in particular then bond with each other to form thymidine dimers, as illustrated in Fig. 20.32(b). However, the short-

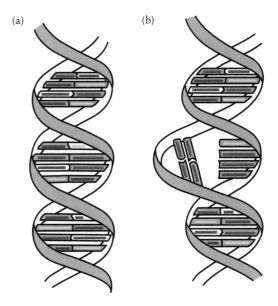

(a)        (b)

**FIGURE 20.32**

DNA molecule before and after typical UV radiation damage occurs. Thymine groups are particularly susceptible to radiation and form stable thymidin dimers that distort and render useless the DNA double-helix.

wavelength UV bands do not penetrate Earth's atmosphere and therefore remain harmless to living organisms. UVC is generated artificially with mercury arc lamps and is used for the sterilization and disinfection of waste and drinking water.

UVA, and to a lesser extent UVB, reaches sea level. Birds, reptiles, and insects can see in the near UV (UVA band), which is referred to as **black light** because we cannot see it. Many fruits and flowers stand out more strongly from the background in UV light to attract insects, such as bees.

UVB is important for reptiles that do not obtain sufficient levels of vitamin $D_3$ from their diet, such as chuckwallas and tortoises. Vitamin $D_3$ is required to prevent metabolic bone disease, which is an illness due to insufficient metabolizing of dietary calcium compounds. The vitamin is synthesized from pro-vitamin $D_3$ (dehydrocholesterin) in the skin of these reptiles with the aid of UVB radiation.

Although invisible, UVA and UVB radiation are still of relevance to humans because of their harmful effects on the skin. UVB causes **sunburn** (erythema), and UVA is the primary cause of age-related **wrinkles** (permanent collagen damage). However, UVB is also linked to **skin cancer** (melanoma, and basal cell and squamous cell carcinoma), based on the mechanism shown in Fig. 20.32. When exposed to moderate sunlight intensities the skin self-protects with release of the brown pigment **melanin**, which blocks UV radiation from reaching deeper, more vulnerable layers of

## TABLE 20.1

### Division of the UV range of the electromagnetic spectrum

| Region | Wavelength range (nm) | Sub-region | Wavelength range (nm) |
|---|---|---|---|
| XUV (deep UV) | 1–30 | | |
| FUV (far UV) | 10–200 | | |
| NUV (near UV) | 200–400 | UVC | 200–290 |
| | | UVB | 290–320 |
| | | UVA | 320–400 |

Irradiance [J/(sm² nm)]

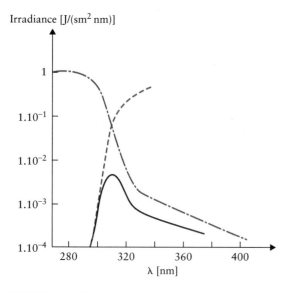

## FIGURE 20.33

Origin of the enhanced sensitivity of skin to the UVB band of the electromagnetic spectrum. The dashed line shows the irradiance spectrum of sunlight at sea level, with a steeply diminishing intensity toward smaller wavelengths due to absorption in the atmosphere. The dash-dotted curve is called the erythemal-action spectrum and indicates the relative sensitivity of skin to radiation of the respective wavelength. A larger value means that the skin shows a higher rate of sunburn. The product of both curves (red curve) causes a sensitivity peak in the UVB band.

the skin. This melanin production is insufficient as a protection against sunlight (even on a cloudy day, as UVA and UVB are not blocked by water vapour). Even though UVA radiation is more intense, UVB is of primary concern for two reasons:

- it is stopped within a shorter range of the skin, thus depositing its energy in a smaller tissue volume, and

- the skin is sensitive to increasingly shorter wavelengths (called the **erythemal-action spectrum**). The erythemal-action spectrum (dash-dotted line) and the irradiance spectrum of sunlight at sea level (dashed line) are illustrated in Fig. 20.33. A skin-sensitivity peak (red curve) results in the UVB band because the net harmful effect of radiation is the product of the erythemal-action spectrum and the intensity spectrum of light.

## Colour as a Physiological Concept

As complex and subjective as the process of interpretation of wavelengths in our brain may be, interesting physics are included in the physiological aspects of colour vision. We want to establish these in this sec-

tion. Once the light from an object reaches the retina, the colour you see depends on the relative excitation of three **colour-sensitive receptor** types embedded at each point in your retina. We already mentioned that Young postulated three different receptors are needed. Their respective sensitivity as a function of the wavelength of the incoming light is shown in Fig. 20.34. Corresponding to the range of greatest sensitivity, the three receptors are labelled $R$, $G$, and $B$ for **red receptor**, **green receptor**, and **blue receptor**. The significant overlap of the peaks in Fig. 20.34 rules out a simple colour composition concept. Instead, each colour we perceive in our brain is associated with light that has excited at least two different cones, and most colour impressions result from an excitation of all three types of cones.

How we use Fig. 20.34 to predict a colour impression is illustrated next. We start with the definition of the **colour triangle**. For an object with a given colour, let the absolute excitation intensity of the red receptor be $R$, the absolute excitation intensity of the green receptor be $G$, and the absolute excitation intensity of the blue receptor be $B$. The total excitation intensity is then $R + G + B$. The total excitation intensity determines whether the object appears bright or dim and duplicates the information the brain receives from the retinal rods. Using the total excitation in-

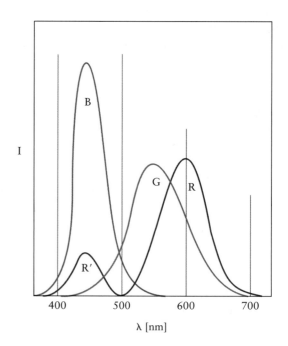

## FIGURE 20.34

Sensitivity of the three types of colour-detecting cones as a function of the wavelength in the visible range of the electromagnetic spectrum. The cones are labelled $R$ (red), $G$ (green), and $B$ (blue), according to the colour at the wavelength of the maximum of each curve.

tensity, we define a relative excitation intensity for each of the three receptor types:

$$r = \frac{R}{R + G + B} \quad \text{with } 0 \leq r \leq 1$$

$$g = \frac{G}{R + G + B} \quad \text{with } 0 \leq g \leq 1 \qquad [30]$$

$$b = \frac{B}{R + G + B} \quad \text{with } 0 \leq b \leq 1$$

with

$$r + g + b = 1 \qquad [31]$$

The red and the green relative excitation intensities, $r$ and $g$, are used to form the two perpendicular sides of the colour triangle in Fig. 20.35. With $r$ and $g$ given in the figure, the value of $b$ is derived from $b = 1 - g - r$.

Not all relative intensity combinations represented in the colour triangle are accessible. For example, the point $g = 1$ and $r = b = 0$ is inaccessible due to the overlap of the three receptors in Fig. 20.34, which shows that no wavelength of light excites only the green receptor. In Fig. 20.35 the accessible part of the colour triangle is shown as a white area, with the corresponding colour impressions included. Points near the centre of the triangle are perceived as white (additive colour sensitivity). Fig. 20.36 illustrates the use of the colour triangle for sunflower yellow and the blue colour of the sky on a beautiful day.

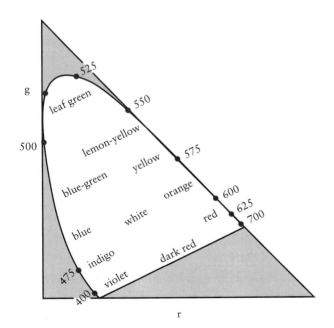

**FIGURE 20.35**

The visible part of the colour triangle (white area) and the respective colour impressions. No colour impressions are possible in the grey areas due to the overlap of the sensitivity peaks in Fig. 20.34.

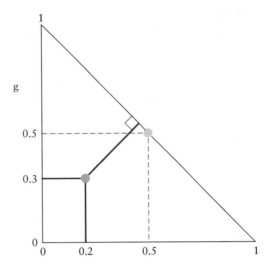

**FIGURE 20.36**

The position of sunflower yellow ($r = g = 0.5$, $b = 0$) and sky blue ($r = 0.2$, $g = 0.3$, $b = 0.5$) in the colour triangle.

## Concept Question 20.8

**Do all humans see colours the same way? More specifically, did Homer, who lived around 750 BC to 700 BC, see colours as we do? Homer wrote works including the *Iliad* and the *Odyssey*. In these he repeatedly referred to the Aegean Sea (part of the Mediterranean Sea) as "a sea coloured like violets" or a "wine-coloured sea," descriptions most of us would disagree with. So, did he see colours differently?**

ANSWER: Homer most likely saw colours the same way you see them! For him to have seen colours differently at the blue end of the spectrum, the sensitivity of the eyes of the ancient Greek people must have stretched slightly farther toward shorter wavelengths into ultraviolet. To allow for this, Figs. 20.34 and 20.35 must be modified for Homer's eyes. This could occur in two ways:

• A first possibility for Homer's vision is to shift the sensitivity peak of the blue receptor toward the left in Fig. 20.34, and shift the minor peak of the red receptor accordingly. Using Fig. 20.35, we find that Homer would have seen in the UVA band as we see blue today. The only difference would be that he might have perceived the colour of the Aegean Sea as more intense due to the high reflection of UVA light from a water surface.

• A second possibility for Homer's eye would be to again shift the sensitivity peak of the blue receptor toward the left in Fig. 20.34, but leave the minor peak of the red receptor where it is in our eye. In this case we simply cannot say what Homer would have seen. Where looking at the Aegean Sea, his brain would have

## Concept Question 20.8 (*continued*)

received signals corresponding to a point in the grey area near $b = 1$ in Fig. 20.35. We don't know what the brain would do with such a signal, as none of our brains has ever had to deal with it. The only thing we know is that the **physiological rule of specific sensory perception** applies, i.e., that the retina responds even to inadequate stimuli (e.g., electrical or mechanical stimulation) with a visual perception.

Of course, Homer, as a poet, might just have been exercising his artistic freedom when describing the sea beloved by the Greeks.

## Concept Question 20.9

**Why do all cats look grey at night?**

ANSWER: Our eye contains retinal cones for colour vision and retinal rods for black and white vision. As the intensity of light diminishes at night, a lower threshold for colour vision is passed and the colour vision shuts off. Once the light intensity has fallen below this threshold, only the black and white vision remains active and everything we see looks grey (somewhere between black and white). Since cats are active at night, they are typical objects for this observation.

## Concept Question 20.10

**Why do we see ghosts only in the dark?**

*Answer.* Rods and cones are not equally distributed across our retina. The density of the black-and-white-sensitive rods in particular is larger farther away from the fovea centralis ((8) in Fig. 18.1), while the colour-sensitive cones are

concentrated near the fovea, as illustrated in Fig. 20.37. This is a result of the mammalian evolutionary development that displays an effective adjustment to nocturnal life, including well-developed olfaction and limited colour vision. Humans are, in that sense, exceptional mammals in that we have fully developed colour vision. However, our fields of view for black/white vision and for colour vision developed at very different stages of evolution.

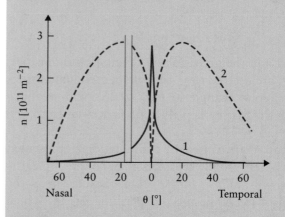

**FIGURE 20.37**
Number density of cones (1) and rods (2) in the retina as a function of distance from the fovea centralis. The gap is due to the blind spot.

During daytime we use our brain to process information primarily transmitted from the colour-sensitive area near the fovea centralis, defining our **normal field of vision** (see Fig. 18.4). At night, with only the retinal rods operational because of low light intensities, the brain receives a higher fraction of information from outside the normal field of vision. Thus, we respond more sensitively to motions near the edge of our field of vision, overreacting to objects at the fringes. This is perceived as unusual or frightening since we are used to daytime vision. Thus, ghostly impressions are night-time phenomena and always try to creep in on us from the edge of our field of vision.

# MULTIPLE CHOICE AND CONCEPTUAL QUESTIONS

### MAGNETISM

**Q–20.1.** In a presentation, you use Fig. 20.7 to describe the magnetic force between two current-carrying wires. Someone in the audience challenges your statement that $F_{2\,on\,1}$ and $F_{1\,on\,2}$ are an action–reaction pair of forces. Which of the following statements would you not make in response? (A) The two forces act on different objects. (B) The forces are equal in magnitude. (C) The forces are opposite to each other in direction. (D) The electric currents flow in parallel directions.

**Q–20.2.** Which of the following is not a suitable unit for the magnitude of a magnetic field? (A) G (gauss), (B) T (tesla), (C) Oe (oersted), (D) N/(A · m), (E) (N · m)/(C · s).

**Q–20.3.** Fig. 20.38 shows a long wire that carries a current $I$. In what direction does the magnetic field point at point $P$, which lies in a common $yz$-plane with the wire? Answer the question based on the coordinate system shown in the figure. (A) along the positive $x$-axis, (B) along the negative $x$-axis, (C) along the positive $y$-axis, (D) along the negative $y$-axis, (E) along the positive or negative $z$-axis.

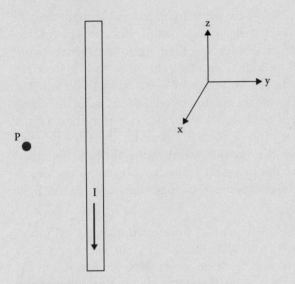

**FIGURE 20.38**

A long wire carries current $I$. A point $P$ is located in the common $yz$-plane with the wire. The coordinate system is shown at the right.

**Q–20.4.** In which of the following locations is the magnetic field uniform in direction and constant in magnitude? (A) inside a solenoid through which a current flows, (B) between the plates of a parallel plate capacitor, (C) outside a solenoid through which a current flows, (D) between two parallel current-carrying wires, (E) far from an antenna operated as a high-frequency sender.

**Q–20.5.** Consider once again Fig. 20.11. In which quadrants does one conductor contribute to the magnetic field in the positive $z$-direction and the other in the negative $z$-direction? (A) in quadrants I and II, (B) in quadrants I and III, (C) in quadrants I and IV, (D) in quadrants II and III, (E) in quadrants II and IV, (F) in quadrants III and IV. (G) None of these choices is correct.

**Q–20.6.** A thin cylinder of copper has mass $m = 50\ g$ and is 1 metre long. What is the minimum current that has to flow through the cylinder for it to levitate in a

magnetic field of 0.1 $T$? Choose the closest value, (A) 1.2 A, (B) 2.5 A, (C) 4.9 A, (D) 9.8 A.

**Q–20.7.** In which arrangement is a conductor with a current not subjected to a magnetic force?

**Q–20.8.** Which way does a compass point when you are at the North magnetic pole?

**Q–20.9.** We move with the drift speed parallel to the electrons in a current-carrying conductor. Do we measure a zero magnetic field?

**Q–20.10.** (a) Two parallel conductors are located one above the other, with both carrying currents in opposite directions. As a result, they repel each other. Is the upper conductor in a stable state of levitation? (b) Now we reverse one current so that the two conductors attract each other. Is the lower conductor in a stable state of levitation?

**Q–20.11.** Parallel conductors exert magnetic forces on each other. What about two current-carrying conductors that are oriented perpendicular to each other?

### ELECTROMAGNETIC WAVES

**Q–20.12.** In Michael Faraday's experiment a permanent magnet is moved through a wire loop. If you measure the electric current in the wire loop, you find a non-zero current when (A) the south pole of the magnet is held in the plane of the loop, (B) the north pole of the magnet is held in the plane of the loop, (C) the bar magnet is held such that its north and south poles are equally far from the plane of the loop, (D) the bar magnet moves with constant speed through the wire loop, (E) the bar magnet is moved toward the wire loop from below with its acceleration vector in the plane defined by the loop.

**Q–20.13.** Light travels in the direction that is (A) parallel to the electric field vector, (B) parallel to the magnetic field vector, (C) at an angle of 45° with the electric field vector, (D) at an angle of 45° with the magnetic field vector, (E) none of the above.

**Q–20.14.** Light waves and sound waves have the following in common: (A) Both travel in a vacuum. (B) Both are transverse waves. (C) Both travel at the same speed. (D) When they reach the water surface from air, both refract and reflect. (E) None of the above is correct.

**Q–20.15.** We use a conducting line as a receiving antenna. What should the orientation of this antenna be relative to the antenna that emits electromagnetic waves?

**Q–20.16.** A vibrating object is the source of sound. What is the physical source of an electromagnetic wave?

**Q–20.17.** What is it that actually moves when a light wave travels through outer space?

**Q–20.18.** Assume your eyes were sensitive in the infrared wavelength range. Look around the room you are in. What would you see?

**Q–20.19.** Why does an infrared photograph taken of a person look different from a photograph taken with visible light?

## LIGHT POLARIZATION

**Q–20.20.** In the skin of animals exposed to sunlight, 7-dehydrocholesterol is converted into the hormone cholecalciferol (vitamin $D_3$). Fig. 20.39 shows this reaction. How many carbon atoms in 7-dehydrocholesterol are optically active? (A) none, (B) 1–3, (C) 4–6, (D) 7–9, (E) all.

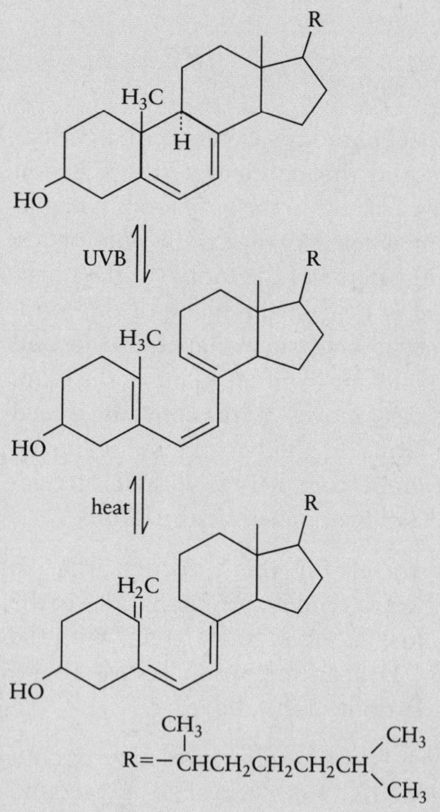

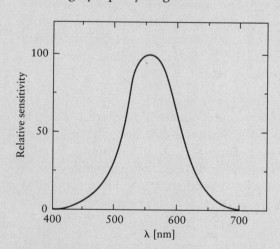

### FIGURE 20.39

7-dehydrocholesterol (top) is converted into the hormone cholecalciferol, also called vitamin $D_3$ (bottom). The reaction occurs in two steps; the first step to provitamin $D_3$ (centre) requires UVB radiation.

**Q–20.21.** Light is fully polarized if it is reflected off a planar surface and the incoming light ray (A) forms an angle of 60° with the normal, (B) forms an angle

of 45° with the normal, (C) forms an angle of 30° with the normal, (D) hits the surface perpendicular, (E) none of the above.

**Q–20.22.** Linearly polarized light is sent through two consecutive polarizers. The first polarizer has an angle of 45° with the original plane of polarization, and the second has an angle of 90°. What fraction of the incident light intensity passes through both polarizers? (A) zero, (B) 25%, (C) 50%, (D) 12.5%, (E) none of the above.

## COLOUR VISION

**Q–20.23.** When white light passes through a prism it is split into the colours of the rainbow. The following feature does not contribute to this observation: (A) White light contains light of all visible frequencies (between 360 nm and 760 nm). (B) The index of refraction of the prism material depends on the wavelength of the light. (C) The prism material displays a non-constant dispersion relation. (D) The speed of light for the various wavelengths varies in the glass body of the prism. (E) The frequencies of the different light components change unequally as the light enters the prism.

**Q–20.24.** The peak of the electromagnetic radiation intensity from the Sun lies (A) in the microwave range, (B) in the range of radiofrequencies, (C) in the far infrared range, (D) in the visible/near-ultra-violet range, (E) in the range of X-rays, because the Sun is a cosmic object.

**Q–20.25.** Fig. 20.40 shows that our eye is much more sensitive to absolute intensities of green light in comparison to absolute intensities of red light. Why then do the green and red lights of a traffic light still look roughly equally bright?

### FIGURE 20.40

Relative sensitivity of the human eye as a function of wavelength.

**Q–20.26.** Describe the colour vision of an alien if the sensitivity of the three colour receptors in the alien's eye is as shown in Fig. 20.41.

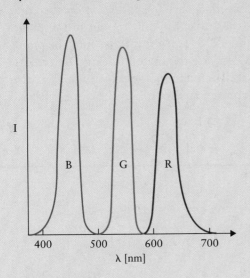

**FIGURE 20.41**

**Q–20.27.** Why is a rainbow red at the top and blue at the bottom?

**Q–20.28.** A light ray of given wavelength travels from air into glass ($n > 1$). Does the wavelength of the light change? Does its frequency change? Does its speed change? Does its colour change?

**Q–20.29.** A mixed light beam of two colours, $X$ and $Y$, is sent through a prism. In the prism, the $X$ component is bent more than the $Y$ component. Which component travelled more slowly in the prism?

# ANALYTICAL PROBLEMS

## MAGNETISM

**P–20.1.** Two long, parallel wires are separated by a distance of $l_2 = 5$ cm, as shown in Fig. 20.42. The wires carry currents $I_1 = 4$ A and $I_2 = 3$ A in opposite directions. Find the direction and magnitude of the net magnetic field (a) at point $P_1$ that is a distance $l_1 = 6$ cm to the left of the wire carrying current $I_1$, and (b) at point $P_2$ that is a distance $l_3 = 5$ cm to the right of the wire carrying current $I_2$. (c) At what point is the magnitude of the magnetic field zero, i.e., $|B| = 0$?

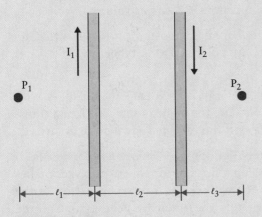

**FIGURE 20.42**

**P–20.2.** At what distance from a long, straight conductor that carries a current of 1 A is the magnitude of the magnetic field due to the wire equal to the magnitude of Earth's magnetic field at the surface of Earth, i.e., $|B| = 50 \ \mu T$?

**P–20.3.** A conducting wire has a mass of 10 g per metre of length. The wire carries a current of 20 A and is suspended directly above a second wire of the same type that carries a current of 35 A. How far do you have to close the separation distance between the wires so that the upper wire is balanced at rest by magnetic repulsion?

**P–20.4.** Two parallel conductors each carry a current of 2 A and are 6 cm apart. (a) If the currents flow in opposite directions, find the force per unit length exerted on either of the two conductors. Is the force attractive or repulsive? (b) How do the results in part (a) change if the currents flow parallel to each other?

**P–20.5.** Fig. 20.43 shows two parallel wires that carry currents $I_1 = 100$ A and $I_2$. The top wire is held in position; the bottom wire is prevented from moving sideways but can slide up and down without friction. If the wires have a mass of 10 g per metre of length, calculate current $I_2$ such that the lower wire levitates at a position 4 cm below the top wire.

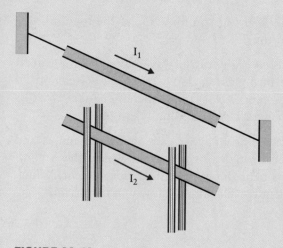

**FIGURE 20.43**

**P–20.6.** A current of $I = 15$ A flows through a conductor in the positive $x$-direction. Perpendicular to the current is a magnetic field, causing a magnetic force on the conductor per unit length of 0.12 N/m in the negative $y$-direction. Calculate the magnitude and determine the direction of the magnetic field in the region through which the current flows.

**P–20.7.** A conductor carries a current of 10 A in a direction that makes a 30° angle with the magnetic field of strength $B = 0.3$ T. What is the magnitude of the magnetic force on a 5-m segment of the conductor?

**P–20.8.** Fig. 20.44 shows two conductors that carry currents in opposite directions. The right conductor carries a current $I_1 = 10$ A. Point $A$ is the midpoint between the conductors, which are separated by $L = 10$ cm, and point $B$ is located 5.0 cm to the right of $I_1$. The current $I_2$ is adjusted such that the magnetic field at point $B$ is zero. (a) Find $I_2$, and (b) find the magnitude of the magnetic field at point $A$.

**P–20.9.** Fig. 20.45 shows the cross-sections of four long, parallel, current-carrying conductors. Each current is 4.0 A, and the distance between neighbouring conductors is $L = 0.2$ m. A dot on the conductor means the current is flowing out of the plane of the paper and a cross means it flows into the plane of the paper. Calculate the magnitude and determine the direction of the magnetic field at point $P$ at the centre of the square shown.

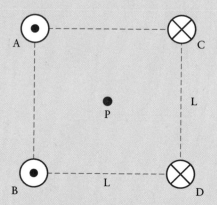

**FIGURE 20.45**

## LIGHT POLARIZATION

**P–20.10.** Assume that the angle of incidence of a light ray in air onto a reflecting surface is continuously variable. The reflected beam is completely polarized when the angle of incidence is 48°. (a) What is the index of refraction of the reflecting material? (b) What is the angle of refraction of the part of the light that travels through the reflecting material?

**P–20.11.** The index of refraction of a slab of glass is $n = 1.52$. (a) What is Brewster's angle if the glass is located in air? (b) Modify the formulas in the text such that you can calculate Brewster's angle if the glass slab is in water. What is its value?

**P–20.12.** At what angle above the horizon is the Sun if its light is fully polarized after reflecting off a water surface?

**P–20.13.** A light ray is incident on flint glass with $n = 1.65$. Calculate the angle of refraction of a transmitted light ray if the reflected ray is fully polarized.

**P–20.14.** Light of intensity $I_0$ leaves a polarizer. (a) If the transmission axis of a subsequent analyzer makes an angle of 45° with the axis of transmission of the polarizer, what is the intensity of the transmitted light? (b) What should be the angle between the two transmission axes for the final intensity to be $I_0/3$?

**P–20.15.** If light is incident at an angle $\theta$ from a medium of index of refraction $n_1$ to a medium with $n_2$

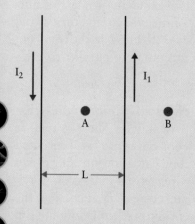

**FIGURE 20.44**

such that the angle between the reflected and refracted beams is $\beta$, show that:

$$\tan \theta = \frac{n_2 \cdot \sin \beta}{n_1 - n_2 \cdot \cos \beta} \quad [32]$$

*Hint:* Use the formula for $\sin(\alpha_1 + \alpha_2)$ from the Math Review "Trigonometry" at the end of Chapter 17.

## DISPERSION

**P–20.16.** The index of refraction for violet light in silica flint glass is 1.66, and that for red light is 1.62. What is the angular dispersion of visible light (expressed as the angle $\phi$) passing through the equilateral prism shown in Fig. 20.46, if the angle of incidence is 50°? Compare with Fig. 20.6.

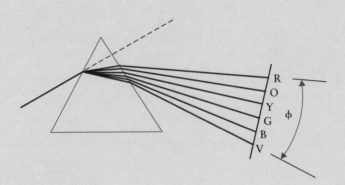

**FIGURE 20.46**

**P–20.17.** Light of wavelength $\lambda_0$ in vacuum has a wavelength of $\lambda_w = 438$ nm in water and a wavelength of $\lambda_b = 390$ nm in benzene. (a) What is the wavelength $\lambda_0$ in a vacuum? (b) Using only the given information, determine the ratio of the index of refraction of benzene to that of water.

**P–20.18.** A 400-nm-wavelength light ray is incident at an angle of 45° on acrylic glass and is refracted. What wavelength of light, also incident at an angle of 45° but on fused quartz, refracts at the same angle? *Hint:* Use Fig. 20.26.

**P–20.19.** The index of refraction of red light in water is $n = 1.331$, and for blue light it is $n = 1.340$. If a ray of white light enters the water at an angle of incidence of 83°, what are the underwater angles of refraction for the two light components?

**P–20.20.** A glass has an index of refraction for blue light at $\lambda = 430$ nm of $n = 1.650$, and for red light at $\lambda = 680$ nm it is $n = 1.615$. If a light ray containing these two colours is incident at an angle of 30° on the glass, what is the angle between the two light components inside the glass?

## BLACKBODY RADIATION

**P–20.21.** A typical human skin temperature is 35°C. At what wavelength does the radiation emitted by the human body reach its peak?

# SUMMARY

## DEFINITIONS

- Permeability of vacuum: $\mu_0 = 1.26 \times 10^{-6}$ N/A$^2$
- $\sigma$ is the Stefan–Boltzmann constant:
  $\sigma = 5.67 \times 10^{-8}$ J/(m$^2$ · s · K$^4$)

## UNITS

- Magnetic field |**B**|: T = N/(A · m)

## LAWS

- Magnetic force between two parallel currents in wires of length $l$ and distance $d$:

$$|\mathbf{F}_{\text{mag}}| \propto \frac{I_1 \cdot I_2}{d} l \quad \Rightarrow \quad \frac{|\mathbf{F}_{\text{mag}}|}{l} \propto \frac{I_1 \cdot I_2}{d}$$

- Magnetic field
  - for a current in a straight wire:

$$|\mathbf{B}| = \frac{\mu_0}{2 \cdot \pi} \frac{I}{d}$$

- for a solenoid:

$$|\mathbf{B}_{\text{solenoid}}| = \mu_0 \frac{N}{l} I$$

  where $N$ is the number of windings.
- Stefan's law
  - for blackbody radiation:

$$\frac{\Delta Q}{\Delta t} = -\sigma \cdot A \cdot T^4$$

  where $\Delta Q/\Delta t$ is the total energy emitted, $A$ is the surface area, and $\sigma$ is the Stefan–Boltzmann constant.
  - for arbitrary objects:

$$\frac{\Delta Q}{\Delta t} = -\sigma \cdot \varepsilon \cdot A \cdot T^4$$

  with $\varepsilon$ the emissivity, $0 < \varepsilon \leq 1$.

# PART 5

# KA

The last group of three chapters addresses the theme **future** as we take a look into the future at several levels. Atomic and nuclear physics were often referred to as *modern physics* during the 20th century. The non-classical ideas of quantum mechanics in particular open a window on the microscopic structure of molecules and therefore form the cornerstone of many modern sciences, from biochemistry to cell biology. The study of the atomic nucleus and its radioactive decay further opens access to medical physics and nuclear medicine.

On a second level, these chapters allow the reader to complete a comprehensive overview of the basic physics principles that play a role in the modern sciences by also covering angular momentum, magnetism of free charged particles, and magnetic resonance. These chapters are written so as to motivate further reading on techniques and principles, specifically in medical physics or even more broadly in physics as a life science.

In ancient Egyptian mythology, Ka—often depicted by a pair of arms pointing upward—differentiates a living person from the dead. It is the life force, complementing Ba, a person's personality, and Akh, the spirit that is fully resurrected in the afterlife. While Ba and Akh are the domains of the social sciences and theology, respectively, Ka has always been of great interest to natural scientists, who later referred to it as *vis vitalis*. While a life force was never found, it has motivated inquisitive minds throughout the ages: more recently, for example, Erwin Schrödinger (winner of a 1933 Nobel Prize for his contributions to quantum mechanics), who in 1945 published a book entitled *What Is Life?* When you finish reading this book, we hope that you continue to wonder about Schrödinger's question and that you continue to see the important contributions physics has made, can make, and will make in the future in our quest to embrace the *vis vitalis*.

# CHAPTER 21

# THE HUMAN BODY IN OUTER SPACE
## Circular Motion and a First Look at Radiation

Two phenomena unique to low-orbit space flight, weightlessness and the occurrence of radiation belts, are linked to the concept of uniform circular motion. This type of motion results when an object encounters constant centripetal acceleration. Gravity provides such an acceleration for objects in the vicinity of a planet or star; a uniform magnetic field causes it for a moving charged particle. The radius of the circular motion of the object depends on its speed. The centripetal acceleration is used in Newton's second law to characterize the motion of the system.

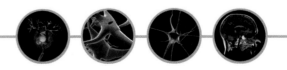

When we think of life on Earth we imagine an abundant diversity of life forms that have developed over the past four billion years, conquering every corner of the vast seas and huge continents. However, when we include the third dimension, we realize that the **biosphere** is limited to a very thin, almost two-dimensional layer sandwiched between the solid lithosphere and the sterile tranquillity of outer space. With the deepest trenches in the oceans reaching about 10 km below sea level, and our ability to breathe limited to altitudes of less than 10 km above sea level, life has adapted to a layer that is only 0.3% of the distance to the centre of Earth.

Challenging these limitations has been a human dream for centuries. The idea of reaching into the lithosphere remains a topic for science fiction (such as *A Journey to the Centre of the Earth* by Jules Verne, written in 1864). On the other hand, expanding our reach into outer space has become an option for human civilization during the past 50 years.

# Outer Space: The Challenges

The environment beyond 15 km above sea level becomes extremely hostile. A whole range of physical parameters reach values that are intolerable for all known forms of life, including humans. Fig. 21.1 illustrates the most important changes. The axis at the left shows the altitude above sea level. Note that this is a logarithmic scale, ranging from 1 km to 100 000 km. The average distance of the Moon is about 384 000 km; thus, the Moon is off the scale—but not by much.

The first parameter that changes significantly with height is **air pressure**. Gravity prevents atmospheric gases from escaping into outer space and holds most of their components near the surface. The pressure already drops noticeably below altitudes of 13 km (the limit of oxygen breathing), with an air pressure decrease by about a factor of 10, as shown on the first axis on the right-hand side of Fig. 21.1. The pressure diminishes faster at higher altitudes, to about 0.1% at 50 km and to about 1 billionth of the pressure at ground at the altitude where the **International Space Station** (ISS) orbits Earth (between 370 km and 460 km). Exposure to such low pressures causes instant death. The human body must be protected with a pressurized suit at altitudes above 19 km.

The planet Mars has a much thinner atmosphere than Earth. This is due to the mass of Mars, which is only about 10% that of Earth. The gravitational pull of Mars is not sufficient to prevent light molecules such as oxygen and nitrogen from escaping over a period of millions or billions of years.

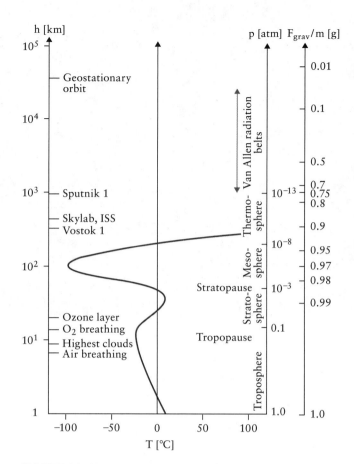

**FIGURE 21.1**

Temperature profile of the atmosphere. The left axis is a logarithmic scale of the altitude. The two axes at the right indicate the pressure profile in unit atm and the gravitational acceleration relative to the gravitational acceleration at sea level as a function of altitude.

The second parameter that changes notably with altitude is the **environmental temperature**. The temperature profile of the atmosphere is shown as the red curve at the centre of Fig. 21.1. Several zones are identified on the basis of their temperature due to complex composition variations and dynamic processes in the atmosphere. The human body cannot withstand temperatures outside the interval from 0°C to +50°C for extended periods. Thus, temperature becomes a problem within a few kilometres from the ground, as we already know from mountain climbing.

Since the effects of temperature and pressure variations on the human body have been discussed in previous chapters, in this chapter we focus on changes in two other parameters: the reduction of gravity and the exposure to energetic particles and X-rays. That these factors play a unique role at high altitudes is evident from the fact that the field of their study, **aerospace medicine**, is a distinct discipline within medicine. It emerged as an extension of aviation medicine, which started about 1784 when physiological experiments were made on the newly developed hot-air balloons (the first manned ascent was in November 1783, by Joseph Montgolfier). This type of research yielded the oxygen mask in 1894 and the pressurized suit in 1934. **Space medicine** began in 1948 with animal testing on rockets. In 1957, Russia sent a dog into orbit, followed by a monkey launched in 1958 by the United States. The first human in space was Yuri Gagarin on *Vostok I*, which orbited Earth once on April 12, 1961, during a 1-hour-and-48-minute flight (Gagarin was killed seven years later in a test-airplane crash).

The early space explorations eliminated some space-travel concerns; for example, the 21-day quarantine of the first Apollo missions to the Moon were scrapped during later missions as no extraterrestrial microbes were detected, and the worries about emotional stress due to close confinement proved unfounded thanks to the intensive training of the astronauts.

However, as missions became longer, two serious health issues moved into the forefront of aerospace medical research: **weightlessness** was found to severely diminish bone development and muscle strength, and radiation levels were found to be more critical than anticipated.

Since we have not yet discussed in this textbook the physics associated with both of these issues, we will focus on them in detail in this last group of chapters. Before we do so, we take another look at Fig. 21.1 to see what implications these issues have for our modern, space station–based exploration of outer space.

First, we focus on the axis at the far right of the figure. It shows the magnitude of the gravitational force divided by the mass of the object. What does this axis mean? We start with **Newton's law of gravity**:

$$F_{gravity} = G* \frac{m \cdot M}{r^2} \qquad [1]$$

in which $M$ is the mass of Earth. Note that the radius in the denominator is kept variable (not set equal to $R_{Earth}$) because we want to describe the distance to the centre of the planet from any point, not just points on the surface of Earth. This way we don't limit our considerations to the gravitational effect at the surface of Earth—as we did in Chapter 3, where we found that we can rewrite the gravitational force as the weight $W = m \cdot g$ at sea level. Dividing Eq. [1] by the mass $m$ of the object attracted by Earth, we find for the gravitational acceleration (in unit m/s²):

$$\frac{F_{gravity}}{m} = G* \frac{M_{Earth}}{r^2} \qquad [2]$$

i.e., the gravitational pull on the object decreases with the square of the distance of the object from the

centre of Earth. The right axis in Fig. 21.1 does not provide the gravitational acceleration in absolute units but as a multiple of $g$, which is the gravitational acceleration at sea level introduced in Chapter 3 as:

$$g = \frac{G* \cdot M_{Earth}}{r_{Earth}^2} = 9.8 \frac{m}{s^2} \qquad [3]$$

To quantify values on the right axis of Fig. 21.1, we divide Eq. [2] by $g$:

$$\frac{F_{gravity}/m}{g} = \left( \frac{R_{Earth}}{r} \right)^2 \qquad [4]$$

which now provides us with the relative gravitational acceleration, which diminishes with height as the factor on the right-hand side of Eq. [4].

## Concept Question 21.1

**Fig. 21.2 shows four plots of the relative gravity as a multiple of *g* versus the distance from the centre of Earth. The graphs begin at *r* = *R*<sub>Earth</sub>; i.e., they represent positions above Earth's surface. Which of the plots shown is correct?**

ANSWER: Choice (D). The first two plots do not show a reduction in gravity with distance. The third plot is linear; i.e., the right-hand side of the formula would have to be of the form $a - b \cdot r$, with $a$ and $b$ constants. The actual dependence is $F_{gravity}/(m \cdot g) \propto 1/r^2$ in Eq. [4].

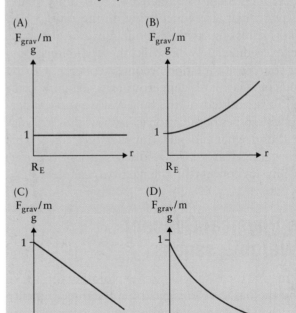

**FIGURE 21.2**

Four plots of the relative gravity as a multiple of *g* versus the distance from the centre of Earth. The graphs begin at *r* = *R*<sub>E</sub> = *R*<sub>Earth</sub>; i.e., they represent positions above Earth's surface.

Inspecting the axis of the relative gravitational acceleration in Fig. 21.1 more closely, we notice that the ISS, like its U.S. forerunner Skylab, orbits at a height where the gravitational acceleration is still about 90% of the value at sea level. This means that people at that height should weigh about 90% of what they weigh down here on the surface of Earth. Why, then, do astronauts float weightlessly in the ISS? The first section of this chapter will answer that question.

All the original plans for manned space exploration were dashed when Explorer I, a U.S. satellite sent into space in February 1958, discovered a belt of high-intensity ionizing radiation starting at an altitude of about 1000 km above Earth. The belt was named the **van Allen belt** in honour of the Explorer mission chief. By now we know of three such belts, reaching out into space as far as 25 000 km. The radiation exposure in the inner belt can exceed in an hour the annual limit allowed for professionals exposed to radioactive materials by a factor of 10! This limits the possible altitudes for orbiting space stations, such as the ISS, to a narrow gap above the point where the atmosphere is still too dense and would slow the station down too much, and the lower end of the van Allen radiation belt.

The radiation belts are not too dangerous for interplanetary travel because astronauts in a spaceship pass through them in a relatively short time, as did 27 Americans twice when flying on the *Apollo 8* to *Apollo 17* missions to the Moon. However, for space travel exceeding a few days (like the *Apollo* missions) other sources of radiation become a concern. During periods of solar flares dangerous levels of gamma radiation are emitted by the Sun. We want to understand what types of radiation exist, how they are generated, and what biological impact they have. This will become clear when we discuss atomic and nuclear physics concepts in the next two chapters.

# The Physical Concept of Weightlessness

The major focus of human exploration of space during the past 50 years has been the direct vicinity of Earth. Once the Moon-landing programs were completed by the end of 1972 (with a total of 80 hours spent on its surface), attention turned to the development of space stations. Russia maintained seven Salyut stations in orbit between 1971 and 1991 and operated the Mir station from 1986 to 2001. The United States started with the Skylab program, active from 1973 to 1979, but NASA then turned its attention to the space shuttle program, for which the longest stay was just over 16 days in orbit. Since 2000, an international group of space agencies has operated the International Space Station. The longest period an individual astronaut has stayed in space was 84 days on the Skylab mission, and 437 days on the Mir station.

While no adverse effects due to weightlessness were observed during earlier missions, which were always completed within a few days, extended periods of time spent under conditions of weightlessness were found to lead to serious structural decay of the human bones, with a **calcium loss** of 1% to 2% per month. Recovery after the space flight is partially possible, but the recovery time is very long. But how can this happen to an astronaut in the ISS? Doesn't Fig. 21.1 imply that the gravitational force in the ISS is about 90% of the gravitational force at ground? To clarify this apparent discrepancy in the argument we must first study the concept of circular motion.

## Concept Question 21.2

**Can we create the condition of weightlessness without space travel?**

ANSWER: Yes. Many amusement parks offer rollercoaster rides or similar attractions in which the paying customer falls freely for a very short period of time. This can be extended up to several minutes with a **parabola flight**. In this approach, an airplane is allowed to fall just fast enough to have the passengers float freely in mid-air. It is called a parabola flight because it simulates the motion of a rock thrown upward at an angle. Assume you were in a cavity inside the rock: you would float apparently weightless relative to the mantle of the rock until the rock hits the ground. In the case of an airplane, the pilot doesn't shut the engines off (that could not be reversed in time to prevent a crash landing) but carefully flies a parabolic trajectory to simulate the same situation as occurs in the stone cavity.

This isn't a thrill for everyone; not only is it a stomach-wrenching experience, but it is also very expensive to book such a flight. Most of these flights are done for research purposes, for example, to test materials properties or fast biological and chemical processes under zero-$g$ conditions.

## Uniform Circular Motion

When we studied Newton's laws in Chapter 3 we focussed on the motion of an object along a straight line, even when applying the second law to cases

(a)

(b)

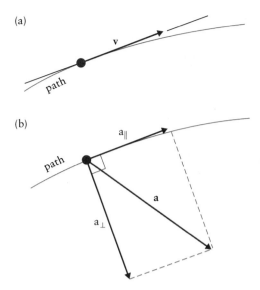

**FIGURE 21.3**

An object (blue dot) moving along a curved path. The indicated velocity components (a) and acceleration components (b) are derived for an object-centred coordinate system. The index ∥ indicates components tangential and the index ⊥ components perpendicular to the path.

where an acceleration changes the velocity of the object. While the restriction to linear motion is a useful simplification for many mechanical problems, it must be lifted when we want to include the motion of an object along a curved path.

Such a motion is illustrated in Fig. 21.3. The line labelled **path** is the line connecting all successive positions of the object, which is shown as a blue dot. At the instant shown, the object moves with a given velocity **v**, as illustrated in Fig. 21.3(a), and a given acceleration **a**, as illustrated in Fig. 21.3(b). Velocity is defined as the change of position with time. Thus, the direction of the velocity is tangential to the path of the object; i.e., it has a component along the path but not perpendicular to it. One way to write this is to use a Cartesian coordinate system that introduces fixed $x$- and $y$-axes in space:

$$\lim_{\Delta t \to 0} \frac{\Delta x}{\Delta t} = v_x$$

$$\lim_{\Delta t \to 0} \frac{\Delta y}{\Delta t} = v_y$$

[5]

Both $x$- and $y$-components of the velocity change with time: $v_x = v_x(t)$ and $v_y = v_y(t)$. Alternatively, we can substitute the Cartesian coordinates with a **coordinate system that is attached to the object**. The two directions that replace the fixed $x$- and $y$-axes are an axis along the direction tangential to the path of the object, leading to a velocity component $v_\parallel = |v|$, and an axis perpendicular to the tangential direction, leading to a velocity component $v_\perp = 0$. This coordinate

system therefore allows us to reduce the number of time-dependent variables to one, $v_\parallel = v_\parallel(t)$.

If a velocity changes with time, e.g., to obtain a curved path, an acceleration is needed. This acceleration is illustrated in Fig. 21.3(b). To quantify it, we start again with the general definition of acceleration based on a Cartesian coordinate system:

$$\lim_{\Delta t \to 0} \frac{\Delta v_x}{\Delta t} = a_x$$

$$\lim_{\Delta t \to 0} \frac{\Delta v_y}{\Delta t} = a_y$$

[6]

in which, then, both components are a function of time, $a_x = a_x(t)$ and $a_y = a_y(t)$, to obtain a curved path. We can again use the object-centred coordinate system, which leads to the two components shown in Fig. 21.3(b): $a_\parallel$ and $a_\perp$. Choosing this coordinate system represents a great simplification for uniform circular motion, as we will see next.

*Objects that travel on curved paths are best described by an object-centred coordinate system with one axis parallel and one axis perpendicular to the path of the object. In this case, the velocity and acceleration are written as:* **v** $= (v_\parallel, 0)$ *and* **a** $= (a_\parallel, a_\perp)$.

We justify a further simplification regarding the tangential acceleration component: we limit our discussion to cases in which the tangential acceleration is zero, i.e., the object moves with a constant tangential velocity component. A first argument in support of this assumption is that the motion associated with a tangential acceleration component has already been described fully in Chapter 3: the object accelerates in the direction of the velocity vector, which results in motion along a straight line. The more important argument is that the assumption is one of two assumptions that lead to **uniform circular motion**, which is a type of motion observed often in nature. The second assumption we need for uniform circular motion is that the perpendicular acceleration component is constant; i.e., $a_\parallel = 0$ and $a_\perp = $ const. The term *uniform* refers to the fact that the magnitude of the velocity of the object does not change; i.e.,

$$a_\parallel = 0 \quad \Rightarrow \quad v_\parallel = |v| = \text{const} \qquad [7]$$

The term *circular* indicates that the path becomes a circular path. You can convince yourself that the assumption $a_\perp = $ const indeed results in circular motion by using an object that is attached to a string. When you swing the object horizontally, the fixed length of the string forces the object onto a circular path around your hand. Throughout the swing you need the same magnitude of force to keep the object

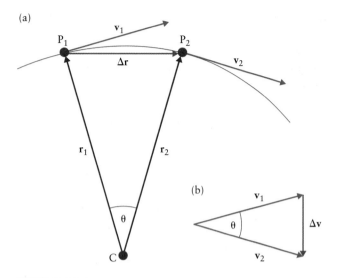

**FIGURE 21.4**

Position and velocity components for an object moving along a circular path, shown at two different times that we label with indices 1 and 2.

on its path; the constant magnitude of force is associated with a constant magnitude of acceleration due to Newton's second law. Note, however, that neither the acceleration nor the needed force are constant, as both are vectors that continuously change their directions.

We want to further quantify the relations between the various parameters describing a uniform circular motion. To do so, we specify several parameters in Fig. 21.4. Part (a) shows two points, $P_1$ and $P_2$, along the circular path with centre $C$. The two points are characterized by position vectors $\mathbf{r}_1$ and $\mathbf{r}_2$, which subtend an angle $\theta$. The two points on the path are separated by a distance $\Delta r$. An object at point $P_1$ has the velocity $\mathbf{v}_1$, and at point $P_2$ it has the velocity $\mathbf{v}_2$. Sketch 21.4(b) illustrates the corresponding relation between the two velocity vectors: they also describe an angle $\theta$ due to the geometrical fact that both $\mathbf{r}_1 \mathrel{\rotatebox[origin=c]{90}{$\sqsubset$}} \mathbf{v}_1$ and $\mathbf{r}_2 \mathrel{\rotatebox[origin=c]{90}{$\sqsubset$}} \mathbf{v}_2$. The difference between $\mathbf{v}_1$ and $\mathbf{v}_2$ is defined as $\Delta \mathbf{v}$.

We relate the perpendicular acceleration component $a_\perp$ to the velocity and the radius of the path by using the two sketches in Fig. 21.4. For this we assume that only a very short time $\Delta t$ has elapsed as the object moves from point $P_1$ to point $P_2$. That means that both $\Delta \mathbf{r}$ and $\Delta \mathbf{v}$ are very short vectors and $\theta$ is a small angle. Using trigonometry we find from the two parts of Fig. 21.4, respectively:

$$\sin \theta = \frac{|\Delta \mathbf{r}|}{r}$$

$$\sin \theta = \frac{|\Delta \mathbf{v}|}{v} \qquad [8]$$

In Eq. [8], we simplified the notation to $|\mathbf{r}_1| = |\mathbf{r}_2| = r$ and $|\mathbf{v}_1| = |\mathbf{v}_2| = v$ since both position vectors and both velocity vectors have the same magnitude. Next we combine both formulas in Eq. [8]:

$$|\Delta \mathbf{v}| = \frac{v}{r}|\Delta \mathbf{r}| \qquad [9]$$

We divide Eq. [9] on both sides by the elapsed time interval $\Delta t$:

$$\frac{\Delta v}{\Delta t} = \frac{v}{r}\frac{\Delta r}{\Delta t} \qquad [10]$$

Taking the limit $\Delta t \to 0$ on both sides, we get:

$$a_\perp = \frac{v^2}{r} \qquad [11]$$

in which the limit of $\Delta v/\Delta t$ is $a_\perp$, and the limit of $\Delta r/\Delta t$ is $v$, because $a_\perp$ and $v$ are instantaneous values. This acceleration is called the **centripetal acceleration** because it is a constant acceleration toward the centre of the circular path. It is important to note again that the acceleration in Eq. [11] is not an $x$- or a $y$-component in the $xy$-plane of the circular motion; in respect to fixed $x$- and $y$-axes the components of the centripetal acceleration continuously change.

*Uniform circular motion results when the velocity of an object along its path is constant and a constant acceleration toward the centre of the circular path occurs. This is called the centripetal acceleration.*

The period $T$ is the time to complete a full cycle. Since the circumference of a circle has the length $2 \cdot \pi \cdot r$, this definition allows us to rewrite the velocity as $2 \cdot \pi \cdot r/T$. Substituting this in Eq. [11] leads to a second formula for the centripetal acceleration:

$$a_\perp = \frac{4 \cdot \pi^2 \cdot r}{T^2} \qquad [12]$$

The centripetal acceleration is larger for an object moving around the centre with a shorter period, and it is larger for an object at a greater distance from the centre of the path. The angular frequency is the angle (in unit radians) through which an object on a cyclic path passes in one second: $\omega = 2 \cdot \pi/T$. This allows us to rewrite the centripetal acceleration in Eq. [11] in a third form:

$$a_\perp = \omega^2 \cdot r \qquad [13]$$

## Concept Question 21.3

**Where on planet Earth is $a_\perp = 0$?**

ANSWER: At the geographical North and South Poles, which are the points at which the rotation axis intersects with the surface of Earth. People standing at one of the poles spin about their own axis once in 24 hours. Note that the person does not move about the centre of Earth on a circle of radius $R_{Earth}$, since Earth rotates about an axis connecting its geographical North and South Poles. Thus, the distance to the axis is $r = 0$ at the poles and we find $a_\perp = 0$.

## ● EXAMPLE 21.1

Calculate the centripetal acceleration due to the rotation of Earth of a person in New York. New York is located at 40.8° northern geographical latitude. Note that this acceleration is independent from the gravitational acceleration caused by the attraction between the two objects Earth and person. Use $R_{Earth} = 6370$ km for the radius of Earth.

*Solution:* The period of Earth is 1 day, which corresponds to 86 400 s. As noted in Concept Question 21.3, a point at $\theta = 40.8°$ above the equator moves on a circle with a radius $r = R_{Earth} \cdot \cos \theta$, as illustrated in Fig. 21.5. This allows us to calculate the centripetal acceleration required to keep a person in New York on the ground:

$$a = \frac{4 \cdot \pi^2 \cdot R_{Earth} \cdot \cos \theta}{T_{Earth}^2} \quad [14]$$

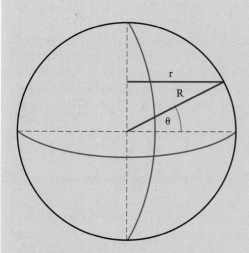

**FIGURE 21.5**

Illustration of the position of New York, at latitude $\theta = 40.8°$. Note that the distance to the axis, $r$, is different from Earth's radius, $R$.

which leads with the specific values of the example text to:

$$a = \frac{4 \cdot \pi^2 (6.37 \times 10^6 \, \text{m})\cos 40.8°}{(8.64 \times 10^4 \, \text{s})^2}$$

$$= 0.026 \, \frac{\text{m}}{\text{s}^2} \quad [15]$$

Note that this result is much smaller than the gravitational acceleration. Thus, gravity provides a more than sufficient downward force to keep us from floating off the ground.

## ● EXAMPLE 21.2

How fast would Earth have to spin to have a person in New York float apparently weightlessly across the room?

*Solution:* This would happen if the centripetal acceleration were equal to the gravitational acceleration. In this case the entire gravitational pull would be needed to keep us on a circular path as Earth spins and no fraction of gravity would be left to pull us down onto the ground. We rewrite Eq. [12] to determine the period of Earth required for this case:

$$T = 2 \cdot \pi \sqrt{\frac{r}{a_\perp}} = 2 \cdot \pi \sqrt{\frac{R_{Earth} \cdot \cos \theta}{g}} \quad [16]$$

in which we can substitute the specific values given in the example text:

$$T = 2 \cdot \pi \sqrt{\frac{(6.37 \times 10^6 \, \text{m})\cos 40.8°}{9.8 \, \frac{\text{m}}{\text{s}^2}}}$$

$$= 4410 \, \text{s} \quad [17]$$

This result means that Earth would have to spin around once every 1 hour and 13.5 minutes, which would be the length of a day in this case. Such fast-spinning planets don't exist in our planetary system. The fastest is Jupiter, with 0.41 days for one revolution.

## Centripetal Acceleration and Newton's Laws

What causes the centripetal acceleration? As before, we consider Newton's laws when trying to address force issues. However, we have to be careful because we do not want to return to the Cartesian coordinates used for **Newton's second law** in component form in Chapter 3. Trying to do this here would require us to determine the $x$- and $y$-components of the acceleration in Eq. [11].

For circular motion, we have to rewrite Newton's second law with a different set of three perpendicular axes, two representing the plane in which the circular motion occurs and one that we call the $z$-component, which is perpendicular to the plane of the circular motion. In this textbook, we will consider only cases in which the velocity component in this $z$-direction is constant or zero, i.e., cases where Newton's first law applies in the $z$-direction.

In the plane of circular motion (the $xy$-plane), we use the directions parallel and perpendicular to the object's path as our coordinates. Continuing to use the simplification $a_\parallel = 0$, we write Newton's laws for the case of a uniform circular motion in the form:

$$\text{(I)} \quad \sum_i F_{i,\perp} = m\,\frac{v^2}{r}$$

$$\text{(II)} \quad \sum_i F_{i,\parallel} = 0 \qquad \qquad \text{[18]}$$

$$\text{(III)} \quad \sum_i F_{i,z} = 0$$

The formulas in Eq. [18] replace Eq. [3.30] in the case of circular motion. Without the simplifying assumptions we made, the right-hand side of the second and third formulas in Eq. [18] would be written as $m \cdot a_\parallel$ and $m \cdot a_z$, respectively.

*Newton's second law applies to circular motion, with the acceleration identified as the centripetal acceleration.*

Newton's laws in Eq. [18] reveal the direction in which the net force acts in a circular motion: perpendicular to the path within the plane in which the circular motion occurs. It is interesting to note that no identifiable force exists that we can call the centripetal force; i.e., no additional force exists in a system with a circular motion. The sum of forces (i.e., the net force) on the left-hand side of the first formula in Eq. [18] is unfortunately sometimes referred to as centripetal force.

An important assumption of Newton's mechanics is that we must be able to find a physical object causing each force. In turn, we should not find any object causing a force if the force is not individually identified in Newton's laws. Although it is always hard to prove that something doesn't exist (since there are an infinite number of possibilities one may have to test), it are instructive to try—and fail—to find an object causing an independent "centripetal force" in the examples we discuss below.

# Centripetal Acceleration Caused by Contact Forces

In this section, we illustrate how tension and normal forces can cause uniform circular motion. The conical pendulum, the Ferris wheel, and blood rushing through the aortic arch serve as examples.

## ● EXAMPLE 21.3

An object of mass $m$ is placed at the end of a string of length $L$. It swings along a horizontal circle with constant speed $|v|$ at angle $\beta$ with the vertical direction, as illustrated in Fig. 21.6(a). How does the time $T$ for a single revolution depend on the angle $\beta$? *Note:* This arrangement is called a **conical pendulum**, and is shown in a photograph in Fig. 21.6(b).

*Solution:* Although it is undesirable, in this example we use the same letter for two different quantities, the period and the tension. This is possible because one is a scalar (the period) and the other is a vector (the tension). By maintaining the notation $|\mathbf{T}|$ for the magnitude of the tension, no confusion should occur.

First, we identify the object as the system. The forces acting on the system are the tension, caused by the string, and the weight, caused by Earth. Note that we do *not* identify a separate centripetal force, because no further force acts on the system in Fig. 21.6! Next, we draw the free-body diagram. In accordance with the discussion earlier in this section, we identify the vertical direction as the $z$-direction because this direction is perpendicular to the $xy$-plane of the circular motion. In the $xy$-plane, the directions perpendicular and tangential to the path are identified. To draw a two-dimensional free-body diagram we neglect the direction tangential to the path, because we know that the second formula of Eq. [18] applies in the given form. The resulting free-body diagram is illustrated in Fig. 21.7. Using this figure we write the two non-trivial formulas from Eq. [18] for the present example:

$$\sum_i F_{i,\perp} = |\mathbf{T}| \cdot \sin\beta = m\,\frac{v^2}{r}$$

$$\sum_i F_{i,z} = |\mathbf{T}| \cdot \cos\beta - m \cdot g = 0 \qquad \text{[19]}$$

In the first formula of Eq. [19], the net force directed toward the centre of the circular path is identified as the horizontal component of the tension $\mathbf{T}$ in the string. The second formula in Eq. [19] states that a mechanical equilibrium exists in the vertical direction.

(a)

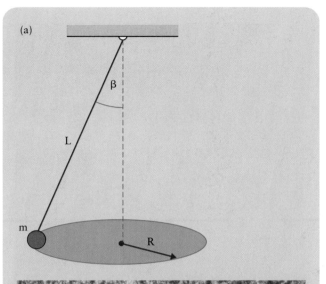

**FIGURE 21.6**

(a) An object of mass $m$ is attached to a string of length $L$ and moves along a circular path of radius $R$. The string forms an angle $\beta$ with the vertical. (b) Photograph of a conical pendulum.

It is useful to distinguish between the known and unknown variables in Eq. [19] and compare them with the parameters we are asked to quantify in the example text. The text refers to four quantities: the mass $m$, the length $L$, the speed $v$, and the angle $\beta$. Of these, the mass and the length

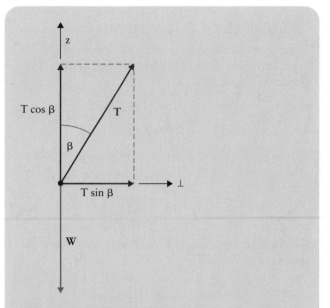

**FIGURE 21.7**

Free-body diagram for the object (red dot) shown in Fig. 21.6(a). Note that an object-centred coordinate system is used with the horizontal axis labelled $\perp$, i.e., pointing in a direction perpendicular to the path of the object.

are fixed and the angle is variable. Further, the period of the motion varies, which means the speed is also a variable.

Now we check Eq. [19]. The two formulas in the equation contain a total of four variables: the magnitude of the tension $|\mathbf{T}|$, the angle $\beta$, the speed of the object $v$, and the radius of the circular path $R$. From geometrical considerations based on Fig. 21.6(a), one additional formula is written that connects some of the unknown variables: the radius of the circular path $R$ is related to the length of the string and $\beta$ by $R = L \cdot \sin \beta$.

The two formulas in Eq. [19] and this geometrical relation do not introduce the period of the motion. Since the example text asks about this quantity, we need to introduce a fourth formula relating the speed, the circumference of the circular path, and the period: $v = 2 \cdot \pi \cdot R/T$. This formula allows us to exchange the variable speed for the period. Thus, the four formulas we have written for this example contain five unknown variables: (i) tension $|\mathbf{T}|$, (ii) period $T$, (iii) velocity $|v|$, (iv) radius $R$, and (v) angle $\beta$. Consequently, we cannot calculate any of these unknown parameters, but we can write how any one of them depends on any one of the others.

The example text asks us specifically to calculate $T = f(\beta)$; i.e., the tension, velocity, and radius have to be eliminated. We use the two formulas in Eq. [19] to eliminate the tension, then use $R = L \cdot \sin \beta$ to eliminate the radius, and finally eliminate the velocity with $v = 2 \cdot \pi \cdot R/T$. We show

## ● EXAMPLE 21.3 (continued)

step by step how this is done. We first combine the two formulas in Eq. [19] by dividing the first formula by the second:

$$\tan \beta = \frac{v^2}{g \cdot R} \qquad [20]$$

Then we eliminate the radius in the equation for the velocity:

$$v = \frac{2 \cdot \pi \cdot R}{T} = \frac{2 \cdot \pi \cdot L \cdot \sin \beta}{T} \qquad [21]$$

In the next step, Eq. [21] is used to substitute the velocity in Eq. [20]:

$$\tan \beta = \frac{\left( \dfrac{2 \cdot \pi \cdot L \cdot \sin \beta}{T} \right)^2}{g \cdot L \cdot \sin \beta}$$

$$= \frac{4 \cdot \pi^2 \cdot L \cdot \sin \beta}{g \cdot T^2} \qquad [22]$$

which, with $\tan \beta = \sin \beta / \cos \beta$, leads to:

$$\cos \beta = \frac{g \cdot T^2}{4 \cdot \pi^2 \cdot L} \qquad [23]$$

Eq. [23] is then solved for the period:

$$T = 2 \cdot \pi \sqrt{\frac{L \cdot \cos \beta}{g}} \qquad [24]$$

This is the formula sought in the problem text.

We can test this relation with an object attached to a string. Hold the string and vary the speed with which you let the object move in a horizontal circle. If it moves slowly (long period) the object is at a small angle $\beta$ (which corresponds to a large $\cos \beta$). When you let the object move faster, the angle $\beta$ becomes larger.

## ● EXAMPLE 21.4

We compare one person at the top and one at the bottom on a **Ferris wheel**, as shown in Fig. 21.8(b). The Ferris wheel rotates with a constant tangential speed, $|v|_{top} = |v|_{bottom}$. Determine the force the seats exert on each person.

*Solution:* A large Ferris wheel is shown in Fig. 21.8(a). Two forces act on people in a Ferris

(a)

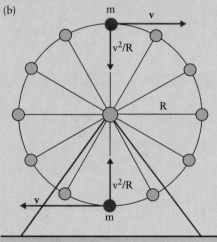

(b)

**FIGURE 21.8**

(a) Photograph of a Ferris wheel. (b) A Ferris wheel with two persons (blue dots) in the seats at top and at bottom. The Ferris wheel has a radius $R$ and rotates such that both persons move with a speed $|v|$.

wheel: the weight and the normal force exerted by the seat. This leads to the two free-body diagrams shown in Fig. 21.9 for a person at the top and a person at the bottom. Since no forces

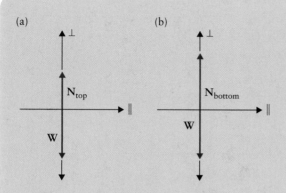

**FIGURE 21.9**

Free-body diagram for (a) a person in the top seat, and (b) a person in the bottom seat of the Ferris wheel shown in Fig. 21.8(b). Note that the coordinate system is attached to the person, and therefore is not fixed in space.

act perpendicular to the plane or in the tangential direction, only the first formula in Eq. [18] is used. For the person at the top, it reads:

$$\sum_i F_{i,\perp} = N_{top} - m \cdot g = -m\frac{v^2}{r} \quad [25]$$

in which the negative sign on the right-hand side establishes the centripetal acceleration as directed downward, consistent with Fig. 21.8(b). Eq. [25] allows us to calculate the force exerted by the seat:

$$N_{top} = m\left(g - \frac{v^2}{r}\right) < m \cdot g \quad [26]$$

Thus, the person at the top feels lighter, which is an effect that is obviously felt more strongly at higher speeds, e.g., on a rollercoaster ride. The corresponding Newtonian equation for the person at the bottom reads:

$$\sum_i F_{i,\perp} = N_{bottom} - m \cdot g = +m\frac{v^2}{r} \quad [27]$$

with the direction of the centripetal acceleration being the only difference between Eqs. [25] and [27], based on Fig. 21.9. This leads to the following form for the force exerted by the seat:

$$N_{bottom} = m\left(g + \frac{v^2}{r}\right) > m \cdot g \quad [28]$$

i.e., the person feels heavier than on steady ground.

**Concept Question 21.4**

Explain the Windkessel effect, as illustrated in Fig. 16.11, with the concept of circular motion.

ANSWER: The Windkessel effect is the result of the blood ejected from the heart moving through the 180° arch of the aorta. Like the person at the top of the Ferris wheel, the blood has to be accelerated toward the centre of the arch (centripetal acceleration). The necessary force is exerted on the blood by the wall of the aorta. In a system with two objects interacting, an equal but opposite force must act on the wall of the aorta. Since the wall of the aorta is elastic, it responds to this apparent force by stretching outward.

## Centrifugation

In Chapter 4 we discussed the terminal speed of an object moving with friction through a medium. Terminal speeds are observed for the frictional force proportional to the speed of the object, $\mathcal{F} \propto v$, and, as discussed in Chapter 4, for $\mathcal{F} \propto v^2$. The linear case applies to objects sinking more slowly through a solution. The mechanical equilibrium condition that leads to a constant (terminal) speed is:

$$F_{net} = F_{buoyant} + \mathcal{F} - W = 0 \quad [29]$$

in which the buoyant force and the frictional force act upward and the weight of the object downward. Substituting the buoyant force from Chapter 11 and $\mathcal{F} = k \cdot v$ for the object's friction, we find:

$$F_{net} = \frac{\rho_{fluid}}{\rho_{object}} m \cdot g + k \cdot v_{terminal} - W = 0 \quad [30]$$

in which $m$ is the mass of the object. Eq. [30] allows us to write the terminal speed $v_{terminal}$:

$$v_{terminal} = \frac{m \cdot g}{k}\left(1 - \frac{\rho_{fluid}}{\rho_{object}}\right) \quad [31]$$

This speed is called the **sedimentation rate**. Sedimentation rates are quite small for most biological samples of interest; e.g., a blood cell sinks in blood plasma at a rate of about 5 cm per hour. Biomolecules are even slower, as they are smaller than a cell. These rates therefore limit the speed with which biological samples can be analyzed.

Centrifuges are used to increase the sedimentation rate. Instead of the gravitational acceleration $g$ in Eq. [31], a radial acceleration applies that is caused by a rapid rotation of the solution in a test tube. The

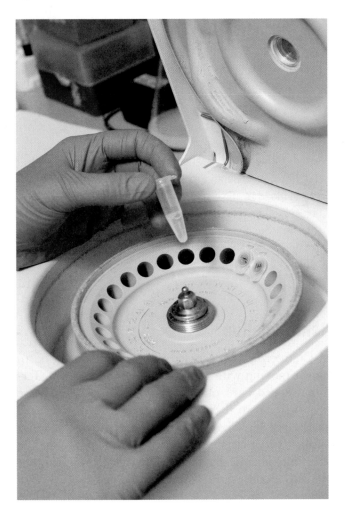

**FIGURE 21.10**

A laboratory centrifuge.

radial acceleration is $a_{\text{radial}} = \omega^2 \cdot r$, with $\omega$ the angular frequency of the centrifuge and $r$ the distance of the sample from the rotation axis. In a centrifuge, Eq. [31] is written in the form:

$$v_{\text{terminal}} = \frac{m \cdot \omega^2 \cdot r}{k}\left(1 - \frac{\rho_{\text{fluid}}}{\rho_{\text{object}}}\right) \qquad [32]$$

The sedimentation rate is proportional to the mass of the object. Thus, the heaviest components in a solution collect at the bottom of the test tube. A modern laboratory centrifuge is shown in Fig. 21.10.

### Concept Question 21.5

A typical centrifuge spins with an angular frequency of 5250 rad/s. The top end of an 8-cm-long test tube in this centrifuge is 5 cm from the axis of rotation. Find the effective value of the radial acceleration as a multiple of the gravitational acceleration $g$ at the bottom of the test tube.

ANSWER: We use $a_{\text{radial}} = \omega^2 \cdot r$ with $r = 8\text{ cm} + 5\text{ cm} = 13\text{ cm}$:

$$\frac{a_{\text{radial}}}{g} = \frac{\omega^2 \cdot r_{\text{bottom}}}{g}$$

$$= \frac{\left(5250\,\dfrac{\text{rad}}{\text{s}}\right)^2 (0.13\text{ m})}{9.8\,\dfrac{\text{m}}{\text{s}^2}}$$

$$= 3.7 \times 10^5 \qquad [33]$$

The test tubes must be carefully supported in the centrifuge to withstand more than 350 000 $g$!

## Centripetal Acceleration Caused by Contact-Free Forces

Contact and **contact-free forces** cause the same effect with respect to circular motion. We have seen this already in Example 21.4, where the gravitational force was used in the form of the weight of the person. Thus, Eq. [18] remains applicable when studying circular motion in these cases. Applications include:

- for gravity: the motion of satellites, including the Moon or human-made structures, the motion of planets around their central star, or even the rotation of galaxies. This case also allows us to explain in this section why astronauts in the ISS appear weightless.

- for the electric force: Bohr's atomic model in Chapter 22.

- for the magnetic force: cosmic ray particles in Earth's magnetic field, and magnetic separators such as in a mass spectrometer (discussed later in this chapter).

### ● EXAMPLE 21.5

How fast would Earth have to spin so that we could tread as lightly at the equator as the **Apollo astronaut** in Fig. 21.11 did on the Moon? *Hint:* Neglect the rotation of the Moon around its own axis.

*Solution:* We first determine the gravitational acceleration the astronaut felt on the surface of the Moon. For that, we need the following data for the Moon:

$$m_{\text{Moon}} = 7.35 \times 10^{22}\text{ kg} \cong 1.2\%\ m_{\text{Earth}}$$

$$r_{\text{Moon}} = 1.74 \times 10^6\text{m} = 27\%\ r_{\text{Earth}} \qquad [34]$$

**FIGURE 21.11**

An Apollo astronaut on the Moon.

Note that these values allow us to calculate a density for the Moon that is significantly different from that of Earth (the average density of Earth is $\rho = 5.52$ g/cm$^3$ and the average density of the Moon is $\rho = 3.33$ g/cm$^3$), implying differences in the geophysical development of the Moon and Earth. Next, we use Eq. [3] to determine the gravitational acceleration on the Moon:

$$g_{\text{Moon}} = G* \frac{m_{\text{Moon}}}{r^2_{\text{Moon}}}$$

$$= \left(6.67 \times 10^{-11} \frac{\text{m}^3}{\text{kg} \cdot \text{s}^2}\right)$$

$$\times \frac{7.35 \times 10^{22}\,\text{kg}}{(1.74 \times 10^6\,\text{m})^2} \qquad [35]$$

which leads to:

$$g_{\text{Moon}} = 1.62\,\frac{\text{m}}{\text{s}^2} = 16.5\%\ g_{\text{Earth}} \qquad [36]$$

In the second step, the required rotational speed of Earth is calculated to obtain this gravitational acceleration on Earth. The free-body diagram for a person standing on ground is very simple, and exactly the same as for the person sitting in the seat at the top of the Ferris wheel in Example 21.4. Using Eq. [26], the normal force becomes $N_{\text{top}} = m \cdot g_{\text{Moon}}$ in the present example. Thus:

$$m \cdot g_{\text{Moon}} = m\left(g_{\text{Earth}} - \frac{v^2}{R_{\text{Earth}}}\right) \qquad [37]$$

in which we use $R_{\text{Earth}}$ since the person stands on the equator. Using $v = 2 \cdot \pi \cdot r/T$ to replace the speed with the period in Eq. [37], we find:

$$g_{\text{Earth}} - g_{\text{Moon}} = \frac{v^2}{R_{\text{Earth}}} = \frac{4 \cdot \pi^2 \cdot R_{\text{Earth}}}{T^2} \qquad [38]$$

which is solved for the period $T$:

$$T = 2 \cdot \pi \sqrt{\frac{R_{\text{Earth}}}{g_{\text{Earth}} - g_{\text{Moon}}}}$$

$$= 5544\,\text{s} = 92\,\text{min} \qquad [39]$$

which is $T = 1$ hour, 32 min. Compare this result with Example 21.2.

## ● EXAMPLE 21.6

(a) The International Space Station orbits at an average altitude of $h = 430$ km. How long does the ISS need to complete one full orbit? (b) At what distance above Earth must a satellite be positioned to be in **geostationary orbit**? A satellite in geostationary orbit remains located above the same longitude on Earth all the time.

*Solution to part (a):* For the ISS to neither crash like the Mir station did in 2001, nor float to higher altitudes where the intensive radiation of the van Allen belt would force its occupants to abandon ship, the net force acting on the station perpendicular to the circular path around Earth (gravitational force) must be equal to the centripetal acceleration multiplied by the station's mass. We find from the first formula in Eq. [18], with gravity the only force contributing to the net force perpendicular to the station's motion:

$$G* \frac{m_{\text{Earth}} \cdot m_{\text{ISS}}}{(R_{\text{Earth}} + h)^2} = m_{\text{ISS}} \frac{v^2_{\text{ISS}}}{R_{\text{Earth}} + h} \qquad [40]$$

in which $R_{\text{Earth}} + h$ is the distance of the satellite from the centre of Earth. From Eq. [40] we obtain a formula for the speed of the ISS:

$$v_{\text{ISS}} = \sqrt{G* \frac{m_{\text{Earth}}}{R_{\text{Earth}} + h}} \qquad [41]$$

and with the specific values from the example text:

$$v_{\text{ISS}} = \sqrt{\left(6.67 \times 10^{-11} \frac{\text{m}^3}{\text{kg} \cdot \text{s}^2}\right) \frac{5.98 \times 10^{24}\,\text{kg}}{6800\,\text{km}}}$$

$$= 7660\,\frac{\text{m}}{\text{s}} \qquad [42]$$

This high speed is not apparent from the TV images we are used to seeing from the station, because the TV camera moves with the station!

● **EXAMPLE 21.6 (continued)**

We use the relation $v = 2 \cdot \pi \cdot r/T$ to connect the speed to the period for a full orbit:

$$v_{ISS} = \frac{2 \cdot \pi \cdot r_{orbit}}{T} \qquad [43]$$

the period for the ISS can be calculated as:

$$T = \frac{2 \cdot \pi (R_{Earth} + h)}{v_{ISS}} = \frac{2 \cdot \pi (6800 \text{ km})}{7660 \frac{m}{s}}$$

$$= 5580 \text{ s} \qquad [44]$$

i.e., the ISS moves around Earth once every 93 minutes!

*Solution to part (b):* For a geostationary orbit, the altitude $h$ in Eq. [40] must be chosen such that $T = 24$ hours. For this calculation, we again use Eq. [40] but rewrite the right-hand side with Eq. [43] in order to replace the unknown speed of the geostationary satellite with its period and radius:

$$G^* \frac{m_{Earth} \cdot m_{satellite}}{(R_{Earth} + h_{satellite})^2}$$

$$= m_{satellite} \frac{4 \cdot \pi^2 (R_{Earth} + h_{satellite})}{T^2} \qquad [45]$$

Eq. [45] allows us to express the height above ground for the geostationary satellite:

$$h_{satellite} = \left( G^* \frac{m_{Earth} \cdot T^2}{4 \cdot \pi^2} \right)^{1/3} - R_{Earth} \qquad [46]$$

The term in parentheses in Eq. [46] reads:

$$\frac{\left[ \left( 6.67 \times 10^{-11} \frac{m^3}{kg \cdot s^2} \right)(5.98 \times 10^{24} \text{ kg})(8.64 \times 10^4 \text{ s})^2 \right]^{1/3}}{4 \cdot \pi^2}$$

$$[47]$$

Thus, Eq. [46] yields:

$$h_{satellite} = 3.59 \times 10^7 \text{ m} = 35\,900 \text{ km} \qquad [48]$$

This position of the geostationary orbit is indicated in Fig. 21.1. It is used for TV and telephone transmission satellites, which have to stay continuously in contact with the ground station.

# The Physiological Effect of Weightlessness

Example 21.6(a) indicates that the weightlessness of astronauts on board the ISS is not due to the value of the gravitational force at the altitude at which the ISS

orbits Earth. The ISS and the astronauts aboard are in perpetual freefall toward Earth, but don't come closer to the surface, as they are moving with a high speed sideways.

The issues of weightlessness during a long-distance space flight—e.g., during a **Mars mission**, when the gravitational pull of Earth or Mars would be negligible for practically the entire trip—are equivalent to the problems with weightlessness encountered in the ISS. For this reason, endurance tests on the space station are of interest in aerospace medicine to determine preventive measures for future missions. To date, the longest stay on a space station was recorded for Valeriy Polyakov in 1995, who stayed on the Russian station Mir for 437 days. His program included 2 hours per day of intensive exercise to counterbalance the lack of use of his bones and muscles. Polyakov was able to walk away from the landing site under his own power.

Polyakov's record still falls short of the anticipated time that a trip to Mars would take. This is illustrated in Fig. 21.12, which shows the relative constellation of Earth and Mars at the two respective launch dates. Note that the spaceship does not travel straight outward in (b) or straight inward in (d), as it does have a tangential velocity component at launch due to the motion of each planet. Since only certain relative constellations of Earth and Mars at each launch lead to a suitable passage, there is a minimum stay of 455 days for the mission on Mars (which is

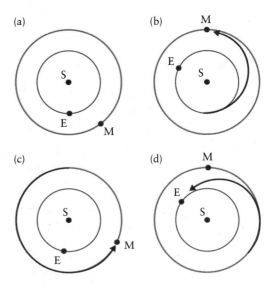

**FIGURE 21.12**

The relative positions of Earth (E) and Mars (M) in their respective orbits around the Sun (S) during (a) launch time of a Mars mission (day 0), (b) arrival time of the mission at Mars (day 257), (c) launch time for the return trip to Earth (day 714), and (d) arrival time at the completion of the mission (day 972).

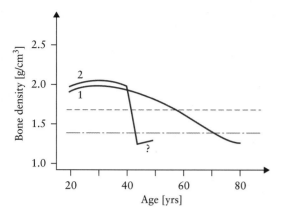

**FIGURE 21.13**

Density of human bones as a function of age (curve 1). A trained astronaut may have a slightly denser bone structure (curve 2), but encounters a significant bone density loss during a Mars mission as scheduled in Fig. 21.12. The dashed line indicates the threshold for osteopenia, and the dash-dotted line indicates the threshold for osteoporosis.

still less than a Mars year) until a return time window opens. Thus, the entire mission will last 972 days, assuming currently available technology, with a total of about 520 days under weightless conditions while travelling between the two planets.

Those 520 days of weightlessness will have a major effect on the human body, as illustrated in Fig. 21.13. Curve (1) shows the change in **bone density** for humans as a function of age for the average healthy person. The density peaks at age 30, with $\rho = 2.0$ g/cm$^3$, and then decreases steadily. The two horizontal lines indicate two critical thresholds: below the upper dashed line we speak clinically of **osteopenia,** a state of reduced bone tissue density that is considered normal in older people. Below the lower dash-dotted line we speak clinically of **osteoporosis,** which causes pain in the part of the body where the bones are affected, causes general back pain, and leads to a characteristic bent-over posture due to the collapse of vertebrae.

Using data from previous endurance stays under weightlessness, we know that a 1% to 2% loss of calcium occurs in human bones per month. Weightlessness means that the stress on our bones caused by gravity is eliminated. The body reacts by redirecting calcium to other uses in our metabolism. Thus, we would anticipate a loss of bone strength due to a loss of about 15% to 30% of bone calcium during a Mars trip. This is illustrated in curve (2) of Fig. 21.13. The curve starts at a somewhat higher density, assuming that intensive training precedes the mission. The steep reduction in bone density is due to weightlessness during the Mars mission for astronauts in their early 40s. The individual would return with a bone

structure resembling that of a fragile 80-year-old person! Note the question mark on the anticipated recovery curve. We simply don't know whether there would be a recovery, but even if there is one it must be a very slow process.

Note also that the program that the astronauts would be able to perform on Mars would be limited, as they would arrive with already weakened bones resembling those of a person in his/her mid 60s.

How do bones lose calcium? Bones are not static structures in our body, nor are they inorganic or lifeless. Bones are refurbished in very much the same fashion as other body tissues. The bones undergo a continuous process of adding and removing calcium minerals to and from a frame-like template of collagen. Collagen, a rubber-like protein, allows bones to bend slightly without breaking. The large, calcium-containing phosphate molecules filling the structure are called hydroxyapatite. These make the entire structure almost as strong as concrete. Two additional components of the bone structure are osteoblasts and osteoclasts. Osteoblasts are bone-growing cells secreting minerals that eventually entomb the cell. In spite of being immobilized in this fashion, they stay alive and contribute to the porous, spongy nature of the bones. Osteoclasts are bone-removing cells that tear down the bone structure for replacement or for scavenging calcium if it is needed elsewhere in the body.

Heavy use of certain bones can lead to significant bone diameter increases. For example, the bones in the playing arm of a professional tennis player are up to 30% thicker than normal.

# Radiation Exposure

## Cosmic Rays

The first indication of intensive radiation outside of Earth's atmosphere was found in 1910, when Viktor Hess noted that the intensity of environmental radiation increases with altitude. He correctly concluded that the radiation must come from outer space, and therefore called it **cosmic rays.**

The intensity of cosmic rays reaching sea level is rather low, at about 1 particle/cm$^2$ min. What arrives at sea level is secondary radiation, caused by reactions between the primary radiation and the molecules in the atmosphere at about 20 km altitude. The primary radiation consists of 85% protons, 14% helium nuclei ($\alpha$-particles), and about 1% nuclei of heavier elements ranging from lithium to iron. This distribution matches the composition of stars, hinting at the radiation's origin in supernova explosions.

The next important discovery was that the cosmic radiation is not reaching Earth uniformly from all directions. Instead, the intensity varies with geographic latitude, as shown in Fig. 21.14. At sea level the variation is weaker (indicated by the curve labelled with the pressure value of 760 torr), but at greater altitudes, where the atmospheric pressure is reduced to 600 torr (centre curve) and 450 torr (top curve), the intensity of the radiation not only is increased, as originally found by Hess, but also shows a strong latitude dependence, with higher levels of radiation close to the poles. This effect is not the result of unevenly distributed events in the deep universe, but is an Earth-bound effect. This was established when the U.S. satellite **Explorer I** discovered the radiation belts in 1958. These belts span the outer parts of the atmosphere, between 1000 and 25 000 km altitude. Three distinct belts exist, with the innermost belt containing high electron densities with particle energies of 0.8 MeV and protons of extremely high energy, reaching beyond 150 MeV. The outer belts are populated only by electrons.

We want to study the effect that this radiation has on astronauts. From war- and peacetime testing of atomic and hydrogen bombs, as well from medical applications, we know that these effects may be severe. A first example is given by Fig. 21.15, which shows the fraction of surviving cells after various doses of radiation. The unit **gray** (Gy) quantifies the **dose**, which is defined as the total amount of radiation energy deposited in tissue. The figure shows that

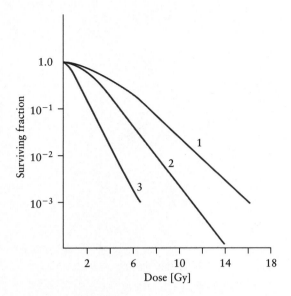

**FIGURE 21.15**

The surviving fraction of three types of human cells as a function of energy dose in unit Gy. The energy dose is the energy deposited by the radiation per kilogram of tissue. Note the lower steepness at doses below 1 Gy, which is due to self-repair mechanisms in living cells. Various cells respond with different sensitivity to radiation: (1) thyroid cells, (2) mammary cells, and (3) bone marrow.

essentially all cell types in the human body resist lower doses, but get damaged beyond repair at higher doses.

Luckily, higher doses are rare, as shown in Fig. 21.16. In this figure, a different definition for dose, called **equivalent dose**, is used. The equivalent dose includes a correction factor for the biological effect of the radiation. This correction factor is quantified in the next chapter with the introduction of the unit **sievert** (Sv) for the equivalent dose. Fig. 21.16 compares various activities and the corresponding risk of exposure to biologically damaging radiation.

It is important to recognize that Fig. 21.16 has a logarithmic ordinate. Compared to the natural background radiation to which we are all exposed and which corresponds to an equivalent dose of 1 mSv/year, even relatively short space missions represent a significant increase in exposure. This brings us back to the risks of space travel. The longest stay on the U.S. Skylab station was 84 days. The radiation exposure of those astronauts was equivalent to what they would be exposed to over 70 years on the surface of our planet, i.e., equivalent to the radiation dose received during an average lifespan. Polyakov, the cosmonaut with the current record for endurance stay in space, was exposed to more radiation than any human has ever received naturally, because a person would have to live 350 years to receive that dose in a natural environment. The Mars mission discussed earlier would again triple that amount.

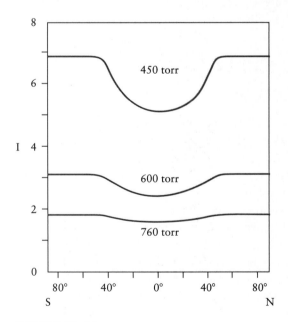

**FIGURE 21.14**

The intensity of cosmic rays as a function of altitude (expressed in unit pressure, which can be correlated to altitudes with Fig. 21.1) and as a function of geographic latitude.

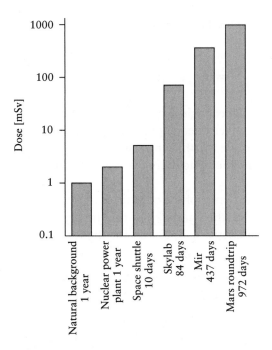

**FIGURE 21.16**

The equivalent full-body dose received by a person under various conditions. The lowest full-body dose corresponds to the natural background radiation. The full-body doses received on the longest Skylab or Mir missions are significantly less than what we have to anticipate during a Mars mission. The equivalent dose, which is closely related to the energy dose but corrected by a biological impact factor, is given in unit milli-sievert.

---

**Concept Question 21.6**

**In this section, the units sievert and gray have been used. We have introduced two different units for the same physical quantity several times before in this textbook. Find an example—e.g., in Chapter 17—and discuss the rationale for taking this approach.**

ANSWER: In Chapter 17, we introduced the units dB and phon for loudness. This is often done when a physical property and its impact on humans are distinguished. A particularly illustrative example emphasizing the need to work with this distinction is the impact of UVA and UVB radiation, as we discussed in the previous chapter.

---

In this section we have identified several questions we have to discuss in more detail for space travel applications:

- What explains the radiation belts and their non-uniformity with geographic latitude?

- How can the Sun generate electromagnetic radiation at very short wavelengths?

- What distinguishes particle radiation from electromagnetic radiation?

The answers to these questions come from very different subfields of physics, and therefore are split over the remainder of this and the next two chapters. If we accept that charged particles continuously approach Earth at high speeds from outer space, then the radiation belts become primarily an issue of magnetism and the motion of charged particles in a magnetic field. This will be illustrated below.

The difference between electromagnetic radiation and cosmic rays is significant in that the former can be explained with an atomic model, while the latter require nuclear physics models. The next two chapters deal with the atomic model and the formation of X-rays first, followed by nuclear physics concepts as required for biological and medical applications. The biological impacts of both types of radiation have to be discussed separately as they differ in several ways, such as penetration depth and energy deposition in tissue.

## Origin of the Radiation Belts

We discussed magnetism in the previous chapter to establish the electromagnetic nature of light, which was needed to explain the phenomena of light polarization and colour. We return to the concept of **magnetism** in the current section to supplement its effect on currents by its effect on moving charged particles. Since Earth has a magnetic field, charged particles approaching the planet from outer space are subject to magnetic interactions that explain several of the observations discussed above. But we also will see that the interaction of charged particles with magnetic fields allows us to get a step closer to understanding the molecular nature of matter.

The magnetic force was defined in Chapter 20 as the force acting between two parallel electric currents:

$$|\mathbf{F}_{mag}| \propto \frac{I_1 \cdot I_2}{d} l \quad \Rightarrow \quad \frac{|\mathbf{F}_{mag}|}{l} \propto \frac{I_1 \cdot I_2}{d} \quad [49]$$

in which $I_1$ and $I_2$ are two parallel currents, $d$ is the distance between the two conductors, and $l$ is the length over which the conductors interact. The magnitude of the magnetic field $|\mathbf{B}|$ followed from Eq. [49] with one of the currents identified as a test current and removed from the system:

$$|\mathbf{B}| = \frac{\mu_0}{2 \cdot \pi} \frac{I}{d} \quad [50]$$

In the present context we want to move beyond the concept of electric current and focus on single charged particles in motion. In a first step toward single charges, we maintain the two parallel conductors but use the definition of current from Chapter 14 to identify the current as the flow of electrons:

$$I = \frac{\Delta Q}{\Delta t} = n \cdot e \cdot v_d \cdot A \qquad [51]$$

in which $n$ is the particle density of mobile charges in the conductor, $e$ is the elementary charge, $v_d$ is the magnitude of the drift velocity, and $A$ is the cross-sectional area of the conductor.

We substitute Eqs. [50] and [51] into Eq. [49] to remove the currents and replace the magnetic force with the magnetic field. This leads to the following formula for the magnetic force between parallel conductors:

$$\frac{F_{\mathrm{mag}}}{l} = B \cdot I = B \cdot n_e \cdot e \cdot v_d \cdot A \qquad [52]$$

We generalize this formula by replacing the elementary charge $e$ of the electron in a wire with the charge $q$, which may represent, alternatively, the charge of an ion. The product of length $l$ and cross-sectional area $A$ in Eq. [52] equals the volume, $V = l \cdot A$. The volume can be combined with the density of the moving charges, $n_e$, to yield the total number of charged particles, $N_q$:

$$l \cdot A \cdot n_e = V \cdot n_e = N_q \qquad [53]$$

With this equation, Eq. [52] is rewritten for a single point charge as:

$$\frac{F_{\mathrm{mag}}}{N_q} = B \cdot q \cdot v \qquad [54]$$

in which the index $d$ for *drift* from Eq. [52] has been dropped, as the speed of any moving charged particle obeys this formula, not only the electrons drifting in a conducting wire. Eq. [54] provides us with the magnitude of the magnetic force per charged particle as the product of the magnitude of the magnetic field, the charge of the particle, and the speed of the particle. We introduce a new parameter for the force per particle in the form $\mathbf{f}_{\mathrm{mag}} = F_{\mathrm{mag}}/N_q$. Thus, $\mathbf{F}_{\mathrm{mag}}$ represents the total force on a larger number of charged particles, while $\mathbf{f}_{\mathrm{mag}}$ is the force on a single particle. Note that Eq. [54] is written in scalar form; i.e., all vector quantities are represented by their respective magnitudes. If the direction of the magnetic field vector $\mathbf{B}$ and the direction of the velocity of the particle $\mathbf{v}$ are taken into account, a vector product formula replaces Eq. [54]:

$$\mathbf{f}_{\mathrm{mag}} = q[\mathbf{v} \times \mathbf{B}] \qquad [55]$$

Applying Eq. [55], we note that the magnitude of the magnetic force for cases in which the magnetic field and the velocity are not perpendicular to each other becomes:

$$\frac{F_{\mathrm{mag}}}{N_q} = f_{\mathrm{mag}} = q \cdot v \cdot B \cdot \sin\phi \qquad [56]$$

in which $\phi$ is the angle between $\mathbf{B}$ and $\mathbf{v}$. We use Eq. [56] whenever the magnitude of the magnetic force on a particle is sufficient. The directional properties of the magnetic field are discussed further later in this chapter.

The standard units of the quantities in Eq. [56] are coulomb (C) for the charge, m/s for the speed, tesla (T) for the magnetic field, and N for the force.

*The magnetic force on a moving point charge is proportional to its charge, its speed, and the magnetic field. It also depends on the angle between the magnetic field and the path of the particle.*

## ● EXAMPLE 21.7

A 10.0-keV proton beam (i.e., protons extracted from a vacuum ion source with a potential difference of 10 kV) enters a magnetic field of magnitude 2 T perpendicular to the field. (a) What is the speed of the protons? (b) What force acts on each proton in the beam?

*Solution to part (a):* 10 keV is the kinetic energy of each proton. We use for the energy conversion $10\,\mathrm{keV} = 1.6 \times 10^{-15}$ J, and for the mass of the proton $m_{\mathrm{p}} = 1.67 \times 10^{-27}$ kg. With these values, we calculate the speed of the protons in the beam:

$$v = \sqrt{\frac{2 \cdot E}{m}} = \sqrt{\frac{2 \cdot (1.6 \times 10^{-15}\,\mathrm{J})}{1.67 \times 10^{-27}\,\mathrm{kg}}}$$

$$= 1.38 \times 10^6 \frac{\mathrm{m}}{\mathrm{s}} \qquad [57]$$

Note that we applied the classical formula for the kinetic energy, $E_{\mathrm{kin}} = \frac{1}{2} \cdot m \cdot v^2$. This is justified because the speed of the protons is only about 0.5% of the speed of light.

*Solution to part (b):* We substitute the given values in Eq. [56], including the result in part (a). The angle between the velocity direction and the magnetic field direction is $\phi = 90°$; thus, $\sin\phi = 1$:

$$f_{\mathrm{mag}} = (1.6 \times 10^{-19}\,\mathrm{C})\left(1.38 \times 10^6 \frac{\mathrm{m}}{\mathrm{s}}\right)(2.0\,\mathrm{T})$$

$$= 4.4 \times 10^{-13}\,\mathrm{N} \qquad [58]$$

It is interesting to compare this force with the forces listed in Table 3.4. While its magnitude is small, we have to keep in mind that this is a force acting on an atomic-size particle. It is certainly smaller than the electric force between a proton and an electron in a hydrogen atom; however, it is much stronger than the gravitational force represented by the weight of a hydrogen atom.

When a charged particle enters an area where electric and magnetic fields are present, the electric and the magnetic force are added. The resulting force is called the **Lorentz force,** named for Hendrik Lorentz, and reads for a force acting on a single point charge:

$$\mathbf{F}_{\text{Lorentz}} = q(\mathbf{E} + [\mathbf{v} \times \mathbf{B}]) \qquad [59]$$

Before we discuss important applications of the Lorentz force, we need to emphasize the differences between the electric and magnetic contributions in Eq. [59]. The electric force acts in the direction parallel or antiparallel to the electric field. The magnetic force is perpendicular to the magnetic field. More specifically, the direction of the magnetic force for a positive point charge results as the direction of the middle finger of your right hand if you point the thumb in the direction of the velocity and the index finger in the direction of the magnetic field. The directions related to magnetic interactions are illustrated in Fig. 21.17. Note that the sketch is two-dimensional; i.e., it shows the plane defined by the force and the velocity. The directional information for the magnetic field in the third dimension is given in a standard notation for vectors pointing into or out of a plane: a circle with a cross (⊗) stands for a

vector pointing into the plane and a circle with a dot (⊙) stands for a vector pointing out of the plane. This notation is easiest to remember by using the inset in the lower right corner of Fig. 21.17, which shows an arrow as used with a bow in the Middle Ages. When you shoot the arrow, you see the cross of feathers at the end of the arrow moving away, i.e., into the plane of the paper. If you are shot at, you see the sharp tip of the arrow approaching, i.e., coming out of the plane of the paper.

The magnetic field in Fig. 21.17 is directed into the plane of the figure. On a positive point charge moving with velocity **v** toward the lower left, a force is exerted toward the lower right; when it moves toward the lower right, a force is exerted toward the upper right. Confirm these directions by using the right-hand rule.

Since force and velocity are perpendicular to each other, we have a situation analogous to that in Fig. 21.4, where a force with constant magnitude and perpendicular to the direction of motion of the object led to uniform circular motion. This type of motion also results when the magnitude of the magnetic field does not change along the path of the particle. Thus, the particle in Fig. 21.17 moves in a circular fashion.

*The Lorentz force is the force acting on a charged particle. It has two components: the electric force leads to a linear acceleration and the magnetic force leads to a circular motion.*

Eq. [18] allows us to quantify the circular motion in response to the magnetic field. The net force acting in the direction perpendicular to the path of the object in Newton's law is the magnetic force:

$$\sum_i F_{i,\perp} = q \cdot v \cdot B = m \frac{v^2}{r} \qquad [60]$$

This equation relates the magnitude of the magnetic field, the mass and charge of the particle, and the radius and speed of the motion of the particle. The radius of the circular motion is given by:

$$r = \frac{m \cdot v}{q \cdot B} \qquad [61]$$

From Eq. [61] an angular frequency for the point charge can be calculated. For this we start with the speed of the object in circular motion and divide by the radius of the circular path:

$$v = \frac{2 \cdot \pi \cdot r}{T} \quad \Rightarrow \quad \frac{v}{r} = \frac{2 \cdot \pi}{T} = \omega \qquad [62]$$

Thus, isolating the term $v/r$ in Eq. [61] yields:

$$\omega = \frac{q \cdot B}{m} \qquad [63]$$

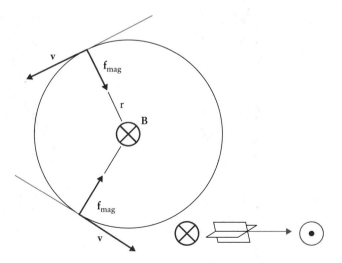

**FIGURE 21.17**

The magnetic force $\mathbf{f}_{\text{mag}}$, acting on a positive point charge moving along a circle of radius $r$ in a magnetic field that is directed into the plane. The blue arrow at the lower right illustrates the standard notation for a vector pointing into the plane (⊗) or out of the plane (⊙).

The frequency, $f = \omega/(2 \cdot \pi)$, and the period, $T = 2 \cdot \pi/\omega$, of the circular motion can then be derived. This angular frequency is called the **cyclotron frequency**, because a cyclotron is a setup that uses the concept of circular motion of charged particles. The synchrotron, a particular example of a cyclotron, is used as a particle accelerator and also to generate intensive and highly focussed X-ray beams. We will discuss in the next chapter why particles moving in circles in a cyclotron emit such radiation.

*A charged particle that moves through a constant magnetic field displays uniform circular motion. The path of the particle winds around the magnetic field lines. Its radius is proportional to the mass and speed of the particle. It is further inversely proportional to the charge of the particle and the magnitude of the magnetic field.*

## Concept Question 21.7

**(a) If a charged particle moves in a straight line through a chosen region in space, can you conclude that no magnetic field exists in that region? (b) How can the motion of a charged particle be used to distinguish between magnetic and electric fields?**

ANSWER TO PART (a): No. Other forces, such as an electric force or gravity, can compensate a magnetic force such that the net force is zero. Later in this chapter we discuss devices called Wien filters, in which magnetic and electric fields exist, but through which particles can move along a straight line.

ANSWER TO PART (b): The magnetic force always acts perpendicular to the velocity vector of the particle. No magnetic force acts on the charged particle when it moves parallel to the magnetic field. The force on a charged particle in an electric field is always parallel to the electric field, no matter in which way the particle moves. Thus, sampling a region with charged particles moving along different directions allows us to distinguish the two types of fields.

## ● EXAMPLE 21.8

Food in a **microwave oven** becomes heated as the water molecules in the food absorb energy from radiation at $f = 2450$ MHz. What kind of magnet is needed for a microwave oven in which the radiation is obtained from electrons circling in a magnetic field?

*Supplementary physical information:* We will discuss the interaction of electromagnetic radiation with matter in the next chapter. We know

that electromagnetic radiation of a given frequency $f$ is associated with an energy, $E = h \cdot f$, where $h$ is the Planck constant. This energy is carried by a photon. Photons in the microwave region, which lies between radio waves and infrared, cause molecules to rotate. Thus, during microwave cooking, the water molecules in the food are set into fast rotations. As a result of intermolecular collisions the surrounding molecules slow that rotation down, which turns the rotational energy into thermal energy and thus raises the temperature of the food.

*Solution:* To find the magnetic field, we first convert the given frequency into an angular frequency:

$$\omega = 2 \cdot \pi \cdot f = 2 \cdot \pi \cdot (2.45 \times 10^9 \, \text{s}^{-1})$$
$$= 1.54 \times 10^{10} \, \text{rad/s} \qquad [64]$$

Using Eq. [63] with the electron mass and charge from Table 13.1, this yields:

$$B = \frac{m \cdot \omega}{q}$$
$$= \frac{(9.11 \times 10^{-31} \, \text{kg})(1.54 \times 10^{10} \, \text{Hz})}{1.6 \times 10^{-19} \, \text{C}}$$
$$= 0.09 \, \text{T} \qquad [65]$$

This is a moderate magnetic field, but the magnet still represents a major fraction of the weight of the microwave oven. Note that electrons move in the opposite direction of positive charges in a magnetic field. However, Eq. [63] remains valid as it relates the *magnitudes* of vector quantities.

## ● EXAMPLE 21.9

A proton moves along a circular path with radius 20 cm in a uniform magnetic field. The magnitude of the magnetic field is 0.5 T and it is directed perpendicular to the velocity of the proton. (a) What is the speed of the proton along its path? (b) If the proton is replaced with an electron moving with the same speed, what is the radius of the circular path of the electron?

*Solution to part (a):* We solve Eq. [61] for the speed and use the mass and charge of the proton from Table 13.1:

$$v = \frac{q \cdot B \cdot r}{m}$$
$$= \frac{(1.6 \times 10^{-19} \, \text{C})(0.5 \, \text{T})(0.2 \, \text{m})}{1.67 \times 10^{-27} \, \text{kg}}$$
$$= 9.6 \times 10^6 \, \frac{\text{m}}{\text{s}} \qquad [66]$$

*Solution to part (b):* We could use Eq. [61] directly or, as done here, rewrite it in terms of these two cases:

$$\frac{r_{e^-}}{r_{p^+}} = \frac{\left(\dfrac{m_{e^-} \cdot v}{q \cdot B}\right)}{\left(\dfrac{m_{p^+} \cdot v}{q \cdot B}\right)} = \frac{m_{e^-}}{m_{p^+}} \qquad [67]$$

which leads to:

$$r_{e^-} = \frac{m_{e^-}}{m_{p^+}} r_{p^+} = 1.1 \times 10^{-4}\,\text{m} \qquad [68]$$

in which the mass of the electron is again taken from Table 13.1.

How can the circular motion of charged particles in a magnetic field explain the existence of the radiation belts at high altitudes? We begin with Earth's magnetic field. Fig. 21.18 is an artist's view of Earth's magnetic field lines, which resemble the field lines of a regular bar magnet. The corresponding bar magnet's south pole lies below the surface of the Northern Hemisphere (in the Arctic Ocean off Canada's Queen Elizabeth Islands), and its north pole lies below the surface of the Southern Hemisphere. The magnetic poles of Earth are not stationary (a phenomenon called **polar wandering**). At moderate latitudes the magnetic field vector points north with a horizontal component of 50 $\mu$T.

In reality, however, Earth cannot contain a permanent magnet (like a bar magnet), since matter inside Earth cannot sustain a magnetization beyond temperatures of 540°C, a value that the material in Earth's core significantly exceeds. The mechanism by which Earth generates its magnetic field has not yet been fully explained, although the **dynamo theory** is widely accepted. This theory assumes that huge convection currents in the liquid outer core carry charges. The moving charges in turn cause the magnetic field. The depth range of this liquid zone is shown in Table 21.1.

Fig. 21.19 illustrates the paths that fast charged particles take when approaching Earth from outer space. The magnetic field lines of Fig. 21.18 act as a trap for the particles, forcing them onto circular paths around the magnetic field lines. The narrowing of the field lines toward the poles causes the particles to bounce back and remain trapped between both poles. This explains the non-uniformity of the radiation belts shown in Fig. 21.14. Only particles with a very high energy or travelling at an unusually steep angle to the magnetic field lines—e.g., after a collision with the dilute atmospheric molecules in the radiation belts—escape. Thus, Earth's magnetic field shields us from intensive particle showers from the outer universe by trapping these particles in the belts. However, locating a space mission in the van Allen belt would expose the astronauts to intensive radiation, as high as 4.5 million times the natural radiation exposure at sea level.

**FIGURE 21.18**

An artist's view of the magnetic field of Earth.

## TABLE 21.1

### Composition of Earth

| Structure | Distance from centre (km) | Density (g/cm³) |
|---|---|---|
| Solid core* | 0–1400 | 13.0 |
| Liquid core | 1400–3500 | 10.0 |
| Solid mantle | 3500–6000 | 3.3–6.0 |
| Crust | 6000–6300 | |
| Lithosphere | 6300–6400 | 2.7 |

*$T \cong 6650°C$.

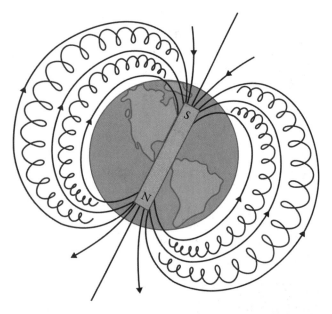

**FIGURE 21.19**

The magnetic field of Earth, represented for simplicity by a bar magnet. The real origin of the magnetic field must differ from the sketch as no permanent magnet can exist at the temperatures at the centre of Earth. The sketch illustrates the spiral paths of charged particles trapped in Earth's magnetic field. Trapped electrons and protons cause the innermost radiation belt, which is called the van Allen belt.

## Mass Spectrometer

Francis William Aston developed the first mass spectrometer in 1919 by combining two devices, (i) a **velocity selector** based on a magnetic and an electric field and (ii) a **mass selector** based on a magnetic field. In this section we discuss how this instrument allows us to measure the mass of molecules and fragments of molecules, making it one of the most versatile instruments in analytical organic chemistry.

Fig. 21.20 is a conceptual sketch of a **mass spectrometer**. The instrument consists of an ion source, which is usually a simple hot filament that ionizes molecules as they leave a gas chromatography setup used to separate the vapour phases of the sample of interest. The ion source is shown at the top of the figure. The generated ions travel through a set of slits. These slits serve two purposes: (i) they confine the beam of particles, and (ii) they are electrically charged to operate as parallel plate capacitors to accelerate the ions. Two devices are then required to separate the components of the ion beam on the basis of their masses: a velocity selector (called a Wien filter) and a magnetic mass analyzer.

In Aston's setup the final mass separation was obtained when the charged ions hit a photographic plate, which was developed afterward. In modern instruments the charged ions are measured as a current with a device called a Faraday cage. The main components of the instrument are discussed in more detail first, followed by an application of mass spectrometry in chemistry.

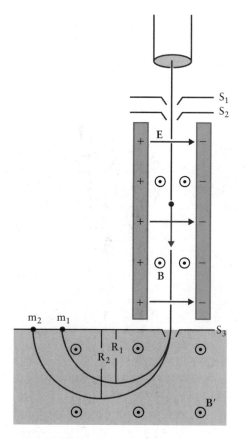

**FIGURE 21.20**

Aston's mass spectrometer. The ions, collimated with slits $S_1$ and $S_2$, first pass through a velocity selector (Wien filter) with perpendicular electric and magnetic fields and then enter a mass selector with magnetic field **B'**.

# Wien Filter

The **Wien filter** (named for Wilhelm Wien) serves as a velocity selector. The ionization process of a typical mass spectrometer produces almost exclusively ions with a single positive charge. After these ions pass through the acceleration section, the beam contains a range of ionized molecular fragments, each with a range of different velocities. All of these ions enter the Wien filter parallel to each other. The Wien filter contains magnetic and electric fields that are arranged perpendicular to each other and perpendicular to the direction of the motion of the charged particles. This is illustrated in Fig. 21.21(a). The magnetic field points into the plane and the electric field is directed downward. Fig. 21.21(b) shows the free-body diagram for a positively charged ion: the electric force acts downward and the magnetic force acts upward.

The Wien filter, which includes a narrow slit at its exit ($S_3$ in Fig. 21.20), allows us to select particles of a single velocity by using Newton's first law based on the free-body diagram shown in Fig. 21.21(b). Newton's first law defines the condition under which the particle is not accelerated, i.e., the condition under which it moves straight through the Wien filter. Any particle not satisfying Newton's first law is accelerated moving away from the straight line, and is then blocked at the exit slit. Labelling the direction upward as the positive $y$-axis, the condition of mechanical equilibrium is:

$$\sum_i F_{i,y} = -q \cdot E + q \cdot v \cdot B = 0 \qquad [69]$$

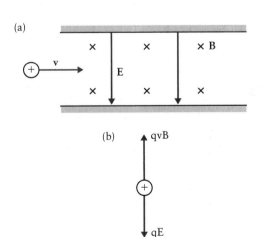

**FIGURE 21.21**

(a) Sketch of a Wien filter. Positive ions enter horizontally from the left, with the electric field of the parallel plate capacitor oriented vertically and the magnetic field perpendicular to the plane of the paper. A uniform magnetic field is usually generated with two solenoids. (b) Free-body diagram for the particle shown in part (a).

which yields:

$$v = \frac{E}{B} \qquad [70]$$

Thus, to select a certain velocity with a Wien filter, the ratio of the magnitudes of the electric and magnetic fields must be chosen according to Eq. [70].

## Concept Question 21.8

A Wien filter is used to select protons of a given speed $v_0$. In the ion source used in the experiment He$^{2+}$ ions are also generated, which we assume have four times the mass of protons. Do helium ions pass through the Wien filter, and if so, at what speed? Is there a way to obtain a pure proton beam from the mixture leaving the ion source?

ANSWER: Helium ions pass at the same speed, $v_0$, due to Eq. [70], in which the mass of the ions does not enter and the charge state $q$ of the ions is cancelled. A sector magnet following the Wien filter can separate the protons and helium ions, as discussed in the next section.

# Role of the 180° Sector Magnet

Once a single velocity is selected with the Wien filter, the beam of particles enters a **180° sector magnet** in Fig. 21.20. The charged particles move in a circular fashion through the magnetic field, with a radius of the path described by Eq. [61]. Because all particles enter the magnet with the same speed, the only variable term on the right-hand side of Eq. [61] is the mass of the ions. Thus, the heavier the ion, the farther to the left it hits the photographic plate in Fig. 21.20. The analysis of the obtained data is very simple as the distances along the photographic plate are directly proportional to the ion's mass, $R \propto m$.

# Applications of Mass Spectrometry

Five mass spectra in Fig. 21.22 illustrate typical applications of this technique. Plotted is the particle current passing through the 180° sector magnet as a function of $m/Z$, which is the particle mass per charge carried by the particle. Organic molecules usually contain a large number of atoms. A mass spectrometric analysis contains a great amount of information about the molecule, as usually not only the positively charged molecule itself but also a range of its stable fragments are observed. In modern instruments, the information about the fragments includes not only the mass but

**FIGURE 21.22**

Mass spectra for five different organic molecules. Note that spectra (d) and (e) are given for two different organic molecules with the same chemical formula.

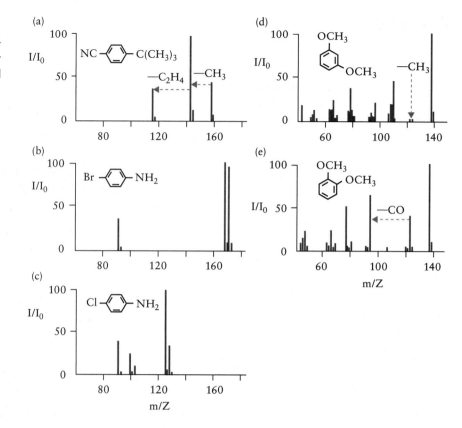

also the relative probability of each fragment's being formed in the source.

The study of the mass and formation probability of various fragments is useful since the ionization process in a mass spectrometer is not an indiscriminate process. Weaker chemical bonds in the molecule break more easily, causing characteristic fragments to occur. Fig. 21.22(a–c) compares the mass spectra for three benzene-ring systems: (a) a benzene ring with a cyano- and a butyl-ligand, (b) a benzene ring with an amino- and a bromine-ligand, and (c) a benzene ring with an amino- and a chlorine-ligand. Characteristic fragmentation for the first molecule includes the loss of a methyl group (15 mass units) and the subsequent loss of a $C_2H_4$ group. The bromine compound prefers to lose the bromine atom (79 and 81 mass units for the two stable bromine isotopes), while the loss of the chlorine and amino groups is about equally likely for the last molecule.

The second comparison of spectra in Fig. 21.22 (d, e) illustrates another strength of the technique. Organic molecules are rather similar to each other as they usually consist of only a few types of atoms: carbon, oxygen, nitrogen, and hydrogen. The greater the molecular similarity of two species, the fewer the differences in properties that allow us to distin-

guish the compounds. An extreme case is **steric modification** of molecules that have the same composition, such as the two benzene-ring-based ether molecules in Fig. 21.22(d, e). In spite of the great similarity of the molecules, the mass spectra shown are quite distinct, with a characteristic loss of 15 mass units of a methyl group in the lower spectrum that is not observed in the upper spectrum.

**Concept Question 21.9**

Why do scientific laboratories use a gas chromatograph placed in front of a mass spectrometer for analyzing unknown samples? Check the literature or the internet for examples.

ANSWER: An unknown sample may consist of more than one chemical compound. If the compounds enter a mass spectrometer simultaneously, the resulting spectrum is a combination of fragments of several compounds. In most cases, data analysis will no longer be possible. Gas chromatography causes the various components to arrive at the mass spectrometer at different times, allowing us to analyze each component separately.

# MULTIPLE CHOICE AND CONCEPTUAL QUESTIONS

## OUTER SPACE

**Q–21.1.** Fig. 21.1 contains four axes for the temperature, height, pressure, and $F_{gravity}/m$ as a multiple of $g$. (a) Which axis is linear? (b) Which axis is logarithmic?

**Q–21.2.** The temperature curve in Fig. 21.1 is shown to a height of a few hundred kilometres, where it ends with a slope of fast temperature increase with height. Does this imply that outer space is a hot environment?

**Q–21.3.** What happens to a gas-filled balloon that rises high in the atmosphere, such as a weather balloon? Will it collapse or expand? Will it leave the atmosphere or come to rest?

**Q–21.4.** You carry an airtight bag of potato chips onto an airplane. What has happened to the bag when the plane has reached its cruising height?

## GRAVITATIONAL EFFECTS

**Q–21.5.** (a) Can the space shuttle be located stationary above its mission control centre in Texas? (b) Can a European TV satellite be located above a ground station in Athens, Greece?

**Q–21.6.** Where in our solar system does an object encounter a gravitational acceleration that is larger than $g$?

**Q–21.7.** The mass of Mars is $m_{Mars} = 0.102 \cdot m_{Earth}$. What gravitational acceleration $g_{Mars}$ as a multiple of $g_{Earth}$ affects an astronaut on Mars? *Note:* $R_{Mars} = 3400$ km and $R_{Earth} = 6370$ km.

**Q–21.8.** Why is the route for a Mars mission in Fig. 21.12 not a straight line between Earth and the planet? Does the mechanical argument that a straight line is the shortest connection between two points not apply?

**Q–21.9.** An object moves in uniform circular motion when a constant force acts perpendicular to its velocity vector. What happens if the force is not perpendicular?

**Q–21.10.** Describe the path of a moving object if its acceleration is constant in magnitude and (a) perpendicular to its velocity vector, or (b) parallel to its velocity vector.

**Q–21.11.** An object moves with uniform circular motion. (a) Is its velocity constant? (b) Is its speed constant? (c) Is its acceleration constant?

**Q–21.12.** Centrifuges are often used to separate blood cells from blood plasma. Which ends up at the bottom of the test tube?

**Q–21.13.** A bucket of water can be whirled in a vertical loop without any water being spilled. Why does the water not flow out when the bucket is at the top of the loop?

## CHARGED PARTICLES IN MAGNETIC FIELDS

**Q–21.14.** Describe the path of a charged particle that travels with velocity **v** straight toward the North Pole along the north–south axis of a bar magnet.

**Q–21.15.** What happens to a mobile but initially stationary point charge if a magnet travels past its location?

**Q–21.16.** What changes take place in Fig. 21.17 if the direction of the magnetic field is reversed, i.e., if **B** points out of the plane of the page?

**Q–21.17.** In Fig. 21.19, the bar magnet within Earth is shown with its south pole underneath northern Canada. Is this correct?

**Q–21.18.** Why does the picture on a computer screen become distorted when a magnet is brought close to it? *Note:* Don't try this, because it may cause permanent damage.

**Q–21.19.** Two charged particles travel into a region in which a magnetic field acts perpendicular to the particles' velocity vectors. What do you conclude if they are deflected in opposite directions?

**Q–21.20.** What work does the magnetic force do on a charged particle that moves through a uniform magnetic field?

**Q–21.21.** Why do cosmic-ray particles strike Earth more often near the poles than near the equator?

**Q–21.22.** Can a constant magnetic field set into motion a charged particle from rest?

## MASS SPECTROMETRY

**Q–21.23.** What happens in Fig. 21.20 if the three slits $S_1$ to $S_3$ are opened to twice their width?

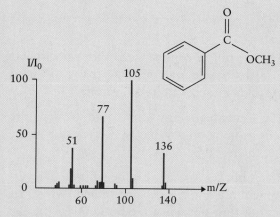

**FIGURE 21.23**

The mass spectrum of benzoic acid methylester. The chemical formula of the molecule is shown as an inset in the figure.

**Q-21.24.** Fig. 21.23 shows the mass spectrum of benzoic acid methylester (the molecule is shown as an inset of the figure). What functional groups have been split off the molecule to generate the peaks at 105, 77, and 51 mass units, respectively?

## ANALYTICAL PROBLEMS

### CIRCULAR MOTION

**P-21.1.** A rollercoaster ride includes a circular loop with radius $R = 10$ m. (a) What minimum speed must the car have at the top to stay in contact with the tracks? (b) What minimum speed must the car have when entering the loop to satisfy the solution in part (a)?

**P-21.2.** The gravitational constant $G^*$, and the gravitational acceleration on the surface of Earth $g$ can be measured in independent laboratory experiments. (a) What other information do you need about Earth to determine Earth's mass? (b) Find this information (it is used in the current chapter) and calculate the mass of Earth.

**P-21.3.** Calculate the orbital speed for the two Russian missions shown in Fig. 21.1. Use the mass and the radius of Earth from the examples in this chapter.

**P-21.4.** A centrifuge of radius 12 cm is used to separate a blood sample. The force needed to obtain sedimentation of red blood cells in a plasma solution is about $4 \times 10^{-11}$ N, acting on an erythrocyte of average mass of $3 \times 10^{-16}$ kg. At what number of revolutions per second must the centrifuge be operated?

**P-21.5.** Eq. [40] also applies to the circular motion of a planet around the Sun. Derive from this equation Kepler's third law, which states that $T^2 \propto r^3$ if $T$ is the planet's period and $r$ its distance from the Sun.

**P-21.6.** In science fiction the idea was brought up of using large rotating cylinders for space travel of long duration. The colony would live a reasonably normal life if the cylinder rotates at the right speed. To simulate Earth's gravity in a cylinder of 8.0 km diameter, what must be the period of the cylinder?

**P-21.7.** An airplane flies in a horizontal circle with a speed of 100 m/s. The pilot is a standard man (see Table 3.3). The maximum acceleration of the pilot should not exceed $7 \cdot g$, with $g$ the gravitational acceleration. What is the minimum radius of the airplane's circular path?

**P-21.8.** Fig. 21.24 shows an object of mass $m = 250$ g that is attached to a massless string and slides on a frictionless horizontal surface. Its circular path has a radius of 1.0 m. The other end of the string passes through a hole at the centre of the object's path and is connected to a hanging object of mass $M = 1.0$ kg. (a) What is the tension in the string if the hanging object is in mechanical equilibrium? (b) What is the speed of the object in uniform circular motion?

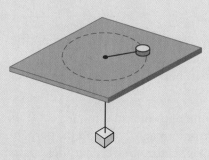

**FIGURE 21.24**

**P–21.9.** A child of mass $m = 40$ kg takes a ride on a Ferris wheel that has a radius of 9.0 m and spins four times per minute. (a) What is the child's centripetal acceleration? (b) What is the force the seat exerts on the child at the highest and lowest points, and when the child is halfway between?

## CHARGED PARTICLES IN MAGNETIC FIELDS

**P–21.10.** A proton (mass and charge are given in Table 13.1) moves with a speed of 100 km/s through the magnetic field of Earth, which has at a particular location a magnitude of 50 $\mu$T. What is the ratio of the gravitational force to the magnetic force on the proton when the proton travels perpendicular to the magnetic field?

**P–21.11.** A long, straight wire in a vacuum system carries a current of 1.5 A. A low-density, 20-eV electron beam is directed parallel to the wire at a distance of 0.5 cm. The electron beam travels against the direction of the current in the wire. Find (a) the magnitude of the magnetic force acting on the electrons in the electron beam, and (b) the direction in which the electrons are deflected from their initial direction.

**P–21.12.** A proton travels with $v = 3.0 \times 10^6$ m/s at an angle of 37° with the direction of the magnetic field of a magnet of strength $B = 0.3$ T. The magnetic field is oriented along the $y$-axis. (a) Calculate the magnitude of the magnetic force acting on the proton. (b) Calculate the magnitude of the acceleration of the proton.

**P–21.13.** Sodium ions $Na^+$ move at 0.5 m/s through a blood vessel. The blood vessel is in a magnetic field of $B = 1.0$ T. The blood flow direction subtends an angle of 45° with the magnetic field. What is the magnetic force on the blood vessel due to sodium ions if the blood vessel contains 0.1 L blood with a sodium concentration of $c = 70$ mmol/L?

**P–21.14.** A positive charged particle carries 0.2 $\mu$C and moves with a kinetic energy of 0.09 J. It travels through a uniform magnetic field of $B = 0.1$ T. What is the mass of the particle if it moves in the magnetic field in circular fashion with a radius $r = 3.0$ m?

**P–21.15.** A proton moves in uniform circular motion perpendicular to a uniform magnetic field with $B = 0.8$ T. What is the period of its motion?

## MASS SPECTROMETRY

**P–21.16.** We consider Aston's mass spectrometer, as illustrated in Fig. 21.20. The magnitude of the electric field is $E = 1.0$ kV/m and the magnitude of the magnetic fields in both the Wien filter and the mass selector are 1.0 T. Calculate the radius of the path in the mass selector for an ion with a single positive charge and with a mass of $m = 2.0 \times 10^{-26}$ kg.

**P–21.17.** A mass spectrometer is used to separate isotopes. If the beam emerges with a speed of 250 km/s and the magnetic field in the mass selector is 2 T, what is the distance between the collectors for (a) $^{235}U$ and $^{238}U$, and (b) $^{12}C$ and $^{14}C$?

**P–21.18.** An ion carrying a single positive elementary charge has a mass of $2.5 \times 10^{-23}$ g. It is accelerated through an electric potential difference of 0.25 kV and then enters a uniform magnetic field of $B = 0.5$ T along a direction perpendicular to the field. What is the radius of the circular path of the ion in the magnetic field?

# SUMMARY

## DEFINITIONS

- Uniform circular motion
  - tangential velocity component:

$$v_{\parallel} = \frac{2 \cdot \pi \cdot r}{T}$$

  where $r$ is the radius of the circular path, and $T$ is the period.

- perpendicular velocity component: $v_{\perp} = 0$
- tangential acceleration component: $a_{\parallel} = 0$
- centripetal acceleration component:

$$a_{\perp} = \frac{v^2}{r} = \omega^2 \cdot r = \frac{4 \cdot \pi^2 \cdot r}{T^2}$$

where $v = v_{\parallel}$, and $\omega$ is the angular frequency.

## LAWS

- Newton's law for a system with uniform circular motion in the $xy$-plane:

$$\text{(I)} \quad \sum_i F_{i,\perp} = m\,\frac{v^2}{r}$$

$$\text{(II)} \quad \sum_i F_{i,\parallel} = 0$$

$$\text{(III)} \quad \sum_i F_{i,z} = 0$$

- Magnetic force per particle $\mathbf{f}_{\text{mag}}$:

$$\frac{F_{\text{mag}}}{N_q} = \mathbf{f}_{\text{mag}} = q \cdot v \cdot B \cdot \sin\phi$$

where $F_{\text{mag}}$ is the magnitude of the total magnetic force, $N_q$ is the number of charged particles with charge $q$, and $\phi$ is the angle between the magnetic field $\mathbf{B}$ and the velocity vector of the particle $\mathbf{v}$.

- Motion of a charged particle in a uniform magnetic field
  - radius of circular path:

$$r = \frac{m \cdot v}{q \cdot B}$$

  - cyclotron frequency:

$$\omega = \frac{q \cdot B}{m}$$

- Velocity selected in a Wien filter: $v = E/B$, with $E$ the magnitude of the electric field and $B$ the magnitude of the magnetic field.

# CHAPTER 22

## CHEMICAL BONDS AND X-RAYS
## Atomic and Molecular Physics

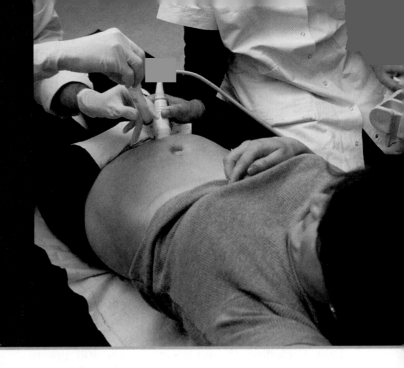

Matter consists of discrete units called atoms. Each electrically neutral atom has a positively charged nucleus and a shell of negatively charged electrons. Bohr's model of the hydrogen atom is based on two postulates: that electrons in a discrete set of orbits do not lose energy through radiation, and that radiation absorbed by or emitted from an atom is due to intra-atomic electron transfer between these allowed orbits. An atom is in its stable ground state when its electrons occupy the energetically lowest orbits. Bohr's second postulate leads to discrete absorption and emission spectra, allowing for spectral analysis of matter.

Molecules are formed when two or more atoms form chemical bonds, which result when their atomic orbitals overlap and are rearranged into stationary molecular orbitals. The molecular orbitals often can be represented as linear combinations of atomic orbitals (LCAO method). The molecule is stable if energetically favoured binding orbitals are occupied by more electrons than are antibinding orbitals.

X-rays are emitted when a core electron of a heavy atom is removed and electrons from higher shells release energy while transferring to the vacancy in the lower orbital.

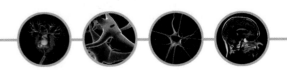

In this chapter we focus on the processes of light generation and absorption in matter. These processes play an important role in medical imaging, for example CT scans (computed tomography) with X-rays, and in laboratory-based diagnostic procedures, as illustrated with the analysis of amniotic fluid. One of the original applications of **amniocentesis** (see the opening photo for this chapter) was to diagnose fetal erythroblastosis based on a sample of amniotic fluid. *Erythroblastosis* is the term used to describe all those illnesses that lead to a presence of immature red blood cells in the blood. In the case of a fetus, this usually occurs as an immune system reaction due to the transfer of antibodies across the placenta, triggered by an incompatibility of blood types between mother and fetus.

To diagnose fetal erythroblastosis, a ray of white light (including all wavelengths from 300 nm to 700 nm) is sent through the amniotic fluid and the intensity of the transmitted light is analyzed as a function of wavelength. This method is called **spectroscopic analysis**. Fig. 22.1 shows the fraction of light absorbed from an incident light intensity plotted versus the wavelength. The four spectra correspond, from left to right, to a normal pregnancy and minor, medium, and severe cases of fetal erythroblastosis.

The relative light absorption in Fig. 22.1 is shown with a logarithmic scale. This means that the amniotic fluid is quite transparent for red light around 700 nm, where almost 90% of the incident light passes through the sample, while it is almost opaque for violet light around 350 nm, where only 20% to 25% of the incident light passes through the sample. In

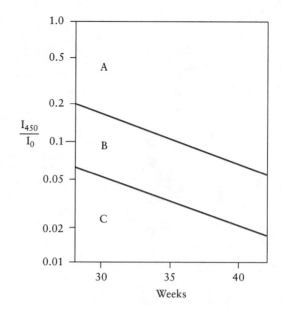

**FIGURE 22.2**

Liley's method to allow a physician to determine the severity of fetal erythroblastosis as a function of the week of gestation in a pregnancy. The ordinate shows the difference between the peak height at $\lambda = 450$ nm from Fig. 22.1 and the corresponding level along the extrapolated background. The chart allows us to distinguish light cases (C), medium cases (B), and severe cases (A). During the early years of amniocentesis, a severe case would have led to induction of labour or an intra-uterine blood transfusion.

addition to the steady decrease in transparency with decreasing wavelength, a characteristic absorption of light occurs in the range between 410 nm and 460 nm if the fetus suffers from fetal erythroblastosis. This additional absorption is quantified by the difference between the peak height and the corresponding level along the extrapolated background at 450 nm (**Liley's method**). For example, for the severe case in Fig. 22.1 the peak value is 64.5% and the corresponding extrapolated base value is 19.8%, leading to an additional absorption of 64.5% − 19.8% = 44.7%. This value is then used by a physician to determine from Fig. 22.2 the severity of the case: 44.7% corresponds as a fraction to 0.447 in this plot, which is indeed a severe case at any stage of the pregnancy.

But how is the light absorption of the amniotic fluid linked to fetal erythroblastosis? i.e., why does the above analysis yield a diagnosis? In an affected fetus, heme, which is a component of the hemoglobin molecule of the red blood cells, is chemically degraded to bilirubin, which the fetus's body in turn disposes of into the amniotic fluid. The higher the bilirubin concentration in this fluid, the higher its absorption of light in the wavelength range at 450 nm. This means that the more severe the fetal erythroblastosis, the higher the absorption in the interval from 410 nm to 460 nm of the electromagnetic spectrum.

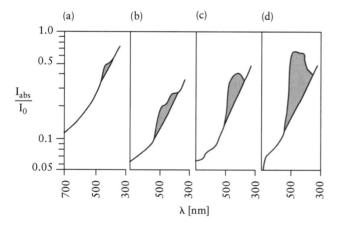

**FIGURE 22.1**

Spectroscopic analysis of the amniotic fluid obtained in an amniocentesis for (a) a healthy baby, (b) a light case, (c) a medium case, and (d) a severe case of fetal erythroblastosis. The shaded peak at wavelength $\lambda = 450$ nm is a measure of the severity of the illness. The ordinate is a logarithmic axis and shows the relative absorbed intensity, $I_{abs}/I_0$, with $I_0$ the incident intensity.

Implicit in the discussion above is the assumption that the bilirubin molecule is able to pick light of a certain wavelength out of a ray of white light passing through the solution. How does the molecule do this? And can the bilirubin molecule in turn generate light of the same wavelength? Are there other molecules that can do the same in other parts of the electromagnetic spectrum? In order to answer these questions, we must develop a model for a molecule. We can no longer treat molecules as structureless particles, since these effects hint at an internal structure that must be characteristic for each type of molecules.

# Early Atomic Models

Before we can interpret molecular spectra such as Fig. 22.1 or the radiation effects we identified in the previous chapter, we must establish a quantitative model for the atom. Only with this fundamental building block in place can more complex structures, such as molecules, be understood.

The idea that matter is not infinitely divisible was already discussed in antiquity. However, Avogadro's hypothesis in Chapter 7 and Dalton's law in Chapter 9 were the first serious experimental hints at the atomic or molecular structure of matter. The success of the kinetic gas theory in Chapter 7 added credibility to the concept. Still, at the end of the nineteenth century the atomic hypothesis was considered only a useful mathematical approach rather than a theory describing actual, physical particles.

In 1897, Sir Joseph Thomson discovered the **electron** with an apparatus in which electric and magnetic fields deflected the rays emerging from a hot metallic wire in a vacuum. He was able to demonstrate that the particles in the ray were negatively charged and had a very small mass. This apparatus was developed further by Aston to become the mass spectrometer, which we discussed in the previous chapter.

Thomson's experiment was the first direct evidence of an elementary particle. Since the electron is negatively charged and the matter from which it came is electrically neutral, Thomson concluded that atoms must consist of something positively charged and electrons. His model is shown in Fig. 22.3: electrons oscillate back and forth within an area defined by a diffusely spread positive charge. The positive charge distribution defines the boundaries of the atom, which has a diameter on the order of 0.1 nm. While this model describes a stable state for the electron in Newton's classical framework, it is contradicted by all experimental evidence about atoms that

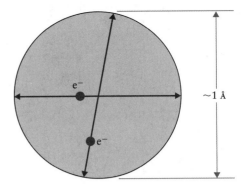

**FIGURE 22.3**

Thomson's atomic model: electrons oscillate in a uniform spherical distribution of positive electric charge (grey area). Note that 1 Å = 0.1 nm.

had been collected by the late 1800s. Thus, it had to be dismissed.

The next model was proposed by Ernest Rutherford in 1911. Bombarding a gold foil with $\alpha$-particles, which are energetic helium nuclei emitted from natural sources such as thorium or uranium, he found that the mass and the positive charge of an atom are concentrated at its centre. Note that we were already able to quantify Rutherford's experiment in Example 13.15, because the $\alpha$-particle and the gold nucleus in the foil interact electrically. We can illustrate the significant difference between the size of the entire atom and its nucleus. Choosing a carbon atom for illustration, we note that its atomic mass is 12 g/mol. With this value we calculate the radius of the carbon nucleus:

$$r_{nucleus} = 1.2 \times 10^{-15} \cdot A^{1/3} = 2.75 \times 10^{-15}\, m \quad [1]$$

in which $A$ is the atomic mass in unit g/mol. The atomic radius of carbon is $7.7 \times 10^{-11}$ m, which can be obtained from chemical bond lengths or diamond crystals. Thus, the atom is 28 000 times larger than its nucleus. This tremendous difference in size is also the reason why atomic concepts were developed and understood in the 1920s while our understanding of the internal structure of the nucleus developed only after World War II. We follow this chronological order and develop nuclear concepts in the next chapter, after we discuss the atomic model.

Rutherford tried to explain his findings with an intriguing analogy. The mass of the solar system has a distribution that is very similar to that of an atom: almost the entire mass is centred in the Sun, while the planets define the size of the solar system by their **orbits**. Thus, he proposed that the nucleus carries most of the mass and all the positive charge of the atom, and the electrons, which carry the negative charge, orbit the nucleus like planets. This model is called **Rutherford's model** and is sketched in Fig. 22.4.

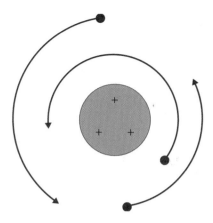

**FIGURE 22.4**

Rutherford's planetary atomic model: the electrons (blue dots) circle around a massive nucleus like planets move around the Sun.

### Concept Question 22.1

Unlike the planets that move around a star, the electrons and the nucleus are electrically charged. Based on the discussion of the circular motion of charged particles in the previous chapter, can you articulate a fundamental problem with Rutherford's model?

ANSWER: Circular motion is an accelerated motion. In Chapter 20 we showed that an accelerating electric charge (e.g., in an antenna) emits electromagnetic radiation. Thus, the electrons in Rutherford's model would continuously lose energy through radiation and would, therefore, rapidly spiral into the nucleus.

## The Hydrogen Atom

In 1913, Niels Bohr concluded that all possible explanations based on classical physics—i.e., the physical ideas derived from Newton's laws and the electromagnetic theory—were failing for the atom. He formulated instead two postulates that contradict classical physics, but describe the atomic structure very well. These postulates and the quantitative description of the possible energy levels of electrons in a hydrogen atom are discussed in this section. In the next section we then review the predictions for the atom based on the theory of quantum mechanics, which was developed in the 1920s and completely abandons the classical concepts. That discussion will lead us to the next step toward biological systems, the step from the atom to the molecule. Bohr's model is still used at the beginning of this chapter since it provides useful insights in our understanding of the

atom. Given the later developments of a quantum-mechanical view of the atom, we should consider Bohr's model in the same fashion we used hard spheres as a model for gas particles when discussing the gas laws in Chapter 7.

> **Bohr's model** is based on two postulates: (i) Electrons do not lose energy via radiation while they are in a discrete set of orbits around the nucleus. These orbits are called **allowed orbits**. (ii) An electron loses or gains energy when it transfers between two allowed orbits. The energy lost or gained is equal to the energy difference of the initial and final orbits of the transition.

Bohr's second postulate is written quantitatively in the form:

$$\Delta E = E_{\text{final}} - E_{\text{initial}} = hf \qquad [2]$$

in which $h$ is Planck's constant and $f$ is the frequency of the electromagnetic radiation absorbed or emitted by the atom during the transition of the electron from one orbit to the other. Bohr could not have written Eq. [2] without Max Planck's prior work. Eq. [2] in its general form is credited to Planck; its application to the hydrogen atom was Bohr's idea. We want to use Bohr's two postulates to describe the simplest possible atom quantitatively. That atom is the **hydrogen atom**, since it consists of only one electron and a nucleus with only one positive elementary charge.

### Concept Question 22.2

Why is Bohr's second postulate important?

ANSWER: The first postulate defines which orbits are allowed. However, this postulate does not provide us with a method to measure and verify its content. The second postulate addresses changes in the total energy of the atom that occur when we interact with the atom (i.e., the atom is thermodynamically a closed system). Energy absorbed by or emitted from the atom provides us with a measurable quantity that will be used to verify the model assumptions.

## The Angular Momentum

We begin with Bohr's postulate that only a discrete set of orbits are allowed in which an electron can be placed without losing energy via radiation. According to Concept Question 22.1, no such orbit should exist. In 1923, Louis de Broglie provided a useful idea to circumvent this problem. Let us assume that the electron is a wave. This idea leads to the non-classical concept of **particle-wave dualism**, because we know with certainty that the electron can act like a particle. Once we accept this assumption, we apply wave concepts instead of mechanical concepts to determine the properties of the electron. In this context it proves useful that in Chapter 17 we studied waves also in a confined space, because the atom confines the electron. In a confined space the wave equation has time-independent solutions that we defined as standing waves. We will focus on such standing waves because the atom does not change with time. Forcing the electron onto a circular path around the nucleus defines the length of the confining space as the circumference of the path. We now require an integer number $n$ of wavelengths ($n = 1, 2, 3, \ldots$) to fit into the circumference as shown for two complete wavelengths in Fig. 22.5. This leads to a general condition for standing-wave solutions for the electron orbits in the atom:

$$2 \cdot \pi \cdot r = n \cdot \lambda \qquad [3]$$

But what is the wavelength of an electron? The fact that an electron can act as a particle or a wave requires that its respective parameter sets are related to each other. This led to **de Broglie's wavelength** formula for the electron:

$$\lambda = \frac{h}{p} = \frac{h}{m \cdot v} \qquad [4]$$

in which $h$ is Planck's constant, $p$ is the momentum, $m$ is the mass, and $v$ is the speed of the electron (when the electron is considered to be a particle). With J · s the unit of Planck's constant and the units of the momentum kg · m/s, we confirm the unit m for the wavelength. We must emphasize that the wavelength

in Eq. [4] is a wave property and the mass and the momentum are particle properties. Both are related to each other with Planck's constant.

### ● EXAMPLE 22.1

Determine de Broglie's wavelength for an electron with energy 1.5 eV.

*Solution:* We use the equation for the kinetic energy, rewritten for the momentum with $p = m \cdot v$:

$$E_{kin} = \frac{1}{2} m \cdot v^2 = \frac{p^2}{2 \cdot m} \qquad [5]$$

which yields:

$$p = \sqrt{2 \cdot m \cdot E_{kin}} \qquad [6]$$

Using Eq. [4], we find:

$$\lambda = \frac{h}{\sqrt{2 \cdot m \cdot E_{kin}}} = 1.0 \, nm \qquad [7]$$

*Note:* A correction for possible relativistic properties, i.e., properties due to velocities close to the speed of light, is needed for electrons of kinetic energies larger than 1 keV. For example, the wavelength calculated for an electron at 50 keV is off by 2.5 % if calculated with Eq. [6].

Substituting Eq. [4] to introduce the electron's particle parameters in the standing wave condition of Eq. [3] yields:

$$2 \cdot \pi \cdot r = n \frac{h}{m \cdot v} \qquad [8]$$

which leads to:

$$m \cdot v \cdot r = \frac{n \cdot h}{2 \cdot \pi} = n \cdot \hbar \qquad [9]$$

in which $\hbar = h/(2 \cdot \pi)$ is a commonly used abbreviation. Eq. [9] indicates that the term on the left-hand side, $m \cdot v \cdot r$, is constant for the electron in an atomic orbit. This quantity is defined as the angular momentum.

Bohr himself derived Eq. [9] in a different fashion. He did not rely on the intuitive wave idea for the electron introduced later by de Broglie, but instead worked with an argument from the classical mechanics of circular motion. It is worthwhile to follow this argument because it reinforces the importance of the conservation of the angular momentum we found in Eq. [9]. We motivate Bohr's approach with a Concept Question.

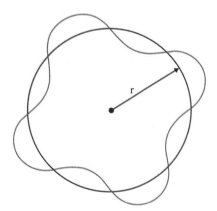

**FIGURE 22.5**

An electron forming a standing wave in an orbit of radius $r$ around the nucleus.

## Concept Question 22.3

**Bohr wanted to describe the circular path of an electron in a hydrogen atom. Why would he look for inspiration to classical mechanics, including the laws describing the motion of planets in the solar system?**

ANSWER: Coulomb's law governs the interaction between a light electron and a massive proton in a hydrogen atom. For opposite charges, it is mathematically similar to Newton's law of gravity for the interaction of a light planet and a massive star in that both forces are **central forces** (acting on the satellite toward the centre) with a magnitude that is inversely proportional to the distance square of the satellite, $|F| \propto 1/r^2$. The law of gravity and its role in describing planetary motion in the solar system goes back at least to the year 1609, when Johannes Kepler, holding the post of imperial court astronomer to the Holy Roman emperor, published his first two laws of planetary motion. The second law is called the **area rule** and states that the hypothetical line drawn from the Sun to the planet sweeps out equal areas during equal intervals of time. This law was generalized 56 years later when Sir Isaac Newton quantified the gravitational force. Bohr used these similarities to avoid reinventing a formalism that was already in place.

In Newton's equation for circular motion (Eq. [21.18]), the centripetal acceleration is caused by a single force if that force is a central force, such as gravity or the electric force. A special result of circular motion with a central force is that we find a new physical quantity to be conserved: the **angular momentum**. Parameters that are conserved in nature command special interest in physics. Indeed we have found so far very few that are conserved: momentum in an isolated system in Chapter 4, energy in an isolated system in Chapter 6, and the net charge of a system in Chapter 13. Thus, we want to learn more about the concept of angular momentum.

As the name implies, the angular momentum is a concept closely related to momentum. The conservation of momentum has been derived in Chapter 4. There we showed that the change of the momentum with time is zero when no external forces act on the system. We can proceed in an analogous fashion when studying the circular motion of an object on which a central force acts. For the circular motion it is more appropriate to consider the torque than the force, as circular motion represents a rotation about the centre. The magnitude of torque is:

$$\tau = r \cdot F \cdot \sin \phi \qquad [10]$$

in which $r$ is the distance of the point of attack from the rotation axis and $F$ is the force applied at the point of attack. The $\sin \phi$ term selects the force component perpendicular to the radius vector, as the force component parallel to it does not contribute to the torque. Motivated by the approach we took in Chapter 4, we study Eq. [10] with respect to changes with time. For this, the force on the right-hand side is rewritten in the form $F = \Delta p/\Delta t$, which is the change of the momentum with time:

$$\tau = r \frac{\Delta p}{\Delta t} \sin \phi = r \frac{\Delta(m \cdot v)}{\Delta t} \sin \phi \qquad [11]$$

The radius does not vary with time for a circular motion. Since neither $\sin \phi$ nor the radius change with time, Eq. [11] remains mathematically unchanged when we move these terms into the parentheses:

$$\tau = \frac{\Delta(r \cdot p \cdot \sin \phi)}{\Delta t} = \frac{\Delta(r \cdot m \cdot v \cdot \sin \phi)}{\Delta t} \qquad [12]$$

From Eq. [12], we establish a new conservation law with the same argument we used for the momentum before. Let's consider an isolated system, i.e., a system in which no external forces—and therefore no net torque—act on the system. For such a system, both sides of Eq. [12] are zero:

$$0 = \frac{\Delta(r \cdot m \cdot v \cdot \sin \phi)}{\Delta t} \qquad [13]$$

which yields:

$$r \cdot m \cdot v \cdot \sin \phi = L = \text{const} \qquad [14]$$

Thus, for a system without external forces the angular momentum $L$ is conserved. We note that angular momentum has the following properties:

- The unit of angular momentum is kg · m²/s, which is the same as J · s.

- Like torque, the angular momentum is a vector quantity, resulting from the product of two other vectors, the momentum and the radius vector. Also, the sine term for the angle between the two vectors suggests a vector product. Eq. [14] is indeed the magnitude of the angular momentum with the proper vector-product notation:

$$\mathbf{L} = [\mathbf{r} \times \mathbf{p}] = m [\mathbf{r} \times \mathbf{v}] \qquad [15]$$

The magnitude of the angular momentum in Eq. [14] is sufficient for our further discussion.

## The Radius of the Hydrogen Atom

Bohr used Eq. [14] to derive his model of the atom. Since the atom is a system with a central force and no other force acts on the electron externally, the angular momentum for the atom must be conserved. Bohr chose the constant term on the right-hand side of Eq. [14] such that only discrete values for $L$ are possible:

$$L = n \cdot \hbar = \frac{n \cdot h}{2 \cdot \pi} \qquad [16]$$

in which $n$ is a positive integer. This statement is equivalent to Eq. [9] and is called **Bohr's quantum condition**.

Next we show how Bohr's quantum condition leads to discrete orbits, as Bohr's first postulate requires. Newton's second law for the circular motion of an electron in a hydrogen atom is based on Eq. [21.18]. The force causing the centripetal acceleration is Coulomb's force. We apply Coulomb's law specifically to the interaction of a proton ($q_1 = +e$) and an electron ($q_2 = -e$). For the magnitude of the net force we find:

$$F_{net} = F_{Coulomb} = \frac{e^2}{4 \cdot \pi \cdot \varepsilon_0 \cdot r^2} = m \frac{v^2}{r} \qquad [17]$$

Multiplying both sides of this equation by $m \cdot r^2$ yields:

$$\frac{m \cdot e^2}{4 \cdot \pi \cdot \varepsilon_0} = \frac{m^2 \cdot v^2 \cdot r^2}{r} \qquad [18]$$

The numerator on the right-hand side is then replaced by Bohr's quantum condition from Eq. [16], but used in quadratic form as $L^2 = (m \cdot v \cdot r)^2 = (n \cdot h)^2 / (2 \cdot \pi)^2$:

$$\frac{m \cdot e^2}{4 \cdot \pi \cdot \varepsilon_0} = \frac{n^2 \cdot h^2}{4 \cdot \pi^2 \cdot r} \qquad [19]$$

which yields for the radius:

$$r = n^2 \frac{\varepsilon_0 \cdot h^2}{m \cdot e^2 \cdot \pi} \qquad [20]$$

Since the right-hand side of Eq. [20] contains only the integer number $n$ as a variable, it describes discrete radii. We therefore call $n$ a **quantum number**. The smallest radius, for which the quantum number is $n = 1$, is called the **Bohr radius**:

$$r_{Bohr} = \frac{\varepsilon_0 \cdot h^2}{m \cdot e^2 \cdot \pi} = 5.29 \times 10^{-11} \, \text{m}$$
$$= 0.053 \, \text{nm} \qquad [21]$$

Note that the radius in Eq. [21] does not depend on any variable; all terms on the right-hand side are constants. Mathematically, Bohr's radius is constant because it is based on three independent equations

with three variables: Eqs. [14] and [17] with variable speed and radius, and Eq. [16] that introduces $n$, which is variable but with discrete values. We then set $n = 1$ and combined the three equations to obtain Eq. [21].

## The Energy of the Hydrogen Atom

With this radius calculated, we now determine the energy of the electron in the hydrogen atom. We start with the electric potential energy between electron and nucleus as defined in Chapter 13:

$$E_{el} = -\frac{e^2}{4 \cdot \pi \cdot \varepsilon_0 \cdot r} \qquad [22]$$

We substitute Bohr's radius for $r$:

$$E_{el} = -\frac{m \cdot e^4}{4 \cdot \varepsilon_0^2 \cdot h^2} \cdot \frac{1}{n^2} \qquad [23]$$

Since the electron is in motion, its total energy is larger than the electric potential energy in Eq. [23]. The kinetic energy is obtained from multiplying both sides of Eq. [17] by $r$:

$$\frac{e^2}{4 \cdot \pi \cdot \varepsilon_0 \cdot r} = -E_{el} = m \cdot v^2 = 2 \cdot E_{kin} \qquad [24]$$

This leads to the total energy of the electron in the hydrogen atom, written as a function of the quantum number $n$ of the orbit:

$$E_{total} = E_{el} + E_{kin} = \frac{1}{2} E_{el} = -\frac{m \cdot e^4}{8 \cdot \varepsilon_0^2 \cdot h^2} \cdot \frac{1}{n^2} \qquad [25]$$

## The Hydrogen Spectrum

Eq. [25] allows for a measurement that tests Bohr's model, as discussed in Concept Question 22.2: the radiation frequency in Bohr's second postulate is calculated from Eq. [25] in the form:

$$h \cdot f = \Delta E_{total} = \frac{m \cdot e^4}{8 \cdot \varepsilon_0^2 \cdot h^2} \left( \frac{1}{n_{initial}^2} - \frac{1}{n_{final}^2} \right) \qquad [26]$$

Eq. [26] is rewritten for the frequency of the **emitted light** or **absorbed light** by dividing the equation by Planck's constant:

$$f = R_H \left| \left( \frac{1}{n_{initial}^2} - \frac{1}{n_{final}^2} \right) \right| \qquad [27]$$

Eq. [27] defines the **Rydberg constant** $R_H$ with:

$$R_H = \frac{m \cdot e^4}{8 \cdot \varepsilon_0^2 \cdot h^3} = 3.29 \times 10^{15} \, \frac{1}{\text{s}} \qquad [28]$$

Bohr's model can be tested in two ways based on Eq. [27]. The first approach is called **absorption spectroscopy**. Light is sent through a transparent hydrogen-filled gas cylinder. The frequency of the incident light is scanned through a wide range as the intensity of the transmitted light beam is detected. When the frequency of the incident light is consistent with Eq. [27], hydrogen atoms absorb the radiation as energy $h \cdot f$. Electrons are transferred from an initial to a final orbit, where $n_{\text{initial}} < n_{\text{final}}$. The energy difference in Eq. [26] is positive in this case because the total energy of the system is increased by the energy absorbed from the incident light ray. The energy lost by the light ray to the system corresponds to a loss of light intensity as recorded by a light detector.

The second way to verify Bohr's model is called **emission spectroscopy**. In this case, light with a wide range of frequencies is passed through a hydrogen-filled gas cell. A detector that measures the intensity of light as a function of frequency is placed at an angle with the direction of the incident beam. Thus, the detector records no light when the gas cell is empty. However, when hydrogen atoms absorb energy from the incident light beam, the electrons that have moved into orbits with higher energy (leading to an **excited atom**) will quickly drop back to the lowest energy state $n = 1$. As electrons return to the lower orbit, Eq. [26] leads to a negative energy, which is the energy lost by the system. This energy leaves the atom as a photon in random directions, including by chance the direction to the detector.

Absorption spectra result in a constant intensity across the observed frequency range with intensity gaps at certain frequencies. Sunlight reaching Earth has such a spectrum. Light from deeper, hotter zones of the Sun's surface is radiated in the direction of Earth. It passes through the outer, cooler layers of the Sun where atoms absorb some of the light at frequencies determined by Eq. [27]. Note that the Sun's outer layers do not exclusively consist of atomic hydrogen. The missing lines in the Sun's spectrum reveal the chemical composition of this layer. The element helium was discovered this way. Its name indicates that it was initially believed to be a metallic element present exclusively in the Sun. The spectra shown in Fig. 22.1 for the amniotic fluid are a second example, however, with the absorbed intensity plotted instead of the transmitted intensity.

Emission spectra in turn consist of the complementary information, i.e., single intensity lines at characteristic frequencies. These correspond to the

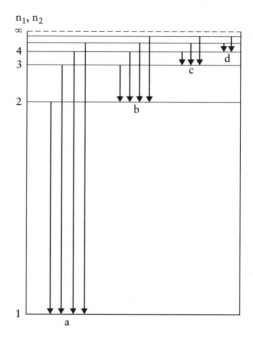

**FIGURE 22.6**

The allowed electronic states in Bohr's atomic model. The ground state has quantum number $n = 1$; the excited states have quantum numbers $n > 1$. The frequency of emitted electromagnetic radiation (photon energy) is proportional to the energy difference of the involved term scheme levels. (a) Lyman series, (b) Balmer series, (c) Paschen series, (d) Brackett series.

transitions shown in Fig. 22.6. The figure shows the transitions of electrons from higher-energy orbits (excited states) to lower orbits. The transitions are grouped in so-called **spectroscopic series**, with (a) the **Lyman series** with transitions to the lowest orbit, (b) the **Balmer series** with transitions to the orbit with $n_{\text{final}} = 2$, (c) the **Paschen series** with $n_{\text{final}} = 3$, and (d) the **Brackett series** with $n_{\text{final}} = 4$. Some of these series of emission lines had been observed before Bohr's model was proposed. The excellent agreement between measurements and the model helped Bohr's postulates to be accepted quickly.

In principle, the quantum number $n$ can take any value between 1 and $\infty$. From a practical point of view, however, only the smaller values are of interest as the energy difference between higher $n$ values becomes smaller and smaller due to Eq. [25]. This is indicated in Fig. 22.6 by the dashed line labelled $\infty$, which we interpret as the ionization energy level, i.e., the energy level beyond which the electron leaves the atom. When an electron leaves, the atom becomes a positive ion. The energy values calculated in Eq. [25] are, therefore, energies relative to the ionization energy of the atom with $E = 0$ eV at $n = \infty$. For the hydrogen atom, we find these values listed in Table 22.1.

## TABLE 22.1

**The total energy of an electron in a hydrogen atom and a He$^+$ ion as a function of the principal quantum number of the occupied orbital**

| $n$ | $E_{total}$(H) (eV) | $E_{total}$(He) (eV) |
|---|---|---|
| 1 | −13.6 | −54.4 |
| 2 | −3.4 | −13.6 |
| 3 | −1.51 | −6.0 |
| 4 | −0.85 | −3.4 |
| 5 | −0.54 | −2.2 |

The origin of the energy scale ($E = 0$) is chosen at the ionization threshold.

## Concept Question 22.4

**Does the hydrogen atom have transitions in the visible range of the electromagnetic spectrum?**

*Solution:* The visible spectrum is defined in Fig. 20.28 as wavelengths between 380 nm and 750 nm. Several lines of the Balmer series, which are transitions to the second-lowest state in the hydrogen atom with $n = 2$, fall within this interval. These Balmer series lines are listed in Table 22.2.

### TABLE 22.2

**Wavelengths of the lowest four transitions in the Balmer series of the hydrogen atom**

| $n_{initial} \rightarrow n_{final}$ | Wavelength (nm) |
|---|---|
| $3 \rightarrow 2$ | 655 |
| $4 \rightarrow 2$ | 485 |
| $5 \rightarrow 2$ | 433 |
| $6 \rightarrow 2$ | 409 |

## ● EXAMPLE 22.2

What are the wavelength and the frequency of light emitted by a hydrogen atom in which the electron makes a transition from the orbit $n = 2$ to the orbit $n = 1$ (called the **ground state**)?

*Solution:* For the frequency emitted as a result of this transition we use Eq. [27]:

$$f = R_H \left| \left( \frac{1}{2^2} - \frac{1}{1^2} \right) \right| = \frac{3}{4} R_H$$
$$= 2.47 \times 10^{15}\,\text{Hz} \qquad [29]$$

The corresponding wavelength is calculated from $c = \lambda \cdot f$ with $c$ the speed of light:

$$\lambda = \frac{c}{f} = \frac{3 \times 10^8\,\dfrac{\text{m}}{\text{s}}}{2.47 \times 10^{15}\,\text{Hz}}$$
$$= 1.21 \times 10^{-7}\,\text{m} = 121\,\text{nm} \qquad [30]$$

Thus, the lowest Lyman-series transition in hydrogen is not visible; the emitted light lies in the UV part of the electromagnetic spectrum. This transition is seen as a sharp peak in the spectrum of Fig. 20.31 just to the left of the broad main peak, indicating strong excitation of atomic hydrogen near the Sun's surface.

## ● EXAMPLE 22.3

How much energy is required to ionize hydrogen atoms when they are (a) in the ground state, and (b) in an excited state with quantum number $n = 3$?

*Solution:* Ionizing an atom means to remove an electron. This is achieved when the atom absorbs at least an amount of energy such that the electron is lifted into the state with $n_{final} = \infty$.

*Solution to part (a):* We insert $n_{initial} = 1$ and $n_{final} = \infty$ in Eq. [26]:

$$\Delta E = h \cdot R_H \left( \frac{1}{n_{initial}^2} - \frac{1}{n_{final}^2} \right) = h \cdot R_H$$
$$= 2.17 \times 10^{-18}\,\text{J} = 13.6\,\text{eV} \qquad [31]$$

*Solution to part (b):* We insert $n_{initial} = 3$ and $n_{final} = \infty$ in Eq. [26]:

$$\Delta E = h \cdot R_H \left( \frac{1}{n_{initial}^2} - \frac{1}{n_{final}^2} \right) = \frac{h \cdot R_H}{9}$$
$$= 2.4 \times 10^{-19}\,\text{J} = 1.5\,\text{eV} \qquad [32]$$

# Toward a Quantum Mechanical Model

When Bohr's model for the hydrogen atom was proposed, it was immediately clear that it would require modifications or extensions to be suitable for atoms of other elements that have many more spectral lines than varying Bohr's quantum number $n$ can explain.

Bohr's model has been shown to apply beyond hydrogen for only one group of particles: single-electron ions such as He$^+$ and Li$^{2+}$. In that case, the elementary charge $e$ for the nucleus is replaced by $Z \cdot e$, where $Z$ is the atomic number taken from the periodic table.

---

### ● EXAMPLE 22.4

Calculate with Bohr's model the five lowest-energy orbits for the He$^+$ ion.

*Solution:* We repeat the calculation that led from Eq. [17] to Eq. [25]. The numerator of Eq. [17] becomes $Ze \cdot e = Ze^2$. This additional factor $Z$ carries through the calculation to Eq. [21], where it leads to an additional factor $Z$ in the denominator for the corrected Bohr radius.

A second factor $Z$ has to be included in the numerator of Eq. [22] for the electric potential energy. Thus, when we substitute the radius in Eq. [22], a factor of $Z^2$ results. Consequently, we find for the total energy of the single electron in heavy single-electron ions:

$$E_{\text{total}}(Z) = Z^2 \cdot E_{\text{total}}(Z = 1) \qquad [33]$$

This allows us to calculate the values for the helium ion with a single positive charge for $Z = 2$ (He). The data are shown in the third column of Table 22.1.

---

Niels Bohr himself, together with Arnold Sommerfeld, made the first attempt to extend Bohr's model to include other types of atoms. They argued that an electron should have three independent quantum numbers (instead of only one), since it moves in three dimensions and its motion in each of the three dimensions of space is independent. We obtain a first idea of what to look for when studying the description of a position in space in three-dimensional polar coordinates. In this case, we use one length parameter (radial distance to origin) and two angles (east–west, and above horizon or below) to identify a position. Thus, one radial and two angular quantum numbers are sought. Continuing to hold on to classical physics to justify this set of quantum numbers, the **Bohr–Sommerfeld model** identified them as:

• The **principal quantum number** $n$ refers to the radial dependence of the electron's orbit. It is due to a quantization of the orbits with discrete total energy values for the electron. This quantum number has already been discussed above in the context of Bohr's original calculations.

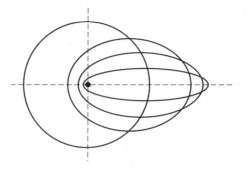

**FIGURE 22.7**

Illustration of circular and elliptical orbits of varying eccentricity.

• The **orbital quantum number** $l$ refers to an angular dependence of the orbit. It is due to the quantization of the angular momentum of the electron. This means that different electrons move on circular or elliptical orbits with different eccentricity around the nucleus, very much like the planets around the Sun. Possible circular and elliptical orbits are illustrated in Fig. 22.7, with the dot at the origin representing the nucleus. Quantization means that only a discrete set of ellipses represent allowed orbits for the electron.

• The **magnetic quantum number** $m_l$ then provides a second angular dependence. It is due to a quantization of the orientation of the orbit of the electron in an external magnetic field, thus further dividing the overall angular dependence provided by the orbital quantum number. This quantum number is called the magnetic quantum number because a non-uniform magnetic field allows us to physically split an atomic beam into as many components as there are allowed values for the magnetic quantum number.

Later, a fourth quantum number was added to make the Bohr–Sommerfeld model consistent with the periodic table of the elements. This quantum number is called **spin** and allows for two values (up or down). The classical concept behind the spin is the rotation of the electron about its own axis. This is another possible motion of the electron, similar to the rotation of Earth about its own axis while it revolves around the Sun. The two values of the spin correspond in this classical picture to the possible east–west or west–east rotation of a planet.

These semi-classical explanations for the quantum numbers are useful as long as they are used cautiously. The classical picture of planet-like electrons moving on ellipses of various eccentricity and orientation around the Sun-like nucleus cannot explain many of the properties of atoms. In particular, the possible locations of a given electron (which we call **orbitals**) differ significantly from the planetary model. This is a significant deficiency as it is the actual orientation of an orbital that determines the chemical properties of an atom or a molecule. We will, therefore, briefly review the quantum mechanical concepts that allow us to determine the actual orbitals.

Quantum mechanics was developed in the 1920s by a new generation of physicists who were more willing to abandon classical concepts. Following Louis de Broglie's idea that an electron may act as either a particle or a wave, Erwin Schrödinger developed a wave equation model for the electron in an atom in 1926. What is very different from the planetary model that considers the electron as a particle is the interpretation of the solutions of **Schrödinger's wave equation**. The solutions, called **wave functions**, are not given any direct meaning but lead after further mathematical operations to **probability functions** that describe the probability of finding an electron at a given time at a given position. Of particular interest are the solutions to Schrödinger's equation that are time-independent (i.e., associated with standing waves), since these lead to time-independent probability functions (i.e., functions that describe the probability of finding an electron at a given position relative to the nucleus at any time). Schrödinger identified these solutions with **stationary orbitals**.

The fact that we can provide only a probability for an electron to be at a certain point is an inherent feature of the wave–particle dualism. When you consider an electron to be a wave, for example as illustrated in a simplified fashion in Fig. 22.5, assigning the electron a specific position is not possible. On the other hand, when you consider an electron to be a particle, as illustrated in Fig. 22.4, locating the electron should be possible. Describing the location of an electron in an atom in the form of probabilities is, therefore, a compromise between the wave and the particle properties of the electron.

Mathematically, the solutions to Schrödinger's equation for the atom are rather complex since they deal with three-dimensional standing waves. In analogy to the solutions to the one-dimensional wave equation in a confined tube discussed in Chapter 17, which allowed only certain frequency values, Schrödinger's equation also permits only certain values of the total energy of the electron for time-independent solutions. These values of the total energy are called **eigenvalues**. The energy eigenvalues predicted by Schrödinger's equation are consistent with the values predicted by Bohr's model for the hydrogen atom.

The time-independent solutions to Schrödinger's equation contain much more information than Bohr's model. They provide a justification of the three quantum numbers that Bohr and Sommerfeld pro-

## TABLE 22.3

### Quantum numbers and orbitals

| $n$ | $l$ | $m_l$ | Name |
|---|---|---|---|
| 1 | 0 | 0 | 1s |
| 2 | 0 | 0 | 2s |
| 2 | 1 | −1, 0, +1 | 2p |
| 3 | 0 | 0 | 3s |
| 3 | 1 | −1, 0, +1 | 3p |
| 3 | 2 | −2, −1, 0, +1, +2 | 3d |
| 4 | 0 | 0 | 4s |
| 4 | 1 | −1, 0, +1 | 4p |
| 4 | 2 | −2, −1, 0, +1, +2 | 4d |
| 4 | 3 | −3, −2, −1, 0, +1, +2, +3 | 4f |

The quantum numbers are: $n$, the principal quantum number; $l$, the orbital quantum number; $m_l$, the magnetic quantum number. The name of an orbital combines the number of the principal quantum number and a letter representing the orbital quantum number: s = sharp, p = principal, d = diffuse, f = fundamental. The magnetic quantum number is then identified as an index (see examples in Figs. 22.9 and 22.10).

posed arbitrarily: Schrödinger's orbitals are mostly not spherical. Three independent quantum numbers are needed to characterize all possible solutions (the fourth quantum number, spin, was integrated into these formulas later). These obey the following selection rules for the orbital quantum number:

$$0 \leq l \leq n - 1 \qquad [34]$$

and for the magnetic quantum number:

$$-l \leq m_l \leq +l \qquad [35]$$

The nomenclature of the orbitals is based on spectroscopic observations of transitions that involve the respective orbital. Table 22.3 summarizes the possible combinations of quantum numbers.

The orbitals can be illustrated in various ways:

- Two-dimensional plots of the radial probability show the probability of finding the electron as a function of distance $r$ from the nucleus. Radial probability plots for six of the orbitals in Table 22.3 are shown in Fig. 22.8.

- Two-dimensional plots of the angular probability show the probability of finding the electron as a function of angle.

- The combination of radial and angular probability plots produces three-dimensional images. In these, the surfaces shown enclose the region in

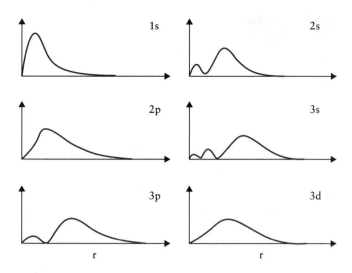

**FIGURE 22.8**

The probability of finding an electron as a function of distance $r$ from the nucleus in various orbitals of an atom. Note that only the s-orbitals are spherically symmetric.

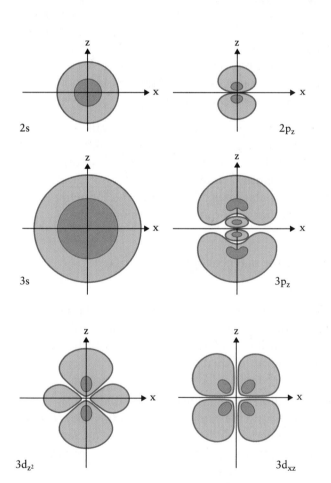

**FIGURE 22.9**

Cross-section through a three-dimensional representation of the probability of finding an electron in an atom as a function of position. The green areas indicate the volume within which the electron is found 50% of the time, and the purple areas 99% of the time. The notation of the orbitals is defined in Table 22.3.

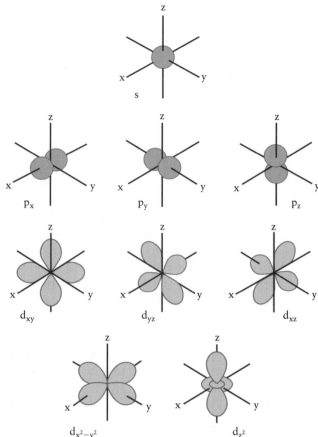

**FIGURE 22.10**

Three-dimensional artist's sketch of atomic orbitals. Shown are the surfaces within which the electron is found 99% of the time (green).

which the electron is to be found with a certain probability. Fig. 22.9 shows cross-sections of such plots, representing the areas with a 50% (green area) and a 99% (purple area) probability of finding the electron inside. In turn, Fig. 22.10 is an artist's sketch of the 99% surfaces in three dimensions. The latter are very useful when trying to envisage processes in stereo-chemistry.

---

**Concept Question 22.5**

**In Fig. 22.8, how can an electron in the 2s orbital be left or right of the minimum between the two peaks, but not at the position of the minimum, where its probability is zero?**

ANSWER: This is one of many similar questions that address the inadequacy of a macroscopic classical interpretation for features that are quantum-mechanical in nature. In this particular case, no answer exists based on a classical corpuscle model of the electron. However, a classical wave model can address this particular paradox: we have seen in Chapter 17 that standing waves have nodes where the wave amplitude remains continuously zero.

Once the orbitals of the atom are identified, quantum theory allows us to predict the order in which these orbitals are filled with electrons. This procedure is based on two principles:

- The **minimum energy principle** states that any electron added to an atom will occupy a free orbital with the least total energy.

- The **Pauli principle** (named for Wolfgang Pauli) states that no two electrons in the same atom may have the same four quantum numbers (including spin).

Due to the Pauli principle, each atomic orbital can accommodate two electrons (due to the existence of two possible values for the spin quantum number). Thus, up to 2 electrons can be placed in each s-orbital; up to 6 electrons in the p-orbitals with a given quantum number $n$; up to 10 electrons in the d-orbitals with a given quantum number $n$; and up to 14 electrons in corresponding f-orbitals.

This explains the periodic table. Hydrogen has one electron in its 1s-orbital. Helium has two electrons in its 1s-orbital; therefore, this orbital is full. A single electron in an orbital is reactive; therefore, hydrogen is usually not found in atomic form. In contrast, an electron pair in an orbital is chemically inert; consequently, helium does not undergo chemical reactions and is called a **noble gas**.

The third element in the periodic table accepts its third electron into the 2s-orbital since the 1s-orbital is already filled by the first two electrons. Thus, lithium behaves chemically similar to hydrogen; it likes to form chemical bonds by releasing its single 2s-electron (valence electron). When a lithium atom releases its valence electron, it becomes a positive ion with a noble gas electron configuration, which is characterized as an atom or ion for which all orbitals of a given quantum number $n$ are filled with electrons. The propensity of lithium to release an electron to obtain a noble gas configuration is called **electropositive behaviour**. A second reason why the lithium atom tends to release its valence electron is the fact that this electron orbits much farther out than the 1s-electrons, increasing the radius from $Li^+$ to Li by a factor of more than 2.5.

The fourth element, beryllium, also accepts the next electron into the 2s-orbital. Different from helium, however, beryllium is extremely reactive. It is actually among the most dangerous elementary metals handled in the laboratory (highly flammable, poisonous). This indicates that a filled 2s-orbital is not sufficient to complete the second period in the periodic table. The second period is completed only when another six electrons are added, i.e., when we reach the element neon. We can predict this from Table 22.3. Beryllium still has three empty 2p-orbitals. These p-orbitals correspond to electron states with slightly higher energy; however, the energy difference is minimal and the two 2s-electrons can easily mix with the empty p-orbitals to form hybrid orbitals. This is not observed in isolated atoms, but it is an important property when forming molecules, as discussed below.

The fifth element, boron, is the first element with an electron in a p-orbital. The sixth element, carbon, has a distinguished position in the periodic system. With two 2s- and two 2p-electrons it has exactly half as many electrons as the second period can accommodate. This allows carbon to form chemical bonds with elements on both sides in the periodic table, e.g., $CO_2$ with oxygen and $CH_4$ with hydrogen. As the example of the methane molecule indicates, carbon can form up to four bonds, the maximum possible for an element in the second period. This enables carbon to form a wide range of different and complex compounds, an ability that is unparalleled in the periodic table. Thus, it is not surprising that life, which depends on such flexibility for the many biochemical tasks necessary for survival, is based on carbon compounds (organic chemistry).

# Molecules

## Molecular Structure

Studying isolated atoms is of limited interest, as the materials around us and in our body are very rarely found in atomic form. Atoms form three types of chemical bonds. We already discussed some properties of the first two types in Chapter 13: (i) ionic systems, in which an electronegative element receives an electron from a more electropositive atom, and (ii) metallic systems, in which many electropositive atoms release their valence electrons into a common, loosely bound electron sea.

The third type of chemical bond is the **covalent bond**. We can discuss covalent bonds only now, because we need to know the atomic orbital structure of the elements to develop a suitable model for molecules. The approach is based on a **linear combination of atomic orbitals**, or the **LCAO method**. This method is useful for predicting the orbital structures and their respective potential energies, as illustrated for the simplest possible example, which is the formation of a hydrogen molecule from two hydrogen atoms:

$$2H \rightarrow H_2 \qquad [36]$$

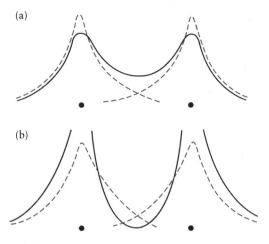

**FIGURE 22.11**

Formation of (a) a binding $\sigma$-orbital and (b) an anti-binding $\sigma^*$-orbital from two atomic s-orbitals, as observed during the formation of an $H_2$ molecule. The two dots indicate the position of the two nuclei. The dashed lines represent the radial probability distribution for the electron in the separate atoms. The red lines represent the combined molecular orbitals.

When applying the LCAO method, we follow the same two steps we used for the atom before: (i) we determine the orbitals and their order with increasing energy, and then (ii) we fill all electrons into the orbitals from lowest to highest energy.

The orbitals of the hydrogen molecule result from the overlap of the atomic orbitals, as shown in Fig. 22.11. The dashed and solid lines represent the probability distribution of finding an electron at distance $r$ from each nucleus for the 1s-orbitals of the hydrogen atoms (dashed lines) and the molecular orbital (red lines). When the two hydrogen atoms come close and the atomic orbitals overlap, they are no longer possible solutions of the Schrödinger equation because the Pauli principle disallows two equivalent electrons to be present in the same space. Instead, new molecular orbitals form—in Fig. 22.11(a) a binding orbital and in Fig. 22.11(b) a non-binding orbital.

We identify the chemical bond in Fig. 22.11(a) as the zone where the greatest overlap occurs. A molecular orbital with the greatest overlap along the line between the two nuclei is called a **sigma bond** ($\sigma$-**orbital**).

As in atomic orbitals, two electrons can be accommodated in each molecular orbital due to the Pauli exclusion principle (since the two electrons have different spins). A simple arithmetic argument demonstrates that we have not yet completed the discussion of the formation of molecular orbitals when we have considered only the formation of a $\sigma$-orbital. Two atomic 1s-orbitals can accommodate a total of four electrons, two for each atom. The newly formed

$\sigma$-orbital can accommodate only two electrons. Thus, a second orbital has to be formed from the two atomic 1s-orbitals. This is illustrated in Fig. 22.11(b). The second molecular orbital is an **anti-binding orbital**, i.e., an orbital that minimizes the overlap between the two original atomic orbitals. This orbital is labelled a $\sigma^*$-orbital, where the superscript * indicates the anti-binding character of the bond. Since the $\sigma^*$-orbital can also accommodate up to two electrons, we have provided as many molecular orbital places for electrons as were present in the combined atomic orbitals. Thus, our model of the hydrogen molecule is complete.

Fig. 22.12 shows the same orbitals; however, it assigns to each orbital an energy level relative to the energy of the atomic orbital. Such a display is called a **term scheme**. The energies of the two molecular orbitals are different from each other and different from the energies of the original atomic orbitals. How can we justify the term scheme shown in Fig. 22.12? For this, we need to introduce another quantum mechanical principle: **Heisenberg's uncertainty principle**, introduced by Werner Heisenberg in 1927. The uncertainty principle states that it is impossible to know precisely both the position and the momentum of a particle at any given time instant.

Studying the following attempt to measure both as precisely as possible leads to a mathematical expression of the principle. We consider a particle that has been placed under a microscope. By looking through the microscope we try to pin down the position of the particle to within an uncertainty of a small distance $\Delta x$. To do this, we must interfere with the particle. To be sure that it is within a distance interval $\Delta x$, we

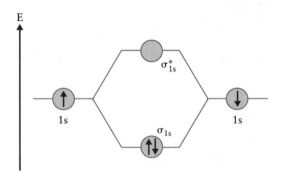

**FIGURE 22.12**

The term scheme for the formation of a hydrogen molecule. Shown at left and right are the 1s-orbital energies of the two hydrogen atoms. The two molecular orbitals differ in energy, with the binding orbital at a lower energy and the anti-binding orbital at a higher energy than the respective atomic orbitals. The arrows in the green circles indicate electrons. Each orbital can accept two with different spin quantum numbers. This is indicated by the up and down direction of the arrows.

need to use light of wavelength $\lambda \le \Delta x$ for the observation. Based on de Broglie's arguments, light of wavelength $\lambda$ carries a momentum $p$ with $\lambda = h/p$, where $h$ is Planck's constant. Thus, the momentum the light carries into the system during observation is at least $p = h/\lambda$. Since we cannot know what fraction of this momentum is transferred to the particle we observe, we find that the product of the uncertainty of the position of the particle after the observation, $\Delta x$, and the uncertainty of the momentum after the observation, $\Delta p$, is given by:

$$\Delta p \cdot \Delta x \ge \frac{h}{\lambda} \cdot \lambda = h \qquad [37]$$

Uncertainty of this kind does not exist in the realm of classical physics, because in classical physics it is implicitly assumed that $h = 0$. We used the classical view whenever we treated phenomena as **deterministic**, which means they are fully predictable. In reality, Planck's constant is very small, but not zero. Therefore, we have to accept that we cannot know precisely both the momentum (from which we can calculate the energy when knowing the mass of the particle) and the position of a particle; the better we know the position, the greater is the uncertainty of the momentum, and vice versa, since the uncertainties in Eq. [37] are related by multiplication.

*The uncertainty principle states that the position and momentum of a particle cannot be measured precisely at the same time.*

## Concept Question 22.6

**Fig. 22.13 shows the ground-state energies, $E_g$ in unit eV, for about 25 hydrogen-containing systems as a function of the distance between the hydrogen atom, H, and its molecular partner, R, in unit nm. The data include non-polar molecules, such as hydrogen and silane, polar molecules, such as water and HF, and solid metal hydrides. The ground state is the state of lowest total energy of a molecule. How would you explain the decreasing ground-state energy with increasing hydrogen bond length?**

ANSWER: Ground-state energies are governed by Heisenberg's uncertainty principle. The closer a hydrogen atom is located to its molecular partner, the greater the uncertainty of its momentum. Thus, a smaller molecule requires a larger momentum, and therefore a larger total energy of the bond.

Specifically, Eq. [37] states that the uncertainty of the momentum is inversely proportional to the uncertainty of the position, $\Delta p \ge h/\Delta x$. Momentum and kinetic energy are related as $E = p^2/(2 \cdot m)$. Thus, the spatial restriction $\Delta x$ of the hydrogen atom and its kinetic energy are related as $\Delta E_{kin} \propto 1/\Delta x^2$. This causes the total energy of a hydrogen atom to increase with spatial confinement.

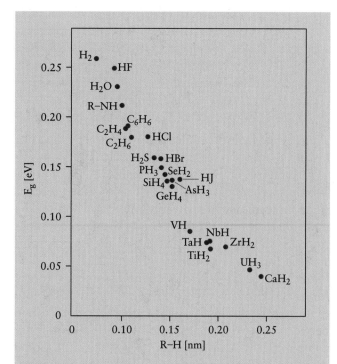

**FIGURE 22.13**

Ground-state energies in unit eV for hydrogen-containing chemical systems as a function of the distance between the hydrogen atom and its molecular partner. The data include non-polar and polar molecules, and solid metal hydrides.

We can apply Heisenberg's uncertainty principle to the orbitals that we developed for the hydrogen molecule. In comparison to the atomic orbital, the binding $\sigma$-orbital in Fig. 22.11 provides more space (larger $\Delta x$) to its electrons. The uncertainty principle implies that the uncertainty in the energy of this orbital is less than that for the atomic orbital; i.e., the orbital can have a lower energy. The $\sigma^*$-orbital, on the other side, restricts the space where electrons can be found more than the atomic orbital. This requires a larger uncertainty in energy, and therefore a higher energy level for the orbital.

The term scheme shown in Fig. 22.12 explains why $H_2$ molecules form and why $He_2$ molecules do not exist. In agreement with the minimum energy principle and Pauli's principle, the hydrogen molecule has two electrons in the $\sigma$-orbital while its $\sigma^*$-orbital is empty. Thus, the formation of the hydrogen molecule is energetically favourable because the hydrogen molecule has a lower total energy than the system of two

separate hydrogen atoms. The energy difference is released during the formation of the molecule. In turn,
to break a hydrogen molecule into two hydrogen
atoms, the energy difference must be added to the
molecule from the environment. On the other hand,
when two helium atoms try to form a molecule, both
the $\sigma$- and $\sigma^*$-orbitals are occupied by two electrons.
Thus, the helium molecule is energetically not
favoured over two separate helium atoms.

Orbitals other than s-orbitals can overlap and contribute to chemical bonds. For this we have to consider molecules with partially filled p-orbitals. The
molecular orbitals for the elements in the second period are shown in Fig. 22.14, and the energy term
scheme for oxygen is shown in Fig. 22.15. The orbitals in Fig. 22.14 are derived in the same fashion as
for the hydrogen molecule (LCAO method). Note
that each overlapping orbital that forms along a line
between the two nuclei is called a $\sigma$-orbital and is accompanied by a non-overlapping $\sigma^*$-orbital. Some
atomic p-orbitals can overlap as well, leading to orbitals that are not rotationally symmetric to the axis
of the bond. Such orbitals are called $\pi$-**orbitals**.
Again, each binding $\pi$-orbital must be accompanied
by a non-binding $\pi^*$-orbital to accommodate the
same number of electrons as the separate p-orbitals.

The term scheme in Fig. 22.14 indicates that the
overlap between two p-orbitals is less effective than
that between two s-orbitals. Thus, the energy difference between a $\pi$-orbital and the p-orbital from
which it formed is less than that between a $\sigma$-orbital
and the respective s-orbital.

The next step is to study the formation of molecules with more than two atoms, e.g., $CH_4$, $NH_3$, and
$H_2O$. In the formation of these molecules, we observe

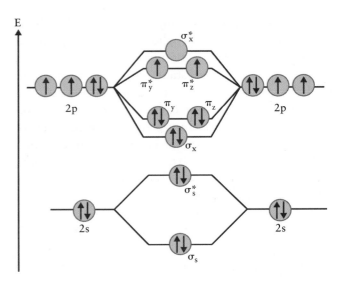

**FIGURE 22.15**

Term scheme of the oxygen molecule. The greater stability of the molecule
compared to the separate atoms is explained by the energy of the respectively
highest occupied orbital. Unpaired electrons participate in chemical reactions; all orbitals of equal energy are occupied by a single electron before a
second electron is added to an orbital.

a new phenomenon called **hybridization**. Hybrid orbitals are orbitals that hypothetically form in a single
atom by mixing the various solutions of the Schrödinger equation, e.g., the s-orbital and all or some of
the p-orbitals in the elements of the second period.
This does not occur in isolated atoms because the
atomic orbitals that we discussed earlier represent the
lowest energies for the respective atoms. However, as
atoms or molecules approach each other, the mutual
overlapping of orbitals can lead to hybridization
when this produces a term scheme that allows for a
lower energy of the molecule formed.

Hybridization is illustrated in Fig. 22.16 for the
case in which all three p-orbitals participate, e.g., in
the case of the formation of a $CH_4$ molecule. We see
that the four resulting $sp^3$-orbitals are directed toward
the corners of a tetrahedron, which leads to a bond
angle $\theta = 109.47°$. The angles between the chemical
bonds of $CH_4$, $NH_3$, and $H_2O$ are compared to this
value in Fig. 22.17. The centre atoms in all three molecules are $sp^3$-hybridized; the minor variation in the
bond angle is due to the electrostatic repulsion between orbitals occupied by two electrons.

Note that hybridization may sometimes involve
only one or two p-orbitals. For example, the
carbon–carbon bond in organic molecules can be
based on either $sp^3$-orbitals (single bond, e.g., in
ethane ($C_2H_6$)); $sp^2$-orbitals (leading to a double
bond, e.g., in ethylene ($C_2H_4$)); or sp-orbitals (leading to a triple bond, e.g., in acetylene ($C_2H_2$)).

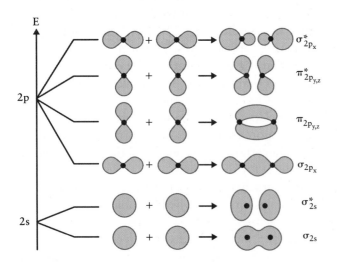

**FIGURE 22.14**

Molecular orbitals formed by linear combination of equivalent orbitals in the
first and second period of the periodic system.

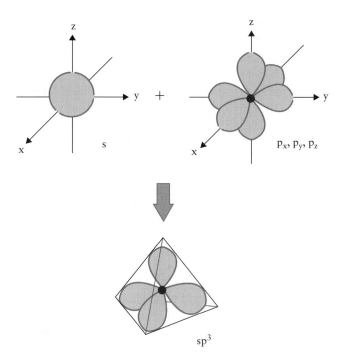

**FIGURE 22.16**

Geometric sketch illustrating the formation of a hybrid sp³-orbital that is formed by combining one atomic s- and three p-orbitals.

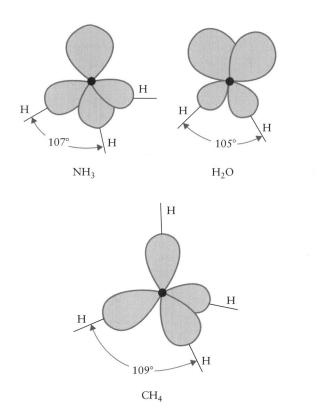

**FIGURE 22.17**

Comparison of the bond angles in three sp³-hybridized molecules. Only methane displays the theoretical angle of $\theta = 109.47°$. Asymmetric occupation of orbitals and the electrostatic repulsion between electrons lead to slightly lower H—N—H and H—O—H angles in the ammonia and water molecules.

# Light Emission

For both atoms and molecules, we return to Bohr's postulates to describe in more detail how light is emitted. The second postulate states that electrons lose or gain energy when they transfer between two allowed orbits. Since energy conservation applies, the energy difference between the initial and final orbits of the transition must be accounted for after the transition has occurred. If the transition is associated with an increase in the total energy of the electron, the energy must be provided to the atom or molecule, and if the transition is associated with a decrease in the total energy of the electron, the energy must be emitted from the atom or molecule.

A system can change its total energy in essentially two ways: either it is a closed system that exchanges only heat with the environment, or it is an open system that exchanges both heat and matter with the environment. At the microscopic scale of atoms and molecules, both of these forms of exchange are possible, although they must be interpreted in a new way. An atom or a molecule acts as a closed system when the total energy is changed by absorbing or emitting electromagnetic radiation (**photons**). The emission may be in the form of visible light, but it may also be in the form of other types of electromagnetic radiation, ranging from microwave frequencies (this type of radiation excites the rotation of molecules, e.g., the rotation of water molecules in a microwave oven) to X-rays, which we discuss below.

Atoms and molecules can also be open systems. In most cases this involves the addition or removal of an electron. In the next chapter we will also discuss cases in which other particles leave an atom, such as alpha particles. These originate from the nucleus.

Here we focus on the atom or molecule as a closed system; i.e., we assume that the number and type of particles constituting the atom or molecule do not change. These are indeed the cases Bohr had in mind when he formulated the second postulate. He provided a classical interpretation for his second postulate: we allow an electron in an atom to be briefly in two orbits at the same time, which must be the case during a transition from one orbit to the other since it cannot be anywhere between the two orbits. If we consider the electron to oscillate between the two orbits during the transition, like electrons oscillating in an antenna, then it emits electromagnetic radiation. The radiation represents a loss of energy, and thus the total energy of the electron is reduced. This occurs only if an unoccupied allowed orbit of lower energy exists. If not, the atom cannot lose energy as it is in the lowest energy state (ground state). However, the inverse process can happen, in which we provide electromagnetic radiation externally and allow the electron to pick some of it up (absorption) to move to an allowed orbit at higher energy.

The absorption and emission processes of electromagnetic radiation were early tools for analyzing atoms and molecules. Depending on the type of electromagnetic radiation, different experimental analytical methods are required including infrared spectroscopy (IR), which samples vibrational excitations of molecules, and ultraviolet spectroscopy (UV), for electronic excitations.

A typical spectroscopic experiment for sodium can be conducted in the following way: sodium at room temperature is a solid metal, and as such is not well suited for spectroscopy. The preferred state of matter for spectroscopy is either a gas or a dilute solution in an inert matrix (e.g., an organic powder embedded in a potassium chloride (KCl) matrix for infrared spectroscopy). In the case of sodium, a piece of the metal is placed in a vacuum chamber and heated to $100°C$ at a pressure of $10^{-7}$ torr. Sodium has an unusually high vapour pressure and, thus, an appreciable sodium vapour density develops in the chamber. The chamber has several windows that are transparent to visible light. We now shine light through the sodium vapour and analyze the intensity as a function of frequency for (i) light passing straight through the chamber, and (ii) light emerging from the vapour in other directions.

When shining white light (which is light with equal intensities across the visible range) through the chamber, we notice a loss of intensity at $\lambda = 589$ nm. This wavelength corresponds to the absorption of energy for a transition between two allowed orbitals in the sodium atom. Electromagnetic radiation is also detected in directions other than the direction of the incident light beam. This electromagnetic radiation is yellow light, again with a wavelength of 589 nm. Thus, the atomic absorption and instantaneous re-emission processes allow for a selective scattering of light with well-defined frequencies. This process is called **fluorescence**. The scattered light is isotropic; i.e., it is observed to have the same intensity in all directions. We also refer to this process more specifically as resonant fluorescence: the external light interacts with the electron in the atom by forcing its oscillation between the two orbitals involved in the transition. Since external light does this only with exactly the right transition frequency, the term **resonant**, as defined in Chapter 17, applies.

George Gabriel Stokes noted that resonant fluorescence is not the only type of fluorescence that occurs in the experiment described above. Particularly for

molecules, we also observe fluorescence light at wavelengths shorter than the wavelength required to excite the atom or molecule; i.e., fluorescence also occurs when the incoming light has higher energy than the atomic transition. The spectrum in Fig. 22.18 illustrates this for an eosine solution (eosine is an organic sodium-containing dye, used to enhance contrast in bacteriological studies). The primary beam in this experiment is monochromatic, which means that we do not shine white light through the solution, but use only light of a particular wavelength. The wavelength of the incident light is scanned. We use two intensity detectors, one placed in the path of the beam passing straight through the chamber to detect the absorption process, and one at a large angle with the incident beam to analyze the re-emission process. Both detectors are tuned to a given wavelength that corresponds to an allowed electron transition in the eosine molecule.

We note from Fig. 22.18 that eosine molecules absorb energy most effectively at wavelengths shorter than those at which they re-emit light. The difference in energy represents energy lost by the molecule during a collision with another molecule; i.e., the energy is either redistributed as kinetic energy (thermal energy) or is used to excite the collision partner. This fluorescence phenomenon is called **non-resonant fluorescence**. But how is it possible that an excited eosine molecule collides with another molecule if re-emission is instantaneous? Most excited atomic states have a lifetime of less than $10^{-8}$ s. This time is, however, sufficient for molecular interactions to take place, particularly at higher temperatures and in solutions that are denser than gases.

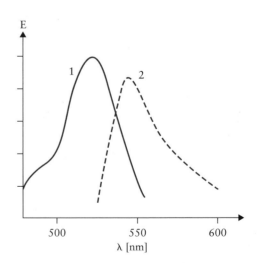

**FIGURE 22.18**

Non-resonant fluorescence of eosine molecules. A monochromatic light beam is scanned from 450 nm to 600 nm. Both absorption (1) and re-emission (2) intensities of light are recorded.

**FIGURE 22.19**

A firefly.

In some cases, re-emission occurs after much longer times, as long as milliseconds. This phenomenon is called **phosphorescence**. It is associated with a forbidden transition that traps the electron in the higher-energy orbital despite an empty orbital at lower energy. The reason why a transition may be forbidden lies in the four quantum numbers that characterize each orbital. Transitions require an adjustment for the electron to the new set of quantum numbers; some of these adjustments are not possible. The same transition is then forbidden for absorption as well. This does not render the trapping impossible, since the initial absorption may have occurred into a higher-energy orbital because the re-emission can involve several transition steps of the electron. Examples of phosphorescence include the radiation emitted by zinc sulphide (ZnS) layers in TV screens and the luminous dials of some clocks. **Luminescence** is a generic term for fluorescence and phosphorescence.

Excitation may occur chemically rather than electromagnetically. Chemiluminescence or bioluminescence occurs in some plants and animals, like the lightning bug or firefly shown in Fig. 22.19.

# X-Rays

## Origin of X-Rays

X-rays are a type of electromagnetic radiation with high frequencies and high photon energies, discovered by Wilhelm Konrad Röntgen in 1895. The maximum range in medical applications lies between 30 keV (mammography) and 150 keV (high kilovoltage radiology). These energies correspond to wave-

lengths in the range from $10^{-10}$ m to $10^{-12}$ m. X-rays are generated when high-energy electrons interact with matter. For medical applications, X-rays are generated in **X-ray tubes**, as illustrated in Fig. 22.20(a) for a typical chest X-ray setup. A chest X-ray is shown in Fig. 22.20(b). The X-ray tube consists of an evacuated glass tube and two electrodes. The vacuum is needed because the technique is based on accelerating free electrons toward a solid target electrode. In air, an electron would not be able to travel more than 1 millimetre. To generate the free electrons, a current $I_T$ is sent through a thin metallic electrode, causing thermal evaporation of electrons. The electrons are then

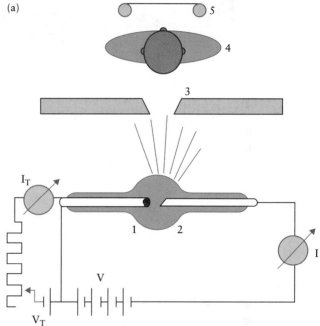

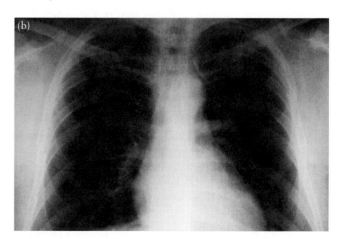

**FIGURE 22.20**

(a) X-ray tube and sketch of its standard use in medicine. Electrons are evaporated from a hot negative electrode in a vacuum chamber (1). The free electrons are then accelerated with a high potential difference to strike the positive electrode (2). The generated X-rays leave the tube, are confined by a collimator (3), pass through the body of the patient (4), and reach a photographic film (5). (b) A typical chest X-ray.

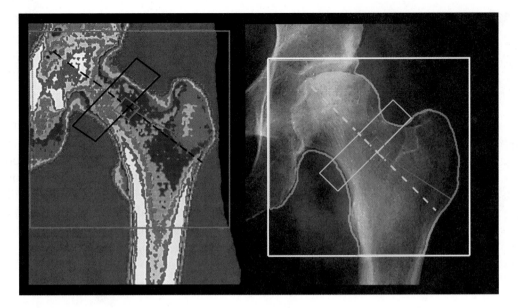

**FIGURE 22.21**

Coloured bone densitometry scan (left) and an X-ray (right) of the same area of a left hip. The rectangle highlights the joint of femur to the acetabulum of the hip (at upper left). X-rays are used to obtain the bone density measurement. The bone density is colour coded, ranging from blue-green for least dense to white for most dense. The bone density of the average menopausal patient shown is normal.

accelerated through a large potential difference $\Delta V$ toward a metallic anode. When the electrons strike the anode X-rays are generated, which are called cathode rays for historical reasons. The glass tube is transparent for these rays (in the same fashion as it is transparent for visible light). The X-rays then travel through a collimator toward the patient. After penetrating the tissue they expose a film behind the patient; the film is developed and used for diagnosis. X-rays are also used in other techniques, such as bone density measurements, as illustrated in Fig. 22.21.

The above process can be used to generate X-rays with a wide range of energies, as illustrated in Fig. 22.22. The figure shows the result of using a molybdenum anode and an X-ray tube potential difference of $\Delta V = 37$ kV between cathode and anode. We need to discuss several features of the spectrum in Fig. 22.22 to understand the processes by which X-rays are generated at the atomic level:

- The figure shows that there is a minimum wavelength, or, correspondingly, a maximum energy of X-rays with the cutoff at $\lambda = 33 \times 10^{-12}$ m.

- A broad peak occurs that tails off toward larger wavelengths. This radiation is called **bremsstrahlung**.

- Two sharp peaks occur at $\lambda = 61 \times 10^{-12}$ m and $\lambda = 70 \times 10^{-12}$ m. These peaks are due to **characteristic X-rays**. We discuss their nomenclature below.

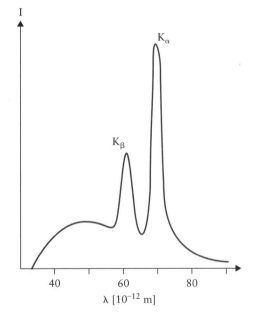

**FIGURE 22.22**

The intensity as a function of wavelength for the electromagnetic radiation emitted by a molybdenum electrode bombarded with 37-keV electrons. Note the cutoff at $\lambda = 33 \times 10^{-12}$ m. Two main features characterize the spectrum: a broad bremsstrahlung peak, and several sharp peaks of characteristic X-rays, labelled $K_\alpha$ and $K_\beta$.

The observation of a sharp cutoff energy is the result of the conservation of energy: even if an electron quickly slows down in the metal, it cannot radiate more than its entire kinetic energy. The interpretation

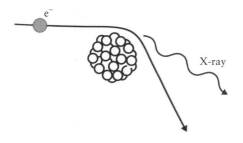

**FIGURE 22.23**

Sketch of the process causing bremsstrahlung. An electron passes a nucleus at close proximity. A large angle deflection occurs due to the strong attraction between the two charges. The electron emits X-rays while accelerating along a curved path.

of the broad bremsstrahlung spectrum then expands on the cutoff argument. An electron with high energy penetrating a piece of solid matter may slow down more slowly, losing its kinetic energy in several steps. Fig. 22.23 illustrates a typical process in which an electron loses some of its energy. When the electron comes in close proximity to an atomic nucleus within the anode, the direction of its motion changes significantly due to electrostatic attraction. Deviation from straight motion is an acceleration during which the electron emits electromagnetic radiation. In the case of the strong acceleration near a nucleus, that radiation has short wavelengths in the X-ray part of the electromagnetic spectrum. The term *bremsstrahlung* (*bremsen* = to brake, *strahlung* = radiation, both terms from German) was adopted as only electrons with a large negative acceleration contribute to the X-ray intensity. Most other interaction processes, like the interaction with valence electrons in the anode atoms, lead to loss of energy in small amounts, which is converted into heat rather than radiation.

The explanation of the sharp peaks in Fig. 22.22 requires the atomic model. This can experimentally be illustrated by changing the material in the anode; while the bremsstrahlung part of the X-ray spectrum varies little, the sharp peaks shift to new wavelengths. This is the reason why this part of the spectrum is called characteristic X-rays: the peaks are characteristic of the anodic material.

We saw already in the discussion of Bohr's model for elements heavier than hydrogen that the same transitions require more energy; the transition from $n = 2$ to $n = 1$ releases 13.6 eV in hydrogen, but 54.4 eV in $He^+$. However, these values apply only to atoms and ions with a single electron. To remove a valence electron from heavier atoms usually requires little energy. The situation during the bombardment with energetic electrons is different. The energetic

electrons act like particles and can kick electrons out of one of the inner orbitals of the anode atoms. Once an inner electron is removed, electrons in higher orbitals fill the vacancy. The energy difference for electrons involved in such transitions is large on account of the large positive charge in the nucleus and the large energy difference between the lower-lying orbitals.

Several possible transitions of electrons into a lower orbital vacancy occur, as illustrated in Fig. 22.24. For an electron removed from the innermost orbital (the orbitals with quantum number $n = 1$ are called the K shell), four possible transitions are shown, labelled with Greek letter indices. Other transitions leading to X-ray emission involve the initial removal of an electron from the L shell (i.e., from orbitals with $n = 2$) or from the M shell (i.e., from orbitals with $n = 3$).

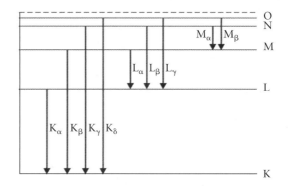

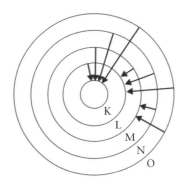

**FIGURE 22.24**

Electron transitions in an atom in which an electron has been removed from a low-energy orbital. Electrons from higher-energy orbitals make transitions to the vacancy, either in one or in several steps. This leads to several possible transitions in heavier atoms, with many of them in the X-ray part of the electromagnetic spectrum (characteristic X-rays). The figure indicates the standard notation used for these transitions, with a capital letter indicating the principal quantum number of the orbital with the vacancy (K shell corresponds to $n = 1$). The Greek subscript indicates the difference in the principal quantum numbers of the initial and final orbitals of the electron that makes the transition ($\alpha$ corresponds to $\Delta n = 1$).

NEL

## Concept Question 22.7

**Assume that we increase the energy with which electrons hit the metal target in an X-ray tube. How does the wavelength of the emitted characteristic X-rays change?**

ANSWER: Not at all. Characteristic X-rays are the result of certain electron transitions in an atom; these do not change due to the velocity of external electrons.

## ● EXAMPLE 22.5

(a) Estimate the photon energy of the characteristic X-rays emitted from a tungsten anode when an electron from the M shell ($n = 3$) drops into a vacancy created in the K shell ($n = 1$). (b) What is the corresponding wavelength of the X-rays?

*Solution to part (a):* We start from Eq. [33]. We cannot simply substitute $Z = 74$, which is the number of positive charges in the tungsten nucleus, since the electrostatic force between a particular electron and the positive charge in the nucleus is partially screened by other electrons in the atom. In 1914, Henry Moseley showed that the effective value for $Z$ is given by the number of protons in the nucleus, diminished by the number of electrons in shells at lower energy than the electron that makes the transition we study. In the K shell we use Eq. [33], modified in the form $E_K = (Z - 1)^2 \cdot E_1$, where $E_1$ is the ionization energy for the hydrogen atom. In the M shell, we use $E_M = (Z - 9)^2 \cdot E_3$ since there are eight electrons in the L shell and one electron in the K shell (the other one has been kicked out), shielding the M shell electron before the transition. Further, we know from Eq. [25] that $E_3 = E_1/3^2$. Thus, using $E_1 = -13.6$ eV from Table 22.1, we find for the transition:

$$\Delta E = E_K - E_M$$
$$= (-72.5 \, \text{keV}) - (-6.4 \, \text{keV})$$
$$= -66.1 \, \text{keV} \qquad [38]$$

*Solution to part (b):* The wavelength is calculated from the relation $\Delta E = h \cdot f = h \cdot c/\lambda$, with $c$ the vacuum speed of light, $h$ Planck's constant, and $\lambda$ the wavelength. This leads to $\lambda = 0.019$ nm.

## The Biological Impact of X-Rays

What effect do X-rays have on the human body? Are there parts of the electromagnetic spectrum we have to fear? Does radiation in these parts of the spectrum reach dangerous levels of intensity, either in a hospital X-ray machine or in outer space?

It is important to answer these questions, of course, and we will do so in this section. However, before we start it may be useful to note that it is not appropriate to see the interaction of X-rays with tissue as something destructive and dangerous. If handled appropriately, X-rays are an invaluable tool in diagnosis and therapy—e.g., when used to obtain CT (computed axial tomography) scans. It might be interesting to note further that X-rays often are used for other scientific purposes. As an example, two pivotal contributions to the development of modern genetics are noted in which X-rays played a key role: Hermann Joe Muller's 1927 experiment that proved genes are (artificially) mutable, and Francis Crick and James Watson's 1953 proposal for the DNA structure.

Once Gregor Mendel's genetics experiments had been rediscovered in the early years of the 20th century, an apparent discrepancy between Mendelism and Darwinism was noted, in that the latter needs a steady change for evolutionary progress, while the former is based on the stability of the genetic code. To test the apparent immutability of genes, Muller bombarded fruit flies with X-rays and linked new deformities in the offspring to the radiation, proving that he had artificially altered genes in the insects. In 1940, George Beadle and Edward Tatum used the same X-ray technique on a species of bread mould (*neurospora*) to prove the correlation between genes and enzymes: the mutation of certain genes led to the lack of certain enzymes in the offspring.

Crick and Watson discovered the double-helix structure of DNA from an X-ray crystallographic analysis. In this technique, usually applied in solid-state physics to characterize crystal structures, patterns in X-rays scattered off the sample are used to determine bond lengths and bond angles. Crick and Watson's collaboration was characterized by one science historian as "the young, ambitious, supple minded American who knew some biology (Watson) and the effortlessly brilliant but unfocussed older Briton who knew some physics (Crick)."

We know from the medical use of X-rays that this type of electromagnetic radiation penetrates biological matter much more easily than does light. Thus, whatever adverse effect radiation has on living biological material, the effect of light is limited to the surface (e.g., skin cancer due to UV radiation) while the damage done by X-rays may reach much deeper.

The ability to penetrate various materials depends on the actual energy of the X-rays and the consistency of the penetrated matter. For this discussion it is beneficial to think of the X-ray beam as a stream of particles (photons). If such a beam has an energy of less than 1 MeV it loses intensity in matter by three processes: (i) scattering, which changes only the direction but not the energy of the X-ray photon; (ii) the photoelectric effect, in which an electron absorbs an X-ray photon entirely, converting the photon energy into kinetic energy; and (iii) the **Compton effect**, which is an elastic collision between the photon and an electron. The combined attenuation of these processes along the $x$-direction of the incident beam can be written as:

$$I(x) = I_0 \cdot e^{-\mu \cdot x} \qquad [39]$$

in which $I_0$ is the incident X-ray intensity and $I(x)$ is the intensity at the depth $x$. $\mu$ is the **attenuation coefficient** in unit $m^{-1}$. That means that the X-ray intensity decreases with the same exponential law (**Beer's law**) we found in Chapter 17 for sound.

Table 22.4 illustrates how the attenuation varies with the energy of the X-ray beam. X-ray attenuation is usually quantified in the form of a **mass attenuation coefficient** $\mu/\rho$, which is the attenuation coefficient per unit density of the material penetrated by the radiation, in unit $m^2/kg$. This definition allows us to exclude variations due to density changes for the same material, which is useful particularly for biological materials. Table 22.4 reports values of $\mu/\rho$ for aluminium and copper for three different X-ray wavelengths. We see that the higher the X-ray energy (i.e., the shorter their wavelengths), the farther the X-rays penetrate.

The role of X-ray attenuation in biological materials is discussed for a typical setup used in medical applications. Such an X-ray facility consists of a tungsten anode in a vacuum tube with an electron acceleration potential of 100 kV. Fig. 22.25 shows in logarithmic representation the intensity fraction of 100 keV (solid lines) and 50 keV (dashed lines) X-rays reaching various depths $d$ in bone material (1), and in muscle tissue or water (2). The $x$-axis is given as the product of path lengths and density,

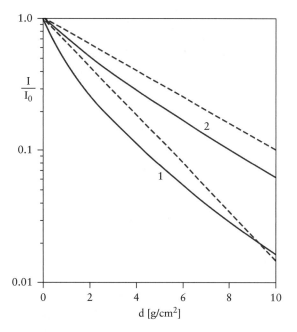

**FIGURE 22.25**

Intensity attenuation of X-ray beams of 100 keV (solid lines) and 50 keV (dashed lines) in human bones (curves 1) and muscle tissues (curves 2). The depth is given in unit $g/cm^2$, which results from the product of density and the path length in the tissue.

because only the combination of both factors is physiologically important in this context. For muscle tissues, the transmitted intensity is reduced to 10% at a tissue thickness of $d = \rho/\mu \cong 8$–10 $g/cm^2$, which corresponds to an actual thickness of about 9 cm. The same intensity reduction is reached for bone material at thicknesses $d = \rho/\mu \cong 4$–5 $g/cm^2$, which corresponds to a bone thickness of about 2 to 3 cm.

Note that the lost X-ray intensity in Fig. 22.25 is not reflected, but either scattered (Compton effect) or absorbed by the bone and the tissue. This absorbed fraction causes the adverse biological impact. It is measured and reported in two ways:

- as the amount of ionization occurring in the material due to the radiation (exposure dose), and

- as the energy deposited by the radiation in the material (absorbed dose).

Before we can quantify the biological impact of X-rays, we must define the unit systems used to measure the respective dose or dose rate. The **dose** is the total amount of ionization or energy deposited in a given amount of material, and the **dose rate** is the amount of ionization or energy deposited in a given amount of material per time unit (often reported per hour).

The first dose we define was also the first one introduced historically: the **exposure dose** is defined as the total charge generated by the ionizing radiation

**TABLE 22.4**

**Mass attenuation coefficient $\mu/\rho$, in unit $m^2/kg$, as a function of X-ray wavelength for aluminium and copper**

| $\lambda$ (nm) | $\mu/\rho_{Al}$ | $\mu/\rho_{Cu}$ |
| --- | --- | --- |
| 0.01 | 0.016 | 0.033 |
| 0.1 | 1.5 | 13.1 |
| 0.2 | 10.2 | 18.8 |

per kilogram of air (unit C/kg). The reference to air at standard conditions (sea-level pressure) originates from the early interest in cosmic radiation. Cosmic radiation at sea level generates about 1 ion/(cm³ · s). As a result, a steady-state concentration of ions is present; this concentration is about $1 \times 10^3$ ions/cm³. Another, non-standard unit often used for the exposure dose is the unit roentgen (R). It is defined as:

$$1 \text{ R} = 2.08 \times 10^9 \frac{\text{ion pairs}}{\text{cm}^3}$$

$$1 \text{ R} = 2.58 \times 10^{-4} \frac{\text{C}}{\text{kg}}$$

[40]

Thus, cosmic rays cause an ionization dose rate of $1.7 \times 10^{-6}$ R/h, which is about 10% of the total ionization dose rate on the surface of Earth, with the rest due to natural radioactive elements in the environment. The ionization dose rate in the van Allen belt is as high as 50 R/h, and strong samples in therapeutic nuclear medicine (cobalt source) have ionization dose rates as high as $10^4$ R/h at a distance of 100 cm from the source.

The radiation measure that is now more commonly used is the **energy dose**. The energy dose is the amount of energy deposited per kilogram of air in J/kg. The unit **gray** is introduced as a derived standard unit for the energy dose, 1 Gy = 1 J/kg. This unit has replaced an older, non-standard unit that you may still find in the literature (and which should not be mixed up with the unit radians), the unit rad with the conversion 1 Gy = 100 rad. Note that for most biological materials both doses are roughly equivalent, with 1 R ≅ 1 rad = 0.01 Gy.

Penetrating radiation, such as X-rays, is capable of destroying live tissue either through ionization, which leads to the breaking of chemical bonds, or though energy deposition. Energy deposition is damaging because a large amount of localized heat can break chemical bonds, particularly in large molecules such as DNA. The consequences for the surviving fraction of affected cells are illustrated in Fig. 21.15. Note the logarithmic scale used in that figure to illustrate the fraction of cells surviving a given energy dose in unit Gy. Curve 1 represents thyroid cells, curve 2 mammary cells, and curve 3 bone marrow. While an interval of minor sensitivity exists at low doses, all three curves have the same steep slope at larger energy doses. The initial non-exponential behaviour is due to DNA-repair mechanisms operating in live cells. Even intensive UV radiation does not destroy tissue with the same efficiency, primarily due to the limited penetration depth of UV radiation, which does not allow it to reach many body cells, such as thyroid cells.

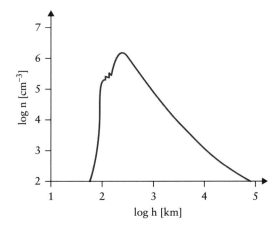

**FIGURE 22.26**

Double-logarithmic plot of the density of free electrons as a function of altitude. The interactions of these energetic electrons with atmospheric molecules are the primary origin of X-rays in the upper part of the atmosphere.

As dangerous as X-rays are for biological tissue we usually don't have to worry about them, thanks to the low doses of environmental X-rays we are exposed to. Inspecting Fig. 20.31, we note that the X-ray portion of the solar spectrum is not too intensive. This is partially due to the fact that the Sun consists mainly of very light elements, and partially due to the outer gas layers of the Sun that absorb most of the more intense radiation generated in the nuclear fusion processes that fuel the Sun's core. The remaining radiation is absorbed by the upper layers of Earth's atmosphere.

However, for an astronaut, the danger of exposure to X-rays is significantly higher because of indirect processes. Particularly in the radiation belts, where intensive streams of energetic particles, mostly electrons, are coupled with an extremely low concentration of gas molecules, any such particle that strikes the spaceship or, even worse, the astronaut's suit during an **extra-vehicular activity** (EVA) generates X-rays in the form of bremsstrahlung. Fig. 22.26 illustrates that this is a serious issue in the radiation belts around Earth. The figure shows a double-logarithmic plot of the electron density as a function of altitude. The high density of energetic electrons in the radiation belts and their ability to generate penetrating X-rays is the main reason why orbiting missions remain at altitudes below 1000 km above Earth's surface, as shown in Fig. 21.1. On the other hand, as soon as a mission has passed beyond 25 000 km above Earth's surface, the density of energetic electrons is reduced. However, radiation remains dangerous because the absorbing atmosphere no longer protects the astronauts against more intensive high-energy electromagnetic radiation—e.g., during Sun flares.

# MULTIPLE CHOICE AND CONCEPTUAL QUESTIONS

## ANGULAR MOMENTUM AND ITS CONSERVATION

**Q–22.1.** Once a helicopter takes off from its landing platform, one would expect that the non-zero friction between the rotor axis and its bearings causes the helicopter cabin to spin out of control. Look at a photograph of a helicopter and determine how this effect is prevented.

**Q–22.2.** Cats are very agile animals; a cat will usually land on its feet following a fall from any position. If you have ever seen a cat fall out of a tree, you may have noticed that the animal's upper body twists one way while its lower part rotates the other way. Why does this counter-rotation occur?

**Q–22.3.** Why do figure skaters pull their arms close to their chests when they want to spin fast, e.g., during a fast spin or a triple jump?

**Q–22.4.** A figure skater finishes a performance with a fast spin, then suddenly stops the rotation and bows to the audience. In the process, the angular momentum of the athlete changed from a finite value to zero. Did the athlete violate the conservation of angular momentum?

## ATOMIC MODELS

**Q–22.5.** What is wrong with Rutherford's atomic model (see Fig. 22.4), which is based on an analogy to the planetary system? (A) The planetary system has eight planets, but the atom may have more or fewer electrons. (B) The planetary system formed after a supernova ejected large amounts of gas/dust into space. No such event precedes the formation of an atom. (C) The planets are not charged electrically like the electron. (D) An electron orbiting a positive charge must lose energy via electromagnetic radiation. (E) The International Astronomic Society can decide how many objects in the solar system qualify as planets, but it has no jurisdiction to decide how many electrons are present in the shell of an atom.

**Q–22.6.** Why did Thomson postulate a diffuse positive charge as the background for oscillating electrons in his atomic model? (A) Because he needed to define the size of the atom independently. (B) Because such diffuse positive charges had been observed experimentally. (C) Because he needed the atom to be an ion. (D) Because the electron wouldn't oscillate without it. (E) Because he needed this so that his model would match the spectroscopic data available at the time.

**Q–22.7.** Bohr postulated that an electron in a particular orbit does not radiate. What consequence does this assumption have? (A) The linear momentum of the electron is conserved. (B) The total energy of the electron is conserved. (C) The kinetic energy of the electron is conserved. (D) The angular momentum of the electron varies only with time.

**Q–22.8.** To explain the quantum condition Bohr introduced, the following idea was presented: (A) A slight eccentricity of the orbit, like that of Earth on its path around the Sun. (B) A standing wave describes the electron in its orbit. (C) The position of the orbit is uncertain (derived from Heisenberg's uncertainty principle). (D) The electron moves along an ellipse, with the nucleus at one of its foci. (E) None of the above.

**Q–22.9.** De Broglie's wavelength of a subatomic particle depends on its kinetic energy $E$ as: (A) $\lambda \propto E$, (B) $\lambda \propto E^{1/2}$, (C) $\lambda \propto E^{-1/2}$, (D) $\lambda \propto E^2$, (E) $\lambda \propto E^{-2}$, (F) $\lambda \propto E^{-1}$.

**Q–22.10.** Niels Bohr calculated the radius of the smallest stable electron orbit in the hydrogen atom. It is called the Bohr radius and depends on the following variable: (A) the kinetic energy of the electron, (B) the total energy of the electron, (C) the wavelength of the electron, (D) the speed of the electron, (E) none of the above.

**Q–22.11.** Bohr used Newton's second law in the form $F_{net} = m \cdot v^2/r$, not in the form $F_{net} = m \cdot a$ ($a$ is acceleration, $m$ is mass, $v$ is speed, and $r$ is radius). When is Newton's second law used in this form? (A) when objects move with constant velocity, (B) when objects move along circular paths, (C) when the total energy is conserved, (D) in cases of uniform circular motion, (E) when the system consists of two interacting objects.

**Q–22.12.** When an electron makes a transition from $n = 1$ to $n = 2$ in a hydrogen atom, the following is a correct statement about this transition: (A) The electron emits UV radiation. (B) The electron releases thermal energy. (C) The electron transfers to an orbit that lies closer to the nucleus. (D) The nucleus must pick up the difference in angular momentum and spin faster. (E) None of the above.

**Q–22.13.** On which variable does the frequency of radiation emitted from a hydrogen atom depend linearly? (A) the quantum number of the initial orbit, (B) the quantum number of the final orbit, (C) the

Rydberg constant, (D) the wavelength of the emitted radiation in a vacuum, (E) none of the above.

**Q–22.14.** What does a transition to $n = \infty$ (infinity) imply? (A) That the atom explodes (atomic bomb). (B) That the electron becomes electrically neutral. (C) That the atom loses an (almost) infinite amount of energy (big bang). (D) That the electron moves to an orbit that is larger than the radius of the universe. (E) That the atom becomes an ion.

**Q–22.15.** When a hydrogen atom absorbs a photon of energy $h \cdot f$, the kinetic energy of the electron that transfers to an excited state changes by: (A) zero, (B) $\frac{1}{2} \cdot h \cdot f$, (C) $h \cdot f$, (D) $2 \cdot h \cdot f$, (E) $-h \cdot f$.

**Q–22.16.** When a hydrogen atom absorbs a photon of energy $h \cdot f$, the potential energy of the electron that transfers to an excited state changes by: (A) zero, (B) $-\frac{1}{2} \cdot h \cdot f$, (C) $-h \cdot f$, (D) $-2 \cdot h \cdot f$, (E) $+2 \cdot h \cdot f$.

**Q–22.17.** The quantum number $n$ can increase to infinity in Bohr's hydrogen atom. Does this mean that the possible frequencies of its spectral lines also increase without limit?

**Q–22.18.** Can a hydrogen atom in the ground state absorb a photon of energy less than 13.6 eV? Can it absorb a photon of energy greater than 13.6 eV?

## HEAVY ATOMS AND MOLECULES

**Q–22.19.** Why has an electron in the binding $\sigma$-orbital in an $H_2$ molecule a lower total energy than in the lowest-energy state of the hydrogen atom ($n = 1$)? (A) Because it is attracted by two positive charges at the same time. (B) Because it is screened by the other electron in that orbital. (C) Because it occupies a larger space (Heisenberg's uncertainty principle). (D) Because it can no longer radiate. (E) None of the above.

**Q–22.20.** LCAO stands for (A) localized convolution of atomic orbitals, (B) linear conversion of atomic orbitals, (C) linear combination of alternative organizations, (D) linear combination of atomic orbitals, (E) molecular orbital calculation (the acronym doesn't fit because the original is in French).

**Q–22.21.** Identify the molecule for which Fig. 22.27 shows the term scheme of the linear combination of atomic orbitals.

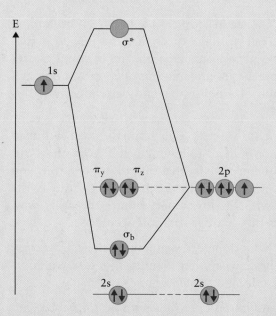

**FIGURE 22.27**

**Q–22.22.** Krypton has atomic number 36. How many electrons does this noble gas hold in its next-to-outer shell, i.e., in the orbit with $n = 3$? (A) 2, (B) 4, (C) 8, (D) 18, (E) none of the above.

**Q–22.23.** Must an atom first be ionized to emit light?

**Q–22.24.** Why do lithium, sodium, and potassium display similar chemical properties? Which of the following atoms should vary chemically the most from the others? (A) chlorine, (B) oxygen, (C) bromine, (D) fluorine. Consult the periodic table.

**Q–22.25.** The ionization energies for Na, K, and Rb are 5.14 eV, 4.34 eV, and 4.18 eV, respectively. Why are the values decreasing in this order?

## X-RAYS

**Q–22.26.** Is it possible to obtain from an X-ray tube a continuous spectrum of X-rays without the presence of any characteristic X-rays?

# ANALYTICAL PROBLEMS

## ANGULAR MOMENTUM AND ITS CONSERVATION

**P–22.1.** Calculate the angular momentum of Earth as it moves around the Sun.

**P–22.2.** Halley's Comet moves around the Sun along an elliptical path. Its closest point to the Sun is 0.59 A.U., and its farthest point is 35 A.U.; A.U. is the astronomical unit (1 A.U. = distance Earth to

Sun). What is the speed of Halley's Comet at its farthest point from the Sun if it moves with 54 km/s through the closest point? Neglect any changes in the comet's mass while orbiting.

**P–22.3.** Fig. 22.28 shows four point-like objects that are connected by massless strings and rotate about the origin with an angular speed of 2 revolutions per second. Use $L = 1.0$ m. If we shorten their distances to the origin to 0.5 m by pulling the strings shorter, what is their new angular speed? Can you use the result to draw conclusions about the rotation of a collapsing star?

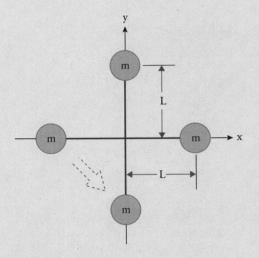

**FIGURE 22.28**

**BOHR'S ATOMIC MODEL**

**P–22.4.** In the spectrum of helium ions, a series of absorption lines exists (Pickering series) for which every other line coincides with a Balmer series line of the hydrogen atom (the remaining lines fall in between the Balmer series lines). Which transitions in the helium ion are responsible for the Pickering series?

**P–22.5.** A hydrogen atom is in its first excited state ($n = 2$). Using Bohr's atomic model, calculate (a) the radius of the electron's orbit, (b) the potential energy of the electron, and (c) the total energy of the electron.

**P–22.6.** The size of Rutherford's atom is about 0.1 nm. (a) Calculate the attractive electrostatic force between an electron and a proton at that distance. (b) Calculate the electrostatic potential energy of that atom. Express the result in unit eV. (c) The size of Rutherford's atomic nucleus is about 1 fm. Calculate the repulsive electrostatic force between two protons at that distance. (d) Calculate the electrostatic potential energy of a pair of protons in such a nucleus. Express the result in unit MeV.

**P–22.7.** Calculate the electric force on the electron in the ground state of the hydrogen atom.

**P–22.8.** What is the wavelength of light that can cause a transition of an electron in the hydrogen atom from the orbit with $n = 3$ to $n = 5$?

**P–22.9.** A hydrogen atom emits a photon of wavelength $\lambda = 656$ nm. Which transition did the hydrogen atom undergo to emit this photon?

**P–22.10.** Calculate the wavelength of an electron in a hydrogen atom that is in the orbit with $n = 3$.

**P–22.11.** The size of Rutherford's atom is about 0.1 nm. (a) Calculate the speed of an electron that moves around a proton, based on their electrostatic attraction, if they are separated by 0.1 nm. (b) Calculate the corresponding de Broglie wavelength for Rutherford's electron.

**P–22.12.** Show that the speed of the electron in the $n$-th orbit of a hydrogen atom in Bohr's model is:

$$v = \frac{1}{4 \cdot \pi \cdot \varepsilon_0} \cdot \frac{e^2}{n \cdot \hbar} \qquad [41]$$

**P–22.13.** How much energy is required to ionize hydrogen when it is in the state with $n = 3$?

**P–22.14.** Calculate for Bohr's atomic model the speed of the orbiting electron in the ground state.

**PHOTONS AND X-RAYS**

**P–22.15.** The intensity threshold of human dark-adapted vision at $\lambda = 500$ nm is $4.0 \times 10^{-11}$ J/(m$^2 \cdot$ s). When a person's pupil is open, light enters the eye through a circular area with a diameter of 8.5 mm. How many photons reach the retina per second at the dark-adaptation threshold?

**P–22.16.** Using the approach taken in Example 22.5, estimate the energy of K$_\alpha$ X-rays emitted from a gold anode.

**P–22.17.** The K shell ionization energy of Cu is 8980 eV and the L shell ionization energy is 950 eV. Determine the wavelength of the K$_\alpha$ X-ray emission of Cu.

**P–22.18.** Calculate the minimum wavelength produced when electrons are accelerated through a potential difference of 100 kV in an X-ray tube. Base the calculation on an electron that converts all its kinetic energy into a single photon during a collision. For the photon, note that the relation $c = \lambda \cdot f$ holds, with $c$ the speed of light in a vacuum.

# SUMMARY

## DEFINITIONS

- Bohr radius of the hydrogen atom:

$$r_{\text{Bohr}} = \frac{\varepsilon_0 \cdot h^2}{m \cdot e^2 \cdot \pi} = 5.29 \times 10^{-11}\,\text{m}$$

- Rydberg constant:

$$R_{\text{H}} = \frac{m \cdot e^4}{8 \cdot \varepsilon_0^2 \cdot h^3} = 3.29 \times 10^{15}\,\frac{1}{\text{s}}$$

where $e$ is the elementary charge, and $m$ is the mass of the electron.

## UNITS

- Exposure dose: roentgen (R), with

$$1.0\,\text{R} = 2.08 \times 10^9\,\frac{\text{ion pairs}}{\text{cm}^3}$$

$$1.0\,\text{R} = 2.58 \times 10^{-4}\,\frac{\text{C}}{\text{kg}}$$

- Energy dose: gray (Gy) with 1 Gy = 1 J/kg. Non-standard unit rad: 1 rad = 0.01 Gy.

## LAWS

- Bohr's postulates:
  - electrons do not lose energy while they are in certain orbits.
  - electrons lose or gain energy when they transfer between two allowed orbits:

$$\Delta E = E_{\text{final}} - E_{\text{initial}} = h \cdot f$$

where $h$ is Planck's constant, and $f$ is the frequency of the photon absorbed or emitted.

- Bohr's quantum condition for the atom:

$$m \cdot v \cdot r = \frac{n \cdot h}{2 \cdot \pi} = n \cdot \hbar$$

with $\hbar = h/(2 \cdot \pi)$ and $n$ the quantum number (integer).

- De Broglie's wavelength of a particle:

$$\lambda = \frac{h}{p} = \frac{h}{m \cdot v}$$

where $p$ is momentum, $m$ mass, and $v$ the speed of the particle.

- Energy levels of the hydrogen atom (ionization energy level is at $E = 0$):

$$E_{\text{total}} = -\frac{m \cdot e^4}{8 \cdot \varepsilon_0^2 \cdot h^2} \cdot \frac{1}{n^2}$$

- Electronic transitions in the hydrogen atom:
  - written as an energy:

$$h \cdot f = \Delta E_{\text{total}} = \frac{m \cdot e^4}{8 \cdot \varepsilon_0^2 \cdot h^2}\left(\frac{1}{n_{\text{initial}}^2} - \frac{1}{n_{\text{final}}^2}\right)$$

  - written as a frequency:

$$f = R_{\text{H}}\left|\left(\frac{1}{n_{\text{initial}}^2} - \frac{1}{n_{\text{final}}^2}\right)\right|$$

with $R_{\text{H}}$ the Rydberg constant.

- Selection rules for atomic orbitals:

$$(\text{I}) \quad 0 \leq l \leq n - 1$$

$$(\text{II}) \quad -l \leq m_l \leq +l$$

where $n$ is the principal quantum number, $l$ is the orbital quantum number, and $m_l$ is the magnetic quantum number. The spin quantum number $m_s$ can take two values: $+\frac{1}{2}$, $-\frac{1}{2}$.

- Order of occupying atomic orbitals:
  - minimum energy principle: an electron added to an atom occupies the free orbital with the least total energy.
  - Pauli principle: no two electrons in the same atom can have the same four quantum numbers.

# CHAPTER 23

# RADIATION
## Nuclear Physics and Magnetic Resonance

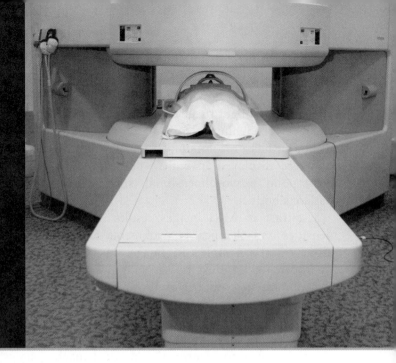

The atomic nucleus is five orders of magnitude smaller than the atom, but carries most of its mass. The nucleus contains neutrons and protons and is held together by the nuclear force, which is stronger than the electrostatic repulsion between its protons. This force has a very short range of only about $1 \times 10^{-15}$ m.

Stable nuclei are characterized by certain ratios of protons and neutrons; other isotopes are radioactive and decay with a characteristic half-life. Four decay mechanisms are associated with the loss of $\alpha$-, $\beta^{-}$-, $\beta^{+}$-, and/or $\gamma$-particles. Together with a nuclear transition due to the capture of an inner-shell electron, these four decay mechanisms describe all processes observed up to thorium. The specific energy of the emitted particle allows for the use of radioactive isotopes in chemistry and medicine as radio tracers. Natural radioactivity is used for dating purposes, e.g., the radiocarbon method allows us to date organic material up to 50 000 years old.

Several state-of-the-art medical diagnosis and therapy methods rely on nuclear physics principles. In magnetic resonance imaging (see the photo above), the nuclear concepts of spin and spin coupling combine with classical concepts from electromagnetism and thermodynamics to establish one of the most powerful imaging methods in medicine.

Fig. 23.1 shows a magnetic resonance imaging (MRI) picture of the cross-section of a human head. Note the wide range of grey tones: the greyscale has been chosen to highlight tissue differences, e.g., the difference between white and grey matter in the brain. The technique has a resolution of about $1.0 \text{ mm}^3$, and the data are displayed in scans—like Fig. 23.1—that correspond to two-dimensional "slices" through the patient's body.

Contrast in MRI images results from different densities and chemical environments for hydrogen atoms in the sample. To image this feature, the hydrogen nuclei must possess a physical property that can interact with neighbouring nuclei and external fields, in particular the magnetic field that is varied to obtain images such as the one shown in Fig. 23.1. We need to focus on the properties of the atomic nucleus to identify the physical mechanism that is used to generate MRI images. Note that we referred to the atomic nucleus in the previous chapter, but did not discuss its composition and structure. In the current chapter, we therefore expect to find a range of new features as we study atomic nuclei more closely.

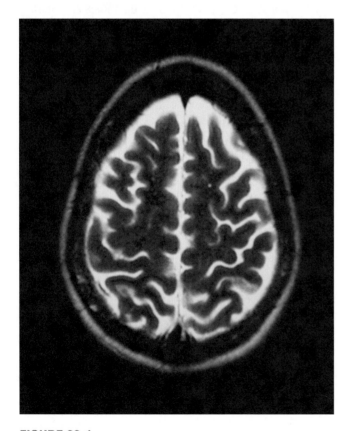

**FIGURE 23.1**

Magnetic resonance image (MRI) of a human head at the level of the brain. Greyscale is used to distinguish various tissues.

# The Stable Atomic Nucleus

Once the atomic hypothesis had been accepted, questions arose about the composition and structure of the atom. These questions were split into two separate parts early in the discussion: Heinrich Hertz (1891) and Philipp Lenard (1900) had shown that atoms consist of a tiny nucleus, which contains essentially all the mass of the atom, and a large space around the nucleus that they said is "as empty as the outer space in the universe."

In the previous chapter we established the structure and composition of the atom beyond the nucleus: the electron is the elementary particle present in the atomic shell and, by the 1930s, quantum mechanics properly described the structure of the orbitals.

The nucleus remained more elusive, primarily due to its small size in comparison to the atom as a whole. The first indication of its composition came from studying cosmic rays and instable—i.e., **radioactive**—elements. Since the primary cosmic rays, protons and $\alpha$-particles, travel vast distances in outer space before reaching Earth, they must be stable. The interaction of the primary cosmic rays with molecules of the atmosphere at altitudes of 20 to 30 km results in secondary cosmic rays that reach the surface of Earth. Due to the short period of time it takes for secondary cosmic rays to penetrate Earth's atmosphere, they can include unstable particles, e.g., neutrons and muons, and anti-matter particles, e.g., positrons (which are identical to electrons but carry a positive charge). As these particles were discovered, it became clear that a large number of additional phenomena exist in which they are involved and that are not explained by the atomic model.

In the 1930s, the first conclusive discoveries and theoretical models for the nucleus emerged. The field was defined as nuclear physics, a discipline that investigates the stable nuclei in the atoms of regular matter, and the limits of stability that are evident in radioactivity. In more recent decades, the field has evolved into a discipline called high-energy physics or subatomic physics, which is focussed on the systematic study of the large number of particles that are smaller than the atom.

In this chapter we focus on two aspects of nuclear physics—the composition of stable nuclei and the radioactive decay process—that are linked to modern subfields in medicine, such as radiology and nuclear medicine.

From the onset of atomic research it was clear that the nucleus must contain as many positive charges as electrons in its shell, because atoms are electrically neutral. Let us assume that we want to build a nucleus from fundamental particles, which we call **nucleons**. Based on the hydrogen atom, one could think we need only one type of nucleon that carries a positive charge, which we call a **proton**. We immediately run into a problem with this approach, though, because the nucleus of a helium atom has two positive charges but four times the mass of a hydrogen nucleus.

Since a single positive nucleon is, therefore, not sufficient to explain the mass and charge properties of all nuclei, the question was whether two different nucleons would do. Two possibilities were considered in the 1920s, either a combination of positive and negative particles, or positive and electrically neutral particles. The first proposals were based on combining protons and electrons to make up the nucleus. Both particles were known to exist: the electron ($e^-$) had been discovered in 1897 by Thomson, and the proton ($p^+$) had been observed in the primary cosmic rays. In turn, no neutral particles had at that time been found.

With the development of quantum mechanical concepts in the mid 1920s it became clear that the helium nucleus cannot contain four protons and two captured electrons, because this would require a violation of Heisenberg's uncertainty relation: if we confine an electron to a space as small as the nucleus (i.e., accept a very small uncertainty in the position of the electron), the energy of the electron must significantly exceed the energy needed for the electron to escape from the nucleus. The same problem does not apply to the protons in the nucleus because of their much larger mass.

Thus, it was theoretically postulated that the atomic nuclei must contain protons and an electrically neutral nucleon, called the **neutron**. The neutron ($n^0$), however, remained elusive until 1932, when James Chadwick discovered it indirectly (by observing protons set free from hydrogen atoms in collisions with neutrons). The neutron is hard to observe experimentally for two reasons:

- *A neutral particle interacts with matter much less than does a charged particle.* Most interactions we observe are based on the electrostatic force, because it is the only strong and far-reaching fundamental force; gravity is too weak, and the nuclear and weak forces act only across distances of the size of the atomic nucleus.

- *Free neutrons are not stable; they are stable only as part of a nucleus.* We quantify stability later

with the concept of the half-life. This is the time by which 50% of an initial amount of unstable particles have decayed. Protons and electrons are stable since their half-life at least exceeds the age of the universe. This also applies to a neutron in a nucleus. However, when the neutron is separated from a nucleus, its half-life is only 12.5 minutes; i.e., after this short period, half of the isolated neutrons no longer exist. What happens when a neutron decays is written in the following form:

$$n^0 \rightarrow p^+ + e^- + \bar{\nu} + \Delta E \qquad [1]$$

The neutron decays into a proton, an electron, and an anti-neutrino (which is the anti-matter particle to the neutrino; neutrinos are not further discussed in this textbook). The $\Delta E$ term in Eq. [1] indicates that energy is also released, in this particular case $\Delta E = 0.77$ MeV. The fact that the neutron decays rather quickly when isolated but is stable when it is part of a nucleus indicates that nucleons behave differently as part of nuclear matter.

First, a convenient mass scale is introduced to characterize a quantitative parameter on which the various properties of atomic and nuclear matter depend. The atomic mass is expressed as a multiple of the atomic unit u, where 1 u is defined as one-twelfth the mass of a $^{12}$C atom (stable and most abundant carbon nuclide): $1 \text{ u} = 1.6605677 \times 10^{-27}$ kg. A proton has a mass of $1.007276 \cdot$ u, a neutron $1.008665 \cdot$ u, an alpha-particle (helium nucleus) $4.002604 \cdot$ u, and an electron $5.49 \times 10^{-4} \cdot$ u.

## ● EXAMPLE 23.1

Calculate the binding energy of the helium nucleus.

*Solution:* We establish the uniqueness of the intra-nuclear environment by first calculating the change in mass when two protons and two neutrons form a helium nucleus ($\alpha$-particle):

$$\begin{aligned} \Delta m &= m_\alpha - (2m_{p^+} + 2m_{n^0}) \\ &= (4.002604 - 2 \cdot 1.007825 \\ &\quad - 2 \cdot 1.00665) \text{ u} \end{aligned} \qquad [2]$$

which yields:

$$\Delta m = -0.03076 \text{ u} \qquad [3]$$

i.e., the helium nucleus is lighter than the four nucleons it is made of. This is a surprising result we cannot understand using the classical concepts we have studied so far: mass was conserved in all our

● **EXAMPLE 23.1** (*continued*)

previous experiments. However, in 1905 Albert Einstein showed that mass can be interpreted as a form of energy with the conversion formula:

$$E = m \cdot c^2 \qquad [4]$$

in which $c$ is the speed of light in a vacuum. Thus, even a small amount of mass corresponds to a tremendous amount of energy. When the helium nucleus forms, the mass difference in Eq. [3] is converted into binding energy that holds the four nucleons together:

$$E_{binding}(\text{He}) = (0.03076 \, \text{u})\left(3 \times 10^8 \, \frac{\text{m}}{\text{s}}\right)^2$$

$$= 28.3 \, \text{MeV} \qquad [5]$$

Calculating binding energies for all stable elements allows us to compare the contribution of each nucleon to the total binding energy. In the case of the helium nucleus this energy is 7.1 MeV, which is 28.3 MeV divided by four nucleons. Fig. 23.2 shows that this value roughly holds constant across the periodic table; the binding energy per nucleon $E_{nucleon}$ varies between 5.5 MeV and 8.5 MeV, from deuterium to uranium.

That such extremely large binding energies hold stable nuclei together (in comparison, typical chemical energies are on the order of 1 eV) had already been anticipated when Hertz, Lenard, and Rutherford illustrated how small atomic nuclei indeed

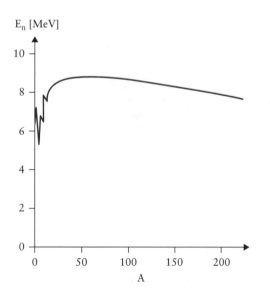

$E_n$ [MeV]

**FIGURE 23.2**

Binding energy per nucleon $E_n$ in nuclear matter as a function of the mass of the nucleus. The binding energy per nucleon varies only slightly, with an average value of about 8 MeV.

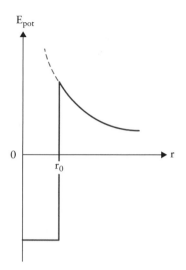

**FIGURE 23.3**

Potential energy profile for an approaching proton as a function of distance from the centre of a typical nucleus. The energy barrier near the edge of the nucleus is due to electrostatic repulsion; the significantly lower energy within the nucleus is due to the attractive nuclear force.

are: a factor of $10^5$ difference exists between the size of an atom and the size of a nucleus. To obtain a stable nucleus, a nuclear force must exist that exceeds the repulsive Coulomb force acting between any two protons in the nucleus, i.e., at a distance of about $10^{-14}$ m. Hideki Yukawa developed a potential energy model for the nuclear force, taking into account its very short range. Fig. 23.3 shows that potential energy for a proton in a typical nucleus. An approaching proton at first encounters the repulsive Coulomb force, as we observed in Rutherford's experiment. However, when the proton penetrates the nuclear matter it suddenly feels an attractive force, which is essentially constant across the nucleus.

## Concept Question 23.1

**(a) How would Fig. 23.3 look if it were drawn for a neutron in the nucleus? (b) Is the nucleus in Fig. 23.3 stable?**

ANSWER TO PART (a): The nuclear attraction part of the potential energy curve remains the same; however, once the neutron leaves the nucleus it isn't repelled electrostatically. Fig. 23.4(a) shows the corresponding potential curve.

ANSWER TO PART (b): Fig. 23.3 shows the potential energy for a proton and Fig. 23.4(a) for a neutron. Since the curves are different, obviously we must first clarify whether we mean stable against losing a proton or a

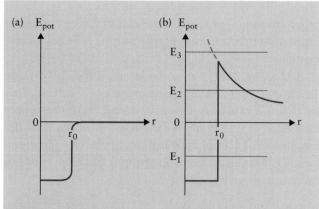

**FIGURE 23.4**

(a) Potential energy profile for an approaching neutron as a function of distance from the centre of a typical nucleus. No energy barrier appears near the edge of the nucleus because the approaching particle is electrically neutral. (b) Potential energy profile for a proton as a function of distance from the centre of a typical nucleus, as shown in Fig. 23.3. Three energy levels for the total energy of the proton are shown, with the lowest level leading to a stable nucleus, the centre level a metastable nucleus, and the highest level an unstable nucleus.

neutron. In either case, next we must determine the kinetic energy of the particle. If we focus on a proton, three possibilities exist as illustrated in Fig. 23.4(b): (i) the nucleus is stable for a proton with total energy $E_1$, since that proton cannot be anywhere but inside the nucleus. (ii) The nucleus is **metastable** for a proton with total energy $E_2$, because that proton can also exist outside the nucleus but would have to penetrate an energy barrier to leave the nucleus. Classically, it cannot overcome that barrier unless its kinetic energy is significantly increased. Quantum-mechanically, it has a finite probability of escaping the nucleus in a process called **tunnelling**. (iii) The nucleus is unstable for a proton with total energy $E_3$; i.e., that proton will leave the nucleus immediately.

With variations in both the number of protons and number of neutrons in the nucleus, a wide range of different nuclei can be formed. More than 1700 known nuclei exist, of which 271 are stable. We must always report two of three numbers to unequivocally identify a nucleus: (i) the **mass number** $A$, which corresponds to the number of nucleons in the nucleus, (ii) the **atomic number** $Z$, which corresponds to the number of protons in the nucleus, and (iii) the number of neutrons, $N$. These numbers are related by:

$$A = Z + N \qquad [6]$$

It is common practice to identify the atomic number $Z$ and the mass number $A$, and to connect them with the familiar chemical symbol $X$ (although the

atomic number and the chemical symbol are synonymous terms). The general notation is illustrated for two common cases, carbon and oxygen:

$$^A_Z X \quad \text{e.g.: } ^{12}_6 C , \ ^{16}_8 O \qquad [7]$$

Various terms have been introduced to identify relations between different nuclei. The most frequently used terms are:

- **isobaric nuclei**, which refers to nuclei with the same mass number, $A = $ const. An example is the three nuclei:

$$^{96}_{38}Sr \ ^{96}_{39}Y \ ^{96}_{40}Zr \qquad [8]$$

- **isotopic nuclei (isotopes)**, which refers to nuclei with the same atomic number, $Z = $ const. Two examples are:

$$^1_1H \quad ^2_1H \quad ^3_1H \qquad ^{11}_6C \quad ^{12}_6C \quad ^{13}_6C \quad ^{14}_6C \qquad [9]$$

in which the names of the isotopes at the left are, in order, hydrogen, deuterium, and tritium. Eighty-one elements in the periodic table have stable isotopes. When referring to isotopes, the atomic number is often omitted, since the information is already contained in the chemical symbol. For example, we later discuss a carbon-dating method for determining the age of biologically formed matter based on the carbon isotope with $A = 14$. You often find this isotope referred to in the abbreviated notation $^{14}C$ instead of the form shown in Eq. [9].

- **Isomers**, which refers to identical nuclear composition, $A = $ const and $Z = $ const, but different energy states of the nucleus. Nuclei that result from radioactive decay or a nuclear reaction are often initially not in the ground state (labelled g) but in an excited state (labelled m for metastable). Several such isomers are important in nuclear medicine. An example is technetium:

$$^{99m}Tc \quad ^{99g}Tc \qquad [10]$$

# Radioactivity
## Radioactive Decay Law

Of the 1700 nuclei that have been studied, more than 1400 are not stable. Many of these occur naturally: some, such as uranium, decay so slowly that they are still around from the time the solar system formed; others are formed in nuclear reactions of stable isotopes with particles of the cosmic rays, e.g., $^{14}C$. The first radioactive decay was observed in 1896 by

Henri Becquerel, when he noticed that a uranium salt emits invisible radiation that darkens a photographic plate. Systematic studies by Marie and Pierre Curie led to the discovery of several radioactive isotopes by the beginning of the 20th century.

An isotope is radioactive if a non-zero probability exists that a nucleus of this isotope decays after a finite time. For each **radioactive isotope**, we know its type of decay. Three types of particles are emitted by all but the heaviest radioactive nuclei (which may undergo fission): emission of a helium nucleus (**α-decay**), emission of an electron (**β⁻-decay**), or emission of a positron (**β⁺-decay**). Many of the decay processes are accompanied by the emission of X-rays, which are called **γ-rays** when they originate in a nuclear process. Using the notation of Eq. [10], we can determine which nucleus results from a decay process:

$$\alpha\text{-decay:} \quad {}_{Z}^{A}X \rightarrow {}_{Z-2}^{A-4}Y + {}_{2}^{4}He$$

$$\beta^{+}\text{-decay:} \quad {}_{Z}^{A}X \rightarrow {}_{Z-1}^{A}Y + e^{+} \qquad [11]$$

$$\beta^{-}\text{-decay:} \quad {}_{Z}^{A}X \rightarrow {}_{Z+1}^{A}Y + e^{-}$$

The isotope X is called the **parent nucleus**, and Y is the **daughter nucleus**. The same daughter nucleus as in β⁺-decay follows from an electron capture, which is a process in which an inner-shell electron is absorbed into the nucleus. The transition of the nucleus is accompanied by a cascade of X-rays due to other shell electrons filling the lower-level vacancy.

---

### Concept Question 23.2

**(a) ²³⁸U decays with a half-life of 4.47 billion years to form ²³⁴Th (a thorium isotope). What type of decay is this? (b) ²³⁴Th in turn decays with a half-life of 24.1 days in a β⁻-decay. What daughter nucleus is formed?**

ANSWER TO PART (a): The uranium decay causes a loss of four mass units: $\Delta A = 238 - 234 = 4$. Thorium is located two places before uranium in the periodic system; i.e., $\Delta Z = 2$. This corresponds to the loss of an α-particle—i.e., an α-decay.

ANSWER TO PART (b): We use the third line in Eq. [11]: the daughter nucleus has the same mass number 234, but the atomic number is increased by one. The element located after thorium in the periodic system is protactinium, i.e., ²³⁴Pa. This isotope then again undergoes a β⁻-decay, leading to ²³⁴U.

---

When an individual radioactive nucleus decays cannot be predicted. Radioactive decay is a statistical process, which means that each nucleus decays randomly and independently of the others. As in other statistical processes, we can make only quantitative statements about a large number of radioactive nuclei.

Assuming that we consider a sufficiently large amount of one unstable isotope, e.g., N nuclei, then we define a **rate of radioactive decay**, $-\Delta N/\Delta t$, where the negative sign indicates the number of nuclei is decreasing. For any type of radioactive decay the decay rate is observed to be proportional to the number of radioactive nuclei at time $t$:

$$-\frac{\Delta N}{\Delta t} = \lambda \cdot N \qquad [12]$$

where $\lambda$ is the **decay constant** and has the unit 1/s. We have come across this type of equation several times before in this textbook. The linear proportionality between decay rate and absolute amount of a quantity leads to an exponential law describing, in the case of Eq. [12], the time dependence of the number of radioactive nuclei present in a sample if we start with $N_0$ radioactive nuclei at time $t = 0$:

$$N(t) = N_0 \cdot e^{-\lambda \cdot t} \qquad [13]$$

Instead of the decay constant $\lambda$, or the **mean lifetime** $T_{mean} = \lambda^{-1}$, the **half-life** $T_{1/2}$ is usually given. This time represents the time after which 50% of the initial number of radioactive nuclei in the sample have decayed. We can relate the half-life to the decay constant $\lambda$. To develop this relation we substitute $N(t) = N_0/2$ for $t = T_{1/2}$ in Eq. [13]:

$$\frac{N_0}{2} = N_0 \cdot e^{-\lambda \cdot T_{1/2}} \qquad [14]$$

After dividing both sides by $N_0$, the natural logarithm of each side is taken:

$$\ln \frac{1}{2} = -\lambda \cdot T_{1/2} \qquad [15]$$

which is the same as:

$$\ln 2 = \lambda \cdot T_{1/2} \qquad [16]$$

Solving Eq. [16] for the half-life yields:

$$T_{1/2} = \frac{\ln 2}{\lambda} \qquad [17]$$

The radioactive decay law in Eq. [13] is illustrated in Fig. 23.5, highlighting the half-life. Note that the decay of three-fourths of the initial amount of radioactive nuclei requires a time of $2 \cdot T_{1/2}$. We can relate the mean lifetime and the half-life using Eq. [17]:

$$T_{mean} = \frac{1}{\lambda} = 1.44 \cdot T_{1/2} \qquad [18]$$

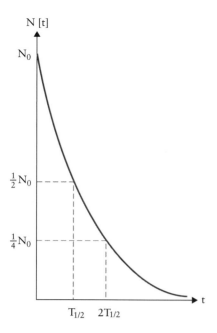

**FIGURE 23.5**

Sketch of the number of nuclei of a given radioactive isotope in a sample as a function of time. The dashed lines indicate the reduction after one half-life (at $t = T_{1/2}$) and two half-life periods (at $t = 2 \cdot T_{1/2}$).

We define one more term for practical applications. The absolute value of the number of decays per time unit of a radioactive sample, $\Delta N/\Delta t$, is defined as **activity** $A$; i.e., $\Delta N/\Delta t = A$. The standard unit for activity is the unit **becquerel** (Bq), with the definition 1 Bq = 1 decay/s.

**EXAMPLE 23.2**

We consider a sample that contains $3 \times 10^{16}$ nuclei of $^{226}$Ra, which has a half-life of 1600 years. What is the activity of the sample at $t = T_{1/2}$?

*Solution:* This is not a laboratory experiment, since the two reference times are 1600 years apart. In the first step we determine the decay constant $\lambda$. For this, we express the half-life in standard unit second: $T_{1/2} = 5 \times 10^{10}$ s. Thus:

$$\lambda = \frac{\ln 2}{T_{1/2}} = 1.4 \times 10^{-11}\,\text{s}^{-1} \qquad [19]$$

We substitute this value into Eq. [12] to determine the activity at $t = 0$ (initially):

$$A = \lambda \cdot N_0 = (1.4 \times 10^{-11}\text{s}^{-1})(3 \times 10^{16})$$

$$= 4.1 \times 10^5\,\text{Bq} \qquad [20]$$

We use the same formula to calculate the activity at the half-life of the sample:

$$A = \lambda \frac{N_0}{2} = 2.05 \times 10^5\,\text{Bq} \qquad [21]$$

**Concept Question 23.3**

**How long will it take for a radioactive sample to drop below 1% of its current activity?**

ANSWER: For each half-life, the activity drops to 50%. After two half-life periods, the activity is down to $(1/2)^2$ and after $n$ half-life periods it is down to $(1/2)^n = 1/2^n$. We are asked to find $n$ in $1/2^n = 1/100$, or $2^n = 100$. The best way to calculate $n$ is to take the natural logarithm on both sides: $n = \ln(100)/(\ln 2) = 6.6$. It takes almost seven half-life periods for a radioactive source to diminish its activity to less than 1 percent of the initial value.

## Biological Impact of Particle Radiation

Having defined several new types of energetic radiation in this section, we return to the question of their impact on a biological sample. In principle the same issues are relevant, as in the case of X-rays. Due to the high energy of the particles emitted in nuclear processes, they can penetrate into biological tissues—even though not to the same depth as X-rays—as illustrated qualitatively in Fig. 23.6 and confirmed by quantitative examples in Table 23.1.

The biological impact of high-energy particles is due to the deposition of their kinetic energy in the tissue and to the ionization close to the trajectory of the penetrating particle. Thus, the same dose units defined for X-rays in the previous chapter are useful: the unit roentgen (R) for the exposure dose, and the unit gray (Gy) for the absorbed dose $D_{\text{absorbed}}$. The range values in Table 23.1 allow us further to calculate the affected tissue volume.

When comparing the effect of equal amounts of radiation on the same biological sample (e.g., human tissue), different types of radiation have different

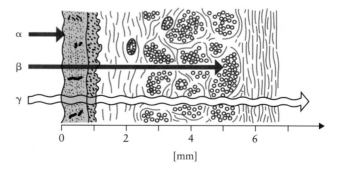

**FIGURE 23.6**

Sketch illustrating the range of different types of radiation at 1 MeV incident energy. $\alpha$-particles cannot penetrate even the outermost layer of the skin, $\beta$-particles reach several millimetres deep into the skin, and $\gamma$-rays pass through the entire body.

## TABLE 23.1

**Range of various forms of radiation in biological tissue or water**

| Radiation type | Energy | Range |
|---|---|---|
| $\alpha$-particles | 5 MeV | 40 $\mu$m |
| $\beta$-radiation | 20 keV | 10 $\mu$m |
| $\beta$-radiation | 1 MeV | 7 mm |
| $\gamma$-radiation | 20 keV | 6.4 cm |
| $\gamma$-radiation | 1 MeV | 65 cm |
| neutrons | 1 MeV | 20 cm |

## TABLE 23.2

**Radiation factor $w_R$ for the biological impact of various types of radiation**

| Radiation type | $w_R$ |
|---|---|
| X-ray and $\gamma$-radiation | 1 |
| $\beta^+, \beta^-$ | 1 |
| $n^0$ | 5–10 |
| $\alpha$ | 10 |

degrees of adverse impact. This leads to the definition of a new variable, the **equivalent dose** $D_{equivalent}$, with the unit sievert (Sv). The equivalent dose is defined such that the same equivalent dose of any type of radiation has the same degree of impact on live tissue. This is achieved by introducing two weighting factors:

- the **radiation factor** $w_R$, which expresses the physiological damage relative to an equal amount of X-ray radiation, and
- the **tissue factor** $w_T$, which expresses the physiological damage relative to a whole-body exposure:

$$D_{equivalent} = w_R \cdot w_T \cdot D_{absorbed} \qquad [22]$$

with $D_{equivalent}$ measured in unit Sv and $D_{absorbed}$ in Gy.

Typical values of the radiation factor are given in Table 23.2 for the different types of radiation. The list also includes neutrons that are generated in nuclear reactors. The table illustrates that, as a general rule, the heavier the emitted particle in a nuclear process the higher the adverse biological impact.

The equivalent dose is used when various types of radiation are compared, as in Fig. 21.16. Table 23.3

## TABLE 23.3

**Medical impact of various whole-body equivalent doses**

| Equivalent dose (Sv) | Pathological diagnosis |
|---|---|
| 1–5 | Serious temporary alterations of the blood count |
| 4–5 | 50% death rate in 30 days |
| 10–50 | Vomiting and nausea |
| 50–100 | Brain and nerve damage, death in one week |

lists some typical pathological consequences of whole-body exposures to various equivalent doses. Note that the biological effect is dependent on whether the dose is received over a long period or within a short time. Protracted exposure is better tolerated due to the damage-repair mechanisms operating in living cells. These repair mechanisms were noted to cause the initial plateau in Fig. 21.15. However, alterations in the cells may lead to long-term effects, which often are diagnosed only years after the dose has been received. These effects usually include degenerative changes or organ malfunctions due to the damage to blood vessels. For leukemia, the risk factor for whole-body exposure is given as $10^{-4}$ 1/Sv, i.e., 0.01%/Sv.

## ● EXAMPLE 23.3

During an accident, a standard man ingests an amount of 0.05 MBq of a radioactive isotope that releases 1.5 MeV per decay. Assume that the radioactive element is distributed uniformly throughout the person's body. The half-life of the radioactive element is 30 years. Calculate (a) the energy dose rate in unit Gy/s of the initially ingested radioactive element, and (b) the whole-body energy dose in unit Gy after a period of 30 years.

*Solution to part (a):* The energy released by the ingested amount of the radioactive isotope per second is calculated from the number of decays (given in MBq) and the energy released per decay event:

$$\frac{\Delta E}{\Delta t} = \left(5 \times 10^4 \, \frac{decays}{s}\right)\left(1.5 \times 10^6 \, \frac{eV}{decay}\right)$$

$$= 7.5 \times 10^{10} \, \frac{eV}{s}$$

$$= 1.2 \times 10^{-8} \, \frac{J}{s} \qquad [23]$$

in which we converted $1.0$ eV $= 1.6 \times 10^{-19}$ J. With this result we calculate the initial dose rate by dividing by the mass of the person:

$$\frac{1}{m}\frac{\Delta E}{\Delta t} = \frac{1.2 \times 10^{-8}\,\frac{J}{s}}{70\,kg}$$

$$= 1.7 \times 10^{-10}\,\frac{Gy}{s} \qquad [24]$$

*Solution to part (b):* We use the same approach as in Example 23.2. The decay constant $\lambda$ is obtained from Eq. [17]:

$$\lambda = \frac{\ln 2}{T_{1/2}} = \frac{0.693}{9.46 \times 10^8\,s}$$

$$= 7.3 \times 10^{-10}\,s^{-1} \qquad [25]$$

Next, we calculate the initial number of radioactive nuclei in the ingested sample, using the initial activity $A_0$ in Eq. [12]:

$$N_0 = \frac{A_0}{\lambda} = \frac{5 \times 10^4\,Bq}{7.3 \times 10^{-10}\,Hz}$$

$$= 6.85 \times 10^{13}\,particles \qquad [26]$$

After 30 years, which is the half-life of the radioactive isotope in the sample, 50% of the material in Eq. [26] has decayed. The total energy released into the person's body is obtained by multiplying this number by the energy released in every decay event (the same energy conversion as above is used):

$$E_{total} = \frac{1}{2}(6.85 \times 10^{13}\,decays)$$

$$\times \left(1.5 \times 10^6\,\frac{eV}{decay}\right)$$

$$\times \left(1.6 \times 10^{-19}\,\frac{J}{eV}\right)$$

$$= 8.2\,J \qquad [27]$$

The whole-body energy dose is obtained by dividing this result by the mass of the person, with a result of $0.12$ Gy. This corresponds to $0.1$–$1.0$ Sv, depending on the type of radiation emitted. Based on Table 23.3, we judge the accident as serious, but not severe.

## Applications of Radioactivity: Radioactive Markers in Chemistry

Mass spectrometers (see Chapter 21) are capable of separating identical fragments of organic molecules when they are marked with isotopes, e.g., a fragment

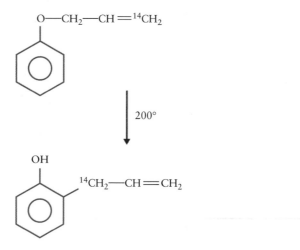

**FIGURE 23.7**
Claisen reaction with the terminal carbon atom radioactively marked.

in which a $^{12}C$ atom is replaced by a $^{14}C$ isotope that is heavier by two mass units. Carbon is usually introduced into the molecules through synthesis from $Ba^{14}CO_3$. A well-established example is the determination of the mechanism of the **Claisen reaction** in Fig. 23.7, where isotope marking shows where a particular carbon atom moved in an aromatic rearrangement. Note that the isotope-marked carbon is not at the end of the ligand chain after the reaction takes place.

## Diagnostic Nuclear Medicine with Tracers

A wide range of radioactive isotopes is used in **medical diagnosis**. An example is shown in Fig. 23.8. The top of the figure shows a thyroid gland ultrasound diagnosed as enlarged on the patient's left side. A normal thyroid gland weighs 20 g. It produces two hormones, an amount of 100 μg/day of thyroxine (tetraiodothyronine $T_4$), and 10 μg/day triiodothyronine $T_3$. Various organs are able to transform $T_4$ into $T_3$, which increases the metabolic rate.

Frames (a) and (b) of Fig. 23.8 show two possible results of a tracer study in nuclear medicine. This technique is based on the selective absorption of iodine in the thyroid gland. The patient is orally given a radioactive iodine sample containing $^{131}I$. $^{131}I$ undergoes a $\beta^-$-decay with a half-life period of $T_{1/2} =$ 8.04 days.

If the radiological image resembles frame (a) in Fig. 23.8, a thyroid overproduction in the enlarged part of the thyroid is diagnosed; if the image resembles frame (b), a reduced absorption of iodine in

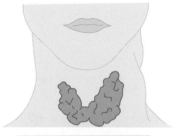

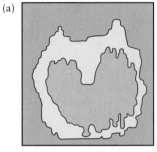

(a)

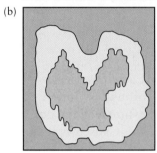

(b)

**FIGURE 23.8**

A patient with an enlarged thyroid is given an oral dose of an [131]I-containing drug. (a) and (b) show two possible outcomes of the radio-tracer diagnosis: in (a), the increased radiation from the enlarged part of the thyroid indicates an overproduction; in (b), the lack of iodine absorption may indicate cancer.

the enlarged part of the thyroid is diagnosed, which may be explained by thyroid cancer.

## Carbon-Dating with $^{14}C$

Until a radioactive isotope has been decaying up to ten times its half-life, it is reasonably easy for us to determine the time interval over which it has been decaying if we know its initial activity. A short half-life (hours to months) makes a radioisotope useful in nuclear medicine or for marking chemical compounds. A half-life on the order of millions of years enables us to measure the age of geological events.

Carbon-14 with $T_{1/2} = 5730$ years is used to analyze the age of biological tissues up to 50 000 years old. This is a rather accurate method for determining the time of death of the organism that contained the tissue based on the way $^{14}C$ is produced and stored in the biosphere.

The primary cosmic rays continuously interact with the upper layers of the atmosphere and create a secondary shower of particles, which include short-lived neutrons. These neutrons can undergo a nuclear reaction with the most abundant nitrogen isotope in the atmosphere, $^{14}N$. If a $^{14}N$ nucleus captures a neutron it becomes unstable and decays into a proton and a $^{14}C$ nucleus. The production rate of $^{14}C$ due to cosmic rays varies little, and is given as a rate of 2.4 $^{14}C/(cm^2 \cdot s)$.

The nuclear reaction process with the secondary cosmic neutron releases enough energy to break the chemical bond of the atmospheric nitrogen molecule. The newly formed $^{14}C$ atom is highly reactive and forms carbon dioxide with oxygen in the air:

$$^{14}C + O_2 \rightarrow {}^{14}CO_2 \qquad [28]$$

All living organisms participate in a continuous exchange of carbon-containing molecules within the biosphere and with the carbon dioxide in the atmosphere through their metabolisms. This leads to a steady-state amount of $^{14}C$ in a living body, characterized by a decay rate of 16.1 decays per minute and gram of carbon in the organism.

When an organism dies, its metabolism ceases. No more $^{14}C$ is incorporated in the organism's remains, but the $^{14}C$ present at the time of death decays. This allows us to determine the age of biological samples, including wood, skin, hair, linen, and parchment, by using Eqs. [12] to [18]. Famous examples include carbon-dating of wood from the death ship of the Egyptian king Sesostris III, who died about 3800 years ago; the scrolls at Qumram near the Dead Sea, which are more than 1900 years old; and the Shroud of Turin (said to be the burial shroud of Jesus), which was made in AD 1320 ($\pm 60$ years).

The $^{14}C$ dating method is slightly less reliable than a simple half-life measurement. The main question is to what extent the cosmic ray intensity, and thus the $^{14}C$ production, varied in the past 50 000 years. The standard method of calibrating the $^{14}C$-measured age of wood by independently counting the rings in old trees is illustrated in Fig. 23.9. The averaged data (red line) show variations as large as 900 years, which are attributed to changes in the geomagnetic field over the past 8000 years. Using $^{14}C$ methods for very recent samples is possible only to a limited extent because of two significant effects of human interference: the intensive burning of fossil fuels (lowering the $^{14}C$ concentration in the active biosphere), and the frequent test detonations of atomic and hydrogen bombs in the atmosphere in the 1950s and 1960s, which increased the $^{14}C$ concentration in the biosphere.

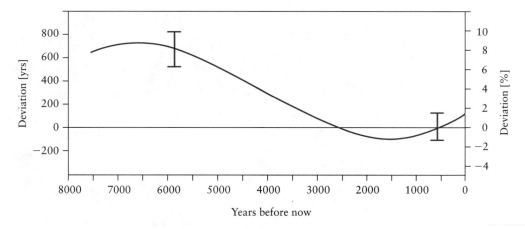

**FIGURE 23.9**

Calibration of the carbon-dating technique. The curve is based on a large number of wood samples that have been dated by the $^{14}C$ method and by counting tree rings. Two bars indicate how these data vary about the solid curve that represents the average correction factor as a function of sample age. The solid curve oscillates because of the environmental production of $^{14}C$ based on nuclear reactions between neutrons from the secondary cosmic rays and atmospheric nitrogen nuclei.

## The Spin of an Atomic Nucleus

The textbook to this point presents the concepts of physics as a cornerstone of physiology and biology. With all fundamental physical principles developed we are now able to study all physiological phenomena in a healthy living organism, and we are able to understand the impact of environmental conditions on individuals as well as entire species during their evolution. Physics concepts play an equally pivotal role in human and veterinary medicine in two ways:

- Physics allows us to establish sickness- and accident-related alterations in human and animal physiology. We have referred to such examples several times, e.g., when describing edemas in Chapter 9.

- Physics allows us to understand the principles and applications of equipment and techniques used in the medical field, ranging from research tools such as electrophoresis (used to separate proteins in biochemistry laboratories), to advanced diagnostic and therapeutic methods such as computed tomography (used to obtain spatially resolved X-ray maps of a patient).

The last part of this chapter focusses on an example, magnetic resonance imaging (MRI), to illustrate how a combination of several fundamental physics concepts is required to take advantage of an advanced medical technique.

Our approach can be divided into two steps. First, we establish nuclear magnetic resonance (NMR). As the technical term implies, the observation is based on

(i) the properties of atomic nuclei, (ii) the use of magnetic fields, and (iii) a resonance phenomenon. These three concepts combine topics we discussed in Chapter 17 (resonance), Chapters 20 and 21 (magnetism), and Chapter 22 (angular momentum), and nuclear properties discussed in the first part of the current chapter. From the NMR principle it is a small step to its use in an imaging mode, although the actual performance of the imaging and the interpretation of the images is quite challenging in its own right.

A second issue we must address is the question of medically relevant information contained in an NMR signal. The most frequent use of the technique is to detect and locate tumours in the body of a patient. Thus, the NMR signal from a tumorous cell must differ from the NMR signal from a healthy cell. This discussion will allow us to distinguish the medical use of NMR. The ultimate purpose of this last section is, however, to stimulate readers to apply the same physics-based analytical approach to the wide range of medical research, diagnosis, and therapeutic techniques they will encounter during their further course of study or professional career.

### Classical Concept of a Spin

We studied physical phenomena associated with rotational motion of objects in Chapter 21. The discussion then focussed primarily on the orbiting of a satellite in a gravitational force field, e.g., the orbiting of the Moon or the International Space Station about Earth, or the rotation of an electron about the nucleus in the electric field of a hydrogen atom.

**FIGURE 23.10**

Earth/Moon system.

For circular motion, we introduced the **angular momentum** $L$ as:

$$L = p \cdot r \cdot \sin \phi = m \cdot v \cdot r \cdot \sin \phi \qquad [29]$$

in which $p = m \cdot v$ is the linear momentum of the object, $r$ is the distance from the axis of the circular motion, and $\phi$ is the angle between the momentum vector and the radius vector, $\phi = \sphericalangle(\mathbf{p}, \mathbf{r})$. The angular momentum of a system is conserved when no external net torque acts on it.

We want to investigate the system Earth/Moon, shown in Fig. 23.10, for the role of the conservation of angular momentum. In this system, we find two contributions to the total angular momentum. The first is due to the orbiting of the Moon about Earth. The distance from Earth to the Moon is $r = 384\,000$ km (a distance that light travels in about 1 second). The speed of the Moon along its orbit is obtained from the radius of the orbit and the time for a complete revolution, with the circumference given as $2 \cdot \pi \cdot r$ and the period given as 28 days (which defines a month). Treating the Moon as a point-like object, which in this context is a reasonable approximation, provides us with the Moon's contribution to the total angular momentum of the Earth/Moon system:

$$
\begin{aligned}
L_{\text{Moon}} &= m_{\text{Moon}} \frac{2 \cdot \pi \cdot r}{T} r \\
&= m_{\text{Moon}} \frac{2 \cdot \pi \cdot r^2}{T} \\
&= 7.3 \times 10^{22} \, \text{kg} \, \frac{2 \cdot \pi (3.84 \times 10^8 \, \text{m})^2}{2.42 \times 10^6 \, \text{s}} \qquad [30]
\end{aligned}
$$

which yields:

$$L_{\text{Moon}} = 2.8 \times 10^{34} \frac{\text{kg} \cdot \text{m}^2}{\text{s}} \qquad [31]$$

A second contribution to the angular momentum is due to the rotation of Earth itself. Since Earth rotates about its own axis, this does not lead to a motion along an orbit. To distinguish this rotation from the rotation of the Moon about Earth, we call a rotation of a body about its own axis a **spin**. Quantitatively, the term *spin* stands for the angular momentum of this motion, with the same unit of $\text{kg} \cdot \text{m}^2/\text{s} = \text{J} \cdot \text{s}$. The spin of Earth would not contribute to the angular momentum if we could neglect Earth's radius and treat it as a point-like object. Point-like objects do not rotate or, at least, their rotation can be neglected. However, we know that Earth is not a point, but is an extended (nearly spherical) planet with a radius of 6370 km. Thus, would an assumption that Earth is a point-like object be justified? The way to answer this question is to determine the contribution of Earth's spin to the total angular momentum of the Earth/Moon system and then to see whether we can indeed neglect this contribution.

How do we calculate the contribution of a spin to the angular momentum? The best approach is to imagine Earth cut into a very large number of small segments, each of which we can treat as if it were a point-like object. The angular momentum of Earth is, then, the sum of the contributions of all segments:

$$L_{\text{Earth}} = \sum_i m_i \cdot v_i \cdot r_i \qquad [32]$$

in which $m_i$ is the mass, $v_i$ is the speed, and $r_i$ is the distance from the axis of the $i$-th segment. Since the velocity and the position vectors are perpendicular to each other for each segment, $\sin \phi_i = 1$ for all values of index $i$. Eq. [32] can be simplified by replacing the speed by the angular frequency:

$$\omega = \frac{v_i}{r_i} \qquad [33]$$

This is a simplification since various segments have different speeds, but all have the same angular frequency with $\omega = 2 \cdot \pi / T$ and the period $T$ equal to 24 hours for Earth. Thus, $\omega$ carries no index $i$, and Eq. [32] is rewritten in the form:

$$L_{\text{Earth}} = \omega \cdot \sum_i m_i \cdot r_i^2 = \omega \cdot \Theta \qquad [34]$$

in which the sum has been replaced by $\Theta$, which is called the **moment of inertia**.

The formula for the moment of inertia is similar to that of the centre of mass we introduced in Eq. [4.36]: a rigid object is divided into a very large number of segments, leading to a sum over the product of the mass and some geometrical properties of the segment. In the case of the centre of mass, the geometrical term is the distance to a reference point on the rigid object; in the case of the moment of inertia, the geometrical term is the square of the distance to its axis. Evaluating $\Theta$ leads to simple expressions for highly symmetric objects. If a body is irregular in shape or density, the effort to analyze the sum in Eq. [34] in turn becomes extensive. An example of a highly symmetric body for which $\Theta$ takes a simple form is a sphere of uniform density:

$$\Theta_{\text{uniform sphere}} = 0.4 \cdot M \cdot R^2 \qquad [35]$$

with $M$ the total mass of the sphere and $R$ its radius. Using this formula for Earth is only approximately justified, as the mass distribution of Earth is not uniform since it has a massive iron core, as noted in Table 21.1. Assuming a spherical Earth of uniform density, we rewrite Eq. [34] in the form:

$$L_{\text{Earth}} = \omega \cdot \Theta_{\text{uniform sphere}}$$

$$= \frac{2 \cdot \pi}{T} \left( \frac{2}{5} m_{\text{Earth}} \cdot r_{\text{Earth}}^2 \right) \qquad [36]$$

which leads to a numerical value:

$$L_{\text{Earth}} = \frac{4 \cdot \pi}{5} \frac{(5.98 \times 10^{24} \text{ kg})(6.37 \times 10^6 \text{ m})^2}{8.64 \times 10^4 \text{ s}}$$

$$= 7 \times 10^{33} \frac{\text{kg} \cdot \text{m}^2}{\text{s}} \qquad [37]$$

Comparing the angular momentums in Eqs. [31] and [37], we find that the major contribution to the total angular momentum of the Earth/Moon system arises from the rotation of the Moon; however, 20% of the total value is attributed to Earth's spin.

The fact that Earth's contribution is a non-negligible contribution becomes evident when we study how the length of a day has changed in the course of time. This change is due to a slowing of Earth's spin. The gravitational attraction of the Moon on the water of Earth's oceans causes two tidal domes, one stationary beneath the Moon and one on Earth's opposite side. Due to the rotation of Earth, the two tidal domes move as tidal waves continuously around the planet, with a high tide every 12 hours and 26 minutes at any point along the seashore (called a semi-diurnal tidal sequence). Every time the tidal waves crash into a continent, Earth's rotation is slowed by a tiny fraction. One of the largest tidal differences on Earth is observed in the Bay of Fundy in New Brunswick, as depicted in Fig. 23.11.

The tidal slowing of Earth's rotation is only about $20 \pm 5$ $\mu$s/year. Nevertheless, this effect was already proposed in 1700 by Immanuel Kant, who interpreted data from Edmund Halley (famous for Halley's comet), who in turn had noticed a discrepancy in the historical records of a total eclipse in the year 484 AD. The historical record shows that the total eclipse was seen along a line from the Greek island of Rhodes to Lebanon, but Halley's precise calculations showed that it should have been observed along a line from Lisbon in Portugal to Cyprus. Thus, there had been a small but indisputable slowing of Earth's spin over the 1200 years from the eclipse to Kant's and Halley's time.

Modern scientific research has revealed direct proof for the tidal slowing of Earth's spin, in particular in the form of annual and daily variations in the deposits of chalk in 300-million-year-old Devonian coral reefs that indicate a Devonian year was $400 \pm 10$ days. Note the discrepancy between the current rate of 0.05 $\mu$s/day and the average rate since the Devonian period of 0.07 $\mu$s/day. This indicates that the effect depends on the location of the continents, which varies over long periods due to continental drift.

The tidal slowing will eventually (although very slowly) reduce the contribution of Earth's spin to the total angular momentum to a negligible amount. To conserve the angular momentum of the Earth/Moon system, the Moon must pick up the difference. The Moon can do this in two ways, as shown in Eq. [29]: it can increase its distance from Earth, and it can change its orbiting speed. These two developments are not independent, however, but are governed by

**FIGURE 23.11**

Tidal effect at the Bay of Fundy, New Brunswick.

Johannes Kepler's area law. This law states that the ratio of the cube of a satellite's mean distance, $r$, to the square of its orbiting period, $T$, is constant: $r^3/T^2 = \text{const}$. This allows us to determine the final state of motion of the Earth/Moon system: its final angular frequency value will be $\omega = 1.33 \times 10^{-6}\,\text{s}^{-1}$, which corresponds to the length of a day as well as a month, each lasting 56 of our current days; the distance from Earth to the Moon will have increased to 1.56 times the current distance.

We leave this topic with a final comment on the issue of spin in the Earth/Moon system. You notice that we did not discuss a contribution due to the Moon's spin. This is due to the fact that the Moon spins very slowly. It takes exactly one month to spin once, which leads to the well-known effect that it is always the same side of the Moon that faces Earth. This is not accidental; the Moon's mass is not evenly distributed and, therefore, the heavier end points toward Earth while the lighter end points away from the source of the gravitational attraction.

## The Nuclear Spin

The discussion of spin in the Earth/Moon system prepares us to tackle an invisible but related system, the spin of an atomic nucleus. Like the Moon, the electrons orbit the nucleus in Rutherford's model. An angular momentum can be attributed to their motion. At the centre of the atom, the nucleus may also rotate about its own axis. This is again a classical picture, but a useful one as we see below. The rotation of the nucleus leads to a **nuclear spin** contribution to the total angular momentum of the atom. At that point, however, the similarities to the Earth/Moon system end:

- Different from the Moon, the orbiting electrons each carry a spin of their own. We used this fact implicitly when we allowed two electrons (differing only in their spin-quantum number) to fill each of the orbitals identified in Table 22.3. For this reason, Pauli's principle was written such that any two electrons in the same atom must differ in at least one of four quantum numbers: either one of the three listed in Table 22.3 or the spin-quantum number. Helium, as an example, has two electrons that have the same three quantum numbers as found in Table 22.3—i.e., $n = 1$, $l = 0$, $m_l = 0$—but they do not violate Pauli's principle since they differ in their spin. This can be pictured in a classical model: one electron spins in the direction east to west, the other west to east. Since we want to develop the basic physical principles for MRI next, we do not discuss the electron spin further. Note, however, that interesting experimental methods are based on the measurement of effects due to the electron spin. In particular, **electron spin resonance** (ESR) is used to identify unpaired electrons, e.g., in electrically neutral molecules called **radicals**.

- No tidal wave or any other mechanism exists to allow electrons to exert a torque on the nuclear

## TABLE 23.4

### Nuclear spin for selected elementary particles and atomic nuclei

| Nucleus | Spin | Nucleus | Spin |
|---|---|---|---|
| Neutron | $\frac{1}{2}\hbar$ | proton ($^{1}$H) | $\frac{1}{2}\hbar$ |
| Deuteron ($^{2}$H) | $\hbar$ | $\alpha$ ($^{4}$He) | 0 |
| $^{12}$C | 0 | $^{13}$C | $\frac{1}{2}\hbar$ |
| $^{14}$N | $\hbar$ | $^{16}$O | 0 |
| $^{19}$F | $\frac{1}{2}\hbar$ | $^{31}$P | $\frac{1}{2}\hbar$ |

spin. Thus, the spin is fixed and can be used to identify a particular nucleus.

- The underlying forces in the Earth/Moon and atomic systems are different. Gravity causes the Moon and Earth to constantly fall toward each other, but the electric force holds the atom together. This leads to additional effects we discuss in this section, such as a magnetic dipole moment of the nucleus.

- Electrons and nuclei are much smaller than the Moon and Earth. In Chapter 22 we found that we must use quantum-mechanical models to describe physical properties at the atomic level. This remains true in the current discussion: nuclear spins have features that classical spin systems do not have. Of these the most important is the quantization of the spin. The spins of a nucleus can be only zero or an integer multiple of the value $h/(4 \cdot \pi) = \hbar/2$, in which $h$ is Planck's constant. The values for various nuclei are shown in Table 23.4. Nuclei with a zero spin cannot be used for nuclear magnetic resonance techniques such as MRI. Therefore, of the most common elements in biochemical molecules, hydrogen in particular is sensitive to the process discussed in this section.

# The Nuclear Spin in a Magnetic Field

## The Magnetic Dipole Moment of a Nucleus

The spin is observed not directly but indirectly, due to a magnetic dipole moment of the nucleus that is a consequence of the presence of the spin. A spin leads to a magnetic dipole because the nucleus is not electrically neutral. It contains neutrons and protons, while the electric neutrality of an atom follows from the presence of a number of electrons in the shell that matches the number of protons in the nucleus. When a charged particle spins about its axis, the individual charges describe a circular motion, i.e., they form an electric current loop. How this current loop causes a magnetic dipole moment is shown by analogy to the electric case.

In electricity we started with the concept of a separate charge. The electric force is defined as the product of the charge and the electric field present at the position of the charge. In turn, this allowed us to define the electric field as the electric force per unit charge:

$$\mathbf{F}_{Coulomb} = q \cdot \mathbf{E} \quad \Rightarrow \quad \mathbf{E} = \frac{\mathbf{F}_{Coulomb}}{q} \quad [38]$$

The same approach cannot be taken to define a magnetic field, because no separate magnetic charges (magnetic monopoles) exist.

Thus, to develop an analogy to electricity, we need to look at the next simplest case, which is the electric dipole that has two equal but opposite charges with a separation distance $d$. The electric dipole was introduced in Chapter 13, where we found that the combination of charge $q$ and distance $d$ characterized the dipole in the form:

$$\mu_{el} = q \cdot d \quad [39]$$

in which $\mu_{el}$ is called the **electric dipole moment**. The electric dipole moment can be interpreted as a vector pointing in the direction of the line connecting the two charges, in which case $d$ is written as a position vector: $\boldsymbol{\mu}_{el} = q \cdot \mathbf{d}$. For such an electric dipole the electric field is shown in Fig. 23.12. The electric field of a dipole is anisotropic, i.e., varying in a different fashion in the various directions away from the dipole. For example, perpendicular to the dipole,

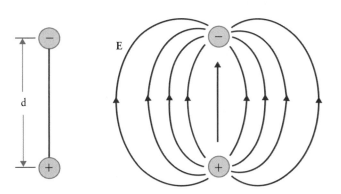

**FIGURE 23.12**

Electric field of an electric dipole.

a larger value of the electric field is observed at a given distance than in any other direction.

We have seen similarly shaped magnetic fields before, e.g., Earth's magnetic field in Fig. 21.19. The magnetic field of a bar magnet is shown in Fig. 23.13(a). The sketch illustrates that the magnetic field in this case looks exactly like the electric field of a dipole. This is not surprising, because a bar magnet consists of a north and a south pole at a fixed distance $d$ from each other, i.e., a structure very similar to the two separated charges of an electric dipole.

A magnetic field of the same shape is found in Fig. 20.14, which applies to a solenoid. Allowing a circular current to flow in a fixed loop resembles the solenoid closely. This is illustrated in Fig. 23.13(b), where the magnetic field of a single, circular current is shown.

The similarities between this magnetic field and the electric field of an electric dipole allow us to identify the bar magnet or the circular current as a magnetic dipole. In analogy to the electric case, a **magnetic dipole moment** is identified. For the current loop, the current replaces the charges in the electric case, and the area (expressed as a magnitude $A$ and a normal vector) replaces the distance vector:

$$\mu_{mag} = I \cdot A \cdot \mathbf{n}^0 \qquad [40]$$

where $A$ is defined as the area enclosed by the current loop. The current loop is a good model for the spinning nucleus, in which protons describe circular paths around the axis of the spin. The current for a spinning nucleus is calculated from the charge and the speed of the charge along its orbiting path.

With the electric and magnetic dipoles defined, we can establish the interactions between a dipole and an external field. We develop this concept again for the electric and magnetic cases by analogy.

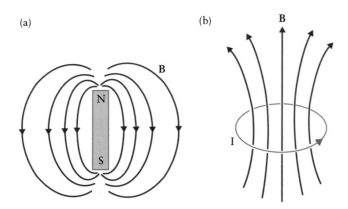

**FIGURE 23.13**

Magnetic field of (a) a bar magnet and (b) a circular current loop.

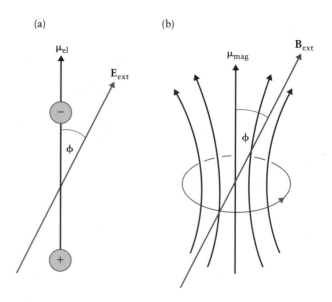

**FIGURE 23.14**

(a) Electric dipole moment, oriented with an angle $\phi$ relative to an external electric field $\mathbf{E}_{ext}$. (b) Magnetic dipole moment of a current loop, oriented with an angle $\phi$ relative to an external magnetic field $\mathbf{B}_{ext}$.

A dipole is an extended object. An electric field causes a force acting on the dipole. We saw in Chapter 5 that a force can act in two different ways on an extended object, either causing a linear acceleration or causing a rotation. The latter case occurs when the external force does not act in the direction of the axis of the extended object, causing a torque. A torque on the dipole results when the direction of the electric field and the axis of the dipole are not parallel. This is illustrated in Fig. 23.14(a) with the angle $\phi$ between the dipole vector and the electric field vector. Note that the torque, the dipole moment, and the electric field are three vectors and their relation is properly given as a vector product. We limit our discussion here to the magnitude of the torque. We write in analogy to the mechanical case:

$$\tau = \mu_{el} \cdot E_{ext} \cdot \sin \phi = q \cdot d \cdot E_{ext} \cdot \sin \phi \qquad [41]$$

i.e., the torque is zero when $\phi = 0°$, which occurs when the dipole is aligned with the electric field. For any other orientation of the dipole, the net torque causes a rotation of the dipole until it is aligned with the external field. Dipole alignment in an electric field led to the very large capacitance values for polar molecules in Table 14.2.

The magnetic case is developed with the same line of arguments based on Fig. 23.14(b). A current loop is shown that causes a magnetic dipole moment as given in Eq. [40]. An external magnetic field (e.g., caused by a horseshoe magnet) acts under an angle $\phi$

on the magnetic dipole. The torque is again a vector, for which we quantify its magnitude only:

$$\tau = \mu_{mag} \cdot B_{ext} \cdot \sin\phi = I \cdot A \cdot B_{ext} \cdot \sin\phi \quad [42]$$

The torque disappears when the external magnetic field and the normal vector, representing the area enclosed by the loop, are parallel, $\phi = 0°$. Thus, we expect magnetic dipoles (be it small pieces of iron as in a compass, or small circular current loops like atomic nuclei) to align with the external magnetic field.

Small bar magnets succeed in aligning with the external field when they are mobile. This effect is observed in volcanic lava, where small crystallites with a magnetic dipole moment are frozen in alignment with Earth's magnetic field. Since Earth's magnetic field changes its north–south polarity once in a while, we can use this effect for rough dating of fossils that are found in volcanic ash layers. This method was used to independently confirm radioisotope dating of the *Australophithecus afarensis* (Lucy) fossil, which we discussed toward the end of Chapter 5.

The magnetic dipole moments of atomic nuclei with a non-zero spin also align in external magnetic fields. This is illustrated in Fig. 23.15 for hydrogen atoms. Note that part (b) of the figure shows, however, that two orientations occur: one with parallel and one with anti-parallel alignment. Fig. 23.15 oversimplifies the situation: the actual orientations of the magnetic dipole moment for a nucleus with spin of $\frac{1}{2}\hbar$ are shown in Fig. 23.16 for an external magnetic field along the z-axis; one orientation has a z-component parallel to the magnetic field and the other has an anti-parallel z-component.

Thus, the orientation of an atomic nucleus differs from the orientation of the magnetic crystallites in the volcanic ash. For the atomic nuclei, the orienta-

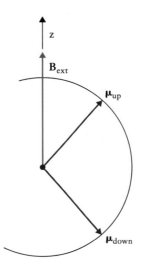

**FIGURE 23.16**

Quantum-mechanically allowed orientations of a $\frac{1}{2}\hbar$-spin nucleus with an external magnetic field, which is oriented in the $+z$-direction.

tion is a quantum-mechanical effect. That means, for a nucleus with spin of $\frac{1}{2}\hbar$, only two orientations are possible; these are shown in Fig. 23.16.

# Energy of a Nuclear Spin in a Magnetic Field

Now we establish the energy for a particle with a magnetic dipole moment in a magnetic field. We do this again in analogy to an electric dipole that is brought into an electric field. For simplicity, we confine both discussions to uniform fields. The energy of an electric dipole in a uniform electric field is calculated with Fig. 23.17. The electric field lines are horizontal, with the electric field directed toward the right. The electric dipole forms an angle $\alpha$ with the field lines. Using the definition of the electric energy

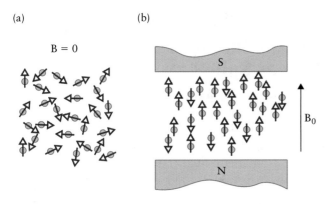

**FIGURE 23.15**

Sketch of the alignment of the magnetic dipole moments of a sample in an external magnetic field.

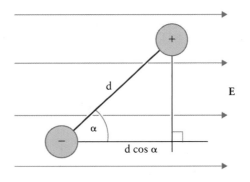

**FIGURE 23.17**

An electric dipole in a uniform external electric field. This sketch allows us to calculate the electric energy of the dipole as a function of its orientation relative to the field.

for a point charge for each of the two charges forming the dipole, we find:

$$E_{el} = q_+ \cdot V_+ + q_- \cdot V_- = q(V_+ - V_-) \qquad [43]$$

in which $V_+$ and $V_-$ are the electric potential at the positions of the positive and negative charge, respectively. We know from Chapter 13 that the electric energy, and thus the electric potential, vary linearly in a uniform electric field. Therefore, we need to find the difference in the position along the direction of the external field for the two charges forming the dipole in Fig. 23.17. As the figure illustrates, the difference in position is $d \cdot \cos \alpha$. With this distance, we rewrite Eq. [43] in the form:

$$E_{el} = q \cdot (|E| \cdot d \cdot \cos \alpha) = \boldsymbol{\mu}_{el} \cdot \mathbf{E} \qquad [44]$$

in which the charge $q$ and the distance between the charges $d$ are combined to the electric dipole moment $\boldsymbol{\mu}_{el}$. The $\cos \alpha$ term is due to the dot product between the electric field and the electric dipole moment. The energy of a magnetic dipole in a uniform magnetic field is written in analogy, leading to:

$$E_{mag} = \boldsymbol{\mu}_{mag} \cdot \mathbf{B} = I \cdot A \cdot B \cdot \cos \alpha \qquad [45]$$

In this case, $\alpha$ is the angle between the direction of the magnetic field **B** and the unit vector $\mathbf{n}^0$, which is normal to the area of the current loop.

From Eq. [45] we calculate the difference in energy for two nuclei with the two allowed orientations of a $\frac{1}{2}\hbar$ spin in a magnetic field, as shown in Fig. 23.16:

$$\Delta E_{mag} = \mu_{mag} \cdot B \qquad [46]$$

Eq. [46] is illustrated in Fig. 23.18. The figure shows the magnetic energy of a nucleus with a spin $\frac{1}{2}\hbar$ as a function of the external magnetic field for both the parallel and anti-parallel orientations. The two orientations are labelled with the respective spin quantum-numbers $m_s$. The energy difference for a partic-

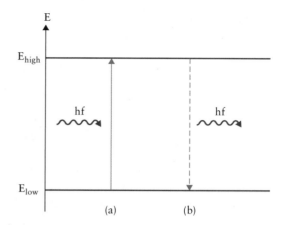

**FIGURE 23.19**

Transition processes for a nuclear spin in an external magnetic field: absorption of radiation allows us to excite the nucleus (spin flips into anti-parallel orientation), and emission of radiation allows the nucleus to return to the lower-energy state (spin flips into parallel orientation).

ular external field of magnitude $B_0$ is highlighted. Note that the energy difference increases linearly with the magnitude of the external magnetic field.

In the same fashion as we discussed this topic for electrons in atomic shells, a system that occupies a state of higher energy can relax by emitting a photon while transferring into a state of lower energy. Equally, external photons can be absorbed to excite a system from a lower to a higher state. This is a resonance effect. Fig. 23.19 indicates how a resonant transition occurs for nuclei in the lower of the two spin states in a uniform magnetic field. If photons with the right amount of energy are used, a nucleus in the parallel state can be brought into the anti-parallel state. The energy of the photon absorbed in this process, $h \cdot f$, is determined by the energy difference between the two states from Eq. [46]:

$$h \cdot f = \mu_{mag} \cdot B \qquad [47]$$

# Experiments with Nuclear Spins

## Measuring the Atomic Spin

In 1922, Otto Stern and Walther Gerlach proved experimentally that the orientation of the spin is quantized in a magnetic field. Different from our discussion above, however, their experiment focussed on the atomic spin, not the nuclear spin. The **Stern–Gerlach experiment** is shown in Fig. 23.20. It consists of a non-uniform horseshoe magnet and a vacuum chamber. Silver metal is evaporated thermally from a

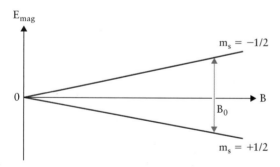

**FIGURE 23.18**

The magnetic energy of a magnetic dipole splits into two energy levels for a nucleus with $\frac{1}{2}\hbar$-spin when brought into a uniform external magnetic field. The energy difference is proportional to the magnitude of the magnetic field.

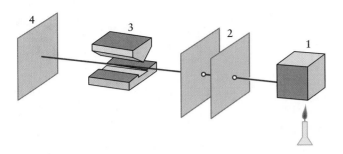

**FIGURE 23.20**

Stern–Gerlach experiment to measure the atomic spin. An atomic silver beam from an oven (1) travels in a vacuum. After passing through a collimator (2) and a non-uniform magnetic field (3) the beam is split on the screen (4) due to the atomic spin of the silver atoms.

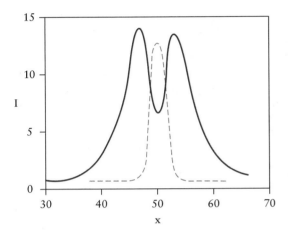

**FIGURE 23.21**

Result of the experiment by Stern and Gerlach, showing the intensity of the measured atomic beam as a function of position on the observation screen. Without a magnetic field, a single peak (blue dashed line) is observed with a width representing the Maxwell–Boltzmann velocity distribution of the atoms coming from the source. With the magnetic field, the beam splits into two components, one associated with the z-component of the spin in the direction of the magnetic field and one with the z-component anti-parallel to the field.

crucible in the vacuum system. An atomic silver beam is selected with collimators in the direction of the gap of the magnet. In this setup the atomic beam passes through the magnetic poles perpendicularly to the magnetic field lines. Since silver atoms have a spin of $\frac{1}{2}\hbar$ due to an unpaired electron in the outer shell, two orientations are possible in the external magnetic field, one parallel and one anti-parallel to the field. A force is exerted on the atom due to the interaction between the magnetic dipole moment and the magnetic field, with the two orientations leading to a splitting of the beam.

The intensity of the silver atomic beam as a function of position on the screen is shown in Fig. 23.21; the red line is observed with the magnetic field turned

on and the blue dashed line with the magnetic field turned off. The two peaks in the first case are not perfectly separated, because of the high thermal energy of the evaporated silver atoms, which display a broad Maxwell–Boltzmann velocity distribution.

On closer inspection, it is possible to illustrate that each of the two peaks in Fig. 23.21 splits again, although to a much lesser degree than the split due to the spin of the valence-electrons. This secondary split is due to the nuclear spin of the silver atoms. For atoms where no effect is expected on account of the electrons in the atomic shell (so-called **diamagnetic atoms**), only a splitting due to the nuclear spin is observed. The number of the observed peaks in such measurements reveals the spin, and the distance between the peaks is a measure of the nuclear magnetic dipole moment.

## Resonance Measurements

The transition energy between the states of a nuclear spin in an external magnetic field is small in comparison to transitions between electronic states in atoms that we discussed in Chapter 22. Even for strong fields, such as $|\mathbf{B}| = 10$ T, the frequency of the photon causing the resonance in a $\frac{1}{2}\hbar$-spin system is only 500 MHz, and for a typical field of $|\mathbf{B}| = 1$ T the transition occurs at 50 MHz. This leads to a thermodynamic question: Is there enough thermal energy in the system that the nuclear spins are already fully excited?

Whether a transition energy is small or large is decided by a quantitative comparison between the thermal energy available to the system and the energy needed to observe a **resonance transition** between two states of the system, $\Delta E_{\text{excitation}}$. We distinguish two cases:

$$\text{(i)} \quad \Delta E_{\text{excitation}} \ll k \cdot T$$
$$\text{(ii)} \quad \Delta E_{\text{excitation}} \gg k \cdot T \qquad [48]$$

We use $k \cdot T$, the product of the Boltzmann constant and the temperature, as a measure of the thermal energy available per atom or molecule.

In case (i) of Eq. [48], enough thermal energy is present that every atom or molecule can easily undergo a transition from the lower to the higher energy state, without need of externally provided photons. Thus, the system is fully excited with an equal number of atoms or molecules in the excited and the lower state in Fig. 23.19. In case (ii) of Eq. [48] the thermal energy of the system is insufficient to allow atoms or molecules to obtain the energy to undergo an excitation. Consequently, essentially all atoms or molecules are in the lower state.

We found in earlier chapters examples for both cases: rotational excitation states for gas molecules are separated from their ground state by very small energies in the microwave part of the electromagnetic spectrum. Thus, most molecules occupy higher rotation states at room temperature. On the other hand, electronic excitation states are separated by larger energy gaps from the ground state (in the visible-to-UV range), and thus atoms and molecules are exclusively occupying the ground state (lowest energy state) with respect to electronic excitations.

We want to decide which case in Eq. [48] we are dealing with for the spin orientations of a nucleus in an external magnetic field. For this we assume a large magnetic field of 10 T, which is associated with an excitation frequency of 500 MHz. We further assume that the probe is at room temperature during the experiment. This assumption is particularly useful for MRI studies, as cooling of human patients is not possible without causing damage to tissues. This leads to:

$$h \cdot f = (500 \text{ MHz})(6.63 \times 10^{-34} \text{ J} \cdot \text{s})$$
$$= 3.3 \times 10^{-25} \text{ J} \qquad [49]$$

for the energy of the transition, and to:

$$k \cdot T = \left(1.38 \times 10^{-23} \frac{\text{J}}{\text{K}}\right)(298 \text{ K})$$
$$= 4.1 \times 10^{-21} \text{ J} \qquad [50]$$

for the thermal energy of the system. Thus, the thermal energy exceeds the energy needed for the transition between the two states of a spin in the external magnetic field by more than a factor of $10^4$. As a consequence, both states in Fig. 23.19 are almost equally occupied in the probe, with a difference in favour of the lower level on the order of only $1 \times 10^{-4}$%!

This means that a resonance technique using the transition between spin orientations differs significantly from other resonance techniques such as infrared (IR) or ultraviolet (UV) spectroscopy. In the latter techniques, externally provided photons of the resonance energy lead to strong absorption as practically all molecules are in the ground state. In the nuclear spin resonance case we expect much weaker signals, as almost all spins that could be excited already are.

## Nuclear Magnetic Resonance (NMR)

Fig. 23.22 illustrates the experimental setup with which we can excite resonant transitions in the orientation of nuclear spins in an external magnetic

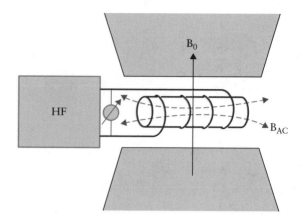

**FIGURE 23.22**

Experimental setup of the NMR experiment.

field. A magnet with a large magnetic field $B_0$ is needed, indicated by the grey areas, to provide a constant and uniform external magnetic field. This field causes the two orientations of the spin to split into two separate energy levels. For resonance experiments with hydrogen nuclei in chemical molecules, a magnetic field of 2.349 T is used in a standard setup. This magnitude of the magnetic field leads to a resonance frequency of 100 MHz, values typically used in nuclear magnetic resonance (NMR) measurements.

The resonance radiation of about 100 MHz is provided by an external high-frequency generator. The frequency can be scanned across a range of $\pm 500$ Hz, which is a minor variation of $1 \times 10^{-3}$%. The ability to sweep the frequency through this range is needed for two reasons: (i) to adjust for minor variations of the actual external magnetic field, and (ii) to allow for a chemical composition analysis in NMR.

How do we analyze chemical samples for their hydrogen composition with this setup? Fig. 23.22 indicates that the high-frequency signal provided through an electric solenoid arrangement can also be interpreted as causing an alternating magnetic field. This relates to the classical interpretation of the resonance effect, in which the nuclear spins are treated as tops that undergo a precessional motion about the magnetic axis. With the external push due to the alternating magnetic field, which wiggles on the top, it is possible to cause the top to flip to an inverted precessional motion. If we now sweep the external high frequency (HF) through a $\pm 500$ Hz range near 100 MHz a spectrum results—with peaks whenever the external frequency passes through an actual resonance frequency. At that instant, nuclear spins absorb energy from the high-frequency field and change their orientation to their excited state. The energy absorption in the probe leads to the need for a higher

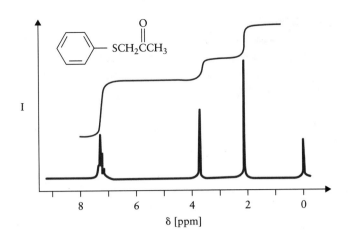

**FIGURE 23.23**

A typical NMR spectrum, showing peaks that correspond to various resonances (thick line). The corresponding area under the signal (thin line) is used to quantify the number of equivalent hydrogen atoms involved in the respective transitions.

power input from the high-frequency generator, which is recorded with a separate instrument (indicated as a circle with an arrow in Fig. 23.22).

A $^1$H–NMR spectrum is shown in Fig. 23.23. A chemically pure sample of 1-thiophenylpropanone-(2) is dissolved in an NMR-inert solvent, i.e., a solvent that does not contain hydrogen. Typically, we use $CCl_4$ as a non-polar solvent, (in the present case) or $D_2O$ as a polar solvent. The sample is then brought into the magnet of the NMR apparatus and a resonance measurement is obtained. Several features of the resulting spectrum are noted:

- The abscissa is given not as frequencies but as a dimensionless parameter (in parts per million (ppm)). In addition, a peak occurs at a zero-reference point. The reference point is the result of a calibration with a separate sample of tetramethylsilane, $(CH_3)_4Si$, which has 12 equivalent hydrogen atoms. This compound is used as a reference point such that any peak at a resonance frequency different from the resonance frequency of tetramethylsilane, $f_{TMS}$, is considered to be chemically shifted. The chemical shift $\delta$ is quantified in the form:

$$\delta = \frac{f_{sample} - f_{TMS}}{f_0} \cdot 10^6 \qquad [51]$$

The basic frequency $f_0$ for the spectrum shown in Fig. 23.23 is 100 MHz. The factor $10^6$ causes the chemical shift to be given in ppm.

- Two curves are shown in Fig. 23.23, a step function and a spectrum of discrete peaks at various resonance frequencies. The step function

represents the area under each of the peaks, cumulatively from left to right. This measurement is provided since its step height is proportional to the number of equivalent hydrogen atoms in each molecule.

- The hydrogen atoms in the thiophenylpropanone molecule give rise to three peaks at different chemical shifts. This is the most important aspect of the application of the NMR technique in structural analysis studies in chemistry. The external magnetic field $B_0$ determines the magnetic field at positions of hydrogen nuclei within the molecule only to the first order. The actual magnetic field varies slightly due to minor magnetic field contributions at the position of the hydrogen nucleus, caused by atomic electrons that move within the molecule. This contribution varies with the relative location of functional groups in chemical compounds. For example, in the thiophenylpropanone molecule shown as an inset in Fig. 23.23, three types of hydrogen atoms with variable environments can be identified: (a) five hydrogen atoms attached to the benzene ring at $\delta = 7.25$ ppm, (b) two hydrogen atoms in the double-substituted methyl-group ($-CH_2-$) at the centre of the molecule at $\delta = 3.73$ ppm, and (c) three hydrogen atoms in the methyl-group at the end ($-CH_3$) with $\delta = 2.16$ ppm. The step height of the integral measurement identifies the ratio of the peak areas as 5:2:3 from lower- to higher-resonance frequency in the spectrum.

Chemical shifts and signal splitting—as can be seen in Fig. 23.23 for the five hydrogen atoms of the benzene group—are important tools for identifying unknown chemical compounds based on their NMR spectra. At the same time, these fingerprint-type details are useful only when a single chemical compound has been isolated for the NMR measurement. These features cannot be used in MRI, where a separation of chemical compounds in the human body is not possible.

# Magnetic Resonance Imaging as a Medical NMR Application

Magnetic resonance imaging (MRI) combines the material-sensitive information of NMR with modern computer-based imaging techniques. At first glance one may expect little useful information from an NMR signal obtained from a sample of human tissue. The range of complex molecules and the multitude of hydrogen atoms in widely varying local magnetic environments should lead to an indifferent signal.

Indeed, no chemical-shift information is collected. However, it has been experimentally established that the relaxation times associated with the relaxation process in Fig. 23.19 vary with tissue material.

The time-dependence of the relaxation process following a high-frequency pulse is illustrated in Fig. 23.24. The figure shows the difference in occupation of the upper and the lower energy state for the nuclear spins in a probe as a function of time after the pulse. The relaxation time is defined as the time it takes for the signal to decay to 37% of its initial value.

In Table 23.5 we compare the relaxation times for various forms of tissue in their healthy state and when diseased by a tumour. The table shows for a wide range of tissues that significant changes in the relaxation time take place when tumours are present.

A second difference between NMR and MRI is the need for a spatial resolution of the technique in MRI. We do not want to dissect the patient to analyze a particular tissue; rather, we want to do the analysis non-intrusively with the tissue remaining in the patient! This requires that the entire patient (or at least the part

### TABLE 23.5

**Relaxation time of hydrogen nuclear spins in an external magnetic field as a function of tissue with and without tumours**

| Tissue | Relaxation time $T_{relax}$ (s) | |
| --- | --- | --- |
| | Healthy | With tumour |
| Breast | 0.37 | 1.08 |
| Skin | 0.62 | 1.05 |
| Muscle | 1.02 | 1.41 |
| Liver | 0.57 | 0.83 |
| Stomach | 0.77 | 1.24 |
| Lung | 0.79 | 1.10 |
| Bone | 0.55 | 1.03 |
| Water | 3.6 | — |

of the patient we want to survey for tumours) be placed in the magnet and within the solenoid. To obtain a signal from only a given sampling depth within the patient (relative to a fixed reference plane, not relative to the patient's skin), a constant-gradient magnetic field is superimposed on the constant magnetic field $B_0$. As this gradient field is varied, the fixed high frequency is the proper resonance frequency in only a thin layer at any given time. Alternatively, the gradient field can be held fixed and the high frequency can be varied, as Figs. 23.18 and 23.19 suggest.

When we use multiple projections and analyze the data appropriately with a computer, overlapping planes produce stripes and overlapping stripes produce single segments of information. This information is processed such that relaxation times are usually shown in false-colour codes.

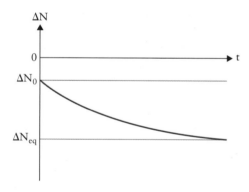

**FIGURE 23.24**

Decay of the population change of a spin system in a magnetic field after a high-frequency pulse has been sent through the sample. A characteristic decay time constant is calculated from the curve.

# MULTIPLE CHOICE AND CONCEPTUAL QUESTIONS

## NUCLEAR ENERGY AND RADIOACTIVE DECAY

**Q–23.1.** A tremendous amount of energy is released per nuclear decay in the fuel cells of a nuclear power plant or in an atomic bomb explosion. Where does this energy come from?

**Q–23.2.** Particles and their corresponding anti-matter particles annihilate when they meet. (a) Does this not violate the conservation of energy? (b) Why

does Earth or the Sun not rapidly dissolve in such energy bursts?

**Q–23.3.** Why is the binding energy of a nucleon in an atomic nucleus much larger than the chemical binding energy in a molecule?

**Q–23.4.** For which of the following two nuclei is the range of the nuclear force smaller, $^4$He or $^{238}$U? Why is this so?

**Q–23.5.** Is the radioactive decay law linear? If not, can you rewrite it such that a plot yields a straight line?

**Q–23.6.** Safe, long-term storage of nuclear waste is a major problem. Would you be satisfied if a particular storage facility could guarantee the concealment of waste for its half-life?

**Q–23.7.** Fig. 23.6 and Table 23.1 indicate that alpha particles penetrate the skin only to a shallow depth. Why, then, is this type of radiation considered particularly dangerous, as indicated by its large radiation factor in Table 23.2?

**Q–23.8.** You are asked to find a radioactive isotope better suited for the study in Fig. 23.8 than $^{131}$I. When surveying potential nuclides, what criteria would you apply?

**Q–23.9.** You work in a lab that uses radioactive materials. A spill occurs due to an accident. What is your first reaction?

**Q–23.10.** Fig. 23.9 indicates that the age determination with carbon dating also depends on the age of the sample. What do you conclude from Fig. 23.9? (A) That carbon dating is unreliable. (B) That carbon dating gives a perfect result once the calculated age is corrected with the curve shown in the figure. (C) That carbon dating is subject to a statistical error indicated by the variation of the curve in the figure. (D) That carbon dating is subject to a systematic error indicated by the variation of the curve in the figure.

**Q–23.11.** The activity of an unknown radioactive isotope reduces to 96% of the original value in 120 minutes. What is its half-life? Choose the closest value. (A) 610 min, (B) 2040 min, (C) 2640 min, (D) 4120 min.

**Q–23.12.** Why do isotopes have identical chemical properties?

**Q–23.13.** The emitted particle in beta decay has a wide range of possible energies, but the energy of the helium nucleus emitted in alpha decay has a decay-specific value. What explains this difference?

**Q–23.14.** A heavy isotope undergoes an alpha decay from rest. Does the daughter nucleus or the alpha particle carry away a greater kinetic energy?

**Q–23.15.** Why are X-ray cassettes in hospitals not affected when an alpha emitter is in close proximity, but deteriorate when a beta-emitter comes close?

**Q–23.16.** Can dating with $^{14}$C be used to determine the age of a rock formation?

### SPIN

**Q–23.17.** In this chapter we discussed the tidal waves and their effect on Earth's rotation. Given that the Sun is much bigger than the Moon, shouldn't the effect due to the Sun be larger than that due to the Moon?

**Q–23.18.** One prediction of global warming is that the polar ice caps will melt during this century. Would this event affect the angular momentum of Earth? If the ice caps melt, would the length of a day increase or decrease?

# ANALYTICAL PROBLEMS

## NUCLEAR ENERGY AND RADIOACTIVE DECAY

**P–23.1.** The nucleus of the deuterium atom consists of one proton and one neutron. What is the binding energy of this nucleus if the mass of the deuterium nucleus is given as $2.014102 \cdot u$?

**P–23.2.** A living organism has $16.1 \pm 0.1$ $^{14}$C decays per minute and per gram carbon. A particular wood sample found in an ancient Egyptian grave measures $505 \pm 10$ decays/(hour $\cdot$ g). When was the tree cut from which this wood came?

**P–23.3.** Nuclear waste from power plants may contain $^{239}$Pu, a plutonium isotope with a half-life of 24 000 years. How long does it take for the stored waste to decay to 10% of its current activity level?

**P–23.4.** A radioactive $^{210}$Po source of 0.05 MBq is placed on a biological sample. This polonium isotope is a 5.4-MeV $\alpha$-emitter. The range of the $\alpha$-particles in the sample is 20 $\mu$m. What is the energy dose rate (dose per hour) absorbed by the biological sample? *Hint:* Treat the source as a point source and use the density of water for the density of the sample.

**P–23.5.** A tracer study drug contains 11 kBq of a technetium isotope, $^{99}$Tc, which has a half-life of $T_{1/2} = 363$ minutes. Technetium can be used as a substitute for $^{131}$I in tracer studies of the thyroid gland. What is the activity of the drug when it is used after 3 hours?

**P–23.6.** The activity of radon gas is of interest since this gas can be trapped in basements. How many radioactive radon atoms are left after half a day if a gas space initially contained $6.7 \times 10^{-16}$ mol $^{222}$Rn? (The half-life of $^{222}$Rn is 3.824 days.)

**P–23.7.** An archaeological wood sample is analyzed. What is its age if its $^{14}$C content is 15% of a living wood sample?

**P–23.8.** $^{131}$I has a half-life of 8.04 days. (a) What is its decay constant? (b) How many mol of this isotope are required for a sample to have an activity of 18.5 kBq?

**P–23.9.** A radioactive sample contains 5.0 μg of pure $^{15}$O with a half-life of 2.03 min. (a) How many radioactive nuclei does the sample contain? (b) What is the activity of the sample after 5 hours?

**P–23.10.** The age of rocks can be determined with the decay $^{87}$Rb $\rightarrow$ $^{87}$Sr $+ e^-$, which has a half-life of $T_{1/2} = 4.7 \times 10^{10}$ years. Assume that a rock sample did not contain any strontium initially. We find a 1-g sample to contain $1.8 \times 10^{10}$ atoms radioactive rubidium and $1.1 \times 10^9$ strontium. (a) How old is the rock? (b) What assumptions are necessary for this age to be reliable?

### MEDICAL AND OCCUPATIONAL APPLICATIONS

**P–23.11.** How much heavy ion radiation does the same damage as 10-Sv X-rays?

**P–23.12.** A radioactive source emits 1.0 mGy of 2.0-MeV γ-rays per hour, as measured at a distance of 1 m. (a) How long could a person stand at that distance before receiving a dose of 10 mSv? (b) Assuming that the γ-emission is spatially uniform, at what distance would a person receive a dose rate of 0.1 mGy/h?

**P–23.13.** A standard man is exposed to a whole-body radiation of 0.25 Gy. What amount of energy (in unit J) is added to the person's body?

**P–23.14.** In a clinical study, a standard man swallows a 1.3-MBq sample of $^{32}$P. $^{32}$P is a $\beta^-$-emitter with a half-life of 14.3 days; the emitted electron carries on average a kinetic energy of 700 keV. (a) How many decays occur in a 10-day period in the standard man's body, assuming that none of the phosphorous sample is discharged? (b) What is the total energy absorbed by the standard man's body during the same 10-day period?

**P–23.15.** A sample of 2.0 Gy is administered during a cancer treatment. If the entire radiation is absorbed by a tumour of mass $m = 250$ g, (a) how much energy does it absorb, and (b) how much does its temperature increase? *Hint:* Use the thermodynamic data for water to simulate tissue.

### SPIN

**P–23.16.** A 2.0-m-long single-looped conductor carries a current $I = 2.0$ A. The loop has the shape of an equilateral triangle and is placed in a uniform magnetic field with $B = 0.5$ T. Determine the maximum torque that acts on the loop.

**P–23.17.** A conductor forms a single circular loop of 0.5 m radius. It carries a current of $I = 2.0$ A and is located in a uniform magnetic field of $B = 0.4$ T. (a) What is the maximum torque that acts on the loop? (b) What is the angle between the magnetic field and the plane of the loop when the torque is one-half of the value found in part (a)?

# SUMMARY

### DEFINITIONS

- Notation of nuclei:
  - mass number $A$: number of nucleons in nucleus
  - atomic number $Z$: number of protons in nucleus
  - number of neutrons, $N$ with $A = Z + N$

    $$^A_Z X \quad \text{e.g.:} \quad ^{12}_6 C, \ ^{16}_8 O$$

- Decay processes:

    $\alpha$-decay: $\quad ^A_Z X \rightarrow \ ^{A-4}_{Z-2} Y + \ ^4_2 He$

    $\beta^+$-decay: $\quad ^A_Z X \rightarrow \ ^A_{Z-1} Y + e^+$

    $\beta^-$-decay: $\quad ^A_Z X \rightarrow \ ^A_{Z+1} Y + e^-$

### UNITS

- Equivalent dose $D_{equivalent}$: sievert (Sv)

    $$D_{equivalent} = w_R \cdot w_T \cdot D_{absorbed}$$

    where $w_R$ is the radiation factor, $w_T$ is the tissue factor, and $D_{absorbed}$ is the absorbed dose in unit gray.

    Non-standard unit 1 rem = 10 mSv. The unit rem stands for "radiation equivalent man."

- Activity: becquerel (Bq) with 1 Bq = 1 decay/s.

## LAWS

- Radioactive decay law
  - for activity $A$:

$$A = -\frac{\Delta N}{\Delta t} = \lambda \cdot N$$

  where $\lambda$ is the decay constant with unit 1/s.
  - for number of radioactive nuclei in sample, $N$:

$$N(t) = N_0 \cdot e^{-\lambda \cdot t}$$

  where $N_0$ is the number of radioactive nuclei at $t = 0$.

- Half-life $T_{1/2}$: time after which 50% of initial radioactive nuclei have decayed.

$$T_{1/2} = \frac{\ln 2}{\lambda}$$

- Mean life-time: $T_{mean}$:

$$T_{mean} = \frac{1}{\lambda} = 1.44 \cdot T_{1/2}$$

# PHOTO CREDITS

## Cover

**top:** Mike Powell/Getty Images; **bottom, left to right:** Jim Wehtje/Getty Images, © iStockphoto.com/James Steidl, © iStockphoto.com/Christian, © iStockphoto.com/Eraxion.

## Chapter 1

1: © iStockphoto 2: IFA Bilderteam/Jupiter Image.

## Part 1: PANTA RHEI

13: © Shutterstock/Wally Stemberger 15: © Shutterstock 25: Stephen Dalton/Photo Researchers/First Light 27: Norbert Wu/Science Faction/Getty Images 31: © Shutterstock/Sebastian Kaulitzki 31: © Shutterstock/Sebastian Kaulitzki 39: © Phototake/Alamy 42: © SPL/Photo Researchers 49: Anatomical Travelogue/Science Photo Library/Custom Medical Stock Photo 65: © Aflo Foto Agency/Alamy 67: © Shutterstock/Philip Date 71: CNRI/Science Photo Library/Custom Medical Stock Photo 77: © Shutterstock/Philip Date 80: © Shutterstock/Lucian Coman 83: Andrewartha Gary & Terry/Oxford Scientific/Jupiter Images 85: © Andrew Syred/Photo Researchers 90: © Bruce Coleman Incl./Alamy 92: © Shutterstock/Adam Tinney 97: © Shutterstock/Bruce Yeung 108: © Randall Ingalls/Alamy 113: © Shutterstock/Herbert Kratky 139: © Morton Beebe/Corbis 142: © Shutterstock/Jeff Cleveland 144: © allOver photography/Alamy 147: Scott Boehm/Getty Images Sport.

## Part 2: SEMPER IDEM

151: © Shutterstock/gary718 153: David T. Roberts/Nature's Images/Science Photo Library/Custom Medical Stock Photo 155: © Professors Pietro M. Motta & Tomonori Naguro/Photo Researchers 157: Highlights for Children/Oxford Scientific/Jupiter Images 177: Astrid & Hans-Frieder Michler/Science Photo Library/Custom Medical Stock Photo 192: Comstock/Jupiter Images 196: Dallas and John Heaton/Stock Connection/Jupiter Images 201: © Shutterstock/Fernando Jose Vasconcelos Soares 206: Patrick McDonnell/Science Photo Library/Custom Medical Stock Photo 251: Dr. Dennis Kunkel/Visuals Unlimited/Getty Images 252: 3D4Medical.com/Getty Images 253: © Phototake/Alamy 263: © Roger Ressmeyer/Corbis

270: Charles D. Winters/Science Photo Library/Custom Medical Stock Photo 275: Philippe Psaila/Science Photo Library/Custom Medical Stock Photo 278: © Shutterstock/wheatley 281: © Shutterstock/Daniel Gustavsson 291: © Shutterstock/Linda Armstrong 292: © Dr. P. Marazzi/Photo Researchers.

## Part 3: YIN AND YANG

297: © Shutterstock/Elena Elisseeva 299: © Shutterstock/PMLD 302: Hybrid Medical Animation/Science Photo Library 303: Russell Kightley/Science Photo Library/Custom Medical Stock Photo 309: Philippe Psaila/Science Photo Library/Custom Medical Stock Photo 310: © Martin Harvey/Alamy 313: NASA Jet Propulsion Laboratory (NASA-JPL) 315: © Shutterstock/FloridaStock 323, **left:** Eye of Science/Science Photo Library, **right:** John Bavosi/Science Photo Library/Custom Medical Stock Photo 339: © blickwinkel/Alamy 342: Richard Megna/Fundamental Photos/Science Photo Library/Custom Medical Stock Photo 345: © Shutterstock/Ian Klein 350: Juan Carlos Calvin/A.G.E. Foto Stock/First Light 352: © Shutterstock/Johanna Goodyear 355: © iStockphoto 357, **left:** Andrew Lambert Photography/Science Photo Library/Custom Medical Stock Photo, **right:** Andrew Lambert Photography/Science Photo Library/Custom Medical Stock Photo 358: Biomedical Imaging Unit, Southamptom General Hospital/Science Photo Library/Custom Medical Stock Photo 360: © Shutterstock/Megan Gayle 364: Herman Eisenbeiss/Photo Researchers/First Light 367: © Shutterstock/David Starling 377, **left:** © Kevin A. Somerville/Phototake, **right:** © Shutterstock/Gary L. Brewer 378: Brian Evans/Photo Researchers, Inc. 389: Alfred Pasieka/Science Photo Library/Custom Medical Stock Photo 391: © Shutterstock/Nick Stubbs 392: © Shutterstock/Gary L. Brewer 396: Steve Gschmeissner/Science Photo Library/Custom Medical Stock Photo 400: © Shutterstock/Jozsef Szasz-Fabian 403: © Photos.com 404: © Photos.com 405: Sigit Pamungkas/Reuters/Landov 425: © Stockfolio/Alamy 433, **top:** Gregory Ochocki/Photo Researchers/First Light, **right:** Richard T. Nowitz/Photo Researchers/First Light 443: © Kevin A. Somerville/Phototake/Alamy 451: Adam Hart-Davis/Science Photo Library/Custom Medical Stock Photo 481: © Shutterstock/Franc Podgoršek 488: FPG/Hulton Archive/Getty Images 489: Annabella Bluesky/Science Photo Library/Custom Medical Stock Photo.

## Part 4: TAMASO MA JYOTIR

493: © Shutterstock/coko 495: Alain Pol, ISM/Science Photo Library/Custom Medical Stock Photo 502: CNRI/Science Photo Library/Custom Medical Stock Photo 504: Brian Evans/Photo Researchers, Inc. 518: Dominique Douieb/PhotoAlto/Getty Images 524: © Shutterstock/Beth Van Trees 525: © Shutterstock/Morgan Lane Photography 527: © Shutterstock/Alexandru Verinciuc 545: David B. Fleetham/Oxford Scientific/Jupiter Images 549: © R. Spencer Phippen/Phototake/Alamy 554: Dr. John D. Cunningham/Visuals Unlimited/Getty Images 554: © Educational Images/Custom Medical Stock Photo 560: © Shutterstock/Lucian Coman 562, top: Alain Pol, ISM/Science Photo Library/Custom Medical Stock Photo, centre: Simon Fraser/Science Photo Library/Custom Medical Stock Photo 564: © Arco Images/Alamy 569: © Shutterstock/Andrey Armyagov 575: Dorling Kindersley/Getty Images 578: Andrew Lambert Photography/Science Photo Library/Custom Medical Stock Photo 579: © Andrew Lambert/Leslie Garland Picture Library/Alamy 586: Kent Wood/Photo Researchers/First Light 595: © Shutterstock/Nik Niklz 597: Erich Schrempp/Science Photo Library/Custom Medical Stock Photo 598, left: © Shutterstock/coko, right: © Shutterstock/coko 603: © Shutterstock/Ismael

Montero Verdu 604: © Shutterstock/bhathaway 609: Steve Allen/Brand X/Jupiter Images 610: Martin Zinke-Allmang 613, top: Waterlilies: The Japanese Bridge, or Japanese Bridge at Giverny, c.1923, Monet, Claude (1840-1926)/Minneapolis Institute of Arts, MN, USA/The Bridgeman Art Library, bottom: Waterlily Pond: Pink Harmony, 1900 (oil on canvas), Monet, Claude (1840-1926)/Musee d'Orsay, Paris, France, Lauros/Giraudon/The Bridgeman Art Library 617: © Carol Donner/Phototake/Alamy 617: © Shutterstock/Yakobchuk Vasyl.

## Part 5: KA

645: © Shutterstock/Norman Pogson 647: © The Print Collector/Alamy 655: Don Farrall/Photodisc/Getty Images 656: © Photos.com 658: Hemera Technologies/AbleStock/Jupiter Images 659: NASA Johnson Space Center (NASA-JSC) 667: © Carol and Mike Werner/Alamy 693: © Runk/Schoenberger/Alamy 693: © Shutterstock/Stuart Monk 694: Zephyr/Science Photo Library/Custom Medical Stock 704: © Shutterstock/Katrina Brown 714: © Shutterstock/Tomasz Szymanski 716: © Shutterstock/V. J. Matthew.

# INDEX

# Standard Units

These basic seven units were internationally adopted in 1969 under the title *Système International* (SI units).

| | | |
|---|---|---|
| Length | m | metre |
| Time | s | second |
| Mass | kg | kilogram |
| Temperature | K | kelvin |
| Amount of material | mol | mole |
| Electric current | A | ampere |
| Luminous intensity | Cd | candela |

# The Greek Alphabet

Greek capital and lower case letters

| | | | | | |
|---|---|---|---|---|---|
| Alpha | $A, \alpha$ | Beta | $B, \beta$ | Gamma | $\Gamma, \gamma$ |
| Delta | $\Delta, \delta$ | Epsilon | $E, \varepsilon$ | Zeta | $Z, \zeta$ |
| Eta | $H, \eta$ | Theta | $\Theta, \theta$ | Iota | $I, \iota$ |
| Kappa | $K, \kappa$ | Lambda | $\Lambda, \lambda$ | Mu | $M, \mu$ |
| Nu | $N, \nu$ | Xi | $\Xi, \xi$ | Omicron | $O, o$ |
| Pi | $\Pi, \pi$ | Rho | $P, \rho$ | Sigma | $\Sigma, \sigma$ |
| Tau | $T, \tau$ | Upsilon | $\Upsilon, \upsilon$ | Phi | $\Phi, \phi$ |
| Chi | $X, \chi$ | Psi | $\Psi, \psi$ | Omega | $\Omega, \omega$ |

# Standard Prefixes

Standard prefixes for terms of the form $10^n$

| | |
|---|---|
| $n = 9$: G for "giga-" | $n = 6$: M for "mega-" |
| $n = 3$: k for "kilo-" | $n = -1$: d for "deci-" |
| $n = -2$: c for "centi-" | $n = -3$: m for "milli-" |
| $n = -6$: $\mu$ for "micro-" | $n = -9$: n for "nano-" |
| $n = -12$: p for "pico-" | $n = -15$: f for "femto-" |

Examples: $1.0 \ \mu m = 1.0 \times 10^{-6}$ m; $6.5$ cm$^2 = 6.5 \ (10^{-2}$ m$)^2 =$ $6.5 \times 10^{-4}$ m$^2$; $1.0$ L (litre) $= 1.0$ dm$^3 = 1 \ (10^{-1}$ m$)^3 = 1 \times 10^{-3}$ m$^3$. The radius of Earth is written as 6370 km and the diameter of a chlorine ion is 0.181 nm.